D0271588

ORGANIC CHEMISTRY

A Man would do nothing, if he waited until he could do it so well that no one would find fault with what he has done.

CARDINAL NEWMAN.

ORGANIC CHEMISTRY

VOLUME ONE
THE FUNDAMENTAL PRINCIPLES

By

I. L. FINAR
B.Sc., Ph.D.(Lond.), A.R.I.C.
Senior Lecturer in Organic Chemistry,
Northern Polytechnic, Holloway, London

LONGMANS

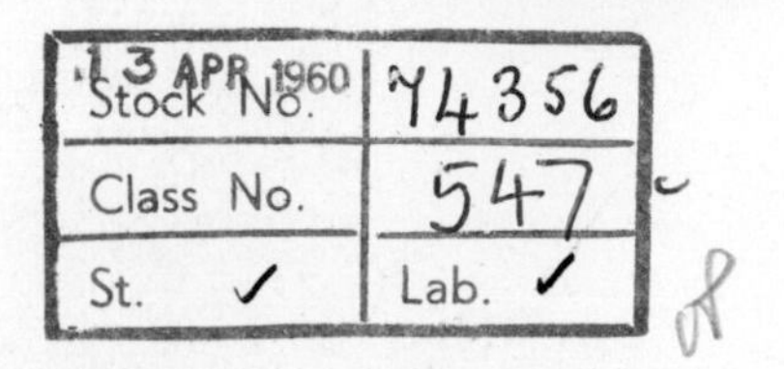

LONGMANS, GREEN AND CO LTD
6 & 7 CLIFFORD STREET, LONDON W I
THIBAULT HOUSE, THIBAULT SQUARE, CAPE TOWN
605-611 LONSDALE STREET, MELBOURNE C I
443 LOCKHART ROAD, HONG KONG
ACCRA, AUCKLAND, IBADAN
KINGSTON (JAMAICA), KUALA LUMPUR
LAHORE, NAIROBI, SALISBURY (RHODESIA)

LONGMANS, GREEN AND CO INC
119 WEST 40TH STREET, NEW YORK 18

LONGMANS, GREEN AND CO
20 CRANFIELD ROAD, TORONTO 16

ORIENT LONGMANS PRIVATE LTD
CALCUTTA, BOMBAY, MADRAS
DELHI, HYDERABAD, DACCA

First published 1951
Second Edition 1954
Third impression 1955
Fourth impression 1956
Fifth impression 1957
Third Edition 1959
Seventh impression 1960

The fourth impression of this book was retitled *Organic Chemistry Volume One: The Fundamental Principles,* as a second volume, dealing with Stereochemistry and the Chemistry of Natural Products, is now published and is designated Volume Two.

Printed in Great Britain by Richard Clay and Company, Ltd., Bungay, Suffolk

PREFACE TO THE THIRD EDITION

THE fourth impression of this book (1956) was retitled *Organic Chemistry Volume One: The Fundamental Principles*, and since then *Volume Two: Stereochemistry and the Chemistry of Natural Products* (1956) has appeared. The latter volume is, in effect, a continuation of the former, and so some material that has been described in this volume (I) in a relatively elementary manner, particularly Stereochemistry, has been dealt with far more fully in Volume II.

Volume I has now been revised in order to bring it up to date. This has meant rewriting many sections, and at the same time I have made some additions which, I hope, will improve the value of this book. It may be useful if I indicate briefly the more important changes I have made in this new edition. Rewritten and expanded subjects include dipole moments, resonance, S1 and S2 mechanisms, steric effects, tautomerism, hyperconjugation, organolithium compounds, stereochemistry, Diene synthesis, carbohydrates, aromatic substitution, transition state, and heterocyclic compounds. Additions include the use of isotopes, molecular diagrams, molecular crowding, E1 and E2 mechanisms, inclusion complexes, conformation, ferrocene, *cyclo*alkynes, paracyclophanes, *ortho-para* ratio in aromatic substitution, and cine-substitution.

In addition to these changes, I have added many mechanisms for various reactions and at the same time have used the more recent methods of writing mechanisms. I have also rewritten aromatic systems with double bonds.

Once again I wish to thank those reviewers, correspondents and many of my students who have pointed out errors and have made suggestions for improving the book.

I. L. FINAR.

October, 1957.

PREFACE TO THE SECOND EDITION

THE aim of this book has remained unchanged. Since I do not consider the chemistry of natural products fundamental chemistry but rather the application of fundamental principles, I have excluded almost completely the study of natural products. It is my hope, however, to write a companion volume in which I shall deal with further aspects of stereochemistry and also with the chemistry of many classes of natural products.

In this second edition, I have taken the opportunity to correct various errors in the text. I wish to thank those reviewers, correspondents and many of my students who brought these errors to my notice, and also made suggestions for improving the book.

In this edition I have used the alphabetical order of naming prefixes, and I have described the older method on p. 784. The principal additions include a more detailed account of molecular orbital theory, some further aspects of stereochemistry, various heterocyclic compounds, and a number of dyestuffs.

My original intention was to deal with molecular orbital theory in the future companion volume. I came to the conclusion, however, that the treatment of this subject is best dealt with in this book. I have therefore given an elementary account of molecular orbitals in Chapter II, and I have discussed their applications throughout the text alongside the resonance theory so that the student can gain some knowledge of both theories. In order to keep the size of this book within reasonable limits, I have used smaller type for much of the additional matter.

It is impossible to express my indebtedness to those authors of monographs, articles, etc., from which I have gained so much information. I can only hope that some measure of my gratitude is expressed by the references I have given to their works.

I. L. FINAR.

1953

PREFACE TO THE FIRST EDITION

In this book my aim has been to describe the fundamental principles of organic chemistry. Although the book has not been written with any particular examination in view, nevertheless the subject matter covers most of the organic chemistry required for the General Honours degree of the London University. It also covers a large amount of the organic chemistry of Part I of the Special Honours degree in chemistry of the London University, and a number of sections of this book should serve as an introduction to Part II.

To many beginners organic chemistry may seem to consist of a large variety of methods and reactions which appear to be isolated and, consequently, only to be learned by heart. After many years' experience of teaching organic chemistry to degree students, I have found that the best method of instruction is by the introduction of electronic theories as early as possible, with a constant application of their principles. These electronic theories give to organic chemistry a certain coherence that is soon appreciated by the beginner, and thus facilitate his study in this branch of chemistry. Stress has been laid on structural formulæ, properties of compounds, and reaction mechanisms. Special attention has been given to the systematic nomenclature of organic compounds. The alphabetical order of naming prefixes was adopted by the Chemical Society in April, 1950. This book was completed before this date and so this method has not been used. The reader, however, should have no difficulty in locating a compound in the index.

It is my experience that only a fairly detailed study of the subject matter enables the student to appreciate the problems involved. Too short an account usually leaves the impression that " everything works according to plan ". This is undesirable for those who are expected to acquire a certain amount of factual knowledge and at the same time learn to think for themselves. I have therefore included detailed discussions on developments of a straightforward nature and also of a controversial nature, in the hope of encouraging the student to weigh up the evidence for himself. This will also give him an idea of some of the problems being investigated at the present time, and will show him that many " facts " are subject to change. Controversial material and the more advanced sections have generally been printed in small type.

Only by reading original papers in which are described the " whys and wherefores " can the student hope to gain a more mature outlook. A selected number of reading references have therefore been given at the end of each chapter. Since summaries of various topics by workers in special fields are of great value in extending the student's knowledge, references of this type have also been included. An account of the literature of organic chemistry has been given in an appendix.

In describing methods of preparation of various compounds, I have given, wherever possible, actual percentage yields (taken mainly from *Organic Syntheses*). The student will thus be enabled to assess the value of a particular method. Where general methods of preparation have been described, the yields have been indicated according to the following (arbitrary) scheme:

> 0–15% very poor (*v.p.*); 16–30% poor (*p.*); 31–45% fair (*f.*); 46–60% fairly good (*f.g.*); 61–75% good (*g.*); 76–90% very good (*v.g.*); 91–100% excellent (*ex.*).

At the end of each chapter there are questions designed to test the student's " book knowledge " and to test the application of his book knowledge. At the end of the book there are also fifty questions chosen from various examinations—B.Sc. General and Special Honours of the University of London, and the Associateship and Fellowship of The Royal Institute of Chemistry. I should here like to thank these Examining Boards for permission to reproduce these questions.

It is hoped that the method of presentation in this book will stimulate the reader's interest in organic chemistry and enable him to read with understanding original papers and monographs covering specialised fields.

I should like to acknowledge the valuable help given me by Mr. K. Merton in reading the manuscript and by Miss A. B. Simmonds, B.Sc., Ph.C., A.R.I.C., in reading the proofs.

I. L. FINAR.

July, 1950.

LIST OF JOURNAL ABBREVIATIONS

Abbreviations.	Journals.
Angew. Chem.	Angewandte Chemie (the name Die Chemie was used for vol. 55, 1942, to vol. 58, 1945).
Ann. Reports (*Chem. Soc.*)	Annual Reports of the Progress of Chemistry (The Chemical Society, London).
Ber.	Berichte der Deutschen Chemischen Gesellschaft (name now changed to Chemische Berichte).
Chem. Eng. News	Chemical and Engineering News (American Chemical Society).
Chem. Reviews	Chemical Reviews.
Chem. and Ind.	Chemistry and Industry.
Helv. Chim. Acta	Helvetica Chimica Acta.
Ind. Eng. Chem.	Industrial and Engineering Chemistry.
Ind. Eng. Chem. (*Anal. Ed.*)	Industrial and Engineering Chemistry (Analytical Edition) [name now changed to Analytical Chemistry].
Ind. Eng. Chem. (*News Ed.*)	Industrial and Engineering Chemistry (News Edition).
J. Amer. Chem. Soc.	Journal of the American Chemical Society.
J. Chem. Educ.	Journal of Chemical Education.
J.C.S.	Journal of the Chemical Society.
J. Org. Chem.	Journal of Organic Chemistry.
J.S.C.I.	Journal of the Society of Chemical Industry.
J. Soc. Dyers and Col.	Journal of the Society of Dyers and Colourists.
Nature	Nature.
Quart. Reviews (*Chem. Soc.*)	Quarterly Reviews of the Chemical Society (London).
Rec. trav. chim.	Recueil des Travaux Chimiques des Pays-Bas.
Research	Research.
Science	Science.
Trans. Faraday Soc.	Transactions of the Faraday Society.

CONTENTS

ALICYCLIC COMPOUNDS

AROMATIC COMPOUNDS

CHAPTER I

INTRODUCTION

HISTORICAL INTRODUCTION

ALTHOUGH organic substances such as sugar, starch, alcohol, resins, oils, indigo, etc., had been known from earliest times, very little progress in their chemistry was made until about the beginning of the eighteenth century. In 1675, Lemery published his famous *Cours de Chymie*, in which he divided compounds from natural sources into three classes: *mineral*, *vegetable* and *animal*. This classification was accepted very quickly, but it was Lavoisier who first showed, in 1784, that all compounds obtained from vegetable and animal sources always contained at least carbon and hydrogen, and frequently, nitrogen and phosphorus. Lavoisier, in spite of showing this close relationship between vegetable and animal products, still retained Lemery's classification. Lavoisier's analytical work, however, stimulated further research in this direction, and resulted in much-improved technique, due to which Lemery's classification had to be modified. Lemery had based his classification on the *origin* of the compound, but it was now found (undoubtedly due to the improved analytical methods) that in a number of cases the *same* compound could be obtained from both vegetable and animal sources. Thus no difference existed between these two classes of compounds, and hence it was no longer justifiable to consider them under separate headings. This led to the reclassification of substances into two groups: all those which could be obtained from vegetables or animals, *i.e.*, substances that were produced by the *living organism*, were classified as *organic*; and all those substances which were not prepared from the living organism were classified as *inorganic*.

At this stage of the investigation of organic compounds it appeared that there were definite differences between organic and inorganic compounds, *e.g.*, complexity of composition and the combustibility of the former. Berzelius (1815) thought that organic compounds were produced from their elements by laws different from those governing the formation of inorganic compounds. This then led him to believe that organic compounds were produced under the influence of a *vital force*, and that they could not be prepared artificially.

In 1828, Wöhler converted ammonium cyanate into urea, a substance hitherto obtained only from animal sources. This synthesis, however, had very little effect on the belief in the vital force theory because it did not start from the elements. Wöhler had prepared his ammonium cyanate from ammonia and cyanic acid, both of which were of animal origin. Wöhler himself appreciated this point, but at that time no methods were known for obtaining ammonia and cyanic acid from their elements. Thus Wöhler's synthesis remained incomplete for the time being. It was not until 1845 that the complete synthesis of an organic compound was carried out. In that year Kolbe synthesised acetic acid from its elements. This synthesis was later followed by others, *e.g.*, in 1856 Berthelot synthesised methane, and so belief in a vital force disappeared.

Since the supposed differences between the two classes of compounds have been disproved, the terms organic and inorganic would appear to be no longer necessary. Nevertheless, they have been retained, but it should be appreciated that they have lost their original meaning. The retention of the terms organic and inorganic may be ascribed to several reasons: (i) all so-called organic compounds contain carbon; (ii) the compounds of carbon are far more numerous (over 750,000) than the known compounds of *all* the other elements put together; (iii) carbon has the power to combine with other carbon atoms to form long chains. This property, known as *catenation*, is not shown to such an extent by any other element.

Hence organic chemistry is the chemistry of the carbon compounds.

This definition includes compounds such as carbon monoxide, carbon dioxide, carbonates, carbon disulphide, etc. Since these occur chiefly in the inorganic kingdom (*original meaning*), they are usually described in text-books of inorganic chemistry.

ANALYSIS OF ORGANIC COMPOUNDS

The following is an outline of the methods used in the study of organic compounds.

(1) **Purification.** Before the properties and structure of an organic compound can be completely investigated, the compound must be prepared in the pure state. Common methods of purification are:

(i) Recrystallisation from suitable solvents.

(ii) Distillation: (*a*) at atmospheric pressure; (*b*) under reduced pressure or *in vacuo*; (*c*) under increased pressure.

(iii) Steam distillation.

(iv) Sublimation.

(v) Chromatography. This method is based on the differential adsorption of the different components of a mixture on various adsorbents. Chromatography offers a means of concentrating a product that occurs naturally in great dilution, and is an extremely valuable method for the separation, isolation, purification and identification of the constituents of a mixture.

It is surprising how much information has often been obtained about the properties and structure of a substance that has not been isolated in a pure state. Even so, purification should always be attempted, since it is much simpler to investigate a pure substance than an impure one.

(2) **Qualitative analysis.** The elements commonly found in organic substances are: carbon (always: by definition), hydrogen, oxygen, nitrogen, halogens, sulphur, phosphorus and metals.

(i) **Carbon and hydrogen.** The compound is intimately mixed with dry cupric oxide and the mixture then heated in a tube. Carbon is oxidised to carbon dioxide (detected by means of calcium hydroxide solution), and hydrogen is oxidised to water (detected by condensation on the cooler parts of the tube).

(ii) **Nitrogen, halogens and sulphur.** These are all detected by the *Lassaigne method*. The compound is fused with metallic sodium, whereby nitrogen is converted into sodium cyanide, halogen into sodium halide, and sulphur into sodium sulphide. The presence of these sodium salts is then detected by inorganic qualitative methods.

(iii) **Phosphorus.** The compound is heated with fusion mixture, whereby the phosphorus is converted into metallic phosphate, which is then detected by the usual inorganic tests.

(iv) **Metals.** When organic compounds containing metals are strongly heated, the organic part usually burns away, leaving behind a residue. This residue is usually the oxide of the metal, but in certain cases it may be the free metal, *e.g.*, silver, or the carbonate, *e.g.*, sodium carbonate.

As a rule, no attempt is made to carry out any test for oxygen; its presence is usually inferred from the chemical properties of the compound.

The non-metallic elements which occur in *natural* organic compounds, in order of decreasing occurrence, are hydrogen, oxygen, nitrogen, sulphur, phosphorus, iodine, bromine and chlorine. Halogen compounds are essentially synthetic compounds, and are not found to any extent naturally. Some important exceptions are chloramphenicol (chlorine), Tyrian Purple (bromine) and thyroxine (iodine). In addition to these non-metallic elements, various metallic elements occur in combination with natural organic compounds, *e.g.*, sodium, potassium, calcium, iron, magnesium, copper.

(3) **Quantitative analysis.** The methods used in the determination of the composition by weight of an organic compound are based on simple principles.

(i) **Carbon and hydrogen** are estimated by burning a known weight of the substance in a current of dry oxygen, and weighing the carbon dioxide and water formed. If elements (non-metallic) other than carbon, hydrogen and oxygen are present, special precautions must be taken to prevent their interfering with the estimation of the carbon and hydrogen.

(ii) **Nitrogen** may be estimated in several ways, but only two are commonly used.

(*a*) **Dumas' method.** This consists in oxidising the compound with copper oxide, and measuring the volume of nitrogen formed. This method is applicable to all organic compounds containing nitrogen.

(*b*) **Kjeldahl's method.** This depends on the fact that when organic compounds containing nitrogen are heated with concentrated sulphuric acid, the organic nitrogen is converted into ammonium sulphate. This method, however, has certain limitations.

(iii) **Halogens** may be estimated in several ways. One is the classical method of *Carius*. The substance is heated in a sealed tube with fuming nitric acid in the presence of silver nitrate. Silver halide is formed, and this is estimated gravimetrically.

A simpler method for *non-volatile* compounds is to fuse the substance with sodium peroxide in a nickel crucible, whereupon the halogen is converted into sodium halide, which is then estimated as before.

(iv) **Sulphur** may be estimated by the methods used for the halogens. In the Carius method for sulphur, no silver nitrate is used. Organic sulphur is converted into sulphuric acid (Carius method) or sodium sulphate (sodium peroxide fusion). In both cases the sulphate is precipitated as barium sulphate and weighed.

(v) **Phosphorus** may be estimated by heating the compound with fusion mixture and weighing the phosphate as magnesium pyrophosphate.

The Carius determination (no silver nitrate used, *cf.* sulphur) invariably gives low results for phosphorus. Olivier (1940) found that exact results were obtained by heating the organic compound mixed with calcium oxide in a stream of oxygen. The phosphate was then estimated as above.

(vi) **Oxygen** is usually estimated by difference. All direct methods are still not completely satisfactory, but recently Aluise and co-workers (1947) claim to have evolved a satisfactory technique. The organic compound is subjected to pyrolysis in a stream of nitrogen, and all the oxygen in the pyrolysis products is converted into carbon monoxide by passage over carbon heated at 1120°. The carbon monoxide is then passed over iodine pentoxide, and the iodine liberated is estimated titrimetrically.

Quantitative analysis falls into three groups according to the amount of material used for the estimation:

(i) **Macro-methods** which require about 0·1–0·5 g. of material (actual amount depends on the element being estimated).

(ii) **Semi-micro methods** which require 20–50 mg. of material.
(iii) **Micro-methods** which require 3–5 mg. of material.

Nowadays the tendency is to use method (ii) or (iii). Although all the methods are simple in theory, their successful application (particularly when using micro- or semi-micro methods) requires a great deal of technical skill. These methods have become standardised, and are described in detail in many books on practical organic chemistry. Improvements and new methods for analysis, however, are always being published; *e.g.*, chlorine and sulphur may be determined by wrapping the sample of the compound in filter paper, igniting and lowering it into a flask filled with oxygen. The acid gases are absorbed in hydrogen peroxide; the sulphuric acid formed is titrated with standard alkali, and the chloride is determined by titrating the neutralised solution with mercuric nitrate (Mikl *et al.*, 1953). Fluorine, chlorine and nitrogen may be determined by decomposition in a nickel bomb (Brown *et al.*, 1955).

(4) **Empirical formula determination.** The empirical formula indicates the *relative numbers* of each kind of atom in the molecule, and is calculated from the percentage composition of the compound.

(5) **Molecular weight determination.** The molecular formula—this gives the *actual* number of atoms of each kind in the molecule—is obtained by multiplying the empirical formula by some whole number which is obtained from consideration of the molecular weight of the compound. In many cases this whole number is *one*.

The methods used for the determination of molecular weights fall into two main groups: physical and chemical. The standard physical methods are the determination of: (i) vapour density; (ii) elevation of boiling point; (iii) depression of freezing point. These methods are described fully in text-books of physical chemistry. In addition to these standard methods, which are used mainly for relatively simple molecules, there are also other physical methods used for compounds having high molecular weights, *e.g.*, rate of diffusion, rate of sedimentation, viscosity of the solution, osmotic pressure, etc.

The chemical methods, since they are only useful in organic work, will be here described in detail.

(i) **Molecular weights of organic acids (method of silver salt).** If the basicity of the acid is known, then the molecular weight of that acid may be determined from the analysis of its silver salt. The silver salt is chosen because: (*a*) Most silver salts are insoluble in water, and hence they are readily prepared. (*b*) Most silver salts are anhydrous; this is a definite advantage, since it does not introduce a possible source of error (*i.e.*, the determination of water of crystallisation). (*c*) All silver salts are readily decomposed on ignition, leaving a residue of metallic silver.

The method of calculation is shown in the following example: 0·701 g. of the silver salt of a dibasic acid on ignition yielded 0·497 g. of metallic silver. Calculate the M.Wt. of the acid, given that the A.Wt. of silver is 108.

Since the acid is dibasic, its molecule can be represented by the formula H_2A, where A is that part of the molecule other than replaceable hydrogen atoms. Hence the silver salt will be Ag_2A, *i.e.*, one gram molecule of it contains 216 g. of silver.

There is 0·497 g. silver in 0·701 g. of Ag_2A

$$\therefore \text{ there is 216 g. silver in } \frac{0{\cdot}701 \times 216}{0{\cdot}497} \text{ g. of } Ag_2A = 304{\cdot}7 \text{ g.}$$

i.e., the M.Wt. of Ag_2A is 304·7.

$$\therefore \text{ the M.Wt. of acid } H_2A \text{ is } (Ag_2A - 2Ag + 2H) = (304{\cdot}7 - 216 + 2) = 90{\cdot}7.$$

(ii) **Molecular weights of organic bases (method of chloroplatinate).** Organic bases combine with chloroplatinic acid, H_2PtCl_6, to form insoluble, anhydrous chloroplatinates (platinichlorides) which, on ignition, leave a residue of metallic platinum. Let B represent one molecule of the base. If it is a "monoacid" base, the formula of its chloroplatinate will be $B_2H_2PtCl_6$; if a "diacid" base, BH_2PtCl_6.

EXAMPLE. 0·800 g. of the chloroplatinate of a "monoacid" base on ignition gave 0·262 g. of platinum. Calculate the M.Wt. of the base, given that the A.Wt. of platinum is 195.

Since the base is "monoacid", the formula of its chloroplatinate will be $B_2H_2PtCl_6$, *i.e.*, one gram molecule of the chloroplatinate contains 195 g. of platinum.

There is 0·262 g. of platinum in 0·800 g. of $B_2H_2PtCl_6$.

$$\therefore \text{ there is 195 g. of platinum } \frac{0{\cdot}800 \times 195}{0{\cdot}262} = 595{\cdot}4 \text{ g. of } B_2H_2PtCl_6.$$

i.e., the M.Wt. of $B_2H_2PtCl_6$ is 595·4.

∴ the M.Wt. of B is

$$\frac{B_2H_2PtCl_6 - H_2PtCl_6}{2} = \frac{595{\cdot}4 - (2 + 195 + 213)}{2} = 92{\cdot}7.$$

(iii) The *molecular formula* of any *gaseous hydrocarbon* (compound containing carbon and hydrogen only) may be determined by exploding a measured volume of the gas with a measured excess of oxygen, in a eudiometer tube.

EXAMPLE. 10 ml. of a gaseous hydrocarbon was mixed with 80 ml. of oxygen and the mixture exploded. 70 ml. of gas remained (after cooling to room temperature), and this was reduced to 50 ml. (of oxygen) after treatment with potassium hydroxide solution. What is the formula of the hydrocarbon?

There are two ways of solving this problem:

(*a*) $$C + O_2 \longrightarrow CO_2$$

Thus one atom of carbon requires one molecule of oxygen.

$$2H_2 + O_2 \longrightarrow 2H_2O.$$

Thus one atom of hydrogen requires $\frac{1}{4}$ molecule of oxygen. Let the formula of the hydrocarbon be C_xH_y. Then x molecules of oxygen will be required to burn the carbon to carbon dioxide, and $\frac{y}{4}$ molecules of oxygen to burn the hydrogen to water. Thus we have

$$C_xH_y + \left(x + \frac{y}{4}\right)O_2 \longrightarrow xCO_2 + \frac{y}{2}H_2O \quad . \quad . \quad . \quad . \quad (i)$$

From Avogadro's law, it follows that

$$1 \text{ vol. of } C_xH_y + \left(x + \frac{y}{4}\right) \text{ vol. of } O_2 \longrightarrow x \text{ vol. } CO_2 + \frac{y}{2} \text{ vol. } H_2O \text{ (as steam)} \quad (ii)$$

Since measurements of volume are carried out at room temperature, the water will be present as liquid, the volume of which may be ignored. Therefore, contraction after sparking $= \left(1 + x + \frac{y}{4}\right) - x = \left(1 + \frac{y}{4}\right)$ vol.

After treatment with potassium hydroxide solution, the contraction will be x vol. (*i.e.*, vol. of CO_2).

From the figures of the experiment, we have

First contraction[1] = 90 − 70 = 20 ml.
Second contraction = 70 − 50 = 20 ml.

∴ since 10 ml. of C_xH_y is to be taken as 1 vol. (from equation ii), then $1 + \frac{y}{4} = 2$.

∴ $y = 4$ and $x = 2$.

Hence the hydrocarbon is C_2H_4.

(*b*) Total amount of oxygen used = 80 − 50 = 30 ml.

Of this, 20 ml. was required for burning the carbon (vol. of CO_2 is equal to vol. of O_2 used). Hence 10 ml. was required for the hydrogen which gives 20 ml. of steam.

∴ 10 ml. C_xH_y + 30 ml. $O_2 \longrightarrow$ 20 ml. CO_2 + 20 ml. H_2O (steam).

∴ from Avogadro's law

$$C_xH_y + 3O_2 \longrightarrow 2CO_2 + 2H_2O$$

∴ $x = 2, y = 4$; and the hydrocarbon is C_2H_4.

(6) **Determination of structure,** *i.e.*, the manner in which the atoms are arranged in the molecule. The usual procedure for elucidating the structure of an unknown compound is to make a detailed study of its chemical reactions. This procedure is known as the *analytical method*, and includes breaking down (*degrading*) the compound into smaller molecules of *known* structure.

In addition to the purely chemical means, there are also various physical properties which are used to elucidate structure, *e.g.*:

(i) *Dipole moment.* This gives information on the spatial arrangement of atoms in a molecule, and so offers a means of distinguishing between alternative arrangements.

(ii) *Refractive index.* This may be used to distinguish between two types of structure, *e.g.*, between a keto and an enol form.

(iii) *Parachor.* This has been used to distinguish between alternative structures.

(iv) *X-Ray analysis.* This offers a means of studying the arrangement of atoms in crystalline solids, but it may also be used for liquids and gases. Since most organic compounds are complex from the point of view of structure, X-ray analysis has mainly been used to " round off " information obtained by purely chemical means. Bond lengths may be measured by X-ray analysis, and deviations from " normal " values give information on structure.

(v) *Electron diffraction.* This has been used in the same way as X-ray analysis, and is applicable to gases, liquid and solids. It is, however, usually confined to gases or compounds in the vapour state.

(vi) *Absorption spectra.* All organic compounds absorb light, which may be in one or more of the following regions: infra-red, visible or ultra-violet. Many bands are associated with particular groups, and it is therefore possible to ascertain the presence of these various groups in a new compound. In general, compounds possessing similar structures show similar absorption spectra. Hence the structure of a new compound may be elucidated by comparing its absorption spectrum with known spectra.

The *Raman effect* also is characteristic of a particular group, and has been widely used to ascertain the nature of the groups present in a compound.

When sufficient evidence has been accumulated, a tentative structure which best fits the facts is accepted. Sometimes two (or even more) structures fit the facts almost equally well, and it has been shown in certain cases that the compound exists in both forms which are in equilibrium. This phenomenon is known as *tautomerism*. Where tautomerism has not been shown to be present, one must accept (with reserve) the structure that has been chosen (see also next section).

(7) **Synthesis of the compound.** The term *synthesis* means the building up of a compound, step by step, from a simpler substance of *known* structure. The term *complete synthesis* means the building up of a compound, step by step, *starting from its elements* (and any others that may be necessary). In either case (synthesis or complete synthesis), *the structure of each intermediate compound is taken as proved by its synthesis from the compound that preceded it.*

The synthesis of a compound is necessary to establish its structure beyond doubt. There is always the possibility of one or more steps not proceeding " according to plan ". Hence the larger the number of syntheses of a compound by *different* routes, the more reliable will be the structure assigned to that compound.

STRUCTURAL FORMULÆ AND ISOMERISM

In 1857, Kekulé postulated the *constant* quadrivalency (tetravalency) of carbon. From 1900 onwards, however, compounds containing *tervalent* carbon have been prepared, and their number is increasing rapidly. These compounds usually require special methods of preparation, and many have a very short life (see text). Since their properties are different from those compounds containing quadrivalent carbon, they are fairly easily recognised. More recently, compounds containing bivalent carbon (*carbenes*) are believed to be formed as intermediates during certain reactions. Hence, unless there is definite evidence to the contrary, carbon is always assumed to be quadrivalent.

If " valency units " or " valency bonds " (see Ch. II) are represented by lines, then the number of lines drawn from the symbol shows the valency of that atom, *e.g.*,

$$\begin{array}{c} | \\ -\mathrm{C}- \\ | \end{array};\quad -\mathrm{O}-;\quad \begin{array}{c} | \\ -\mathrm{N}- \end{array};\quad \mathrm{H}-$$

The molecular formula shows the number of each kind of atom present in the molecule, but does not indicate their arrangement. In organic chemistry there are many cases where a given formula represents two or more compounds that differ in physical and chemical properties, *e.g.*, there are at least seven compounds having the same molecular formula $C_4H_{10}O$. Such compounds, having the same molecular formula, but differing in physical and chemical properties, are known as *isomers* or *isomerides*, the phenomenon itself being known as *isomerism*. The existence of isomerism may be explained by assuming that the atoms are arranged in a definite manner in a molecule, and that there is a different arrangement in each isomer, *i.e.*, the isomers differ in *structure* or *constitution*. This type of isomerism is known as *structural isomerism*.

Obviously, then, from what has been said above, it is always desirable to show the arrangement (if known) of the atoms in the molecule, and this is done by means of *structural formulæ* or *bond-diagrams*; *e.g.*, the molecular formula of ethanol is C_2H_6O; its structural formula is

$$\begin{array}{ccccccc} & & \mathrm{H} & & \mathrm{H} & & \\ & & | & & | & & \\ \mathrm{H} & - & \mathrm{C} & - & \mathrm{C} & - & \mathrm{O}-\mathrm{H}. \\ & & | & & | & & \\ & & \mathrm{H} & & \mathrm{H} & & \end{array}$$

So far nothing has been said about the *spatial* disposition of the four valencies of carbon. Later (Ch. II) it will be shown that when carbon is joined to four univalent atoms or groups, the four valencies are directed towards the four corners of a tetrahedron. Thus the above plane-structural formula does not show the disposition of the atoms in space; a three-dimensional formula is necessary for this. Usually the plane-formula is satisfactory.

A structural formula is really a short-hand description of the properties of the compound. Hence the study of organic chemistry is facilitated by mastering the structural formula of every compound the reader meets. An organic molecule, however, is only completely described when the following facts are known: *structure* or *constitution* (this includes a knowledge of the electron distribution; see resonance, p. 17), *configuration* (p. 381), and *conformation* (p. 465).

SATURATED AND UNSATURATED COMPOUNDS

If, in an organic compound containing two or more carbon atoms, there are only *single* bonds linking any two adjacent carbon atoms, then that compound is said to be *saturated, e.g.*, ethane, C_2H_6 (I), *normal* propanol, C_3H_8O (II), acetaldehyde, C_2H_4O (III).

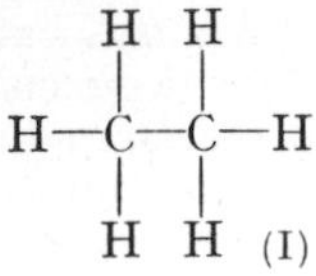

```
    H  H             H  H  H                  H
    |  |             |  |  |                  |    //O
 H—C—C—H          H—C—C—C—O—H             H—C—C
    |  |             |  |  |                  |    \
    H  H  (I)        H  H  H   (II)           H  (III) H
```

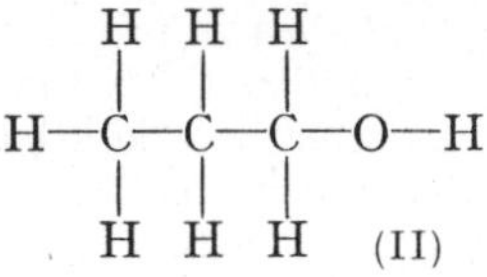

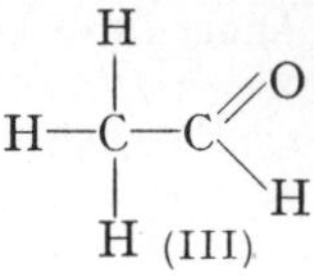

On the other hand, if the compound contains at least one pair of adjacent carbon atoms linked by a *multiple* bond, then that compound is said to be *unsaturated, e.g.*, ethylene, C_2H_4 (IV); this compound contains a *double* bond. Acetylene, C_2H_2 (V); this contains a *triple* bond. Acraldehyde, C_3H_4O (IV); this contains a double bond. *The double bond between the carbon and oxygen atoms is not a sign of unsaturation* (*cf.* acetaldehyde above).

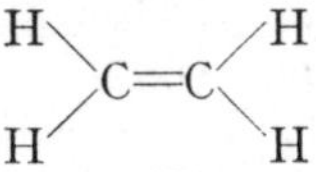

```
                                                      H
 H\      /H                                    H\     |    //O
   C=C          H—C≡C—H                          C=C—C
 H/      \H                                    H/          \H
   (IV)              (V)                            (VI)
```

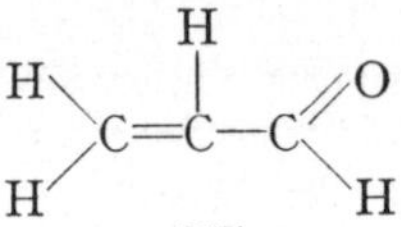

CLASSIFICATION OF ORGANIC COMPOUNDS

Organic compounds are classified into three major groups:

(1) (*a*) **Aliphatic** or **open-chain** compounds.

(*b*) **Alicyclic** compounds. These are **carbocyclic** or **ring** compounds which resemble aliphatic compounds in many ways.

(2) **Aromatic** compounds. These are carbocyclic or ring compounds *containing at least one benzene ring*.

(3) **Heterocyclic** compounds. These are cyclic (ring) compounds containing other elements besides carbon in the ring. In a few cases *no* carbon atom is in the ring.

READING REFERENCES

Partington, *A Short History of Chemistry*, Macmillan (1957, 3rd ed.). Ch. X. The Beginnings of Organic Chemistry.

Schorlemmer, *The Rise and Development of Organic Chemistry*, Macmillan (1894).

Japp, Kekulé Memorial Lecture, *J.C.S.*, 1898, **73**, 97.

Mann and Saunders, *Practical Organic Chemistry*, Longmans, Green (1952, 3rd ed.). Part IV. Quantitative Analysis.

Belcher and Godbert, *Semi-Micro Quantitative Organic Analysis*, Longmans, Green (1954, 2nd ed.).

Pregl, *Quantitative Organic Microanalysis*, Churchill (1937).

Aluise *et al.*, Oxygen in Organic Compounds, *Ind. Eng. Chem.* (*Anal. Ed.*), 1947, **19**, 347.

Vogel, *Practical Organic Chemistry*, Longmans, Green (1956, 3rd ed.), Ch. 12. Semi-micro Technique.

Ann. Reports (*Chem. Soc.*), 1955, **52**, 353. Classical Organic Analysis.

Ingram, The Rapid Micro-combustion Procedure, *Chem. and Ind.*, **1956**, 103.

CHAPTER II

STRUCTURE OF THE ATOM

ACCORDING to modern theory, an atom consists of a *nucleus* which contains *protons* and *neutrons*, and which is surrounded by *electrons*. The mass of a proton is almost the same as that of a neutron, but whereas the proton carries a unit of *positive* charge, the neutron is electrically *neutral*. The electron has about $\frac{1}{1850}$th of the mass of a proton, and carries a unit of *negative* charge. The electrons are arranged in shells around the nucleus, each shell being able to contain up to a maximum number of electrons, this maximum depending on the number of the shell, n. n is known as the *principal quantum number*, and indicates the main energy level of the electrons in that shell. n has *whole* number values, 1, 2, 3, 4 . . ., the shells corresponding to which are also denoted by the letters K, L, M, N . . . respectively. Within each shell there are energy sublevels; these are indicated by l, the *orbital quantum number* (also known as the *azimuthal* or *serial* quantum number). l may have *whole* number values 0 to $n - 1$, each sublevel being also designated by a letter; thus $l = 0, 1, 2, 3, \ldots$ refer respectively to the s, p, d, f . . . sublevels.

In organic chemistry we are concerned only with the s and p levels. In the K shell there can be electrons only in the s level, and they are designated as 1s electrons. In the L shell electrons occur in both s and p levels, and they are known as the 2s and 2p electrons, respectively. The potential energy of an electron is greater the farther it is from the nucleus, and the order of increasing energy for the levels mentioned above is 1s, 2s, 2p.

The existence of spectral lines has been explained on the supposition of one s level, three p, five d, and seven f levels of energy. These levels are known as *orbitals* (see later for a more detailed description of an orbital). By the fundamental *Pauli Exclusion Principle* (1925), no two electrons, in any system, can be assigned the same set of four quantum numbers. Hence there can be only *two* electrons in any one orbital, and these must be differentiated from each other by their spins, which *must* be *antiparallel*, *i.e.*, in the opposite sense. Such electrons are said to be *paired*, and a pair of electrons with antiparallel spins in the same orbital is represented by the symbol $\downarrow\uparrow$. Since a moving charge is accompanied by a magnetic field, a spinning electron behaves as a small bar-magnet, and consequently two paired electrons will give a zero resultant magnetic field.

The hydrogen atom consists of one proton and one electron. When the hydrogen atom is in the " *ground* " state, *i.e.*, the state of lowest energy, its electron will be in the lowest energy level, *i.e.*, the 1s level, and is represented by (1s). When hydrogen is in an " *excited* " state, its electron will occupy a higher energy level, the actual level depending on the amount of " excitation ".

Helium has two electrons; hence its electron configuration in the ground state is represented as $(1s)^2$. Lithium has three electrons. Since the maximum number of electrons in the K shell ($n = 1, l = 0$) is two, the third electron must start the L shell ($n = 2, l = 0, 1$). Electrons occupy lowest energy levels first. Thus this third electron occupies the 2s orbital, and not the 2p, because the 2p is a higher energy level than the 2s. Hence the electron configuration of lithium is $(1s)^2(2s)$. Thus the K shell is filled first. Then the electrons enter the L shell until that is filled. In this shell the s level is filled before the p. In fitting electrons into shells containing orbitals of *equivalent* energy, Hund's rules are used to assign the electrons to their orbitals. These rules are: (i) electrons tend to avoid being in the same orbital as far as possible; (ii) two electrons, each singly occupying a given pair of *equivalent* orbitals, tend to have their spins parallel when the atom is in the ground state. Thus carbon, with six electrons, may be represented as $(1s)^2(2s)^2(2p)^2$. The K shell is filled first; the L shell is filled next, the $2s$ orbital being doubly filled before a higher level is used; then singly two of the $2p$ orbitals. Nitrogen, with seven electrons, is $(1s)^2(2s)^2(2p)^3$: all three $2p$ orbitals each contain one electron. Oxygen, with eight electrons, is $(1s)^2(2s)^2(2p)^4$: here one of the $2p$ orbitals is doubly filled.

THE ELECTRONIC THEORY OF VALENCY

The electronic theory of valency starts with the assumption that valency involves the electrons in the outer shells: in some cases only those in the highest sublevel in the outermost shell; in other cases those in the highest and penultimate sublevels, even though the penultimate sublevel may be in a lower quantum shell. Lewis (1916) assumed that the electron configuration in the rare gases was particularly stable (since these gases are chemically inert), and that chemical combination between atoms took place by achieving this configuration. The outermost shell of the rare gases always contains an *octet* of two s and six p electrons. Since both the s and p sublevels are completely filled, the octet will be a stable configuration. In the case of helium, however, an octet is impossible; here the stable arrangement is the *duplet*, the two $1s$ electrons of which completely fill the first quantum shell.

There are exceptions to the octet rule, *e.g.*, PBr_5 (10 electrons), SF_6 (12 electrons), IF_7 (14 electrons) and OsF_8 (16 electrons).

Lewis also suggested that there was a definite tendency for electrons in a molecule to form pairs. This rule of 2, as we have seen, became established by the developments of quantum mechanics. There are few molecules that contain an odd number of valency electrons: where such *odd electron molecules* do exist, unusual properties are found to be associated with them (see free radicals).

There are *three* ways whereby atoms may achieve their stable states, which correspond to an outermost shell of 2, 8, 10, 12, 14 or 16 electrons, according to the nature of the atom involved.

1. **Electrovalency** is manifested by the *transfer* of electrons, and gives rise to the *electrovalent, polar, heteropolar* or *ionic* bond. Consider sodium chloride. Sodium is $(1s)^2(2s)^2(2p)^6(3s)$: chlorine is $(1s)^2(2s)^2(2p)^6(3s)^2(3p)^5$. Sodium has completed K and L shells, and is starting the M shell with one electron. This electron (the $3s$ electron) is the valency electron of sodium. Chlorine has completed K and L shells, and has seven electrons in the M shell. These M electrons are the valency electrons of chlorine. If the sodium completely transfers its valency electron to the chlorine atom, then each atom will have eight electrons in its outermost shell, and this, as we have seen, is a stable arrangement. Since both atoms were originally electrically neutral, the sodium atom, in losing one electron, will now have a single positive charge, *i.e.*, the neutral atom has become a positive ion. Similarly, the neutral chlorine atom, in gaining one electron, has become a negative ion. In the sodium chloride crystal these ions are held together by electrostatic forces. If the symbol of an element is used to represent the nucleus of an atom and all the electrons other than the valency electrons, and dots are used to represent the valency electrons, then the combination of the sodium and chlorine atoms to form sodium chloride may be represented as follows:

$$\mathrm{Na}^{\cdot} + :\ddot{\underset{\cdot\cdot}{\mathrm{Cl}}}\cdot \longrightarrow \overbrace{\overset{+}{\mathrm{Na}}\ :\ddot{\underset{\cdot\cdot}{\mathrm{Cl}}}:^{-}}$$

2. **Covalency.** Another type of bonding involves a *sharing* of electrons in pairs, each atom contributing one electron to form a shared pair, each pair of electrons having their spins antiparallel. This method of completing an octet (or any of the other possible values) gives rise to the *covalent, non-polar* or *homopolar* bond.

Hydrogen is usually *unicovalent*: occasionally it is unielectrovalent, *e.g.*, in sodium hydride, hydrogen exists as the hydride anion, formed by accepting an electron from the sodium:

$$\mathrm{Na}^{\bullet} + \mathrm{H}^{\bullet} \longrightarrow \underbrace{\overset{+}{\mathrm{Na}}\ \overset{-}{\mathrm{H}}\!:}$$

Carbon almost invariably forms covalent compounds. The electron configuration of carbon is $(1s)^2(2s)^2(2p)^2$. Since the two $2s$ electrons are paired, it would appear that carbon is bivalent, only the two single $2p$ electrons being involved in compound formation. As pointed out previously, carbon is almost always quadrivalent; thus the $2s$ and $2p$ electrons must be involved. Just how these four electrons readjust themselves to give quadrivalent carbon will be described later; at this stage we shall assume it done, and write quadrivalent carbon as $\cdot\dot{\underset{\cdot}{\mathrm{C}}}\cdot$.

In methane the four hydrogen atoms each contribute one electron and the carbon atom four electrons towards the formation of four shared pairs:

$$4\mathrm{H}^{\bullet} + \cdot\dot{\underset{\cdot}{\mathrm{C}}}\cdot \longrightarrow \begin{array}{c} \mathrm{H} \\ \mathrm{H}:\ddot{\underset{\cdot\cdot}{\mathrm{C}}}:\mathrm{H} \\ \mathrm{H} \end{array}$$

Each hydrogen atom has its duplet (as in helium), and the carbon atom has an octet.

Nitrogen, with electron configuration $(1s)^2(2s)^2(2p)^3$, has three $2p$ orbitals each containing one electron, all with parallel spins. Thus each of these orbitals can add one electron to form a pair, thereby giving rise to *tercovalent* nitrogen. The two $2s$ electrons are not used in tervalent nitrogen, and are known as the " lone pair ". It is possible, however, for them to be used as valency electrons, and when this happens a *co-ordinate* valency bond is formed (see below).

Oxygen, with electron configuration $(1s)^2(2s)^2(2p)^4$, has one $2p$ orbital doubly filled, and the other two singly. Thus oxygen can behave bicovalently, with two lone pairs (two $2s$ and the two paired $2p$ electrons). It is also possible for at least one of these lone pairs to be used in co-ordinate valency (see below).

Sulphur may exhibit a covalency of 2, 4 or 6; in certain cases, 3, but when it does so, the sulphur simultaneously becomes unielectrovalent (see below). **Fluorine** and **chlorine** are apparently always unicovalent in organic compounds. **Bromine** may be uni- or bi-covalent. **Iodine** may be uni-, bi- or ter-covalent (and possibly quadricovalent).

Each pair of shared electrons is equivalent to the ordinary " valency-bond ", and so electronic formulæ are readily transformed into the usual structural formulæ, each bond representing a shared pair, *e.g.*,

$$\mathrm{H}:\ddot{\underset{\cdot\cdot}{\mathrm{O}}}:\mathrm{H} \text{ or } \mathrm{H{-}O{-}H};\quad \mathrm{H}:\mathrm{C}\vdots\mathrm{C}:\mathrm{H} \text{ or } \mathrm{H{-}C{\equiv}C{-}H};$$

$$\begin{array}{c} \mathrm{H}:\ddot{\underset{\cdot\cdot}{\mathrm{N}}}:\mathrm{H} \\ \mathrm{H} \end{array} \text{ or } \begin{array}{c} \mathrm{H{-}N{-}H} \\ | \\ \mathrm{H} \end{array}$$

From these examples it can be seen that there is a very important difference between an electronic formula and its equivalent structural formula. In the former, all valency electrons are shown whether they are used to form covalent bonds or not; in the latter, only those electrons which are actually used to form covalent bonds are indicated. This is a limitation of the usual structural formula. Some writers indicate lone pairs by dots, *e.g.*, $\mathrm{H{-}\underset{\cdot\cdot}{\ddot{O}}{-}H}$; others, by short lines, *e.g.*, $\mathrm{H{-}\underline{\overline{O}}{-}H}$ or $\mathrm{H{-}\overset{|}{\underset{|}{O}}{-}H}$. Neither scheme has gained general acceptance. In this book, only when lone pairs are under discussion will they be indicated in the structural formula.

Although bonds are used to represent valency, they are not *material bonds*; their exact nature is still uncertain, but they are probably electromagnetic in character. The term " bond " is used for convenience.

3. **Co-ordinate valency** is a special type of covalency. Its distinguishing feature is that *both* of the shared electrons forming the bond are supplied by only one of the two atoms linked together, *e.g.*, when ammonia combines with boron trifluoride to form a " molecular compound ", it is the lone pair of the nitrogen atom that is involved in the formation of the new bond. In boron trifluoride, the boron has only six electrons in its valency shell; hence it can accommodate two more to complete its octet. Thus, if the nitrogen atom uses its lone pair, the combination of ammonia with boron trifluoride may be shown as:

$$\begin{array}{ccc} & \mathrm{H} & \\ \mathrm{H}: & \mathrm{\ddot{\underset{\cdot\cdot}{N}}}: & \end{array} + \begin{array}{cc} & :\mathrm{\ddot{F}}: \\ & \mathrm{\underset{\cdot\cdot}{\ddot{B}}}:\mathrm{\underset{\cdot\cdot}{\ddot{F}}}: \\ & :\mathrm{\underset{\cdot\cdot}{F}}: \end{array} \longrightarrow \begin{array}{cccc} & \mathrm{H} & :\mathrm{\ddot{F}}: & \\ \mathrm{H}: & \mathrm{\underset{\cdot\cdot}{\ddot{N}}} & :\mathrm{\underset{\cdot\cdot}{\ddot{B}}}: & \mathrm{\underset{\cdot\cdot}{\ddot{F}}}: \\ & \mathrm{H} & :\mathrm{\underset{\cdot\cdot}{F}}: & \end{array}$$

In the usual structural formula notation, a co-ordinate bond may be represented by an arrow pointing *away* from the atom supplying the lone pair (Sidgwick, 1927); thus:

$$\begin{array}{ccc} & \mathrm{H} & \\ & | & \\ \mathrm{H}- & \mathrm{N}: & \\ & | & \\ & \mathrm{H} & \end{array} + \begin{array}{cc} \mathrm{F} & \\ | & \\ \mathrm{B} & -\mathrm{F} \\ | & \\ \mathrm{F} & \end{array} \longrightarrow \begin{array}{cccc} & \mathrm{H} & & \mathrm{F} \\ & | & & | \\ \mathrm{H}- & \mathrm{N} & \rightarrow & \mathrm{B}-\mathrm{F} \\ & | & & | \\ & \mathrm{H} & & \mathrm{F} \end{array}$$

The atom that supplies the lone pair is known as the *donor*, and the atom that receives a share is the *acceptor*. Since it is one atom that donates the lone pair, the co-ordinate link is also known as the *dative* link (Sidgwick, 1927).

Before combination, both donor and acceptor are electrically neutral: after combination, the donor has lost a share in the lone pair, and the acceptor has gained a share. Therefore the donor acquires a positive charge and the acceptor a negative charge, and the presence of these charges may be indicated by writing the formula $\mathrm{H_3\overset{+}{N}{-}\overset{-}{B}F_3}$.

Hence we have a covalent bond holding together two charged portions, and because of this the co-ordinate link is also known as the *semi-polar* or *semi-ionic* bond (Noyes, 1933). The co-ordinate link has also been named the " *mixed double bond* " (Lowry, 1923), and the " *semi-polar double bond* " (Sugden, 1925); in both of these the bond is represented $\mathrm{H_3N \rightleftharpoons BF_3}$. In this book Sidgwick's dative formula will be used.

If water were a purely covalent compound, it should have no electrical conductivity at all. Actually pure water has a definite, although very small, conductivity. This implies a small degree of ionisation. The obvious ions are hydrogen and hydroxyl ions:

$$H_2O \rightleftharpoons H^+ + OH^-$$

The proton, however, is co-ordinated by the lone pair of electrons associated with the oxygen atom of another undissociated water molecule to form the so-called *hydronium* or *hydroxonium* ion, H_3O^+, so that the whole process may be represented as follows:

$$H:\underset{\cdot\cdot}{\overset{\cdot\cdot}{O}}:H + H:\underset{\cdot\cdot}{\overset{\cdot\cdot}{O}}:H \rightleftharpoons \left[\begin{matrix} & H & \\ & \cdot\cdot & \\ H: & \underset{\cdot\cdot}{O} & :H \end{matrix}\right]^+ + \left[:\underset{\cdot\cdot}{\overset{\cdot\cdot}{O}}:H\right]^-$$

The final result is that in the donating water molecule the oxygen atom which was originally bicovalent is now *tercovalent uni-electrovalent.*

At first sight it may appear that in the hydroxonium ion one hydrogen is bound by a dative bond, whereas the other two are bound by covalent bonds, *i.e.*, the hydroxonium ion should be written $H_2O \rightarrow H^+$. All work shows that the three hydrogen atoms are equivalent, and so the positive charge is regarded as being centred on the oxygen atom, or possibly distributed over the molecule as a whole; and so the ion is written $\left[\begin{matrix} & H & \\ & | & \\ H— & O & —H \end{matrix}\right]^+$.

In the same way sulphur, in compounds in which it is bicovalent, may act as a donor, and thereby become tercovalent uni-electrovalent.

In ammonia, nitrogen is tercovalent. When ammonia reacts with, for example, hydrochloric acid, the nitrogen donates its lone pair to the proton from the HCl, forming the ammonium ion:

$$\begin{matrix} & H & \\ & \cdot\cdot & \\ H: & N & : \\ & \cdot\cdot & \\ & H & \end{matrix} + H:\underset{\cdot\cdot}{\overset{\cdot\cdot}{Cl}}: \longrightarrow \left[\begin{matrix} & H & \\ & \cdot\cdot & \\ H: & N & :H \\ & \cdot\cdot & \\ & H & \end{matrix}\right]^+ + :\underset{\cdot\cdot}{\overset{\cdot\cdot}{Cl}}:^-$$

Again, as for the hydroxonium ion, there is no difference between these four hydrogen atoms. In the ammonium chloride crystal the ammonium ion NH_4^+, by virtue of its positive charge, attracts the negative chloride ion electrostatically. Hence in ammonium salts the nitrogen atom is *quadricovalent uni-electrovalent.*

Once the co-ordinate bond has been formed, there may be no way of distinguishing it from any other covalent bond, but since one atom has supplied the pair of shared electrons, charges are produced in the molecule. When a covalent bond is formed, charges may also be produced in the molecule, giving rise to a dipole (*q.v.*). Hence the co-ordinate bond is effectively a covalent bond. The extent of the charge on each atom in a dative (or covalent) bond may be found as follows. Add the number of unshared electrons to one half of the shared electrons, and compare the result with the number of valency electrons of the neutral atom, *e.g.*, (i) methane, CH_4. Here there are 8 shared electrons; $\frac{1}{2} \times 8 = 4 =$ number of electrons in the neutral carbon atom; therefore methane is uncharged. (ii) $H_3N \rightarrow BF_3$. For the nitrogen atom we have $\frac{1}{2} \times 8 = 4$; but since the neutral nitrogen atom has 5 valency electrons, in the compound $H_3N \rightarrow BF_3$ the nitrogen has a charge of $+1$. For boron we have $\frac{1}{2} \times 8 = 4$; but since the neutral boron atom has 3 electrons, in this molecular compound the boron has a charge of -1.

Electrovalent compounds are good electrical conductors in the fused state or in solution. They are generally non-volatile, and are usually insoluble in hydrocarbons and allied solvents. Covalent compounds are non-electrical conductors, are generally volatile, and are usually soluble in hydrocarbons and allied solvents. Since the covalent bond is directional, *stereoisomerism* (space-isomerism) is possible (see p. 381). Co-ordinated compounds behave very much like covalent compounds, but they are usually less volatile than purely covalent compounds.

CHELATE COMPOUNDS

In the co-ordinated compounds discussed above, one donor atom has shared its lone pair with one acceptor atom. It is possible, however, for an acceptor atom to receive a number of shares in lone pairs, *e.g.*, cobalt-ammine chloride, $[Co(NH_3)_6]^{3+}3Cl^-$. In this complex, the cobalt atom receives shares from six lone pairs, each ammonia molecule donating its nitrogen lone pair (I). Now let us consider ethylenediamine as the donating molecule. Its structure is $\ddot{N}H_2—CH_2—CH_2—\ddot{N}H_2$. In this molecule there

$$\text{(I)}\quad \left[\begin{array}{c} NH_3 \\ H_3N \searrow \downarrow \swarrow NH_3 \\ Co \\ H_3N \nearrow \uparrow \nwarrow NH_3 \\ NH_3 \end{array}\right]^{3+} 3Cl^- \qquad \left[Co\left\{\begin{array}{l} \swarrow NH_2{\cdot}CH_2 \\ \qquad\quad | \\ \nwarrow NH_2{\cdot}CH_2 \end{array}\right\}_3\right]^{3+} \quad \text{(II)}$$

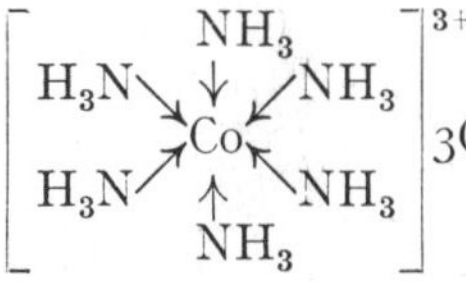

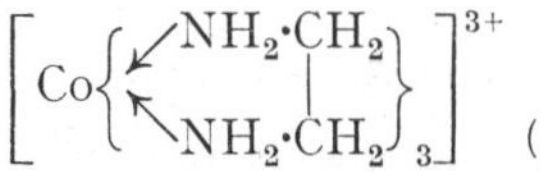

are two lone pairs, and it has been found that each nitrogen atom can act independently as a donor. Thus one ethylenediamine molecule can occupy two positions in the complex, producing the cation (II). This complex will, therefore, contain three rings. Compounds such as this are known as *chelate* compounds, *chelation* taking place when the donating molecule shares two lone pairs on different atoms within the molecule with a single acceptor atom, thereby producing a ring. Chelation may also take place *intra-molecularly*, *i.e.*, between two atoms in the *same* molecule; but in these cases the chelate rings are formed, not by co-ordinate bonds, but by hydrogen bonds (see later).

DIPOLE MOMENTS

When a covalent bond is formed between two identical atoms, *e.g.*, H—H, Cl—Cl, etc., the two electrons forming the covalent bond may be regarded as being symmetrically disposed between the two atoms. The centres of gravity of the electrons and nuclei therefore coincide. With two *dissimilar* atoms the two electrons are no longer symmetrically disposed, because each atom has a different *electron-affinity* (*electronegativity*), *i.e.*, attraction for electrons. Chlorine has a much greater electron-affinity than hydrogen; so that when chlorine and hydrogen combine to form covalent hydrogen chloride, the electrons forming the covalent bond are displaced towards the chlorine atom without any separation of the nuclei:

$$H\cdot + :\ddot{\underset{\cdot\cdot}{Cl}}\cdot \longrightarrow H:\ddot{\underset{\cdot\cdot}{Cl}}: \text{ or } \overset{\delta+}{H}—\overset{\delta-}{Cl}$$

The hydrogen atom will, therefore, be slightly positively charged, and the chlorine atom slightly negatively charged. Thus, owing to the greater electron-attracting power of the chlorine atom, the covalent bond in hydrogen chloride is characterised by the separation of small charges in the bond. A covalent bond such as this, in which one atom has a larger share of the electron-pair, is said to possess *partial ionic character*.

In the foregoing account, it has been assumed that a dipole moment is produced because of the unequal electronegativity of the two atoms concerned. This explanation, although satisfactory for many simple molecules, is not satisfactory in other cases. Thus other factors (besides electronegativity) must operate in determining the value of the dipole moment (see, *e.g.*, p. 27).

In analogy with a magnet, such a molecule is called a *dipole*, and the product of the electronic charge, *e*, and the distance *d*, between the charges (positive and negative centres) is called the *dipole moment*, μ; *i.e.*, $\mu = e \times d$. *e* is of the order of 10^{-10} e.s.u.; *d*, 10^{-8} cm. Therefore μ is of the order 10^{-18} e.s.u., and this unit is known as the Debye (D), in honour of Debye, who did a large amount of work on dipole moments.

The dipole moment is a vector quantity, and its direction is often indicated by an arrow parallel to the line joining the points of charge, and pointing towards the negative end, *e.g.*, $\overrightarrow{\text{H—Cl}}$. The greater the value of the dipole moment, the greater is the *polarity* of the bond. The terms *polar* and *non-polar* are used to describe bonds, molecules and groups, and the reader is advised to make sure he appreciates how the terms are applied in each case under consideration.

The following points are useful in organic chemistry:

(i) In the bond H—X, where X is any atom other than hydrogen or carbon, the hydrogen atom is the positive end of the dipole, *i.e.*, $\overrightarrow{\text{H—X}}$.

(ii) In the bond C—X, where X is any atom other than carbon, the carbon atom is the positive end of the dipole, *i.e.*, $\overrightarrow{\text{C—X}}$. Earlier work appeared to show that in saturated compounds of carbon, the dipole for the C—H bond was $\overleftarrow{\text{C—H}}$. Work by Coulson (1942), however, indicates that the dipole is in the opposite direction, *i.e.*, $\overrightarrow{\text{C—H}}$, and that in methane the value is 0·30D. Both the direction and value, however, are not constant, but depend on the nature of the hybridisation. According to Walsh (1947), the more *s* character a hybridised orbital possesses, the more negative will be the carbon atom. Thus in methane the dipole is $\overrightarrow{\text{C—H}}$, but in ethylene the dipole is $\overleftarrow{\text{C—H}}$ and has a value of 0·40D. This also holds good for benzene, and is even greater in acetylene.

(iii) When a molecule contains two or more polar bonds, the resultant dipole moment of the molecule is obtained by the vectorial addition of the constituent bond dipole moments.

(iv) A symmetrical molecule is non-polar, although it may contain polar bonds.

ELECTRON DISPLACEMENTS IN A MOLECULE

1. **Inductive effect.** Consider a carbon chain in which one terminal carbon atom is joined to a chlorine atom: —C_3—C_2—C_1—Cl. Chlorine has a greater electron-affinity than carbon; therefore the electron pair forming the covalent bond between the chlorine atom and C_1 will be displaced towards the chlorine atom. This causes the chlorine atom to acquire a small negative charge, and C_1 a small positive charge. Since C_1 is positively charged, it will attract towards itself the electron pair forming the covalent bond between C_1 and C_2. This will cause C_2 to acquire a small positive charge, but the charge will be smaller than that on C_1 because the effect of the chlorine atom has been transmitted through C_1 to C_2. Similarly, C_3 acquires a positive charge which will be smaller than that on C_2. This type of electron displacement along a chain is known as the *inductive effect*; it is *permanent*, and decreases rapidly as the distance from the source increases. From the practical point of view, it may be ignored after the second carbon atom. It is important to note that the electron pairs, although permanently displaced, *remain in the same valency shells*.

This inductive effect is sometimes referred to as a *transmission effect*, since it takes place by a displacement of the intervening electrons in the molecule.

There is also another effect possible, the *direct* or *field effect*, which results from the electrostatic interaction across space or through a solvent of two charged centres in the same molecule, *i.e.*, the direct effect takes place independently of the electronic system in the molecule (Ingold, 1934). Apparently it has not been possible to separate these two modes of inductive effect in practice.

The inductive effect may be represented in several ways. The following will be adopted in this book: —C→—C→—C→—Cl.

Inductive effects may be due to atoms or groups, and the following is the order of decreasing inductive effects:

$$NO_2, F, Cl, Br, I, OCH_3, C_6H_5, H, CH_3, C_2H_5, (CH_3)_2CH, (CH_3)_3C$$

For measurement of relative inductive effects, hydrogen is chosen as reference; any atom or group that attracts electrons more strongly than hydrogen is said to have a − I effect (electron-attracting). Any atom or group that attracts electrons less strongly than hydrogen is said to have a + I effect (electron-repelling), *e.g.*, Br is − I; C_2H_5 is + I. This terminology is due to Ingold (1926); Robinson suggests the opposite signs for I, *i.e.*, Br is + I; C_2H_5, − I. Ingold's terminology will be used in this book.

2. **Electromeric effect.** This is a *temporary* effect involving the *complete transfer* of a shared pair of electrons to one or other atom joined by a multiple bond, *i.e.*, a double or triple bond. The electromeric effect is brought into play only at the requirements of the attacking reagent, and takes place almost instantaneously. Consider the following: C═O or C⁞Ö:. At the moment of reaction the oxygen atom takes complete control of one of the shared electron pairs, the electronic structure becoming $\overset{+}{C}$:Ö:$^{-}$. Since the carbon has lost its share in the electron pair, and the oxygen gained a share, the carbon acquires a positive charge and the oxygen a negative one. Removal of the attacking reagent causes the charged molecule to revert to its original electronic condition. It should be noted that the original condition of the molecule will have *small* charges on both the carbon and oxygen atoms (positive and negative, respectively), due to the inductive effect of the oxygen, which is more strongly electron-attracting than carbon. Another effect may also operate to give each atom a small charge (see resonance).

The electromeric effect is represented as follows:

$$C{=}O \longrightarrow \overset{+}{C}{-}\overset{-}{O}$$

The curved arrow shows the displacement of the shared electron pair, beginning at the position where the pair was originally, and ending where the pair has migrated. It should be noted that the electromeric effect might have taken place:

$$C{=}O \longrightarrow \overset{-}{C}{-}\overset{+}{O}$$

However, this is most unlikely, since oxygen is strongly electron-attracting, and therefore " assists " the displacement towards itself, and " opposes " the displacement away from itself. This is an example of the electromeric and inductive effects aiding each other. It is possible, however, for them to oppose each other, and when they do so, the electromeric effect generally overcomes the inductive effect, but this happens only when the chain has conjugated double bonds (see *e.g.*, benzene).

The displacement of the electron pair forming a covalent bond when a unit charge is brought up is a measure of the *polarisability* of that bond. It is not a permanent polarisation since, when the charge is removed, the electron displacement disappears.

3. **Mesomerism or Resonance.** The theory of mesomerism was developed on chemical grounds. It was found that no structural formula could satisfactorily explain all the properties of certain compounds, *e.g.*, benzene. This led to the idea that such compounds exist in a state which is some combination of two or more electronic structures, all of which seem equally capable of describing most of the properties of the compound, but none of describing *all* the properties. Ingold (1933) called this phenomenon *mesomerism* (" between the parts ", *i.e.*, an intermediate structure). Heisenberg (1926), from quantum mechanics, supplied a theoretical background for mesomerism; he called it *resonance*, and this is the name which is widely used.

The chief conditions for resonance are:

(i) The positions of the nuclei in each structure must be the same or nearly the same.

(ii) The number of unpaired electrons in each structure must be the same.

(iii) Each structure must have about the same internal energy, *i.e.*, the various structures have approximately the same stability.

Let us consider carbon dioxide as an example. The electronic structure of carbon dioxide may be represented by at least three possible electronic arrangements which satisfy the above conditions:

```
 ..   ..        -   +              +   -
 O::C::O      :O:C:::O:        :O:::C:O:
 ..   ..       ..                    ..
  (I)           (II)              (III)
```

Structures (II) and (III) are identical *as a whole*, since both oxygen atoms are the same.* Each structure, however, shows a given oxygen atom to be in a *different* state, *e.g.*, the oxygen atom on the left in (II) is negative, whereas in (III) it is positive. Although two (or more) of the electronic structures may be the same when the molecule is considered as a whole, each one must be treated as a separate individual which makes its own contribution to the resonance state. Structures (I), (II) and (III) are called the *resonating*, *unperturbed*, or *canonical* structures of carbon dioxide, and carbon dioxide is said to be a *resonance hybrid* of these structures, or in the *mesomeric state*.

It is hoped that the following crude analogy will help the reader to grasp the concept of resonance. Most readers will be familiar with the rotating disc experiment that shows the composite nature of white light. When stationary, the disc is seen to be coloured with the seven colours of the rainbow. When rotating quickly, the disc appears to be white. The resonating structures of a resonance hybrid may be compared to the seven colours, and the actual state of the resonance hybrid to the " white "; *i.e.*, the resonating structures may be regarded as superimposed on one another, the final result being *one kind of molecule*. **In a resonance hybrid all the molecules are the same; a resonance hybrid cannot be expressed by any single structure.**

In a resonance hybrid the molecules have, to some extent, the properties of each resonating structure. The greater the contribution of any one structure, the more closely does the actual state approach to that structure. At the same time, however, a number of properties differ from those of any one structure. The observed heat of formation of carbon dioxide is greater than the calculated value by 31·6 kg. cal. In other words, carbon dioxide

* If the two oxygen atoms are not the same but one is isotope ^{16}O and the other isotope ^{18}O, then clearly structures (II) and (III) are different.

requires 31·6 kg. cal. more energy than expected to break it up into its elements, *i.e.*, carbon dioxide is more stable than anticipated on the structure O=C=O. How can this be explained? Arguments based on quantum mechanics show that a resonance hybrid would be more stable than any single resonating structure, *i.e.*, the internal energy of a resonance hybrid is less than that calculated for any one of the resonating structures. The difference between the heat of formation of the *actual* compound, *i.e.*, the *observed* value, and that of the resonating structure which has the *lowest* internal energy (obtained by *calculation*) is called the **resonance energy**. Thus the value of the resonance energy of any resonance hybrid is *not an absolute value*; it is a *relative* value, the resonating structure containing the least internal energy being chosen as the arbitrary standard for the resonance hybrid. The greater the resonance energy, the greater is the stabilisation due to resonance. The resonance energy is a maximum when the resonating structures have equal energy content, and the more resonating structures there are, the greater is the resonance energy. When the resonating structures are identical in energy content, and consequently the resonance energy is a maximum, the compound is said to be completely *degenerate*.

Another property of the resonance hybrid which differs from that of any of the resonating structures, is that of the bond length, *i.e.*, the distance between atoms joined by a covalent bond. The normal length of the carbonyl double bond (C=O) in ketones is about 1·22 A; the value found in carbon dioxide is 1·15 A. For a given pair of atoms, the length of a single bond is greater than that of a double bond, which, in turn, is greater than that of a triple bond. Resonance, therefore, accounts for the carbonyl bond in carbon dioxide not being single, double or triple (see also butadiene, p. 80, and benzene, p. 484).

In a resonance hybrid, the electronic arrangement and bond lengths will be different from those of the resonating structures. Consequently the observed dipole moment may differ from that calculated for any one structure.

As we have seen above, in a resonance hybrid all the molecules have the same structure. A difficulty that arises with the resonance theory is the representation of a resonance hybrid. The molecules corresponding to the structures chosen as the resonating structures do not necessarily have an actual existence. Thus, if these resonating structures are fictitious, what fictitious structures are we to choose? The normal way of solving this problem is first to ascertain the structure of the molecule by the usual methods, and then describe it by means of the classical valency-bond formula. Let us consider again the case of carbon dioxide. The classical structure is (I) (see above). As we have also seen, it has been found that not all the properties of carbon dioxide are described by this classical formula. Thus the classical structure is an approximation, and it is in this sense that classical structures are fictitious. By *postulating* other electronic structures (II) and (III), wave functions can then also be obtained for these fictitious structures. By a linear combination of all three functions, a " structure " is obtained which describes the properties of carbon dioxide. This " structure " is called the resonance hybrid of the classical (I) and the two postulated electronic structures (II) and (III).

It is very important to note here that wave-mechanics offers a theoretical method of studying the electron distribution in a molecule, but starts with a knowledge of the relative positions of all the nuclei concerned, *i.e.*, with the " classical structure ". Theoretically, it is possible to start from a molecular formula, and then solve the structure. The number of possibilities and mathematical difficulties, however, are far too great at present, and so it seems that the classical chemist, who arrives at the classical structures by classical methods, will still be " in business " for a long time to come. Since, however, by means of wave-mechanics one can calculate the density of electronic charge at all points in a molecule (of known classical structure), it is possible from this information to deduce charge distributions, bond lengths and bond angles, and consequently the size and shape of a molecule.

The question that now arises is: Starting with the classical structure, what other electronic structures are we justified in postulating? A very important point in this connection is that *resonance can occur only when all the atoms involved lie in the same plane* (*or nearly in the same plane*). Thus any change in structure which prevents planarity will diminish or inhibit resonance. This phenomenon is known as *steric inhibition of resonance* (p. 659).

In practice, then, the conditions described above must be considered when choosing canonical structures. At the same time, the following observations will be a useful guide:

(i) Elements of the first two rows never violate the octet rule (hydrogen, of course, can never have more than a duplet).

(ii) The more stable a structure, then generally the larger will be its contribution to the resonance state. The stability of a molecule can be found from its bond energies. The bond energy is the amount of energy required to dissociate a compound, say AB, in the gaseous state, into the neutral atoms A· and B·. Generally, the structure with the largest number of bonds is the most stable.

(iii) If the different resonating structures have the same number of bonds, but some structures are charged, then the charged molecules will be less stable than the uncharged. The high energy content of a charged molecule is due to the work put into the molecule to separate the charges, and the greater the distance of charge separation, the less stable is that structure. Even so, charged structures may make a considerable contribution to the resonance state, since resonance among a number of charged structures gives a resonance hybrid that is more stable than any one resonating structure.

The final problem is the method of representing a resonance hybrid. Various methods have been used, and the one used in this book is that introduced by Bury (1935). This consists of writing down the resonating structures with a double-headed arrow between each pair:

$$\mathrm{O{=}C{=}O} \longleftrightarrow \overset{-}{\mathrm{O}}{-}\mathrm{C}{\equiv}\overset{+}{\mathrm{O}} \longleftrightarrow \overset{+}{\mathrm{O}}{\equiv}\mathrm{C}{-}\overset{-}{\mathrm{O}}$$

Inductive and resonance (mesomeric) effects are permanently operating in the " real " molecule; collectively they are known as the *polarisation effects*. On the other hand, there are also two temporary (time-variable) effects, the *electromeric effect* and the *inductomeric effect* (which operates by an inductive mechanism). Both of these are brought into play by the attacking reagent, and collectively they are known as the *polarisability effects*. Remick (1943) has suggested the use of subscripts *s* and *d* to represent the *static* (permanent) and *dynamic* (time-variable) effects. Thus the inductive effect may be represented by the symbol I_s, and the inductomeric effect by I_d.

THE HYDROGEN BOND OR HYDROGEN BRIDGE

Compounds containing OH or NH groups often exhibit unexpected properties such as relatively high boiling points, and it was soon felt necessary to assume that the elements oxygen or nitrogen were linked by means of hydrogen, thereby producing the *hydrogen bond*. Detailed study has shown that the unexpected properties were exhibited only when the atoms participating in the bond had high electron-affinity—fluorine, oxygen and nitrogen (decreasing in this order), and to a less extent, chlorine and sulphur. Thus the hydrogen bond explained, for example, the existence of the HF_2^- ion, the association of hydroxylic compounds such as water, alcohols, etc., and the association of ammonia.

The exact nature of the hydrogen bond is still undecided. It was explained originally by assuming hydrogen to be bicovalent, *e.g.*,

$$[F \rightarrow H - F]^-$$

This assumption was soon rejected on physical grounds. It was then suggested that resonance could explain the existence of the hydrogen bond, *e.g.*,

$$[:\ddot{\underset{..}{F}}:^- \; H-\ddot{\underset{..}{F}}:] \longleftrightarrow [:\ddot{\underset{..}{F}}-H \; :\ddot{\underset{..}{F}}:^-]$$

It now appears that resonance plays only a small part, if any, in hydrogen bonding. The theory now favoured is purely an electrostatic union. In bond Z—H, if Z has high electron-affinity, there will be a relatively large amount of polarity, *i.e.*, the state of affairs will be $\overset{\delta-}{Z}-\overset{\delta+}{H}$, where $\delta+$ is relatively large. Since the hydrogen atom has a tiny volume, the $\overset{\delta+}{H}$ will exert a large electrostatic force and so can attract atoms with a relatively large $\delta-$ charge, providing these atoms have a small atomic radius. Fluorine, oxygen and nitrogen are of this character. If the atom has a greater radius the electrostatic forces are weaker; thus chlorine, although it has about the same electron-affinity as nitrogen, forms very weak hydrogen bonds since its atomic radius is greater.

This theory of electrostatic union has much to support it. The hydrogen bond is very weak, and has more in common with the " van der Waals forces " (which are electrical in nature) than with anything else. Infrared spectroscopy shows that the Z—H bond (Z = F, O or N) is very little affected when the hydrogen enters into hydrogen bonding; actually it has been found that the polarity of the Z—H bond increases slightly. Values obtained for the energy of the hydrogen bond are H—F---H, 10 k.cal./mole; H—O---H, 7; H—N---H, 2.

Hydrogen bond formation *intramolecularly*, *i.e.*, involving one molecule only, gives rise to ring formation or chelation, and this only when the formation of a five- or six-membered ring is possible. Hydrogen bonding *intermolecularly*, *i.e.*, between two or more molecules, gives rise to association. Many examples of hydrogen bonding will be found in the text, and this is represented by a dotted line between the hydrogen and other atom involved (as shown above).

Association produces a higher boiling point than expected (*e.g.*, from the molecular weight of the compound). On the other hand, chelation usually produces a lower boiling point than expected, *e.g.*, a nitro-compound usually has a higher boiling point than its parent compound, but if chelation is possible in the nitro-compound, the boiling point is lowered (see, *e.g.*, nitrophenols, p. 599).

ATOMIC AND MOLECULAR ORBITALS

So far, we have discussed the structure of molecules in terms of valency bonds. There is an alternative method of investigating the structure of molecules, and to appreciate this approach—and to extend the other—it is necessary to consider the structure of matter from the point of view of wave-mechanics. It has already been pointed out that the electron may be regarded as a tiny mass carrying a negative charge. In 1923, de Broglie proposed that every moving particle has wave properties associated with it. This was first experimentally verified in the case of the electron (Davisson and Germer, 1927; G. P. Thomson, 1928). Thus an electron has a dual nature, particle and wave, but it behaves as one or the other according to the nature of the experiment; *it cannot at the same time behave as both.* According to wave-mechanics, a moving particle is represented by a wave function ψ such that $\psi^2 dv$ is the *probability* of finding the particle in the element of volume dv. The greater the value of ψ^2, the greater is the probability of finding the electron in that volume dv. Theoretically, ψ has a finite value at a large distance (compared with atomic dimensions) from the nucleus, but in practice there is very little probability of finding the electron beyond a distance of 2–3A. It is therefore possible to map out regions or contours within which the probability of finding the electron is high, and outside which there is very little likelihood of finding the electron.

An alternative interpretation of the wave function ψ is to regard the electron as a cloud (*charge-cloud*), the density of the cloud at any point being proportional to ψ^2. Hence once again it is possible to draw contours within which almost all the electron charge is to be found. These regions (of probability or of density of charge-cloud) are known as *atomic orbitals* (A.O.s), and have characteristic shapes.

In 1926, Schrödinger developed the wave-equation, which connected the wave function ψ of an electron with its energy, E. This equation has an infinite number of solutions for E, but only certain values are permissible since certain conditions must be satisfied. The solutions for ψ are called the *eigenfunctions*, and the corresponding values of E are called the *eigenvalues*. A number of eigenfunctions exist, the simplest being those which possess *spherical symmetry* (ψ_s function), and the next simplest being those which possess an *axis of symmetry* (ψ_p function). The eigenvalues (*i.e.*, the energy values) for the ψ_s functions are not, in general, the same as those for the ψ_p functions. Since $\psi^2\ dv$ measures the probability of finding the electron in the element of volume dv, we can therefore picture "probability regions" which will be generated by the expressions $\psi^2{}_s$ and $\psi^2{}_p$. Such regions are those we have called *atomic orbitals*, and we can speak of the energy of an A.O. if we mean the eigenvalue (energy value) corresponding to that wave function ψ.

In addition to its wave function ψ, an electron also has spin. Two electrons can have the same wave function, *i.e.*, can occupy the same orbital *provided their spins are opposite* (Pauli exclusion principle). In this case the electrons are said to be paired.

The various A.O.s are classified as $s, p, d, f, \ldots$ orbitals. Only the s and p orbitals need concern us, and Fig. 1* shows their shapes. The s-orbital is spherically symmetrical, which means that the region within which it is reasonable to expect to find the electron is a sphere having the nucleus as centre. The p-orbitals are dumb-bell in shape, and the two halves are separated by a *nodal plane*, over which the value of ψ is zero, *i.e.*, there is no likelihood of finding the electron in this plane. In these p-orbitals, the electron is confined to regions which have a marked directional character, each orbital having an axis at right angles to those of the other two, and hence they are known as the p_x, p_y, p_z orbitals, respectively. These orbitals are entirely equivalent except for their directional property.

The order of orbital energies is $1s < 2s < 2p < 3s < 3p < 3d \ldots$ Since an electron must occupy some *particular* orbital, when the electron "jumps" from that orbital to another, it acquires the energy of the new

* Each diagram has been given two numbers, the first indicating the chapter, and the second the order in that chapter. Reference to a diagram in its *own* chapter will be indicated by the *second* number only.

orbital, absorbing or emitting the difference in a "discrete energy packet" or *quantum*. Not all transitions between different energy levels are allowable; a definite rule of selection exists, *e.g.*, permitted transitions are $s \longrightarrow p$, $p \longrightarrow s$ or d, etc.; $s \longrightarrow s$ is *not* permitted. When an electron absorbs a quantum of energy, it is driven into an (allowable) orbital of

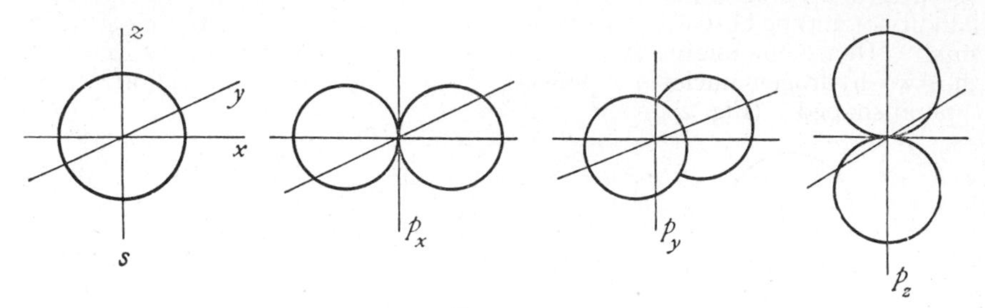

FIG. 2.1.

higher energy. The atom is then said to be "*excited*", and is more reactive. On returning to its normal orbital, the electron emits the quantum of energy at a definite wave-length, giving rise to a particular line in the emission spectrum (see p. 743). When all the electrons in an atom are in their normal orbitals, *i.e.*, orbitals of lowest energy, the atom is said to be in the "*ground*" state.

So far, we have dealt only with atoms, *i.e.*, with electrons associated with *one* nucleus. The wave-equations for molecules cannot be solved without making some approximations. Two types of approximations have been made, one set giving rise to the *valence-bond* method (V.B.); and the other set to the *molecular orbital* method (M.O.). The V.B. method—due mainly to the work of Heitler, London, Slater and Pauling—considers the molecule as being made up of atoms *with electrons in atomic orbitals on each atom*. Thus a molecule is treated as if it were composed of atoms which, to some extent, retain their individual character when linked to other atoms. The M.O. method—due mainly to the work of Hund, Lennard-Jones and Mulliken—treats a molecule in the same way as an atom, except that in the molecule an electron moves in the field of *more than one nucleus*, i.e., *molecular orbitals* are *polycentric*. Thus each electron in a molecule is described by a certain wave function, the *molecular* orbital, for which contours can be drawn as for A.O.s, but differing in that the former are polycentric and the latter monocentric. In general, the greater the freedom (*i.e.*, the larger the region for movement) allowed to an electron, the lower will be its energy. Thus atoms combine to form a molecule because, owing to the overlap of the A.O.s when the atoms are brought together, the electrons acquire a greater freedom, and the energy of the system is lowered below that of the separate atoms. Energy would therefore have to be supplied to separate the atoms in the molecule, and the greater the amount of energy necessary, the stronger are the bonds formed between the various atoms.

Let us now consider the case of the hydrogen molecule. A hydrogen atom has one $1s$ electron. When the bond is formed between two hydrogen atoms to form the hydrogen molecule, these two $1s$ electrons become *paired* to form *molecular electrons*, *i.e.*, both occupy the same M.O., a state of affairs which is possible provided their spins are antiparallel. A very important principle for obtaining the M.O. is that the bond energy is greatest when the component A.O.s overlap one another as much as possible. To get the maximum amount of overlap of orbitals, the orbitals should be in the same plane. Thus the M.O. is considered as being a *linear combination of atomic orbitals with maximum overlap* (L.C.A.O.). Furthermore, according to L.C.A.O. theory, the binding energy is greater the more nearly equal are the energies of the component A.O.s. If these energies differ very much, then there will be no significant combination between the two atoms concerned.

Since the hydrogen molecule is composed of two identical atoms, the probability of finding both electrons simultaneously near the same nucleus is very small. Hence one might expect the M.O. to be symmetrical with respect to the two hydrogen nuclei, *i.e.*, the M.O. in the hydrogen molecule will be " plum-shaped " (Fig. 2).

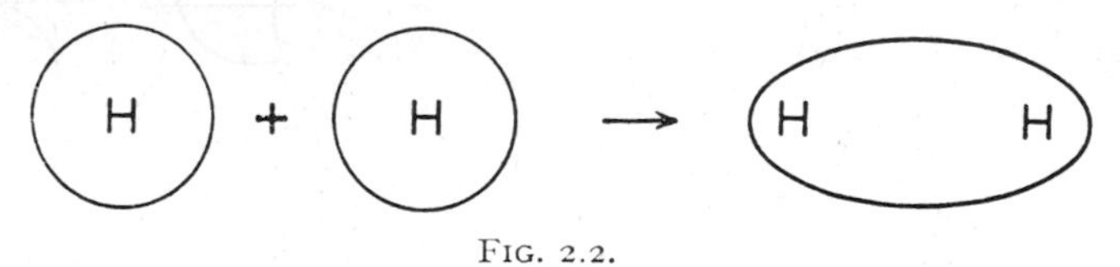

FIG. 2.2.

Although the probability of finding the two electrons simultaneously near the same nucleus is very small, nevertheless this probability exists, and gives rise to the two *ionic* structures H^+H^- and H^-H^+. Thus the hydrogen molecule will be a resonance hybrid of three resonating structures, one purely covalent (*i.e.*, the two electrons are *equally* shared), and two ionic (*i.e.*, the pair of electrons are associated with *one* nucleus all the time):

$$H{:}H \longleftrightarrow \overset{+}{H}\,{:}\overset{-}{H} \longleftrightarrow \overset{-}{H}{:}\,\overset{+}{H}$$

Calculation has shown that the ionic structures contribute very little to the actual state of the hydrogen molecule, and the bond between the two hydrogen atoms is described as a *covalent bond with partial ionic character.* It should here be noted that when the single bond is formed between the two hydrogen atoms, the probability of finding the electrons is greatest in the region *between* the two nuclei. Such a bond is said to be a *localised* M.O., and preserves the idea of a bond connecting the two atoms. This localisation (in a covalent bond) gives rise to the properties of bond lengths, dipole moments, polarisability and force constants.

The electron configuration of carbon is $(1s)^2(2s)^2(2p_x, 2p_y)$. It therefore appears to be bivalent. To be quadrivalent, the $(2s)^2$ and the $(2p_x, 2p_y)$ electrons must be involved. One way is to *uncouple* the paired $2s$ electrons, and then *promote* one of them to the empty $2p_z$ orbital. Should this be done, four valencies would be obtained, since each of the electrons could now be paired with an electron of another atom. The resulting bonds, however, would not all be equivalent, since we would now have the component A.O.s $2s$, $2p_x$, $2p_y$, $2p_z$. All work on *saturated* carbon compounds indicates that the four valencies of carbon are equivalent (but see below). In order to get four equivalent valencies, the four " pure " A.O.s must be " mixed " or *hybridised.* It is possible, however, to hybridise these four " pure " A.O.s in a number of ways to give four valencies which may, or may not, be equivalent. Three methods of hybridisation are important: (i) *tetrahedral* (sp^3 bond), (ii) *trigonal* (sp^2 bond), (iii) *digonal* (sp bond).

(i) In **tetrahedral hybridisation,** the $(2s)$ and $(2p_x, 2p_y, 2p_z)$ electrons are *all* hybridised, resulting in **four equivalent orbitals arranged tetrahedrally,** *i.e.*, pointing towards the four corners of a *regular* tetrahedron (Fig. 3). The orbitals are greatly concentrated along these four directions (Fig. *a* shows the shape along one of these directions). Then by linear combination with the $1s$ orbitals of four hydrogen atoms, four equivalent M.O.s are obtained for methane. Because of the large amount of overlapping between the hybridised A.O.s of the carbon and the *s* A.O. of the hydrogen atom, there will be strong binding between the nuclei. As in the case of the hydrogen molecule, each M.O. is almost completely confined to the region between the two nuclei concerned, *i.e.*, in methane are four *localised* molecular orbitals. This scheme of localised M.O.s may be satisfactorily applied to all compounds containing single covalent bonds. Bond orbitals which are symmetrical about the line joining the two nuclei concerned are known as **σ-bonds.**

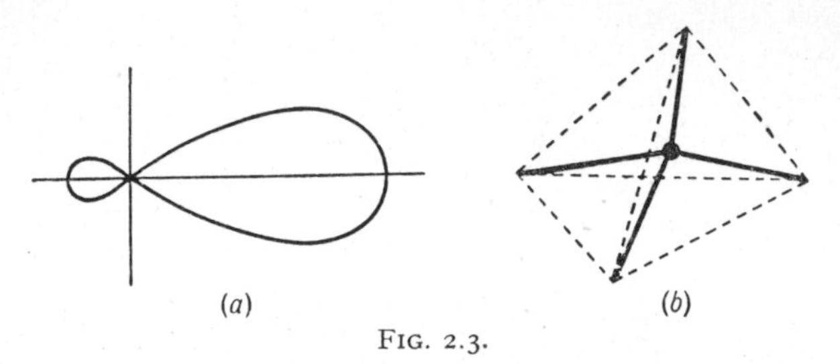

FIG. 2.3.

The above state of affairs holds good only so long as four *identical* groups are attached to the carbon atom, *e.g.*, in CH_4, CCl_4, $C(CH_3)_4$, etc. When the groups are different, *e.g.*, in $CHCl_3$, the four bonds are no longer equivalent. The four carbon valencies are now hybridised in a *non-equivalent* fashion, pointing towards the four corners of an *irregular* tetrahedron. In $CHCl_3$, the three Cl—C—Cl angles are increased from the normal angle of 109° 28′ to about 111°, and the three Cl—C—H angles decreased to about 108°.

(ii) In **trigonal hybridisation,** the $2s$, $2p_x$ and $2p_y$ orbitals are hybridised,

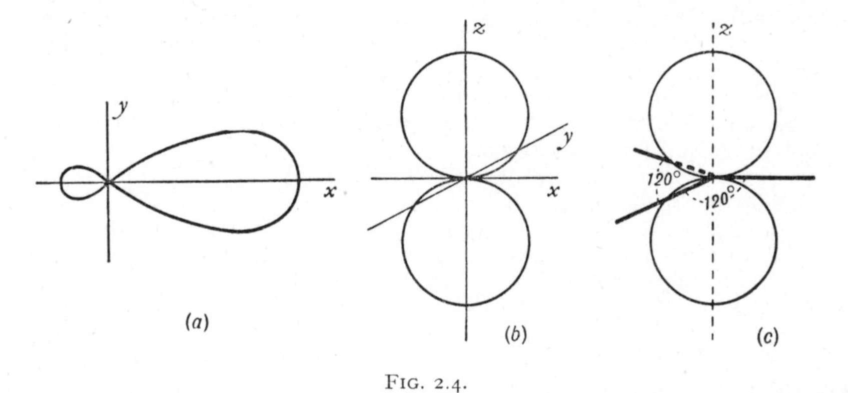

FIG. 2.4.

resulting in **three equivalent coplanar orbitals pointing at angles of 120° in the *xy* plane** (Fig. 4*a*). The remaining orbital is the undisturbed $2p_z$ (Fig. *b*). Thus there will be three equivalent valencies in one plane and a fourth pointing at right angles to this plane (Fig. *c*). The three coplanar valencies form σ-bonds, and the $2p_z$ valency forms the so-called π-bond. The $2p_z$ electrons are known as π-electrons, *mobile* electrons, or *unsaturation* electrons when they form the π-bond. The trigonal arrangement occurs in compounds containing a *double* bond, which is regarded as being made up of a strong bond (σ-bond) between two trigonal hybrid A.O.s of carbon, and a weaker bond (π-bond) due to the relatively small overlap of the two pure

p_z orbitals in a plane *at right angles* to the trigonal hybrids. Fig. 5(*a*) shows the plan, and (*b*) the elevation of ethylene, $CH_2{=}CH_2$ (see also p. 406).

The H—C—H angle in ethylene has been measured spectroscopically, and it has been found to be 119° 55′ (Gallaway *et al.*, 1942). This is in agreement with the value expected for trigonal hybridisation.

It is the π-electrons which are involved in the electromeric and resonance effects.

When a compound contains two or more double bonds, the resulting

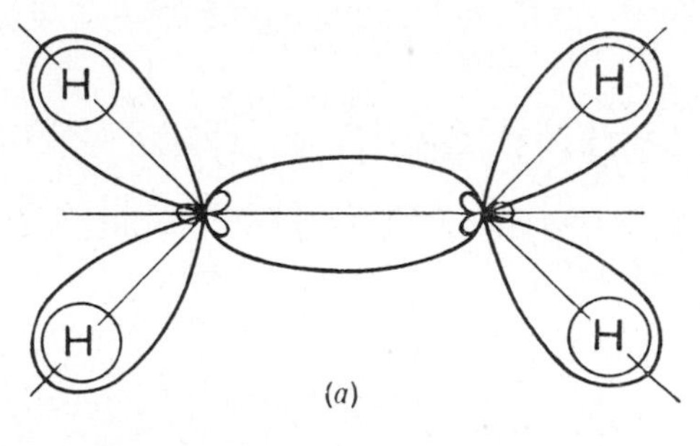

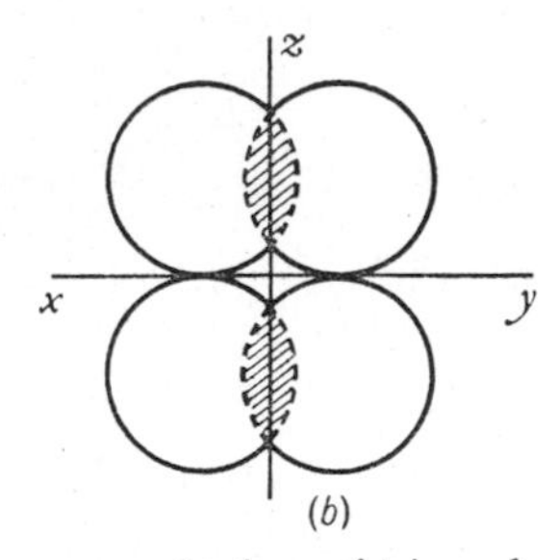

FIG. 2.5.

xy is plane of trigonal hybridisation

M.O.s depend on the positions of these bonds with respect to one another (see, *e.g.*, butadiene, p. 80, and benzene, p. 485).

(iii) In **digonal hybridisation,** only one 2*s* electron and the $2p_x$ electron are hybridised, resulting in **two equivalent collinear orbitals** (Fig. 6); the $2p_y$ and $2p_z$ electrons remain undisturbed. Thus we get two equivalent valencies (forming the σ-type of bond) pointing in opposite directions along a straight line, and two other valencies (each forming a π-type of bond), one concentrated along the *y*-axis (the $2p_y$ orbital), and the other along the *z*-axis (the $2p_z$ orbital). The digonal arrangement occurs in compounds containing a *triple* bond, *e.g.*, acetylene.

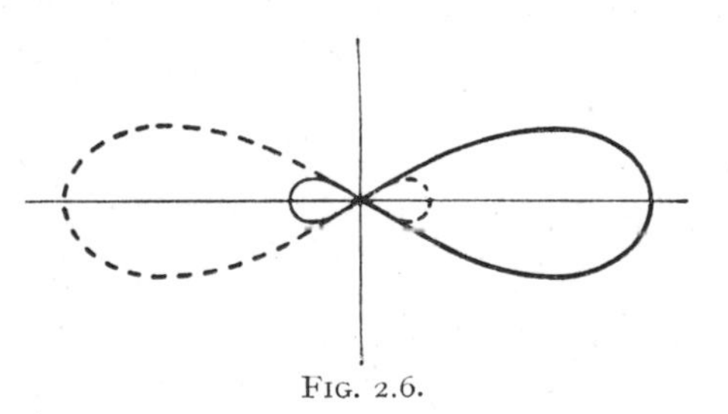

FIG. 2.6.

When the electrons of any atom have been placed in hybridised orbitals, that atom is said to be in a "valence state". The atom on its own cannot exist in a valence state; energy is required to promote the atom to this condition. This energy is obtained through the formation of bonds which are stronger with the hybridised orbitals than with the "pure" orbitals, *i.e.*, more energy is released with the former than with the latter.

Now let us consider the hydrogen chloride molecule. Here we have two *dissimilar* atoms linked together. In the separate atoms the electrons which form the bond are in the H(1*s*) and the Cl($3p_x$) A.O.s, since only these electrons have approximately the same energy. The greatest overlap for these two will be obtained when the *x* direction from Cl points directly towards the hydrogen atom. In this molecule, however, since chlorine is more strongly electron-attracting than hydrogen, the electrons are more likely to be simultaneously near the former atom than the latter. Thus, although the electrons will be found with great probability in the region between the atoms, *i.e.*, we have a localised M.O., nevertheless the region near the chlorine atom will tend to be occupied more than that near the hydrogen atom (Fig. 7; note the "tail" attached to the chlorine atom).

In other words, in addition to the covalent structure H—Cl, there will also be a significant contribution of the ionic structure H^+Cl^-, the contribution of H^-Cl^+ being negligible. Thus we may say that hydrogen chloride is a resonance hybrid of the two resonating structures H—Cl and H^+Cl^-. The actual hydrogen chloride molecule will therefore have a dipole moment $\overrightarrow{\text{H—Cl}}$.

In general, when two dissimilar atoms are linked, the contribution of the two ionic structures, A^+B^- and A^-B^+, will *not* be equally important. The

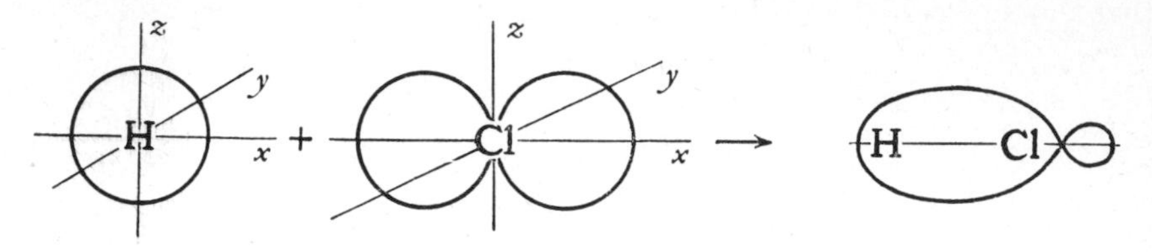

FIG. 2.7.

greater the electron-affinity of B with respect to A, the greater will be the contribution of A^+B^- to the actual state of the molecule. The problem is then to decide what are the weights of the contributions of the resonating structures. The importance of this problem is readily seen from a consideration of carbon dioxide.

$$\underset{\text{(I)}}{\text{O=C=O}} \qquad \underset{\text{(II)}}{\overset{-}{\text{O}}\text{—C}\equiv\overset{+}{\text{O}}} \qquad \underset{\text{(III)}}{\overset{+}{\text{O}}\equiv\text{C—}\overset{-}{\text{O}}}$$

Suppose these three structures are described by the wave functions ψ_1, ψ_2 and ψ_3. Then the actual molecule will be represented by a wave function which is a linear combination of the three structures:

$$\psi = a_1\psi_1 + a_2\psi_2 + a_3\psi_3$$

The best approximation is given by values for the coefficients a_1, a_2 and a_3 that give the *lowest energy* to the resonance hybrid, *i.e.*, coefficients a_1, a_2 and a_3 are a measure of the weights of the resonating structures. This may be done by calculation. On the other hand, in *qualitative* resonance arguments, it is usual to assume that the weight of a resonating structure is directly related to its energy content. This, however, appears to be satisfactory only when two structures are involved, but often leads to erroneous results when three or more are involved.

Now let us consider the problem of ionic character of a bond, and for this purpose let us examine the hydrogen chloride molecule. There are two important structures for this molecule, one purely covalent and the other purely ionic: H—Cl and H^+Cl^-. The wave function of the resonance hybrid is:

$$\psi = \psi_{\text{covalent}} + a\psi_{\text{ionic}}$$

When the value of a is such that minimum energy is obtained, then $(a^2/1 + a^2) \times 100$ is called the *per cent. ionic character* of the bond. This may be calculated from a knowledge of the dipole moment of the bond. The following values have been found for the hydrogen halides:

HF, 60; HCl, 17; HBr, 11; HI, 5.

Thus HF is largely ionic, and HI is mainly covalent.

In hydrogen chloride, the two sets of lone pairs on the chlorine atom $(3p_y)^2$ and $(3p_z)^2$, will point at right angles to the H—Cl bond. Hence the electrons in these pairs are referred to as *pπ-electrons*, *p* because they are in *p* A.O.s, and π because their axes are perpendicular to the valency bond. There is also a third lone pair on the chlorine atom, the $(3s)^2$. It appears, however, from recent work, that these are not " pure " 3*s* electrons. The dipole moment of H—Cl is too great to be accounted for on the basis of the electron affinity of the chlorine atom (see above). It has therefore been suggested that this lone pair of 3*s* electrons is hybridised with the $3p_x$ electron, one hybrid being used for the formation of the H—Cl bond, and the other two hybrids behaving as the " impure " lone pair $(3s)^2$. Calculation has shown that the dipole moment of hydrogen chloride in this condition is reasonably close to the observed value.

We have already discussed the problem of the ground and excited states of an atom. Now let us consider the analogous position of molecules. Suppose we are dealing with a diatomic molecule in which each atom has supplied one electron to form the bond. By means of the L.C.A.O. theory, the solution for the M.O. is found by ultimately solving a *quadratic* equation derived from the combination of the two wave functions (A.O.s). Two *real* roots are obtained, *i.e.*, *two* M.O.s of different energy levels are possible when two A.O.s are combined. Now it is possible for both electrons to occupy either M.O., or for one electron to be in the M.O. of the lower energy level and the other in the higher energy level. When both electrons occupy the lower M.O., the molecule is in the *ground* state, and when one or both electrons occupy the higher M.O., the molecule is in an *excited* state. Suppose E_1 and E_2 (where $E_1 < E_2$) are the energies of the two contributing A.O.s, and $\mathscr{E}_1$ and $\mathscr{E}_2$ (where $\mathscr{E}_1 < \mathscr{E}_2$) are the energies of the two resulting M.O.s. On comparing these energies, it will be found that $\mathscr{E}_1 < E_1$ and $\mathscr{E}_2 > E_2$, *i.e.*, one M.O. has lower energy than the lower of its components (this is the *ground* state), and the other M.O. has a higher energy than the higher of its components (this is an *excited* state). In general, if *n* A.O.s are combined, then there are *n* resultant M.O.s, and any two consecutive M.O.s embrace one of the contributing A.O.s (see Fig. 8).

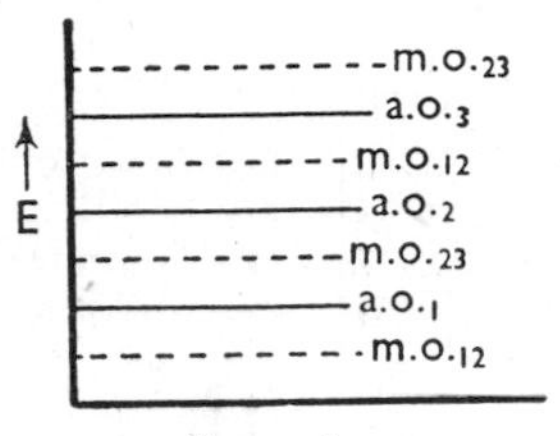

FIG. 2.8.

It can now be seen that when two atoms combine to form a bond, two types of bonding are possible. In one M.O., the energy level is lower than either of its component A.O.s. In this M.O., the electron charge is concentrated in the region *between* the two nuclei, resulting in strong bonding between the

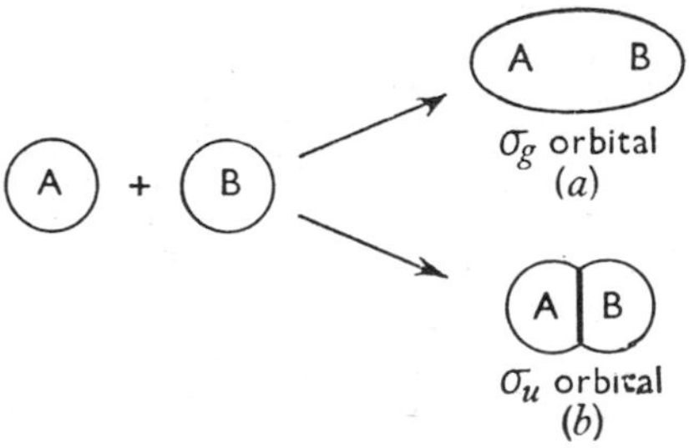

σ_g orbital (*a*)

σ_u orbital (*b*)

FIG. 2.9.

π_u orbital (*a*)

π_g orbital (*b*)

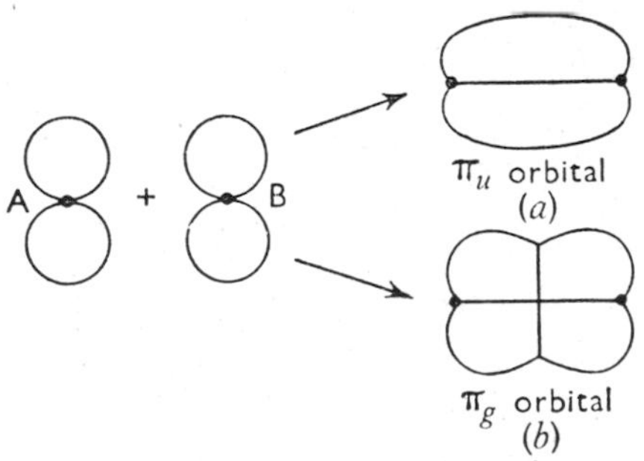

FIG. 2.10.

atoms. This type of M.O. is called a *bonding* orbital or σ_g bond (Fig. 9*a*). In the other M.O., the energy level is higher than either of its component A.O.s. In this M.O., the charge is pushed *away* from the region between the two nuclei, resulting in a nodal plane midway between A and B. In this condition A and B repel each other, and this M.O. is said to be *anti*-bonding or a σ_u bond (Fig. 9*b*).

Any two A.O.s can be combined provided their energies are approximately the same. In the above example of bonding and anti-bonding orbitals, A and B were atoms with *s* electrons. Combination of two $2p$ electrons also gives one bonding and one anti-bonding orbital (Fig. 10*a* and *b*). In the bonding orbital, a π_u-bond, there is *one* nodal plane (which contains the molecular axis), but in the anti-bonding orbital, a π_g-bond, there are *two* nodal planes (one containing the molecular axis, and the other perpendicular to it). It should here be noted that as the number of nodes in a bond increases, the energy level rises, and consequently the bond becomes weaker. When a molecule undergoes transitions from one energy level to another (with emission or absorption of light), a *g* state must go to a *u* state, or vice-versa. Transitions from one *g* state to another *g* state, and from one *u* state to another *u* state are forbidden.

An important difference between V.B. and M.O. theories is that when dealing with energy levels of electrons in *molecules*, in the V.B. method, electrons are dealt with in *pairs*, whereas in the M.O. method, electrons can be dealt with individually (see also p. 747).

THE GENERAL NATURE OF ORGANIC REACTIONS

Much work has been done on reaction mechanisms, *i.e.*, the actual steps by which a reaction takes place. A chemical equation indicates the initial and final products of a reaction; rarely does it indicate *how* the reaction proceeds. Many reactions take place via intermediates which may or may not have been isolated. When a reaction proceeds without any intermediates, that reaction is said to be a *one-step* (or *elementary*) reaction. Furthermore, in every one-step reaction there is a transition state (see below). As a result of much experimental work, particularly from kinetic studies of reactions, it has been shown that most chemical reactions take place in successive steps. The rate of the overall reaction must be controlled by the slowest step; this is known as the *rate-determining step*. Suppose a reaction proceeds by the following two equations:

$$A + B \longrightarrow C + D \qquad \text{(i)}$$

$$C + XY \longrightarrow CX + Y \qquad \text{(ii)}$$

where reaction (i) is slower than reaction (ii). As fast as C is formed it is destroyed by XY. Therefore the amount of XY reacting is conditioned solely by C, and not by the actual concentration of XY, provided that the latter is always present in excess. The rate of formation of C is determined by the concentrations of A and B, which therefore control the rate of the complete reaction. Thus if a reaction is independent of the concentration of one of the reactants, the actual step (or steps) involving this reactant must be faster than the rate-determining step.

Now let us examine in more detail what happens when molecules containing *covalent* bonds undergo chemical reaction. Consider the reaction

$$Y + R - X \longrightarrow Y - R + X$$

where RX and RY are both covalent molecules. It can be seen that in this reaction, bond R—X has been broken and the new bond Y—R has been formed. The mechanism of the reaction depends on the way in which these bonds are broken. There are three possible ways in which this may occur, and the result of much work has shown that the actual way in which the break occurs depends on the nature of R, X and Y, and the experimental conditions.

(i) Each atom (forming the X—R bond) retains one electron of the shared pair, *i.e.*,

$$X\text{-}|\text{-}R \longrightarrow X\cdot + R\cdot$$

This equation is usually written:

$$X\text{—}R \longrightarrow X\cdot + R\cdot$$

This gives rise to *free radicals*, and the breaking of the bond in this manner is known as *homolytic* fission (*homolysis*). Free radicals are *odd electron molecules*, *e.g.*, methyl radical $CH_3\cdot$, triphenylmethyl radical $(C_6H_5)_3C\cdot$, etc. The majority are electrically neutral (a few free radical ions are known). All possess addition properties, and are extremely reactive; when a free radical is stable, its stability is believed to be due to resonance. Free radicals are *paramagnetic*, *i.e.*, possess a small permanent magnetic moment, due to the presence of the odd (unpaired) electron. This property is used to detect the presence of free radicals. Diradicals are also known; these have an even number of electrons, but *two are unpaired* (see, *e.g.*, methylene, anthracene). In general, free-radical reactions are catalysed or initiated by compounds which generate free radicals on decomposition, or by heat or light. Furthermore, a reaction which proceeds by a free-radical mechanism can be inhibited by the presence of compounds that are known to combine with free radicals. Another important characteristic is that a free-radical mechanism leads to abnormal orientation in aromatic substitution.

(ii) Atom (or group) R retains the shared pair. This may be represented as:

$$X|—R \longrightarrow \overset{+}{X} + :\overset{-}{R}$$

This equation is now usually written:

$$X\frown R \longrightarrow X^+ + R^-$$

This is known as *heterolytic* fission (*heterolysis*), and Y is said to be an *electrophilic* (electron-seeking) or *cationoid* reagent, since it *gains* a share in the two electrons retained by R. Obviously an electrophilic reagent attacks a molecule at the point of *high* electron density. When an electrophilic reagent is involved in a *substitution* or a replacement reaction, that reaction is represented by S_E (S referring to substitution, and E to the electrophilic reagent). When $\bar{R}:$ is a negative group in which the carbon atom carries the negative charge, *i.e.*, has an unshared pair of electrons, the group is known as a **carbanion.** Carbanions appear to be capable of leading a separate existence.

(iii) Atom (or group) R loses the shared pair, *i.e.*, the shared pair remains with X. This may be represented as:

$$X—|R \longrightarrow \bar{X}: + \overset{+}{R}$$

or

$$X\frown R \longrightarrow X^- + R^+$$

This also is heterolytic fission (heterolysis), and Y is said to be a *nucleophilic* (nucleus-seeking) or *anionoid* reagent, since it *supplies* the electron pair. Obviously a nucleophilic reagent attacks a molecule at the point of *low* electron density. When a nucleophilic reagent is involved in a substitution or a replacement reaction, that reaction is represented by S_N. When R^+ is a positive group in which the carbon atom carries the positive charge, *i.e.*, lacks a pair of electrons in its valency shell, the group is known as a **carbonium ion,** and is in a trigonal state of hybridisation. It appears that carbonium ions do not have a separate existence but can, however, lead a separate existence in a solvated form.

Mechanisms involving free radicals are known as *free-radical mechanisms*, and those involving carbanions or carbonium ions are known as *ionic mechanisms*.

Although these various ways of breaking the R—X bond occur *ultimately*, it does not necessarily mean that each occurs *first* and then combination of R with Y occurs afterwards. Before a molecule can enter into chemical reaction, it must be *activated, i.e.*, it must attain a certain amount of energy above the average value. As a result of the mathematical work of London (1928, 1929) and Polanyi *et al.* (1931–38), it has been shown that in the reaction

$$Y^- \curvearrowright R{-}X \longrightarrow Y{-}R + X^-$$

the reaction requires a *minimum* energy of activation if:

(i) Y approaches RX *along the bonding line* R—X and on the side *remote* from X.

(ii) The bond R—X stretches at the same time until Y and X can compete on *equal* terms for R.

Thus a point is reached when the distance Y—R and R—X are such that the forces between each pair are the same. This geometrical arrangement of Y, R and X is known as the *transition state* or *activated complex*, and

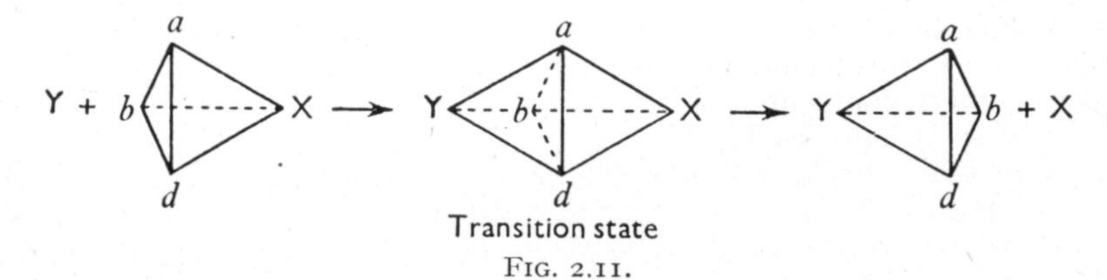

FIG. 2.11.

represents a condition when neither molecule YR nor RX exists independently. From the activated condition, the system can now proceed in either direction, forming Y + RX or YR + X. Thus the reaction may be imagined to proceed as follows:

$$Y + R - X \longrightarrow Y \cdots R \cdots X \longrightarrow Y - R + X$$

Y is approaching RX — **transition state** — X is receding from YR

This reaction is called a *three-centre* reaction, and is said to take place by an *end-on* approach. It should here be noted that the *new* bond Y—R is formed at R on the side *opposite* to that of the *original* bond R—X. Thus if RX is a molecule of the type *abd*CX (where *a*, *b* and *d* are any three univalent atoms or groups), then in the formation of *abd*CY, the original molecule is turned " inside out ", *i.e.*, *inverted* when the new molecule is formed (Fig. 11; see also the Walden Inversion, p. 395).

In addition to three-centre reactions, there are also *four-centre* reactions, *e.g.*:

$$Y - Z + R - X \longrightarrow R - Y + X - Z$$

This type of reaction is believed to occur by a *side-approach* (*broadside-collision*):

$$\begin{matrix} Y & & R \\ | & + & | \\ Z & & X \end{matrix} \longrightarrow \begin{matrix} Y & \cdots & R \\ \vdots & & \vdots \\ Z & \cdots & X \end{matrix} \longrightarrow \begin{matrix} Y - R \\ + \\ Z - X \end{matrix}$$

transition state (planar)

When a reaction proceeds in this manner, no inversion occurs.

The reactions so far discussed have involved the activated complex. On the other hand, organic *ionic* reactions may be promoted by electrophilic and nucleophilic reagents. Examples of these various types of reactions will be found distributed throughout the text.

Use of isotopes in organic chemistry. In recent years the use of isotopes has been extremely helpful in the study of reaction mechanisms and rearrangements, in the elucidation of structures, and also in quantitative analysis. The application of isotopes in biochemistry has also been particularly fruitful, since they offer a means of identifying intermediates and the " brickwork " of the final products. The common isotopes that have been used in organic chemistry are: deuterium (^{2}H, D; stable), tritium (^{3}H, T; radioactive), ^{13}C (stable), ^{14}C (radioactive), ^{15}N (stable), ^{18}O (stable), ^{32}P (radioactive), ^{35}S (radioactive), ^{37}Cl (stable), ^{82}Br (radioactive), ^{131}I (radioactive).

Various methods of analysis are used. Radioactive isotopes are usually analysed with the Geiger–Müller counter, and the stable isotopes by means of the mass spectrograph. Deuterium is often determined by means of infrared spectroscopy; and there are also the older methods for deuterium and ^{18}O of density, or refractive index measurements (of the water produced after combustion of the compound). A new method is that of nuclear magnetic resonance, this technique being applicable only to those isotopes having nuclear magnetic moments, *e.g.*, D, T, ^{13}C and ^{15}N.

Isotopes are usually used as *tracers*, *i.e.*, the starting material is labelled at some particular position, and after reaction the labelled atom is then located in the product. This does not mean that labelled compounds contain 100 per cent. of the isotope, but that they usually contain an abnormal amount of the isotope. Many examples of the use of isotopic indicators will be found in the text (see Index, Isotopic indicators).

The use of isotopes, stable or radioactive, is based on the fact that the chemical behaviour of any particular isotope is the same as that of the other atoms isotopic with it (the chemical properties of an element depend on the nuclear positive charge and the number of electrons surrounding the nucleus, and not on the number of neutrons in the nucleus). This identity in chemical behaviour is essentially true for the heavy atoms, but in the case of the lightest elements, reactions involving heavier isotopes are slower, but so long as identical paths are followed, the final result is unaffected. Furthermore, since the isotopic effect is greater the greater the ratio of the two nuclear masses, deuterium is of particular value as a tracer.

Ion accelerators and nuclear reactors produce, as by-products, artificial isotopes, particularly those which are radioactive. These isotopes are then supplied in the form of some compound from which a labelled compound can be synthesised, *e.g.*, ^{14}C is usually supplied as $Ba^{14}CO_3$, ^{15}N as $^{15}NH_4Cl$, etc. A simple example of the synthesis of a labelled compound is that of acetic acid (in the following equations, which involve a Grignard reagent, $\overset{*}{C}$ is ^{14}C; this is a common method of representing a tracer atom, provided its nature has been specified).

$$Ba\overset{*}{C}O_3 + 2HCl \longrightarrow BaCl_2 + H_2O + \overset{*}{C}O_2$$

$$\text{(i)} \qquad \overset{*}{C}O_2 + CH_3MgI \longrightarrow CH_3\cdot\overset{*}{C}O_2H$$

$$\text{(ii)} \qquad \overset{*}{C}O_2 + 3H_2 \xrightarrow{\text{catalyst}} H_2O + \overset{*}{C}H_3OH \xrightarrow{I_2/P} \overset{*}{C}H_3I \xrightarrow{Mg} \overset{*}{C}H_3MgI$$

$$\overset{*}{C}H_3MgI \xrightarrow{CO_2} \overset{*}{C}H_3\cdot CO_2H \qquad \overset{*}{C}H_3MgI \xrightarrow{\overset{*}{C}O_2} \overset{*}{C}H_3\cdot\overset{*}{C}O_2H$$

In a number of cases, an exchange reaction is a very simple means of preparing a labelled compound, *e.g.*, dissolving a fatty acid in water enriched with deuterium.

$$R{\cdot}CO_2H + D_2O \rightleftharpoons R{\cdot}CO_2D + DHO$$

Because of the possibility of this exchange reaction, it is often necessary to carry out control experiments.

Isotopes are also very useful in the analysis of mixtures, particularly for the determination of the yield of products in a chemical reaction when isolation is difficult. A simple method is that of *isotopic dilution*. The labelled compound is prepared, and a known amount is then added to the mixture to be analysed. A portion of the substance is now taken and analysed for its isotopic content. From a knowledge of the isotopic content of the labelled compound added and recovered, and the weight of the labelled compound added, it is thus possible to calculate the weight of the labelled compound in the mixture. This method can only be used as long as there is no isotopic exchange during the isolation.

READING REFERENCES

Sidgwick, *Electronic Theory of Valency*, Oxford Press (1927).
Watson, *Modern Theories of Organic Chemistry*, Oxford Press (1941, 2nd ed.).
Remick, *Electronic Interpretations of Organic Chemistry*, Wiley (1943).
Pauling, *The Nature of the Chemical Bond*, Cornell University Press (1945, 2nd ed.).
Hammett, *Physical Organic Chemistry*, McGraw-Hill (1940).
Branch and Calvin, *The Theory of Organic Chemistry (An Advanced Course)*, Prentice-Hall (1941).
Dewar, *The Electronic Theory of Organic Chemistry*, Oxford Press (1949).
Walsh, Remarks on the Strengths of Bonds, *Trans. Faraday Soc.*, 1947, **43**, 60 (also pp. 158, 342).
Coulson, Representation of Simple Molecules by Molecular Orbitals, *Quart. Reviews (Chem. Soc.)*, 1947, **1**, 144.
Coulson, *Valence*, Oxford Press (1952).
Wheland, *Resonance in Organic Chemistry*, Wiley (1955).
Wheland, *Advanced Organic Chemistry*, Wiley (1949, 2nd ed.).
Ferguson, *Electronic Structures of Organic Molecules*, Prentice-Hall (1952).
Ferguson, Hydrogen Bonding and Physical Properties of Substances, *J. Chem., Educ.*, 1956, **33**, 267.
Hermans, *Theoretical Organic Chemistry*, Elsevier (1954).
Ingold, *Structure and Mechanism in Organic Chemistry*, Bell and Sons (1953).
Cartmell and Fowles, *Valency and Molecular Structure*, Butterworths (1956).
Hine, *Physical Organic Chemistry*, McGraw-Hill (1956).
Orville-Thomas, Nuclear Quadruple Coupling and Chemical Bonding, *Quart. Reviews (Chem. Soc.)*, 1957, **11**, 162.
Pople, The Molecular-Orbital and Equivalent Orbital Approach to Molecular Structure, *ibid.*, 1957, **11**, 273.
Arnstein and Bentley, Isotopic Tracer Technique, *ibid.*, 1950, **4**, 172.
Thomas and Turner, The Syntheses of Isotopically Labelled Organic Compounds, *ibid.*, 1953, **7**, 407.
Gold and Satchell, The Principles of Hydrogen Isotope Exchange Reactions in Solution, *ibid.*, 1955, **9**, 51.
Semenow and Roberts, Uses of Isotopes in Organic Chemistry, *J. Chem. Educ.*, 1956, **33**, 2.
Popják, Chemistry, Biochemistry, and Isotopic Tracer Technique, Lectures, Monographs and Reports of the Royal Institute of Chemistry, 1955, No. 2.

CHAPTER III

ALIPHATIC COMPOUNDS

PARAFFINS

ALIPHATIC compounds are *open-chain* or *acyclic* compounds, and the name aliphatic arises from the fact that the first compounds of this class to be studied were the fatty acids (Greek: *aliphos*, fat).

Carbon forms a large number of compounds with hydrogen only and these are known collectively as *hydrocarbons*. There are two groups of hydrocarbons: (i) *saturated* hydrocarbons; (ii) *unsaturated* hydrocarbons.

The paraffin hydrocarbons or the *paraffins* are the saturated hydrocarbons. Many occur naturally, and the chief source of the paraffins is *mineral oil* or *petroleum*, which occurs in many parts of the world.

The simplest paraffin is **methane,** CH_4, which occurs in "natural gas" (*q.v.*) and the gases from oil-wells. Methane is the principal product of organic decay in swamps and marshes, the gas being set free by the action of bacteria; this method of formation in nature has given rise to the name "marsh-gas" for methane. Sewage sludge which has been fermented by bacteria yields a gas containing about 70 per cent. methane, and this is used as a liquid fuel. Methane also forms about 40 per cent. by volume of coal-gas.

Methane may be synthesised as follows:

(i) By striking an electric arc between carbon electrodes in an atmosphere of hydrogen. Only a very small amount of methane is obtained in this way.

(ii) A mixture of carbon and reduced nickel is heated at 475° in the presence of hydrogen.

(iii) The first synthesis of methane was carried out by Berthelot in 1856, who passed a mixture of carbon disulphide and hydrogen sulphide over heated copper:

$$CS_2 + 2H_2S + 8Cu \longrightarrow CH_4 + 4Cu_2S$$

(iv) A mixture of carbon monoxide or dioxide and hydrogen is passed over finely divided nickel heated at about 300°:

$$CO + 3H_2 \longrightarrow CH_4 + H_2O$$
$$CO_2 + 4H_2 \longrightarrow CH_4 + 2H_2O$$

This synthesis is due to Sabatier and Senderens (1897). Until recently the nickel catalyst was usually prepared by reducing with hydrogen nickel oxide deposited on a suitable inert, porous support, *e.g.*, kieselguhr. The support is impregnated with a nickel salt, treated with sodium hydroxide, washed and dried, and the resulting nickel oxide reduced with hydrogen at 300–450°. Many organic compounds may be reduced by passing their vapours mixed with hydrogen over nickel heated at 200–300°. Any reduction that is carried out in this manner is referred to as the *Sabatier–Senderens reduction,* in honour of the workers who first introduced this method. It is quite a common feature in organic chemistry to name a reaction after its discoverer or, in certain cases, after a worker who investigated the reaction and extended its application. The reader should always make himself familiar with the reaction *associated* with a particular name.

The most common nickel catalyst used to-day is that prepared by the method introduced by Raney (1927). An alloy containing equal amounts of nickel and aluminium is digested with sodium hydroxide; the aluminium is dissolved away, and the residual very finely divided nickel is washed and stored under water, ethanol, or any other suitable liquid. Raney nickel is more reactive than the supported nickel catalyst, and is usually effective at lower temperatures, often at room temperature.

None of the syntheses described above is of any *practical* importance as a method of preparing methane in quantity. The following methods are those which may be used in the laboratory, *i.e.*, convenient methods of preparing methane in reasonable quantities. The degree of purity of the product depends on the particular method used. Quite often it is the purification of the crude product which causes an appreciable loss of material, and the more we aim at getting the " pure " compound, the smaller is the final yield.

1. The most convenient method is to heat a mixture of anhydrous sodium acetate and soda-lime (see also p. 44):

$$CH_3 \cdot CO_2Na + NaOH(CaO) \longrightarrow CH_4 + Na_2CO_3$$

In chemical reactions soda-lime behaves as sodium hydroxide (or calcium hydroxide); it is not deliquescent and does not attack glass, and is therefore more convenient to use than solid sodium hydroxide.

2. By boiling aluminium carbide with water:

$$Al_4C_3 + 12H_2O \longrightarrow 3CH_4 + 4Al(OH)_3$$

The methane is impure; it contains hydrogen.

3. Almost pure methane (it contains traces of hydrogen) is obtained by the reduction of methyl iodide with nascent hydrogen:

$$CH_3I + 2[H] \longrightarrow CH_4 + HI$$

A common method for generating hydrogen uses zinc and acetic acid saturated with hydrogen chloride, or hydrochloric acid alone, or with aqueous sodium hydroxide. Another useful method is by the action of a zinc–copper couple on ethanol.

Lithium aluminium hydride or lithium hydride may also be used for reducing alkyl bromides.

4. By the action of water on:

(*a*) dimethylzinc, $(CH_3)_2Zn + 2H_2O \longrightarrow 2CH_4 + Zn(OH)_2$
(*b*) Methylmagnesium iodide,

$$CH_3 - Mg - I + H_2O \longrightarrow CH_4 + MgI(OH).$$

Method (*b*) is far more convenient than (*a*). Methylmagnesium iodide is a member of a group of compounds known as the *Grignard reagents* (p. 331).

Methane is obtained in vast quantities from natural gas, gas from the oil-wells, and from cracked petroleum (*q.v.*).

Properties of methane. Methane is a colourless, odourless, non-poisonous gas; its b.p. is $-164°/760$ mm., and m.p. $-184°$. It is somewhat soluble in water, 100 ml. of water dissolving about 5 ml. of methane at 20°; but is quite soluble in ethanol and ether. It burns with a non-luminous flame in air or oxygen, forming carbon dioxide and water:

$$CH_4 + 2O_2 \longrightarrow CO_2 + 2H_2O$$

It explodes violently when mixed with air (or oxygen) and ignited, and this is believed to be the cause of explosions in coal-mines, where methane is known as *fire-damp*. Methane may be *catalytically* oxidised to methanol and formaldehyde.

Substitution reactions of methane. Chlorine has no action on methane in the dark. In bright sunlight the reaction is explosive, and hydrogen chloride and carbon are formed:

$$CH_4 + 2Cl_2 \longrightarrow C + 4HCl$$

In diffused sunlight no explosion occurs, but a series of reactions takes place whereby the four hydrogen atoms in methane are successively replaced by chlorine atoms:

$$\begin{array}{rll} CH_4 + Cl_2 \longrightarrow & CH_3Cl + HCl & \text{methyl chloride} \\ CH_3Cl + Cl_2 \longrightarrow & CH_2Cl_2 + HCl & \text{methylene chloride} \\ CH_2Cl_2 + Cl_2 \longrightarrow & CHCl_3 + HCl & \text{chloroform} \\ CHCl_3 + Cl_2 \longrightarrow & CCl_4 + HCl & \text{carbon tetrachloride} \end{array}$$

In methane the four carbon valencies are satisfied by combination with four hydrogen atoms. Carbon never exhibits a valency of more than four, and so cannot combine with more than four hydrogen atoms or four other univalent atoms or groups. Hence in the reaction with chlorine, the hydrogen atoms are displaced, and chlorine atoms take their place. This type of reaction is known as *substitution*, and is the *direct replacement of hydrogen* by some other atom or group. The products so formed are known as *substitution products*. The atom or group that has replaced the hydrogen atom is called the *substituent*, and when a substituent atom or group is replaced by some other atom or group, the reaction is referred to as a *replacement* (or *displacement*) reaction. It should be noted that in substitution or replacement reactions there is *no change in structure*. The *spatial* arrangement of the molecule, however, may have changed (see p. 395).

In the substitution reaction between methane and chlorine, all four substitution products are obtained, since it is impossible to stop the reaction at any particular stage. It has been found possible, however, to control the reaction so as to obtain mainly methyl chloride (*q.v.*).

Methane also undergoes substitution with bromine, but the reaction is less vigorous than that with chlorine. With iodine the reaction is reversible:

$$CH_4 + I_2 \rightleftharpoons CH_3I + HI$$

The equilibrium lies almost completely on the left, and consequently the yield of methyl iodide is negligible. On the other hand, in the presence of an oxidising agent, *e.g.*, iodic acid, nitric acid, mercuric oxide, etc., the reaction proceeds to the right, since the equilibrium is upset by the removal of the hydrogen iodide which is oxidised, *e.g.*,

$$5HI + HIO_3 \longrightarrow 3I_2 + 3H_2O$$

Methane reacts explosively with gaseous fluorine. The initial reaction is possibly:

$$CH_4 + 2F_2 \longrightarrow C + 4HF$$

Structure of methane. The molecular formula of methane is CH_4. Assuming the quadrivalency of carbon and the univalency of hydrogen, we find that there is only one structure possible for methane, *viz.*, (I). Study of

$$\begin{array}{ccc} \begin{array}{c} H \\ | \\ H-C-H \\ | \\ H \end{array} & \begin{array}{c} Cl \\ | \\ H-C-H \\ | \\ Cl \end{array} & \begin{array}{c} Cl \\ | \\ H-C-Cl \\ | \\ H \end{array} \\ (I) & (II) & (III) \end{array}$$

the reactions of methane shows that all four hydrogen atoms are equivalent, *e.g.*, methylene chloride, CH_2Cl_2, prepared by totally different methods, is always the same. Thus (II) and (III) are different ways of writing the *same* structure. At first sight it may appear that these two structural formulæ are different. They *are* different if the molecule is two-dimensional, but, as we have seen (p. 23), in saturated compounds the four valencies of carbon are arranged tetrahedrally. Examination of the two structures as tetrahedral figures shows that they are identical.* The chief disadvantage of the plane-structural formula is that it does not show the spatial arrangement of the atoms. On the other hand, the three-dimensional structural formula is cumbersome, and for many complicated molecules cannot easily be drawn on paper. Hence we usually adopt the plane-formulæ when dealing with compounds from the point of view of their structure; only when we wish to stress the spatial arrangement of the atoms or groups in a molecule do we resort to solid diagrams (see, *e.g.*, Ch. XVII). How we show the relative positions of the various atoms or groups in the plane-structural formula of a given compound usually depends on ourselves but where possible the simplest method of writing the structure should be chosen. Consider 1 : 5-dichloropentane, $C_5H_{10}Cl_2$. This is a "straight" chain compound, and its structural formula is usually written $CH_2Cl{\cdot}CH_2{\cdot}CH_2{\cdot}CH_2{\cdot}CH_2Cl$. Now, 1 : 5-dichloropentane gives *cyclo*pentane when treated with zinc. *cyclo*Pentane is a ring compound, and to show its formation from 1 : 5-dichloropentane, we write the structure of the latter as follows:

$$CH_2\begin{cases}CH_2{\cdot}CH_2Cl\\CH_2{\cdot}CH_2Cl\end{cases} + Zn \longrightarrow CH_2\begin{cases}CH_2{-}CH_2\\ \quad\;\;\,|\\CH_2{-}CH_2\end{cases} + ZnCl_2$$

Thus "straight" chains may be "bent" to stress a particular point we may have in mind.

Uses of methane. (i) When heated at 1000°, methane is decomposed into carbon and hydrogen:

$$CH_4 \longrightarrow C + 2H_2$$

The carbon is formed in a very finely divided state, and is known as *carbon black*. This is used in making printers' ink and paints; it is also used in the rubber industry for motor tyres, etc.

(ii) Methane is used as a source of hydrogen (for synthetic ammonia and for synthesis gas). Methane is mixed with steam and passed over nickel supported on alumina heated at 725°:

$$CH_4 + H_2O \longrightarrow CO + 3H_2$$

(iii) For the technical preparation of methyl chloride and methylene chloride (*q.v.*).

(iv) For the technical preparation of methanol and formaldehyde (*q.v.*).

(v) As a liquid fuel.

Ethane, C_2H_6, occurs with methane in natural gas and the gases from the oil-wells. It is formed to a slight extent when an electric arc is struck between carbon rods in an atmosphere of hydrogen. It may be *prepared* by any of the following methods:

1. By reduction of ethyl iodide with nascent hydrogen using, for example, the zinc–copper couple and ethanol:

$$C_2H_5I + 2[H] \longrightarrow C_2H_6 + HI$$

* "Atomic models" are very useful to the organic chemist. Sets of these models may be bought; alternatively the reader can build his models from plasticine and matchsticks, which provide crude but usually satisfactory models.

The ethane is contaminated with traces of hydrogen:

$$Zn/Cu + 2C_2H_5OH \longrightarrow H_2 + (C_2H_5O)_2Zn + Cu$$

2. By treating a dry ethereal solution of methyl iodide with sodium:

$$2CH_3I + 2Na \longrightarrow C_2H_6 + 2NaI$$

This is an example of the *Wurtz* reaction. It is not so straightforward as the equation indicates; other products are obtained in addition to ethane (see p. 45).

3. By the electrolysis of a concentrated solution of sodium or potassium acetate. A mixture of ethane and carbon dioxide is evolved at the anode, and hydrogen is evolved at the cathode:

$$2CH_3{\cdot}CO_2Na + 2H_2O \longrightarrow C_2H_6 + 2CO_2 + 2NaOH + H_2$$

This means of preparation is an example of *Kolbe's electrolytic method.* The ethane may be freed from carbon dioxide by washing the mixture with aqueous sodium hydroxide, but still contains other impurities (see p. 46).

4. Pure ethane may be obtained by the action of water on ethylmagnesium iodide (a Grignard reagent):

$$C_2H_5{-}Mg{-}I + H_2O \longrightarrow C_2H_6 + MgI(OH)$$

5. The best way of preparing pure ethane in large quantity is by the catalytic hydrogenation of ethylene:

$$C_2H_4 + H_2 \xrightarrow[300^\circ]{Ni} C_2H_6$$

Properties of ethane. Ethane is a colourless gas, b.p. -89°, sparingly soluble in water but readily soluble in ethanol. It burns in air or oxygen to form carbon dioxide and water:

$$2C_2H_6 + 7O_2 \longrightarrow 4CO_2 + 6H_2O$$

It reacts with halogens in a similar manner to methane to form substitution products, but a much greater number of products are possible due, firstly to the presence of six hydrogen atoms in ethane compared with four in methane, and secondly, to the fact that isomerism is possible in the substitution products of ethane, and not in those of methane. Thus, for example, two dichloroethanes are possible: $CH_3{\cdot}CHCl_2$ and $CH_2Cl{\cdot}CH_2Cl$ (see later).

Structure of ethane. The molecular formula of ethane is C_2H_6. Assuming the quadrivalency of carbon and the univalency of hydrogen, the only possible structure for ethane is (I). This structure agrees with all the known properties of ethane. Writing the structural formula of ethane in the bond-diagram way uses up a lot of space. Hence it has become customary to use a "contracted" structural formula: $CH_3{-}CH_3$ or $CH_3{\cdot}CH_3$ or CH_3CH_3. The reader should make himself familiar with these different ways of writing structural formulæ as soon as possible.

```
   H  H
   |  |
H—C—C—H
   |  |
   H  H
   (I)
```

Propane. C_3H_8 is a constituent of natural gas and gas from the oil-wells. It may be prepared by the following methods:

1. By reduction of propyl iodide with nascent hydrogen:

$$C_3H_7I + 2[H] \xrightarrow[C_2H_5OH]{Zn/Cu} C_3H_8 + HI$$

2. By the Wurtz reaction, using a mixture of methyl and ethyl halides, *e.g.*,

$$CH_3Br + CH_3{\cdot}CH_2Br + 2Na \xrightarrow{\text{ether}} CH_3{\cdot}CH_2{\cdot}CH_3 + 2NaBr$$

The yield of propane is poor, since ethane and butane, C_4H_{10} (as well as other compounds), are obtained as by-products:

$$2CH_3Br + 2Na \longrightarrow C_2H_6 + 2NaBr$$
$$2C_2H_5Br + 2Na \longrightarrow C_4H_{10} + 2NaBr$$

3. By Kolbe's electrolytic method, using a mixture of sodium acetate and sodium propionate:

$$CH_3{\cdot}CO_2Na + C_2H_5{\cdot}CO_2Na + 2H_2O \longrightarrow C_3H_8 + 2CO_2 + 2NaOH + H_2$$

Apart from other products, ethane and butane are obtained in relatively large quantities, resulting in a poor yield of propane (*cf.* 2 above).

4. By the action of water on propylmagnesium iodide:

$$C_3H_7{-}Mg{-}I + H_2O \longrightarrow C_3H_8 + MgI(OH)$$

Properties of propane. Propane is a colourless gas, b.p. $-44{\cdot}5°$. It resembles methane and ethane in many of its chemical properties.

Structure of propane. The molecular formula of propane is C_3H_8. Assuming the quadrivalency of carbon and univalency of hydrogen, the only possible structure for propane is $CH_3{\cdot}CH_2{\cdot}CH_3$. This structure agrees with all the known properties of propane.

Butanes, C_4H_{10}. Theoretical consideration of this formula shows that two structures are possible:

```
                                         H
                                         |
     H  H  H  H                  H    H—C—H    H
     |  |  |  |                  |       |       |
  H—C—C—C—C—H               H—C———————C———————C—H
     |  |  |  |                  |       |       |
     H  H  H  H                  H       H       H

                                     CH3
                                     |
  CH3·CH2·CH2·CH3               CH3·CH·CH3 or (CH3)3CH
        (I)                            (II)
```

(I) has a *straight* chain, and (II) a *branched* chain. Both isomers are known, and thus "butane" is the first paraffin to exhibit structural isomerism. This is an example of *chain* or *nuclear* isomerism, and is characterised by the manner of linking of the *carbon chain.* (I) is known as *normal* butane, and (II) as *iso*butane. Both occur in natural gas and in petroleum gas, and they may be separated by fractional distillation under pressure.

normal Butane may be prepared by the Wurtz reaction using ethyl iodide:

$$2CH_3{\cdot}CH_2I + 2Na \xrightarrow{\text{ether}} CH_3{\cdot}CH_2{\cdot}CH_2{\cdot}CH_3 + 2NaI$$

It is a colourless gas, b.p. $-0{\cdot}5°$.

*iso*Butane may be prepared by reducing tertiary *butyl iodide* with nascent hydrogen:

$$(CH_3)_3CI + 2[H] \xrightarrow[C_2H_5OH]{Zn/Cu} (CH_3)_3CH + HI$$

It is a colourless gas, b.p. $-10{\cdot}2°$.

Examination of the two butane structures shows that all the carbon atoms are not equivalent, and also that all the hydrogen atoms are not equivalent. A *primary* carbon atom is one that is joined to *one* other carbon atom; a *secondary* carbon atom to *two* other carbon atoms; and a *tertiary* carbon atom to *three* other carbon atoms. Hydrogen atoms joined to primary, secondary, and tertiary carbon atoms are known as primary, secondary, or tertiary hydrogen atoms, respectively. Thus *normal* butane contains two primary carbon atoms, two secondary carbon atoms, six primary and four secondary hydrogen atoms. *iso*Butane contains three primary carbon atoms, one tertiary carbon atom, nine primary hydrogen atoms, and one tertiary hydrogen atom. As we shall see later, the behaviour of these various types of hydrogen atoms differs considerably.

Pentanes, C_5H_{12}. Three pentanes are possible theoretically, and all are known.

Structure.	*Name.*	*b.p.*
$CH_3{\cdot}CH_2{\cdot}CH_2{\cdot}CH_2{\cdot}CH_3$	*normal* pentane	36°
$(CH_3)_2CH{\cdot}CH_2{\cdot}CH_3$	*iso*pentane	28°
$CH_3{-}C(CH_3)_2{-}CH_3$	*neo*pentane	9·4°

All the pentanes occur in natural gas and petroleum gas. *neo*Pentane contains a *quaternary* carbon atom, *i.e.*, a carbon atom joined to *four* other carbon atoms.

As the number of carbon atoms in the paraffin increases, the number of possible isomers increases rapidly, *e.g.*, the paraffin $C_{15}H_{32}$ can exist in 4347 isomeric forms. The number of isomers of a given paraffin may be calculated by means of mathematical formulæ; in most cases very few have actually been prepared.

Nomenclature of the Paraffins

Whenever a new branch of knowledge is opened up, there is always the problem of introducing a system of nomenclature. The early chemists usually named a compound on the basis of its history, *e.g.*, methane. This is the parent hydrocarbon of methyl alcohol, CH_3OH. Methyl alcohol was originally obtained by the destructive distillation of wood, and was named " wood-spirit ". From this arose the word methyl, which is a combination of two Greek words, *methu* (wine) and *hule* (wood). Other examples of this way of naming compounds are acetic acid, which is the chief constituent of vinegar (Latin: *acetum*, vinegar); malic acid, which was first isolated from apples (Latin: *malum*, apple), and so on. Thus grew up a system of *common* or *trivial* names, and in many cases the origin of the name has been forgotten. One advantage of the trivial system is that the names are usually short and easily remembered, but a disadvantage is that a particular compound may have a number of names.

As the number of known organic compounds increased, it became apparent that it was necessary to systematise the method of nomenclature. The most satisfactory system is one which indicates the structure of the compound. This task was originally begun in 1892 by an international committee of chemists at Geneva, and hence is referred to as the *Geneva system of nomenclature.* The work was carried on by the *International Union of Chemists* (I.U.C.) by a committee appointed in 1922, and in 1931 these drew up a report which is often referred to as the I.U.C. system. The disadvantage of the Geneva (or I.U.C.) system is that systematic names for fairly complex compounds may be long or complicated, and so cannot be remembered. In some cases it is almost, if not actually, impossible to name a very complex compound systematically.

Dyson (1946) has developed " a new notation for organic chemistry ". This scheme does not provide a new means of *naming* compounds, but shows how it is possible to portray the structure of an organic compound irrespective of its complexity, and how it may be used for indexing.

There are at least three systems in use for naming paraffins, and in all three the *class-suffix*, *i.e.*, the ending of the name which indicates the particular homologous series (see later), is *-ane*.

1. In the **trivial system** of nomenclature the straight-chain compounds are always designated as *normal* compounds, and the word *normal* is usually abbreviated to *n*-. If the compound contains the grouping $(CH_3)_2C—H$, it is known as the *iso*-compound; if it contains a quaternary carbon atom, the compound is known as the *neo*-compound. It is impossible to name many of the more complex paraffins by the trivial system (see later for examples of the trivial system).

The first four paraffins have special names (related to their history); from the fifth member onwards, Latin or Greek numerals are used to indicate the number of carbon atoms in the molecule.

Name.	*Formula.*	*Name.*	*Formula.*
methane	CH_4	hexadecane	$C_{16}H_{34}$
ethane	C_2H_6	heptadecane	$C_{17}H_{36}$
propane	C_3H_8	octadecane	$C_{18}H_{38}$
butane	C_4H_{10}	nonadecane	$C_{19}H_{40}$
pentane	C_5H_{12}	eicosane	$C_{20}H_{42}$
hexane	C_6H_{14}	heneicosane	$C_{21}H_{44}$
heptane	C_7H_{16}	docosane	$C_{22}H_{46}$
octane	C_8H_{18}	tricosane, etc.	$C_{23}H_{48}$, etc.
nonane	C_9H_{20}	triacontane	$C_{30}H_{62}$
decane	$C_{10}H_{22}$	hexatriacontane	$C_{36}H_{74}$
undecane / hendecane	$C_{11}H_{24}$	tetracontane	$C_{40}H_{82}$
		pentacontane	$C_{50}H_{102}$
dodecane	$C_{12}H_{26}$	hexacontane	$C_{60}H_{122}$
tridecane	$C_{13}H_{28}$	heptacontane	$C_{70}H_{142}$
tetradecane	$C_{14}H_{30}$	octacontane	$C_{80}H_{162}$
pentadecane	$C_{15}H_{32}$		

Univalent radicals that are formed by the removal of one hydrogen atom from a paraffin are known as *alkyl* or *alphyl* radicals or groups. The name of each individual radical is obtained by changing the suffix *-ane* of the parent hydrocarbon into *-yl*. The first five alkyl radicals are often represented by a shorthand notation, particularly in abstracting journals.

Paraffin.	*Radical.*	*Short-hand notation.*
methane	methyl $CH_3—$	Me
ethane	ethyl $C_2H_5—$	Et
propane	*n*-propyl $CH_3·CH_2·CH_2—$	*n*-Pr, Prα, or Pr
	*iso*propyl $CH_3·CH(—)·CH_3$	*iso*Pr, Prβ, or Pr^i
butane	*n*-butyl $CH_3·CH_2·CH_2·CH_2—$	*n*-Bu, Buα, or Bu
	sec.-butyl $CH_3·CH_2·CH(—)·CH_3$	*sec.*-Bu, Buβ, or Bu^s
	iso-butyl $(CH_3)_2CH·CH_2—$	*iso*Bu or Bu^i
	tert.-butyl $(CH_3)_3C—$	*tert.*-Bu or Bu^t
pentane	amyl $CH_3·(CH_2)_3·CH_2—$	*n*-Am
	*iso*amyl $(CH_3)_2CH·CH_2·CH_2—$	*iso*Am or Am^i

The radical derived from pentane is usually named amyl, but there is a growing tendency to call it pentyl. The name amyl arose from the fact that amyl alcohol, $C_5H_{11}OH$, was first obtained from starch, the Latin name of which is *amylum*.

The paraffins are also known as the *alkanes*, since an alkyl radical plus one hydrogen atom gives a paraffin, *i.e.*, *alkyl* + H = alk*ane*.

In chemical equations, if we are dealing with alkyl compounds as a group and we do not wish to specify any particular member, we use the symbol R to represent the unspecified alkyl radical, *e.g.*, RCl represents *any* alkyl chloride.

2. In this system of nomenclature the hydrocarbon, except the *n*-compound, is regarded as a substitution product of methane. The most highly branched carbon atom in the compound is named as the methane nucleus, and the alkyl groups attached to this carbon atom are named in order of increasing molecular weight of the groups (or in alphabetical order). If two groups have the same molecular weight, the simpler is named before the more complex, *e.g.*, propyl before *iso*propyl. Hydrogen atoms, if joined to the carbon atom chosen as the methane nucleus, are not named. Since April, 1950, however, the *Chemical Society* has adopted an alphabetical order for prefixes denoting substituents. This order follows in general that adopted in *Chemical Abstracts* except for differences in nomenclature, spelling, italicising, or punctuation. *Italicised prefixes* are neglected when assembling substituents, *e.g.*, *iso*butyl will be named before ethyl. Isomeric substituents, however, are arranged in alphabetical order of the italicised prefixes, except that *iso* follows directly after *n*, *e.g.*, *n*-butyl, *iso*butyl, *sec.*-butyl, *tert.*-butyl (see p. 784 for further information on nomenclature).

This system of nomenclature is fairly good, since the name indicates the structure of the compound. It is impossible, however, to name the complex paraffins by this system.

3. In the **I.U.C. system** of nomenclature the longest chain possible is chosen, and the compound is named as a derivative of this *n*-hydrocarbon. The carbon chain is numbered from one end to the other by arabic numerals, and the positions of *side-chains* are indicated by numbers. Usually the end for starting the numbering is so chosen that the *sum of the numbers used to name the compound is a minimum*. If the sums are equal, the end chosen as the starting point is that which includes the lowest individual number or numbers, *e.g.*, 1 : 2 : 5 is regarded as lower than 1 : 3 : 4; 1 : 1 : 3 : 4 lower than 1 : 2 : 2 : 4. If the sums are *not* equal, then the *rule of lowest numbers* takes precedence over the *rule of lowest sum*, *e.g.*, if two alternative numberings were 1 : 5 : 5 and 2 : 2 : 6, then the first set of numbers must be used, since it includes the *lowest individual numbers*. When two sets of numbers are equally possible, then the order of the prefixes in the name decides which shall be used, *e.g.*, 1-bromo-3-chloropropane and *not* 3-bromo-1-chloropropane. It should also be noted that the names of prefixes are arranged alphabetically, regardless of the number of each, *e.g.*, 5-ethyl-2 : 3-dimethyloctane.

The I.U.C. system of nomenclature is undoubtedly superior to the other two, since it permits the naming of any paraffin on sight.

The following are examples of the three systems of nomenclature:

	1.	2.	3.
$CH_3{\cdot}CH_2{\cdot}CH_2{\cdot}CH_3$	*n*-butane	*n*-butane	*n*-butane
$\overset{1}{C}H_3{\cdot}\overset{2}{C}H{\cdot}\overset{3}{C}H_2{\cdot}\overset{4}{C}H_3$ (with CH_3 on C-2)	*iso*pentane	ethyldimethylmethane ($\overset{2}{C}$ is most highly branched)	2-methylbutane

	1.	2.	3.
$\overset{1}{CH_3}\cdot\overset{2}{C}(CH_3)_2\cdot\overset{3}{CH_2}\cdot\overset{4}{CH_3}$	*neo*hexane	ethyltrimethylmethane ($\overset{2}{C}$ is most highly branched)	2 : 2-dimethylbutane
$CH_3\cdot CH_2\cdot\overset{5}{C}H\cdot\overset{6}{C}H_2\cdot\overset{7}{C}H_2\cdot\overset{8}{C}H_3$ with $^4CH_2$—^3CH(—CH_3)—^2CH(—CH_3)—$^1CH_3$ on C_5	—	—	5-ethyl-2 : 3-dimethyloctane

The reader should note that the prefixes *iso*- and *neo*- are not used in the I.U.C. system.

When several chains are of equal length, that chain which allows the maximum substitutions is chosen. Where there is a side-chain within a side-chain, the latter is also numbered, *e.g.*,

$$\begin{array}{l} \qquad\qquad\qquad\quad \overset{3}{C}HMe\cdot\overset{2}{C}HMe\cdot\overset{1}{C}H_3 \\ \qquad\qquad\qquad\quad |^{4} \\ \overset{7}{C}H_3\cdot\overset{6}{C}H\cdot\overset{5}{C}H_2\cdot C\cdot CH_3 \\ \qquad\ \ | \qquad\qquad\ |^{1'} \\ \qquad CH_3 \qquad\ \ CMe_2\cdot\overset{2'}{C}HMe\cdot\overset{3'}{C}H_3 \end{array}$$

1′ : 1′ : 2 : 2′ : 3 : 4 : 6-heptamethyl-4-propylheptane. Alternatively, it may be named as 2 : 3 : 4 : 6-tetramethyl-4-(1 : 1 : 2-trimethylpropyl)heptane.

There are three chains each containing seven carbon atoms: chain C_1–C_7 contains four, chain C_3'–C_7, five, and chain C_2–C_3', seven substituents. Since chain C_1–C_7 contains the least number of substituents, it will allow the maximum number of substitutions and is, therefore, chosen as the fundamental chain.

Homologous Series

If we examine the formulæ of the various paraffins we find that the formula of each individual differs from that of its " neighbour " by CH_2, *e.g.*, CH_4, C_2H_6, C_3H_8, C_4H_{10}, C_5H_{12}, . . . A set of compounds, such as the paraffins, in which the members differ in composition from one another by CH_2, is known as an *homologous series*, the individual members being known as *homologues*.

Throughout organic chemistry we find homologous series, each series being characterised by the presence of a *functional group*. The functional group is an atom or a group of atoms that causes a compound to behave in a particular way, *i.e.*, it is the functional group that gives rise to homologous series. Some of the more important functional groups and the classes of compounds to which they give rise are shown in Table I.

It is also possible for a compound to contain two (or more) identical or different functional groups, and this gives rise to *polyfunctional* compounds (see text).

If we examine the formulæ of the various paraffins, we find that the formula C_nH_{2n+2} will represent any particular homologue when n is given the appropriate value, *e.g.*, for pentane n is 5; therefore the formula of pentane is C_5H_{12}. The formula C_nH_{2n+2} is known as the *general formula* of the paraffins. The composition of any homologous series can be expressed by means of a general formula.

When we study the methods of preparation of the different paraffins, we find that several methods are common to all, *i.e.*, similar methods may be used for the preparation of all the homologues. This gives rise to the *general methods of preparation* of a particular homologous series.

TABLE I

Class of Compound.	Functional Group.	
	Formula.	Name.*
Alcohols	—OH	Hydroxyl group
Aldehydes and ketones .	$>C{=}O$	Carbonyl group
Carboxylic acids . . .	$-C(=O)OH$	Carboxyl group
Cyanides	$-C{\equiv}N$	Cyano group
Nitro-compounds . .	$-NO_2$	Nitro group
Amines	$-NH_2$	Amino group
Mercaptans	—SH	Mercapto group
Sulphonic acids . . .	$-SO_3H$	Sulphonic acid group

* Many functional groups are known by more than one name. Nomenclature is dealt with in each homologous series described in the text.

Examination of the properties of the paraffins shows that many properties are, more or less, common to all the paraffin homologues. This gives rise to the *general properties* of an homologous series.

The occurrence of homologous series facilitates the study of organic chemistry, since it groups together compounds having many resemblances. If we know the properties of several of the lower homologues, we can obtain a fair idea of the properties of higher homologues, *i.e.*, we can forecast (within limits) the properties of a compound that we have not yet prepared. The reader, however, must never be too hasty in predicting the properties of an unknown homologue. The idea of homologous series should be used as a guide, not as a hard-and-fast rule.

In view of what has been said above, we can see that in studying organic chemistry it is advantageous to describe first the general methods of preparation of an homologous series, and then the general properties of that series. It is also usual to describe the more important members individually, and to indicate, at this stage, any *special* methods of preparation and any *special* properties. This is the way (wherever possible) in which we shall deal with organic chemistry throughout this book, and we shall start by reconsidering the paraffins from this point of view.

The general methods of preparation of the paraffins fall into three groups.

A. From compounds containing the same number of carbon atoms.

1. By the catalytic reduction of unsaturated hydrocarbons, *e.g.*, reduction of ethylene:

$$C_2H_4 + H_2 \xrightarrow[300^\circ]{Ni} C_2H_6 \quad (ex.)\dagger$$

2. (*a*) An alcohol, ROH, is converted into its corresponding alkyl iodide using, *e.g.*, phosphorus triodide (see alkyl halides):

$$3ROH + PI_3 \longrightarrow 3RI + H_3PO_3 \quad (v.g.)$$

† See preface for the significance of these terms in parentheses.

The alkyl iodide may then be converted into the paraffin by various means:

(i) Reduction with nascent hydrogen:

$$RI + 2[H] \longrightarrow RH + HI \quad (g.\text{–}v.g.)$$

(ii) Catalytic reduction using palladium as catalyst (see p. 60 for the preparation of this catalyst):

$$RI + H_2 \xrightarrow{Pd} RH + HI \quad (v.g.)$$

(iii) Reduction by heating with concentrated hydriodic acid at 150°. This high temperature necessitates heating under pressure, since the maximum boiling point of hydriodic acid (57 per cent. HI) is 126°. High-pressure work is carried out in *autoclaves*, but where the pressure is not excessive, sealed, thick-walled glass tubes may be used. Reductions with hydriodic acid under pressure are carried out in sealed tubes:

$$RI + HI \longrightarrow RH + I_2 \quad (g.\text{–}ex.)$$

The reduction can be performed directly on the alcohol, using excess of hydriodic acid:

$$ROH + 2HI \xrightarrow{150^\circ} RH + I_2 + H_2O \quad (g.\text{–}ex.)$$

Reduction with concentrated hydriodic acid is usually carried out in the presence of a small amount of red phosphorus which regenerates the hydriodic acid from the iodine formed. The hydriodic acid–red phosphorus mixture is one of the most powerful reducing agents used in organic chemistry.

Instead of reduction, the alkyl iodide may be converted into the corresponding Grignard reagent, which is then decomposed by water to form the paraffin:

$$RI + Mg \xrightarrow{ether} R\text{—}Mg\text{—}I \xrightarrow{H_2O} RH \quad (v.g.)$$

(*b*) By the reduction of a carbonyl compound with concentrated hydriodic acid and red phosphorus, heated under pressure at 150°, *e.g.*, acetone is converted into propane:

$$CH_3{\cdot}CO{\cdot}CH_3 \xrightarrow[150^\circ]{HI/P} CH_3{\cdot}CH_2{\cdot}CH_3 \quad (v.g.)$$

Alternatively, the carbonyl compound can be reduced to the corresponding alcohol, which is then reduced by HI/P (*cf.* above). On the other hand, ketones may be converted into the corresponding paraffins by the *Clemmensen* (see p. 140) and *Wolff-Kishner* (see p. 143) reductions.

(*c*) By the reduction of fatty acids, $R{\cdot}CO_2H$, with HI/P in a sealed tube at 200°:

$$R{\cdot}CO_2H \xrightarrow[200^\circ]{HI/P} R{\cdot}CH_3$$

The yields are very good for the higher paraffins, and may even be improved by heating the fatty acids with hydrogen under pressure in the presence of a nickel catalyst.

B. From compounds containing a larger number of carbon atoms.

1. By heating a mixture of the sodium salt of a fatty acid and soda-lime:

$$R{\cdot}CO_2Na + NaOH(CaO) \longrightarrow RH + Na_2CO_3$$

This process of eliminating carbon dioxide from a carboxylic acid is known as *decarboxylation*. Soda-lime is a very useful reagent for this process, but various other reagents may also be used (see also p. 166).

Oakwood *et al.* (1950) have shown that only sodium acetate decomposes according to the equation given above. In all of the other cases tested—propionate, butyrate and caproate—various products were obtained, *e.g.*, with sodium propionate:

$$C_2H_5{\cdot}CO_2Na \xrightarrow{NaOH} \underset{(44\%)}{C_2H_6} + \underset{(20\%)}{CH_4} + \underset{(33\%)}{H_2} + \text{Unsaturated compounds.}$$

This method, therefore, is not suitable for the preparation of simple paraffins since, apart from the low yield of the desired product, it is very difficult to separate the mixtures obtained.

2. By heating a mixture of the disodium salt of a dicarboxylic acid and soda-lime, *e.g.*, sodium adipate gives *n*-butane:

$$CO_2Na{\cdot}CH_2{\cdot}CH_2{\cdot}CH_2{\cdot}CH_2{\cdot}CO_2Na + 2NaOH(CaO) \longrightarrow CH_3{\cdot}CH_2{\cdot}CH_2{\cdot}CH_3 + 2Na_2CO_3$$

The reader may well ask: why not use tricarboxylic acids, etc.? When dealing with a preparation, there are at least three important points that must be considered: (i) the yield of crude product; (ii) the yield of pure product; (iii) the *accessibility* of the starting materials. In certain cases the yield of crude material is high, but the nature of the impurities is such that purification causes a large loss of material, resulting in a poor yield of pure product. On the other hand, it often happens that the product of one reaction is to be used as the starting material for some other compound which can readily be freed (*i.e.*, purified with very little loss) from the original impurity. Provided, then, that this impurity does not interfere with the second reaction, the crude material of the first step can be used as the starting material for the second. Thus the yield alone of a particular reaction cannot decide the usefulness of that method of preparation; the subsequent history of the product must also be taken into consideration. Furthermore, all things being equal, the more accessible materials, *i.e.*, readily prepared or purchased, are used as the starting materials.

With respect to the decarboxylation of acids as a means of preparing paraffins, the reader will find that tricarboxylic acids, etc., are not readily accessible; in fact, they are less accessible than the paraffins that can be prepared from them. It would, therefore, be useless, from the practical point of view, to use these acids as starting materials for paraffins. From the point of view of learning the subject, however, some useful purpose is served in carrying out "paper reactions" with inaccessible materials, since the reader may then master reactions of practical value.

C. From compounds containing fewer carbon atoms.

1. By the **Wurtz reaction** (1854). An ethereal solution of an alkyl halide (preferably the bromide or iodide) is treated with sodium, *e.g.*,

$$RX + R'X + 2Na \longrightarrow R{-}R' + 2NaX$$

As previously pointed out, when we do not wish to specify a particular alkyl radical, we use the symbol R. When we deal with two unspecified alkyl radicals which may, or may not, be the same, we can indicate this by R and R′: also, when dealing with compounds containing a halogen atom, and we do not wish to specify the halogen, we can indicate the presence of the unspecified halogen atom by means of X.

Consideration of the equation given above shows that in addition to the desired paraffin R—R′, there will also be present the paraffins R—R and R′—R′. It is usually difficult to isolate the individuals from such a mixture. Unsaturated hydrocarbons are also obtained. Obviously, then, the best yield of a paraffin will be obtained when R and R′ are the same, *i.e.*, when the paraffin contains an even number of carbon atoms and is symmetrical. It has been found that the Wurtz reaction gives good yields only for " even carbon " paraffins of high molecular weight, and that the reaction generally fails with tertiary alkyl halides (*q.v.*).

Sodium is used in the Wurtz reaction. Other metals, however, in a finely-divided state, may also be used, *e.g.*, Ag, Cu (see text).

Two mechanisms have been suggested for the Wurtz reaction, and there is evidence in favour of both. It is even possible that both take place simultaneously.

(i) The intermediate formation of an *organo-metallic* compound, *e.g.*, the formation of *n*-butane from ethyl bromide:

$$C_2H_5—Br + 2Na\cdot \longrightarrow C_2\overset{-}{H_5}\overset{+}{Na} + NaBr$$
$$C_2\overset{-}{H_5}\overset{+}{Na} + C_2H_5Br \longrightarrow C_2H_5—C_2H_5 + NaBr$$

(ii) The intermediate formation of free radicals, *e.g.*,

$$C_2H_5—Br + Na\cdot \longrightarrow C_2H_5\cdot + NaBr$$
$$C_2H_5\cdot + C_2H_5\cdot \longrightarrow C_2H_5—C_2H_5$$

One of the properties of free radicals is *disproportionation*. *i.e.*, intermolecular hydrogenation, one molecule acquiring hydrogen at the expense of the other, *e.g.*,

$$C_2H_5\cdot + C_2H_5\cdot \longrightarrow C_2H_6 + C_2H_4$$

This would account for the presence of ethane and ethylene in the products. According to Morton *et al.* (1942), however, ethane and ethylene may be produced as follows:

$$\begin{matrix} Na^+ & & Br & & & & & \\ H_2C^- & \leftarrow & CH_2 & \longrightarrow & CH_3 & + & CH_2 & + NaBr \\ | & & | & & | & & \| & \\ CH_3 & H— & CH_2 & & CH_3 & & CH_2 & \end{matrix}$$

This mechanism is particularly interesting in view of the fact that disproportionation is commonly accepted as a criterion for a free-radical mechanism. Furthermore, Bryce-Smith (1956) has obtained evidence that free radicals play only a minor part in the formation of the usual Wurtz coupling and disproportionation products.

2. **Kolbe's electrolytic method** (1849). A concentrated solution of the sodium or potassium salt of a fatty acid or mixture of fatty acids is electrolysed, *e.g.*,

$$R\cdot CO_2K + R'\cdot CO_2K + 2H_2O \longrightarrow R—R' + 2CO_2 + H_2 + 2KOH$$

If R and R′ are different, then hydrocarbons R—R and R′—R′ are also obtained (*cf.* Wurtz reaction). The yields are *g.–v.g.* if R and R′ are the same, *i.e.*, only if a *single* substance is electrolysed; but in any case by-products are always obtained. The amount of by-products depends on the structure of the acid and the experimental conditions used. The best type of anode has been found to be one of smooth platinum or iridium, and a high anode current is required. The by-products are olefins, alcohols (particularly in alkaline solution), and esters. Methanolic solutions of salts give the best yields of paraffin, and the yields are higher when the acids contain six or more carbon atoms.

The mechanism of the reaction is still obscure; a possibility is via free radicals, *e.g.*, when sodium propionate is electrolysed, *n*-butane, ethane, ethylene and ethyl propionate are obtained. The propionate ion discharges at the anode to form a free radical:

$$C_2H_5CO_2{:}^{-} \longrightarrow C_2H_5CO_2\cdot + e$$

This free propionate radical then breaks up into the free ethyl radical and carbon dioxide:

$$C_2H_5CO_2\cdot \longrightarrow C_2H_5\cdot + CO_2$$

Then:

$$\text{(i)} \quad 2C_2H_5\cdot \longrightarrow C_4H_{10}$$

$$\text{(ii)} \quad C_2H_5\cdot + C_2H_5\cdot \longrightarrow C_2H_6 + C_2H_4$$

$$\text{(iii)} \quad C_2H_5\cdot + C_2H_5CO_2\cdot \longrightarrow C_2H_5{\cdot}CO_2C_2H_5$$

Reaction (i) gives *n*-butane; (ii) gives ethane and ethylene by disproportionation (*cf.* Wurtz reaction); and (iii) gives ethyl propionate.

3. By the action of an alkyl halide on a Grignard reagent:

$$R{-}Mg{-}I + R'I \xrightarrow{\text{ether}} R{-}R' + MgI_2 \quad (g.\text{–}v.g.)$$

4. **Frankland's method** (1850). Dialkyl-zinc compounds readily react with alkyl halides to form hydrocarbons:

$$R_2Zn + R'I \longrightarrow R{-}R' + R{-}Zn{-}I$$

Dialkyl-zinc compounds are difficult to handle and as far as hydrocarbons are concerned, are used only for the preparation of paraffins containing a quaternary carbon atom, *e.g.*,

$$(CH_3)_3CCl + (CH_3)_2Zn \longrightarrow (CH_3)_4C + CH_3{-}Zn{-}Cl$$

General properties of the paraffins. The name paraffin arose through contracting the two Latin words "*parum affinis*", which means "little affinity". This name was suggested because these hydrocarbons were apparently very unreactive. It is difficult to define the terms "reactive" and "unreactive", since a compound may be reactive under one set of conditions and unreactive under another. Under "ordinary" conditions, the paraffins are inert towards reagents such as acids, alkalis, oxidising reagents, reducing reagents, etc. In recent years, however, it has been shown that the paraffins are reactive if the "right" conditions are used (see below).

General physical properties of the paraffins. The normal paraffins from C_1 to C_4 are colourless gases; C_5 to C_{17}, colourless liquids; and from C_{18} onwards, colourless solids. The b.ps. rise fairly regularly as the number of carbon atoms in the compound increases. This holds good only for the normal compounds, and the difference in b.ps. decreases as the higher homologues are reached. Other physical properties, such as m.p., specific gravity, viscosity, also increase in the same way as the b.ps. (of the normal paraffins), *e.g.*, the specific gravity of the normal paraffins increases fairly steadily for the lower members, and eventually tends to a maximum value of about 0·79. Straight-chain paraffins containing at least six carbon atoms form *inclusion compounds* with urea (see p. 369).

At the moment comparatively little is known about the quantitative relationships between physical properties and chemical constitution. It is believed that variation in b.p.s of compounds is due to different *intermolecular* forces such as hydrogen bonding, dipole moments, etc. Hydrogen bonding may produce association, and this will cause the b.p. to be higher than anticipated (see, *e.g.*, alcohols). The greater the dipole moment of the compound, the higher is the b.p., since, owing to the charges, more work is required to separate the molecules, *e.g.*, nitro-compounds, $R{\cdot}NO_2$, which have large dipole moments, have much higher b.ps. than the paraffins in which the dipole moment is absent or very small.

Observation has shown that in a group of isomeric compounds (acyclic), the normal compound *always* has the highest b.p. and m.p., and generally, the greater the branching, the lower the b.p.

The paraffins are almost insoluble in water, but readily soluble in ethanol and ether, the solubility diminishing with increase in molecular weight.

It is believed that solubility depends on the following intermolecular forces: solvent/solute; solute/solute; solvent/solvent. A non-electrolyte dissolves readily in water only if it can form hydrogen bonds with the water. Thus paraffins are insoluble, or almost insoluble, in water. Methane is more soluble than any of its homologues; hydrogen bonding with the water is unlikely, and so other factors—possibly molecular size—must also play a part. A useful rule in organic chemistry with respect to solubility is that " like dissolves like ", *e.g.*, if a compound contains a hydroxyl group, then the best solvents usually contain hydroxyl groups. This rule is not rigid (*cf.* paraffins).

X-Ray analysis of *solid* paraffins has shown that the carbon chains are fully extended, *i.e.*, zigzag. In the *liquid* state this extended form is also one of the

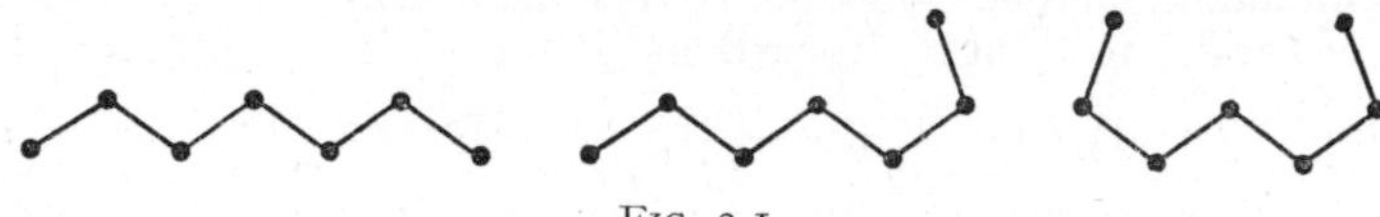

FIG. 3.1.

stable conformations provided that the carbon chain is not very long. When the number of carbon atoms is sixteen or more, the extended form is no longer present in the liquid state. The presence of a number of these different *conformations* (or *rotational isomers*) has been shown by a study of infra-red and Raman spectra of liquid paraffins. The various conformations arise from the fact that groups can rotate about single bonds (p. 386). Furthermore, it has been found that not all possible conformations are present, *e.g.*, *n*-heptane shows the presence of three conformations (Sheppard *et al.*, 1948, 1949). Fig. 1 shows diagrammatically three possible forms.

Since the dipole moment of methane is zero, the dipole moment of the methyl group is equal to that of the fourth C—H bond (in methane) and is directed along this axis. Thus replacement of hydrogen by a methyl group will not be expected to change the dipole moment, *i.e.*, the dipole moment of all paraffins, whether straight- or branched-chain, will be zero. This has been found to be so in practice. This will always hold good whatever conformation is taken up by the paraffin provided that no deformation of the normal carbon valency angle (of 109° 28′) is produced in the twisting, since all methyl groups will be balanced by a C—H bond. It therefore follows that the electronegativity of *all* alkyl groups is equal to that of hydrogen, namely zero (p. 16). As soon as one hydrogen atom is replaced by another atom or group (other than alkyl), the resultant molecule will now be found to possess a dipole moment (see also p. 97).

General Chemical Properties of the Paraffins

1. **Halogenation** (see also the alkyl halides). Chlorination has been studied in very great detail. It may be brought about by light, heat or

catalysts, and the extent of chlorination depends largely on the amount of chlorine used. A mixture of all possible isomeric monochlorides is obtained, but the isomers are formed in unequal amounts, due to the difference of the reactivity of primary, secondary and tertiary hydrogen atoms. Markownikoff (1875) found experimentally that the order of ease of substitution is tertiary hydrogen>secondary>primary. This observation is very useful for predicting the possible courses of a reaction, and qualitatively, to what extent each course will proceed, *e.g.*, chlorination of *iso*butane at 300° gives a mixture of two isomeric monochlorides:

$$\underset{\text{(I)}}{CH_3{\cdot}\overset{\overset{\displaystyle CH_3}{|}}{C}H{\cdot}CH_2Cl} \quad \text{and} \quad \underset{\text{(II)}}{CH_3{\cdot}\overset{\overset{\displaystyle CH_3}{|}}{C}Cl{\cdot}CH_3}$$

We should expect to find more of (II) than (I); quantitative experiments show that this is so.

Bromination is similar to chlorination, but not so vigorous. Iodination is reversible, but it may be carried out in the presence of an oxidising agent, such as HIO_3, HNO_3, HgO, etc., which destroys the hydrogen iodide as it is formed (see p. 35). Iodides are more conveniently prepared by treating the chloro- or bromo-derivative with sodium iodide in methanol or acetone solution, *e.g.*,

$$RCl + NaI \xrightarrow{\text{acetone}} RI + NaCl$$

This reaction is possible because sodium iodide is soluble in methanol or acetone, whereas sodium chloride and sodium bromide are not.

Direct fluorination is usually explosive; special conditions are necessary for the preparation of the fluorine derivatives of the paraffins (see p. 109).

2. **Nitration** (see also p. 285). Under certain conditions, paraffins react with nitric acid, a hydrogen atom being replaced by a *nitro-group*, NO_2. This process is known as *nitration*. Nitration of the paraffins may be carried out in the vapour phase between 150° and 475°, whereupon a complex mixture of mononitroparaffins is obtained. The mixture consists of all the possible mononitro-derivatives and the nitro-compounds formed by every possibility of *chain fission* of the paraffin; *e.g.*, propane gives a mixture of 1-nitropropane, 2-nitropropane, nitroethane and nitromethane:

$$CH_3{\cdot}CH_2{\cdot}CH_3 \xrightarrow[400^\circ]{HNO_3} CH_3{\cdot}CH_2{\cdot}CH_2{\cdot}NO_2 + CH_3{\cdot}\overset{\overset{\displaystyle NO_2}{|}}{C}H{\cdot}CH_3 + C_2H_5{\cdot}NO_2 + CH_3{\cdot}NO_2$$

As in the case of halogenation, the various hydrogen atoms in propane are not replaced with equal ease.

3. **Sulphonation** (see also p. 581) is the process of replacing a hydrogen atom by a *sulphonic acid group*, SO_3H. Sulphonation of a normal paraffin from hexane onwards may be carried out by treating the paraffin with oleum (fuming sulphuric acid). The ease of replacement of hydrogen atoms is: tertiary very much greater than secondary, and secondary greater than primary; replacement of a primary hydrogen atom in sulphonation is very slow indeed. *iso*Butane, which contains a tertiary hydrogen atom, is readily sulphonated to give *tert.*-butylsulphonic acid:

$$(CH_3)_3CH + H_2SO_4/SO_3 \longrightarrow (CH_3)_3C{\cdot}SO_3H + H_2SO_4$$

Sulphuryl chloride, in the presence of light and a catalyst, converts hydrocarbons into sulphonyl chlorides (p. 322).

It has been shown that in concentrated sulphuric acid, hydrocarbons containing a tertiary hydrogen atom undergo hydrogen exchange (Ingold *et al.*, 1936). The mechanism is believed to occur via a carbonium ion:

$$R_3CH + 2H_2SO_4 \longrightarrow R_3C^+ + HSO_4^- + SO_2 + 2H_2O$$
$$R_3C^+ + R_3CH \longrightarrow R_3CH + R_3C^+, \text{ etc.}$$

This reaction is of particular interest since optically active hydrocarbons have been racemised in sulphuric acid (see p. 394); *e.g.*, Burwell *et al.* (1948) have shown that optically active 3-methylheptane is racemised in sulphuric acid.

4. **Oxidation.** All paraffins readily burn in excess of air or oxygen to form carbon dioxide and water. Incomplete oxidation, due to insufficient air, produces carbon-black in variable yields. The mechanism of the oxidation of paraffins in the vapour state appears to take place via the formation of a hydrocarbon peroxide; *e.g.*,

$$R{\cdot}CH_3 + O_2 \longrightarrow R{\cdot}CH_2O{\cdot}OH \longrightarrow R{\cdot}CHO + H_2O$$

Other products are also obtained by fission of the carbon chain.

Oxidising reagents such as potassium permanganate readily oxidise a *tertiary* hydrogen atom to a hydroxyl group, *e.g.*, *iso*butane is oxidised to *tert.*-butanol:

$$(CH_3)_3CH + [O] \xrightarrow{KMnO_4} (CH_3)_3{\cdot}COH$$

The *catalytic oxidation* of methane produces methanol, CH_3OH, and formaldehyde, H·CHO. The catalytic oxidation of higher homologues (C_{16}--) produces long-chain fatty acids and some other products.

5. **Isomerisation** of *n*-paraffins into branched-chain paraffins in which the side-chain is a methyl group, may be brought about by heating the *n*-paraffin with aluminium chloride at 300°, *e.g.*, *n*-hexane isomerises into 2- and 3-methylpentanes:

$$CH_3{\cdot}CH_2{\cdot}CH_2{\cdot}CH_2{\cdot}CH_2{\cdot}CH_3 \xrightarrow[300^\circ]{AlCl_3} CH_3{\cdot}\underset{\displaystyle CH_3}{\overset{|}{CH}}{\cdot}CH_2{\cdot}CH_2{\cdot}CH_3 + CH_3{\cdot}CH_2{\cdot}\underset{\displaystyle CH_3}{\overset{|}{CH}}{\cdot}CH_2{\cdot}CH_3$$

According to Pines *et al.* (1946), this isomerisation does not occur unless a trace of water is present (to form HCl from the $AlCl_3$) together with a trace of alkyl halide or an olefin.

Instead of writing out the formulæ of the 2- and 3-methylpentanes as shown in the equation, an alternative way is to write the formula in a " straight " line, enclosing in parentheses any side-chain; thus: $CH_3{\cdot}CH(CH_3){\cdot}CH_2{\cdot}CH_2{\cdot}CH_3$ and $CH_3{\cdot}CH_2{\cdot}CH(CH_3){\cdot}CH_2{\cdot}CH_3$. The atoms or groups in parentheses are joined directly to the *preceding* carbon atom in the chain not placed in parentheses, *e.g.*,

$$CH_3{\cdot}\underset{\displaystyle N{\cdot}OH}{\overset{}{\underset{\|}{C}}}{-}CH\begin{cases}OH\\CH_3\end{cases} \text{ may be written as } CH_3{\cdot}C({:}N{\cdot}OH){\cdot}CH(OH){\cdot}CH_3$$

In many cases where there is no ambiguity, the parentheses may be omitted, *e.g.*, *iso*propanol is $CH_3{\cdot}\underset{\displaystyle OH}{\underset{|}{CH}}{\cdot}CH_3$; this is often written $CH_3{\cdot}CHOH{\cdot}CH_3$, but if the rules are strictly adhered to, it should be written $CH_3{\cdot}CH(OH){\cdot}CH_3$.

6. **The thermal decomposition of the paraffins** (see below).

PETROLEUM AND NATURAL GAS

Crude **petroleum** (*mineral oil*) is the term usually applied to the gases occurring naturally in the oilfields, the liquid from the wells, and the solids which are dissolved in, or have separated from, the liquid. The composition of crude petroleum varies with the locality of occurrence, but all contain paraffins (from about C_1 to C_{40}), *cyclo*paraffins or naphthenes, and aromatic hydrocarbons. The low-boiling fractions of almost all petroleums are composed of paraffins; it is the composition of the higher-boiling fractions which differs according to the source of the petroleum. In addition to hydrocarbons, there are also present compounds containing oxygen, nitrogen and sulphur.

Natural gas is the term applied to the large quantities of gas associated with or unassociated with liquid petroleum. The composition of natural gas varies with the source, and consists chiefly of the first six paraffins, the percentage of each decreasing with increasing molecular weight. Other gases such as water vapour, hydrogen, nitrogen, carbon dioxide and hydrogen sulphide may be present in amounts that vary with the locality of occurrence.

The origin of petroleum and natural gas is still uncertain. Many theories have been suggested, but not one explains all the known facts. There is now, however, general agreement that petroleum has organic origin, and this is due to the fact that the higher boiling fractions of petroleum contain optically active compounds (p. 381) and that petroleum has been shown to contain both animal and plant type of porphyrins, *i.e.*, hæmin and chlorophyll (Treibs, 1934–36). The problem is how organic matter is converted into petroleum. A very highly favoured theory is that it takes place by means of bacterial decomposition, but there is a growing belief that bacterial action is only the first stage in the conversion and this is then followed by physical and chemical stages.

Another highly favoured theory is that petroleum is formed from organic matter by the catalytic activity of certain natural inorganic compounds. There is a great deal of experimental work that supports this theory which, in many ways, appears superior to any other. It is probable that both mechanisms are operating.

Distribution and general composition of crude petroleum. If the residue of petroleum, after removal of volatile compounds, contains a large amount of paraffins or wax, the petroleum is classified as *paraffinic* or *paraffin base oil*. If naphthenes predominate, the petroleum is classified as *asphaltic* or *asphalt base oil*. The crudes from the wells in Pennsylvania, Iran, Irak and Rumania are paraffinic; those from Baku and Venezuela are asphaltic; and those from Oklahoma, Texas and Mexico are intermediate in composition, and may be classified as paraffinic and asphaltic.

Distillation of petroleum. The crude oil is nearly always associated with water and sand; hence the crude petroleum discharged from the top of the well contains water and sand in suspension. The mixture is passed, under pressure, into cylindrical tanks, and the gas, oil and solids are drawn off separately.

Except for the low-boiling hydrocarbons, no attempt is made to separate the individual hydrocarbons. The crude oil is fractionated by continuous distillation into four main fractions: **petrol** (*gasoline*), **kerosene** (*kerosine, paraffin oil*), **gas oil** (*heavy oil*) and **lubricating oil.** The residue may be fractionated by means of vacuum-distillation to give light, medium and heavy lubricating oils, paraffin wax, and asphaltic bitumen. Each of the four main fractions may be further split up by batch distillation into fractions of narrow boiling range. Recently, it has been possible to isolate individuals by "superfractionation". The *final* number of fractions taken depends on the purpose in view.

Table II shows one set of fractions that may be obtained.

Refining of the various fractions. It appears that refining was originally introduced to remove the bad colour and objectionable odour of petrol. To-day it is realised that it is more important to remove sulphur compounds which lower the response of petrol to added tetraethyl-lead.

An internal-combustion engine, *i.e.*, one which burns fuel within the working cylinder, is more efficient the higher the compression ratio. Petrol engines use "spark ignition", and as the compression ratio increases, a point is reached when "knocking" is observed, *i.e.*, after passage of the firing spark, instead of

TABLE II

Name.	B.P. ° C.	Approximate Composition.	Uses.
Light petrol	20–100	C_5H_{12}–C_7H_{16}	Solvent
Benzine	70–90	C_6–C_7	Dry cleaning
Ligroin	80–120	C_6–C_8	Solvent
Petrol (gasoline) . . .	70–200	C_6–C_{11}	Motor fuel
Kerosene (paraffin oil) . .	200–300	C_{12}–C_{16}	Lighting
Gas oil (heavy oil) . . .	above 300	C_{13}–C_{18}	Fuel oil
Lubricating oil (mineral oil) .	,,	C_{16}–C_{20}	Lubricants
Greases, vaseline, petrolatum .	,,	C_{18}–C_{22}	Pharmaceutical preparations
Paraffin wax (hard wax) .	,,	C_{20}–C_{30}	Candles, waxed paper, etc.
Residue (asphaltic bitumen) .	,,	C_{30}–C_{40}	Asphalt tar; petroleum coke

all the fuel gas burning smoothly, the end portion burns with explosive violence, giving rise to a metallic rattle. The phenomenon of knocking is still not fully understood, but it has been found that, among other factors, the tendency to knock depends on the nature of the petrol. *n*-Paraffins tend to produce knocking far more than branched-chain paraffins. Edgar (1927) introduced 2 : 2 : 4-trimethylpentane (incorrectly known as *iso*-octane), which has higher antiknock properties, and *n*-heptane, which has lower antiknock properties than any commercial petrol, as standards for rating fuels. "*iso*-Octane" is arbitrarily given the value of 100 and *n*-heptane, 0, and the *octane number* of any fuel is the per cent. of "*iso*-octane" in a mixture of this compound and *n*-heptane which will knock under the same conditions as the fuel being tested.

Olefins and aromatic compounds have high octane numbers. Tetraethyl-lead also raises the octane number of a given petrol, but if sulphur compounds are present, the response to this "dope" is lowered. Hence it is very important to remove sulphur compounds from petrol. The method of refining depends on the particular fraction concerned, and it is not practicable to refine before distillation (of the petroleum).

Gasoline refining. 1. Petroleum may be treated with concentrated sulphuric acid which reduces the sulphur content and also removes unsaturated compounds which polymerise on standing to form gums (see olefins). For straight-run gasoline, *i.e.*, gasoline obtained directly from crude petroleum, 98 per cent. sulphuric acid is used; for cracked gasoline (see later), 80 per cent. acid is used. This diluted acid removes only unstable unsaturated hydrocarbons, *i.e.*, those which tend to polymerise, leaving the stable unsaturated hydrocarbons, which raise the octane number of the gasoline. The diluted acid, however, causes some polymerisation to take place, but the gasoline is readily separated from these high-boiling polymers by distillation.

2. Instead of sulphuric acid the *adsorption process* can be used to remove thioalcohols (the chief group of sulphur compounds occurring in petroleum) from straight-run gasoline. The gasoline vapour is passed, under pressure, over an adsorbent such as clays, bauxite, etc., heated at about 450° C. Cracked gasoline contains sulphur as thiophens, and these cannot be removed so easily this way. Thiophens, however, are not so objectionable as thioalcohols.

3. Straight-run gasolines may be refined by sodium hydroxide washing, which may remove almost all thioalcohol sulphur. Where this simple sodium hydroxide treatment is insufficient, it is followed by "sweetening". By sweetening, the thioalcohols (which give gasoline an unpleasant odour) are converted into disulphides, thereby improving the odour. Common sweetening agents are:

(i) An alkaline solution of sodium plumbite ("doctor solution"):

$$2RSH + Na_2PbO_2 + S \longrightarrow R—S—S—R + PbS + 2NaOH$$

Free sulphur is added as required in carefully controlled amounts. The spent doctor solution is regenerated by blowing with air.

(ii) Sodium hypochlorite:

$$2RSH + [O] \xrightarrow{NaOCl} R—S—S—R + H_2O$$

(iii) Cupric chloride:

$$2RSH + 2CuCl_2 \longrightarrow R—S—S—R + 2CuCl + 2HCl$$

Sweetening of "sour" gasoline does not appreciably alter the total sulphur content, and will not improve the octane number or lead susceptibility; in fact sweetened gasoline may have a lower octane number and lead susceptibility than unsweetened; only the odour is improved.

4. The *solutiser process* involves the use of solvents, and the more common ones are a methanolic solution of sodium hydroxide, sodium hydroxide and sodium butyrate, and potassium hydroxide and potassium butyrate. By this means the thioalcohols are removed completely, and thus the octane number and lead susceptibility are raised.

Kerosene refining. (i) The kerosene is washed first with sulphuric acid, then with sodium hydroxide solution, and finally with water. (ii) The kerosene is treated with liquid sulphur dioxide, which removes most of the sulphur compounds and aromatic hydrocarbons. Because of the removal of the latter, this method of refining cannot be used for gasoline.

Gas oil and lubricating oil refining is carried out by extraction with liquid sulphur dioxide.

CRACKING

The thermal decomposition of organic compounds is known as *pyrolysis*; pyrolysis, when applied to paraffins, is known as *cracking*.

When heated to about 500–600°, paraffins are decomposed into smaller molecules, and the products obtained from a given paraffin depend on: (i) the structure of the paraffin; (ii) the pressure under which cracking is carried out; and (iii) the presence or absence of catalysts such as silica–alumina, silica–alumina–thoria, silica–alumina–zirconia.

The mechanism of cracking is still obscure. Many theories have been suggested, and one that is highly favoured is a free-radical mechanism, evidence for which has been obtained from the observation that at cracking temperatures many hydrocarbons produce free alkyl radicals. On the other hand, Hansford (1947) suggests that when cracking takes place, ions are produced rather than free radicals.

When petroleum is cracked, of all the compounds produced, the most important are those containing up to four carbon atoms: methane, ethane, ethylene, propane, propylene, butane, butylene and *iso*butylene. All of these have found wide application as the materials for the preparation of a large number of chemicals (see text).

By using suitable catalysts, paraffins containing six or more carbon atoms may be catalytically cyclised, *e.g.*, *n*-hexane, under pressure, passed over chromic oxide carried on an alumina support and heated at 480–550°, gives benzene (see also p. 476):

$$C_6H_{14} \longrightarrow C_6H_6 + 4H_2$$

There are two main types of cracking: (i) liquid phase, and (ii) vapour phase.

(i) **Liquid phase cracking.** Heavy oil (from the petroleum distillation) is cracked by heating at a suitable temperature (475–530°) and under pressure (100–1000 lb/sq. in.), by means of which the cracked material is maintained in the liquid condition. The heavy oil is converted into gasoline to the extent of 60–65 per cent. of the oil (by volume), and has an octane number of 65–70. If attempts are made to increase the yield of gasoline, the octane number decreases.

(ii) **In vapour phase cracking** the cracking temperature is 600° and the pressure is 50–150 lb/sq. in. The cracking stock may be gasoline, kerosene, gas oils, but not the heavy oils, since these cannot be completely vaporised under the above conditions.

Reforming is the process whereby straight-run gasoline is cracked in order to raise the octane number. The gasoline is heated to about 600° and under pressure of 400–750 lb/sq. in., and the yield varies from 60 to 90 per cent.; the greater the yield, the lower is the octane number. Catalysts—the oxides of silicon and aluminium, plus small amounts of other oxides such as magnesia, zirconia, etc.—are usually employed in the reforming process, and their use produces a higher octane number (which is partly due to the increased content of benzene and toluene), and also increases the yield of gasoline.

Catalytic cracking is also increasing in use, since it has been found that catalytically cracked gasoline contains few olefins that readily polymerise. Gum formation in cracked gasolines is prevented by the addition of *inhibitors*, which are mainly phenols or aromatic amines, *e.g.*, catechol, *p*-benzylaminophenol, naphthylamine.

As pointed out above, large quantities of gases up to C_4 (and small amounts of C_5, *i.e.*, the pentanes and pentenes) are produced in cracking. These gases may be used as the starting materials for various chemicals. Alternatively, by polymerising the olefins under the influence of a catalyst, *e.g.*, phosphoric acid on kieselguhr, or sulphuric acid, a high-octane (80–85) gasoline can be obtained.

Treatment of natural gas. When natural gas does not contain hydrocarbons above ethane, it is said to be "lean" or "dry"; when it contains the higher hydrocarbons (up to hexane) it is said to be "rich" or "wet". The paraffins may be separated by fractional distillation under increased pressure, thereby giving methane, ethane, propane, *n*- and *iso*butanes, *n*-, *iso*- and *neo*pentanes, and hexane. These gases are used for various purposes (see text). On the other hand, natural gas itself may be used in the manufacture of various compounds. Oxidation of natural gas under carefully controlled conditions produces a complex mixture of compounds, among which are formaldehyde, acetaldehyde, acetic acid, acetone, methanol, ethanol, propanols and butanols. These are separated by distillation, solvent extraction, etc.

Wet gas is also used as a source of gasoline. The vapours of the liquid hydrocarbons (pentanes and hexane) in the wet gas are removed by various methods, *e.g.*, compression, and cooling. The liquid product obtained from wet gas is known as "natural" or "casinghead" gas, and is "wild" because of the dissolved gases in it. These gases may be removed by distillation under pressure, and the resulting liquid is known as "stabilised natural gasoline"; this has very high antiknock properties.

Synthetic Fuels. (i) **Fischer–Tropsch Gasoline Synthesis or Synthine Process.** Synthesis gas, which is water-gas mixed with half its volume of hydrogen, at about 200–300° and a pressure of 1–200 atm., is passed over a catalyst:

$$x\text{CO} + y\text{H}_2 \longrightarrow \underset{\text{(saturated and unsaturated)}}{\text{mixture of hydrocarbons}} + \text{water}$$

The water-gas is made from coke. One third of the water-gas is passed with steam at 400° over iron, and the hydrogen-enriched water-gas is then mixed with the rest of the water-gas to produce the synthesis gas. This contains about 20 per cent. of inert gases. If the synthine process is carried out at atmospheric pressure, the carbon dioxide (about one third of the volume of the inert gases) is left in; if the synthesis is carried out under pressure, most of the carbon dioxide is washed out.

Synthesis gas contains sulphur compounds, and since these poison the catalyst, their removal is necessary. Hydrogen sulphide is removed by bog-iron ore. Organic sulphur compounds are oxidised under carefully controlled conditions, the sulphur being retained as sodium sulphate. If the synthesis gas contains large amounts of hydrocarbons, the latter are almost completely removed by passing through active carbon adsorbers before removing the sulphur compounds. The purified gas is then passed to the catalyst chambers, with or without compression. Other methods of preparing synthesis gas are also available, *e.g.*, from methane and steam (p. 36).

Various metals and oxides have been used as catalysts. One of the best is: cobalt (100 parts), thoria (5 parts), magnesia (8 parts) and kieselguhr (200 parts). When synthesis gas is passed over the catalyst at moderate pressure (9–11 atm.), more of the high-boiling fraction is obtained than when the process is carried out at atmospheric pressure. The liquid products are fractionally distilled, and refined in the same way as are the petroleum fractions; furthermore the higher-boiling fractions are cracked.

Gasoline from the synthine process costs more than that from petroleum. The Fischer–Tropsch oils appear to be more valuable as chemical raw materials than as fuels, and have been used for the production of higher olefins, fatty acids, detergents and in the *oxo*-process (see p. 115).

(ii) **Petrol from coal.** (*a*) Distillation of coal-tar gives a fuel oil, fractionation of which yields petrol (about one sixth of the volume). On the other hand, hydrogenation of the fuel oil under a pressure of 200 atm. and at about 475° produces petrol in 100 per cent. yield.

(*b*) In the *Bergius process* coal dust is heated to 400–500° in hydrogen at 250 atm., preferably in the presence of a catalyst, one of the best being an organic compound of tin. The yield of petrol may be as high as 60 per cent. (on the coal used).

(*c*) In the I.C.I. process coal dust is mixed with heavy oil to form a paste (50 per cent. of oil), which is pumped, with hydrogen, under pressure (250 atm.), into chambers containing the catalyst (organic tin compound) heated at 450°. The gases produced are scrubbed and condensed, and the liquid fractions are distilled to give the petrol fraction. The higher-boiling oils may be further hydrogenated to give more petrol.

QUESTIONS

1. Write out the structures and names (by the three methods described in the text) of the isomeric hexanes. State how many primary, secondary, tertiary and quaternary carbon atoms there are in each isomer.
2. By means of equations, show how you would convert methane into propane.
3. What is the percentage of carbon and hydrogen in the paraffin $C_{30}H_{62}$? Could you distinguish this paraffin from its next homologue by determining the percentage composition of each hydrocarbon?
4. Synthesise all the alkanes you can, by methods dealt with so far, from (*a*) $CH_3{\cdot}CH_2{\cdot}CH(OH){\cdot}CH_3$; (*b*) $CH_3{\cdot}CH_2{\cdot}CH_2{\cdot}CH_2{\cdot}CO_2H$.
5. Define and give examples of:—(*a*) isomerism, (*b*) substitution, (*c*) homologous series, (*d*) cracking, (*e*) nitration, (*f*) sulphonation, (*g*) decarboxylation.
6. What reagents could you use to convert:—(*a*) a monohalogen derivative of a paraffin and (*b*) carbonyl compounds, into the corresponding and higher paraffins?
7. Write notes on:—(*a*) the Wurtz reaction, (*b*) Kolbe's electrolytic method, (*c*) Frankland's method, (*d*) Fischer–Tropsch reaction.

The reader should test himself on the general methods of preparation and general properties of any homologous series.

READING REFERENCES

Definitive Report of the Committee for the Reform of Nomenclature in Organic Chemistry, *J.C.S.*, **1931**, 1067.
Smith, Modern Chemical Nomenclature, *ibid.*, **1936**, 1071.
Editorial Report on Nomenclature, *ibid.*, **1950**, 3699; **1951**, 3515; **1952**, 5057; **1953**, 4201; **1954**, 4714; **1955**, 4497.

Dyson, *A New Notation and Enumeration System for Organic Compounds*, Longmans, Green (1947).
Beezer, Latin and Greek Roots in Chemical Terminology, *J. Chem. Educ.*, 1940, **17**, 63.
Gilman, *Advanced Organic Chemistry*, Wiley (1942, 2nd ed.), (i) Vol. I, Ch. 1. Reactions of the Paraffins. (ii) Vol. II, Ch. 23. Constitution and Physical Properties of Organic Compounds.
Mitchell, *British Chemical Nomenclature*, Arnold (1948).
Haensel and Sterba, Pyrolytic and Catalytic Decomposition of Hydrocarbons, *Ind. Eng. Chem.*, 1950, **42**, 1739.
Goldstein, *The Petroleum Chemicals Industry*, Spon (1949).
Brooks, *The Chemistry of the Non-benzenoid Hydrocarbons*, Reinhold (1950, 2nd ed.).
Nelson, The Origin of Petroleum, *J. Chem. Educ.*, 1954, **31**, 399.
Bryce-Smith, Evidence for the Formation of Free Alkyl Radicals during certain Wurtz Reactions, *J.C.S.*, **1956**, 1603.
Weedon, Anodic Syntheses with Carboxylic Acids, *Quart. Reviews* (*Chem. Soc.*), 1952, **6**, 380.
Astle, *The Chemistry of Petrochemicals*, Reinhold (1956).

CHAPTER IV

UNSATURATED HYDROCARBONS

Olefins, Alkylenes or Alkenes

THE olefins are the unsaturated hydrocarbons that contain one double bond. The simplest member of the series is ethylene, $CH_2{=}CH_2$; hence this homologous series is often referred to as the " ethylene series ". The olefins have the general formula C_nH_{2n}, and the double bond is also known as the " olefinic bond " or " ethylenic bond ".

Olefins have recently become very important technically, since they are obtained in huge quantities in the cracking of petroleum, and may be used to prepare a large variety of organic compounds (see text).

Nomenclature. The name olefin arose from the fact that ethylene was called " olefiant gas " (oil-forming gas), since it formed oily liquids when treated with chlorine or bromine. The original name given to this homologous series was olefine; but it was later decided to reserve the suffix *-ine* for *basic* substances only. Since the name olefine had gained wide usage, it was decided to compromise and call the series the olefins.

One method of nomenclature is to name the olefin from the corresponding paraffin by changing the suffix *-ane* of the latter into *-ylene*, *e.g.*, (methylene), ethylene, propylene, etc.

The name alkylene is obtained in a similar manner, alk*ane* being converted into alk*ylene*.

Isomers differing only in the position of the double bond are prefixed by Greek letters or numbers which indicate the position of the double bond. The lowest number is usually given to the double bond (see below), and the number (or Greek letter) indicates the *first* of the two carbon atoms that are joined together by the double bond, *e.g.*,

$CH_3{\cdot}CH_2{\cdot}CH{=}CH_2$	α-Butylene	or	1-Butylene
$CH_3{\cdot}CH{=}CH{\cdot}CH_3$	β-Butylene	or	2-Butylene
$(CH_3)_2C{=}CH_2$	*iso*Butylene		
$(CH_3)_2C{=}CH{\cdot}CH_3$	β-*iso*Amylene (*cf.* pentane and amyl)		

Another method of nomenclature is to consider ethylene as the parent substance and the higher members as derivatives of ethylene. If the compound is a monosubstituted derivative of ethylene, then no difficulty is encountered in naming it; if the compound is a disubstituted derivative of ethylene isomerism is possible, since the alkyl groups can be attached to the same or different carbon atoms. When the groups are attached to the same carbon atom the olefin is named as the *asymmetrical* or *unsymmetrical* compound (abbreviated to *as-* or *unsym-*); when attached to different carbon atoms the olefin is named as the *symmetrical* (*sym-* or *s-*) compound, *e.g.*,

$CH_3{\cdot}CH{=}CH_2$	Methylethylene
$CH_3{\cdot}CH{=}CH{\cdot}CH_3$	*s*-Dimethylethylene
$(CH_3)_2C{=}CH_2$	*as*-Dimethylethylene
$(CH_3)_2C{=}CH{\cdot}CH_3$	Trimethylethylene

According to the I.U.C. system of nomenclature, the class suffix of the olefins is *-ene*, and so the series becomes the alkene series. The longest carbon chain containing the double bond is chosen as the parent alkene, the name of which is obtained by changing the suffix *-ane* of the corresponding paraffin into *-ene*. The positions of the double bond and side-chains are indicated by numbers.

It has already been pointed out that the rule of least numbers shall be used (p. 41). There is, however, another rule according to which the lowest number possible is given, in order of preference, (i) to the principal functional group of a compound, (ii) to the double bond, (iii) to the triple bond, and (iv) to atoms or groups designated by prefixes. As far as the paraffins are concerned, only statement (iv) applies, and the rule of lowest numbers is used. In order to name compounds with two (or more) functional groups, it is necessary, for purposes of naming, to choose one as the principal function; this will be dealt with later (p. 221).

In naming olefins by the I.U.C. system of nomenclature, the lowest number possible is given to the double bond, and the positions of side-chains are indicated accordingly, even though the rule of lowest numbers is violated. The number indicating the position of the double bond may be placed before or after the name of the alkene, or before the suffix,* *e.g.*,

$CH_3{\cdot}CH_2{\cdot}CH{=}CH_2$ 1-Butene, Butene-1 or But-1-ene

$CH_3{\cdot}CH{=}C(CH_3){-}C(CH_3)_2{-}CH_3$ 3 : 4 : 4-Trimethyl-2-pentene, 3 : 4 : 4-Trimethylpentene-2 or 3 : 4 : 4-Trimethylpent-2-ene

$CH_3{\cdot}CH_2{\cdot}C({=}CH_2){\cdot}CH(CH_3){\cdot}CH_3$ 2-Ethyl-3-methylbut-1-ene

In addition to the above method of nomenclature, there still remains the older scheme of denoting the presence of a double (or a triple) bond by the Greek letter Δ, the position of the double bond being indicated by a number placed at the upper right-hand corner of the symbol, *e.g.*,

$CH_3{\cdot}CH{=}C(CH_3){-}CH(CH_3){\cdot}CH_2{\cdot}CH_3$ 3 : 4-Dimethyl-Δ^2-hexene

General Methods of Preparation of the Olefins. 1. By the action of concentrated sulphuric acid, at 160–170°, on primary alcohols. The acid acts as a dehydrating agent, removing one molecule of water from the alcohol to form the olefin, *e.g.*, ethylene from ethanol:

$$C_2H_5OH \xrightarrow{-H_2O} C_2H_4 \quad (f.\text{–}g.)$$

Dehydration of secondary and tertiary alcohols is best carried out using *dilute* sulphuric acid, since the olefins produced from these alcohols (particularly tertiary alcohols) tend to polymerise under the influence of the concentrated acid. The yields of olefin from secondary and tertiary alcohols are very good.

Instead of sulphuric acid, glacial phosphoric acid (HPO_3), phosphorus pentoxide, or alumina may be used. With alumina, at 350°, the yields are *v.g.–ex.* Brandenberg *et al.* (1950) have converted all three classes of alcohols

* See also p. 785.

into olefins in excellent yields by means of boric acid as catalyst (borates are formed as intermediates):

$$3R{\cdot}CH_2{\cdot}CH_2OH + H_3BO_3 \longrightarrow (R{\cdot}CH_2{\cdot}CH_2O)_3B \longrightarrow 3R{\cdot}CH{=}CH_2 + H_3BO_3$$

Methyl xanthates may also be used to prepare olefins (p. 120).

2. By the action of *ethanolic* potassium hydroxide on monohalogen derivatives of the paraffins, *e.g.*, propylene from propyl bromide:

$$CH_3{\cdot}CH_2{\cdot}CH_2Br + KOH \xrightarrow{\text{ethanol}} CH_3{\cdot}CH{=}CH_2 + KBr + H_2O$$

This is not a very important method for the preparation of the lower alkenes, since these may be prepared directly from the corresponding alcohols, which are readily accessible. The reaction, however, is very important, since by means of it a double bond can be introduced into an organic compound (see text). The yield of olefin depends on the nature of the alkyl halide used; it is fair with primary, and very good for secondary and tertiary alkyl halides. Ethylene cannot be prepared by this method from ethyl halide (see alkyl halides for the mechanism of *dehydrohalogenation, i.e.*, removal of halogen acid).

3. (i) By the action of zinc dust on methanolic solutions of *gem*-dihalogen derivatives of the paraffins, *e.g.*, propylene from propylidene bromide:

$$CH_3{\cdot}CH_2{\cdot}CHBr_2 + Zn \longrightarrow ZnBr_2 + [CH_3{\cdot}CH_2{\cdot}CH{<}] \longrightarrow CH_3{\cdot}CH{=}CH_2$$

The mechanism of this reaction is not known, but it seems likely that the unstable propylidene radical $CH_3{\cdot}CH_2{\cdot}CH{=}$ is formed first, and then rearranges to form propylene (which is stable).

If sodium is used instead of zinc, and the reaction is carried out preferably in ether solution, comparatively little propylene is formed, the main product being hex-3-ene:

$$2CH_3{\cdot}CH_2{\cdot}CHBr_2 + 4Na \longrightarrow CH_3{\cdot}CH_2{\cdot}CH{=}CH{\cdot}CH_2{\cdot}CH_3 + 4NaBr$$

This reaction is really an extension of the Wurtz synthesis, and the important point to note is that the use of sodium tends to produce lengthening of the carbon chain.

(ii) By the action of zinc dust in methanol solution on *vic*-dihalogen derivatives of the paraffins, *e.g.*, propylene from propylene bromide:

$$CH_3{\cdot}CHBr{\cdot}CH_2Br + Zn \longrightarrow CH_3{\cdot}CH{=}CH_2 + ZnBr_2$$

Sodium can also be used, but zinc dust is usually more satisfactory.

Neither (i) nor (ii) is used very much for preparing alkenes, since the necessary dihalogen compounds are not readily accessible. The method, however, is very useful for purifying alkenes or for " protecting " a double bond (see, *e.g.*, allyl alcohol). Sodium iodide may be used instead of zinc dust, and its use depends on the fact that the *vic*-di-iodide which is formed is unstable, and readily eliminates iodine to form a double bond:

$$>CBr{\cdot}CBr< + 2NaI \longrightarrow 2NaBr + [>CI{\cdot}CI<] \longrightarrow >C{=}C< + I_2$$

4. By heating a quaternary ammonium hydroxide, *e.g.*, ethylene from tetraethylammonium hydroxide:

$$(C_2H_5)_4NOH \longrightarrow C_2H_4 + (C_2H_5)_3N + H_2O$$

This method of preparation is more important as a means of ascertaining the structure of a compound containing nitrogen in a ring, and is the basis of the Hofmann Exhaustive Methylation reaction (see p. 302).

5. Boord *et al.* (1930–33) have prepared olefins by conversion of an aldehyde into its chloro-ether, treating this with bromine followed by a Grignard reagent, and finally treating the product with zinc and *n*-butanol.

$$R\cdot CH_2\cdot CHO \xrightarrow[HCl]{C_2H_5OH} R\cdot CH_2\cdot CHCl\cdot OC_2H_5 \xrightarrow{Br_2} R\cdot CHBr\cdot CHBr\cdot OC_2H_5$$

$$\xrightarrow{R'MgBr} R\cdot CHBr\cdot CHR'\cdot OC_2H_5 \xrightarrow[C_4H_9OH]{Zn} R\cdot CH{=}CH\cdot R'$$

This method is very useful for preparing olefins of definite structure, and an interesting point about it is the replacement of the α-chlorine atom by bromine when the α-chloro-ether undergoes bromination in the β-position.

6. A number of olefins are prepared by the cracking of petroleum (p. 53), *e.g.*, ethylene, propylene, butylenes, etc. (see also the individuals). For the production of the lower olefins the most suitable starting material is gas oil, whereas for the higher olefins it is best to use paraffin wax or Fischer–Tropsch wax (p. 54). The lower olefins (C_2—C_5) are also prepared by the catalytic dehydrogenation of saturated hydrocarbons, the most satisfactory catalysts being those of the chromium oxide–alumina type.

General properties of the olefins. The members containing two to four carbon atoms are gases; five to fifteen, liquids; sixteen onwards, solids at room temperature. All are lighter than water, in which they are insoluble, and they burn in air with a luminous smoky flame.

Owing to the presence of a double bond, the olefins undergo a large number of *addition* reactions, but under special conditions they also undergo substitution reactions. The high reactivity of the olefinic bond is due to the presence of the two π-electrons. These are less firmly held between the two nuclei than the σ-electrons, and are more exposed to external influences, and so are readily polarisable. It is the π-electrons which undergo the electromeric effect at the requirements of the attacking reagent, and when addition occurs, the trigonal arrangement in the olefin changes to the tetrahedral arrangement in the saturated compound produced (see p. 408).

1. Olefins are readily hydrogenated under pressure in the presence of a catalyst. Finely divided platinum and palladium are effective at room temperature; nickel on a support (Sabatier–Senderens reduction) requires a temperature between 200° and 300°; Raney nickel is effective at room temperature and atmospheric pressure:

$$C_2H_4 + H_2 \xrightarrow{\text{catalyst}} C_2H_6$$

Platinum and palladium-black, *i.e.*, the metals in a very finely divided state, may be prepared by reducing their soluble salts with formaldehyde. Adams' platinum–platinum oxide catalyst is prepared by reducing platinum oxide with hydrogen before the addition of the compound being hydrogenated, or it may be added to the compound, reduction of the oxide taking place during hydrogenation.

One molecule of hydrogen is absorbed for each double bond present in the unsaturated compound.

The olefinic bond is readily reduced *catalytically*, but it is not reduced by metals and acid, or sodium and ethanol, unless the double bond is in the αβ-position with respect to certain groups (see text). On the other hand, all aliphatic double bonds can be reduced by means of concentrated hydriodic acid and red phosphorus.

2. Olefins form addition compounds with the halogens, *e.g.*, ethylene adds bromine to form ethylene bromide:

$$CH_2{=}CH_2 + Br_2 \longrightarrow CH_2Br\cdot CH_2Br \quad (85\%)$$

The order of the reactivity of the addition of halogens is:—chlorine>bromine>iodine. The addition of halogens to olefins in the gaseous phase can take place in the dark, but is accelerated by light. Stewart and Edlund (1923) showed that the reaction between ethylene and bromine (in the absence of light) occurs only at the surface of the reaction vessel. Norrish (1923) showed that the reaction depended on the nature of the surface of the walls of the containing vessel; *e.g.*, ethylene and bromine react in a clean, dry vessel, or one coated with stearic acid, but practically ceased to react when the walls were coated with paraffin wax. Norrish and Jones (1926) also showed that the reaction was catalysed when the glass walls were wet. The "gaseous phase" reaction is also catalysed by inorganic halides (anhydrous) such as aluminium chloride, ferric chloride, etc.

The addition of halogen to olefins takes place readily in the liquid phase or in a solvent such as ethanol, light petrol, etc., and it is catalysed in solution by halide ions.

Since *polar* catalysts facilitate the addition of halogens to ethylene (and other olefins), it would appear that the reaction takes place by a polar mechanism, the catalyst forcing the two π-electrons to move in one direction, thereby polarising the molecule. Consider the reaction between ethylene and bromine. At the requirements of the bromine molecule, and assisted by catalysts if these are present, the ethylene molecule undergoes the electromeric effect:

$$CH_2{=}CH_2 \longrightarrow \overset{+}{C}H_2{-}\overset{-}{\ddot{C}}H_2$$

In the bromine molecule there is a *tendency* for one of the bromine atoms to gain control of the shared electron pair forming the covalent bond, *i.e.*, the bromine *tends* to separate into positive and negative ions:

$$Br{\div}Br \longrightarrow \overset{\delta+}{Br}{-}{:}\overset{\delta-}{Br}$$

It can now be supposed that the bromine molecule approaches the ethylene molecule, each affecting the other, and finally forming the transition complex, which then breaks down as follows:

$$\overset{\delta-}{Br}{:}{-}|\overset{\delta+}{Br}\text{ - - - - }\overset{-}{C}H_2{-}\overset{+}{C}H_2 \longrightarrow \overset{-}{Br} + Br{-}CH_2{-}\overset{+}{C}H_2$$

This is then followed by the addition of the bromide ion to the positively charged carbon atom:

$$Br{-}CH_2{-}\overset{+}{C}H_2 + \overset{-}{Br} \longrightarrow Br{-}CH_2{-}CH_2{-}Br$$

Combining these equations, we have:

$$Br{-}Br \quad CH_2{=}CH_2 \longrightarrow BrCH_2{\cdot}\overset{+}{C}H_2 \quad \overset{-}{Br} \longrightarrow BrCH_2{\cdot}CH_2Br$$

If this is the mechanism, then bromine (and the other halogens) are *electrophilic* reagents, since the bromine atom that adds on first is short of two electrons, and so will attack at a point of high electron density. That the two bromine atoms add on *singly* is supported by the work of Francis (1925), who passed ethylene into an aqueous solution of bromine that contained sodium chloride or sodium nitrate, *i.e.*, Francis brominated ethylene in the presence of chloride or nitrate ions. 1-Bromo-2-chloroethane, $CH_2Cl{\cdot}CH_2Br$, or the nitrate ester, $CH_2Br{\cdot}CH_2{\cdot}O{\cdot}NO_2$, of ethylene bromohydrin ($CH_2Br{\cdot}CH_2OH$) was obtained as well as ethylene bromide. If the two atoms of bromine add on simultaneously to ethylene, then only ethylene bromide should be obtained. Since in the presence of chloride or nitrate ions the chloro- or nitrate derivative was also formed, it can be supposed that when the first bromine atom (positive ion) has added on, there will be in solution the residual bromide ion and chloride or nitrate ions, which will all compete for the positively charged carbon atom in $Br—CH_2—\overset{+}{C}H_2$, and which will form their respective addition products in amounts depending on their relative concentrations. Thus, if addition of the bromine molecule takes place one atom at a time, the experimental results may be explained.

The above mechanism was first put forward by Burton and Ingold (1928), but recently it has been shown that this mechanism, while satisfying some reactions, does not satisfy others. In the latter cases it is suggested that the reaction proceeds first through the formation of a complex, and is followed by addition (Robertson and co-workers, 1937, 1938, 1939; Nozaki and Ogg, 1942; see also p. 408).

Since the addition of halogen to olefin is catalysed by light, it has been suggested that the light-catalysed reaction may proceed via a free-radical mechanism, *e.g.*,

$$Cl_2 \xrightarrow{h\nu} 2Cl\cdot$$
$$CH_2{=}CH_2 + Cl\cdot \longrightarrow CH_2Cl—CH_2\cdot$$
$$CH_2Cl—CH_2\cdot + Cl_2 \longrightarrow CH_2Cl—CH_2Cl + Cl\cdot$$
$$CH_2{=}CH_2 + Cl\cdot \longrightarrow CH_2Cl—CH_2\cdot, \text{ etc.}$$

It may be asked why the free radical $CH_2Cl\cdot CH_2\cdot$ does not combine with the other chlorine atom (free radical). There is, of course, always a chance of this occurring, but since the concentration of the chlorine molecules is infinitely greater, the reaction will therefore proceed as shown above. On the other hand, since the concentration of the ethylene is high, it would appear that the free radical $CH_2Cl\cdot CH_2\cdot$ could react with ethylene molecules. If this were to happen, polymerisation (or at least dimerisation) would take place. There appears to be no evidence for this, and so, if the reaction is via free radicals, we must suppose it to take place as shown. This type of reaction is known as a free-radical chain reaction, and once started, carries on until the reactants are used up, or the chain broken by the destruction of the free radicals (see below, polymerisation).

Instead of addition reactions with the halogens, the olefins may undergo substitution provided the right conditions are used. Thus when straight-chain olefins are treated with chlorine at a high temperature, they form mainly monochlorides of the allyl type, *i.e.*, in the chain $—C—\overset{\times}{C}—C{=}C—$, it is the hydrogen of $\overset{\times}{C}$ that is substituted (see allyl compounds); *e.g.*, propylene heated with chlorine between 400° and 600° gives allyl chloride:

$$CH_3\cdot CH{=}CH_2 + Cl_2 \longrightarrow CH_2Cl\cdot CH{=}CH_2 + HCl$$

Above a certain temperature range, substitution takes place; below this range, addition takes place. The temperature range varies according to the olefin used, but for most olefins lies between 300° and 600°.

On the other hand, substitution is fairly easy with branched-chain olefins, and again occurs in the allyl position (see, *e.g.*, *iso*butene).

The action of fluorine on olefins usually results in the formation of carbon tetrafluoride, but addition to the double bond may be effected by treating the olefin with hydrogen fluoride in the presence of lead dioxide (Henne *et al.*, 1945); the fluorinating agent is lead tetrafluoride:

$$PbO_2 + 4HF \longrightarrow PbF_4 + 2H_2O$$
$$>C{=}C< + PbF_4 \longrightarrow >CF\cdot CF< + PbF_2$$

3. Olefins form addition compounds with the halogen acids, *e.g.*, ethylene adds hydrogen bromide to form ethyl bromide:

$$C_2H_4 + HBr \longrightarrow C_2H_5Br$$

The order of reactivity of the addition of the halogen acids is hydrogen iodide > hydrogen bromide > hydrogen chloride > hydrogen fluoride. The conditions for the addition are similar to those for the halogens; the addition of hydrogen fluoride, however, is effected only under pressure.

In the case of unsymmetrical olefins it is possible for the addition of the halogen acid to take place in two different ways, *e.g.*, propylene might add on hydrogen iodide to form propyl iodide:

$$CH_3{\cdot}CH{=}CH_2 + HI \longrightarrow CH_3{\cdot}CH_2{\cdot}CH_2I$$

or it might form *iso*propyl iodide:

$$CH_3{\cdot}CH{=}CH_2 + HI \longrightarrow CH_3{\cdot}CHI{\cdot}CH_3$$

Markownikoff studied many reactions of this kind, and as a result of his work, formulated the following rule: *the negative part of the addendum adds on to the carbon atom that is joined to the least number of hydrogen atoms.* In the case of the halogen acids the halogen atom is the negative part, and so *iso*propyl halide is obtained. Some authors have claimed that some *n*-propyl halide is also formed in small amounts, but, mainly from the work of Kharasch and his co-workers (see below), it appears that the addition occurs exclusively according to Markownikoff's rule.

Markownikoff's rule is empirical, but it may be explained theoretically as follows. In halogen acids the halogen atom, due to its high electron-affinity, is the negative end of the dipole in the molecule; thus $\overset{\delta+}{H}{-}\overset{\delta-}{X}$. The addition of hydrogen iodide to ethylene may be formulated as follows (*cf.* addition of halogen to ethylene, above):

$$I{-}H \quad CH_2{=}CH_2 \longrightarrow CH_3{\cdot}\overset{+}{C}H_2 \quad \overset{-}{I} \longrightarrow CH_3{\cdot}CH_2I$$

Now consider the addition of hydrogen iodide to propylene. The electromeric effect in propylene can take place in two ways:

$$\text{(i)}\quad CH_3{\cdot}CH{=}CH_2 \longrightarrow CH_3{\cdot}\overset{+}{C}H{-}\overset{\bullet\bullet}{\overset{-}{C}}H_2$$

$$\text{(ii)}\quad CH_3{\cdot}CH{=}CH_2 \longrightarrow CH_3{\cdot}\overset{\bullet\bullet}{\overset{-}{C}}H{-}\overset{+}{C}H_2$$

Since the methyl group is electron-repelling, the electromeric effect will take place according to (i), and hence *iso*propyl iodide will be formed:

$$I{-}H \quad CH_2{=}CH{\cdot}CH_3 \longrightarrow CH_3{\cdot}\overset{+}{C}H{\cdot}CH_3 + \overset{-}{I} \longrightarrow CH_3{\cdot}CHI{\cdot}CH_3$$

Thus with all *polar* addenda of the type $\overset{\delta+}{H}{-}\overset{\delta-}{Z}$, the addition takes place in accordance with Markownikoff's rule (see also p. 255).

Olefins containing at least three carbon atoms will add on a molecule of water when heated with steam at 200–250° under pressure in the presence of oxides of metals such as silver, copper, etc., *e.g.*, propylene forms acetone:

$$CH_3{\cdot}CH{=}CH_2 + H{-}OH \longrightarrow [CH_3{\cdot}CHOH{\cdot}CH_3] \longrightarrow CH_3{\cdot}CO{\cdot}CH_3 + H_2$$

The Peroxide Effect (Kharasch, 1933). The presence of oxygen or peroxides that are formed when the olefin stands exposed to the air, or added peroxides such as benzoyl peroxide, causes the addition of hydrogen bromide to take place in the direction opposite to that predicted by Markownikoff's rule. This departure from the rule is known as the " abnormal " reaction, and was shown to be due to the " peroxide effect " (Kharasch *et al.*, 1933). Hydrogen chloride, hydrogen iodide and hydrogen fluoride do not exhibit the abnormal reaction. The abnormal reaction in the presence of peroxides can be prevented by the addition of an " inhibitor " such as diphenylamine, catechol, etc. It has been found that the addition of hydrogen bromide is " abnormally " effected photochemically as well as by peroxide catalysts (Vaughan *et al.*, 1942).

The mechanism of the peroxide effect is still not settled, but it seems likely that it is a free-radical chain reaction, the peroxide generating the free radical R· (*cf.* polymerisation, below):

$$(R{\cdot}CO_2)_2 \longrightarrow 2RCO_2{\cdot} \longrightarrow 2R{\cdot} + 2CO_2$$

$$R{\cdot} + HBr \longrightarrow RH + Br{\cdot}$$

$$R'{\cdot}CH{=}CH_2 + Br{\cdot} \longrightarrow R'{\cdot}\dot{C}H{\cdot}CH_2Br \xrightarrow{HBr} R'{\cdot}CH_2{\cdot}CH_2Br + Br{\cdot}, \text{ etc.}$$

In the photochemical addition, the bromine atom is produced by a quantum of light:

$$HBr \xrightarrow{h\nu} H{\cdot} + Br{\cdot}$$

At least two explanations may be offered for the fact that the bromine atom attacks the carbon atom *not* joined to the least number of hydrogen atoms:

(i) Free halogen atoms are *electrophilic* reagents owing to their tendency to complete their octets, and hence will attack the olefin at its point of highest electron density. As we have seen above, the electromeric effect in olefins of the type $R{\cdot}CH{=}CH_2$ takes place *away* from the CH group, owing to the electron-repelling effect of the R group, *i.e.*, we have:

$$R{\cdot}CH{=}CH_2 \longrightarrow R{\cdot}\overset{+}{C}H{-}\overset{-}{\ddot{C}}H_2$$

$$R{\cdot}\overset{+}{C}H{-}\overset{-}{\ddot{C}}H_2 + Br{\cdot} \longrightarrow R{\cdot}\dot{C}H{-}CH_2Br \xrightarrow{HBr} R{\cdot}CH_2{\cdot}CH_2Br + Br{\cdot}, \text{ etc.}$$

(ii) Each of two carbon atoms joined by the double bond retains its π-electron. Thus a bromine atom can attack either carbon atom equally well, but of the two free radicals that can be produced, *viz.*, $R{\cdot}\dot{C}H{\cdot}CH_2Br$ and $R{\cdot}CHBr{\cdot}CH_2{\cdot}$, it is the former which has the lower free energy, and hence this one is more likely to be formed.

4. Aqueous hypohalous acid solutions react with olefins to form halohydrins, *e.g.*, ethylene forms ethylene chlorohydrin with hypochlorous acid solution:

$$CH_2{=}CH_2 + HOCl \longrightarrow CH_2Cl{\cdot}CH_2OH$$

In hypohalous acids, HOX, the OH group is the negative end of the dipole, and so the addition may be formulated as:

$$HO{-}Cl \quad CH_2{=}CH_2 \longrightarrow CH_2Cl{\cdot}\overset{+}{C}H_2 \quad \overset{-}{O}H \longrightarrow CH_2Cl{\cdot}CH_2OH$$

Similarly, in unsymmetrical olefins the reaction will be in accordance with Markownikoff's rule:

$$R{\cdot}CH{=}CH_2 \quad Cl{-}OH \longrightarrow R{\cdot}\overset{+}{C}H{\cdot}CH_2Cl + \overset{-}{O}H \longrightarrow R{\cdot}CHOH{\cdot}CH_2Cl$$

Halohydrins are useful in certain syntheses, since they contain two reactive groups (see text).

Various sulphenyl halides form adducts with olefins; 2 : 4-dinitrobenzene-sulphenyl chloride in particular has been found extremely useful for identifying olefins (Kharasch *et al.*, 1949–).

The mechanism of the addition is possibly as follows, the sulphur being the positive end of the dipole:

$$CH_2{=}CH_2 + NO_2C_6H_3(NO_2)\overset{\delta+}{S}{-}\overset{\delta-}{Cl} \longrightarrow ClCH_2{\cdot}CH_2{\cdot}SC_6H_3(NO_2)NO_2$$

Two products are obtained with unsymmetrical olefins, the predominating adduct being the one formed in accordance with Markownikoff's rule.

Compounds containing triple bonds also form adducts with one molecule of the sulphenyl chloride.

5. Olefins are absorbed by concentrated sulphuric acid to form alkyl hydrogen sulphates. Addition takes place according to Markownikoff's rule, *e.g.*, propylene reacts with sulphuric acid to form *iso*propyl hydrogen sulphate:

$$CH_3{\cdot}CH{=}CH_2 \quad H{-}O{\cdot}SO_2{\cdot}OH \longrightarrow$$
$$CH_3{\cdot}\overset{+}{C}H{\cdot}CH_3 + \bar{O}{\cdot}SO_2{\cdot}OH \longrightarrow (CH_3)_2CHO{\cdot}SO_2{\cdot}OH$$

Paraffins are not absorbed by cold concentrated sulphuric acid, and hence may be separated from olefins (see also ethers and alcohols).

6. Olefins add on nitrosyl chloride, nitrosyl bromide and oxides of nitrogen; *e.g.*, ethylene forms ethylene nitrosochloride with nitrosyl chloride:

$$CH_2{=}CH_2 + NOCl \longrightarrow CH_2Cl{\cdot}CH_2{\cdot}NO$$

Since the X atom is the negative end of the dipole in NOX, it will add on to the carbon atom joined to the least number of hydrogen atoms (Markownikoff's rule), *e.g.*, trimethylethylene adds on nitrosyl bromide to form the following trimethylethylene nitrosobromide:

$$(CH_3)_2C{=}CH{\cdot}CH_3 + NO{-}Br \longrightarrow (CH_3)_2CBr{\cdot}CH(NO){\cdot}CH_3$$

The reaction with nitrosyl chloride is usually carried out by treating a solution of the olefin and ethyl or pentyl (amyl) nitrite in glacial acetic acid with concentrated hydrochloric acid, the temperature being maintained at about 10°. The nitrosochlorides (and nitrosobromides) are usually *bimolecular* crystalline solids, *e.g.*,

$$\begin{matrix}CH_2\\ \|\\ CH_2\end{matrix} + NOCl \longrightarrow \begin{bmatrix}CH_2{-}NO\\ |\\ CH_2{-}Cl\end{bmatrix} \xrightarrow{\text{2 molecules}} \begin{bmatrix}CH_2{\cdot}NO\\ |\\ CH_2Cl\end{bmatrix}_2$$

The addition of the oxides of nitrogen to olefins is complicated, and much of the work done is of a doubtful nature. The compound formed depends on the structure of the olefin and the nature of the "nitrous fumes"; usually a mixture of addition products is formed. According to Levy, Scaife *et al.* (1946), when ethylene, propylene, and some other olefins react with dinitrogen tetroxide, N_2O_4, then according to the conditions dinitroparaffin, nitro-alcohols and nitro-alkyl nitrates can be obtained in high yield.

The reaction is best carried out in the liquid phase at $-10°$ to $+25°$. Dinitro-compounds or nitro-nitrites are produced, but the latter are usually partly oxidised to nitro-nitrate. The unchanged nitro-nitrite is unstable, tending to explode, but it may be converted into the stable nitro-alcohol when treated in the cold with water or a lower aliphatic alcohol. The nitrogen tetroxide behaves as (i) two NO_2 groups to give dinitro-compounds, and (ii) one NO_2 group and one ONO group (nitrite radical) to give nitro-nitrites (see also nitro-compounds):

$$>C{=}C< \xrightarrow{(NO_2)(ONO)} >C(NO_2){-}C(O{\cdot}NO)< \xrightarrow{ROH} >C(NO_2){-}C(OH)<$$

(nitro-nitrite) (nitro-alcohol)

$$>C{=}C< \xrightarrow{(NO_2)(NO_2)} >C(NO_2){-}C(NO_2)< \quad \text{(dinitro-paraffin)}$$

$$\text{nitro-nitrite} \xrightarrow{\text{oxidation}} >C(NO_2){-}C(O{\cdot}NO_2)< \quad \text{(nitro-nitrate)}$$

According to Schechter *et al.* (1953), the addition of dinitrogen tetroxide occurs via the formation of the nitronium free-radical:

$$O_2N{-}NO_2 \rightleftharpoons 2{\cdot}NO_2$$

$$>C{=}C< \xrightarrow{\cdot NO_2} >C(NO_2){-}\dot{C}< \xrightarrow{\cdot NO_2} >C(NO_2){-}C(NO_2)< + >C(NO_2){-}C(ONO)<$$

Dinitrogen trioxide in ether adds on to olefins at -70 to $5°$ to give mainly dimeric nitro-nitroso compounds:

$$>C{=}C< + NO{\cdot}NO_2 \longrightarrow >C(NO){-}C(NO_2)< \xrightarrow{2\text{ mols.}} \left[>C(NO){-}C(NO_2)<\right]_2$$

If the olefin is unsymmetrical, then the nitro group adds to the carbon joined to the larger number of hydrogen atoms. This may be explained by assuming that the nitro group is the positive part of the addendum (*i.e.*, the addition takes place according to Markownikoff's rule):

$$CH_3{\cdot}CH{=}CH_2 \quad O_2N{-}NO \longrightarrow CH_3{\cdot}\overset{+}{C}H{\cdot}CH_2{\cdot}NO_2 + \bar{N}O \longrightarrow CH_3{\cdot}CH(NO){\cdot}CH_2{\cdot}NO_2$$

7. Olefins are readily hydroxylated, *i.e.*, add on hydroxyl groups, to form dihydroxy-compounds known as glycols (*q.v.*). Hydroxylation may be effected:

(i) By cold dilute alkaline permanganate solution (*cis*-hydroxylation); *e.g.*, ethylene is converted into ethylene glycol:

$$CH_2{=}CH_2 + H_2O + [O] \xrightarrow{KMnO_4} CH_2OH{\cdot}CH_2OH$$

(ii) By 90 per cent. hydrogen peroxide in glacial acetic acid or better, in formic acid; *e.g.*, oleic acid is converted into 9:10-dihydroxystearic acid (see also reaction 8):

$$CH_3{\cdot}(CH_2)_7{\cdot}CH{=}CH{\cdot}(CH_2)_7{\cdot}CO_2H + H_2O_2 \longrightarrow CH_3{\cdot}(CH_2)_7{\cdot}CH(OH){\cdot}CH(OH){\cdot}(CH_2)_7{\cdot}CO_2H$$

The addition of hydrogen peroxide may be catalysed by various oxides, *e.g.*, osmium tetroxide in *tert.*-butanol (*cis*-addition), selenium dioxide in *tert.*-butanol or acetone (*trans*-addition; see p. 407).

(iii) By means of osmium tetroxide. This compound adds very readily to an ethylenic double bond at room temperature (Criegee, 1936):

$$\begin{matrix} R\cdot CH \\ \| \\ R\cdot CH \end{matrix} + OsO_4 \longrightarrow \begin{matrix} R\cdot CH-O \\ | \\ R\cdot CH-O \end{matrix} \!\!>\! Os \!\begin{matrix} \nearrow O \\ \searrow O \end{matrix} \quad (v.g.\text{-}ex.)$$

These cyclic compounds (*osmic esters*), on refluxing with aqueous ethanolic sodium hydrogen sulphite, are hydrolysed to 1:2-glycols (*cis*-glycols).

If the addition of osmium tetroxide is carried out in the presence of pyridine, coloured crystalline compounds are obtained, usually in theoretical yield:

$$\begin{matrix} R\cdot CH \\ \| \\ R\cdot CH \end{matrix} + OsO_4 + 2C_5H_5N \longrightarrow \begin{matrix} R\cdot CH-O \\ | \\ R\cdot CH-O \end{matrix} \!\!>\! OsO_2,\ 2C_5H_5N$$

cis-Hydroxylation of a double bond may also be effected by treating the olefin with iodine and silver acetate in wet acetic acid, and then hydrolysing the mixed mono- and di-acetates with alkali (Barkley *et al.*, 1954):

$$>C=C< \xrightarrow[CH_3\cdot CO_2Ag]{I_2} \begin{matrix} >C & - & C< \\ | & & | \\ OH & & O\cdot CO\cdot CH_3 \end{matrix} + \begin{matrix} >C & - & C< \\ | & & | \\ CH_3\cdot COO & & O\cdot CO\cdot CH_3 \end{matrix} \xrightarrow{NaOH} \begin{matrix} >C & - & C< \\ | & & | \\ OH & & OH \end{matrix}$$

Glycols are readily oxidised to acids or ketones by means of acid permanganate or acid dichromate, the nature of the products being determined by the structure of the glycol, *e.g.*,

(*a*) propylene glycol gives acetic and formic acid:

$$CH_3\cdot CH(OH)\cdot CH_2OH \xrightarrow{[O]} CH_3\cdot CO_2H + H\cdot CO_2H$$

(*b*) *iso*Butylene glycol gives acetone and formic acid:

$$\begin{matrix} CH_3 \\ CH_3 \end{matrix}\!\!>\! C(OH)\cdot CH_2OH \xrightarrow{[O]} \begin{matrix} CH_3 \\ CH_3 \end{matrix}\!\!>\! CO + H\cdot CO_2H + H_2O$$

Sodium bismuthate, in acid solution, also effects similar oxidations (Rigby, 1950). An advantage of this reagent is that an aldehyde is one of the products (when possible); it is *not* further oxidised.

Oxidation of a glycol may also be effected by lead tetra-acetate, $(CH_3\cdot CO_2)_4Pb$, or by periodic acid, HIO_4 or H_5IO_6, the products being aldehydes or ketones, according to the structure of the glycol, *e.g.*,

(*a*) ethylene glycol gives two molecules of formaldehyde:

$$CH_2OH\cdot CH_2OH \xrightarrow[(CH_3CO_2)_4Pb]{[O]} H\cdot CHO + H\cdot CHO$$

(*b*) *iso*Butylene glycol gives acetone and formaldehyde:

$$\begin{matrix} CH_3 \\ CH_3 \end{matrix}\!\!>\! C(OH)\cdot CH_2OH \xrightarrow[HIO_4]{[O]} \begin{matrix} CH_3 \\ CH_3 \end{matrix}\!\!>\! CO + H\cdot CHO$$

It can be seen that whatever oxidising agent is used the glycol is split into two fragments, the rupture of the carbon chain occurring between the two carbon atoms joined to the hydroxyl groups. Since these two carbon atoms were linked together by the double bond in the original olefin, identification of the two fragments which may be acids, aldehydes or ketones, will indicate the position of the double bond in the olefin, *e.g.*,

$$R{\cdot}CH{=}CH{\cdot}R' \xrightarrow{H_2O_2} R{\cdot}CH(OH){\cdot}CH(OH){\cdot}R' \xrightarrow{HIO_4} R{\cdot}CHO + R'{\cdot}CHO$$

8. **Prileschaiev's reaction** (1912). By means of per-acids, the double bond in olefins is converted into the *epoxide* (olefin oxide). Perbenzoic acid, $C_6H_5{\cdot}CO{\cdot}O_2H$, and monoperphthalic acid, $CO_2H{\cdot}C_6H_4{\cdot}CO{\cdot}O_2H$, have been widely used for this reaction, *e.g.*,

$$R{\cdot}CH{=}CH{\cdot}R' + C_6H_5{\cdot}CO{\cdot}O_2Na \longrightarrow R{\cdot}\overset{\frown O \frown}{CH{\cdot}CH}{\cdot}R' + C_6H_5{\cdot}CO_2Na$$

Emmons *et al.* (1954, 1955) have found that peroxytrifluoroacetic acid ($CF_3{\cdot}CO{\cdot}O_2H$) is a very good reagent for epoxidation and hydroxylation.

$$R{\cdot}CH{=}CH{\cdot}R \xrightarrow{CF_3{\cdot}CO_3H} R{\cdot}\overset{\frown O \frown}{CH{-}CH}{\cdot}R \xrightarrow{CF_3{\cdot}CO_3H}$$

$$R{\cdot}CHOH{\cdot}CH(O{\cdot}CO{\cdot}CF_3){\cdot}R \xrightarrow[CH_3OH]{HCl\ in} R{\cdot}CHOH{\cdot}CHOH{\cdot}R \quad (60\text{–}95\%)$$

This method is particularly useful for high molecular-weight alkenes with a terminal double bond (these are only slowly hydroxylated by other per-acids). Furthermore, peroxytrifluoroacetic acid may be used to hydroxylate negatively substituted olefins, *e.g.*, ethyl acrylate, $CH_2{=}CH{\cdot}CO_2C_2H_5$.

Many mechanisms have been proposed for epoxidation, but none is certain. According to Pausacker *et al.* (1955), the mechanism is:

$$\begin{matrix} | \\ CH \\ \| \\ CH \\ | \end{matrix} + O\begin{matrix} O{-}C{\cdot}C_6H_5 \\ \quad\ \| \\ H{\cdots}O \end{matrix} \longrightarrow \begin{matrix} | \\ CH \\ \vdots \\ CH \\ | \end{matrix}\!\!>O<\!\!\begin{matrix} O{=}C{\cdot}C_6H_5 \\ \vdots \\ H{\cdots}O \end{matrix} \longrightarrow \begin{matrix} | \\ CH \\ | \\ CH \\ | \end{matrix}\!\!>O + \begin{matrix} O{=}C{\cdot}C_6H_5 \\ | \\ H{-}O \end{matrix}$$

transition state

9. Olefins add on ozone to form **ozonides.** These are usually explosive in the free state, and their structure and mechanism of formation have been the subject of a great deal of work. Staudinger (1922) suggested that the *mol-ozonide* is formed first, and this then rearranges to the ozonide, some polymerising as well.

$$R{\cdot}CH{=}CH{\cdot}R' + O_3 \longrightarrow \begin{matrix} R{\cdot}CH{-}CH{\cdot}R' \\ |\qquad |^{+}\quad \\ O{-}O{-}\overset{-}{O} \end{matrix} \longrightarrow \begin{matrix} \quad O \\ R{\cdot}CH \quad CH{\cdot}R' \\ |\qquad | \\ O{-}O \end{matrix} + \text{polymer}$$

molozonide ozonide

According to Criegee *et al.* (1954), the formation of the ozonide takes place as follows:

$$>C{=}C< + O_3 \longrightarrow \left[>\overset{\frown O_3 \frown}{C{-}C}< \right] \longrightarrow$$

$$\left[>C{=}O + \overset{-}{O}{-}O{-}\overset{+}{C}< \right] \longrightarrow >C\begin{matrix} O{-}O \\ O \end{matrix}C<$$

Bailey (1957), however, has proposed a mechanism in which the first step is the formation of a π-complex (p. 408). This then produces a zwitterion which breaks down to produce the zwitterion and carbonyl compound in the Criegee mechanism:

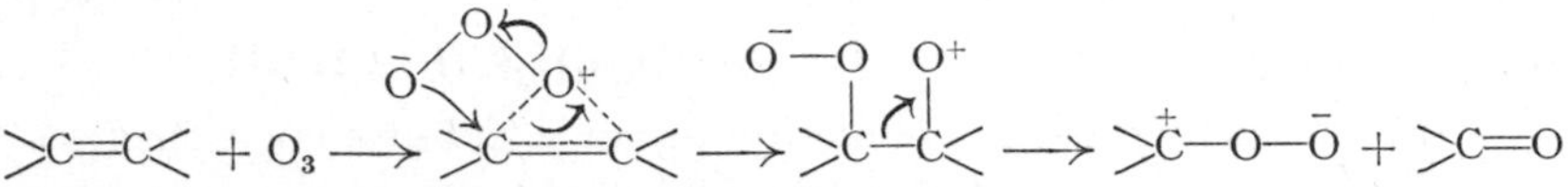

$$>C{=}C< + O_3 \longrightarrow >C\overset{\bar{O}-O-O^+}{=\!=}C< \longrightarrow >\underset{}{C}(\bar{O}{-}O)-C(O^+)< \longrightarrow >\overset{+}{C}-O-\bar{O} + >C{=}O$$

In this way Bailey explains the ready fission of carbon–carbon multiple bonds.

The ozonide is prepared by dissolving the olefinic compound in a solvent that is unaffected by ozone, *e.g.*, chloroform, carbon tetrachloride, glacial acetic acid, light petrol, etc., and a stream of ozonised oxygen is passed through. Subsequent treatment may be by one of the following procedures.

(i) The solvent is evaporated under reduced pressure, and the residual ozonide is treated with water and zinc dust in the presence of traces of silver and hydroquinone (Whitmore, 1932). Aldehydes or ketones are obtained according to the structure of the olefin. The function of the zinc dust is to destroy the hydrogen peroxide which is formed in the reaction, and which tends to oxidise the aldehyde (if this is a primary cleavage product) to the corresponding acid, *e.g.*,

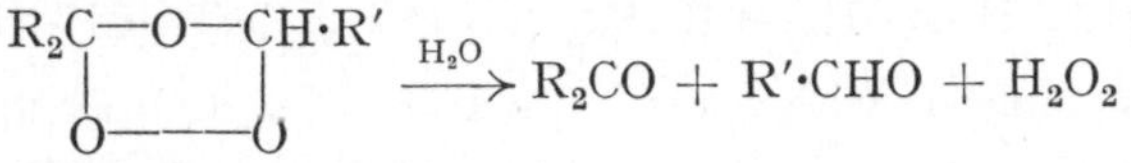

$$R_2C(-O-)CH{\cdot}R' \text{ (with } -O-O- \text{ bridge)} \xrightarrow{H_2O} R_2CO + R'{\cdot}CHO + H_2O_2$$

$$R'{\cdot}CHO + H_2O_2 \longrightarrow R'{\cdot}CO_2H + H_2O$$

In practice both aldehyde and acid are obtained.

(ii) A better method than the above is the *reductive* decomposition of the ozonide (Fischer, 1928, 1932). A palladium catalyst carried on a calcium carbonate support is added to the solution of the ozonide and then hydrogen is passed in. Usually a good yield (50–90 per cent.) of aldehyde or ketone is obtained:

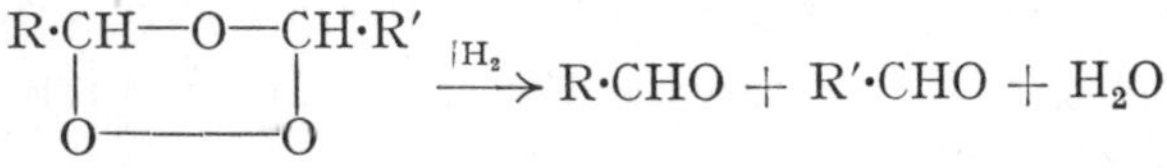

$$R{\cdot}CH(-O-)CH{\cdot}R' \text{ (with } -O-O- \text{ bridge)} \xrightarrow{H_2} R{\cdot}CHO + R'{\cdot}CHO + H_2O$$

(iii) Wilms (1950) has found that peracetic acid in acetic acid oxidises ozonides to carboxylic acids in high yields.

The resulting aldehydes (or acids) and ketones are identified, and thus the position of the double bond in the olefinic compound is found. The complete process of preparing the ozonide and decomposing it (and identifying the products formed) is known as *ozonolysis*, and this is probably the best method for determining the position of a double bond in any olefinic compound. Recently, however, some doubt has been cast on ozonolysis as a means of determining the positions of double bonds in unsaturated compounds, *e.g.*, according to Barnard *et al.* (1950), during the ozonolysis of citral (an acyclic terpene), partial rearrangement from the *iso*propylidene (I) to the *iso*propenyl structure (II) occurs (this is an example of a three-carbon tautomeric system; see p. 206):

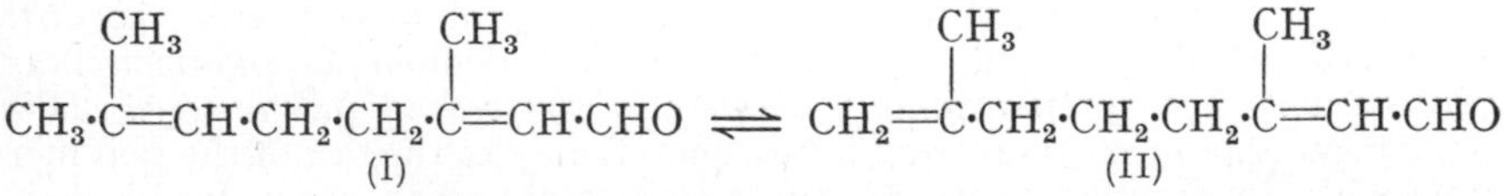

$$\underset{\text{(I)}}{CH_3{\cdot}C(CH_3){=}CH{\cdot}CH_2{\cdot}CH_2{\cdot}C(CH_3){=}CH{\cdot}CHO} \rightleftharpoons \underset{\text{(II)}}{CH_2{=}C(CH_3){\cdot}CH_2{\cdot}CH_2{\cdot}CH_2{\cdot}C(CH_3){=}CH{\cdot}CHO}$$

10. Olefins isomerise when heated at high temperature (500–700°), or at a lower temperature (200–300°) in the presence of various catalysts, *e.g.*, aluminium sulphate. Isomerisation may be due (i) to the change in

position of the double bond, which always tends to move towards the centre of the chain, *e.g.*, pent-1-ene isomerises to pent-2-ene:

$$CH_3{\cdot}CH_2{\cdot}CH_2{\cdot}CH{=}CH_2 \longrightarrow CH_3{\cdot}CH_2{\cdot}CH{=}CH{\cdot}CH_3$$

(ii) To the migration of a methyl group, *e.g.*, but-1-ene isomerises to *iso*butene:

$$CH_3{\cdot}CH_2{\cdot}CH{=}CH_2 \longrightarrow (CH_3)_2C{=}CH_2$$

(i) and (ii) may, or may not, occur together.

11. Olefins add on to *iso*paraffins in the presence of a catalyst, many of which are known, but the one usually employed is concentrated sulphuric acid, *e.g.*, ethylene adds on to *iso*butane to form a mixture of 2-methylpentane and 2 : 3-dimethylbutane:

$$(CH_3)_2CH{\cdot}CH_3 \xrightarrow[H_2SO_4]{C_2H_4} (CH_3)_2CH{\cdot}CH_2{\cdot}CH_2{\cdot}CH_3 + (CH_3)_2CH{\cdot}CH(CH_3)_2$$

This reaction is particularly useful for preparing "*iso*-octane", 2 : 2 : 4-trimethylpentane (see p. 52) by treating *iso*butane with *iso*butene in the presence of concentrated sulphuric acid:

$$(CH_3)_3CH + CH_2{=}C(CH_3)_2 \longrightarrow (CH_3)_3C{\cdot}CH_2{\cdot}CH(CH_3)_2$$

12. Olefins condense with acetic anhydride, $(CH_3{\cdot}CO)_2O$, in the presence of a catalyst, *e.g.*, zinc chloride, to form unsaturated ketones, *e.g.*, ethylene forms methyl vinyl ketone:

$$CH_2{=}CH_2 + (CH_3{\cdot}CO)_2O \xrightarrow{ZnCl_2} CH_2{=}CH{\cdot}CO{\cdot}CH_3 + CH_3{\cdot}CO_2H$$

Acid chlorides and α-halogenated ethers also combine with olefins in the presence of aluminium chloride, *e.g.*,

$$CH_3{\cdot}COCl + CH_2{=}CH_2 \xrightarrow{AlCl_3} CH_3{\cdot}CO{\cdot}CH_2{\cdot}CH_2Cl$$

$$CH_3{\cdot}O{\cdot}CH_2Cl + CH_2{=}CH_2 \xrightarrow{AlCl_3} CH_3{\cdot}O{\cdot}CH_2{\cdot}CH_2{\cdot}CH_2Cl$$

All of these condensations are examples of the Friedel–Crafts reaction in aliphatic compounds (see p. 502).

13. Olefins readily polymerise in the presence of suitable catalysts, *e.g.*, *iso*butene gives a polymer in the presence of concentrated sulphuric acid:

$$nC_4H_8 \longrightarrow (C_4H_8)_n$$

When two compounds have the same empirical formula but differ in molecular weight, the more complicated compound is called a *polymer* of the simpler one. The term *polymerisation* was used originally to indicate the process that took place when a single substance—the *monomer*—gave products having the same empirical formula but different molecular weights, each of these being a multiple of that of the monomer. As the investigation of polymerisation reactions progressed, it was found that many compounds of high molecular weight, although they produced a large number of monomer molecules on suitable treatment, did not always have exactly the same empirical formula as the parent monomer. This led to a modification of the definitions of the terms polymer and polymerisation. According to Carothers (1931, polymerisation is best defined as *intermolecular combinations that are functionally capable of proceeding indefinitely*. This definition implies that there is no limit theoretically to the size of the polymer molecule. In practice, however, the polymer ceases to grow, for various reasons (see below). The terms polymer and polymerisation are now used mainly in connection with high molecular weight compounds, which, in addition to being called polymers, are also known as *macromolecules*.

There are two types of polymerisation, *addition polymerisation* and *condensation polymerisation*.

Addition Polymerisation. Addition polymerisation occurs among molecules containing double or triple bonds; but in certain cases it can also occur between bifunctional compounds that result from the opening of ring structures (see, *e.g.*, ethylene oxide). *There is no liberation of small molecules during addition polymerisation.*

A very important group of olefinic compounds that undergo addition polymerisation is of the type $CH_2{=}CHY$, where Y may be H, X, CO_2R, CN, etc.:

$$nCH_2{=}\underset{\displaystyle Y}{\overset{\displaystyle H}{C}} \longrightarrow \left(-CH_2-\underset{\displaystyle Y}{\overset{\displaystyle H}{C}}-\right)_n$$

There are three possible ways in which this polymerisation can occur:

(i) Head to tail: $-CH_2{\cdot}CHY-CH_2{\cdot}CHY-$

(ii) Head to head and tail to tail:

$$-CHY{\cdot}CH_2-CH_2{\cdot}CHY-CHY{\cdot}CH_2-CH_2{\cdot}CHY-$$

(iii) A random arrangement involving (i) and (ii).

Experimental work seems to indicate that (i) is favoured.

Most polymerisations are carried out in the presence of catalysts, and polymerisation of olefins can be accelerated by ionic-type catalysts or radical-type catalysts. Both types of reaction consist of a number of steps which follow one another consecutively and rapidly, and appear to take place in three principal steps:

(i) The initiation or activation.
(ii) The growth or propagation.
(iii) The termination or cessation.

If M represents the monomer, the series of reactions may be represented as follows:

(i) $M \longrightarrow M^*$
(ii) $M + M^* \longrightarrow MM^* \xrightarrow{M} MMM^* \longrightarrow \cdots \longrightarrow M_n^*$
(iii) $M_n^* \longrightarrow M_n$.

The Ionic Mechanism of Catalysis. The ionic mechanism is believed to take place in the presence of certain metallic and non-metallic halides such as $AlCl_3$, $SnCl_4$ or BF_3. In certain cases sulphuric acid also catalyses polymerisation. Ionic catalysts are usually electrophilic reagents, and Hunter and Yohe (1933) have suggested that the chain-initiating action of these catalysts depends on their electrophilic nature, and consists in the catalyst acquiring a share in a pair of electrons (the π-electrons) from the double bond of the monomer, *e.g.*,

(i) $AlCl_3 + \overset{|}{\underset{|}{C}}{=}\overset{|}{\underset{|}{C}} \longrightarrow Cl_3\bar{A}l-\overset{|}{\underset{|}{C}}-\overset{|}{\underset{|}{C}}{}^{+}$

(ii) $Cl_3\bar{A}l-\overset{|}{\underset{|}{C}}-\overset{|}{\underset{|}{C}}{}^{+} + n\overset{|}{\underset{|}{C}}{=}\overset{|}{\underset{|}{C}} \longrightarrow Cl_3\bar{A}l-(-\overset{|}{\underset{|}{C}}-\overset{|}{\underset{|}{C}}-)_n-\overset{|}{\underset{|}{C}}-\overset{|}{\underset{|}{C}}{}^{+}$

(iii) $Cl_3\bar{A}l-(-\overset{|}{\underset{|}{C}}-\overset{|}{\underset{|}{C}}-)_n-\overset{|}{\underset{|}{C}}-\overset{|}{\underset{|}{C}}{}^{+} \longrightarrow Cl_2Al-(-\overset{|}{\underset{|}{C}}-\overset{|}{\underset{|}{C}}-)_n-\overset{|}{\underset{|}{C}}{=}\overset{|}{\underset{|}{C}} + HCl$

In (iii) a proton is lost, thus producing a double bond at the end of the chain so that the molecule becomes deactivated, and hence ceases to grow (see also below).

The Free-Radical Mechanism of Catalysis. The most important cases of addition polymerisation are those which take place by chain reactions and are brought about by catalysts that are known to generate free radicals. The most widely used catalysts are the organic and inorganic peroxides and the salts of the per-acids, *e.g.*, benzoyl peroxide, acetyl peroxide, hydrogen peroxide, potassium perborate, etc.

Staudinger (1932) was the first to suggest a free-radical mechanism, and it may be as follows for an organic peroxide:

(i) $(R{\cdot}CO_2)_2 \longrightarrow 2RCO_2{\cdot}$

$RCO_2{\cdot} \longrightarrow R{\cdot} + CO_2$

$$R{\cdot} + \geq C{=}C\leq \longrightarrow R{-}\overset{|}{\underset{|}{C}}{-}\overset{|}{\underset{|}{C}}{\cdot}$$

(ii) $$R{-}\overset{|}{\underset{|}{C}}{-}\overset{|}{\underset{|}{C}}{\cdot} + n\geq C{=}C\leq \longrightarrow R{-}({-}\overset{|}{\underset{|}{C}}{-}\overset{|}{\underset{|}{C}}{-})_n{-}\overset{|}{\underset{|}{C}}{-}\overset{|}{\underset{|}{C}}{\cdot}$$

(iii) The cessation reaction may take place:

(*a*) By the collision between two growing chains which unite to form a deactivated molecule:

$$2R{-}M_n{\cdot} \longrightarrow R{-}M_n{-}M_n{-}R$$

Alternatively, disproportionation (see p. 46) may take place, and thereby deactivate the growing molecules:

$$2R{-}({-}\overset{|}{\underset{|}{C}}{-}\overset{|}{\underset{|}{C}}{-})_n{-}\overset{|}{\underset{|}{C}}{-}\overset{H}{\underset{Y}{C}}{\cdot} \longrightarrow R{-}({-}\overset{|}{\underset{|}{C}}{-}\overset{|}{\underset{|}{C}}{-})_n{-}\overset{H}{\underset{|}{C}}{-}\overset{|}{\underset{Y}{C}}{-}H + R{-}({-}\overset{|}{\underset{|}{C}}{-}\overset{|}{\underset{|}{C}}{-})_n{-}\overset{|}{\underset{|}{C}}{=}\overset{H}{\underset{Y}{C}}$$

(*b*) By the collision between the growing chain and a catalyst radical:

$$R{-}M_n{\cdot} + R{\cdot} \longrightarrow R{-}M_n{-}R$$

(*c*) By the collision between the growing chain and impurities which have become activated during the polymerisation, *e.g.*,

$$R{-}M_n{\cdot} + YZ \longrightarrow R{-}M{-}Y + Z{\cdot}$$

$$Z{\cdot} + M \longrightarrow ZM{\cdot} \xrightarrow{M} ZM_n{\cdot}$$

$$ZM_n{\cdot} + YZ \longrightarrow Z{-}M_n{-}Y + Z{\cdot}$$

In "uncatalysed" polymerisation, *i.e.*, in the absence of foreign substances, initiation may begin by *dimerisation* of the monomer:

$$2\geq C{=}C\leq \longrightarrow {\cdot}\overset{|}{\underset{|}{C}}{-}\overset{|}{\underset{|}{C}}{-}\overset{|}{\underset{|}{C}}{-}\overset{|}{\underset{|}{C}}{\cdot}$$

Not only can addition polymerisation take place among molecules of one kind, but it can also take place among molecules of two kinds, when the phenomenon is known as *copolymerisation* or *interpolymerisation*.

Condensation Polymerisation or Polycondensation. In condensation polymerisation, bi- or polyfunctional molecules condense with one another, and in doing so repeatedly eliminate a small molecule such as water, ammonia, hydrogen chloride, etc., as the reaction proceeds. This type of polymerisation takes place by a series of steps, and is discussed in various parts of the text (see, for example, the aldol condensation, the esterification of glycols with dibasic acids, etc.).

Polymers may be classified into three groups:

(i) *natural*, *e.g.*, rubber, proteins, cellulose; (ii) *semi-synthetic*, *e.g.*, nitrocellulose, cellulose acetate; and (iii) *synthetic*, *e.g.*, nylon, bakelite, perspex.

Plastics form a group of high polymers which have a fair range of deformability and mouldability, particularly at high temperatures. In plastics the polymers formed do not all have the same molecular weight, and since the polymers are not amenable to the ordinary methods of separation, the molecular weight of a "polymer" is the *average* molecular weight. Polymerisation is carried out with the object of building up compounds with predicted properties, and since the properties of a plastic depend on the degree of polymerisation, it is necessary to stop polymerisation when the desired average molecular weight is reached. This may be done by various means, *e.g.*, variation of the concentration of the catalyst. The average molecular weight of plastics varies from about 20,000 (*e.g.*, nylon) to several hundred thousand (*e.g.*, polyvinyl chloride, 250,000).

Plastics are generally tough, resistant to the action of acids and alkalis, and not very much affected over a fair range of temperature. They can be moulded to any desired shape or form.

Plastics are of two main types, *thermoplastic* and *thermosetting*. Thermoplastics are linear polymers which are soluble in many organic solvents, and which soften on heating and become rigid on cooling. The process of heat-softening, moulding and cooling can be repeated as often as desired, and hardly affects the properties of the plastic. Typical thermoplastics are cellulose acetate, nitrocellulose and vinyl polymers such as polythene, perspex, etc.

Thermosetting plastics are three-dimensional polymers which are insoluble in any kind of solvent, and which can be heat-treated only once before they set, *i.e.*, their formation, after which heating results in chemical decomposition, and hence they cannot be "reworked". Typical thermosetting plastics are phenol-formaldehyde, urea-formaldehyde, melamine-formaldehyde, silicones, etc.

In thermoplastics the chains are, more or less, free chemically, but are held together by van der Waals' forces. It is possible, however, to link together these linear molecules (*cf.* the rungs of a ladder) and the cross-linking agent converts the thermoplastic into a thermosetting plastic, *e.g.*, in the vulcanisation of rubber the sulphur cross-links the long chains. Furthermore, such thermosetting plastics may be reconverted into thermoplastics by opening the cross-links, *e.g.*, the reclaiming of rubber. Most thermosetting plastics may be regarded as cross-linked polymers.

Those plastics which do not soften very much with rise in temperature are made soft and readily workable by the addition of certain compounds known as *plasticisers*; *e.g.*, polyvinyl chloride is extremely stiff and hard, but addition of tricresyl phosphate makes it soft and rubber-like.

Some Individual Olefins.

The first member of the olefin series is methylene (carbene), CH_2, but it exists only as a free *diradical* with a very short life period. It has been prepared by heating diazomethane at very low pressure:

$$CH_2N_2 \longrightarrow \cdot\dot{C}H_2 + N_2$$

The two electrons must be *unpaired* for methylene to be a diradical.

Ethylene, ethene, C_2H_4. Ethylene may be prepared by any of the general methods of preparation (except 2), but the most convenient laboratory method is to heat ethanol with excess of concentrated sulphuric acid. The mechanism of the reaction is uncertain, but it is widely believed that the acid acts catalytically, removing the elements of water from the ethanol. A co-ordination complex is formed first, the oxygen atom in the ethanol acting as the donor to a proton given up by the acid:

$$C_2H_5—\ddot{\underset{\cdot\cdot}{O}}H \quad H—O\cdot SO_2\cdot OH \longrightarrow C_2H_5—\overset{+}{\underset{\cdot\cdot}{O}}H_2 + \bar{O}\cdot SO_2\cdot OH$$

The complex $[C_2H_5OH_2]^+$ now eliminates a molecule of water to form the *carbonium ion*, $C_2H_5^+$, which has a carbon with only six electrons. This carbonium ion is unstable, and stabilises itself by eliminating a proton to form ethylene (*cf.* the Whitmore mechanism, p. 160):

$$H—CH_2—CH_2—\overset{+}{O}H_2 \longrightarrow H_2O + H—CH_2—\overset{+}{C}H_2 \longrightarrow CH_2{=}CH_2 + \overset{+}{H}$$

$$\overset{+}{H} + \overset{-}{O}{\cdot}SO_2{\cdot}OH \longrightarrow H_2SO_4$$

Since the sulphuric acid acts catalytically there should be no loss of acid; in practice, however, there is always a loss, some of the acid being reduced to sulphur dioxide owing to side reactions taking place in which the concentrated sulphuric acid acts as an oxidising agent. The ethylene may be freed from the sulphur dioxide by passing the gases through aqueous sodium hydroxide.

For each molecule of ethanol converted into ethylene, one molecule of water is produced, and hence, after a time the sulphuric acid becomes too dilute to behave as a dehydrating agent.

Ethylene may also be prepared by the electrolysis of sodium succinate (Kolbe):

$$\begin{array}{l}CH_2{\cdot}COONa\\ |\\ CH_2{\cdot}COONa\end{array} + 2H_2O \longrightarrow \begin{array}{l}CH_2\\ \|\\ CH_2\end{array} + 2CO_2 + 2NaOH + H_2$$

Ethylene is still prepared industrially by passing ethanol vapour over heated alumina at about 350°:

$$C_2H_5OH \longrightarrow C_2H_4 + H_2O$$

It is, however, now being obtained in huge quantities as a by-product in the cracking of crude oil and of ethane, propane and butane. Ethylene is also manufactured by the partial hydrogenation of acetylene, which is mixed with hydrogen and passed, at 200°, over a palladium catalyst carried on a silica-gel support:

$$CH{\equiv}CH + H_2 \longrightarrow CH_2{=}CH_2 \quad (95\%)$$

Ethylene is a colourless gas, b.p. −105°, sparingly soluble in water. It burns with a smoky luminous flame. It has been claimed that carefully purified ethylene does not react with chlorine in the absence of light. When ethylene is heated with chlorine at 350–450°, vinyl chloride is obtained:

$$CH_2{=}CH_2 + Cl_2 \longrightarrow CH_2{=}CHCl + HCl$$

The unsaturated radical $CH_2{=}CH—$ is known as the *vinyl* or *ethenyl* radical.

Ethylene may be oxidised by atmospheric oxygen in the presence of silver as catalyst, and at a temperature of 200–400°, to ethylene oxide:

$$CH_2{=}CH_2 + \tfrac{1}{2}O_2 \longrightarrow \overset{O}{CH_2—CH_2}$$

Ethylene polymerises under high pressure and high temperature to form *polyethylene* or *polythene*:

$$nCH_2{=}CH_2 \longrightarrow —(—CH_2—CH_2—)_n—$$

This polymerisation is catalysed by traces of oxygen (which produces the free radicals). Polythene is very resistant to acids, bases, and most of the usual organic solvents.

Ethylene is used for ripening fruit. Unripe fruit may be transported easily without damage, and ripens on exposure to ethylene gas for a few days, the product being apparently indistinguishable from the natural ripened fruit. Ethylene is also used as an anæsthetic, in the manufacture of mustard gas and plastics (polythene, polystyrene), and in the preparation of various solvents such as glycol, dioxan, cellosolves, etc.

Structure of Ethylene. The molecular formula of ethylene is C_2H_4. Two carbon atoms have the power to combine with six univalent atoms or groups, as in ethane, *neo*pentane, etc. There are only four univalent hydrogen atoms present in ethylene: therefore ethylene is said to be unsaturated, and should be capable of adding on two univalent atoms or groups, and this, as we have seen above, is observed in practice. Thus the structure of ethylene must be such as to be capable of undergoing addition reactions. Assuming carbon to be quadrivalent and hydrogen univalent, three structures are possible for ethylene:

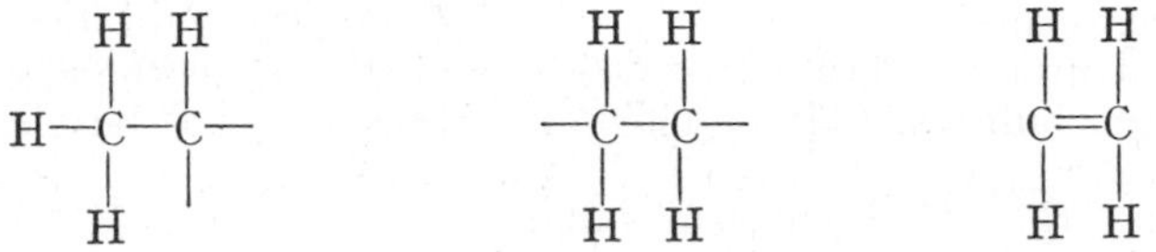

$$\begin{array}{ccc} \begin{array}{c} \mathrm{H}\ \ \mathrm{H} \\ |\ \ \ | \\ \mathrm{H{-}C{-}C{-}} \\ |\ \ \ | \\ \mathrm{H}\ \ \ \ \end{array} & \qquad \begin{array}{c} \mathrm{H}\ \ \mathrm{H} \\ |\ \ \ | \\ \mathrm{{-}C{-}C{-}} \\ |\ \ \ | \\ \mathrm{H}\ \ \mathrm{H} \end{array} & \qquad \begin{array}{c} \mathrm{H}\ \ \mathrm{H} \\ |\ \ \ | \\ \mathrm{C{=}C} \\ |\ \ \ | \\ \mathrm{H}\ \ \mathrm{H} \end{array} \end{array}$$

or

$$\begin{array}{ccc} CH_3{-}CH{<} & \qquad {-}CH_2{\cdot}CH_2{-} & \qquad CH_2{=}CH_2 \\ \text{(I)} & \qquad \text{(II)} & \qquad \text{(III)} \end{array}$$

Two isomeric compounds of molecular formula $C_2H_4Cl_2$ are possible: $CH_3{\cdot}CHCl_2$ and $CH_2Cl{\cdot}CH_2Cl$. Both isomers are known, one (ethylene chloride) being formed by the direct combination between ethylene and chlorine, and the other (ethylidene chloride) by the action of phosphorus pentachloride on acetaldehyde. The structure of ethylidene chloride is $CH_3{\cdot}CHCl_2$ (see p. 106); hence the structure of ethylene chloride is $CH_2Cl{\cdot}CH_2Cl$. If (I) were the structure of ethylene, then the addition of chlorine should give ethylidene chloride, and not ethylene chloride. We may, therefore, reject structure (I). Furthermore, since (I) is unsymmetrical it would have a fairly large dipole moment; actually ethylene has a zero dipole moment.

Structure (II) represents ethylene as possessing " free " bonds by means of which addition compounds are formed. If this is the structure, then we might expect that the " free " carbon valencies could be satisfied one at a time, *i.e.*, a compound such as $CH_2Cl{\cdot}CH_2{-}$ should be possible, since if two " free " valencies can exist independently of each other, it is logical to suppose that one can exist by itself. No such compounds have yet been obtained, and in practice it is found that unsaturated compounds always combine with an *even* number of univalent atoms or groups. Hence structure (III) is accepted for ethylene, and the presence of the double bond (consisting of one σ-bond and one π-bond) is supported by other evidence (length of the carbon–carbon bond; geometrical isomerism).

In structures (I) and (II) the *unconnected* bonds indicate *one* electron. If the two electrons in (II) are *paired*, they form a covalent bond, and so (II) and (III) are the same. On the other hand, if the two electrons in (II) are *unpaired*, then (II) is a diradical. Since ethylene does not exhibit the usual properties of a free diradical, we must reject (II).

The presence of a double (or triple bond) in an organic compound may be found readily by means of bromine water, bromine in chloroform solution, or dilute alkaline permanganate. If the compound under investigation is unsaturated, then the above reagents are decolorised. Perbenzoic acid or monoperphthalic acid can be used to detect the presence of a double bond, and also to estimate the number of double bonds (see also iodine value, p. 247).

Propylene, propene, C_3H_6, may be prepared by heating propanol or *iso*-propanol with sulphuric acid (mechanism as for ethylene from ethanol):

$$CH_3 \cdot CH_2 \cdot CH_2OH \xrightarrow{-H_2O} CH_3 \cdot CH{=}CH_2$$

$$CH_3 \cdot CH(OH) \cdot CH_3 \xrightarrow{-H_2O} CH_3 \cdot CH{=}CH_2$$

It may also be prepared by heating propyl iodide with ethanolic potassium hydroxide:

$$CH_3 \cdot CH_2 \cdot CH_2I + KOH \xrightarrow{\text{ethanol}} CH_3 \cdot CH{=}CH_2 + KI + H_2O$$

Propylene is obtained commercially in huge quantities as a by-product in the cracking of petroleum. It is a colourless gas, b.p. $-48°$, insoluble in water but fairly soluble in ethanol. It is used industrially for the preparation of *iso*propanol, glycerol, etc.

The unsaturated radical $CH_2{=}CHCH_2{-}$ is known as the allyl radical.

Butylenes, butenes, C_4H_8. There are three isomeric butylenes, and all are gases:

$CH_3 \cdot CH_2 \cdot CH{=}CH_2$, α-butylene, but-1-ene (b.p. $-6 \cdot 1°$); $CH_3 \cdot CH{=}CH \cdot CH_3$, β-butylene, but-2-ene (b.p. 1°); $(CH_3)_2C{=}CH_2$, *iso*butylene, *iso*butene * (b.p. $-6 \cdot 6°$).

All the butylenes are obtained from cracked petroleum. The 1- and 2-butenes are used for the preparation of *sec.*-butanol (*q.v.*), and *iso*butene for *tert.*-butanol (*q.v.*). But-2-ene differs from its isomers in that it exhibits geometrical isomerism (see p. 404). *iso*Butene differs from its isomers in that it reacts with chlorine *at room temperature* to give mainly *substitution* products, substitution occurring in the allyl position (see p. 62). Thus 3-chloro-2-methylprop-1-ene is the main product, and is accompanied by a small amount of the addition product 1 : 2-dichloro-2-methylpropane:

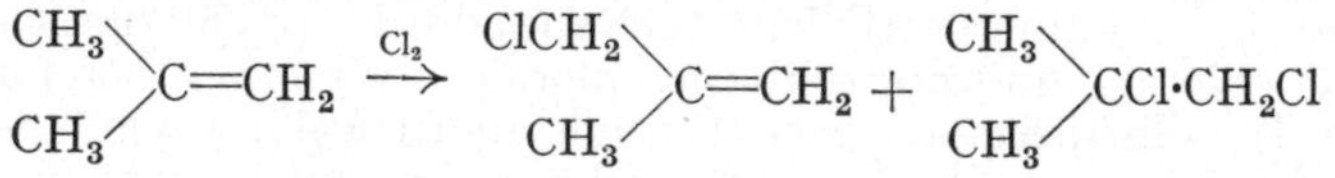

$$(CH_3)_2C{=}CH_2 \xrightarrow{Cl_2} (ClCH_2)(CH_3)C{=}CH_2 + (CH_3)_2CCl \cdot CH_2Cl$$

UNSATURATED COMPOUNDS WITH TWO OR MORE DOUBLE BONDS

When the compound contains two double bonds, it is known as a diolefin or alkadiene, and has the general formula C_nH_{2n-2}; when there are three double bonds present, the compound is known as a triolefin or alkatriene, and has the general formula C_nH_{2n-4}; etc.

Nomenclature. The longest carbon chain containing the maximum number of double bonds is chosen as the parent hydrocarbon, and the positions of side-chains and those of the double bonds are indicated by numbers (see p. 58, rule ii), *e.g.*, $CH{=}CH{-}CH{=}CH_2$ buta-1 : 3-diene:

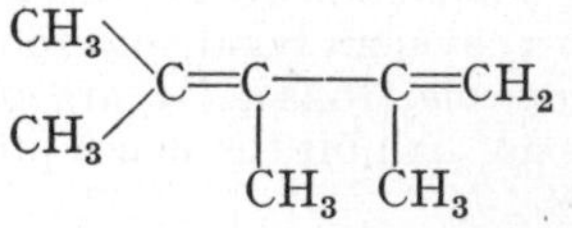

$$(CH_3)_2C{=}C(CH_3){-}C(CH_3){=}CH_2 \quad \text{2 : 3 : 4-trimethylpenta-1 : 3-diene}$$

There are three different types of compounds with two double bonds.

1. **Hydrocarbons with isolated double bonds** contain the arrangement $>C{=}CH \cdot (CH_2)_n \cdot CH{=}C<$, where $n>0$. One of the simplest compounds

* See p. 785.

of this type is **diallyl** or **hexa-1:5-diene**, which may be prepared by the action of soldium on allyl iodide (Wurtz reaction):

$$2CH_2{=}CH{\cdot}CH_2I + 2Na \longrightarrow CH_2{=}CH{\cdot}CH_2{\cdot}CH_2{\cdot}CH{=}CH_2 + 2NaI$$

Diallyl is a liquid, b.p. 59·6°. It resembles the olefins chemically, but since there are two double bonds present, it may add on two or four univalent atoms or groups according to the relative concentration of the addendum; *e.g.*, with excess bromine, diallyl forms 1:2:5:6-tetrabromohexane.

2. **Hydrocarbons with cumulated double bonds** contain the arrangement $>C{=}C{=}C<$. The simplest compound of this type is **allene** or **propadiene,** which may be prepared by heating 1:2:3-tribromopropane with solid potassium hydroxide, and then treating the resulting 2:3-dibromopropylene with zinc dust in methanol solution:

$$CH_2Br{\cdot}CHBr{\cdot}CH_2Br \xrightarrow{KOH} CH_2Br{\cdot}CBr{=}CH_2 \xrightarrow{Zn/CH_3OH} CH_2{=}C{=}CH_2$$

Allene is a gas, b.p. −32°. With bromine it forms 1:2:2:3-tetrabromopropane; with sulphuric acid it forms acetone; and when treated with sodium in ether, the sodium derivative of propyne ($CH_3{\cdot}C{\equiv}CNa$) is produced. Allene compounds are very important from the view of stereochemistry (see p. 410).

In recent years, allenes have been prepared from acetylenes by rearrangement, *e.g.*,

$$CH{\equiv}C{\cdot}CH_2{\cdot}CO_2H \xrightarrow[40^\circ]{aq.\ K_2CO_3} CH_2{=}C{=}CH{\cdot}CO_2H$$

An extended allene type of linkage gives the *cumulene* system, the simplest member of which is butatriene, and this has been prepared by debrominating 1:4-dibromobut-2-yne with zinc (Schubert *et al.*, 1952, 1954):

$$CH_2Br{\cdot}C{\equiv}C{\cdot}CH_2Br \xrightarrow{Zn} CH_2{=}C{=}C{=}CH_2$$

3. **Hydrocarbons with conjugated double bonds** contain single and double bonds arranged *alternately*, *i.e.*, they contain the arrangement $-CH{=}CH{-}CH{=}CH{-}CH{=}CH-$. The simplest member of this group of compounds is **buta-1:3-diene**, which may be prepared by passing *cyclo*hexene over a heated nichrome wire (an alloy of nickel, chromium and iron):

$$cyclo\text{-}C_6H_{10}\ (CH_2{-}CH_2{-}CH_2{-}CH_2{-}CH{=}CH) \longrightarrow CH_2{=}CH{-}CH{=}CH_2 + CH_2{=}CH_2 \quad (65\text{–}75\%)$$

Butadiene is prepared technically:

(i) by dehydrogenating *n*-butane (from natural gas or from petroleum gas) or but-1-ene (from cracked petroleum) by passing the gas over a heated catalyst, *e.g.*, chromic oxide on an alumina support.

(ii) By passing a mixture of butane-1:3-diol and steam, in proportions 4:1, over trisodium phosphate containing 20 per cent. free phosphoric acid, heated at 270°:

$$CH_3{\cdot}CH(OH){\cdot}CH_2{\cdot}CH_2OH \xrightarrow{-2H_2O} CH_2{=}CH{-}CH{=}CH_2 \quad (85\text{–}90\%)$$

(iii) By passing ethanol vapour over a catalyst of alumina–zinc oxide heated at 420–470°:

$$2C_2H_5OH \longrightarrow CH_2{=}CH{-}CH{=}CH_2 + 2H_2O + H_2 \quad (20\%)$$

The yield is low owing to the production of many by-products such as acetic acid, ethyl acetate, ether, etc. The yield of butadiene has been improved by passing a mixture of ethanol and acetaldehyde over a heated catalyst of silica-gel plus 2 per cent. tantalum oxide:

$$C_2H_5OH + CH_3{\cdot}CHO \longrightarrow CH_2{=}CH{-}CH{=}CH_2 + 2H_2O$$

(iv) By passing a mixture of acetylene and formaldehyde over copper acetylide as catalyst, whereupon butynediol $CH_2OH{\cdot}C{\equiv}C{\cdot}CH_2OH$ is formed. This is hydrogenated catalytically to butane-1 : 4-diol, which, on catalytic dehydration, gives butadiene:

$$C_2H_2 + 2H{\cdot}CHO \xrightarrow{Cu_2C_2} CH_2OH{\cdot}C{\equiv}C{\cdot}CH_2OH \xrightarrow[Ni]{H_2}$$

$$CH_2OH{\cdot}CH_2{\cdot}CH_2{\cdot}CH_2OH \xrightarrow{-2H_2O} CH_2{=}CH{-}CH{=}CH_2$$

Butadiene is a gas, b.p. $-2{\cdot}6°$. Under the influence of sodium as catalyst, butadiene readily polymerises to a product which has been used as a rubber substitute known as *buna* (*bu*tadiene + *Na*). The mechanism of this polymerisation is uncertain, but a possibility is discussed in connection with isoprene (see below).

A very important diolefin is **isoprene** or **2-methylbut-1 : 3-diene,** $CH_2{=}C(CH_3){-}CH{=}CH_2$, which may be obtained, in poor yield, by the slow distillation of rubber. It may be prepared by heating *iso*pentanol with hydrogen chloride, and chlorinating the resulting *iso*amyl chloride, three dichlorides thereby being formed:

$$(CH_3)_2CH{\cdot}CH_2{\cdot}CH_2OH + HCl \longrightarrow (CH_3)_2CH{\cdot}CH_2{\cdot}CH_2Cl + H_2O$$

$$(CH_3)_2CH{\cdot}CH_2{\cdot}CH_2Cl \xrightarrow{Cl_2}$$

$$\underset{(I)}{(CH_3)_2CCl{\cdot}CH_2{\cdot}CH_2Cl} + \underset{(II)}{(CH_3)_2CH{\cdot}CHCl{\cdot}CH_2Cl} + \underset{(III)}{(CH_3)(CH_2Cl)CH{\cdot}CH_2{\cdot}CH_2{\cdot}Cl}$$

(I) is the main product (*cf.* p. 49), and this, when passed over soda-lime heated at 500°, gives isoprene:

$$(CH_3)_2CCl{\cdot}CH_2{\cdot}CH_2Cl \xrightarrow{-2HCl} CH_2{=}C(CH_3){-}CH{=}CH_2$$

Isoprene is prepared technically:

(i) by passing *iso*pentane or *iso*pentene over heated chromic oxide on an alumina support (*cf.* butadiene).

(ii) By treating acetone as follows:

$$(CH_3)_2C{=}O \xrightarrow{NaNH_2} CH_3{-}C(ONa){=}CH_2 \xrightarrow{C_2H_2} CH_3{-}C(ONa)(CH_3){-}C{\equiv}CH \xrightarrow{H_2O}$$

$$CH_3{-}C(OH)(CH_3){-}C{\equiv}CH \xrightarrow[(cat.)]{H_2} CH_3{-}C(OH)(CH_3){-}CH{=}CH_2 \xrightarrow[400°]{Al_2O_3} CH_2{=}C(CH_3){-}CH{=}CH_2$$

Isoprene is a liquid, b.p. 35°, and when heated with sodium at 60° it polymerises to a substance resembling natural rubber. The mechanism of this polymerisation is not settled; one that has been suggested is as follows:

$$CH_2{=}C(CH_3){-}CH{=}CH_2 + Na\cdot \longrightarrow \overset{+}{Na}\overset{\cdot\cdot -}{C}H_2{-}C(CH_3){=}CH{-}CH_2\cdot$$

$$\downarrow CH_2{=}C(CH_3)\cdot CH{=}CH_2$$

$$\overset{+}{Na}\overset{\cdot\cdot -}{C}H_2{-}C(CH_3){=}CH{-}CH_2{-}CH_2{-}C(CH_3){=}CH{-}CH_2\cdot, \text{ etc.}$$

Compounds containing conjugated double bonds have physical and chemical properties that are not usually shown by compounds containing isolated or cumulated double bonds, *e.g.*, they show optical exaltation, undergo abnormal addition reactions, readily polymerise, and undergo the Diels–Alder reaction (p. 450). Another typical reaction of conjugated dienes is their combination with sulphur dioxide to form a cyclic sulphone, *e.g.*,

$$CH_2{=}CH{-}CH{=}CH_2 + SO_2 \longrightarrow \begin{matrix} CH{-}CH_2 \\ \| \\ CH{-}CH_2 \end{matrix} \!\!>\! SO_2$$

sulpholene

Thiele's Theory of Partial Valencies. Conjugated compounds undergo abnormal addition reactions, *e.g.*, when butadiene is treated with bromine (one molecule), two dibromo-derivatives are obtained, the "expected" 3 : 4-dibromobut-1-ene (1 : 2-addition), and the "unexpected" 1 : 4-dibromobut-2-ene (1 : 4-addition):

$$CH_2{=}CH{-}CH{=}CH_2 \xrightarrow{Br_2} CH_2Br\cdot CHBr\cdot CH{=}CH_2 + CH_2Br\cdot CH{=}CH\cdot CH_2Br$$

It has been found that 1 : 2- and 1 : 4-additions usually take place together, and the relative amount of each generally depends on the nature of the addendum and the conditions of the experiment, *e.g.*, type of solvent, temperature.

Thiele (1899) suggested his theory of *partial valencies* to account for 1 : 4-addition. According to Thiele, a single bond is sufficient to hold two carbon atoms together, and the two valencies of the double bond are not used completely to link the two carbon atoms, but only one valency and *part* of the other, leaving a surplus on each carbon atom. Thiele called this surplus valency the *residual* or *partial* valency, and if we represent it by a broken line, the formula of butadiene (and similarly for any other conjugated compound) may be written $\underset{\vdots}{C}H_2{=}\underset{\vdots}{C}H{-}\underset{\vdots}{C}H{=}\underset{\vdots}{C}H_2$. Thiele thought that the two middle partial valencies mutually satisfied each other rather than remain free. Thus the actual state of butadiene is

$$\underset{\vdots}{C}H_2{=}\underset{\lfloor}{C}H{-}\underset{\rfloor}{C}H{=}\underset{\vdots}{C}H_2 \text{ or } \underset{\vdots}{C}H_2{=}CH{=}CH{=}\underset{\vdots}{C}H_2.$$

The ends of this molecule are therefore the most active parts, and so addition of, *e.g.*, bromine will occur at these ends, first by attachment through the partial valencies, and then by each bromine atom acquiring a full valency, causing the two middle carbon atoms to utilise completely the two valencies left:

$$\underset{\vdots}{C}H_2{=}CH{=}CH{=}\underset{\vdots}{C}H_2 + Br_2 \longrightarrow \underset{Br}{\underset{\vdots}{C}H_2}{=}CH{=}CH{=}\underset{Br}{\underset{\vdots}{C}H_2} \longrightarrow \underset{Br}{\underset{|}{C}H_2}{-}CH{=}CH{-}\underset{Br}{\underset{|}{C}H_2}$$

Thiele's theory explains 1 : 4-addition so well that it does not account at all for 1 : 2-addition!

The mechanism of addition to conjugated systems is obscure. Burton and Ingold (1928), starting from the scheme of the addition of halogens to a double bond *one atom at a time* (p. 61), suggested the following to explain 1 : 2- and 1 : 4-addition:

$$CH_2{=}CH{-}CH{=}CH_2 \quad Br{-}Br \longrightarrow CH_2{=}CH{-}\overset{+}{C}H{-}CH_2Br + \overset{-}{Br}$$

The resulting positive ion is capable of resonance:

$$CH_2{=}CH{-}\overset{+}{C}H{-}CH_2Br \longleftrightarrow \overset{+}{C}H_2{-}CH{=}CH{-}CH_2Br$$

Hence the addition of the negative bromide ion can occur at either positive carbon atom, resulting in 1 : 2- and 1 : 4-addition. The nature of the solvent also plays a part, since it has been found that in a non-ionising medium, *e.g.*, hexane, 1 : 4-addition occurs to the extent of about 38 per cent.; in ionising solvents, *e.g.*, acetic acid, 1 : 4-addition is about 70 per cent. In an ionising solvent the bromine molecule is more likely to break up as shown in the above equation, whereas in a non-ionising solvent it may be that the bromine molecule tends to add on *as a whole* to the terminal carbon atom by co-ordination, and subsequently the " floating " bromine atom attacks the *adjacent positively charged carbon atom by a " broadside " attack* (bromine can expand its octet):

$$CH_2{=}CH{-}CH{=}CH_2 + Br_2 \longrightarrow$$

$$\begin{array}{c} CH_2{=}CH{\cdot}CH{=}CH_2 \\ \vdots \quad \vdots \\ Br{\cdots}Br \end{array} \longrightarrow \begin{array}{c} CH_2{-}CH{\cdot}CH{=}CH_2 \\ | \quad\; | \\ Br \quad Br \end{array}$$

This mechanism can be extended to include 1 : 4-addition. Butadiene can undergo the electromeric effect in two stages:

$$\text{(i)} \quad CH_2{=}CH{-}CH{=}CH_2 \longrightarrow CH_2{=}CH{-}\overset{+}{C}H{-}\overset{\cdot\cdot}{\bar{C}}H_2$$

$$\text{(ii)} \quad CH_2{=}CH{-}CH{=}CH_2 \longrightarrow \overset{+}{C}H_2{-}CH{=}CH{-}\overset{\cdot\cdot}{\bar{C}}H_2$$

Of the two the second is more stable, since the charges are farther apart than in the first. If the addition complex is formed first, then in an ionising solvent the " floating " bromine atom can break off readily as a negative ion which can then attack the *terminal* carbon atom. In a non-ionising solvent, since the " floating " bromine atom cannot readily break off as an ion, the *extended* electromeric effect plays only a small part in the reaction, the *restricted* electromeric effect producing the activated state of butadiene which can undergo reaction under these conditions.

In the foregoing account of the reactions of butadiene, we have assumed that the molecule has the structure $CH_2{=}CH{-}CH{=}CH_2$. There are, however, alternative electronic structures which are *charged*. Hence butadiene is a resonance hybrid of a number of resonating structures:

$$CH_2{=}CH{-}CH{=}CH_2 \longleftrightarrow CH_2{=}CH{-}\overset{+}{C}H{-}\overset{\cdot\cdot}{\bar{C}}H_2 \longleftrightarrow \overset{+}{C}H_2{-}CH{=}CH{-}\overset{\cdot\cdot}{\bar{C}}H_2, \text{ etc.}$$

There is still, however, another contributing structure of butadiene, *viz.*, (I). The two electrons have antiparallel spins, since the number of unpaired electrons in each resonating structure must be the same (p. 17). Thus these paired electrons would, in the ordinary way, form a covalent bond. The distance between them, however, is too great for them to form an *effective* bond. Consequently this bond is referred to as a *formal bond*, and may be

$\dot{C}H_2—CH{=}CH—\dot{C}H_2$ (I) $\quad$ $\dot{C}H_2—CH{=}CH—\dot{C}H_2$ (II) $\quad$ $CH_2{=}CH—CH{=}CH_2$ (III)

represented by a dotted line (II). Structure (II) carries no charges and so (II) and (III) (also uncharged) are probably the main contributing resonance structures (p. 19). If only these two contribute significantly to the resonance hybrid, the resonance energy can be expected to be small. Actually, calculation has shown it to be about 3·5 k.cal./mole. Thus in butadiene there are no " pure " single or double bonds. The lengths of the bonds will therefore be somewhere between the extremes (of single and double bonds), the actual values depending on the relative contributions of the resonating structures to the resonance hybrid. Furthermore, if we assume that the charged structures make a very small contribution, it might at first sight appear that the butadiene molecule possesses a dipole moment. This, however, is not so in practice, the reason being that the terminal carbon atoms can be either positive or negative, since the electronic displacements can occur equally well in either direction. For this reason butadiene is said to exhibit *balanced conjugation*, and this may be represented as:

$$CH_2{=}CH—CH{=}CH_2$$

So far we have considered the structure of conjugated compounds from V.B. theory. When we consider their structure from M.O. theory, we get a different picture. Each carbon atom in butadiene has the trigonal arrangement, and Fig. 1(*a*) shows the p_z electrons associated with each carbon atom. If the molecule is planar, the p_z electron of C_2 overlaps that of C_1 as much as it does that of C_3, etc. Therefore all four p_z orbitals can be treated as forming an *M.O. covering all four carbon atoms* (*b*). In this condition, a pair of electrons are no longer mainly confined to the region between two nuclei, *i.e.*, the bond formed is no

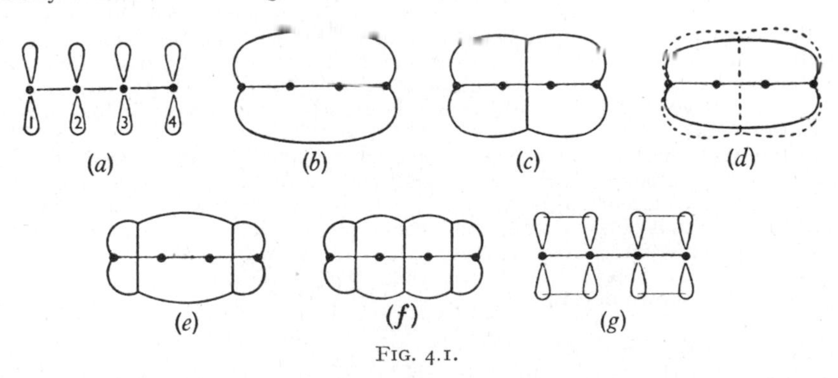

FIG. 4.1.

longer a *localised* bond. The bonds produced are therefore called *delocalised* bonds. In all, there are four delocalised M.O.s possible from the combination of the four π-electrons, two bonding and two anti-bonding M.O.s (p. 27). The two bonding M.O.s are shown in Fig. 1(*b*) and (*c*), the former having one nodal plane, and the latter, two. The two anti-bonding M.O.s are shown in (*e*), with three nodal planes, and in (*f*), with four nodal planes. As pointed out on p. 28, as the number of nodes in an orbital increases, so does the energy associated with that orbital. Furthermore, according to the Pauli exclusion principle, no more than *two* electrons can occupy the same M.O. Therefore in the ground state of butadiene, two of the π-electrons will occupy the M.O. in (*b*), and the other two the M.O. with the next higher energy level, *i.e.*, (*c*). Fig. (*d*) represents these two in one diagram, *i.e.*, (*d*) represents the ground state of butadiene. In any excited state of butadiene, electrons will occupy orbitals (*e*) or (*f*) (see p. 747).

In general, in a conjugated system containing $2n$ π-electrons, there are n bonding and n anti-bonding orbitals, and in the ground state these electrons will occupy, *in pairs*, the n M.O.s of *lowest energy*.

In delocalised bonds, the electrons have greater freedom of movement than in localised bonds. Thus the total energy of the system is lowered, *i.e.*, delocalisation of bonds makes the molecule more stable. Hence the butadiene molecule in state (*d*) is more stable than in state (*g*), in which the π-electrons are paired as " *isolated* " pairs, each pair covering *two* carbon atoms. This energy of stabilisation could be called the *delocalisation energy* (Coulson), but it is more usual to call it the resonance energy. It should here be noted that *delocalisation of bonds* is in M.O. theory what *resonance* is in V.B. theory.

It can be seen from the foregoing discussion that the M.O. treatment of conjugated systems does away with the idea of " bonds " between atoms (this applies to the π-bonds, and not to the σ-bonds). Also the term *conjugation* is used in M.O. theory to indicate the existence in any part of a molecule of *molecular orbitals which embrace three or more nuclei*. It is important to note that a conjugated system (defined as above) *always* contains double bonds, but that the reverse is not necessarily the case, *e.g.*, ethylene.

Since the electron cloud covers the *whole* of the butadiene molecule, an electrical influence in one part of the system is easily propagated to another (*cf.* p. 492). Calculation (Coulson and Longuet-Higgins, 1947) has shown that when, for example, bromine attacks butadiene, the bromine molecule approaches the *end* of butadiene molecule most easily, and produces an *alternate* polarity:

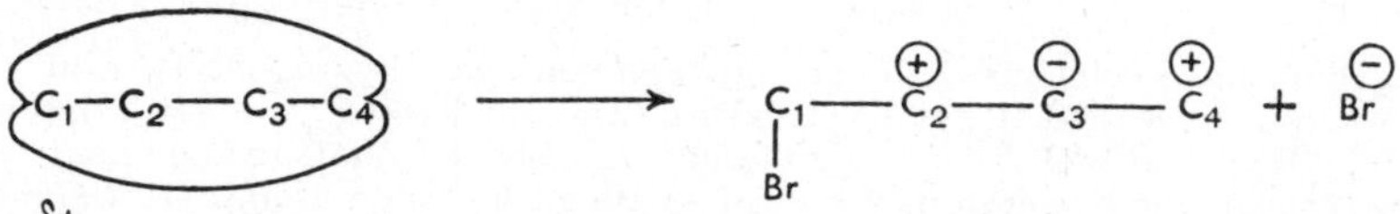

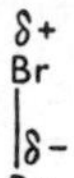

$$C_1—C_2—C_3—C_4 \;\; (\overset{\delta+}{Br}—\overset{\delta-}{Br}) \longrightarrow \underset{\displaystyle Br}{C_1}—\overset{\oplus}{C_2}—\overset{\ominus}{C_3}—\overset{\oplus}{C_4} + \overset{\ominus}{Br}$$

The negative bromide ion can then attack C_2 or C_4.

The relationship between the observed bond-length and the value expected on the assumption that it is a " pure " single or double bond has been put on a quantitative basis. In the V.B. method the *double-bond character* of a bond may be calculated from a knowledge of the observed bond length, the values of the single bond in ethane, and the double bond in ethylene being taken as standard lengths for " pure " single and double bonds, respectively. Calculations by Pauling *et al.* (1933) have shown that the " single " bond in butadiene has about 20 per cent. double-bond character (see also below).

In the M.O. method, the character of a bond is defined by its *fractional bond order*, where the bond orders of 1, 2 and 3 are given to the bonds in ethane, ethylene and acetylene, respectively. Since also the method of calculation is different from that of the V.B. method, the numerical values obtained by the two methods are different. Even so, these values always correspond.

Coulson (1941, 1947) has shown that the butadiene molecule may be represented as shown in (IV).

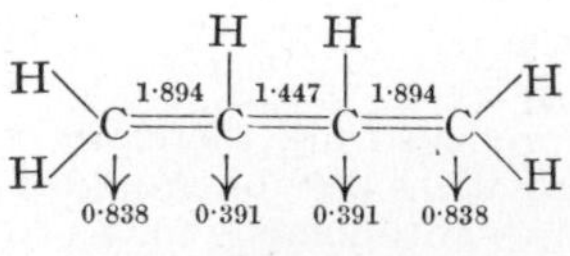

H₂C=CH–CH=CH₂ with bond orders 1·894, 1·447, 1·894 and free valences 0·838, 0·391, 0·391, 0·838

(IV)

Cyclohexane ring with exocyclic bond: 1·670, 0·40

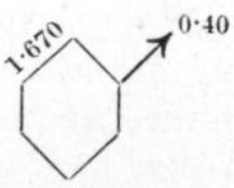

(V)

Calculation gives a bond order of 1·894 to the two outer " double " bonds, and a bond order of 1·447 to the central " single " bond. Thus the total *bond number* of either of the end carbon atoms is $2 \times 1{\cdot}0 + 1{\cdot}894 = 3{\cdot}894$, and the total bond number of either middle carbon is $1{\cdot}0 + 1{\cdot}447 + 1{\cdot}894 = 4{\cdot}341$. Furthermore, since calculation has shown that the maximum bond number for a carbon atom is 4·732, it follows that each carbon atom in butadiene has the "free valency" shown in (IV) (Coulson has suggested that free valency be represented by an arrow). On the other hand, if a structure containing fractional double bonds is written with single bonds labelled with the bond order, and charges are placed on the atoms, then the resulting diagram is known as a *molecular diagram, e.g.*, the molecular diagram for benzene is (V) (see also p. 501). Among other things, a molecular diagram enables one to estimate the most likely points of attack (see, *e.g.*, pyrrole, p. 719).

ACETYLENES OR ALKYNES

The acetylenes are unsaturated hydrocarbons that contain one triple bond. The simplest member of the series is acetylene CH≡CH, and hence this homologous series is often referred to as the "acetylene series". The acetylenes have the general formula C_nH_{2n-2} and the triple bond is also known as the "acetylenic bond".

Nomenclature. One method is to name higher homologues as derivatives of acetylene, the first member of the series, *e.g.*,

$CH_3{\cdot}C{\equiv}CH$ methylacetylene
$CH_3{\cdot}C{\equiv}C{\cdot}CH_2{\cdot}CH_3$ methylethylacetylene

In the I.U.C. system of nomenclature the class suffix is *-yne*, and the rules for numbering are as for the olefins (p. 58), *e.g.*,

$CH{\equiv}CH$ ethyne; $CH_3{\cdot}C{\equiv}C{\cdot}CH_3$ but-2-yne
$(CH_3)_2CH{\cdot}C{\equiv}C{\cdot}CH_3$ 4-methylpent-2-yne

Acetylene or **ethyne,** C_2H_2, is the most important member of this series, and it may be prepared by any of the following methods:

1. By the action of water on calcium carbide:

$$CaC_2 + 2H_2O \longrightarrow C_2H_2 + Ca(OH)_2$$

This method of preparation is used industrially, since calcium carbide is readily manufactured by heating calcium oxide with coke in an electric furnace:

$$CaO + 3C \longrightarrow CaC_2 + CO$$

Acetylene prepared from calcium carbide is not pure, but contains small amounts of phosphine, hydrogen sulphide, arsine, ammonia, etc.; the impurities present depend on the purity of the calcium carbide used. Scrubbing with water is usually sufficient to reduce the amount of all the impurities, except phosphine, below the limit necessary for the safe application of acetylene for technical purposes. Phosphine is removed by means of oxidising agents, *e.g.*, acid dichromate or bleaching-powder, whereby the phosphine is retained as phosphoric acid.

A more recent industrial preparation of acetylene is by the electric arc cracking of methane–ethane mixtures which are derived from coal hydrogenation (p. 55).

2. By the action of ethanolic potassium hydroxide on ethylene bromide. The reaction proceeds in two steps, and under suitable conditions the intermediate product vinyl bromide may be isolated:

$$CH_2Br{\cdot}CH_2Br + KOH \xrightarrow{\text{ethanol}} CH_2{=}CHBr + KBr + H_2O$$
$$CH_2{=}CHBr + KOH \xrightarrow{\text{ethanol}} CH{\equiv}CH + KBr + H_2O$$

Ethylidene chloride may be used instead of ethylene bromide (or chloride), and this reaction also proceeds in two steps:

$$CH_3{\cdot}CHCl_2 \xrightarrow{KOH} CH_2{=}CHCl \xrightarrow{KOH} CH{\equiv}CH$$

Sodamide can be used instead of ethanolic potassium hydroxide, and the yields are usually better since there is less tendency to form by-products, *e.g.*,

$$-CH_2{\cdot}CBr_2- + 2NaNH_2 \longrightarrow -C{\equiv}C- + 2NaBr + 2NH_3$$

3. By the electrolysis of a concentrated solution of sodium (or potassium) salt of maleic or fumaric acid (*q.v.*):

$$CO_2Na{\cdot}CH{=}CH{\cdot}CO_2Na + 2H_2O \longrightarrow CH{\equiv}CH + 2CO_2 + 2NaOH + H_2$$

4. By heating a trihalogen derivative of methane with silver powder; *e.g.*, iodoform gives acetylene when heated with silver powder:

$$2CHI_3 + 6Ag \longrightarrow C_2H_2 + 6AgI$$

Acetylene may be synthesised from its elements by striking an electric arc between carbon rods in an atmosphere of hydrogen. It is also formed by the incomplete combustion of hydrocarbons, *e.g.*, when a bunsen burner "strikes back".

Acetylene is a colourless gas, b.p. −84°, and has an ethereal smell when pure. It is sparingly soluble in water but readily soluble in acetone. When compressed or liquefied acetylene is explosive, but its solution under pressure (10 atm.) in acetone adsorbed on some suitable porous material can be handled with safety. Acetylene burns with a luminous smoky flame (due to the high carbon content), and hence is used for lighting purposes. It is also used in the oxy-acetylene blow-pipe, a temperature above 3000° being reached. Acetylene is used for the preparation of a large number of compounds, *e.g.*, acetaldehyde, ethanol, acetic acid, etc. (see text).

Owing to the presence of a triple bond, acetylene is more unsaturated than ethylene, and forms addition products with two or four univalent atoms or groups, never one or three (*cf.* ethylene). A triple bond consists of one σ-bond and two π-bonds. When two univalent atoms add on to a triple bond the digonal arrangement changes into the trigonal, and the further addition of two univalent atoms changes the trigonal into the tetrahedral arrangement. Under suitable conditions it is possible to isolate the intermediate olefin.

1. Acetylene adds on hydrogen in the presence of a catalyst, the reaction proceeding in two stages:

$$C_2H_2 \xrightarrow[cat.]{H_2} C_2H_4 \xrightarrow[cat.]{H_2} C_2H_6$$

The intermediate product, ethylene, can be obtained in very good yield if the hydrogenation is carried out with a *measured* amount of hydrogen in the presence of Adams' platinum–platinum oxide catalyst (p. 60), or palladium carried on a barium sulphate support.

The partial catalytic reduction of a triple bond in a wide variety of acetylenic compounds has been carried out, but great difficulty has been encountered in partially reducing a triple bond conjugated with a double bond, *i.e.*, the following reduction has proved difficult:

$$-C{\equiv}C-\overset{|}{C}{=}C{<} \longrightarrow -CH{=}CH-\overset{|}{C}{=}C{<}$$

Lindlar (1952), however, has now developed a catalyst for the partial hydrogenation of a triple bond in a wide variety of compounds; it consists of a

Pd—$CaCO_3$ catalyst partially inactivated by treatment with lead acetate, or better, by the addition of quinoline.

Dialkylacetylenes may be catalytically reduced to a mixture of *cis*- and *trans*-olefins, the former predominating. On the other hand, reduction with sodium in liquid ammonia produces the *trans*-olefin. Acetylenes are also reduced to *trans*-olefins by lithium in aliphatic amines of low molecular weight (Benkeser *et al.*, 1955).

$$R—C\equiv C—R \longrightarrow \underset{cis}{(R)(H)C=C(R)(H)} \quad \underset{trans}{(R)(H)C=C(H)(R)}$$

Lithium aluminium hydride may also be used to partially reduce a triple bond provided the molecule contains the grouping —C≡C—C(OH)<.

2. Acetylene adds on gaseous chlorine or bromine in the dark to form acetylene di- and tetrahalides; the addition is catalysed by light and metallic halides (*cf.* olefins):

$$C_2H_2 \xrightarrow{Cl_2} C_2H_2Cl_2 \xrightarrow{Cl_2} C_2H_2Cl_4$$

Direct combination of acetylene with chlorine may be accompanied by explosions, but this is prevented by the presence of a catalyst.

Acetylene reacts with dilute bromine water to produce acetylene dibromide:

$$CH\equiv CH + Br_2 \xrightarrow{aq.} CHBr=CHBr$$

With liquid bromine and in the absence of a solvent, acetylene forms acetylene tetrabromide:

$$C_2H_2 + 2Br_2 \longrightarrow C_2H_2Br_4$$

Acetylene adds on iodine with difficulty, but if the reaction is carried out in ethanolic solution, acetylene di-iodide is obtained:

$$CH\equiv CH + I_2 \xrightarrow{ethanol} CHI=CHI$$

Acetylene also undergoes substitution with halogen provided the right conditions are used, *e.g.*, dichloroacetylene is formed when acetylene is passed into sodium hypochlorite solution at 0° in the absence of air and light:

$$C_2H_2 + 2NaOCl \longrightarrow C_2Cl_2 + 2NaOH$$

Similarly, if acetylene is passed into a solution of iodine in liquid ammonia, di-iodoacetylene is formed (Vaughan and Nieuland, 1932):

$$C_2H_2 + 2I_2 + 2NH_3 \longrightarrow C_2I_2 + 2NH_4I$$

These substitution reactions of acetylene are characteristic of hydrogen only in the ≡CH group. Thus, for example, but-1-yne, but not but-2-yne, can undergo these substitutions. Furthermore, it should be noted that the halogen of the ≡CX group is very unreactive (*cf.* vinyl halides, p. 251).

3. Acetylene can add on the halogen acids, their order of reactivity being HI>HBr>HCl>HF; HF adds on only under pressure (*cf.* ethylene). The addition of the halogen acids can take place in the dark, but is catalysed

by light or metallic halides. The addition is in accordance with Markownikoff's rule, *e.g.*, acetylene combines with hydrogen bromide to form first vinyl bromide, and then ethylidene bromide:

$$CH{\equiv}CH + HBr \longrightarrow CH_2{=}CHBr \xrightarrow{HBr} CH_3{\cdot}CHBr_2$$

Peroxides have the same effect on the addition of hydrogen bromide to acetylene as they have on olefins (p. 63).

The mechanism of the addition of halogens and halogen acids is probably the same as that for the olefins, *e.g.*, the addition of hydrogen bromide may be as follows:

$$CH{\equiv}CH \;\; H{-}Br \longrightarrow \overset{-}{Br} \;\; \overset{+}{C}H{=}CH_2 \longrightarrow CHBr{=}CH_2$$

Vinyl bromide may undergo the electromeric effect in two ways:

$$\text{(i)} \quad CH_2{=}CH{-}Br \longrightarrow \overset{\bar{\cdot\cdot}}{C}H_2{-}\overset{+}{C}H{-}Br$$

$$\text{(ii)} \quad CH_2{=}CH{-}Br \longrightarrow \overset{+}{C}H_2{-}\overset{\bar{\cdot\cdot}}{C}H{-}Br$$

At the same time vinyl bromide is also capable of existing as a resonance hybrid (*cf.*, *e.g.*, chlorobenzene, p. 523):

$$CH_2{=}CH{-}\ddot{\underset{\cdot\cdot}{Br}}{:} \longleftrightarrow \overset{\bar{\cdot\cdot}}{C}H_2{-}CH{=}\overset{+}{\underset{\cdot\cdot}{Br}}{:}$$

Considering the high electron-affinity of bromine, (ii) would seem to be more likely than (i), and the bromine atom would therefore cause the electron drift to take place *towards* itself. Considering the resonance effect, the tendency would be to drive the electrons in the *opposite* direction to that of (ii), and since the resonance effect is much stronger than the inductive effect (p. 493) direction (i) will be the result; hence the addition of a molecule of hydrogen bromide to vinyl bromide is:

$$Br{-}H \;\; CH_2{=}CHBr \longrightarrow CH_3{\cdot}\overset{+}{C}HBr \;\; \overset{-}{Br} \longrightarrow CH_3{\cdot}CHBr_2$$

4. When passed into dilute sulphuric acid at 60° in the presence of mercuric sulphate as catalyst, acetylene adds on one molecule of water to form acetaldehyde. The mechanism of this hydration is not known, but it may be via the formation of vinyl alcohol as an intermediate. Vinyl alcohol has not yet been isolated; all attempts to prepare it result in the formation of acetaldehyde (p. 250). Since we are suggesting it is an intermediate product, but that it has never been isolated in this reaction, we indicate this by enclosing vinyl alcohol in square brackets:*

$$CH{\equiv}CH + H_2O \xrightarrow[Hg^{2+}]{H_2SO_4} [CH_2{=}CHOH] \longrightarrow CH_3{\cdot}CHO$$

The conversion of acetylene into acetaldehyde is very important technically, since acetaldehyde can be used for the preparation of many important compounds (see text).

The homologues of acetylene form ketones when hydrated, *e.g.*, methylacetylene gives acetone:

$$CH_3{\cdot}C{\equiv}CH + H_2O \xrightarrow[Hg^{2+}]{H_2SO_4} [CH_3{\cdot}C(OH){=}CH_2] \longrightarrow CH_3{\cdot}CO{\cdot}CH_3$$

* In this book any compound that is suggested as an intermediate will be enclosed in square brackets *provided that it has not been isolated in the reaction shown.*

5. When acetylene is passed into dilute hydrochloric acid at 65° in the presence of mercuric ions as catalyst, vinyl chloride is formed:

$$CH{\equiv}CH + HCl \xrightarrow{Hg^{2+}} CH_2{=}CHCl$$

Acetylene adds on hydrogen cyanide in the presence of barium cyanide as catalyst to form vinyl cyanide:

$$CH{\equiv}CH + HCN \xrightarrow{Ba(CN)_2} CH_2{=}CHCN$$

Vinyl cyanide is used in the manufacture of *Buna N* synthetic rubber, which is a copolymer of vinyl cyanide and butadiene.

When acetylene is passed into warm acetic acid in the presence of mercuric ions as catalyst, vinyl acetate and ethylidene acetate are formed:

$$CH{\equiv}CH + CH_3{\cdot}CO_2H \xrightarrow{Hg^{2+}} CH_2{=}CH{\cdot}O{\cdot}OC{\cdot}CH_3$$

$$CH_2{=}CH{\cdot}O{\cdot}OC{\cdot}CH_3 + CH_3{\cdot}CO_2H \xrightarrow{Hg^{2+}} CH_3{\cdot}CH(OOC{\cdot}CH_3)_2$$

Vinyl acetate (liquid) is used in the plastic industry. Ethylidene acetate (liquid), when heated rapidly to 300–400°, gives acetic anhydride and acetaldehyde.

Acetylene reacts with nitric acid in the presence of mercuric ions to form nitroform, $CH(NO_3)_3$. Acetylene combines with arsenic trichloride to form Lewisite (p. 327). When acetylene is passed into methanol at 160–200° in the presence of a small amount (1–2 per cent.) of potassium methoxide and under pressure just high enough to prevent boiling, methyl vinyl ether is formed:

$$CH{\equiv}CH + CH_3OH \xrightarrow{CH_3OK} CH_2{=}CH{\cdot}O{\cdot}CH_3$$

This is used for making the polyvinyl ether plastics.

This process whereby acetylene adds on to compounds containing an active hydrogen atom (p. 333) to form vinyl compounds is known as **vinylation.**

Acetylene and formaldehyde interact in the presence of copper acetylide as catalyst to form butynediol, together with smaller amounts of propargyl alcohol, $CH{\equiv}C{\cdot}CH_2OH$:

$$CH{\equiv}CH + HCHO \xrightarrow{Cu_2C_2} CH{\equiv}C{\cdot}CH_2OH$$

$$CH{\equiv}CH + 2HCHO \xrightarrow{Cu_2C_2} CH_2OH{\cdot}C{\equiv}C{\cdot}CH_2OH$$

Propargyl alcohol is used to prepare allyl alcohol, glycerol, etc. Butynediol is used to prepare butadiene, etc.

This reaction in which acetylene (or any compound containing the $\equiv$CH group, *i.e.*, a methyne hydrogen atom) adds on to certain unsaturated links (such as in the carbonyl group), or eliminates a molecule of water by reaction with certain hydroxy-compounds, is known as **ethinylation.** Thus the above reactions with formaldehyde are examples of ethinylation; another example is the following:

$$R_2N{\cdot}CH_2OH + CH{\equiv}CH \longrightarrow R_2N{\cdot}CH_2{\cdot}C{\equiv}CH + H_2O$$

6. When acetylene is passed into hypochlorous acid solution, dichloroacetaldehyde is formed:

$$CH{\equiv}CH + HOCl \longrightarrow [CHCl{=}CHOH] \xrightarrow{HOCl} [CHCl_2{\cdot}CH(OH)_2] \longrightarrow CHCl_2{\cdot}CHO + H_2O$$

Dichloroacetic acid, $CHCl_2 \cdot CO_2H$, is also formed by the oxidation of dichloroacetaldehyde by the hypochlorous acid.

7. Acetylene and its homologues form ozonides with ozone, and these compounds are decomposed by water to form diketones, which are then oxidised to acids by the hydrogen peroxide formed in the reaction :

$$R{\cdot}C{\equiv}C{\cdot}R' + O_3 \longrightarrow R{\cdot}\underset{O-O}{\overset{\;\;O\;\;}{C-C}}{\cdot}R' \xrightarrow{H_2O} R{\cdot}\underset{\|\atop O}{C}-\underset{\|\atop O}{C}{\cdot}R' + H_2O_2 \longrightarrow R{\cdot}CO_2H + R'{\cdot}CO_2H$$

Acetylene is exceptional in that it gives glyoxal as well as formic acid (Hurd and Christ, 1936):

$$CH{\equiv}CH + O_3 \longrightarrow \underset{O-O}{\overset{\;\;O\;\;}{CH-CH}} \xrightarrow{H_2O} \underset{\|\atop O}{CH}{\cdot}\underset{\|\atop O}{CH}$$

The triple bond in acetylenes is usually oxidised by potassium permanganate to give acid fission products:

$$R{\cdot}C{\equiv}C{\cdot}R' \xrightarrow{KMnO_4} R{\cdot}CO{\cdot}CO{\cdot}R' \xrightarrow{KMnO_4} R{\cdot}CO_2H + R'{\cdot}CO_2H$$

The intermediate α-diketone can be isolated if the oxidation is carried out in the presence of magnesium sulphate.

8. When passed through a heated tube acetylene polymerises, to a small extent, to benzene.

$$3C_2H_2 \longrightarrow C_6H_6 \text{ (benzene ring)}$$

Homologues of acetylene behave in a similar manner, *e.g.*, methylacetylene polymerises to *s*-trimethylbenzene, and dimethylacetylene to hexamethylbenzene:

$$3CH_3C{\equiv}CH \longrightarrow C_6H_3(CH_3)_3 \text{ (1,3,5-trimethylbenzene)}$$

$$3CH_3C{\equiv}CCH_3 \longrightarrow C_6(CH_3)_6$$

Under suitable conditions acetylene polymerises to *cyclo*octatetraene (*q.v.*):

$$4C_2H_2 \longrightarrow \text{HC=CH–CH=CH–CH=CH–CH=CH (ring)}$$

In addition to the above type of *cyclic* polymerisation, acetylene undergoes *linear* polymerisation when passed into a solution of cuprous chloride in ammonium chloride to give vinylacetylene and divinylacetylene:

$$CH{\equiv}CH + CH{\equiv}CH \longrightarrow CH_2{=}CH{-}C{\equiv}CH \xrightarrow{C_2H_2} CH_2{=}CH{-}C{\equiv}C{-}CH{=}CH_2$$

Compounds containing both a double and triple bond are named systematically as *alkenynes*. The double bond is expressed first in the name, and is given the lowest number (see rules, p. 58). Thus vinylacetylene is but-1-en-3-yne, and divinylacetylene is hexa-1 : 5-dien-3-yne.

Vinylacetylene adds on one molecule of hydrogen chloride to the triple bond to form *chloroprene* or 2-chlorobuta-1 : 3-diene, the addition taking place in accordance with Markownikoff's rule:

$$CH_2{=}CH{-}C{\equiv}CH + HCl \longrightarrow CH_2{=}CH{-}CCl{=}CH_2$$

Chloroprene readily polymerises to a rubber-like substance known as *neoprene*.

9. Acetylene forms metallic derivatives by replacement of one or both hydrogen atoms, *e.g.*, if acetylene is passed over heated sodium, both the monosodium and disodium acetylides are formed:

$$CH{\equiv}CH \xrightarrow{Na} CH{\equiv}CNa \xrightarrow{Na} NaC{\equiv}CNa$$

By using a large excess of acetylene the main product is monosodium acetylide, which is also obtained by passing acetylene into a solution of sodium in liquid ammonia until the blue colour disappears. The monosodium derivative possesses the interesting property of being able to absorb dry carbon dioxide to form the sodium salt of propiolic acid (*q.v.*):

$$CH{\equiv}C{\cdot}Na + CO_2 \longrightarrow CH{\equiv}C{\cdot}CO_2Na$$

The lithium acetylides are very useful in organic synthesis (p. 345).

When acetylene is passed into an ammoniacal solution of cuprous chloride or silver nitrate, cuprous acetylide Cu_2C_2 (red) or silver acetylide Ag_2C_2 (white) is precipitated. Both these compounds, when dry, explode when struck or heated. When they are treated with potassium cyanide solution pure acetylene is obtained, but on treatment with inorganic acid, the acetylene liberated is impure.

The acidic nature of hydrogen in acetylene is characteristic of hydrogen only in the group $\equiv$CH. The reason for this is obscure, but it appears that the C—H link must have considerable ionic character which may be due to resonance:

$$H{-}C{\equiv}C{-}H \longleftrightarrow H{-}C{\equiv}\overset{-}{C}\overset{+}{H} \longleftrightarrow \overset{+}{H}\overset{-}{C}{\equiv}C{-}H \longleftrightarrow \overset{+}{H}\overset{-}{C}{\equiv}\overset{-}{C}\overset{+}{H}$$

Walsh (1947) has offered an alternative theory. Since one carbon atom is joined to another by a multiple bond, the carbon atoms behave as if they were more electronegative atoms, *i.e.*, they attract electrons more strongly than in saturated compounds. Thus proton release in acetylene is facilitated.

The structure of metallic carbides, *i.e.*, compounds formed between carbon and metals, is still a matter of dispute. It appears certain, so far, that the carbides of the strongly electropositive metals: Na, K, Ca, Sr, Ba, are ionic—X-ray crystal analysis has shown the lattice of these carbides to be ionic, containing the ion $\bar{C}{\equiv}\bar{C}$. These carbides react with water to produce acetylene. Copper and silver carbides are not affected by water, and are explosive when dry. On account of these differences it seems likely that the carbides of these two metals are covalent, *e.g.*, Cu—C$\equiv$C—Cu. Thus these compounds may be regarded as *acetylides*.

In addition to the above carbides, there are a number of carbides which react with water or dilute acids to produce methane, *e.g.*, aluminium carbide; or a mixture of hydrocarbons, *e.g.*, uranium carbide which gives acetylene and other unsaturated hydrocarbons; iron carbide which gives methane and hydrogen. Many authors believe these carbides to be ionic, and include carbides of copper and silver in this group.

There is also one other group of carbides which are highly refractory, and which are extremely stable chemically; *e.g.*, vanadium carbide is not attacked by water or hydrochloric acid even at 600°. These carbides are believed to be *interstitial* compounds, *i.e.*, their lattice is not composed of ions, but resembles a metallic or atomic lattice.

Structure of acetylene. By reasoning similar to that used for ethylene, the structure of acetylene is shown to be H—C≡C—H, and may be repre-

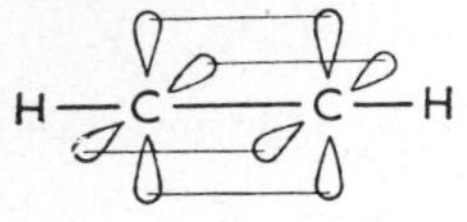

H—C——C—H

(*a*)

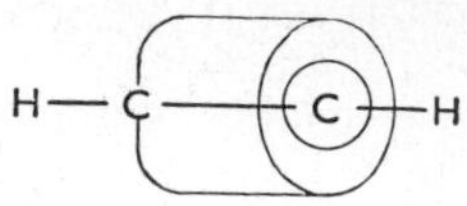

H—C——(C)—H

(*b*)

FIG. 4.2.

sented as Fig. 2(*a*). This representation, however, appears to be inadequate. According to Coulson (1952), the two π-bonds form a charge cloud which has cylindrical symmetry about the carbon–carbon axis (Fig. 2*b*).

HOMOLOGUES OF ACETYLENE

Homologues of acetylene may be prepared by any of the following methods:

1. By the action of ethanolic potassium hydroxide on *vic-* or *gem-*dihalogen derivatives of the paraffins (*cf.* preparation of acetylene, method 2), *e.g.*, methylacetylene from propylene bromide:

$$CH_3\cdot CHBr\cdot CH_2Br + 2KOH \xrightarrow{\text{ethanol}} CH_3\cdot C\equiv CH + 2KBr + 2H_2O$$

Since *gem-*dihalides are not usually readily accessible, and the *vic-*dihalides are, the latter are used.

This method affords a simple means of introducing a triple bond into an organic compound, *e.g.*, *n-*butanol is catalytically dehydrated to but-1-ene, which on treatment with bromine gives 1 : 2-dibromobutane, and this, when heated with ethanolic potassium hydroxide, yields but-1-yne:

$$CH_3\cdot CH_2\cdot CH_2\cdot CH_2OH \xrightarrow[350^\circ]{Al_2O_3} CH_3\cdot CH_2\cdot CH{=}CH_2 \xrightarrow{Br_2}$$
$$CH_3\cdot CH_2\cdot CHBr\cdot CH_2Br \xrightarrow[\text{ethanol}]{KOH} CH_3\cdot CH_2\cdot C\equiv CH$$

2. Monosodium acetylide (see reaction 9 of acetylene) is treated with an alkyl halide, preferably a bromide, whereupon an acetylene homologue is produced:

$$CH\equiv CH + Na \xrightarrow[NH_3]{\text{liquid}} CH\equiv CNa \xrightarrow{RX} CH\equiv C\cdot R + NaX$$

This reaction may be carried further as follows:

$$R\cdot C\equiv CH + Na \xrightarrow[NH_3]{\text{liquid}} R\cdot C\equiv CNa \xrightarrow{R'X} R\cdot C\equiv C\cdot R' + NaX$$

In practice this method is limited to the use of primary alkyl halides, since higher *sec.* and *tert.* halides give mainly olefins when they react with the monosodium derivative of acetylene or its homologues.

3. By the action of acetylene on a Grignard reagent (*q.v.*) and then treating the resulting magnesium complex with an alkyl halide:

$$CH\equiv CH + R{-}Mg{-}Br \longrightarrow RH + CH\equiv C{-}Mg{-}Br \xrightarrow{RBr} CH\equiv C\cdot R$$

The properties of the homologues of acetylene are very similar to those of acetylene, particularly when they are of the type R·C≡CH, *i.e.*, contain the ≡CH group. A very interesting reaction of the acetylene homologues is their ability to isomerise when heated with ethanolic potassium hydroxide, the triple bond moving towards the centre of the chain, *e.g.*, but-1-yne isomerises to but-2-yne:

$$CH_3{\cdot}CH_2{\cdot}C{\equiv}CH \longrightarrow [CH_3{\cdot}CH{=}C{=}CH_2] \longrightarrow CH_3{\cdot}C{\equiv}C{\cdot}CH_3$$

There is a great deal of evidence to show that an allene is formed as an intermediate.

On the other hand, when alkynes are heated with sodamide in an inert solvent, *e.g.*, paraffin, the triple bond moves towards the end of the chain; *e.g.*, but-2-yne gives the sodium derivative of but-1-yne, which is converted into but-1-yne by the action of water:

$$CH_3{\cdot}C{\equiv}C{\cdot}CH_3 + NaNH_2 \xrightarrow{\text{paraffin}} NH_3 + CH_3{\cdot}CH_2{\cdot}C{\equiv}CNa \xrightarrow{H_2O} CH_3{\cdot}CH_2{\cdot}C{\equiv}CH$$

This reaction affords a means of stepping up the alkyne series by method 2 above.

A very useful acetylene derivative for synthetic work is ethoxyacetylene. This may conveniently be prepared by the action of sodamide on chloroacetaldehyde diethyl acetal (Jones *et al.*, 1954):

$$CH_2Cl{\cdot}CH(OC_2H_5)_2 \xrightarrow{NaNH_2} CH{\equiv}C{\cdot}O{\cdot}C_2H_5$$

QUESTIONS

1. Write out the structures of the isomeric pentenes and name them (use three methods of nomenclature).
2. Give an account of the evidence for the structure of propylene.
3. Give as many methods as you can for separating a mixture of *iso*butane and but-1-ene into its constituents.
4. Show how you would distinguish experimentally between the three isomeric butylenes.
5. Name the compounds and indicate the conditions under which they are formed when but-1-ene is treated with:—(*a*) bromine, (*b*) hydrogen bromide, (*c*) hydrogen chloride, (*d*) hypochlorous acid, (*e*) ozone, (*f*) conc. sulphuric acid, (*g*) hydrogen, (*h*) chlorine, (*i*) nitrosyl chloride, (*i*) peracetic acid, (*k*) heat.
6. Define and give examples of:—(*a*) unsaturation, (*b*) dehydration, (*c*) dehydrohalogenation, (*d*) conjugation, (*e*) 1 : 4-addition, (*f*) polymerisation, (*g*) hydroxylation of a double bond, (*h*) peroxide effect, (*i*) ozonolysis, (*j*) Prileschaiev's reaction, (*k*) polycondensation, (*l*) plastics, (*m*) thermoplastic, (*n*) thermo-setting plastic, (*o*) plasticiser, (*p*) ethinylation, (*q*) vinylation.
7. Write out the structures and names (by two methods) of the isomeric pentynes.
8. Give an analytical table to show how you would distinguish between ethane, ethylene and acetylene.
9. Name the compounds and indicate the conditions under which they are formed when acetylene reacts with the reagents named in question 5.
10. Prepare methylpropylacetylene using only acetylene and methyl iodide and any inorganic compounds you wish.
11. Give an account of the evidence for the structure of acetylene.
12. Discuss the structures of butadiene and acetylene from the M.O. point of view.

READING REFERENCES

Gilman, *Advanced Organic Chemistry*, Wiley (1942, 2nd ed.).

Vol. I (*a*) Ch. 1. The Reactions of the Aliphatic Hydrocarbons.
(*b*) Ch. 7. Unsaturation and Conjugation.
(*c*) Ch. 8. Synthetic Polymers.

Mayo and Walling, The Peroxide Effect, *Chem. Reviews*, 1940, **27**, 357.

Riebsomer, Reactions of Nitrogen Tetroxide with Organic Compounds, *ibid.*, 1945, **36**, 197–211.

Levy, Scaife *et al.*, Addition of Dinitrogen Tetroxide to Olefins, *J.C.S.*, **1946**, 1093, 1096, 1100; **1948**, 52.

Gorin, Kuhn, and Miles, Mechanisms of the Catalysed Alkylation of *iso*Butane with Olefins, *Ind. Eng. Chem.*, 1946, **38**, 745.

Groll and Hearne, Substitution in Straight-Chain Olefins, *ibid.*, 1939, **31**, 1530.

Long, Ozonisation Reaction, *Chem. Reviews*, 1940, **27**, 437–454.

Leffler, Cleavages and Rearrangements Involving Oxygen Radicals and Cations, *ibid.*, 1949, **45**, 399. Ozonisation.

Organic Reactions, Wiley. Vol. II (1944), Ch. 8. Periodic Acid Oxidation.
Ann Reports, 1944, **41**, 148–164. Acetylenic Compounds.
ibid., 1945, **42**, 143–145. Oxidation with Lead Tetra-acetate.
De la Mare, Kinetics of Thermal Addition of Halogens to Olefinic Compounds, *Quart. Reviews* (*Chem. Soc.*), 1949, **3**, 126.
Organic Reactions, Wiley. Vol. V (1949), Ch. I. The Synthesis of Acetylenes.
Raphael, *Acetylenic Compounds in Organic Synthesis*, Butterworth (1955).
Organic Reactions, Wiley. Vol. VII (1953), Ch. 7. Epoxidation and Hydroxylation of Ethylenic Compounds with Organic Per-acids.
Lynch and Pausacker, The Oxidation of Olefins with Perbenzoic Acids. A Kinetic Study, *J.C.S.*, **1955**, 1525.
Trapnell, Specificity in Catalysis by Metals, *Quart. Reviews* (*Chem. Soc.*), 1954, **8**, 404.
Bond, The Mechanism of Catalytic Hydrogenation and Related Reactions, *ibid.*, 1954, **8**, 279.
Cadogan and Hey, Free-Radical Addition Reactions to Olefinic Systems, *ibid.*, 1954, **8**, 308.
Bu'Lock, Acetylenic Compounds as Natural Products, *ibid.*, 1956, **10**, 371.
Kharasch, The Unique Properties of 2 : 4-Dinitrobenzenesulphenyl Chloride, *J. Chem. Educ.*, 1956, **33**, 585.
Langford and Lawson, Characterisation of Organic Compounds with 2 : 4-Dinitrobenzenesulphenyl Chloride, *ibid.*, 1957, **34**, 510.

CHAPTER V

HALOGEN DERIVATIVES OF THE PARAFFINS

HALOGEN derivatives of the paraffins are divided into mono-, di-, tri-, etc., substitution products according to the number of halogen atoms in the molecule.

Nomenclature. Monohalogen derivatives are usually named as the halide of the corresponding alkyl group, *e.g.*, C_2H_5Cl ethyl chloride; $CH_3{\cdot}CHBr{\cdot}CH_3$ *iso*propyl bromide; $(CH_3)_3CCl$ *tert.*-butyl chloride.

Dihalogen derivatives. (i) When both halogen atoms are attached to the *same* carbon atom, they are said to be in the *geminal* (*gem*-) position. Since the loss of two hydrogen atoms from the same carbon atom gives the *alkylidene* radical, *gem*-dihalides are named as the alkylidene halides, *e.g.*, $CH_3{\cdot}CHBr_2$ ethylidene bromide; $CH_3{\cdot}CCl_2{\cdot}CH_3$ *iso*propylidene chloride.

(ii) When the two halogen atoms are on *adjacent* carbon atoms they are said to be in the *vicinal* (*vic*-) position, and these dihalides are named as the halide of the olefin from which they may be prepared by the addition of halogen, *e.g.*, $CH_2Cl{\cdot}CH_2Cl$ ethylene chloride; $(CH_3)_2CBr{\cdot}CH_2Br$ *iso*butylene bromide.

(iii) When there is a halogen atom on each of the *terminal* carbon atoms of the chain, *i.e.*, in the αω-position, the compound is named as the polymethylene halide, *e.g.*, $CH_2Cl{\cdot}CH_2{\cdot}CH_2{\cdot}CH_2Cl$ tetramethylene chloride.

(iv) When the two halogen atoms occupy positions other than those mentioned above, the compounds are named as dihalogen derivatives of the parent hydrocarbon, the positions of the halogen atoms being indicated by numbers (use principle of lowest numbers), *e.g.*,

$CH_3{\cdot}CHCl{\cdot}CH_2{\cdot}CHCl{\cdot}CH_2{\cdot}CH_3$ 2 : 4-dichlorohexane

The alkyl halides, *gem*-, *vic*- and αω-dihalides may also be named by this (I.U.C.) system, *e.g.*, $CH_3{\cdot}CH_2{\cdot}CHBr{\cdot}CH_3$ 2-bromobutane; $CH_2Cl{\cdot}CH_2{\cdot}CH_2Cl$ 1 : 3-dichloropropane.

Polyhalogen derivatives are best named by the I.U.C. system (method iv), and the names of the halogens (and any other substituents present) are arranged alphabetically (see also p. 784), *e.g.*,

$CH_2Br{\cdot}CHCl{\cdot}CHCl{\cdot}CH_3$ 1-bromo-2 : 3-dichlorobutane
$CH_2Cl{\cdot}CHI{\cdot}CH(CH_3){\cdot}CH_2{\cdot}CH_2Br$ 5-bromo-1-chloro-2-iodo-3-methylpentane

ALKYL HALIDES

The alkyl halides have the general formula $C_nH_{2n+1}X$ or RX, where X denotes chlorine, bromine or iodine. Fluorine is not included, since fluorides were, until fairly recently, chemical curiosities, and also do not behave like the other halides. Fluorine compounds are discussed separately at the end of this chapter.

General methods of preparation. 1. The method most widely used is to replace the hydroxyl group of an alcohol by an X atom. This may be done by means of various halogen reagents, and the accessibility of the reagent is usually the factor deciding which one is used for the preparation of a particular alkyl halide.

(i) **Alkyl chlorides** may be prepared by passing hydrogen chloride into the alcohol in the presence of anhydrous zinc chloride (Groves' process), *e.g.*, ethyl chloride from ethanol:

$$C_2H_5OH + HCl \xrightarrow{ZnCl_2} C_2H_5Cl + H_2O$$

The yield of alkyl chloride depends on the nature of the alcohol. Primary alcohols of the type $R{\cdot}CH_2{\cdot}CH_2OH$ and $R_2CH{\cdot}CH_2OH$ usually give good yields of alkyl chloride, but when the alcohol is of the type $R_3C{\cdot}CH_2OH$, the main product is a tertiary alkyl chloride formed by rearrangement of the molecule (see *neo*pentyl chloride, p. 100). Secondary alcohols, except for *iso*propanol and *sec.*-butanol, react with hydrogen chloride to give mixtures of chlorides, *e.g.*, pentan-2-ol gives a mixture of 2- and 3-chlorides. Secondary alcohols containing highly branched radicals attached to the carbinol group tend to give tertiary chlorides by molecular rearrangement, *e.g.*, pinacolyl alcohol:

$$(CH_3)_3C{\cdot}CHOH{\cdot}CH_3 \xrightarrow{HCl} (CH_3)_2CCl{\cdot}CH(CH_3)_2$$

Tertiary alcohols give very good yields of tertiary chloride with concentrated hydrochloric acid in the absence of zinc chloride.

The reaction between an alcohol and hydrogen chloride is reversible, and some authors believe that the zinc chloride functions as a dehydrating agent, thus inhibiting the backward reaction. It is possible, however, that the zinc chloride also acts catalytically by helping to break the H—Cl bond as follows:

$$R{-}\ddot{\underset{\cdot\cdot}{O}}{-}H + H|{-}Cl + ZnCl_2 \longrightarrow \left[R{-}\underset{\cdot\cdot}{\overset{\overset{H}{|}}{O}}{-}H\right]^+ + ZnCl_3^-$$

$$[R|{-}OH_2]^+ \longrightarrow R^+ + H_2O$$

$$R^+ + ZnCl_3^- \longrightarrow R{-}Cl + ZnCl_2$$

Alkyl bromides may be prepared:

(*a*) By refluxing the alcohol with excess constant-boiling hydrobromic acid (48 per cent.) in the presence of a little sulphuric acid, which must behave catalytically, since in its absence the reaction is slow.

The yield of alkyl bromide is usually excellent; when a secondary or tertiary alcohol is used, it is better to omit the sulphuric acid, since this would dehydrate these alcohols to olefins and thereby reduce the yield.

(*b*) By heating the alcohol with potassium bromide and concentrated sulphuric acid in excess:

$$ROH + KBr + H_2SO_4 \longrightarrow RBr + KHSO_4 + H_2O$$

The yield is very good for primary alcohols only; secondary and tertiary are readily dehydrated to olefins under these conditions.

Alkyl iodides may be prepared in good yield by refluxing the alcohol with excess of constant-boiling hydriodic acid (57 per cent.). Stone *et al.* (1950) have shown that alkyl iodides may be prepared in good yields by heating alcohols, ethers or olefins with sodium or potassium iodide in 95 per cent. phosphoric acid.

(ii) Any alkyl halide may be prepared by the action of a phosphorus halide on the alcohol. Phosphorus pentachloride gives variable yields depending on the alcohol:

$$ROH + PCl_5 \longrightarrow RCl + HCl + POCl_3$$

Phosphorus trichloride gives poor yields of alkyl chloride except with alcohols which tend to react by an S_N1 mechanism, *e.g.*, *tert.*-alcohols behave in accordance with the equation:

$$PCl_3 + 3ROH \longrightarrow 3RCl + P(OH)_3$$

The yields of alkyl halide with phosphorus tribromide or tri-iodide are *v.g.–ex.* for primary alcohols; less for secondary alcohols, and still less for tertiary. These phosphorus trihalides are usually prepared *in situ*; bromine or iodine is added to a mixture of red phosphorus and alcohol, and warmed.

(iii) Thionyl chloride (one molecule) refluxed with alcohols (one molecule) forms alkyl chlorides in the presence of pyridine (one molecule) [**Darzens procedure**]:

$$ROH + SOCl_2 \xrightarrow{\text{pyridine}} RCl + SO_2 + HCl$$

In a number of cases only a small amount of pyridine need be used to give the same yield of alkyl chloride as in the Darzens procedure.

2. By the addition of halogen acids to an olefin.

3. By direct halogenation, *i.e.*, substitution reactions of the paraffins with halogen, and this may be brought about by (*a*) light, (*b*) catalysts or (*c*) heat.

(*a*) **Photohalogenation** is carried out by treating the paraffin with chlorine or bromine at ordinary temperature in the presence of light. The reaction is believed to take place by a free-radical chain mechanism, the initiation being brought about by the formation of chlorine atoms by the U.V. part of the spectrum of the light:

$$Cl_2 \xrightarrow{h\nu} 2Cl\cdot$$
$$Cl\cdot + CH_4 \longrightarrow HCl + CH_3\cdot$$
$$CH_3\cdot + Cl_2 \longrightarrow CH_3Cl + Cl\cdot$$
$$Cl\cdot + CH_3Cl \longrightarrow HCl + CH_2Cl\cdot$$
$$CH_2Cl\cdot + Cl_2 \longrightarrow CH_2Cl_2 + Cl\cdot \text{ etc.}$$

The termination of the chain reaction may take place by adsorption of the chlorine atoms on the walls of the containing vessel, or by two chlorine atoms combining with each other to form a chlorine molecule. There appears to be no evidence to show that $CH_3\cdot$, $\cdot CH_2Cl$, etc., radicals combine to terminate the chain reaction (*cf.* addition of chlorine to ethylene, p. 62). Ritchie and Winning (1950) suggest that the chain-ending involves the formation of Cl_3 molecules:

$$Cl\cdot + Cl_2 \longrightarrow Cl_3\cdot;\quad 2Cl_3\cdot \longrightarrow 3Cl_2$$

(*b*) **Catalytic halogenation** is carried out by treating the paraffin with halogen in the presence of various metallic halides, *e.g.*, cupric chloride catalyses chlorination; ferric bromide, bromination.

(*c*) **Thermal halogenation.** Thermal chlorination has been studied in great detail by Hass, McBee and their co-workers (1935 onwards), and as a result of their work they suggested a number of rules for chlorination:

(i) If high temperature is avoided, no carbon skeleton rearrangements occur in either thermal or photochemical chlorination.

(ii) Every possible monochloride is formed, and over-chlorination, *i.e.*, chlorination beyond monosubstitution, may be suppressed by controlling the ratio of chlorine to paraffin (this rule also holds good for photochemical chlorination).

(iii) The order of ease of substitution is tertiary hydrogen $>$ secondary $>$ primary. At 300°, with reaction in the vapour phase, the relative rates of substitution of primary, secondary and tertiary hydrogen atoms are 1·00 : 3·25 : 4·43.

(iv) As the temperature rises above 300° the relative rates of substitution tend to become equal, *i.e.*, 1 : 1 : 1. Increased pressure causes an increase in the relative rate of primary substitution.

(v) In vapour-phase chlorination the presence of a chlorine atom on a carbon atom tends to prevent further reaction on that carbon atom during the second substitution.

In the past it was believed that paraffins always tended to *complete* substitution. Rule (ii) shows this is not the case. Methane, however, has been found to be an exception; chlorination of methane always results in a mixture of all four substitution products, their relative amounts depending on the ratio of chlorine to methane (see, *e.g.*, methyl chloride).

Bromination takes place with greater difficulty than chlorination, and there is less tendency for polysubstitution.

The mechanism of thermal halogenation is believed to take place by a free-radical chain reaction (*cf.* photohalogenation). The initiation of the chain reaction is brought about by the thermal dissociation of chlorine molecules into separate atoms:

$$Cl_2 \xrightarrow{\text{heat}} Cl\cdot + Cl\cdot$$

$$Cl\cdot + CH_4 \longrightarrow HCl + CH_3\cdot, \text{ etc.}$$

4. Direct chlorination of paraffins may be effected by means of sulphuryl chloride. Sulphuryl chloride in the absence of light and catalysts does not react with paraffins even at their boiling points, but in the presence of light and a trace of an organic peroxide the reaction is fast:

$$RH + SO_2Cl_2 \longrightarrow RCl + SO_2 + HCl$$

The mechanism of this reaction is still obscure, but in view of the fact that it is catalysed by organic peroxides (which are known to generate free radicals), it is quite likely that chlorination with sulphuryl chloride proceeds by a free-radical chain reaction.

In general, the products obtained by chlorination with sulphuryl chloride are the same as those obtained by photochemical or thermal chlorination, and it has been found that when sulphuryl chloride is used:

(i) The order of ease of replacement of a hydrogen atom is tertiary > secondary > primary.

(ii) The second chlorine atom tends to substitute on that carbon atom which is as far away as possible from the carbon atom already joined to the chlorine atom.

(iii) It is difficult to get two, and impossible to get three, chlorine atoms on the same carbon atom.

Alkyl chlorides and bromides are generally obtained fairly easily, iodides not so easily. Fluorides have to be prepared by special means (see later in this chapter). In many cases the iodide may be obtained from the corresponding chloride or bromide by treating the latter in acetone or methanol solution with sodium iodide (see p. 49):

$$RCl + NaI \longrightarrow RI + NaCl$$

Iodides may also be prepared from the corresponding bromide via the Grignard reagent:

$$RBr + Mg \xrightarrow{\text{ether}} R{-}Mg{-}Br \xrightarrow{I_2} RI$$

5. Hunsdiecker *et al.* (1935) found that various salts of the fatty acids are decomposed by chlorine or bromine to form the alkyl halide, *e.g.*,

$$R{\cdot}CO_2Ag + Br_2 \longrightarrow RBr + CO_2 + AgBr$$

The silver salt appears to give the best yield, but the yield also depends on the solvent used; Stoll *et al.* (1951) found that trichloroethylene is a better solvent than either carbon tetrachloride or carbon disulphide. The yield of halide is primary > secondary > tertiary, and bromine is generally used, chlorine giving a poorer yield of alkyl chloride, and iodine tending to form esters.

$$2R{\cdot}CO_2Ag + I_2 \longrightarrow R{\cdot}CO_2R + CO_2 + 2AgI$$

Apart from preparing alkyl halides, this reaction also offers a means of stepping down the fatty acids and alcohols.

6. Rydon *et al.* (1954) have shown that alkyl halides may be prepared, in good yield, by the addition of halogen to a mixture of an alcohol and triphenyl phosphite:

$$(C_6H_5O)_3P + ROH + X_2 \longrightarrow RX + XPO(OC_6H_5)_2 + C_6H_5OH$$

General properties of the alkyl halides. The lower members methyl chloride, methyl bromide and ethyl chloride are gases; methyl iodide and the majority of the higher members are sweet-smelling liquids. The order of the values of the boiling points (and densities) of the alkyl halides is iodide$>$bromide$>$chloride$>$fluoride. In a group of isomeric alkyl halides, the order of the boiling points is primary$>$secondary$>$tertiary. Many of the alkyl halides burn with a green-edged flame. The chemical reactions of the alkyl halides are similar, but they are not equally reactive, the order of reactivity being iodide$>$bromide$>$chloride; the reactivity of alkyl fluorides depends on the nature of the fluoride (p. 111). Alkyl iodides are sufficiently reactive to be decomposed by light, the iodide darkening due to the liberation of iodide:

$$2RI \longrightarrow R{-}R + I_2$$

Alkyl halides (and the polyhalides) are covalent compounds, insoluble in water, with which they cannot form a hydrogen bond, but soluble in organic solvents. Because of their covalent nature alkyl halides do not give a precipitate of silver halide when treated with aqueous silver nitrate solution.

The alkyl halides are classified as primary, secondary and tertiary, according as the halogen atom is present in the respective groups $-CH_2X$, $=CHX$ and $\equiv CX$, *i.e.*, according as the halogen atom is joined to a primary, secondary or tertiary carbon atom.

For a given halogen atom the order of reactivity of an alkyl halide is tertiary$>$secondary$>$primary. This may be explained as follows. In most of the reactions of the alkyl halides the covalently bound halogen atom is converted into a halogen ion. It is therefore logical to suppose that, in the structure of the alkyl halide, any peculiarity which tends to increase the polarity of the C—X bond will actually weaken this bond, since all the experimental (and theoretical) work shows that as the polarity of a given bond increases so its length increases, with a consequent decrease in strength. In other words, the more " ionic " the character of a bond, the weaker is the bond, and thus the greater is the reactivity of the X atom. Since alkyl groups have a +I effect, *i.e.*, are electron-repelling or electron-releasing, the more alkyl groups attached to the carbon atom of C—X the greater is the electron density on this carbon atom, and so the greater is the repulsion of the electron pair *towards* the X atom of the C—X bond. If we use one arrow-head to represent (qualitatively) the electron-repelling effect of an alkyl group, the following state of affairs will obtain in a primary, secondary or tertiary alkyl halide:

$$R{\rightarrow}{-}X; \qquad \begin{array}{l} R\searrow \\ \quad CH{\rightarrow}{\rightarrow}{-}X; \\ R\nearrow \end{array} \qquad \begin{array}{l} R\searrow \\ R{\rightarrow}C{\rightarrow}{\rightarrow}{\rightarrow}X \\ R\nearrow \end{array}$$

Thus the X atom is released as an X ion most readily in tertiary halides, and least readily in primary. The question that arises from the above explanation is: Why is an alkyl group electron-repelling? Several explanations have been offered; the following is a highly favoured one. As we have seen, methane and ethane are non-polar (p. 48). Thus the methyl group has a zero inductive effect; and this is true for all alkyl groups since all paraffins, whether straight- or branched-chain, have a zero dipole moment. When, however, one hydrogen atom in a paraffin is replaced by some polar atom (or group), the alkyl group now exerts a polar effect which is produced by the presence of the polar atom. Thus, in an alkyl halide, the alkyl group possesses an inductive effect, but it is one which is produced mainly by the mechanism of *interaction polarisation* (*cf.* p. 19). It therefore follows that the alkyl group is more polarisable than a hydrogen atom, and since most of the groups attached to the alkyl group are electron-attracting groups, the alkyl group thus usually becomes an electron-repelling group, *i.e.*, alkyl groups normally have a +I effect.

In addition to the purely electron-attracting power of the halogen atom in alkyl halides, the inductive effect of the alkyl group will also be influenced by the steric factor (p. 99). In the alkyl halides RX, R_2CHX and R_3CX the carbon of the C—X bond (and each of the others) is tetrahedrally hybridised. Owing to the electronegativity of the halogen atom, this bond becomes polar, and in the extreme case where ionisation occurs with formation of a carbonium ion, the latter will be trigonally hybridised (p. 29). In this *flat* ion the hydrogen atoms or alkyl groups attached to the positively charged carbon atom will be furthest apart. Thus crowding will tend to push the halogen atom away, thereby increasing the dipole moment, *i.e.*, the +I effect will increase as the number of alkyl groups increases (see also benzene, p. 496).

The difference in reactivity of the various halogen atoms attached to *identical* alkyl groups may be explained by consideration of the C—X bond energy, the values of which are: C—Cl, 66·5 kg. cal.; C—Br, 54 kg. cal.; C—I, 45·5 kg. cal. Thus the C—I bond is the one most easily broken, and the C—Cl bond least easily; this would account for the fact that iodides are the most reactive and the chlorides the least reactive, with the bromides occupying an intermediate position between the two.

General reactions of the alkyl halides. The alkyl halides are extremely important reagents because they undergo a large variety of reactions that make them valuable in organic syntheses.

1. Alkyl halides are hydrolysed to alcohols very slowly by water, but rapidly by silver oxide suspended in boiling water, or by boiling aqueous alkalis (see also 5):

$$RX + KOH \longrightarrow ROH + KX$$

This type of reaction is an example of nucleophilic substitution (S_N) since the attacking reagent is a nucleophilic reagent (p. 29). It has been assumed that this type of heterolytic reaction in solution can take place by two different mechanisms, unimolecular or bimolecular.

Unimolecular mechanism. This is a *two-stage process*, the first stage consisting of *slow* heterolysis of the compound to form a carbonium ion, followed by *rapid* combination between the carbonium ion and the substituting nucleophilic reagent. Since the rate-determining step is the first one, and since in this step only *one* molecule is undergoing a covalency change, this type of mechanism is called *unimolecular*, and is labelled S_N1 (Ingold *et al.*, 1928, 1933). Thus, if the hydrolysis of an alkyl halide is an S_N1 reaction, it may be written:

$$R\text{—}X \xrightarrow{\text{slow}} X^- + R^+ \xrightarrow[\text{fast}]{OH^-} ROH$$

Bimolecular mechanism. This is a *one-stage process*, two molecules simultaneously undergoing covalency change in the rate-determining step. This type of mechanism is called *bimolecular*, and is labelled S_N2. Since the rate-determining step in this reaction is the formation of the transition state, the hydrolysis of an alkyl halide by an S_N2 reaction may be written:

$$H\bar{O} \curvearrowright R{-}X \longrightarrow \overset{\delta-}{HO}\cdots R \cdots \overset{\delta-}{X} \longrightarrow HO{-}R + X^-$$

It has been found that the mechanism of the reaction depends on the nature of R and the ionising power of the solvent. The greater the electron-repelling (+I) effect of the R group and the greater the ionising power of the solvent, the more likely is the hydrolysis to take place by mechanism (i). It has been shown (Ingold and Hughes) that the hydrolysis of methyl halide is always a bimolecular process; the hydrolysis of ethyl and *iso*propyl halides may be a unimolecular or bimolecular process, depending on the ionising power of the medium; and the hydrolysis of tertiary butyl halide is always unimolecular. It has also been found that *speed* of hydrolysis is in the order tertiary butyl halide > *iso*propyl halide > ethyl halide > methyl halide. This is in keeping with the decreasing tendency of the halogen atom to ionise (see above).

An important point with respect to the ionising power of a solvent is that this property is not entirely dependent on its dielectric constant. If it were, then the greater the dielectric constant, the greater would be the ionising power. Although this is often true, there are examples where the dielectric constant is low and yet the ionising power is very great, *e.g.*, liquid sulphur dioxide. It now seems evident that the important factor in the ionising power of a solvent is dependent on whether the solvent can enter into some sort of combination with the ions produced, *e.g.*, sulphur dioxide has an electrophilic centre (the sulphur atom carries a positive charge); hydroxylic solvents can form hydrogen bonds.

Another factor that plays a part in the mechanism and speed of a reaction is the **steric factor,** *i.e.*, a spatial effect brought into play by mechanical interference between groups. When the steric effects slow down the reaction, that reaction is said to be subject to **steric hindrance,** and when they speed up the reaction, **steric acceleration.** It is difficult to distinguish between steric and polar factors.

In an S_N2 reaction there will be five groups " attached " to the carbon atom at which reaction occurs (see p. 395). Thus there will be " crowding " in the transition state, and the bulkier the groups the greater the crowding, and consequently the transition state will form with greater difficulty, *i.e.*, the reaction will be hindered sterically. On the other hand, steric hindrance is less important in S_N1 reactions. If, however, the molecule contains bulky groups, then by ionising, the molecule can relieve the steric strain, since the carbonium ion produced is flat (trigonal hybridisation) and so there is more room to accommodate the three alkyl groups. Thus, in such S_N1 reactions, there will be steric acceleration. According to Hughes (1951), the rate of reaction is increased only in highly branched compounds; in primary and secondary halides the effects due to steric acceleration are usually negligible.

One other problem may also be considered here. Since steric acceleration increases with increase in size of the alkyl groups, then once the carbonium ion is produced, the more slowly it can be expected to combine with the nucleophilic reagent since, in doing so, steric strain will be re-introduced into the molecule. In cases such as this, the carbonium ion tends to undergo an elimination reaction to form an olefin, and Brown *et al.* (1950) have shown that this elimination process increases as the alkyl groups become larger.

2. Alkyl halides are reduced by nascent hydrogen (Zn/Cu or Na and ethanol, Sn and HCl, etc.) to form the corresponding paraffins:

$$RX + 2[H] \longrightarrow RH + HX$$

Lithium aluminium hydride also effects this reduction.

Alkyl *iodides* may be reduced by heating them with concentrated hydriodic acid and a small amount of red phosphorus at 150°.

$$RI + HI \longrightarrow RH + I_2$$

Since alcohols are readily converted into the corresponding halide, this offers a method of converting alcohols into paraffins with the *same* number of carbon atoms.

3. Alkyl halides undergo the Wurtz reaction to form paraffins (p. 45):

$$2RX + 2Na \longrightarrow R{-}R + 2NaX$$

On the other hand alkyl halides, when heated with certain metallic alloys, form *organo-metallic* compounds, *e.g.*, ethyl chloride heated with a sodium lead alloy under pressure gives tetraethyl-lead:

$$4C_2H_5Cl + 4Na/Pb \longrightarrow (C_2H_5)_4Pb + 4NaCl + 3Pb$$

4. When heated at high temperature (above 300°), alkyl halides tend to eliminate a molecule of hydrogen halide to form olefins, *e.g.*, *iso*propyl iodide gives propylene:

$$CH_3{\cdot}CHI{\cdot}CH_3 \longrightarrow CH_3{\cdot}CH{=}CH_2 + HI$$

For a given alkyl group the tendency to eliminate hydrogen halide is iodide > bromide > chloride; and for a given halogen atom the tendency is tertiary halide > secondary > primary. Tertiary iodides eliminate hydrogen iodide so readily that they are generally useless in organic syntheses.

The mechanism of the elimination of hydrogen halide from an alkyl halide may be as follows (*cf.* the Whitmore mechanism, p. 160). First the halogen atom is released as a halide ion, and the carbonium ion, which is unstable, eliminates a proton to form the olefin, *e.g.*, propylene from *iso*-propyl bromide:

$$\begin{array}{c} CH_3{-}CH{-}Br \\ | \\ CH_2{-}H \end{array} \longrightarrow \begin{array}{c} CH_3{-}\overset{+}{C}H \\ | \\ CH_2{-}H \quad Br^- \end{array} \longrightarrow CH_3{\cdot}CH{=}CH_2 + HBr$$

When an alkyl halide is heated at about 300°, and at a lower temperature in the presence of aluminium chloride as catalyst, the alkyl halide undergoes rearrangement, *e.g.*, 1-bromobutane rearranges to 2-bromobutane:

$$CH_3{\cdot}CH_2{\cdot}CH_2{\cdot}CH_2Br \longrightarrow CH_3{\cdot}CH_2{\cdot}CHBr{\cdot}CH_3$$

The mechanism of this rearrangement is not at all clear and is further complicated by the fact that if there is no hydrogen atom on the carbon adjacent to the C—X group, an alkyl group migrates; *e.g.*, *neo*pentyl chloride rearranges to 2-chloro-2-methylbutane:

$$(CH_3)_3C{\cdot}CH_2Cl \longrightarrow (CH_3)_2CCl{\cdot}CH_2{\cdot}CH_3$$

5. When alkyl halides are boiled with ethanolic potassium hydroxide, olefins are obtained, *e.g.*, propyl bromide gives propylene:

$$CH_3{\cdot}CH_2{\cdot}CH_2Br + KOH \xrightarrow{\text{ethanol}} CH_3{\cdot}CH{=}CH_2 + KBr + H_2O$$

In practice, the reaction between an alkyl halide and alkali in either aqueous or ethanolic solution usually results in the formation of *three* products: alcohol, olefin and an ether. An alcohol is the main product with *aqueous* alkali (or with "silver hydroxide"—see reaction 1), and an olefin with *ethanolic* alkali.

According to Hughes and Ingold (1941), the elimination reaction between an alkyl halide and aqueous potassium hydroxide may take place by either a unimolecular (E1) or a bimolecular (E2) mechanism.

$$\text{(i) E1:}\quad H{-}CH_2{-}CH_2{-}X \xrightarrow{\text{slow}} H{-}CH_2{-}CH_2^+ + X^-$$

$$HO^- \quad H{-}CH_2{-}CH_2^+ \xrightarrow{\text{fast}} H_2O + CH_2{=}CH_2$$

$$\text{(ii) E2:}\quad HO^- \quad H{-}CH_2{-}CH_2{-}X \longrightarrow H_2O + CH_2{=}CH_2 + X^-$$

On the other hand, in ethanolic potassium hydroxide, which contains potassium alkoxide RO^-K^+, the reaction tends to take place by an E2 (iii) or an S_N2 (iv) mechanism.

$$\text{(iii)}\quad RO^- \quad H{-}CH_2{-}CH_2{-}X \longrightarrow ROH + CH_2{=}CH_2 + X^-$$

$$\text{(iv)}\quad RO^- \quad \overset{CH_3}{\dot{C}H_2}{-}X \longrightarrow RO{-}\overset{CH_3}{\dot{C}H_2} + X^-$$

The course of the reaction depends on the nature of the alkyl halide and on the conditions used. Under the most favourable conditions for ethylene formation, ethyl halides give only 1 per cent. ethylene, the main products being replacement products. *iso*Propyl halide gives up to 80 per cent. propylene, and tertiary butyl halide 100 per cent. *iso*butene if the reaction is carried out in *ethanolic* potassium hydroxide, which favours the bimolecular mechanisms (iii) and (iv). Although the unimolecular mechanism (i) is favoured in aqueous solution, it has to compete with the replacement reaction:

$$R{-}X + OH^- \longrightarrow ROH + X^-$$

which is either unimolecular or bimolecular (see reaction 1). Since this replacement reaction predominates in aqueous potassium hydroxide, the reaction proceeds in aqueous solution mainly by replacement rather than by elimination. A better yield of alcohol is often obtained by conversion of the alkyl halide into an ester, which is then hydrolysed.

When two olefins may be formed by dehydrohalogenation of an alkyl halide, the one that predominates is that which is the most substituted olefin, *i.e.*, the one carrying the largest number of alkyl substituents (*Saytzeff's rule*, 1875), *e.g.*,

$$CH_3{\cdot}CHBr{\cdot}CH_2{\cdot}CH_3 \longrightarrow \begin{cases} CH_3{\cdot}CH{=}CH{\cdot}CH_3 & \text{(I)} \\ CH_2{=}CH{\cdot}CH_2{\cdot}CH_3 & \text{(II)} \end{cases}$$

(I) predominates (this is a *disubstituted* ethylene, whereas (II) is a *monosubstituted* ethylene).

Another way of stating Saytzeff's rule is that hydrogen is eliminated from that carbon atom joined to the least number of hydrogen atoms. Ingold *et al.* (1941)

have offered the following explanation for this rule. If (I) and (II) are produced by an E2 mechanism, their formation may be written as follows:

$$\text{(v)}\quad HO^{-}\ H{-}\underset{CH_3}{\underset{|}{CH}}{-}\overset{CH_3}{\overset{|}{CH}}{-}Br \longrightarrow H_2O + \underset{CH_3}{\underset{|}{CH}}{=}\overset{CH_3}{\overset{|}{CH}} + Br^{-} \quad \text{(I)}$$

$$\text{(vi)}\quad HO^{-}\ \ \underset{CH_3}{\underset{|}{CH_2}}{-}\overset{H-CH_2}{\overset{|}{CH}}{-}Br \longrightarrow H_2O + \underset{CH_3}{\underset{|}{CH_2}}{-}\overset{CH_2}{\overset{\|}{CH}} + Br^{-} \quad \text{(II)}$$

In the transition state of (v), the CH_3 group can enter into hyperconjugation with the partly formed double bond (p. 253), thereby lowering the energy of the transition state. In (vi), however, the CH_3 group cannot enter into hyperconjugation with the partly formed double bond, and so the energy of this transition state is higher than that of (v), and consequently the latter path is favoured.

Steric factors also appear to play a part in the direction of olefin formation. Thus Brown *et al.* (1953) have shown that potassium *t.*-butoxide gives 53·4 per cent. of (II), and potassium ethoxide 19 per cent. of (II). Brown *et al.* (1956) have also shown that in the molecule $R{\cdot}CH_2{\cdot}CBr(CH_3)_2$, as R increases in branching (methyl < ethyl < *iso*propyl < *t.*-butyl), a regular increase is obtained in the ratio of 1-/2-olefin in the product. These authors also showed that when the potassium salts of ethanol, *t.*-butanol, *t.*-pentanol and triethylmethanol are used with secondary and tertiary alkyl bromides, the yield of 1-olefin is increased from the left to the right alkoxide.

6. When alkyl halides are heated with ethanolic ammonia under pressure, a mixture of *amines*, *i.e.*, substituted ammonias, is obtained, *e.g.*,

$$RX + NH_3 \longrightarrow R{\cdot}NH_2 + HX \longrightarrow R{\cdot}NH_2{\cdot}HX \text{ or } [R{\cdot}NH_3]^{+}X^{-}$$

Only primary alkyl halides give good yields of amines; secondary—except *iso*propyl halide—and tertiary halides form mainly olefins.

7. When alkyl halides are heated with aqueous ethanolic potassium cyanide, alkyl *cyanides* are obtained:

$$RX + KCN \longrightarrow RCN + KX$$

Tertiary alkyl cyanides cannot usually be prepared this way, since tertiary alkyl halides tend to eliminate hydrogen halide very readily when treated with potassium cyanide.

Alkyl cyanides are very important compounds, since they may be used to prepare many other compounds, *e.g.*, acids, amines, etc.

When alkyl halides are heated with aqueous ethanolic silver cyanide, cyanides and the isomeric iso*cyanides* are formed:

$$RX + AgCN \longrightarrow R{\cdot}CN + AgX$$
$$RX + AgCN \longrightarrow R{\cdot}NC + AgX$$

8. When alkyl halides are heated with an ethanolic solution of a silver salt, *esters* are obtained:

$$R{\cdot}CO_2Ag + R'X \longrightarrow R{\cdot}CO_2R' + AgX$$

The acid may be organic or inorganic. If the salt is silver nitrite two isomeric compounds are obtained, the *nitrite* (ester) and the *nitro*-compound:

$$RX + Ag—O—N{=}O \longrightarrow R—O—N{=}O + AgX$$

$$RX + Ag—O—N{=}O \longrightarrow R—N\begin{smallmatrix}{/\!\!/}O \\ \searrow O\end{smallmatrix} + AgX$$

9. When alkyl halides are heated with sodium alkoxides, *i.e.*, sodium derivatives of the alcohols, *ethers* are obtained. This is the *Williamson synthesis* (see p. 131):

$$RONa + R'X \longrightarrow R{\cdot}O{\cdot}R' + NaX$$

A modification of this reaction is to heat together an alkyl halide and an alcohol in the presence of *dry* silver oxide:

$$2ROH + 2R'I + Ag_2O \longrightarrow 2R{\cdot}O{\cdot}R' + 2AgI + H_2O$$

This reaction is known as the *Purdie method of alkylation*, and is very important in sugar chemistry.

10. Alkyl halides heated with aqueous ethanolic sodium hydrogen sulphide form *thioalcohols*:

$$RX + NaSH \longrightarrow RSH + NaX$$

11. Alkyl halides heated with an ethanolic solution of a mercaptide, *i.e.*, a metallic derivative of a thioalcohol, form *thioethers*:

$$RX + R'SNa \longrightarrow R{\cdot}S{\cdot}R' + NaX$$

12. When alkyl halides are heated with sodium, potassium or ammonium sulphite, a *sulphonate* is formed. This is known as the *Strecker reaction*:

$$RX + Na_2SO_3 \longrightarrow R{\cdot}SO_3Na + NaX$$

13. Alkyl halides may be used in the *Friedel–Crafts* reaction, *e.g.*, benzene reacts with methyl iodide in the presence of anhydrous aluminium chloride to form toluene:

$$C_6H_6 + CH_3I \xrightarrow{AlCl_3} C_6H_5{\cdot}CH_3 + HI$$

14. Alkyl halides are used to prepare Grignard reagents:

$$RX + Mg \xrightarrow{ether} R—Mg—X$$

Methyl chloride, CH_3Cl, is prepared industrially:

(i) By the action of hydrogen chloride on methanol in the presence of anhydrous zinc chloride:

$$CH_3OH + HCl \xrightarrow{ZnCl_2} CH_3Cl + H_2O$$

(ii) By heating trimethylamine hydrochloride with hydrochloric acid under pressure:

$$(CH_3)_3N{\cdot}HCl + 3HCl \longrightarrow 3CH_3Cl + NH_4Cl$$

(iii) By chlorinating methane with chlorine diluted with nitrogen, the ratio by volume of $CH_4 : Cl_2 : N_2$ being 8 : 1 : 80. The reaction is carried out in the presence of partly reduced cupric chloride as catalyst. All four chloromethanes are obtained, the methyl chloride comprising 90 per cent. of the chlorine used:

$$CH_4 + Cl_2 + (N_2) \longrightarrow CH_3Cl + HCl + (N_2) + (CH_2Cl_2 + CHCl_3 + CCl_4)$$

By adjusting the ratio of chlorine to methane, each chloromethane can be obtained as the main product.

Methyl chloride is a colourless gas, b.p. —24°. It is fairly soluble in water, and readily in ethanol. It is used in the manufacture of aniline dyes, as a refrigerating agent, local anæsthetic and as a fire extinguisher.

Methyl iodide, CH_3I, is prepared industrially:

(i) By warming a mixture of methanol and red phosphorus with iodine:

$$6CH_3OH + 2P + 3I_2 \longrightarrow 6CH_3I + 2H_3PO_3$$

(ii) By the action of methyl sulphate on potassium iodide solution in the presence of calcium carbonate:

$$KI + (CH_3)_2SO_4 \longrightarrow CH_3I + K(CH_3)SO_4 \quad (90\text{–}94\%)$$

Methyl iodide is a sweet-smelling liquid, b.p. 42·5°. Since it is a liquid, it is easier to handle than methyl chloride, and so is used a great deal as a methylating agent in laboratory organic syntheses, but the chloride is used industrially, since it is cheaper.

Ethyl chloride, C_2H_5Cl, is prepared industrially:

(i) By the action of hydrogen chloride on ethanol in the presence of anhydrous zinc chloride:

$$C_2H_5OH + HCl \xrightarrow{ZnCl_2} C_2H_5Cl + H_2O$$

(ii) By the addition of hydrogen chloride to ethylene (from cracked petroleum) in the presence of aluminium chloride as catalyst:

$$C_2H_4 + HCl \xrightarrow{AlCl_3} C_2H_5Cl$$

Ethyl chloride is a gas, b.p. 12·5°. It is used in the preparation of tetra-ethyl-lead, sulphonal, etc., and as a refrigerating agent.

DIHALOGEN DERIVATIVES

General methods of preparation. ***gem*-Dihalides** may be prepared:

(i) By the action of phosphorus pentahalides on aldehydes or ketones; *e.g.*, acetone gives *iso*propylidene chloride when treated with phosphorus pentachloride:

$$CH_3{\cdot}CO{\cdot}CH_3 + PCl_5 \longrightarrow CH_3{\cdot}CCl_2{\cdot}CH_3 + POCl_3$$

(ii) By the addition of halogen acids to the acetylenes, *e.g.*, ethylidene bromide from acetylene and hydrogen bromide:

$$CH{\equiv}CH + HBr \longrightarrow CH_2{=}CHBr \xrightarrow{HBr} CH_3{\cdot}CHBr_2$$

***vic*-Dihalides** may be prepared by the addition of halogen to olefins, *e.g.*, propylene bromide from propylene and bromine:

$$CH_3{\cdot}CH{=}CH_2 + Br_2 \longrightarrow CH_3{\cdot}CHBr{\cdot}CH_2Br$$

The method of preparing an **αω-dihalide** is special to the particular halide, *e.g.*, trimethylene bromide may be prepared by the addition of hydrogen bromide to allyl bromide at low temperatures:

$$CH_2{:}CH{\cdot}CH_2Br + HBr \longrightarrow CH_2Br{\cdot}CH_2{\cdot}CH_2Br$$

Oldham (1950), however, has found that αω-dibromides may be prepared by the action of bromine in carbon tetrachloride on the silver salt of a dibasic acid (*cf.* p. 96):

$$(CH_2)_n(CO_2Ag)_2 + 2Br_2 \longrightarrow Br\cdot(CH_2)_n\cdot Br + 2AgBr + 2CO_2.$$

The yields are very good provided n is 5 or more.

General properties and reactions of the dihalides. The dihalides are sweet-smelling, colourless liquids. *gem*-Dihalides are not as reactive as the alkyl halides. It has been found that the polarity of the C—Cl bond *decreases* progressively from methyl chloride, methylene chloride, chloroform and carbon tetrachloride. Therefore the reactivity of chlorine decreases progressively in these compounds in the same order (*i.e.*, from methyl chloride to carbon tetrachloride; *cf.* p. 97).

gem-Dihalides are hydrolysed by aqueous alkalis to the corresponding carbonyl compound (aldehyde or ketone), *e.g.*, *iso*propylidene chloride gives acetone:

$$CH_3\cdot CCl_2\cdot CH_3 + 2KOH \longrightarrow 2KCl + [CH_3\cdot C(OH)_2\cdot CH_3] \longrightarrow CH_3\cdot CO\cdot CH_3 + H_2O$$

It has generally been found that a compound containing two (or more) hydroxyl groups attached to the *same* carbon atom is unstable, and readily eliminates a molecule of water (see p. 157).

gem-Dihalides give olefins when treated with zinc dust and methanol (p. 59), and acetylenes when treated with ethanolic potassium hydroxide (p. 84).

vic- and αω-Dihalides are just as reactive as the alkyl halides. When heated with zinc and methanol, *vic*-dihalides give olefins (p. 59), but αω-dihalides in which the two halogen atoms are in the 1 : 3 to the 1 : 6 positions give cyclic compounds, *e.g.*, trimethylene bromide gives *cyclo*propane:

$$CH_2\begin{cases}CH_2Br\\CH_2Br\end{cases} + Zn \longrightarrow CH_2\begin{cases}CH_2\\ \vert\\CH_2\end{cases} + ZnBr_2$$

vic-Di-iodides tend to eliminate iodine, particularly at raised temperatures, to form olefins, *e.g.*, propylene iodide gives propylene:

$$CH_3\cdot CHI\cdot CH_2I \xrightarrow{\text{heat}} CH_3\cdot CH{=}CH_2 + I_2$$

This property has been used to regenerate the double bond from *vic*-dichlorides or dibromides. These are heated with sodium iodide in ethanol, and the *vic*-di-iodide formed decomposes into the olefin:

$$>CBr\cdot CBr< + 2NaI \xrightarrow{\text{ethanol}} 2NaBr + [>CI\cdot CI<] \longrightarrow >C{=}C< + I_2$$

Methylene chloride, CH_2Cl_2 (liquid, b.p. 40°), was formerly prepared industrially by partially reducing chloroform with zinc and hydrogen chloride in ethanolic solution:

$$CHCl_3 + 2[H] \longrightarrow CH_2Cl_2 + HCl$$

It is now also prepared industrially by the direct chlorination of methane (see methyl chloride). It is used as an industrial solvent.

Methylene bromide, CH_2Br_2 (b.p. 97°), and **methylene iodide,** CH_2I_2 (b.p. 181°), are prepared by the partial reduction of bromoform and iodoform, respectively, with sodium arsenite in alkaline solution (the yield of CH_2Br_2 is 88–90 per cent.; CH_2I_2, 90–97 per cent.), *e.g.*,

$$CHI_3 + Na_3AsO_3 + NaOH \longrightarrow CH_2I_2 + NaI + Na_3AsO_4$$

All the methylene halides are used in organic syntheses.

Ethylene chloride, $CH_2Cl{\cdot}CH_2Cl$ (b.p. 84°), and **ethylidene chloride,** $CH_3{\cdot}CHCl_2$ (b.p. 57°), are isomers; the former is prepared from ethylene and chlorine, and the latter by the action of phosphorus pentachloride on acetaldehyde (*q.v.*).

TRIHALOGEN DERIVATIVES

The most important trihalogen derivatives are those of methane, and they are usually known by their trivial names: chloroform, $CHCl_3$, bromoform, $CHBr_3$ and iodoform, CHI_3.

Chloroform may be prepared in the laboratory or industrially by heating ethanol or acetone with bleaching powder, or with chlorine and alkali (yield about 40 per cent.). The reaction is extremely complicated, and the mechanism is obscure (see chloral, p. 156).

The equations usually given for the action of bleaching powder on ethanol are: (i) oxidation of ethanol to acetaldehyde; (ii) chlorination of acetaldehyde to trichloroacetaldehyde; (iii) decomposition of trichloroacetaldehyde (chloral) by free calcium hydroxide (present in the bleaching powder) into chloroform and formic acid:

$$\text{(i)}\quad CH_3{\cdot}CH_2OH + Cl_2 \longrightarrow CH_3{\cdot}CHO + 2HCl$$
$$\text{(ii)}\quad CH_3{\cdot}CHO + 3Cl_2 \longrightarrow CCl_3{\cdot}CHO + 3HCl$$
$$\text{(iii)}\quad 2CCl_3{\cdot}CHO + Ca(OH)_2 \longrightarrow 2CHCl_3 + (H{\cdot}CO_2)_2Ca$$

When acetone is used, the first product given is trichloroacetone, which is then decomposed by the calcium hydroxide into chloroform and acetic acid:

$$\text{(i)}\quad CH_3{\cdot}CO{\cdot}CH_3 + 3Cl_2 \longrightarrow CCl_3{\cdot}CO{\cdot}CH_3 + 3HCl$$
$$\text{(ii)}\quad 2CCl_3{\cdot}CO{\cdot}CH_3 + Ca(OH)_2 \longrightarrow 2CHCl_3 + (CH_3{\cdot}CO_2)_2Ca$$

Chloroform is also prepared industrially:

(i) By the chlorination of methane (see methyl chloride).

(ii) By the partial reduction of carbon tetrachloride with iron filings and water:

$$CCl_4 + 2[H] \longrightarrow CHCl_3 + HCl$$

When prepared this way chloroform is used for solvent purposes, and not for anæsthesia (see later).

Pure chloroform may be prepared by distilling chloral hydrate with aqueous sodium hydroxide:

$$CCl_3{\cdot}CH(OH)_2 + NaOH \longrightarrow CHCl_3 + H{\cdot}CO_2Na + H_2O$$

Chloroform is a sickly, sweet-smelling, colourless liquid, b.p. 61°. It is sparingly soluble in water but readily soluble in ethanol and ether. It does not burn in air under usual conditions, but its vapour may be ignited, when it burns with a green-edged flame. When heated with concentrated aqueous or ethanolic alkali, chloroform is hydrolysed to formic acid:

$$CHCl_3 + 3KOH \longrightarrow 3KCl + [CH(OH)_3] \longrightarrow H_2O + H{\cdot}CO_2H \xrightarrow{KOH} H{\cdot}CO_2K$$

or

$$CHCl_3 + 4KOH \longrightarrow 3KCl + H{\cdot}CO_2K + 2H_2O$$

When chloroform is treated with zinc and hydrogen chloride in ethanolic solution, methylene chloride (*q.v.*) is obtained; when treated with zinc and water, methane is obtained:

$$CHCl_3 + 6[H] \xrightarrow{Zn/H_2O} CH_4 + 3HCl$$

When chloroform is warmed with silver powder, acetylene is obtained:

$$2CHCl_3 + 6Ag \longrightarrow C_2H_2 + 6AgCl$$

When treated with concentrated nitric acid, chloroform forms *chloropicrin*:

$$CHCl_3 + HNO_3 \longrightarrow CCl_3 \cdot NO_2 + H_2O$$

Chloropicrin or nitrochloroform (liquid, b.p. 112°) is used as an insecticide, and has been used as a war-gas. Chloroform adds on to the carbonyl group of ketones in the presence of potassium hydroxide, *e.g.*, with acetone it forms *chloretone* (colourless needles, m.p. 97°), which is used as a drug:

$$(CH_3)_2C{=}O + CHCl_3 \xrightarrow{KOH} (CH_3)_2C(OH) \cdot CCl_3$$

Chloroform is employed in surgery as an anæsthetic, and for this purpose it should be pure. In the presence of air and light, chloroform slowly forms carbonyl chloride, which is extremely poisonous:

$$CHCl_3 + \tfrac{1}{2}O_2 \longrightarrow COCl_2 + HCl$$

Chlorine, water and carbon dioxide are also produced. Anæsthetic chloroform is therefore kept in well-stoppered dark-brown or blue bottles. Ethanol is also added (1 per cent.), but its function is not quite clear. According to some authors, it *retards* the decomposition of the chloroform. This is supported by the fact that infra-red measurements of such mixtures show the absence of the carbonyl frequency.

A delicate test for chloroform is the " *iso*cyanide test ". This is carried out by heating chloroform with ethanolic potassium hydroxide and aniline, whereby phenyl *iso*cyanide is formed, and is readily detected by its nauseating odour:

$$CHCl_3 + 3KOH + C_6H_5 \cdot NH_2 \longrightarrow C_6H_5 \cdot NC + 3KCl + 3H_2O$$

Chloroform is widely used in industry as a solvent for fats, waxes, resins, rubber, etc.

Bromoform may be prepared by methods similar to those used for chloroform, but it is prepared industrially by the electrolysis of an aqueous solution of acetone or ethanol containing sodium carbonate and potassium bromide (acetone gives a better yield than ethanol). The solution is maintained at about 20°, and hydrobromic acid is run in to neutralise the sodium hydroxide produced during the electrolysis. Bromine is set free at the anode, and probably reacts in the same way as does chlorine in the preparation of chloroform.

Bromoform is a liquid, b.p. 149·5°, and smells like chloroform, which it closely resembles chemically.

Iodoform is prepared industrially by the electrolysis of an aqueous solution of ethanol or acetone containing sodium carbonate and potassium iodide (ethanol gives a better yield than acetone). The solution is maintained at 60–70°, and a current of carbon dioxide is passed through the solution to neutralise the sodium hydroxide formed.

Iodoform crystallises in yellow hexagonal plates, m.p. 119°. It is insoluble in water, but is readily soluble in ethanol and ether. It is used as an antiseptic, but its antiseptic properties are due to the liberation of free iodine, and not to iodoform itself. Iodoform chemically resembles chloroform and bromoform.

POLYHALOGEN DERIVATIVES

Carbon tetrachloride, CCl_4, is prepared industrially in several ways:

(i) By the action of chlorine on carbon disulphide in the presence of aluminium chloride as catalyst:

$$CS_2 + 3Cl_2 \xrightarrow{AlCl_3} CCl_4 + S_2Cl_2$$

The sulphur monochloride is removed by fractional distillation, and the carbon tetrachloride is then shaken with sodium hydroxide, and finally distilled.

(ii) By the chlorination of methane (see methyl chloride).

(iii) By *chlorinolysis*. This term was suggested by McBee, Hass and co-workers (1941) to describe the process of chlorinating an organic compound under conditions which rupture the carbon–carbon bond to yield chloro-compounds with fewer carbon atoms than the original compound. Chlorinolysis may be effected with or without a catalyst, *e.g.*, the hydrocarbon and chlorine are heated at high temperature (300–400°) and under high pressure (about 1000 lb./sq. in.). The product is usually a mixture, *e.g.*, propane gives both carbon tetrachloride and hexachloroethane:

$$C_3H_8 \xrightarrow{Cl_2} CCl_4 + C_2Cl_6$$

Carbon tetrachloride is a colourless liquid, b.p. 77°, which has a sickly smell. It is insoluble in water but readily soluble in ethanol and ether. Since its vapour is non-inflammable, carbon tetrachloride is widely used as an industrial solvent (for fats, oils, resins, lacquers, etc.). It is also used as a fire-extinguisher under the name of *Pyrene.*

Carbon tetrachloride is stable at red heat (about 500°), but when its vapour comes into contact with water vapour at this temperature, some carbonyl chloride is formed:

$$CCl_4 + H_2O \longrightarrow COCl_2 + 2HCl$$

Hence after using pyrene to extinguish a fire, the room should be well ventilated.

Carbon tetrachloride is reduced by moist iron filings to chloroform (*q.v.*). It is hydrolysed by hot ethanolic alkali, *e.g.*, with ethanolic potassium hydroxide it gives potassium chloride and potassium carbonate:

$$CCl_4 + 4KOH \longrightarrow 4KCl + [C(OH)_4] \longrightarrow 2H_2O + CO_2 \xrightarrow{KOH} K_2CO_3$$

Tetrachloroethane or **acetylene tetrachloride,** $CHCl_2{\cdot}CHCl_2$, is prepared by passing acetylene and chlorine into chambers filled with a mixture of kieselguhr and iron filings. This method is used since the combination of acetylene and chlorine is usually explosive unless a catalyst (and preferably a diluent) is present.

Acetylene tetrachloride is a very toxic, colourless liquid, b.p. 146°. It smells like chloroform; it is non-inflammable, and hence is widely used, under the name of *Westron,* as a solvent for oils, fats, paints, varnishes, rubber, etc.

When passed over heated barium chloride as catalyst, acetylene tetrachloride eliminates a molecule of hydrogen chloride to form trichloroethylene:

$$CHCl_2{\cdot}CHCl_2 \xrightarrow{BaCl_2} CHCl{=}CCl_2 + HCl$$

Trichloroethylene is a colourless liquid, b.p. 88–90°. It smells like chloroform, and is non-inflammable. It is more stable and less toxic than acetylene tetrachloride, and hence is more widely used as an industrial solvent, under the name of *Westrosol*, than *Westron*.

Hexachloroethane (*perchloroethane*), C_2Cl_6, may be prepared:

(i) By the chlorinolysis of propane (see carbon tetrachloride).

(ii) By passing ethylene mixed with 10 per cent. excess of chlorine through a pyrex tube packed with activated charcoal at 300–350°:

$$C_2H_4 + 5Cl_2 \longrightarrow C_2Cl_6 + 4HCl$$

The excess chlorine prevents the formation of lower chlorinated products.

(iii) By passing a mixture of acetylene tetrachloride and chlorine over aluminium chloride as catalyst:

$$C_2H_2Cl_4 + 2Cl_2 \xrightarrow{AlCl_3} C_2Cl_6 + 2HCl$$

(iv) By treating trichloroethylene with chlorine and passing the *penta-chloroethane* so produced over heated barium chloride, thus forming *tetra-chloroethylene*, which, in turn, gives hexachloroethane when treated with chlorine:

$$CHCl{=}CCl_2 + Cl_2 \longrightarrow CHCl_2{\cdot}CCl_3 \xrightarrow{BaCl_2} CCl_2{=}CCl_2 \xrightarrow{Cl_2} CCl_3{\cdot}CCl_3$$

Hexachloroethane is a solid, m.p. 187°. It smells like camphor and is used as a substitute for it.

s-Dichloroethylene, $CHCl{=}CHCl$, may be prepared by the action of finely divided zinc on acetylene tetrachloride in the presence of water:

$$CHCl_2{\cdot}CHCl_2 + 2[H] \xrightarrow{Zn/H_2O} CHCl{=}CHCl + 2HCl$$

It is a liquid and exists in two forms, the *cis*, b.p. 60°, and *trans*, b.p. 48° (see p. 406 for the meanings of *cis* and *trans*).

Dichloroethylene is used as a rubber solvent.

The halogen atom in the group $=CHX$ is very unreactive (see p. 251). A remarkable property of the chlorinated unsaturated hydrocarbons is their ability to add on chloroform or carbon tetrachloride in the presence of aluminium chloride as catalyst, *e.g.*, dichloroethylene forms 1 : 1 : 1 : 2 : 3 : 3-hexachloropropane with carbon tetrachloride:

$$CHCl{=}CHCl + CCl_4 \xrightarrow{AlCl_3} CHCl_2{\cdot}CHCl{\cdot}CCl_3$$

Paraffin wax has been chlorinated, and the products are used for dielectric materials, protective coatings for fabrics, etc. Polychloro-derivatives of ethane, propane and butadiene are used as dielectric materials, solvents (non-inflammable), insecticides, plasticisers, etc.

FLUORINE DERIVATIVES OF THE PARAFFINS

Most organic compounds burn or explode when treated with fluorine gas. Carbon heated in fluorine is attacked, sometimes explosively, with the formation of mainly CF_4, and small amounts of C_2F_6, C_2F_4, C_3F_8 and some other products.

Aliphatic fluorine compounds may be obtained in several ways:

(i) Direct fluorination of hydrocarbons may be carried out successfully by diluting the fluorine with nitrogen, and carrying out the reaction in a metal tube packed with copper gauze at a temperature of 150–350°. It is very difficult to control the fluorination, and the product is usually a complex mixture, *e.g.*, methane gives CH_3F, CH_2F_2, CHF_3, CF_4, C_2F_6 and C_3F_8; ethane gives CF_4, C_2F_6, $CH_3{\cdot}CHF_2$, $CH_2F{\cdot}CHF_2$; no mono- or *s*-difluoroethane is obtained.

When catalysts other than copper (actually CuF_2) are used, *e.g.*, AgF, CoF_2, CeF_3, MnF_2, perfluoro-compounds are obtained, *e.g.*, *n*-heptane gives perfluoroheptane:

$$2AgF + F_2 \longrightarrow 2AgF_2$$
$$C_7H_{16} + 32AgF_2 \longrightarrow C_7F_{16} + 16HF + 32AgF$$

It appears that when a catalyst is used, the perfluoro-compound obtained usually has the same number of carbon atoms as the original compound; if no catalyst is used, fluoro-compounds with fewer carbon atoms are usually obtained.

The mechanism of direct fluorination is still obscure, but it appears that the first step is the conversion of the catalyst into a higher fluoride, *e.g.*, AgF into AgF_2; CoF_2 into CoF_3, etc. Some of these higher fluorides have been isolated, *e.g.*, AgF_2.

(ii) Olefins and acetylenes add on hydrogen fluoride under pressure to form fluoro-derivatives of the paraffins, *e.g.*,

$$C_2H_4 + HF \longrightarrow C_2H_5F \quad (\textit{f.g.–g.})$$
$$CH_3{\cdot}C{\equiv}CH + 2HF \longrightarrow CH_3{\cdot}CF_2{\cdot}CH_3 \quad (\textit{f.g.–g.})$$

If the unsaturated compound contains a halogen atom (other than fluorine), this atom may be replaced by fluorine, *e.g.*,

$$R{\cdot}CCl{=}CH_2 + HF \longrightarrow R{\cdot}CFCl{\cdot}CH_3$$
$$R{\cdot}CCl{=}CH_2 + 2HF \longrightarrow R{\cdot}CF_2{\cdot}CH_3 + HCl$$

Lead tetrafluoride (from lead dioxide and hydrogen fluoride) is particularly useful for introducing two fluorine atoms into an olefin containing chlorine, *e.g.*,

$$CCl_2{=}CCl_2 + PbF_4 \xrightarrow{25^\circ} CFCl_2{\cdot}CFCl_2 + PbF_2$$

It is also possible to add fluorine directly without a catalyst to highly halogenated olefins, *e.g.*,

$$CFCl{=}CFCl + F_2 \longrightarrow CF_2Cl{\cdot}CF_2Cl$$

(iii) By esterifying an alcohol with hydrogen fluoride, *e.g.*,

$$C_2H_5OH + HF \longrightarrow C_2H_5F + H_2O$$

This reaction is very little used in practice.

(iv) Fluorine compounds may be prepared indirectly by heating organic halides with inorganic fluorides such as AsF_3, SbF_3, AgF, Hg_2F_2, etc., *e.g.*,

$$C_2H_5Cl + AgF \longrightarrow C_2H_5F + AgCl \quad (\textit{ex.})$$

This method was first used by Swarts (1898), and so is known as the *Swarts reaction*.

When the organic halide contains two or three halogen atoms attached to the same carbon atom, the best yield of fluoride is obtained when CoF_3 is used, but SbF_3 gives yields almost as good (and is more accessible), *e.g.*,

$$3CH_3{\cdot}CCl_2{\cdot}CH_3 + 2SbF_3 \longrightarrow 3CH_3{\cdot}CF_2{\cdot}CH_3 + 2SbCl_3 \quad (\textit{v.g.})$$

Alternatively, hydrogen fluoride may be used under pressure in the presence of a catalyst, *e.g.*,

$$CCl_4 \xrightarrow[(C + FeCl_3)]{HF\,:\,300^\circ} CF_2Cl_2 + CFCl_3 + HCl$$

(v) A newer method of fluorination is the direct electrolytic method. Nickel electrodes are used, and electrochemical fluorination takes place at the anode, the reaction being carried out by the electrolysis of a solution of the organic compound in anhydrous hydrogen fluoride, *e.g.*,

$$CH_3{\cdot}CO_2H \longrightarrow CF_3{\cdot}COF$$
$$C_2H_5{\cdot}O{\cdot}C_2H_5 \longrightarrow C_2H_5{\cdot}O{\cdot}C_2F_5$$

The particular merit of this method is that it usually leaves untouched many types of functional groups.

The lower *n*-alkyl fluorides are gases. The first four members are stable, and the higher members tend to decompose spontaneously into olefin and hydrogen fluoride, *e.g.*,

$$CH_3{\cdot}CH_2{\cdot}CH_2{\cdot}CH_2{\cdot}CH_2F \longrightarrow CH_3{\cdot}CH_2{\cdot}CH_2{\cdot}CH{=}CH_2 + HF$$

Secondary and tertiary alkyl fluorides are so unstable that it is impossible to prepare them free from olefin.

vic-Difluorides are also usually unstable, *e.g.*, ethylene fluoride decomposes spontaneously at 0° into hydrogen fluoride and butadiene:

$$2CH_2F{\cdot}CH_2F \longrightarrow 4HF + CH_2{:}CH{\cdot}CH{:}CH_2$$

Alkyl fluorides are readily hydrolysed by strong acids to the corresponding alcohols; alkalis have no effect. On the other hand, ethylene fluoride is immediately hydrolysed by water to glycol:

$$CH_2F{\cdot}CH_2F + 2H_2O \longrightarrow CH_2OH{\cdot}CH_2OH + 2HF$$

Fluorides with two or three fluorine atoms on the same carbon atom are stable to water and strong acids, *e.g.*, CHF_3, $CHF_2{\cdot}CHF_2$, etc.

Alkyl fluorides do not react with sodium, *i.e.*, do not undergo the Wurtz reaction, and do not form Grignard reagents. An interesting compound is trifluoromethyl iodide, CF_3I. It is converted into fluoroform, CHF_3, by potassium hydroxide, and it combines directly with many non-metals such as P, As, Sb, S, Se, to give, *e.g.*, with phosphorus, $(CF_3)_3P$, $(CF_3)_2PI$ and $CF_3{\cdot}PI_2$.

Chlorofluoro-derivatives of methane and ethane are used as refrigerants and for air-conditioning under the name of *Freons*, which are prepared by the action of hydrogen fluoride on carbon tetrachloride, chloroform and hexachloroethane.

Tetrafluoroethylene, C_2F_4 (gas), is prepared by the action of antimony trifluoride and hydrogen fluoride on chloroform, and then heating the chlorodifluoromethane so produced at 800°:

$$CHCl_3 \xrightarrow[HF]{SbF_3} CHF_2Cl \xrightarrow{800^\circ} C_2F_4 + 2HCl + \text{other products}$$

When tetrafluoroethylene is polymerised, the plastic *Teflon* is produced. Teflon is difficult to work, but is inert to chemical reagents, even to boiling aqua regia.

Polychlorofluoroethylenes are valuable as oils and greases. Perfluoroheptane is useful in a process for the separation of uranium isotopes by gaseous diffusion.

QUESTIONS

1. Write out the structures and names of all the dichloro-derivatives of butane and *iso*butane.
2. By means of equations show how you would convert ethanol into: (*a*) trichloroethylene, (*b*) hexachloroethane, (*c*) *s*-dichloroethylene, (*d*) tetrachloroethylene, (*e*) pentachloroethane.

3. Name the products and state the conditions under which they are obtained when ethyl iodide reacts with: *a*) HI, (*b*) KCN, (*c*) KOH, (*d*) H_2, (*e*) Mg, (*f*) Na, (*g*) NH_3, (*h*) AgCN, (*i*) $NaNO_2$, (*j*) $AgNO_2$, (*k*) $NaHSO_3$, (*l*) C_6H_6.

4. Name the products and state the conditions under which they are obtained when chloroform reacts with (*a*) nascent hydrogen, (*b*) KOH, (*c*) $C_6H_5NH_2$, (*d*) O_2, (*e*) Ag, (*f*) HNO_3, (*g*) $CH_3{\cdot}CO{\cdot}CH_3$, (*h*) CHCl=CHCl.

5. Define and give examples of:—(*a*) halogenation, (*b*) chain reaction, (*c*) Strecker reaction, (*d*) Darzens procedure, (*e*) molecular rearrangement, (*f*) elimination reaction, (*g*) alkylation, (*h*) Williamson synthesis, (*i*) Friedel–Crafts reaction, (*j*) Grignard reagent, (*k*) Groves' process, (*l*) chlorinolysis, (*m*) Swarts reaction.

6. Discuss (i) the inductive effect of the alkyl group, (ii) S_N and E mechanisms, (iii) steric hindrance and steric acceleration, (iv) Saytzeff's rule.

READING REFERENCES

Hass, McBee *et al.*, Chlorination of Paraffins, *Ind. Eng. Chem.*, 1935, **27**, 1190; 1936, **28**, 333; 1941, **33**, 137, 176, 181, 185; 1943, **35**, 317.

Vaughan and Rust, Chlorination of Paraffins, *J. Org. Chem.*, 1940, **5**, 449.

Brown, Sulphuryl Chloride in Organic Chemistry, *Ind. Eng. Chem.*, 1944, **36**, 787.

Organic Reactions, Wiley, Vol. II (1944), Ch. 2. The Preparation of Aliphatic Fluorine Compounds.

Bigelow, Action of Fluorine upon Organic Compounds, *Chem. Reviews*, 1947, **40**, 51.

Ann. Reports (*Chem. Soc.*), 1954, **51**, 279. Perfluoroalkyl Compounds.

Cook (Ed.), *Progress in Organic Chemistry*, Butterworths. Vol. 2 (1953). Ch. 2. Organic Fluorine Compounds.

Musgrave, The Reactions of Organic Fluorine Compounds, *Quart Reviews* (*Chem. Soc.*), 1954, **8**, 331.

Hughes, Mechanism and Kinetics of Substitution at a Saturated Carbon Atom, *Trans. Faraday Soc.*, 1941, **37**, 603.

Hughes and Ingold, The Mechanism and Kinetics of Elimination Reactions, *ibid.*, 1941, **37**, 657.

Hughes, Reactions of Halides in Solution, *Quart. Reviews* (*Chem. Soc.*), 1951, **5**, 245.

Clark and Streight, Systematic Study of the Preparation of Alkyl Chlorides from the Corresponding Alcohols, *Trans. Roy. Soc., Can.*, 1929, [3], **23**, 77.

Huntress, *Organic Chlorine Compounds*, Wiley (1949).

Ingold, *Structure and Mechanism in Organic Chemistry*, Bell & Sons (1953). Ch. 8. Olefin-forming Eliminations.

Johnson, The Degradation of Carboxylic Acids by means of Halogen: The Hunsdiecker Reaction, *Chem. Reviews*, 1956, **56**, 219.

Organic Reactions, Wiley. Vol. IX (1957), Ch. 5. The Reaction of Halogens with Silver Salts of Carboxylic Acids.

Streitwieser, Solvolytic Displacement Reactions at Saturated Carbon Atoms, *Chem. Reviews*, 1956, **56**, 571.

CHAPTER VI

MONOHYDRIC ALCOHOLS

AN alcohol is a compound that contains one or more *hydroxyl* groups, *i.e.*, alcohols are hydroxy-derivatives of the paraffins. They are classified according to the number of hydroxyl groups present. Monohydric alcohols contain one hydroxyl group; dihydric, two; trihydric, three; etc. When the alcohols contain four or more hydroxyl groups, they are usually called polyhydric alcohols.

The monohydric alcohols form an homologous series with the general formula $C_nH_{2n+2}O$, but, since their functional group is the hydroxyl group, their general formula is more satisfactorily written as $C_nH_{2n+1}OH$ or ROH.

Nomenclature. The simpler alcohols are commonly known by their trivial names, which are obtained by naming the alcohol as a derivative of the alkyl radical attached to the hydroxyl group, *e.g.*, CH_3OH, methyl alcohol; $CH_3{\cdot}CH_2{\cdot}CH_2OH$. *n*-propyl alcohol; $CH_3{\cdot}CH(OH){\cdot}CH_3$, *iso*-propyl alcohol; $(CH_3)_3COH$, *tert.*-butyl alcohol.

Another system of nomenclature considers the alcohols as derivatives of methyl alcohol, which is named *carbinol*, *e.g.*, $CH_3{\cdot}CH_2OH$, methylcarbinol. The *Chemical Society*, however, now proposes to use *methanol* instead of carbinol, *e.g.*, $CH_3{\cdot}CH_2{\cdot}CHOH{\cdot}CH_3$, ethylmethylmethanol (both methods have been used in this book).

In the I.U.C. system of nomenclature, the longest carbon chain containing the hydroxyl group is chosen as the parent hydrocarbon. The class suffix is *-ol*, and the positions of side-chains and the hydroxyl group are indicated by numbers, the lowest possible number being given to the hydroxyl group (p. 58), *e.g.*, CH_3OH, methanol; C_2H_5OH, ethanol; $CH_3{\cdot}CH_2{\cdot}CH_2OH$, propan-1-ol; $(CH_3)_2CH{\cdot}CHOH{\cdot}CH_3$, 3-methylbutan-2-ol.

Monohydric alcohols are subdivided into primary, secondary and tertiary alcohols according as the alkyl group attached to the hydroxyl group is a primary, secondary or tertiary group, respectively. Primary alcohols contain the *primary alcoholic group* —CH_2OH, *e.g.*, ethanol, $CH_3{\cdot}CH_2OH$; secondary alcohols, the *secondary alcoholic group* ·$CH(OH)$·, *e.g.*, *iso*propanol, $(CH_3)_2CHOH$; and tertiary alcohols the *tertiary alcoholic group* $\equiv C(OH)$, *e.g.*, *tert.*-butanol, $(CH_3)_3COH$.

General methods of preparation. 1. By the hydrolysis of an alkyl halide with aqueous alkali or silver oxide suspended in water:

$$RX + \text{“ AgOH ”} \longrightarrow ROH + AgX$$

2. By the hydrolysis of esters with alkali:

$$R{\cdot}CO_2R' + KOH \longrightarrow R{\cdot}CO_2K + R'OH$$

This method is important industrially for preparing certain alcohols that occur naturally as esters.

As pointed out previously (p. 101), tertiary halides do not give a good yield of alcohol on hydrolysis. A good yield of alcohol can, however, be obtained by first heating the tertiary halide with silver acetate in ethanolic solution, and then hydrolysing the ester so formed with alkali. Under these conditions the tertiary alkyl radical shows little tendency to form olefin:

$$R_3CX + CH_3{\cdot}CO_2Ag \longrightarrow CH_3{\cdot}CO_2CR_3 + AgX$$
$$CH_3{\cdot}CO_2CR_3 + NaOH \longrightarrow CH_3{\cdot}CO_2Na + R_3COH$$

3. By heating ethers with dilute sulphuric acid under pressure, *e.g.*, diethyl ether forms ethanol:

$$(C_2H_5)_2O + H_2O \xrightarrow{H_2SO_4} 2C_2H_5OH$$

This method is important industrially, since ethers are formed as by-products in the preparation of certain alcohols (see ethanol and propanols).

4. By the reduction of aldehydes, ketones or esters by means of excess sodium and ethanol as the reducing agent (*Bouveault–Blanc reduction*, 1903), *e.g.*,

(i) *Aldehydes*: $R{\cdot}CHO + 2[H] \longrightarrow R{\cdot}CH_2OH$ (*g.–v.g.*)

(ii) *Esters*: $R{\cdot}CO_2R' + 4[H] \longrightarrow R{\cdot}CH_2OH + R'OH$ (*g.*)

(iii) *Ketones*: $R_2CO + 2[H] \longrightarrow R_2CHOH$ (*g.*)

Hansley (1947) has improved the Bouveault–Blanc method by using the *theoretical* quantity of sodium and ethanol (see below), and carrying out the reaction in an inert solvent such as toluene or xylene. The yields are usually 85–90 per cent.

The mechanism of the reaction is uncertain. Hansley has proposed the following:

$$R{-}\overset{\overset{\Large O}{\|}}{C}{-}OC_2H_5 + 2Na \longrightarrow \left[R{-}\overset{\overset{ONa}{|}}{\underset{\underset{Na}{|}}{C}}{-}OC_2H_5\right] \xrightarrow{C_2H_5OH} C_2H_5ONa + \left[R{-}\overset{\overset{O\boxed{Na}}{|}}{\underset{\underset{H}{|}}{C}}{-}\boxed{OC_2H_5}\right]$$

Na ester ketal

Na derivative of the hemiacetal

$$\downarrow$$

$$R{\cdot}CH_2ONa + C_2H_5ONa \xleftarrow{C_2H_5OH} \left[R{-}\overset{\overset{ONa}{|}}{\underset{\underset{H}{|}}{C}}{-}Na\right] \xleftarrow{2Na} R{-}\overset{\overset{O}{\|}}{\underset{\underset{H}{|}}{C}} + C_2H_5ONa$$

$$R{\cdot}CH_2ONa \xrightarrow{H_2O} R{\cdot}CH_2OH + NaOH$$

According to these equations, the theoretical amount of sodium is *four* atoms per molecule of ester and *two* molecules of the reducing alcohol.

Darzens (1947) found that sodium hydride, NaH, gives a better yield of alcohol than does sodium by the Bouveault–Blanc reduction of aldehydes, ketones and esters. Nystrom and Brown (1947) have found that lithium aluminium hydride, $LiAlH_4$, also gives very good yields of alcohols from aldehydes, ketones, esters, acids, acid chlorides and acid anhydrides, and one advantage of this reagent is that it does not normally reduce the olefinic bond, and hence an unsaturated aldehyde, ketone, etc., can be reduced to an unsaturated alcohol. The most remarkable feature of this reagent is the reduction of an *acid* to an alcohol, *e.g.*, stearic acid is reduced to octadecan-1-ol:

$$CH_3{\cdot}(CH_2)_{16}{\cdot}CO_2H \xrightarrow{LiAlH_4} CH_3{\cdot}(CH_2)_{16}{\cdot}CH_2OH \quad (91\%)$$

Reductions with lithium aluminium hydride are usually carried out in ethereal solutions, the compound in ether being added to the lithium aluminium hydride solution. In certain cases the reverse addition is necessary, *i.e.*, the hydride solution is added to the solution of the compound to be reduced.

The reactions for the various compounds have been formulated as follows:

(i) $4R{\cdot}CO{\cdot}R + LiAlH_4 \longrightarrow (R_2CHO)_4LiAl \xrightarrow{H_2O} 4R_2CHOH + LiOH + Al(OH)_3$

(ii) $2R{\cdot}CO_2R' + LiAlH_4 \longrightarrow (R{\cdot}CH_2O)_2(OR')_2LiAl \xrightarrow{H_2O} 2R{\cdot}CH_2OH + 2R'OH$

(iii) $4R{\cdot}CO_2H + 3LiAlH_4 \longrightarrow (R{\cdot}CH_2O)_4LiAl + 2LiAlO_2 + 4H_2 \xrightarrow{H_2O} 4R{\cdot}CH_2OH$

(iv) $2R{\cdot}COCl + LiAlH_4 \longrightarrow (R{\cdot}CH_2O)_2LiAlCl_2 \xrightarrow{H_2O} 2R{\cdot}CH_2OH$

(v) $(R{\cdot}CO)_2O + LiAlH_4 \longrightarrow (R{\cdot}CH_2O)_2LiAlO \xrightarrow{H_2O} 2R{\cdot}CH_2OH$

Sodium borohydride, $NaBH_4$, which is insoluble in ether but soluble in water without decomposition, also reduces carbonyl compounds to alcohols, but does not reduce acids. On the other hand, lithium borohydride, which is soluble in ether and is decomposed by water, behaves like lithium aluminium hydride but is not so vigorous and hence may be used to reduce a more reactive group when the molecule contains two or more reducible groups, *e.g.*, when the compound contains both a carbonyl and a carboxyl group, the former is reduced preferentially:

$$R{\cdot}CO{\cdot}CH_2{\cdot}CH_2{\cdot}CO_2H \xrightarrow{LiBH_4} R{\cdot}CHOH{\cdot}CH_2{\cdot}CH_2{\cdot}CO_2H$$

Aldehydes, ketones, esters, acid chlorides and acid anhydrides can be reduced catalytically to alcohols in very good yields, *e.g.*,

acid chloride: $R{\cdot}COCl + 2H_2 \xrightarrow{cat.} R{\cdot}CH_2OH + HCl$

acid anhydride: $(R{\cdot}CO)_2O + 4H_2 \xrightarrow{cat.} 2R{\cdot}CH_2OH + H_2O$

Catalytic reduction is particularly useful for preparing the higher alcohols from esters. The ester is hydrogenated at 200° and at 150–200 atm. using a copper catalyst, whereupon alcohols free from hydrocarbons are produced. If a nickel catalyst is used and the temperature is above 250°, hydrocarbons are the main product. Cadmium–nickel salts of acids may also be hydrogenated under pressure in the presence of copper chromite to alcohols, the lower members (C_1 to C_5) giving 70–95 per cent. yields (Adams *et al.*, 1952). On the other hand, carboxylic acids can be hydrogenated to primary alcohols in the presence of a ruthenium or copper chromite catalyst (Guyer *et al.*, 1955).

5. Primary, secondary and tertiary alcohols may be prepared by means of a Grignard reagent and the appropriate carbonyl compound (see p. 335).

6. A number of alcohols are obtained by fermentation processes (see later).

7. In recent years synthetic methods have become very important for preparing various alcohols:

(i) By the hydration of olefins, *e.g.*, ethanol, *iso*propanol, etc.

(ii) By heating a mixture of carbon monoxide and hydrogen under pressure in the presence of a catalyst, *e.g.*, zinc chromite plus small amounts of alkali metal or iron salts. A mixture of alcohols containing methyl, ethyl, *n*-propyl, *iso*butyl and higher-branched alcohols is obtained, the individuals being separated by fractional distillation (see below).

(iii) By the "*oxo*" process, which is the process whereby carbon monoxide and hydrogen are added to olefins to yield aldehydes and alcohols (which are separated by fractional distillation). Carbon monoxide, hydrogen and the olefin are compressed to 200 atm. at 125–145°, and passed over a catalyst. One catalyst consists of cobalt, thoria, magnesia and kieselguhr in the proportions of 100 : 5 : 8 : 200—this catalyst is also used in the Fischer–Tropsch synthesis (p. 54); *e.g.*, propylene, CO and H_2 give a mixture of the two straight-chain butanols. The oxo-process is also known as the oxo-synthesis and the carbonylation or hydroformylation reaction.

(iv) Methanol, ethanol, propanols and butanols are prepared industrially by the oxidation of natural gas (p. 54).

Most of the methods given above can be used for the preparation of any particular class of alcohol: it is only a question of starting with the appropriate compound. *Primary* alcohols may be prepared by the hydrolysis of *primary* alkyl halides; by the reduction of aldehydes, esters, acids, acid chlorides and acid anhydrides; and by means of a Grignard reagent and formaldehyde:

$$H{-}C\begin{matrix}{/\!\!/}O\\ \diagdown H\end{matrix} + RMgX \longrightarrow H{-}\underset{\underset{H}{|}}{C}(OMgX){-}R \xrightarrow{H_2O} R{\cdot}CH_2OH$$

In addition to these, primary alcohols may be prepared, in variable yields, by the action of nitrous acid on primary amines of the type $R{\cdot}CH_2{\cdot}NH_2$:

$$R{\cdot}CH_2{\cdot}NH_2 + HNO_2 \longrightarrow R{\cdot}CH_2OH + N_2 + H_2O$$

Secondary alcohols may be prepared by the hydrolysis of *secondary* alkyl halides, or better, via the ester (see above); by the reduction of ketones; and by means of a Grignard reagent and any aldehyde other than formaldehyde:

$$R{-}C\begin{matrix}{/\!\!/}O\\ \diagdown H\end{matrix} + R'MgX \longrightarrow R{-}\underset{\underset{H}{|}}{C}\begin{matrix}\diagup OMgX\\ \diagdown R'\end{matrix} \xrightarrow{H_2O} R{\cdot}CH(OH){\cdot}R'$$

Tertiary alcohols may be prepared by the *indirect* hydrolysis of *tertiary* alkyl halides, *viz.*, via the ester; and by means of a Grignard reagent and a ketone (or an ester):

$$R_2C{=}O + R'MgX \longrightarrow R_2C\begin{matrix}\diagup OMgX\\ \diagdown R'\end{matrix} \xrightarrow{H_2O} R_2C(OH){\cdot}R'$$

General properties of the alcohols. The alcohols are neutral substances: the lower members are liquids, and have a distinctive smell and a burning taste; the higher members are solids and are almost odourless.

In a group of isomeric alcohols, the primary alcohol has the highest boiling point and the tertiary the lowest, with the secondary having an intermediate value. The lower members are far less volatile than is to be expected from their molecular weight, and this is believed to be due to association through hydrogen bonding *extending over a chain of molecules*, thus giving rise to a " large molecule " the volatility of which would be expected to be low:

$$\overset{\overset{R}{|}}{O}{-}H \cdots\cdots \overset{\overset{R}{|}}{O}{-}H \cdots\cdots \overset{\overset{R}{|}}{O}{-}H \cdots$$

The lower alcohols are very soluble in water, and the solubility diminishes as the molecular weight increases. Their solubility in water is to be expected, since the oxygen atom of the hydroxyl group in alcohols can form hydrogen bonds with the water molecules. In the lower alcohols the hydroxyl group constitutes a large part of the molecule, whereas as the molecular weight of the alcohol increases the hydrocarbon character of the molecule increases, and hence the solubility in water decreases. This, however, is not the complete story; the structure of the carbon chain also plays a part, *e.g.*, *n*-butanol is fairly soluble in water, but *tert.*-butanol is miscible with water in all proportions.

General reactions of the alcohols. 1. Alcohols react with organic and inorganic acids to form *esters*:

$$R{\cdot}CO_2H + R'OH \longrightarrow R{\cdot}CO_2R' + H_2O$$

Esters of the halogen acids are, as we have seen (p. 93), the alkyl halides.

Alcohols, when heated with concentrated hydriodic acid and red phosphorus, are converted into paraffins.

The order of reactivity of an alcohol with a given organic acid is primary alcohol>secondary>tertiary, but with a given halogen acid the order is reversed. This implies that the mechanism of *esterification* (p. 176) of organic acids is different from that of halogen acids. It has also been observed that for a given alcohol the order of reactivity of the halogen acids is HI>HBr>HCl. An explanation of all these observations is offered later when the mechanism of esterification is discussed in detail.

2. Alcohols react with phosphorus halides to form alkyl halides (p. 94). Treatment of alcohols with chlorine or bromine results in the formation of halogen-substituted oxidised products (see also p. 156), *e.g.*, chlorination of ethanol gives trichloracetaldehyde (*cf.* chloroform):

$$CH_3{\cdot}CH_2OH \xrightarrow{Cl_2} CCl_3{\cdot}CHO$$

On the other hand, when chlorine is passed into an alcohol (primary or secondary) in the presence of alkali, an organic hypochlorite is formed:

$$R_2CHOH + Cl_2 \xrightarrow{NaOH} R_2CHOCl + HCl$$

These hypochlorites are unstable, and when heated or exposed to light, eliminate hydrogen chloride:

$$R_2CHOCl \longrightarrow R_2CO + HCl$$

3. Alcohols combine with phenyl *iso*cyanate to form phenyl-substituted urethans:

$$C_6H_5{\cdot}NCO + ROH \longrightarrow C_6H_5{\cdot}NH{\cdot}CO_2R$$

Urethans are well-defined crystalline solids, and so may be used to characterise the alcohols.

Readily dehydrated alcohols, particularly tertiary alcohols, do not form urethans but produce olefins and diphenylurea as follows:

$$R_2C(OH){\cdot}CH_2{\cdot}CH_3 \longrightarrow R_2C{=}CH{\cdot}CH_3 + H_2O$$

$$C_6H_5{\cdot}NCO + H_2O \longrightarrow C_6H_5{\cdot}NH_2 + CO_2$$

$$C_6H_5{\cdot}NCO + C_6H_5{\cdot}NH_2 \longrightarrow C_6H_5{\cdot}NH{\cdot}CO{\cdot}NH{\cdot}C_6H_5$$

4. Alcohols are attacked by strongly electropositive metals, *e.g.*, sodium and potassium; hydrogen is liberated and the *alkoxide* is formed; *e.g.*, ethanol reacts with sodium to form sodium ethoxide:

$$2C_2H_5OH + 2Na \longrightarrow 2C_2H_5ONa + H_2$$

Sodium and potassium alkoxides are electrovalent compounds, *i.e.*, their formulæ should be written, *e.g.*, RO^-Na^+; they are white deliquescent solids, readily soluble in water with decomposition:

$$RONa + H_2O \rightleftharpoons ROH + NaOH$$

Alkoxides react with carbon disulphide to form xanthates:

$$RONa + C{\overset{\diagup\!\!\diagup S}{\underset{\diagdown\!\!\diagdown S}{}}} \longrightarrow RO{-}C{\overset{\diagup\!\!\diagup S}{\underset{\diagdown SNa}{}}}$$

The order of ease of formation of an alkoxide with sodium or potassium is primary alcohol > secondary > tertiary. This may be explained as follows. There are two possible ways in which the group COH may undergo fission: C|—O—H and C—O—|H. Since oxygen has a higher electron-affinity than either carbon or hydrogen, the shared electron pairs are displaced towards the oxygen, *i.e.*, we have $\overset{\delta+}{C} \rightarrow \overset{\delta-}{O} \leftarrow \overset{\delta+}{H}$. The greater the displacement of the shared pair towards the oxygen atom in the C—O bond, the larger is the negative charge on the oxygen atom, and consequently the weaker is the attraction of the oxygen atom for the shared pair of the O—H bond. In other words, the greater the polarity of the C—O bond the smaller is the polarity of the O—H bond. As the polarity of a bond increases, the strength of that bond decreases. Hence anything which tends to increase the polarity of the C—O bond weakens this bond and strengthens the O—H bond, and vice versa. Since alkyl groups are electron-releasing, the larger the number of alkyl groups attached to the carbon atom of the COH group, the greater will be the polarity of the C—O bond (*cf.* alkyl halides, p. 97). This may be represented as follows:

$$CH_3 \rightarrow CH_2 \rightarrow O{-}H; \quad \begin{matrix} CH_3 \searrow \\ \\ CH_3 \nearrow \end{matrix} CH \rightarrow\rightarrow O{-}H; \quad \begin{matrix} CH_3 \searrow \\ CH_3 \rightarrow \\ CH_3 \nearrow \end{matrix} C \rightarrow\rightarrow\rightarrow O{-}H$$

Thus the C—O bond is strongest in primary alcohols and weakest in tertiary, and consequently the tendency of the COH group to break as C|—OH is greatest in tertiary alcohols and least in primary; conversely, the tendency of the COH group to break as C—O—|H is greatest in primary alcohols and least in tertiary. Hence reactions involving the breaking of the C—O bond will take place most readily with tertiary alcohols and least readily with primary; but those reactions which involve the breaking of the O—H bond will take place most readily with primary alcohols and least readily with tertiary. When sodium attacks an alcohol, hydrogen is evolved, and since this involves the breaking of the O—H bond, we can now understand why the order of ease of formation of alkoxides is primary alcohol > secondary > tertiary.

A number of alkoxides are important as synthetic reagents; *e.g.*, sodium ethoxide, C_2H_5ONa; aluminium ethoxide, $(C_2H_5O)_3Al$; aluminium *tert.*-butoxide $[(CH_3)_3CO]_3Al$ (see text for their uses). The aluminium alkoxides may be conveniently prepared by the action of aluminium amalgam or aluminium shavings on the alcohol.

5. Primary and secondary alcohols may be acetylated with acetyl chloride, *e.g.*, ethanol gives ethyl acetate:

$$CH_3{\cdot}COCl + C_2H_5OH \longrightarrow CH_3{\cdot}CO_2C_2H_5 + HCl$$

With tertiary alcohols the reaction is often accompanied by dehydration of the alcohol to olefin, or by the formation of a tertiary alkyl chloride; *e.g.*, *tert.*-butanol gives a good yield of *tert.*-butyl chloride:

$$(CH_3)_3COH + CH_3{\cdot}COCl \longrightarrow (CH_3)_3{\cdot}CCl + CH_3{\cdot}CO_2H$$

6. Alcohols may be oxidised, and the products of oxidation depend on the class of the alcohol (see below).

7. Alcohols may be dehydrated to the corresponding olefin, a hydrogen atom being removed from the carbon atom *adjacent* to the COH group. The order of ease of dehydration is tertiary alcohol>secondary>primary, and the reason is probably similar to that for the formation of olefins from the alkyl halides (p. 100). The hydroxyl group is released as a hydroxyl ion, and the carbonium ion then eliminates a proton to form the olefin, *e.g.*,

$$CH_3{\cdot}CH(OH){\cdot}CH_3 \longrightarrow CH_3{\cdot}\overset{+}{C}H{\cdot}CH_3 + O\overset{-}{H} \longrightarrow CH_3{\cdot}CH{=}CH_2 + H_2O$$

Since hydroxyl ion formation is easiest with tertiary alcohols, and most difficult with primary (see above, reaction 4), it can be seen why tertiary alcohols are the most readily dehydrated, and primary the least readily.

Alcohols may be dehydrated to olefins by heat alone, but the temperature must be high (400–800°). Dehydration, however, can be effected at lower temperatures in the presence of catalysts, *e.g.*, all three classes of alcohols are dehydrated by passing over alumina at 350°; primary alcohols are dehydrated by concentrated sulphuric acid at about 170°, and secondary and tertiary alcohols by boiling dilute sulphuric acid (this is used to avoid polymerisation of the olefin). It appears that the function of the catalyst is to weaken the C—O bond of the COH group. With sulphuric acid the mechanism may be:

$$R{-}\ddot{\underset{\cdot\cdot}{O}}H \quad H^+ \longrightarrow R{-}\overset{+}{O}H_2 \longrightarrow R^+ + H_2O$$

The acid supplies a proton which co-ordinates with the oxygen atom, thereby increasing the polarity of the C—O bond, consequently making it weaker. Alumina may possibly act in the same way, an aluminium atom co-ordinating with the oxygen:

$$R{-}\ddot{\underset{\cdot\cdot}{O}}H \quad Al_2O_3 \longrightarrow R{-}\underset{\substack{|\\H}}{\overset{+}{O}}{-}Al_2O_3 \longrightarrow R^+ + HO{-}Al_2O_3$$

With secondary and tertiary alcohols, dehydration may occur in two ways, *e.g.*,

$$CH_3{\cdot}CH_2{\cdot}CH(OH){\cdot}CH_3 \xrightarrow[(1:1H_2SO_4)]{-H_2O} \begin{cases} \rightarrow CH_3{\cdot}CH_2{\cdot}CH{=}CH_2 \\ \rightarrow CH_3{\cdot}CH{=}CH{\cdot}CH_3 \end{cases}$$

Experiment shows that hydrogen attached to the adjacent carbon atom joined to the least number of hydrogen atoms is eliminated most easily. Thus, in the above reaction, the main product is but-2-ene (65–80 per cent.) (*cf.* Saytzeff's rule, p. 101).

When alcohols containing no hydrogen atoms on the carbon atom adjacent to the COH group are dehydrated, dehydration and molecular rearrangement occur together (*cf.* alkyl halides, p. 100), *e.g.*, *neo*pentyl alcohol (*tert.*-butylcarbinol) gives 2-methylbut-2-ene:

$$(CH_3)_3C{\cdot}CH_2OH \xrightarrow{-H_2O} (CH_3)_2C{=}CH{\cdot}CH_3$$

This is an example of the *Wagner rearrangement*, and is believed to occur via a carbonium ion involving the Whitmore mechanism (p. 160):

$$\begin{array}{c}CH_3\ \ OH\\ CH_3{-}C{-}C{-}H\\ CH_3\ \ H\end{array} \xrightarrow{H^+} \begin{array}{c}CH_3\ \ \overset{+}{O}H_2\\ CH_3{-}C{-}C{-}H\\ CH_3\ \ H\end{array} \xrightarrow{-H_2O} \begin{array}{c}CH_3\\ CH_3{-}C{-}\overset{+}{C}{-}H\\ CH_3\ \ H\end{array} \longrightarrow$$

$$\begin{array}{c}CH_3\\ CH_3{-}\overset{+}{C}{-}C{-}H\\ CH_3\ \ H\end{array} \xrightarrow{-H^+} (CH_3)_2C{=}C\begin{array}{l}CH_3\\ H\end{array}$$

Alcohols may also be converted into olefins via their methyl xanthates (*Tschugaev reaction*, 1899):

$$R_2CH{\cdot}CH_2OH \xrightarrow[NaOH]{CS_2} R_2CH{\cdot}CH_2O{\cdot}C\begin{array}{l}{=}S\\ {-}SNa\end{array} \xrightarrow{CH_3I}$$

$$R_2CH{\cdot}CH_2O{\cdot}C\begin{array}{l}{=}S\\ {-}S{\cdot}CH_3\end{array} \xrightarrow{heat} R_2C{=}CH_2 + CH_3SH + COS$$

A very important feature of this reaction is that no rearrangement occurs in the formation of the olefin from alcohols which undergo rearrangement when dehydrated by the usual dehydrating agents.

By means of dehydration, it is possible to convert a primary alcohol into a secondary or tertiary, according to the structure of the primary alcohol, *e.g.*,

(i) $$CH_3{\cdot}CH_2{\cdot}CH_2OH \xrightarrow[350^\circ]{Al_2O_3} CH_3{\cdot}CH{=}CH_2 \xrightarrow{HI} CH_3{\cdot}CHI{\cdot}CH_3 \xrightarrow{\text{“AgOH”}} CH_3{\cdot}CH(OH){\cdot}CH_3$$

(ii) $$(CH_3)_2CH{\cdot}CH_2OH \xrightarrow[350^\circ]{Al_2O_3} (CH_3)_2C{=}CH_2 \xrightarrow{HI} (CH_3)_2CI{\cdot}CH_3 \xrightarrow{\text{“AgOH”}} (CH_3)_2C(OH){\cdot}CH_3$$

In the same way, a secondary alcohol of suitable structure can be converted into a tertiary alcohol, *e.g.*,

$$(CH_3)_2CH{\cdot}CH(OH){\cdot}CH_3 \xrightarrow[350^\circ]{Al_2O_3} (CH_3)_2C{=}CH{\cdot}CH_3 \xrightarrow{HI} (CH_3)_2CI{\cdot}CH_2{\cdot}CH_3 \xrightarrow{\text{“AgOH”}} (CH_3)_2C(OH){\cdot}CH_2{\cdot}CH_3$$

It is also possible to step down the alcohol series by means of dehydration, *e.g.*,

$$R{\cdot}CH_2{\cdot}CH_2OH \xrightarrow[350^\circ]{Al_2O_3} R{\cdot}CH{=}CH_2 \xrightarrow{O_3}$$

$$\begin{array}{c}R{\cdot}CH{-}O{-}CH_2\\ |\qquad\quad |\\ O{-}{-}{-}O\end{array} \xrightarrow{Zn/H_2O} R{\cdot}CHO \xrightarrow[cat.]{H_2} R{\cdot}CH_2OH$$

8. Alcohols also combine with acetylene in the presence of mercury compounds as catalyst to form acetals:

$$2ROH + CH{\equiv}CH \xrightarrow{Hg^{++}} CH_3{\cdot}CH(OR)_2$$

If, however, the reaction is carried out in the presence of potassium alkoxides at high temperature and under pressure, vinyl ethers are obtained (p. 87).

Methods of Distinguishing between the Three Classes of Alcohols. 1. By means of *oxidation*. The nature of the oxidation products of an alcohol depends on whether the alcohol is primary, secondary or tertiary.

(i) A *primary* alcohol on oxidation first gives an *aldehyde*, and this, on further oxidation, gives an acid. *Both the aldehyde and acid contain the same number of carbon atoms as the original alcohol.*

The mechanism of the oxidation of alcohols is still uncertain. One theory is that an oxygen atom (supplied by the oxidising agent) hydroxylates one of the hydrogen atoms attached to the carbon atom of the COH group, *e.g.*, ethanol gives acetaldehyde:

$$CH_3{-}CH_2{-}OH + [O] \longrightarrow \left[CH_3{-}C(H)(OH){-}OH \right] \xrightarrow{-H_2O} CH_3{\cdot}CH{=}O$$

Since a carbon atom cannot usually remain attached to two hydroxyl groups, water is eliminated. The aldehyde is then further oxidised, the hydrogen atom attached to the "oxidised" carbon atom, *i.e.*, the carbon atom linked to oxygen, being hydroxylated to give acetic acid:

$$CH_3{-}C(H){=}O + [O] \longrightarrow CH_3{-}C(OH){=}O$$

Oxidation now ceases, since the "oxidised" carbon atom has no more hydrogen atoms attached to it.

Wieland (1931) offered an alternative theory. He suggested that *dehydrogenation, i.e.*, removal of hydrogen, takes place first when an alcohol is converted into an aldehyde, *e.g.*,

$$CH_3{\cdot}CH_2OH \xrightarrow{-2H} CH_3{\cdot}CHO$$

This mechanism is supported by the fact that a primary alcohol can be converted into an aldehyde in the absence of oxygen, *e.g.*, palladium dehydrogenates an alcohol. Thus, according to Wieland, conversion of a primary alcohol into an aldehyde and then into an acid is by a dehydrogenation mechanism; all that is required is a "hydrogen acceptor":

$$CH_3{\cdot}CH_2OH \xrightarrow{-2H} CH_3{\cdot}C(H){=}O \xrightarrow{H_2O} \left[CH_3{\cdot}C(OH)(H){-}OH \right] \xrightarrow{-2H} CH_3{\cdot}C(OH){=}O$$

Obviously, for Wieland's mechanism for the dehydrogenation of the aldehyde–water complex it is necessary that water be present in the reaction mixture.

Further support for this dehydrogenation mechanism, at least with chromic acid, has been supplied by Westheimer *et al.* (1949), who oxidised 2-deutero*iso*propanol, $CH_3{\cdot}CDOH{\cdot}CH_3$. Since the C—H and C—D bonds differ in reactivity, the former being more reactive than the latter, then if the removal of secondary hydrogen is the rate-determining step, the oxidation of the deutero-alcohol should be slower than that of *iso*propanol itself; this was found to be so.

(ii) A *secondary* alcohol, on oxidation, first gives a *ketone with the same number of carbon atoms as the original alcohol.* Ketones are fairly difficult to oxidise (presumably because there is no hydrogen atom on the "oxidised" carbon), but prolonged action of the oxidising agents produces a mixture of acids, each containing *fewer* carbon atoms than the original alcohol, *e.g.*, methyl-*n*-propylmethanol gives first pentan-2-one, and then a mixture of acetic and propionic acids:

$$CH_3-\overset{\displaystyle H}{\underset{\displaystyle CH_2\cdot CH_2\cdot CH_3}{C}}-OH + [O] \longrightarrow \left[CH_3-\overset{\displaystyle OH}{\underset{\displaystyle CH_2\cdot CH_2\cdot CH_3}{C}}-OH \right] \xrightarrow{-H_2O}$$

$$CH_3-\underset{\displaystyle CH_2\cdot CH_2\cdot CH_3}{C}=O \xrightarrow{[O]} CH_3\cdot CO_2H + CH_3\cdot CH_2\cdot CO_2H$$

Possibly the oxidation of a ketone takes place via the *enol* form (see p. 206), *e.g.*,

$$CH_3\cdot CO\cdot CH_3 \rightleftharpoons CH_3\cdot\overset{\displaystyle OH}{C}=CH_2 \xrightarrow{H_2O + [O]} CH_3-\overset{\displaystyle OH}{\underset{\displaystyle OH}{C}}-CH_2OH \xrightarrow{[O]} CH_3\cdot CO_2H + H\cdot CO_2H$$

The enol is oxidised at the double bond.

(iii) *Tertiary* alcohols are resistant to oxidation in neutral or alkaline solution, but are readily oxidised by acid oxidising agents to a mixture of *ketone and acid, each containing fewer carbon atoms than the original alcohol.* It is possible that the first step in the oxidation is the dehydration of the alcohol to the olefin (which takes place readily in acid solution; see above). The olefin is then oxidised to the mixture of ketone and acid; *e.g.*, ethyldimethylmethanol gives acetone and acetic acid:

$$\begin{matrix} CH_3 \\ CH_3 \end{matrix}\!\!>C(OH)\cdot CH_2\cdot CH_3 \xrightarrow{-H_2O} \left[\begin{matrix} CH_3 \\ CH_3 \end{matrix}\!\!>C=CH\cdot CH_3 \right] \xrightarrow{[O]} \begin{matrix} CH_3 \\ CH_3 \end{matrix}\!\!>C=O + CH_3\cdot CO_2H$$

The oxidising agents usually used for oxidising alcohols are: acid dichromate, acid or alkaline potassium permanganate, and dilute nitric acid.

2. The three classes of alcohols differ in their behaviour when the vapour is passed over copper at 300°:

(i) A primary alcohol is dehydrogenated to an aldehyde, *e.g.*,

$$CH_3\cdot CH_2OH \xrightarrow[300°]{Cu} CH_3\cdot CHO + H_2$$

(ii) A secondary alcohol is dehydrogenated to a ketone, *e.g.*,

$$CH_3\cdot CH(OH)\cdot CH_3 \xrightarrow[300°]{Cu} CH_3\cdot CO\cdot CH_3 + H_2$$

(iii) A tertiary alcohol is dehydrated to an olefin, *e.g.*,

$$(CH_3)_2C(OH)\cdot CH_2\cdot CH_3 \xrightarrow[300°]{Cu} (CH_3)_2C=CH\cdot CH_3 + H_2O$$

3. The alcohol is converted by phosphorus triodide into its corresponding iodide, which is then heated with silver nitrite, and the resulting nitroparaffin is treated with nitrous acid and alkali. Characteristic colours are obtained according as the alkyl group is primary, secondary or tertiary (see p. 289).

Methyl alcohol, methanol (*carbinol*), CH_3OH, is prepared industrially by several methods. The earliest method was by the destructive distillation of wood, whereby tar and an aqueous fraction known as *pyroligneous acid* are obtained. Pyroligneous acid contains methanol, acetone and acetic acid, and all three compounds may be obtained by suitable treatment (see acetic acid, p. 170). It was this method which gave rise to the name "wood spirit" for methanol. The modern methods are synthetic.

(i) Water gas mixed with half its volume of hydrogen—synthesis gas—is passed at a pressure of 200 atmospheres over a catalyst containing the oxides of copper, zinc and chromium at 300°:

$$CO + 2H_2 \longrightarrow CH_3OH$$

If the proper precautions are taken, the yield of methanol is almost 100 per cent., and its purity is above 99 per cent. By changing the catalyst and the ratio of carbon monoxide to hydrogen, methanol and a variety of higher alcohols are produced (p. 115). Another commercial method uses carbon dioxide instead of the monoxide; again a catalyst is required:

$$CO_2 + 3H_2 \longrightarrow CH_3OH + H_2O$$

(ii) By the catalytic oxidation of methane. A mixture of methane and oxygen (ratio by volume of 9 : 1) at a pressure of 100 atmospheres is passed through a copper tube at 200°:

$$CH_4 + \tfrac{1}{2}O_2 \longrightarrow CH_3OH$$

Methanol is a colourless, inflammable liquid, b.p. 64°, and is poisonous. It is miscible with water in all proportions, and is also miscible with most organic solvents. It burns with a faintly luminous flame, and its vapour forms explosive mixtures with air or oxygen when ignited. It combines with calcium chloride to form $CaCl_2{\cdot}4CH_3OH$, and hence cannot be dried this way (*cf.* ethanol).

Methanol is used as a solvent for paints, varnishes, shellac, celluloid cements, etc.; in the manufacture of dyes, perfumes, formaldehyde, etc. It is also used for making methylated spirit and automobile antifreeze mixtures.

Structure of methanol. Analysis and molecular-weight determinations show that the molecular formula of methanol is CH_4O. Assuming that carbon is quadrivalent, oxygen bivalent and hydrogen univalent, only one structure is possible:

$$\begin{array}{c} \quad\ H \\ \quad\ | \\ H{-}C{-}O{-}H \text{ or } CH_3OH \\ \quad\ | \\ \quad\ H \end{array}$$

This is supported by all the chemical reactions of methanol, *e.g.*, (i) only one hydrogen atom in methanol is replaceable by sodium; this suggests that one hydrogen atom is in a different state of combination from the other three.

(ii) Methanol is formed from methyl chloride by hydrolysis with sodium hydroxide. Methyl chloride can have only the structure CH_3Cl. It is reasonable to suppose that the methyl group in methyl chloride is unchanged by the action of dilute alkali, and that the reaction takes place by the replacement of the chlorine atom by a hydroxyl group.

(iii) The presence of the hydroxyl group is confirmed, for example, by the reaction between methanol and phosphorus pentachloride, when methyl chloride, hydrogen chloride and phosphoryl chloride are formed. Thus one oxygen atom (bivalent) and one hydrogen atom (univalent) have been replaced by one chlorine atom (univalent). This implies that the oxygen and hydrogen atoms exist as a univalent radical in methanol: the only possibility is as a hydroxyl group, OH. It is the hydrogen of the hydroxyl group which is displaced by sodium.

All these reactions indicate that the structure of methanol is CH_3OH.

Ethyl alcohol, ethanol (*methylcarbinol*), C_2H_5OH, is prepared industrially by several methods: (i) Ethylene (from cracked petroleum) is absorbed in concentrated sulphuric acid (98 per cent.) at 75–80°, under pressure (250–500 lb./per sq. in.). Ethyl hydrogen sulphate and ethyl sulphate are formed:

$$C_2H_4 + (HO)_2SO_2 \longrightarrow C_2H_5O{\cdot}SO_2{\cdot}OH$$
$$C_2H_5O{\cdot}SO_2{\cdot}OH + C_2H_4 \longrightarrow (C_2H_5O)_2SO_2$$

The reaction mixture is then diluted with about an equal volume of water, and warmed. Hydrolysis takes place and ethanol together with some diethyl ether is formed:

$$C_2H_5O{\cdot}SO_2{\cdot}OH + H_2O \longrightarrow C_2H_5OH + H_2SO_4$$
$$(C_2H_5O)_2SO_2 + 2H_2O \longrightarrow 2C_2H_5OH + H_2SO_4$$
$$(C_2H_5O)_2SO_2 + C_2H_5OH \longrightarrow (C_2H_5)_2O + C_2H_5O{\cdot}SO_2{\cdot}OH$$

The ether is kept to a minimum by separating the ethyl sulphate from the reaction products, and hydrolysing it separately.

The hydrolysed liquids are distilled, and the aqueous ethanol distillate is concentrated by fractional distillation (see also below).

Ethanol is also manufactured by the *direct* hydration of ethylene with steam under pressure in the presence of a suitable catalyst:

$$C_2H_4 + H_2O \longrightarrow C_2H_5OH$$

(ii) Acetaldehyde (from acetylene) is catalytically reduced to ethanol by passing its vapour, mixed with hydrogen, over finely divided nickel at 100–140°:

$$CH_3{\cdot}CHO + H_2 \longrightarrow CH_3{\cdot}CH_2OH$$

(iii) The earliest method of preparing ethanol is by fermentation, and this is still used for the manufacture of beer, wine, brandy, etc., and also as a source of ethanol. The starting material is starch, which is obtained from sources depending on the particular country: common sources of starch are wheat, barley, potato, etc. Recently, molasses (p. 439) has also been used as the starting material for ethanol. The grain, *e.g.*, wheat or barley, is mashed with hot water, and then heated with malt (germinated barley) at 50° for 1 hour. Malt contains the enzyme *diastase* which, by hydrolysis, converts starch into the sugar, maltose (*q.v.*):

$$(C_6H_{10}O_5)_n + \frac{n}{2} H_2O \xrightarrow{\text{diastase}} \frac{n}{2} C_{12}H_{22}O_{11}$$

If molasses is used, then this step is unnecessary, since they contain carbohydrates already present as sugars which can be fermented.

The liquid is cooled to 30° and fermented with yeast for 1–3 days. Yeast contains various enzymes, among which are *maltase*, which converts the maltose into glucose, and *zymase*, which converts the glucose into ethanol:

$$C_{12}H_{22}O_{11} + H_2O \xrightarrow{\text{maltase}} 2C_6H_{12}O_6$$

$$C_6H_{12}O_6 \xrightarrow{\text{zymase}} 2C_2H_5OH + 2CO_2$$

The carbon dioxide is recovered and sold as a by-product. The fermented liquor or " wort ", which contains 6–10 per cent. ethanol and some other compounds, is fractionated into three fractions:

(i) *First runnings*, which consists mainly of acetaldehyde.
(ii) *Rectified spirit*, which is 93–95% w/w ethanol.
(iii) *Final runnings* or *fusel oil*, which contains *n*-propyl, *n*-butyl, *iso*butyl, *n*-amyl, *iso*amyl and " active " amyl alcohol.

Industrial alcohol is ordinary rectified spirit. *Methylated spirit* is of two kinds: (*a*) *Mineralised methylated spirit* is 90 per cent. rectified spirit, 9 per cent. methanol and 1 per cent. petroleum oil, and a purple dye. (*b*) *Industrial methylated spirit* is 95 per cent. rectified spirit and 5 per cent. methanol, whose purpose is to " *denature* " the rectified spirit, *i.e.*, make it unfit for drinking purposes.

Absolute alcohol is 99·5 per cent. ethanol, and is obtained from rectified spirit. When an aqueous solution of ethanol is fractionated, it forms a constant-boiling mixture containing 96 per cent. ethanol from which 100 per cent. ethanol may be obtained by adding a small amount of benzene, and then distilling. The first fraction is the ternary azeotrope, *i.e.*, a constant-boiling mixture containing three constituents, b.p. 64·8° (water, 7·4 per cent.; ethanol, 18·5 per cent.; benzene, 74·1 per cent.). After all the water has been removed, the second fraction that distils over is the binary azeotrope, b.p. 68·2° (ethanol, 32·4 per cent.; benzene, 67·6 per cent.). After all the benzene has been removed, pure ethanol, b.p. 78·1°, distils over.

Ethanol cannot be dried by means of calcium chloride, since a compound (an *alcoholate*) is formed, *e.g.*, $CaCl_2 \cdot 6C_2H_5OH$ (*cf.* methanol). Distillation of rectified spirit over calcium oxide, and then over calcium, gives absolute alcohol. This method is often used in the laboratory, and was formerly used industrially.

Ethanol is a colourless, inflammable liquid, b.p. 78·1°. It is miscible with water in all proportions, and is also miscible with most organic solvents. Ethanol and methanol resemble each other very closely, but they may be distinguished (i) by the fact that ethanol gives the haloform reaction (*q.v.*), whereas methanol does not; and (ii) ethanol gives acetic acid on oxidation; methanol gives formic acid. These two acids are readily distinguished from each other (p. 169).

Ethanol is used for the preparation of esters, ether, chloral, chloroform, etc. It is also used as a solvent for gums, resins, paints, varnishes, etc., and as a fuel.

Structure of ethanol. Analysis and molecular-weight determinations show that the molecular formula of ethanol is C_2H_6O. Assuming that carbon is quadrivalent, oxygen bivalent, and hydrogen univalent, two structures are possible:

$$CH_3\text{—}CH_2\text{—}OH \quad \text{(I)} \qquad\qquad CH_3\text{—}O\text{—}CH_3 \quad \text{(II)}$$

(i) Only one hydrogen atom in ethanol is replaceable by sodium or potassium. This indicates that one hydrogen atom is in a different state of combination from the other five. In (I), one hydrogen atom differs from the other five, but in (II) all the hydrogen atoms are equivalent.

(ii) When ethanol is treated with hydrochloric acid or phosphorus pentachloride, one oxygen atom (bivalent) and one hydrogen atom (univalent) are replaced by one chlorine atom (univalent) to give ethyl chloride, C_2H_5Cl. This implies the presence of a hydroxyl group (*cf.* methanol).

(iii) When ethyl chloride is hydrolysed with dilute alkali, ethanol is obtained. This reaction also indicates the presence of a hydroxyl group in ethanol.

(iv) Ethanol may be prepared as follows:

$$C_2H_6 \xrightarrow{Cl_2} C_2H_5Cl \xrightarrow{NaOH} C_2H_5OH$$

The arrangement of the six hydrogen atoms in ethane is known, and it is reasonable to suppose that five retain their original arrangement in ethyl chloride and ethanol, since these five hydrogen atoms do not enter (presumably) into the above reactions. Thus there is an ethyl radical C_2H_5— in ethanol. This is so in (I), but not in (II).

(v) Structure (II) is definitely eliminated, since it can be shown that it is the structure of dimethyl ether (*q.v.*), a compound that has very little resemblance, physically or chemically, to ethanol.

Thus (I) is accepted as the structure of ethanol, and it accounts for all the known properties of ethanol.

It can be seen from the various examples given on structure determination, *e.g.*, ethane, propane, ethylene, methanol and ethanol, that the method of approach follows certain definite lines. First the molecular formula is obtained. Then, if the compound is simple—in the sense that it contains a small number of unlike atoms, and that the total number of atoms is also small—the valencies of the atoms present are assumed, and various possible structures are written down. If the compound is " simple " the number of possible structures will not be large (four or five at the most). Then by considering the chemical properties of the compound in question, the structure which best fits the observed facts is accepted as the correct one. If the compound is not " simple ", the procedure is to detect the presence of as many functional groups as possible; to degrade the compound into simpler substances whose structures are already known or which may be determined by further degradation; to build up structural formulæ based on the facts obtained; and then to choose that structure which best fits the facts. Finally a synthesis is attempted, and if successful, will usually give proof of the correctness of the structure suggested.

It can be seen from the above arguments that it is necessary to have methods, preferably simple ones, for detecting the presence of functional groups. The reader will become familiar with these methods as he reads the text. At this stage we shall confine our attentions to detecting the presence of a hydroxyl group. The usual tests are: (i) Treatment with sodium; if hydrogen is evolved, a hydroxyl group is present. (ii) Treatment with phosphorus pentachloride or acetyl chloride; the evolution of hydrochloric acid fumes indicates the presence of a hydroxyl group.

Acetyl chloride is usually the most satisfactory (remember, however, alcohols of the type R_3COH, p. 119).

Propyl alcohols, C_3H_7OH. Two isomeric propyl alcohols are possible, and both are known.

n-*Propyl alcohol, propan*-1-*ol,* n-*propanol,* $CH_3{\cdot}CH_2{\cdot}CH_2OH$, was originally obtained from fusel oil (see above), but it is now also produced by the hydrogenation of carbon monoxide. A more recent method is by the catalytic reduction of propargyl alcohol (from acetylene and formaldehyde):

$$CH{\equiv}C{\cdot}CH_2OH + 2H_2 \xrightarrow{Ni} 2CH_3{\cdot}CH_2{\cdot}CH_2OH$$

n-Propanol is a colourless liquid, b.p. 97·4°, and is miscible with water, ethanol and ether. It is used in the preparation of propionic acid, toilet preparations such as lotions, etc.

iso*Propyl alcohol, propan-2-ol,* iso*propanol,** $CH_3{\cdot}CH(OH){\cdot}CH_3$, is prepared industrially:

(i) By the catalytic hydrogenation of acetone under pressure:

$$CH_3{\cdot}CO{\cdot}CH_3 + H_2 \xrightarrow{Ni} CH_3{\cdot}CH(OH){\cdot}CH_3$$

(ii) By passing propylene (from cracked petroleum) into concentrated sulphuric acid, then diluting with water, and distilling off the *iso*-propanol. *iso*Propyl ether is obtained as a by-product (*cf.* ethanol):

$$CH_3{\cdot}CH{=}CH_2 + (HO)_2SO_2 \longrightarrow (CH_3)_2CHO{\cdot}SO_2{\cdot}OH$$

$$(CH_3)_2CHO{\cdot}SO_2{\cdot}OH + CH_3{\cdot}CH{=}CH_2 \longrightarrow [(CH_3)_2CHO]_2SO_2$$

$$(CH_3)_2CHO{\cdot}SO_2{\cdot}OH + H_2O \longrightarrow (CH_3)_2CHOH + H_2SO_4$$

$$[(CH_3)_2CHO]_2SO_2 + 2H_2O \longrightarrow 2(CH_3)_2CHOH + H_2SO_4$$

$$[(CH_3)_2CHO]_2SO_2 + (CH_3)_2CHOH \longrightarrow [(CH_3)_2CH]_2O + (CH_3)_2CHO{\cdot}SO_2{\cdot}OH$$

*iso*Propanol can also be prepared by *direct* hydration, and this can be effected by passing a mixture of propylene and steam at 220–250°, and under pressure (220 atm.), over a catalyst of tungsten oxide plus zinc oxide, on a silica carrier.

*iso*Propanol is a colourless liquid, b.p. 82·4°, and is soluble in water, ethanol and ether. It is used for preparing esters, acetone, keten, as a solvent, and for high-octane fuel.

Butyl alcohols, C_4H_9OH. Four isomers are possible, and all are known.

n-*Butyl alcohol, butan-1-ol,* n-*butanol,* $CH_3{\cdot}CH_2{\cdot}CH_2{\cdot}CH_2OH$, b.p. 117·4°, is prepared industrially:

(i) By the *Weizmann process* (1911). Starch or molasses is fermented with the micro-organism, *Clostridium acetobutylicum,* whereupon acetone and *n*-butanol are obtained.

(ii) Synthetically from acetaldehyde:

$$\underset{}{2CH_3{\cdot}CHO} \xrightarrow{NaOH} \underset{\text{aldol}}{CH_3{\cdot}CH(OH){\cdot}CH_2{\cdot}CHO} \xrightarrow[-H_2O]{heat}$$

$$\underset{\text{crotonaldehyde}}{CH_3{\cdot}CH{=}CH{\cdot}CHO} \xrightarrow{H_2/Ni} CH_3{\cdot}CH_2{\cdot}CH_2{\cdot}CH_2OH$$

n-Butanol is widely used as a solvent.

iso*Butyl alcohol, 2-methylpropan-1-ol,* iso*butanol,* $(CH_3)_2CH{\cdot}CH_2OH$, b.p. 108°, is obtained as a by-product in the preparation of methanol from synthesis gas (p. 123). It behaves as a primary alcohol, but it readily rearranges due to the presence of a branched chain near the COH group, *e.g.*, when it is treated with hydrochloric acid, *iso*butyl chloride and *tert.*-butyl chloride are obtained (*cf.* p. 94):

$$(CH_3)_2CH{\cdot}CH_2OH \xrightarrow{HCl} (CH_3)_2CH{\cdot}CH_2Cl + (CH_3)_3CCl$$

* See p. 785.

sec.-*Butyl alcohol, butan-2-ol,* sec.-*butanol,* $CH_3{\cdot}CH_2{\cdot}CH(OH){\cdot}CH_3$, b.p. 100°, is prepared industrially by the hydration of 1- or 2-butene (from cracked petroleum) by means of concentrated sulphuric acid (*cf.* ethanol and *iso*propanol).

sec.-Butanol is used for the preparation of butanone, esters, and as a lacquer solvent.

tert.-*Butyl alcohol,* tert.-*butanol* (1 : 1-*dimethylethanol*), $(CH_3)_3COH$, m.p. 25·5°, b.p. 83°, is prepared synthetically by the hydration of *iso*butene (from cracked petroleum). It is mainly used as an alkylating agent.

Amyl alcohols, $C_5H_{11}OH$. Eight isomers are possible, and all are known:

1. $CH_3{\cdot}CH_2{\cdot}CH_2{\cdot}CH_2{\cdot}CH_2OH$, *n*-amyl alcohol, pentan-1-ol, *n*-pentanol, b.p. 138°.
2. $(CH_3)_2CH{\cdot}CH_2{\cdot}CH_2OH$, *iso*amyl alcohol, *iso*pentanol, b.p. 130°.
3. $CH_3{\cdot}CH_2{\cdot}CH(CH_3){\cdot}CH_2OH$, "active" amyl alcohol, 2-methylbutan-1-ol, b.p. 128°.
4. $(CH_3)_3C{\cdot}CH_2OH$, *neo*pentyl alcohol, *tert.*-butylcarbinol, b.p. 113°.
5. $CH_3{\cdot}CH_2{\cdot}CH_2{\cdot}CH(OH){\cdot}CH_3$, pentan-2-ol, methyl-*n*-propylcarbinol, b.p. 120°.
6. $CH_3{\cdot}CH_2{\cdot}CH(OH){\cdot}CH_2{\cdot}CH_3$, pentan-3-ol, diethylcarbinol, b.p. 117°.
7. $(CH_3)_2CH{\cdot}CH(OH){\cdot}CH_3$, 3-methylbutan-2-ol, methyl*iso*propylcarbinol, b.p. 114°.
8. $(CH_3)_2C(OH){\cdot}CH_2{\cdot}CH_3$, 2-methylbutan-2-ol, *tert.*-amyl alcohol, *tert.*-pentanol, ethyldimethylcarbinol, b.p. 102°.

Three amyl alcohols, *viz.*, *n*-pentanol, *iso*pentanol and "active" amyl alcohol, have been isolated from fused oil (*q.v.*). The last two are the chief constituents of fusel oil, and all three are produced by the fermentation of protein matter associated with the carbohydrates in starch. This mixture of amyl alcohols (from fusel oil) is used for the preparation of esters (for artificial essences), scents, and as a laboratory reducing agent with sodium it is better than ethanol owing to its higher boiling point (this mixture of amyl alcohols will be referred to in future as *iso*pentanol).

A mixture of amyl alcohols, known as *pentasol,* is prepared industrially by chlorinating at 200°, and in the dark, a mixture of *n*- and *iso*pentanes (from petroleum) to the amyl chlorides which are hydrolysed with dilute sodium hydroxide solution plus a little sodium oleate for emulsification, to the amyl alcohols. Seven isomeric amyl chlorides are theoretically possible by the chlorination of *n*- and *iso*pentanes, but in practice six are obtained—no 2-chloro-3-methylbutane is produced. Pentasol (the mixture of six amyl alcohols) finds great use as a solvent in the lacquer industry.

Commercial "*sec.*-amyl alcohol" (80 per cent. 2- and 20 per cent. 3-pentanol) is made by hydrating 1- and 2-pentenes (from cracked petroleum).

A number of higher alcohols occur as esters in waxes, *e.g.*, cetyl (palmityl) alcohol (hexadecan-1-ol), $C_{16}H_{33}OH$, m.p. 49°, occurs as the palmitate in spermaceti (obtained from the oil of the sperm whale); carnaubyl alcohol (tetracosan-1-ol), $C_{24}H_{49}OH$, m.p. 69°, as esters in wool-grease; ceryl alcohol (hexacosan-1-ol), $C_{26}H_{53}OH$, m.p. 79°, as the cerotate in chinese wax; myricyl (melissyl) alcohol (triacontan-1-ol), $C_{30}H_{61}OH$, m.p. 88°, as esters in bees-wax.

A number of higher alcohols are now prepared industrially by the catalytic reduction of the ethyl (or glyceryl) esters of the higher fatty acids, particularly the alcohols lauryl (dodecan-1-ol), $C_{12}H_{25}OH$, m.p. 24°; myristyl (tetradecan-1-ol), $C_{14}H_{29}OH$, m.p. 38°; palmityl (hexadecan-1-ol), $C_{16}H_{33}OH$, m.p. 49°; and stearyl (octadecan-1-ol), $C_{18}H_{37}OH$, m.p. 59°. These alcohols are used in the form of sodium alkyl sulphates, $RO{\cdot}SO_2{\cdot}ONa$, as detergents, emulsifying agents, wetting agents, insecticides, fungicides, etc. These sodium salts lather well, and are not affected by hard water, and hence can be used as a soap substitute.

QUESTIONS

1. Write out the structures and names (three methods) of the isomeric amyl alcohols. Indicate the class of each alcohol.
2. By means of equations show how you would convert: (*a*) *n*-butanol, (*b*) *n*-pentanol, (*c*) hexan-2-ol, into butan-2-ol.
3. Give as many methods as you can for distinguishing between the three classes of alcohols.
4. Define and give examples of:—(*a*) primary alcohol, (*b*) secondary alcohol, (*c*) tertiary alcohol, (*d*) the Bouveault-Blanc reduction, (*e*) association, (*f*) dehydrogenation, (*g*) fermentation, (*h*) the oxo process, (*i*) dehydration, (*j*) hydration, (*k*) Tschugaev reaction, (*l*) Wagner rearrangement.
5. Name the products and indicate the conditions under which they are formed when ethanol is treated with:—(*a*) AcOH, (*b*) HI, (*c*) PCl_3, (*d*) PBr_5, (*e*) PI_3, (*f*) Na, (*g*) AcCl, (*h*) H_2SO_4, (*i*) $C_6H_5 \cdot NCO$, (*j*) Br_2.
6. Give an account of the evidence for the structure of (*a*) EtOH, (*b*) Pr^iOH.
7. Starting from acetylene, how would you prepare:—(*a*) EtOH, (*b*) C_2H_6, (*c*) CH_4, (*d*) $EtNO_2$, (*e*) Et_2O?
8. Starting with the following compounds, name the alcohol formed and indicate the necessary conditions:—(*a*) acetaldehyde, (*b*) butan-2-one, (*c*) ethyl propionate, (*d*) palmitic acid, (*e*) acetyl chloride, (*f*) propionic anhydride, (*g*) *n*-propylamine, (*h*) EtMgI and HCHO, (*i*) MeMgI and $CH_3 \cdot CHO$, (*j*) MeMgI and Me_2CO.
9. Write brief notes on the industrial preparation of:—(*a*) MeOH, (*b*) EtOH, (*c*) PrOH, (*d*) the four butyl alcohols, (*e*) *iso*PrOH, (*f*) pentasol, (*g*) lauryl alcohol.
10. Suggest why the tertiary alcohols may be dehydrated or converted into alkyl chlorides by AcCl.

READING REFERENCES

Killeffer, Butanol and Acetone from Corn, *Ind. Eng. Chem.*, 1927, **19**, 46.
Wynkoop, *n*-Butanol and Acetone, *ibid.*, 1943, **35**, 1240.
Lee, Fermentation, *ibid.*, 1950, **42**, 1672.
Gabriel, Butanol Fermentation Process, *ibid.*, 1928, **20**, 1063.
Backhaus, Ethyl Alcohol, *ibid.*, 1930, **22**, 1151.
Amyl Alcohols from Pentanes:
(i) Ayres, *ibid.*, 1929, **21**, 899.
(ii) Clark, *ibid.*, 1930, **22**, 439.
Brooks, The Manufacture of Alcohols and Esters, *ibid.*, 1935, **27**, 282.
Park and Donlan, Alcohols other than Butyl, *ibid.*, 1943, **35**, 1031.
Graves, Higher Alcohols formed from Carbon Monoxide and Hydrogen, *ibid.*, 1931, **23**, 1381.
Hansley, Sodium Reduction of Fatty Acid Esters, *ibid.*, 1947, **39**, 55.
Organic Reactions, Wiley. Vol. VI (1951), Ch. 10. Reductions by Lithium Aluminium Hydride.
Wieland, Recent Researches on Biological Oxidation, *J.C.S.*, **1931**, 1055.
Byrkit and Soule, Sodium Methylate and its Uses, *Chem. Eng. News*, 1944, **22**, 1003.
Gaylord, Reduction with Complex Metal Hydrides, *J. Chem. Educ.*, 1957, **34**, 367.

CHAPTER VII

ETHERS

THE general formula of the ethers is $C_nH_{2n+2}O$ (which is the same as that for the monohydric alcohols), and since their general structure is R—O—R′, they may be regarded as alkyl oxides or the anhydrides of the alcohols (see below).

When the two alkyl groups in an ether are the same, the ether is said to be symmetrical or simple, *e.g.*, diethyl ether, $C_2H_5—O—C_2H_5$, is a simple ether. When the two alkyl groups are different, the ether is said to be unsymmetrical or mixed, *e.g.*, ethyl methyl ether, $CH_3—O—C_2H_5$, is a mixed ether.

Nomenclature. 1. In this system of nomenclature all the members are known as ethers, and the individuals are named according to the alkyl groups attached to the oxygen atom, *e.g.*, $CH_3—O—CH_3$, dimethyl ether; $C_2H_5—O—CH(CH_3)_2$, ethyl *iso*propyl ether.

2. According to the I.U.C. system of nomenclature, the ethers are regarded as hydrocarbons in which a hydrogen atom is replaced by an alkoxyl group, –OR, the larger radical being chosen as the alkane. For symmetrical ethers, method 1 is to be used, *e.g.*, $C_2H_5{\cdot}O{\cdot}C_2H_5$, diethyl ether; $CH_3{\cdot}O{\cdot}C_2H_5$, methoxyethane.

General methods of preparation. 1. By heating excess of alcohol with concentrated sulphuric acid or glacial phosphoric acid. One molecule of water is removed from two molecules of alcohol—hence the reason for regarding ethers as the anhydrides of alcohols:

$$2ROH \xrightarrow[-H_2O]{H_2SO_4} R_2O$$

The mechanism of this reaction is obscure. According to Van Alphen (1930), ether is formed from ethanol as follows (*cf.* ethylene):

$$C_2H_5OH + H_2SO_4 \longrightarrow [C_2H_5—\overset{+}{O}H_2]\,HSO_4^- \longrightarrow C_2H_5^+ + H_2O + HSO_4^-$$

The ethyl carbonium ion may eliminate a proton to form ethylene (which is obtained as a by-product), or react with a molecule of ethanol (which is in excess) to form ether:

$$C_2H_5—\underset{H}{\underset{|}{O}}\;\; C_2H_5^+ \longrightarrow C_2H_5—O—C_2H_5 + H^+$$

On the other hand, Brooks (1935) believes that ethyl sulphate is formed first, and this then reacts with the excess alcohol to form ether (*cf.* ethanol):

$$2C_2H_5OH + H_2SO_4 \longrightarrow (C_2H_5O)_2SO_2 + 2H_2O$$

$$(C_2H_5O)_2SO_2 + C_2H_5OH \longrightarrow (C_2H_5)_2O + C_2H_5O{\cdot}SO_2{\cdot}OH$$

The yields of ether are good from primary alcohols and fairly good from secondary. Mixed ethers may also be prepared by this method, *e.g.*, addition of *tert.*-butyl alcohol to a boiling mixture of ethanol and aqueous sulphuric acid gives *tert.*-butyl ethyl ether in excellent yield.

2. By **Williamson's synthesis,** in which the sodium of potassium alkoxide is heated with an alkyl halide:

$$RONa + R'X \longrightarrow R{\cdot}O{\cdot}R' + NaX \quad (g.)$$

The mechanism is possibly:

$$RO^{-} \curvearrowright R'{-}X \longrightarrow \overset{\delta-}{RO}{\cdots}R'{\cdots}\overset{\delta-}{X} \longrightarrow R{\cdot}O{\cdot}R' + X^{-}$$

This method is particularly useful for preparing mixed ethers, and it is best to use the alkoxide of the secondary or tertiary alcohol, and primary alkyl halide because secondary and tertiary alkyl halides readily decompose into olefins.

Williamson's synthesis proves the structure of the ethers.

When R′ is a methyl or ethyl radical, methyl or ethyl sulphate, respectively, can be used instead of the corresponding alkyl halide, *e.g.*,

$$C_2H_5ONa + (CH_3)_2SO_4 \longrightarrow CH_3{\cdot}O{\cdot}C_2H_5 + CH_3NaSO_4$$

3. By heating alkyl halides with *dry* silver oxide:

$$2RX + Ag_2O \longrightarrow R_2O + 2AgX \quad (v.p.)$$

4. By passing the alcohol vapour over a catalyst such as alumina, thoria, etc., at 250° and under pressure:

$$2ROH \longrightarrow R_2O + H_2O$$

5. By passing an olefin into concentrated sulphuric acid, etc. (see ethanol and *iso*propanol).

6. From halogeno-ethers and Grignard reagents (p. 337).

7. Ethers may also be obtained by refluxing alcohols with esters of toluene-*p*-sulphonic acid in the presence of sodium (Drahowzal *et al.*, 1951).

$$ROH + CH_3{-}C_6H_4{-}SO_3R' \xrightarrow{Na} R{\cdot}O{\cdot}R' + CH_3{-}C_6H_4{-}SO_3H$$

General properties of the ethers. The lower members are gases or volatile liquids, and their vapours are highly inflammable. Their boiling points are much lower than those of the alcohols containing the same number of carbon atoms, and this is probably due to the fact that ethers cannot associate through hydrogen bonding. All the ethers are less dense than water in which they are not very soluble, but their solubility is very much increased in the presence of small amounts of alcohol.

The solubility of ethers is not as high as might have been expected in view of the fact that the oxygen in ethers can form hydrogen bonds with water. This low solubility may possibly be due to steric effects of the alkyl groups in the ether.

General reactions. 1. Ethers form stable salts (oxonium compounds) with strong inorganic acids, *e.g.*, $[(C_2H_5)_2OH]^+Cl^-$, $[(C_2H_5)_2OH]^+HSO_4^-$. Because of this, ethers can be separated from paraffins and alkyl halides, *e.g.*, by shaking with concentrated sulphuric acid, ether is removed from a mixture of ether and ethyl bromide.

2. When heated with dilute sulphuric acid under pressure, ethers form the corresponding alcohols:

$$R_2O + H_2O \xrightarrow{H_2SO_4} 2ROH$$

3. When warmed with concentrated sulphuric acid, ethers form alkyl hydrogen sulphates:

$$R_2O + H_2SO_4 \longrightarrow RHSO_4 + ROH$$
$$ROH + H_2SO_4 \longrightarrow RHSO_4 + H_2O$$

4. Ethers are readily attacked by concentrated hydriodic or hydrobromic acid, the final products depending on the temperature of the reaction.

(i) *in the cold*:

$$R_2O + HI \longrightarrow RI + ROH$$

In the case of a mixed ether the iodine atom attaches itself to the *smaller* alkyl radical:

$$CH_3{\cdot}O{\cdot}C_2H_5 + HI \longrightarrow CH_3I + C_2H_5OH$$

If both alkyl radicals contain the same number of carbon atoms, the iodine atom attaches itself to the *less complex* group. Propyl *iso*propyl ether, however, is an exception:

$$CH_3{\cdot}CH_2{\cdot}CH_2{\cdot}O{\cdot}CH(CH_3)_2 + HI \longrightarrow (CH_3)_2CHI + CH_3{\cdot}CH_2{\cdot}CH_2OH$$

(ii) *When heated*:

$$R_2O + 2HI \longrightarrow 2RI + H_2O$$

Reactions (i) and (ii) are very useful for identifying the groups present in an ether. Furthermore, since (i) occurs very easily, it is possible to "protect" a hydroxyl group in a polyfunctional compound by converting the hydroxyl group into an ether, which is later treated with concentrated hydriodic acid to regenerate the hydroxyl group (see, *e.g.*, p. 222).

Decomposition of ethers by concentrated hydriodic acid is the basis of the *Zeisel* method for estimating methoxyl and ethoxyl groups (p. 297).

Although heating ethers with hydriodic acid results mainly in the formation of alkyl iodides, some reduction products are also formed (p. 44). This reduction may be avoided by heating the ether with potassium iodide and phosphoric acid (Stone *et al.*, 1950):

$$R{\cdot}O{\cdot}R + 2KI + 2H_3PO_4 \longrightarrow 2RI + 2KH_2PO_4 + H_2O$$

Birch (1951) has shown that ethers are converted into paraffin and alcohol when treated with sodium in liquid ammonia.

$$R{\cdot}O{\cdot}R' + 2[H] \longrightarrow \begin{cases} RH + R'OH \\ R'H + ROH \end{cases}$$

Which of these two directions occurs is decided by which transition state has the lower energy.

5. When treated with chlorine or bromine, ethers undergo substitution, the extent of which depends on the conditions. Hydrogen joined to the carbon directly attached to the oxygen atom is most readily replaced, *e.g.*, diethyl ether reacts with chlorine in the dark to form 1 : 1'-dichlorodiethyl ether:

$$CH_3{\cdot}CH_2{\cdot}O{\cdot}CH_2{\cdot}CH_3 \xrightarrow{Cl_2} CH_3{\cdot}CHCl{\cdot}O{\cdot}CH_2{\cdot}CH_3 \xrightarrow{Cl_2} CH_3{\cdot}CHCl{\cdot}O{\cdot}CHCl{\cdot}CH_3$$

In the presence of light, perchlorodiethyl ether is obtained:

$$(C_2H_5)_2O \xrightarrow{Cl_2} (C_2Cl_5)_2O$$

Halogeno-ethers may also be prepared in other ways (see, *e.g.*, p. 337).

6. Acid chlorides react with ethers when heated in the presence of anhydrous zinc chloride, aluminium chloride, etc.; *e.g.*,

$$R_2O + CH_3{\cdot}COCl \xrightarrow{ZnCl_2} RCl + CH_3{\cdot}CO_2R$$

Acid anhydrides also split ethers to form esters:

$$R_2O + (CH_3{\cdot}CO)_2O \xrightarrow{ZnCl_2} 2CH_3{\cdot}CO_2R$$

7. Ethers react with carbon monoxide at 125–180° and at a pressure of 500 atmospheres, in the presence of boron trifluoride plus a little water:

$$R_2O + CO \longrightarrow R{\cdot}CO_2R$$

Dimethyl ether (*methyl ether*) is prepared industrially by passing methanol vapour at 350–400°, and at a pressure of 15 atmospheres, over aluminium phosphate as catalyst (p. 131). It is a gas, b.p. —23·6°, and is used as a refrigerating agent.

Diethyl ether (*ether*, " *sulphuric ether* ") is prepared in the laboratory and industrially by the " *continuous etherification process* ", *i.e.*, heating excess ethanol with concentrated sulphuric acid. It is also obtained industrially: (i) as a by-product in the preparation of ethanol from ethylene and sulphuric acid (p. 124); (ii) by passing ethanol vapour, under pressure, over heated alumina or aluminium phosphate (*cf.* dimethyl ether).

Diethyl ether is a colourless liquid, b.p. 34·5°. It is fairly soluble in water, and is miscible with ethanol in all proportions. It is highly inflammable and forms explosive mixtures with air; this is a great disadvantage in its use as an industrial solvent for oils, fats, gums, resins, etc., and as an extracting solvent. It is also used in surgery as an anæsthetic, and is the usual solvent for carrying out Grignard reactions. In the presence of air and light, ether forms ether peroxide $(C_2H_5)_2O{\cdot}O_2$, whose structure, according to Rieche and Meister (1936), is $CH_3{\cdot}CH(O{\cdot}OH){\cdot}O{\cdot}CH_2{\cdot}CH_3$. Ether peroxide is a heavy, pungent, oily liquid, and is explosive. Since its boiling point is higher than that of ether, it is left in the residue after ether distillations, and may cause explosions. Addition of a small amount of a cuprous compound, *e.g.*, cuprous oxide, has been recommended for avoiding the formation of ether peroxide. The chief impurity in ether is ethanol, and this has the property of preventing the formation of ether peroxide.

An important derivative of ether is 2 : 2′-dichlorodiethyl ether, which is prepared by heating ethylene chlorohydrin with concentrated sulphuric acid at 100°:

$$2ClCH_2{\cdot}CH_2OH \xrightarrow[-H_2O]{H_2SO_4} ClCH_2{\cdot}CH_2{\cdot}O{\cdot}CH_2{\cdot}CH_2Cl$$

It may also be prepared by passing a mixture of ethylene and chlorine into ethylene chlorohydrin at 80°:

$$CH_2OH{\cdot}CH_2Cl + C_2H_4 + Cl_2 \longrightarrow (CH_2Cl{\cdot}CH_2)_2O + HCl$$

2 : 2′-Dichlorodiethyl ether is used as a solvent, as a soil fumigant and also as the starting point of many chemicals.

2 : 2′-Dichlorodiethyl ether is also named as bis-(2-chloroethyl) ether. The prefix bis (Latin, twice) indicates that there are *two identical groups* attached to a given atom; it is generally used for complex groups.

Di-*iso*propyl ether is obtained industrially as a by-product in the preparation of *iso*propanol from propylene and sulphuric acid (p. 127). It is also prepared by passing propylene into 75 per cent. sulphuric acid at 75–125° under a pressure of 3–7 atmospheres; very little *iso*propanol is formed under these conditions.

Di-*iso*propyl ether is a colourless liquid, b.p. 69°. It is used as an industrial solvent for extraction operations, and for decreasing the knocking properties of petrol which, mixed with di-*iso*propyl ether, acquires a high octane number.

Di-*iso*amyl ether, $[(CH_3)_2CH{\cdot}CH_2{\cdot}CH_2–]_2O$, is prepared by the action of concentrated sulphuric acid on *iso*pentanol. It is a colourless liquid, b.p. 172°, and has a pear-like odour. It is used as an industrial solvent, and as a solvent in Grignard reactions in which higher temperatures are required than can be obtained by using ether.

Mixed ethers of the following types have been prepared: primary–primary; primary–secondary; primary–tertiary; secondary–secondary; secondary–tertiary; tertiary–tertiary.

Isomerism within the ether series, and any other series in which the isomers differ by the nature of the groups attached to a given atom, *e.g.*, the amines (*q.v.*), is sometimes known as *metamerism*: thus there are three *metamers* of formula $C_4H_{10}O$, *viz.*, diethyl ether, $C_2H_5{\cdot}O{\cdot}C_2H_5$; methyl propyl ether, $CH_3{\cdot}O{\cdot}CH_2{\cdot}CH_2{\cdot}CH_3$; methyl *iso*propyl ether, $CH_3{\cdot}O{\cdot}CH(CH_3)_2$.

The term metamerism was introduced by Berzelius, but he gave it a wider meaning than that which is accepted today (see p. 381).

QUESTIONS

1. Write out the structures and names of the isomeric ethers having the molecular formula $C_5H_{12}O$.
2. Name the compounds and state under what conditions they are formed when ether is treated with:—(*a*) H_2SO_4, (*b*) HBr, (*c*) Br_2, (*d*) PCl_5, (*e*) Na, (*f*) AcCl, (*g*) CO, (*h*) NaOH, (*i*) O_2.
3. Define and give examples of:—(*a*) Williamson's synthesis, (*b*) the Zeisel determination, (*c*) metamerism.
4. A compound has the molecular formula $C_4H_{10}O$. How would you show whether it was an alcohol or an ether? If it is an ether, how would you determine its structure?

READING REFERENCES

Van Alphen, The Formation of Ether from Alcohol, *Rec. trav. chim.*, 1930, **49**, 754.
Brooks, The Manufacture of Alcohols and Esters, *Ind. Eng. Chem.*, 1935, **27**, 284.
Norris and Rigby, Preparation and Properties of Mixed Aliphatic Ethers, *J. Amer. Chem. Soc.*, 1932, **54**, 2088.
Evans and Edlund, Tertiary Alkyl Ethers, *Ind. Eng. Chem.*, 1936, **28**, 1186.

CHAPTER VIII

ALDEHYDES AND KETONES

ALDEHYDES and ketones both have the general formula $C_nH_{2n}O$.

Aldehydes are the first oxidation products of *primary* alcohols, and their functional group is the *aldehyde* group $\cdot CHO$ or $\cdot C\begin{smallmatrix}/\!\!/O \\ \backslash H\end{smallmatrix}$, which can only occur at the *end* of a chain, since the carbon atom of the group has only one available valency. **Ketones** are the first oxidation products of *secondary* alcohols, and their functional group is the *ketonic* group $\begin{smallmatrix}C\diagdown \\ C\diagup\end{smallmatrix}C{=}CO$, which cannot occur at the end of a chain, since in ketones the CO group has two available valencies, each of which is joined to a carbon atom (*cf.*, however, ketens, p. 270).

The C=O group is known as the *carbonyl* group, but when it occurs in ketones, it is referred to as the ketonic group.

Nomenclature. *Aldehydes.* The lower members are commonly named after the acids that they form on oxidation. The suffix of the names of acids is *-ic* (the names of the trivial system are used, see p. 163); this suffix is deleted and replaced by *aldehyde, e.g.*,

$$H\cdot CHO \xrightarrow{[O]} H\cdot CO_2H$$
form*aldehyde* formic acid

$$(CH_3)_2CH\cdot CHO \xrightarrow{[O]} (CH_3)_2CH\cdot CO_2H$$
*iso*butyr*aldehyde* *iso*butyr*ic* acid

The positions of side-chains or substituents are indicated by Greek letters, the α carbon atom being the one *adjacent* to the aldehyde group, *e.g.*,

$$\overset{\gamma}{C}H_3\cdot\overset{\beta}{C}H(OH)\cdot\overset{\alpha}{C}H_2\cdot CHO$$ β-hydroxybutyraldehyde

According to the I.U.C. system of nomenclature, aldehydes are designated by the suffix *-al*, which is added to the name of the hydrocarbon from which they are derived. The longest carbon chain containing the aldehyde group is chosen as the parent hydrocarbon; the positions of side-chains or substituents are indicated by numbers, and the aldehyde group is given the number 1, which may be omitted from the name if the aldehyde group is the only functional group present in the compound (see p. 58), *e.g.*,

$CH_3\cdot CHO$ ethanal

$CH_3\cdot CH_2\cdot CH(CHO)\cdot CH(CH_3)\cdot CH_2\cdot CH_3$ 2-ethyl-3-methylpentanal

Ketones. The lower members are commonly named according to the alkyl groups attached to the ketonic group, *e.g.*,

$CH_3\cdot CO\cdot CH_3$ dimethyl ketone

$CH_3\cdot CH_2\cdot CO\cdot CH(CH_3)_2$ ethyl *iso*propyl ketone

The positions of side-chains or substituents are indicated by Greek letters, the α carbon atom being the one *adjacent* to the ketonic group, *e.g.*,

$$\overset{\beta}{C}H_3{\cdot}\overset{\alpha}{C}HCl{\cdot}CO{\cdot}\overset{\alpha'}{C}H_2{\cdot}\overset{\beta'}{C}H_2Cl \quad \alpha : \beta'\text{-dichlorodiethyl ketone}$$

If the two alkyl groups in a ketone are the same, the ketone is said to be simple or symmetrical; if unlike, mixed or unsymmetrical (*cf.* ethers).

According to the I.U.C. system of nomenclature, ketones are designated by the suffix *-one*, which is added to the name of the hydrocarbons from which they are derived. The longest carbon chain containing the ketonic group is chosen as the parent hydrocarbon; the positions of side-chains or substituents are indicated by numbers, and the ketonic group is given the lowest number possible, *e.g.*,

$$CH_3{\cdot}CO{\cdot}CH_2{\cdot}CH_2{\cdot}CH_3 \qquad \text{pentan-2-one}$$

$$(CH_3)_2CH{\cdot}CO{\cdot}CH(CH_3){\cdot}CH_2{\cdot}CH_3 \qquad 2:4\text{-dimethylhexan-3-one}$$

Since aldehydes and ketones both contain the carbonyl group, it might be expected that they would resemble one another. It is therefore instructive to compare their general methods of preparation and their general properties.

General methods of preparation of aldehydes and ketones

1. *Aldehydes.* By the oxidation of a *primary* alcohol:

$$R{\cdot}CH_2OH \xrightarrow{[O]} R{\cdot}CHO$$

Oxidation may be effected by acid dichromate (yield: *f.g.–g.*); or by passing the alcohol vapour mixed with air over heated silver (250°) as catalyst (yield: *g.*). Alternatively, the alcohol may be *dehydrogenated* by passing the alcohol vapour over heated copper (300°) as catalyst:

$$R{\cdot}CH_2OH \xrightarrow[300^\circ]{Cu} R{\cdot}CHO + H_2 \quad (ex.)$$

tert.-Butyl chromate (prepared by adding chromium trioxide to *tert.*-butanol) oxidises primary alcohols to aldehydes almost quantitatively (Oppenauer *et al.*, 1949).

Ketones. By the oxidation of a *secondary* alcohol (using the same oxidising agents as for aldehydes), or by dehydrogenation over heated copper:

$$R{\cdot}CH(OH){\cdot}R' \xrightarrow{[O]} R{\cdot}CO{\cdot}R' \quad (g.\text{–}ex.)$$

$$R{\cdot}CH(OH){\cdot}R' \xrightarrow[300^\circ]{Cu} R{\cdot}CO{\cdot}R' + H_2 \quad (ex.)$$

There is, however, a specific reagent for oxidising secondary alcohols to ketones, *viz.*, aluminium *tert.*-butoxide, $[(CH_3)_3CO]_3Al$ (the **Oppenauer oxidation,** 1937). The secondary alcohol is refluxed with the reagent in excess acetone solution; *it is the acetone which is reduced*:

$$R{\cdot}CH(OH){\cdot}R' + CH_3{\cdot}CO{\cdot}CH_3 \longrightarrow R{\cdot}CO{\cdot}R' + CH_3{\cdot}CH(OH){\cdot}CH_3 \quad (g.\text{–}v.g.)$$

This reagent is particularly useful for oxidising *unsaturated* secondary alcohols because it does not affect the double bond. On the other hand, *primary* alcohols (particularly unsaturated alcohols) may also be oxidised to aldehydes if acetone is replaced by *p*-benzoquinone. In general, quinones and aromatic ketones are better hydrogen acceptors than acetone.

N-Bromosuccinimide (p. 358) oxidises primary and secondary alcohols to aldehydes and ketones, respectively (Barakat *et al.*, 1952), *e.g.*,

$$CH_3{\cdot}CH_2OH + \begin{array}{l} CH_2{\cdot}CO \\ | \\ CH_2{\cdot}CO \end{array}\!\!\!\!>NBr \longrightarrow CH_3{\cdot}CHO + \begin{array}{l} CH_2{\cdot}CO \\ | \\ CH_2{\cdot}CO \end{array}\!\!\!\!>NH + HBr$$

Primary and secondary alcohols, both saturated and unsaturated, may be oxidised to the corresponding carbonyl compound by means of manganese dioxide in acetone solution (*inter alia*, Bharucha, 1956).

2. *Aldehydes.* By heating a mixture of the calcium salts of formic acid and any one of its homologues:

$$(R{\cdot}CO_2)_2Ca + (H{\cdot}CO_2)_2Ca \longrightarrow 2R{\cdot}CHO + 2CaCO_3$$

The yields are poor on account of the following side reactions:

$$(R{\cdot}CO_2)_2Ca \longrightarrow R{\cdot}CO{\cdot}R + CaCO_3$$

$$(H{\cdot}CO_2)_2Ca \longrightarrow H{\cdot}CHO + CaCO_3$$

The mechanism of this decomposition has been studied by Bell *et al.* (1952), who prepared acetaldehyde by heating a mixture of barium acetate containing ^{13}C and barium formate, and obtained acetaldehyde containing no ^{13}C.

$$Ba\begin{array}{l} \diagup O{\cdot}\overset{*}{C}O{\cdot}\boxed{CH_3 \quad H{\cdot}CO}{\cdot}O\diagdown \\ \qquad\qquad\qquad + \\ \diagdown O{\cdot}\overset{*}{C}O{\cdot}\boxed{CH_3 \quad H{\cdot}CO}{\cdot}O\diagup \end{array}Ba \longrightarrow 2CH_3{\cdot}CHO + 2Ba\overset{*}{C}O_3$$

Ketones. By heating the calcium salt of any fatty acid other than formic acid (yield: variable):

$$(R{\cdot}CO_2)_2Ca \longrightarrow R_2CO + CaCO_3$$

If a mixture of calcium salts is used, mixed ketones are obtained:

$$(R{\cdot}CO_2)_2Ca + (R'{\cdot}CO_2)_2Ca \longrightarrow 2R{\cdot}CO{\cdot}R' + 2CaCO_3$$

The yields for mixed ketones are poor because, in addition to the mixed ketone, the simple ketones R_2CO and R'_2CO are obtained. The mixture may be separated by fractional distillation.

Better yields of ketones (and aldehydes) are obtained by using the barium, manganese or thorium salts instead of the calcium salts.

3. *Aldehydes.* By passing a mixture of the vapours of formic acid and any one of its homologues over manganous oxide as catalyst at 300°:

$$R{\cdot}CO_2H + H{\cdot}CO_2H \xrightarrow{MnO} R{\cdot}CHO + CO_2 + H_2O \quad (f.g.\text{–}g.)$$

R_2CO and $R{\cdot}CHO$ are obtained as by-products, and the reaction probably proceeds via the manganous salt, the manganous carbonate which is formed decomposing at 300° (*cf.* 2):

$$MnCO_3 \longrightarrow MnO + CO_2$$

This mechanism postulating the decomposition of the intermediate manganous salt is supported by experiments using isotopically enriched acid (Reed, 1955).

Ketones. By passing the vapour of any fatty acid other than formic acid over manganous oxide at 300°:

$$2R{\cdot}CO_2H \xrightarrow{MnO} R_2CO + CO_2 + H_2O \quad (g.)$$

A mixture of fatty acids gives mixed ketones:

$$R{\cdot}CO_2H + R'{\cdot}CO_2H \longrightarrow R{\cdot}CO{\cdot}R' + CO_2 + H_2O$$

R_2CO and R'_2CO are obtained as by-products.

4. *Aldehydes.* By the hydrolysis of *gem*-dihalides in which the two halogen atoms are attached to a *terminal* carbon atom:

$$R{\cdot}CHCl_2 \xrightarrow{NaOH} [R{\cdot}CH(OH)_2] \longrightarrow R{\cdot}CHO + H_2O$$

This method is not used much since aldehydes are affected by alkali (see below); furthermore, *gem*-dihalides are usually prepared from the carbonyl compounds (p. 104).

Ketones. By the hydrolysis of *gem*-dihalides in which the two halogen atoms are attached to any carbon atom *other than a terminal one*:

$$R{\cdot}CBr_2{\cdot}R' \xrightarrow{NaOH} [R{\cdot}C(OH)_2{\cdot}R'] \longrightarrow R{\cdot}CO{\cdot}R' + H_2O \quad (g.)$$

5. *Aldehydes.* By the reduction of an acid chloride with hydrogen in boiling xylene using a palladium catalyst suspended on barium sulphate (**Rosenmund's reduction**, 1918):

$$R{\cdot}COCl + H_2 \longrightarrow R{\cdot}CHO + HCl \quad (g.\text{–}v.g.)$$

Aldehydes are more readily reduced than are acid chlorides, and therefore one would expect to obtain the alcohol as the final product. It is the barium sulphate that prevents the aldehyde from being reduced, acting as a poison (to the palladium catalyst) in this reaction. Generally, when the Rosenmund reduction is carried out, a small amount of quinoline and sulphur is added; these are very effective in poisoning the catalyst in the aldehyde reduction. Sakurai *et al.* (1944) have improved the Rosenmund reduction by using $BaSO_4$—$Pd(OH)_2$ as catalyst, and anhydrous acetone or ethyl acetate as solvent (yield: 80–90 per cent.). On the other hand, Davies *et al.* (1943) have shown that aliphatic acid chlorides may be reduced to aldehydes in reasonable yield by means of sodium amalgam.

Brandt (1949) has shown that lithium hydride reduces acid chlorides, anhydrides and thiolesters to the corresponding aldehyde, the yield being best with thiolesters (70 per cent.).

Ketones. There is no analogous method for the preparation of ketones.

6. *Aldehydes.* By the ozonolysis of olefins of the type $R{\cdot}CH{:}CH{\cdot}R'$:

$$R{\cdot}CH{:}CH{\cdot}R' \xrightarrow{O_3} \begin{array}{c} R{\cdot}CH\text{—}O\text{—}CH{\cdot}R' \\ |\qquad\qquad | \\ O\text{————}O \end{array} \xrightarrow[\text{catalyst}]{H_2} R{\cdot}CHO + R'{\cdot}CHO \quad (g.\text{–}v.g.)$$

Ketones. By the ozonolysis of olefins of the type $R_2C{:}CR'_2$:

$$R_2C{:}CR'_2 \xrightarrow{O_3} \begin{array}{c} R_2C\text{—}O\text{—}CR'_2 \\ |\qquad\quad | \\ O\text{———}O \end{array} \xrightarrow[\text{catalyst}]{H_2} R_2CO + R'_2CO \quad (g.\text{–}v.g.)$$

7. *Aldehydes.* By the oxidation of 1 : 2 glycols of the type $R{\cdot}CH(OH){\cdot}CH(OH){\cdot}R'$ with lead tetra-acetate or periodic acid (see p. 67):

$$R{\cdot}CH(OH){\cdot}CH(OH){\cdot}R' \xrightarrow{[O]} R{\cdot}CHO + R'{\cdot}CHO \quad (g.\text{–}v.g.)$$

Ketones. By the oxidation of 1 : 2 glycols of the type $R_2C(OH)\cdot C(OH)R'_2$ with lead tetra-acetate or periodic acid:

$$R_2C(OH)\cdot C(OH)R'_2 \xrightarrow{[O]} R_2CO + R'_2CO \quad (g.\text{–}v.g.)$$

8. *Aldehydes.* Acetylene, when passed into hot dilute sulphuric acid in the presence of mercuric sulphate as catalyst, is converted into acetaldehyde:

$$CH{:}CH + H_2O \longrightarrow [CH_2{:}CHOH] \longrightarrow CH_3\cdot CHO \quad (v.g.)$$

Ketones. All homologues of acetylene, treated in the same way as acetylene, form ketones, *e.g.*,

$$RC{:}CH + H_2O \longrightarrow [R\cdot C(OH){:}CH_2 \longrightarrow R\cdot CO\cdot CH_3 \quad (g.)$$

9. *Aldehydes.* By **Stephen's method** (1925). An alkyl cyanide is dissolved in ether, or better, in ethyl formate or ethyl acetate (Stephen *et al.*, 1956), and reduced with stannous chloride and hydrochloric acid, and then steam distilled. Turner (1956), who has modified Stephen's method, also showed that the yield of aldehyde from *normal*-cyanides increases with increase in chain-length, and that branching in the α-position lowers the yield.

According to Hantzsch (1931), Stephen's reaction proceeds via the iminochloride or aldimine hydrochloride (which is present as the stannichloride):

$$R\cdot C{\equiv}N \xrightarrow{HCl} [R\cdot C{\equiv}NH]^+Cl^- \xrightarrow[HCl]{SnCl_2} [R\cdot CH{=}NH_2]_2{}^+SnCl_6{}^{--} \xrightarrow{H_2O} R\cdot CHO$$

Alkyl cyanides may also be reduced to aldehydes by means of the reverse addition of the calculated amount of lithium aluminium hydride at low temperature (see also p. 114).

$$4R\cdot CN + LiAlH_4 \longrightarrow (R\cdot CH{=}N{-})_4LiAl \xrightarrow{H_2O} 4R\cdot CHO$$

Ketones. There is no analogous method for the preparation of ketones.

10. *Aldehydes.* By means of a Grignard reagent and formic ester (see p. 337).

Ketones. By means of a Grignard reagent and, for example, an alkyl cyanide (see p. 338). Ketones are also formed by reaction between an alkyl cyanide and lithium-alkyls (p. 344).

11. *Ketones.* By the ketonic hydrolysis of the alkyl derivatives of acetoacetic ester (see p. 214), and also from ethyl malonate derivatives (p. 220).

Aldehydes. There is no analogous method for the preparation of aldehydes.

12. *Aldehydes.* Many aldehydes may be prepared by the *oxo* process (p. 115), *e.g.*, propionaldehyde (*q.v.*).

Ketones. There is no analogous method for the preparation of ketones.

13. *Aldehydes.* Aldehydes may be prepared (in yields up to 50 per cent.) by means of the modified *Sommelet reaction* (Angyal *et al.*, 1953; see benzaldehyde, p. 619); *e.g.*, *n*-hexanal is produced by adding an aqueous solution of *n*-hexylamine hydrochloride to a solution of hexamine in acetic acid through which steam is passed.

$$CH_3\cdot(CH_2)_5\cdot NH_2\cdot HCl + (CH_2)_6N_4 \longrightarrow CH_3\cdot(CH_2)_4\cdot CHO \quad (17\%)$$

Ketones. There is no analogous method for the preparation of ketones.

Reactions common to aldehydes and ketones

It has been found that the reactivity of the carbonyl group depends on the nature of the alkyl groups attached to it; the smaller the alkyl group, the more reactive is the carbonyl group. Thus the order of reactivity is:

$$(H)_2C{=}O > (CH_3)(H)C{=}O > (CH_3)_2C{=}O > (C_2H_5)(CH_3)C{=}O > (C_2H_5)_2C{=}O$$

If the alkyl groups are very large, *e.g.*, *tert.*-butyl, the carbonyl group shows very little reactivity. The reason for the decrease of reactivity of the carbonyl group as the attached alkyl groups become larger is not certain, but a contributing factor may be the *spatial effect, i.e.*, mechanical interference between groups. Since chemical reactions take place by " collision " between molecules, large groups will " protect " the carbonyl group from the attacking molecule, and the larger the group the more effective will be the " protection ".

1. Aldehydes and ketones are reduced catalytically or by nascent hydrogen, aldehydes producing primary, and ketones secondary, alcohols, *e.g.*,

$$>C{=}O + 2[H] \xrightarrow{\text{metal/acid}} >CHOH \quad (g.\text{–}v.g.)$$

Aldehydes and ketones are conveniently reduced by Raney nickel in aqueous or ethanolic solution (yield: *g.–v.g.*). Reduction may also be effected by means of the **Meerwein–Ponndorf–Verley reduction** (1925, 1926). The carbonyl compound is heated with aluminium *iso*propoxide in *iso*propanol solution; the *iso*propoxide is oxidised to acetone, which is removed from the equilibrium mixture by slow distillation:

$$R_2CO + (CH_3)_2CHOAl/_3 \rightleftharpoons R_2CHOAl/_3 + CH_3{\cdot}CO{\cdot}CH_3 \xrightarrow[H_2SO_4]{\text{dilute}} R_2CHOH \ (g.)$$

This reducing agent is specific for the carbonyl group, and so may be used for reducing aldehydes and ketones containing some other functional group that is reducible, *e.g.*, a double bond or a nitro-group. The Meerwein–Ponndorf–Verley reduction has been improved by Truett *et al.* (1951). Aldehydes and ketones are also reduced to alcohols by lithium aluminium hydride, lithium borohydride and sodium borohydride (p. 115).

Williams *et al.* (1953) used aluminium *iso*propoxide containing deuterium to reduce *cyclo*hexanone, and concluded that the mechanism involves the formation of a cyclic complex:

$$\text{[RR'C}^{+}{=}O^{-}\cdots D{-}C(CH_3)_2{-}O \text{ cyclic complex with } Al(OC_3H_7)_2] \rightleftharpoons \text{[RR'C(D)}{-}O \cdots (CH_3)_2C^{+}{-}O^{-} \text{ with } Al(OC_3H_7)_2] \xrightarrow{H_2O} RR'C(D)OH + (CH_3)_2C{=}O$$

When carbonyl compounds are heated with concentrated hydriodic acid and red phosphorus, the carbonyl group is reduced to a methylene group —CH_2—. This may also be effected by means of the **Clemmensen reduction** (1913): the carbonyl compound is reduced with *amalgamated zinc* and concentrated hydrochloric acid:

$$R{\cdot}CHO + 4[H] \xrightarrow[HCl]{Zn/Hg} R{\cdot}CH_3 + H_2O$$

$$R{\cdot}CO{\cdot}R' + 4[H] \xrightarrow[HCl]{Zn/Hg} R{\cdot}CH_2{\cdot}R' + H_2O$$

The Clemmensen reduction does not appear to work well for aldehydes, but is reasonably good for many ketones.

2. Aldehydes and ketones add on sodium hydrogen sulphite to form *bisulphite* compounds:

$$>C=O + NaHSO_3 \rightleftharpoons >C\begin{matrix}OH \\ SO_3Na\end{matrix} \quad \text{or} \quad \left[>C\begin{matrix}OH \\ SO_3\end{matrix}\right]^- Na^+$$

These bisulphite compounds are *hydroxysulphonic acid salts*, since the sulphur atom is *directly* attached to the carbon atom. This structure is supported by work with isotope ^{34}S (Sheppard *et al.*, 1954).

Most aldehydes form bisulphite compounds. Ketones of the type $CH_3 \cdot CO \cdot R$, where R is a *primary* alkyl group, form bisulphite compounds fairly readily; but where R is a secondary or tertiary alkyl group, the bisulphite compound is formed very slowly. If the ketone is of the type $R \cdot CO \cdot R'$ where R and R′ are ethyl or higher alkyl groups, the bisulphite compound is not formed at all (*cf.* reactivity of carbonyl compounds, above).

Bisulphite compounds are usually crystalline solids, insoluble in sodium hydrogen sulphite solution. Since they regenerate the carbonyl compound when heated with dilute acid or sodium carbonate solution, their formation affords a convenient means of separating carbonyl compounds from non-carbonyl compounds.

3. Aldehydes and ketones add on hydrogen cyanide to form *cyanohydrins*. The carbonyl compound is treated with sodium cyanide and dilute sulphuric acid:

$$>C=O + HCN \rightleftharpoons >C\begin{matrix}OH \\ CN\end{matrix} \qquad (g.–v.g.)$$

Cyanohydrins are important compounds in organic synthesis since they are readily hydrolysed to α-hydroxy-acids:

$$R \cdot CH(OH) \cdot CN \xrightarrow{H_2O} R \cdot CH(OH) \cdot CO_2H$$

All aldehydes form cyanohydrins; only the ketones acetone, butanone, pentan-3-one, and pinacolone form cyanohydrins.

Cyanohydrins are also prepared, if possible, indirectly from the bisulphite compound, which is treated with sodium (or potassium) cyanide solution:

$$>C(OH) \cdot SO_3Na + NaCN \longrightarrow >C(OH) \cdot CN + Na_2SO_3 \quad (v.g.)$$

It has been suggested that the mechanism of the formation of bisulphite compounds and cyanohydrins is:

Bisulphite compound:

$$O=C< \ :\bar{S}O_3H \rightleftharpoons >C(SO_3H)-\bar{O} \overset{H^+}{\rightleftharpoons} >C(SO_3^-)-OH$$

Cyanohydrin:

$$O=C< \ \bar{C}N \rightleftharpoons >C(CN)-\bar{O} \overset{H^+}{\rightleftharpoons} >C(CN)-OH$$

The carbonyl group undergoes the electromeric effect at the requirements of the attacking reagent, and thus the carbon atom will be the point of attack by a *nucleophilic* reagent, and the oxygen atom by an *electrophilic* reagent. It has been found that a negatively charged oxygen atom is a more stable arrangement than a positively charged carbon atom and so, when the carbonyl group undergoes addition, it is the carbon atom that is attacked first, and then the oxygen atom.

From the M.O. point of view, since the carbonyl group contains one σ- and one π-bond (Fig. 1*a*), and since oxygen is much more strongly electron-attracting than carbon, the π-orbital will be more concentrated round the oxygen than the carbon atom (Fig. *b*) (*cf.* hydrogen chloride, p. 26). Consequently a nucleophilic reagent will approach the carbon atom rather than the oxygen, since the cloud-charge density is less round the former than the latter, *i.e.* a *nucleophilic* reagent will preferentially attack the carbon atom.

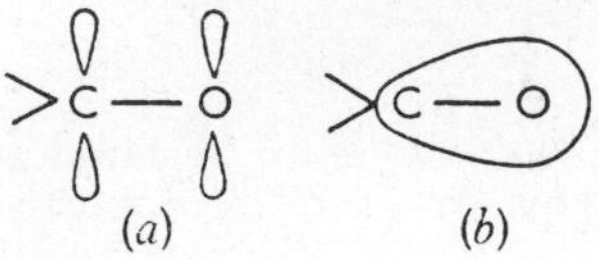

(*a*) (*b*)

FIG. 8.1.

It seems probable that the above mechanisms are over-simplified. According to Svirbely *et al.* (1955), the mechanism of formation of cyanohydrin from propionaldehyde and hydrocyanic acid in methanol solution containing acetate buffers is (HA represents any acid present):

$$>C{=}O + HA \underset{}{\overset{\text{fast}}{\rightleftharpoons}} >C{=}O\text{---}HA$$

$$>C{=}O\text{---}HA + CN^- \xrightarrow{\text{slow}} >C\begin{matrix}CN\\OH\end{matrix} + A^-$$

4. Aldehydes and ketones form *oximes* when treated with hydroxylamine:

$$R_2CO + NH_2OH \longrightarrow \left[R_2C\begin{matrix}OH\\NHOH\end{matrix}\right] \xrightarrow{-H_2O} R_2C{=}NOH \quad (v.g.)$$

The mechanism of this reaction is discussed in connection with semicarbazones (see below).

Oximes are usually well-defined crystalline solids, and may be used to identify carbonyl compounds.

Aldoximes form cyanides when boiled with acetic anhydride, whereas ketoximes form the acetyl derivative of the oxime:

$$R{\cdot}CH{:}N{\cdot}OH \xrightarrow[-H_2O]{(CH_3{\cdot}CO)_2O} R{\cdot}CN$$

$$R_2C{:}N{\cdot}OH \xrightarrow{(CH_3{\cdot}CO)_2O} R_3C{:}N{\cdot}O{\cdot}CO{\cdot}CH_3$$

5. Aldehydes and ketones react with hydrazine to form *hydrazones* and *azines*. The mechanism of their formation is probably similar to that of oxime formation (see above):

Hydrazone:

$$>C{=}O + H_2\ddot{N}{\cdot}\ddot{N}H_2 \longrightarrow \left[>C\begin{matrix}OH\\NH{\cdot}NH_2\end{matrix}\right] \xrightarrow{-H_2O} >C{:}N{\cdot}NH_2$$

Azine:

$$>C{:}N{\cdot}NH_2 + O{=}C< \longrightarrow H_2O + >C{:}N{-}N{:}C<$$

By using suitable derivatives of hydrazine, more well-defined crystalline products are obtained (and azine formation is avoided), *e.g.*,

(i) Phenylhydrazine forms *phenylhydrazones*:

$$C_6H_5{\cdot}NH{\cdot}NH_2 + O{=}C< \longrightarrow H_2O + C_6H_5{\cdot}NH{\cdot}N{:}C>$$

(ii) *p*-Nitrophenylhydrazine forms *p*-nitrophenylhydrazones:

$$NO_2C_6H_4\cdot NH\cdot NH_2 + O{=}C\langle \longrightarrow NO_2C_6H_4\cdot NH\cdot N{:}C\langle + H_2O$$

(iii) 2 : 4-Dinitrophenylhydrazine forms 2 : 4-dinitrophenylhydrazones:

$$(NO_2)_2C_6H_3\cdot NH\cdot NH_2 + O{=}C\langle \longrightarrow (NO_2)_2C_6H_3\cdot NH\cdot N{:}C\langle + H_2O$$

(iv) Semicarbazide forms *semicarbazones*:

$$NH_2\cdot CO\cdot NH\cdot NH_2 + O{=}C\langle \longrightarrow NH_2\cdot CO\cdot NH\cdot N{:}C\langle + H_2O$$

The semicarbazone reaction has been studied in some detail by Conant *et al.* (1932) and Westheimer (1934), and has been shown to be a general acid-catalysed reaction. The following mechanism has been proposed by Bartlett (1953):

$$R_2C{=}O + HA \rightleftharpoons R_2C{=}O\cdots HA \xrightleftharpoons{NH_2\cdot NH\cdot CO\cdot NH_2}$$

$$R_2C\begin{matrix}OH\\ \overset{+}{N}H_2\cdot NH\cdot CO\cdot NH_2\end{matrix} + A^- \rightleftharpoons R_2C\begin{matrix}OH\\ NH\cdot NH\cdot CO\cdot NH_2\end{matrix} + HA \rightleftharpoons$$

(I)

$$R_2C\begin{matrix}\overset{H}{|}\\ O\cdots H{-}A\\ NH\cdot NH\cdot CO\cdot NH_2\end{matrix} \rightleftharpoons R_2C{=}\overset{+}{N}H\cdot NH\cdot CO\cdot NH_2 + H_2O + A^- \rightleftharpoons$$

$$R_2C{=}N\cdot NH\cdot CO\cdot NH_2 + H_2O + HA$$

This mechanism is also believed to operate in the formation of oximes and phenylhydrazones. The addition compound (of type I) has been isolated in certain cases, *e.g.*, with chloral.

The carbonyl compound may be regenerated from the oxime, phenylhydrazone or semicarbazone by boiling with dilute acid (hydrochloric or sulphuric acid).

Wolff–Kishner reduction (1912). When hydrazones (or semicarbazones) are heated with sodium ethoxide at 180°, nitrogen is eliminated, and a hydrocarbon is obtained, *i.e.*, by this means the carbonyl group is converted into the methylene group:

$$\rangle C{:}N\cdot NH_2 \longrightarrow \rangle CH_2 + N_2 \quad (g.\!-\!v.g.)$$

An improved technique is to heat the carbonyl compound in ethylene or trimethylene glycol with 85 per cent. hydrazine hydrate in the presence of three equivalents of sodium, sodium hydroxide or potassium hydroxide, at 180–200°; the yield is usually above 65 per cent. (Huang–Minlon, 1946). The yield of hydrocarbon is better than that obtained by the Clemmensen reduction. Reduction of sterically hindered carbonyl groups by either the Clemmensen reduction or the Wolff–Kishner procedure is not easily effected. Barton *et al.* (1954, 1955) have modified Huang–Minlon's method (by excluding water), and have thereby reduced sterically hindered carbonyl groups.

Girard's reagents for carbonyl compounds (1934, 1936). Girard introduced two reagents for carbonyl compounds: Girard's reagents " T " and " P ", which are respectively trimethylaminoacetohydrazide chloride: $[(CH_3)_3N\cdot CH_2\cdot CO\cdot NH\cdot NH_2]^+Cl^-$, and pyridinium-acetohydrazide chloride, $[C_5H_5N\cdot CH_2\cdot CO\cdot NH\cdot NH_2]^+Cl^-$ (see p. 195). These reagents react with carbonyl compounds to form derivatives of the type $[(CH_3)_3N\cdot CH_2\cdot CO\cdot NH\cdot N{:}C\langle]^+Cl^-$.

These compounds are *soluble* in water, and have been found particularly useful for isolating certain ketonic hormones.

6. Aldehydes and ketones condense with thio-alcohols (mercaptans) to form *mercaptals* and *mercaptols*, respectively:

$$>C{=}O + 2RSH \longrightarrow >C(SR)_2 + H_2O$$

7. Aldehydes and ketones add on a molecule of a Grignard reagent, and the complex formed, when decomposed with water, gives a secondary alcohol from an aldehyde (except formaldehyde, which gives a primary alcohol), and a tertiary alcohol from a ketone (see p. 335):

$$>C{=}O + RMgX \longrightarrow >C\begin{matrix}\diagup OMgX \\ \diagdown R\end{matrix} \xrightarrow{H_2O} >C\begin{matrix}\diagup OH \\ \diagdown R\end{matrix}$$

8. Phosphorus pentachloride reacts with *simple* carbonyl compounds to form *gem*-dichlorides:

$$>C{=}O + PCl_5 \longrightarrow >CCl_2 + POCl_3$$

The yield of *gem*.-dichloride is usually good with aldehydes, but with ketones it is poor. With more complicated carbonyl compounds chlorination also takes place, substitution occurring on the α-carbon atom only; *e.g.*, di-*iso*propyl ketone gives α-chlorodi*iso*propyl ketone when treated with one molecule of phosphorus pentachloride:

$$(CH_3)_2CH{\cdot}CO{\cdot}CH(CH_3)_2 + PCl_5 \longrightarrow (CH_3)_2CCl{\cdot}CO{\cdot}CH(CH_3)_2 + PCl_3 + HCl$$

Very little *gem*-dibromides are obtained with phosphorus pentabromide; the main product from any carbonyl compound is the α-bromo-derivative. Phosphorus pentabromide dissociates more readily than phosphorus pentachloride, and it is probable that the halogenation in the α-position is brought about by the free halogen (see below).

9. Chlorine or bromine replaces one or more α-hydrogen atoms in aldehydes and ketones, *e.g.*, acetone may be brominated in glacial acetic acid to give monobromoacetone:

$$CH_3{\cdot}CO{\cdot}CH_3 + Br_2 \longrightarrow CH_3{\cdot}CO{\cdot}CH_2Br + HBr \quad (43\text{–}44\%)$$

The halogenation of carbonyl compounds is catalysed by bases and by acids, but the details of the mechanisms are not certain. Let us consider the case of acetone. Now it is known that both bases and acids catalyse enolisation of a ketone (see p. 207 for further details).

$$\underset{\text{keto}}{CH_3{\cdot}CO{\cdot}CH_3} \underset{\text{(slow)}}{\overset{\text{base or acid}}{\rightleftharpoons}} \underset{\text{enol}}{CH_3{\cdot}\overset{\overset{OH}{|}}{C}{=}CH_2}$$

If the enol form is the one which is brominated, the bromination can be considered to occur as follows:

$$CH_3{-}\overset{\overset{O-H}{|}}{C}{=}CH_2 \quad Br{-}Br \xrightarrow{\text{fast}} CH_3{-}\overset{\overset{O}{||}}{C}{-}CH_2Br + HBr$$

In both base and acid catalysed reactions it has been shown that the rate of bromination (and of any other halogen) is independent of the concentration of the bromine but is proportional to the concentration of ketone and base or acid present. This is in agreement with at least a two-stage reaction, the first and slow stage being enolisation, and the second and fast stage being bromination.

An alternative mechanism which also agrees with the experimental results is:

$$\begin{matrix} CH_3 \\ | \\ C{=}O \\ | \\ CH_3 \end{matrix} \underset{\text{(slow)}}{\overset{\text{base or acid}}{\rightleftharpoons}} \begin{matrix} CH_3 \\ | \\ C{-}OH \\ \| \\ CH_2 \end{matrix} \underset{\text{(fast)}}{\overset{Br_2}{\longrightarrow}} \left[\begin{matrix} CH_3 \\ | \diagup OH \\ C \\ | \diagdown Br \\ CH_2Br \end{matrix}\right] \underset{\text{(fast)}}{\longrightarrow} \begin{matrix} CH_3 \\ | \\ CO \\ | \\ CH_2Br \end{matrix} + HBr$$

A very interesting point about either of these mechanisms is that if the change from keto to enol could be speeded up to such an extent that it is now faster than the halogenation, then the concentration of the halogen would enter into the rate equation. This has actually been observed in, *e.g.*, the iodination of acetophenone in the presence of sulphuric acid (Hammett *et al.*, 1939).

Another point that we shall discuss here is: How is it possible for a C—H bond to be broken so readily? This must occur whatever the mechanism of enolisation, and has been explained as follows. Owing to the inductive effect of the carbonyl group (caused by the high electron-affinity of the oxygen atom), the electrons of the C—H bonds on the α-carbon atom are displaced towards the carbon atom, thereby increasing the polarity of these bonds and consequently weakening them (*cf.* p. 97), thus giving rise to a condition for an *incipient* proton leaving C_α.

$$\begin{matrix} H & O \\ \downarrow & \| \\ -C_\alpha & \!\!\rightarrow C- \\ \uparrow & \\ H & \end{matrix}$$

Since the inductive effect falls off extremely rapidly from the source, only α-hydrogen atoms will be affected by the inductive effect of the carbonyl group. This offers an explanation for the unusual reactivity of hydrogen in a methyne group (=CH—) or in a methylene group ($—CH_2—$) when adjacent to a carbonyl group or any other strongly electron-attracting group. In such structures the incipient proton is readily removed, and the compound is said to possess an " active " methyne or methylene group.

Aldehydes and ketones with α-hydrogen atoms readily react with sulphuryl chloride at room temperature in the absence of a catalyst, to replace α-hydrogen atoms only, *e.g.*,

$$CH_3{\cdot}CO{\cdot}CH_3 \xrightarrow{SO_2Cl_2} CH_3{\cdot}CO{\cdot}CH_2Cl$$

The halogen atom in the group CX·CO is very reactive, far more so than the halogen atom in alkyl halides. It appears that the adjacent carbonyl group plays a part, but its mode of operation is still not clear.

10. Aldehydes and ketones with a methyl or methylene group adjacent to the carbonyl group are oxidised by selenium dioxide at room temperature to dicarbonyl compounds; *e.g.*, acetaldehyde forms glyoxal, and acetone forms methylglyoxal:

$$CH_3{\cdot}CHO + SeO_2 \longrightarrow CHO{\cdot}CHO + Se + H_2O$$

$$CH_3{\cdot}CO{\cdot}CH_3 + SeO_2 \longrightarrow CH_3{\cdot}CO{\cdot}CHO + Se + H_2O$$

11. Aldehydes and ketones are converted into the formyl derivative of the corresponding primary amine by excess ammonium formate or formamide (**Leuckart reaction,** 1885):

$$>C{=}O + 2H{\cdot}CO_2NH_4 \longrightarrow >CH{\cdot}NH{\cdot}CHO + 2H_2O + CO_2 + NH_3$$

$$>C{=}O + 2H{\cdot}CO{\cdot}NH_2 \longrightarrow >CH{\cdot}NH{\cdot}CHO + CO_2 + NH_3$$

12. Aldehydes and ketones undergo condensation reactions, *i.e.*, two or more (identical or different) molecules unite with, or without, the elimination

of water (or any other simple molecule). There is very little difference between the terms condensation and condensation polymerisation or polycondensation (p. 72); generally, condensation is used for those reactions in which the resulting compound is made up of a small number of the reacting molecules.

Aldol Condensation. Acetaldehyde, in the presence of dilute sodium hydroxide, potassium carbonate or hydrochloric acid, undergoes condensation to form a syrupy liquid known as *aldol*:

$$2CH_3{\cdot}CHO \xrightarrow{NaOH} CH_3{\cdot}CH(OH){\cdot}CH_2{\cdot}CHO \quad (50\%)$$

On heating, aldols eliminate water to form unsaturated compounds, *e.g.*, aldol forms crotonaldehyde:

$$CH_3{\cdot}CH(OH){\cdot}CH_2{\cdot}CHO \longrightarrow CH_3{\cdot}CH{:}CH{\cdot}CHO + H_2O$$

In many cases it is the unsaturated compound that is isolated, and not the aldol, *e.g.*, mesityl oxide and phorone (*q.v.*).

The aldol condensation can occur: (i) between two aldehydes (identical or different); (ii) between two ketones (identical or different); and (iii) between an aldehyde and a ketone. Whatever the nature of the carbonyl compound, *it is only the α-hydrogen atoms which are involved in the aldol condensation.*

(i) Generally, with two different aldehydes all four possible condensation products are obtained; but by using different catalysts one product may be made to predominate in the mixture, *e.g.*,

$$CH_3{\cdot}CHO + CH_3{\cdot}CH_2{\cdot}CHO \underset{}{\overset{NaOH}{\rightleftharpoons}} CH_3{\cdot}CH_2{\cdot}CH(OH){\cdot}CH_2{\cdot}CHO$$

$$CH_3{\cdot}CHO + CH_3{\cdot}CH_2{\cdot}CHO \overset{HCl}{\rightleftharpoons} CH_3{\cdot}CH(OH){\cdot}CH(CH_3){\cdot}CHO$$

(ii) Acetone, in the presence of barium hydroxide, gives diacetone alcohol:

$$2CH_3{\cdot}CO{\cdot}CH_3 \overset{Ba(OH)_2}{\rightleftharpoons} (CH_3)_2C(OH){\cdot}CH_2{\cdot}COCH_3$$

This equilibrium lies almost completely on the left, but the yield of diacetone alcohol may be increased (71 per cent.) by boiling acetone in a Soxhlet with solid barium hydroxide in the thimble. The acetone in the flask gets richer and richer in diacetone alcohol, since the boiling point of the latter is 164°, and that of the former is 56°.

When acetone is treated with hydrochloric acid, mesityl oxide and phorone are formed:

$$2CH_3{\cdot}CO{\cdot}CH_3 \overset{HCl}{\rightleftharpoons} (CH_3)_2C{:}CH{\cdot}CO{\cdot}CH_3 \overset{CH_3{\cdot}CO{\cdot}CH_3}{\rightleftharpoons} (CH_3)_2C{:}CH{\cdot}CO{\cdot}CH{:}C(CH_3)_2$$

(iii) When aldehydes condense with ketones, it is the α-hydrogen atom of the *ketone* which is involved in the condensation, *e.g.*,

$$CH_3{\cdot}CHO + CH_3{\cdot}CO{\cdot}CH_3 \overset{NaOH}{\rightleftharpoons} CH_3{\cdot}CH(OH){\cdot}CH_2{\cdot}CO{\cdot}CH_3 \quad (25\%)$$

The yield of 4-hydroxypentan-2-one is low because aldol and diacetone alcohol are also formed.

The mechanism of the aldol condensation is possibly as follows. In the presence of the base, one molecule of the aldehyde or ketone forms a carbanion:

$$HO^- \; H{-}CH_2{\cdot}CHO \rightleftharpoons H_2O + \bar{C}H_2{\cdot}CHO$$

The carbonyl group in the other molecule (aldehyde or ketone) involved in the aldol condensation undergoes the electromeric effect at the requirements of the attacking reagent—in this case, the carbanion, which is a nucleophilic reagent:

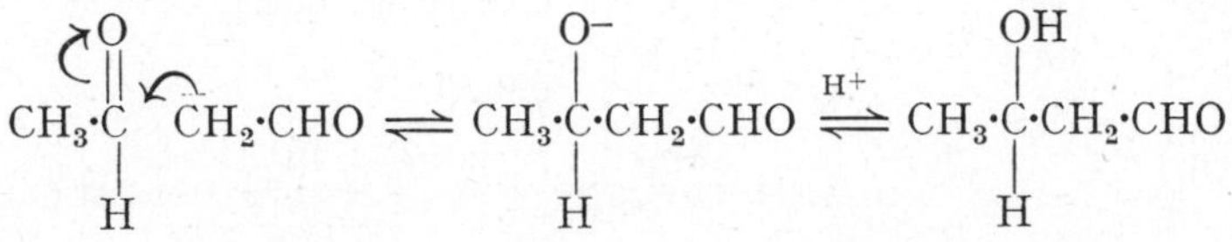

$$CH_3\cdot\underset{H}{\overset{O}{\overset{\|}{C}}}\ \ CH_2\cdot CHO \rightleftharpoons CH_3\cdot\underset{H}{\overset{O^-}{C}}\cdot CH_2\cdot CHO \overset{H^+}{\rightleftharpoons} CH_3\cdot\underset{H}{\overset{OH}{C}}\cdot CH_2\cdot CHO$$

The proton is supplied by the dissociation of water molecules.

Claisen condensation (1881). This is the condensation between an ester and another molecule of an ester or ketone (see p. 209).

Claisen–Schmidt reaction (also known as the **Claisen reaction**) is the condensation between an *aromatic* aldehyde (or ketone) and an aldehyde or ketone, *in the presence of dilute alkali* to form an $\alpha\beta$-unsaturated compound. This reaction is similar to the aldol condensation, and is illustrated by the formation of cinnamaldehyde from benzaldehyde and acetaldehyde:

$$C_6H_5\cdot CHO + CH_3\cdot CHO \xrightarrow{NaOH} C_6H_5\cdot CH{:}CH\cdot CHO + H_2O$$

The mechanism of this reaction is possibly:

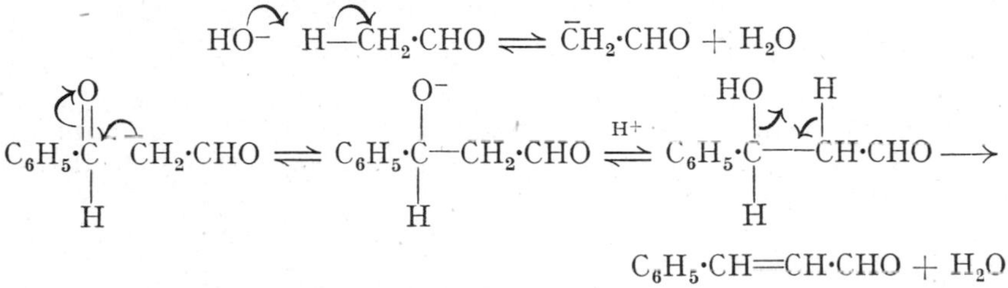

$$HO^- \ \ H—CH_2\cdot CHO \rightleftharpoons \bar{C}H_2\cdot CHO + H_2O$$

$$C_6H_5\cdot\underset{H}{\overset{O}{\overset{\|}{C}}}\ \ CH_2\cdot CHO \rightleftharpoons C_6H_5\cdot\underset{H}{\overset{O^-}{C}}—CH_2\cdot CHO \overset{H^+}{\rightleftharpoons} C_6H_5\cdot\underset{H}{\overset{HO}{C}}—\overset{H}{C}H\cdot CHO \longrightarrow$$

$$C_6H_5\cdot CH{=}CH\cdot CHO + H_2O$$

Other condensations involving aldehydes or ketones are the *Knoevenagel* (p. 263) and *Perkin* (p. 623) reactions.

13. **Darzens Glycidic Ester Condensation** (1904). This reaction involves the condensation of an aldehyde or ketone with an α-halogeno-ester to produce an $\alpha:\beta$-epoxy-ester (*glycidic ester*); the condensing agent is usually sodium ethoxide or sodamide:

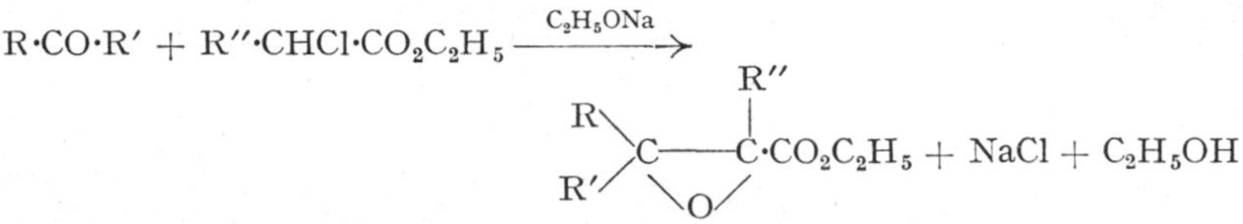

$$R\cdot CO\cdot R' + R''\cdot CHCl\cdot CO_2C_2H_5 \xrightarrow{C_2H_5ONa} \begin{matrix}R\\R'\end{matrix}\!\!>\!C\underset{\diagdown O \diagup}{——}\overset{R''}{C}\cdot CO_2C_2H_5 + NaCl + C_2H_5OH$$

These glycidic esters, on hydrolysis, give the epoxy-acid, and this, on decarboxylation, gives a ketone, or an aldehyde which is formed by rearrangement:

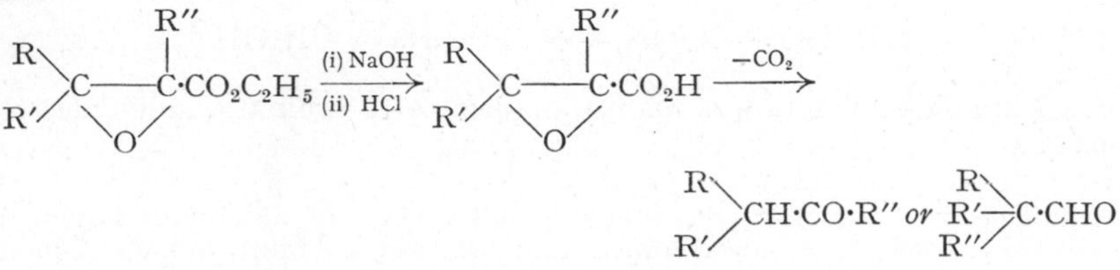

$$\begin{matrix}R\\R'\end{matrix}\!\!>\!C\underset{\diagdown O \diagup}{——}\overset{R''}{C}\cdot CO_2C_2H_5 \xrightarrow[\text{(ii) HCl}]{\text{(i) NaOH}} \begin{matrix}R\\R'\end{matrix}\!\!>\!C\underset{\diagdown O \diagup}{——}\overset{R''}{C}\cdot CO_2H \xrightarrow{-CO_2}$$

$$\begin{matrix}R\\R'\end{matrix}\!\!>\!CH\cdot CO\cdot R'' \ \textit{or}\ \begin{matrix}R\\R'\\R''\end{matrix}\!\!\!>\!C\cdot CHO$$

Darzens (1936, 1937) has also prepared glycidic esters by condensing $\alpha:\alpha$-dihalogeno-esters with an aldehyde or ketone in the presence of dilute magnesium amalgam:

$$R\cdot CO\cdot R' + CHCl_2\cdot CO_2C_2H_5 \xrightarrow{Mg/Hg} \underset{R'}{\overset{R}{>}}\underset{OMgCl}{\underset{|}{C}}-CHCl\cdot CO_2C_2H_5 \xrightarrow{H_2O}$$

$$\underset{R'}{\overset{R}{>}}\underset{OH}{\underset{|}{C}}-CHCl\cdot CO_2C_2H_5 \xrightarrow{C_2H_5ONa} \underset{R'}{\overset{R}{>}}C \overset{O}{\frown} CH\cdot CO_2C_2H_5$$

Reactions given by aldehydes only. 1. Aldehydes restore the magenta colour to Schiff's reagent (rosaniline hydrochloride is dissolved in water, and sulphur dioxide is passed in until the magenta colour is discharged). The mechanism of this reaction is obscure.

2. Aldehydes are very easily oxidised, and hence are powerful reducing agents. Aldehydes reduce Fehling's solution (an alkaline solution containing a complex of copper tartrate) to red cuprous oxide; and Tollens' reagent (ammoniacal silver nitrate solution) to metallic silver, which often appears as a silver mirror on the walls of the containing vessel. In both cases the aldehyde is oxidised to the corresponding acid:

$$R\cdot CHO + [O] \longrightarrow R\cdot CO_2H$$

It is worth noting that Fehling's solution and Tollens' reagent are both weak oxidising agents, and can be used to oxidise *readily oxidisable* groups, *e.g.*, they will oxidise unsaturated aldehydes to the corresponding unsaturated acids; they are not sufficiently strong oxidising agents to attack an ethylenic bond.

According to Veksler (1952), ketones with the structures $Ar\cdot CH_2\cdot CO\cdot CH_3$ and $Ar_2CH\cdot CO\cdot CH_3$ (Ar = aryl radical) reduce cold ammoniacal solutions of *silver oxide* to a silver mirror; it appears that ammoniacal *silver nitrate* is *not* reduced.

3. All aldehydes except formaldehyde form resinous products when warmed with concentrated sodium hydroxide solution. The resin is probably formed via a series of condensations, *e.g.*,

$$2CH_3\cdot CHO \longrightarrow CH_3\cdot CH(OH)\cdot CH_2\cdot CHO \xrightarrow{-H_2O} CH_3\cdot CH{:}CH\cdot CHO \xrightarrow{CH_3\cdot CHO}$$

$$CH_3\cdot CH{:}CH\cdot CH(OH)\cdot CH_2\cdot CHO \xrightarrow{-H_2O} CH_3\cdot CH{:}CH\cdot CH{:}CH\cdot CHO, \text{ etc.}$$

Aldehydes that have no α-hydrogen atoms undergo the **Cannizzaro reaction** (1853), in which two molecules of the aldehyde are involved, one molecule being converted into the corresponding alcohol, and the other into the acid. The usual reagent for bringing about the Cannizzaro reaction is 50 per cent. aqueous or ethanolic alkali, *e.g.*,

$$2H\cdot CHO + NaOH \longrightarrow H\cdot CO_2Na + CH_3OH$$

The Cannizzaro reaction is mainly applicable to aromatic aldehydes (see p. 621).

Although the Cannizzaro reaction is characteristic of aldehydes having no α-hydrogen atoms, it is not confined to them, *e.g.*, certain aliphatic α-monoalkylated aldehydes undergo quantitative disproportionation when heated with aqueous sodium hydroxide at 170–200° (Häusermann, 1951):

$$2(CH_3)_2CH{\cdot}CHO + NaOH \xrightarrow{200^\circ} (CH_3)_2CH{\cdot}CO_2Na + (CH_3)_2CH{\cdot}CH_2OH\ (100\%)$$

The Cannizzaro reaction can take place between two different aldehydes, and is then known as a " crossed " Cannizzaro reaction (see formaldehyde, p. 154).

All aldehydes can be made to undergo the Cannizzaro reaction by treatment with aluminium ethoxide. Under these conditions the acid and alcohol are combined as the ester, and the reaction is then known as the **Tischenko reaction** (1906); *e.g.*, acetaldehyde gives ethyl acetate, and propionaldehyde gives propyl propionate:

$$2CH_3{\cdot}CHO \xrightarrow{Al(OC_2H_5)_3} CH_3{\cdot}CO_2C_2H_5$$

$$2CH_3{\cdot}CH_2{\cdot}CHO \xrightarrow{Al(OC_2H_5)_3} CH_3{\cdot}CH_2{\cdot}CO_2CH_2{\cdot}CH_2{\cdot}CH_3$$

Aldehydes give simple esters with aluminium ethoxide, the aldol condensation with sodium ethoxide, and trimeric glycol esters with magnesium or calcium ethoxides (Villani and Nord, 1947):

$$3R{\cdot}CH_2{\cdot}CHO \xrightarrow{Mg(OC_2H_5)_2} R{\cdot}CH_2{\cdot}CH(OH){\cdot}CHR{\cdot}CH_2O{\cdot}CO{\cdot}CH_2{\cdot}R$$

4. Aldehydes (except formaldehyde) react with ammonia in ethereal solution to give a precipitate of *aldehyde–ammonia, e.g.*,

$$CH_3{\cdot}CHO + NH_3 \longrightarrow CH_3{\cdot}CH(OH){\cdot}NH_2 \quad (50\%)$$

These aldehyde-ammonias are unstable and readily undergo cyclic polymerisation, and it has been suggested, from X-ray crystal analysis, that acetaldehyde-ammonia is the trihydrate of trimethylhexahydrotriazine * (Moerman, 1938):

$$CH_3{\cdot}CHO + NH_3 \longrightarrow CH_3{\cdot}CHO{\cdot}NH_3 \xrightarrow{\text{polymerises}} (CH_3{\cdot}CHO{\cdot}NH_3)_3 \longrightarrow$$

$$CH_3{\cdot}CH\begin{cases} NH{-}CH{\cdot}CH_3 \\ \qquad\qquad >NH{\cdot}3H_2O \\ NH{-}CH{\cdot}CH_3 \end{cases}$$

5. Aldehydes combine with alcohols in the presence of dry hydrogen chloride or calcium chloride to form first the *hemi-acetal*, and then the *acetal*:

$$R{\cdot}CHO + R'OH \underset{}{\overset{HCl}{\rightleftharpoons}} R{\cdot}CH(OH){\cdot}OR' \overset{R'OH}{\rightleftharpoons} R{\cdot}CH(OR')_2 + H_2O \quad (g.)$$

The hemi-acetal is rarely isolated since it very readily forms the acetal. Acetals are diethers of the unstable 1 : 1-dihydroxyalcohols, and may be named as 1 : 1-dialkoxyalkanes. Unlike the parent dihydroxyalcohols these acetals are stable. They are also stable in the presence of alkali, but are converted into the aldehyde by acid. Thus acetal formation may be used to protect the aldehyde group against *alkaline* oxidising agents. On the other hand, the aldehyde group can be protected in *acid* solution by mecaptal formation (p. 317).

* The reaction between aldehydes and ammonia is usually quoted to be simple. Although the first product is simple, the final one is complicated, and so this reaction is not characteristic of aldehydes, since ketones also give complex products with ammonia. In the latter case, however, it is doubtful whether a simple addition product has ever been isolated.

6. Aldehydes react with aniline to form *anils* (azomethines):

$$R{\cdot}CHO + C_6H_5{\cdot}NH_2 \longrightarrow R{\cdot}CH{:}N{\cdot}C_6H_5 + H_2O$$

Aliphatic azomethines tend to polymerise; the aromatic analogues are stable.

7. Aldehydes undergo the **Schmidt reaction.** This is the reaction between a carbonyl compound and hydrazoic acid in the presence of concentrated sulphuric acid (or certain other acids, *e.g.*, trichloroacetic acid). Aldehydes are converted by the Schmidt reaction into cyanides and formyl derivatives of primary amines:

$$R{\cdot}CHO + HN_3 \xrightarrow{H_2SO_4} R{\cdot}CN + R{\cdot}NH{\cdot}CHO$$

The mechanism of the Schmidt reaction is uncertain. According to Smith (1948) it is:

$$H{-}C(R){=}O + H^+ \longrightarrow H{-}C^+(R){-}OH$$

$$H{-}C^+(R)(OH) + {:}\overset{-}{\ddot{N}}(H){-}\overset{+}{N}{\equiv}N{:} \longrightarrow H{-}C(R)(OH){-}\ddot{N}(H){-}\overset{+}{N}{\equiv}N{:} \xrightarrow{-H_2O} H{-}C(R){=}\ddot{N}{-}\overset{+}{N}{\equiv}N{:}$$

$$\xrightarrow{-N_2} H{-}C(R){=}\ddot{N}^+ \xrightarrow{H^-\ \text{migrates}} {}^+C(R){=}\ddot{N}{-}H \longrightarrow R{-}C{\equiv}N + H^+$$

$$\downarrow R^-\ \text{migrates}$$

$$H{-}\overset{+}{C}{=}\ddot{N}{-}R \xrightarrow{H_2O} H{-}C(\overset{+}{O}H_2){=}\ddot{N}{-}R \xrightarrow{-H^+} H{-}C({=}O){-}N(H){-}R$$

8. The lower aldehydes polymerise with great ease (see formaldehyde and acetaldehyde, below).

Reactions given by ketones only. 1. Ketones do not give Schiff's reaction. Acetone, however, restores the magenta colour *very slowly*.

2. Ketones are not easily oxidised (*cf.* p. 122); they do not reduce Fehling's solution or ammoniacal silver nitrate. Hence aldehydes and ketones may readily be distinguished by reactions 1 and 2.

α-Hydroxyketones, *i.e.*, compounds containing the group ·CH(OH)·CO·, readily reduce Fehling's solution and ammoniacal silver nitrate.

Strong oxidising agents, *e.g.*, acid dichromate, nitric acid, etc., oxidise ketones, only the carbon atoms adjacent to the carbonyl group being attacked, and the carbon atom joined to the smaller number of hydrogen atoms is preferentially oxidised:

$$CH_3{\cdot}CO{\cdot}|CH_2{\cdot}CH_3 \xrightarrow{[O]} 2CH_3{\cdot}CO_2H$$

If the adjacent carbon atoms have the same number of hydrogen atoms, the carbonyl group remains chiefly with the *smaller* alkyl group; *e.g.*, when hexan-3-one is oxidised, the main product is propionic acid, and this is accompanied by much smaller amounts of acetic and butyric acids:

$$CH_3{\cdot}CH_2{\cdot}CO{\cdot}|CH_2{\cdot}CH_2{\cdot}CH_3 \xrightarrow{[O]} 2CH_3{\cdot}CH_2{\cdot}CO_2H$$

$$CH_3{\cdot}CH_2|{\cdot}CO{\cdot}CH_2{\cdot}CH_2{\cdot}CH_3 \xrightarrow{[O]} CH_3{\cdot}CO_2H + CH_3{\cdot}CH_2{\cdot}CH_2{\cdot}CO_2H$$

The oxidation of ketones possibly occurs through the enol form (*cf.* p. 206).

All ketones containing the acetyl group, $CH_3{\cdot}CO$, undergo the **haloform reaction**. This reaction is best carried out by dissolving the compound in dioxan, adding dilute sodium hydroxide, then a slight excess of iodine in potassium iodide solution, warming, and finally adding water. If the compound contains the acetyl group, iodoform is precipitated (*cf.* iodoform, p. 107).

The haloform reaction is very useful in organic degradations. A positive iodoform test is given by all compounds containing the acetyl group attached to either carbon or hydrogen, or by compounds which are oxidised under the conditions of the test to derivatives containing the acetyl group, *e.g.*, ethanol, *iso*propanol, etc.

Booth and Saunders (1950) have shown that a number of other compounds besides those mentioned above also give the haloform reaction, *e.g.*, certain quinones, quinols and *m*-dihydric phenols.

In practice, the base-catalysed iodination of aliphatic methyl ketones does *not* occur quantitatively according to the equation:

$$CH_3{\cdot}CO{\cdot}R + 3I_2 + 4NaOH \longrightarrow CHI_3 + R{\cdot}CO_2Na + 3NaI + 3H_2O$$

For example, acetone and butanone consume more than the theoretical amount of iodine, whereas, *e.g.*, methyl *iso*propyl ketone consumes less than this quantity (Cullis *et al.*, 1956). Thus methods based on this reaction for the quantitative estimation of methyl ketones are unsatisfactory.

3. Ketones react with ammonia to form complex condensation products, *e.g.*, if acetone is treated with ammonia and then followed by acidification of the reaction products, *diacetonamine* (I), and *triacetonamine* (II), are formed. If the reaction is carried out at room temperature (I) is the chief product; if heated, (II) is the chief product (Bradbury *et al.*, 1947).

The mechanism of the reactions is uncertain, but it may be as follows. Ammonia (base) causes acetone to undergo the aldol condensation to give mesityl oxide and phorone, which then combine with ammonia to form respectively (I) and (II) (see also p. 261):

$$(CH_3)_2C{:}CH{\cdot}CO{\cdot}CH_3 + NH_3 \longrightarrow \underset{\text{(I)}}{(CH_3)_2C(NH_2){\cdot}CH_2{\cdot}CO{\cdot}CH_3}$$

$$(CH_3)_2C{:}CH{\cdot}CO{\cdot}CH{:}C(CH_3)_2 + 2NH_3 \longrightarrow$$

$$\left[\begin{array}{c} (CH_3)_2\underset{\displaystyle NH_2}{\underset{|}{C}}{\cdot}CH_2{\cdot}CO{\cdot}CH_2{\cdot}\underset{\displaystyle NH_2}{\underset{|}{C}}(CH_3)_2 \end{array}\right] \xrightarrow{-NH_3} \underset{\text{(II)}}{NH\begin{array}{l} \diagup C(CH_3)_2{-}CH_2 \\ \qquad\qquad\qquad\;\; \rangle CO \\ \diagdown C(CH_2)_2{-}CH_2 \end{array}}$$

4. Ketones do not readily form *ketals* when treated with alcohols in the presence of hydrogen chloride or calcium chloride (*cf.* acetals, above). Ketals may, however, be prepared by treating the ketone with ethyl orthoformate (Helferich and Hauser, 1924):

$$R_2CO + H{\cdot}C(OC_2H_5)_3 \longrightarrow R_2C(OC_2H_5)_2 + H{\cdot}CO_2C_2H_5 \quad (g.)$$

5. When ketones are reduced catalytically or in acid solution, secondary alcohols are obtained in good yields, but when they are reduced in neutral or alkaline solution, *pinacols* are the main products; *e.g.*, acetone reduced with magnesium amalgam forms *pinacol*:

$$2CH_3{\cdot}CO{\cdot}CH_3 + 2[H] \xrightarrow[H_2O]{Mg/Hg} (CH_3)_2C(OH){\cdot}C(OH)(CH_3)_2$$

6. When ketones are treated with nitrous acid, the "half oxime" of the α-dicarbonyl compound is formed, *e.g.*, acetone gives oximinoacetone (*iso*nitrosoacetone; see p. 291):

$$CH_3{\cdot}CO{\cdot}CH_3 + HNO_2 \xrightarrow{C_2H_5{\cdot}O{\cdot}NO/HCl} CH_3{\cdot}CO{\cdot}CH{:}N{\cdot}OH + H_2O$$

All compounds containing the $\cdot CH_2{\cdot}CO\cdot$ group form the oximino-derivative with nitrous acid, and this has been used to detect the presence of the $\cdot CH_2{\cdot}CO\cdot$ group.

Benzaldehyde can also be used to detect the presence of the $\cdot CH_2{\cdot}CO\cdot$ group (p. 622):

7. Ketones condense with chloroform in the presence of potassium hydroxide to form chlorohydroxy-compounds:

$$CH_3{\cdot}CO{\cdot}CH_3 + CHCl_3 \xrightarrow{KOH} (CH_3)_2C\begin{matrix} \diagup OH \\ \diagdown CCl_3 \end{matrix}$$

8. Ketones undergo the *Schmidt reaction* (see above) to form amides:

$$R{\cdot}CO{\cdot}R + HN_3 \xrightarrow{H_2SO_4} R{\cdot}CO{\cdot}NH{\cdot}R + N_2$$

9. Ketones form *sodio-derivatives* when treated with sodium or sodamide in ethereal solution (see p. 216), *e.g.*,

$$CH_3{\cdot}CO{\cdot}CH_3 + NaNH_2 \longrightarrow \left[\begin{matrix} O^- \\ | \\ CH_3{\cdot}C{=}CH_2 \end{matrix}\right] \overset{+}{Na} + NH_3$$

Formaldehyde (*methanal*), H·CHO, is prepared industrially:

(i) By passing methanol vapour over copper at 300°:

$$CH_3OH \longrightarrow H{\cdot}CHO + H_2$$

(ii) By passing methanol vapour mixed with air over a copper or silver catalyst at 250–360°:

$$CH_3OH + \tfrac{1}{2}O_2 \longrightarrow H{\cdot}CHO + H_2O$$

The amounts of methanol and air must be carefully controlled, otherwise formic acid will result due to the further oxidation of the formaldehyde:

$$H{\cdot}CHO + \tfrac{1}{2}O_2 \longrightarrow H{\cdot}CO_2H$$

The vapours are cooled, and the condensate obtained is a mixture of formaldehyde, methanol and water. It is freed from excess methanol by distillation, and the resulting mixture is known as *formalin* (40 per cent. formaldehyde, 8 per cent. methanol, 52 per cent. water).

(iii) By passing a mixture of methane and oxygen over certain catalysts, *e.g.*, molybdenum oxides:

$$CH_4 + O_2 \longrightarrow H{\cdot}CHO + H_2O$$

(iv) By the oxidation of natural gas.

Formaldehyde is a colourless, pungent-smelling gas, b.p. −21°, extremely soluble in water. The low boiling points of aldehydes (and ketones) compared with those of alcohols are probably due to the inability of carbonyl compounds to associate through hydrogen bonding. On the other hand, since the carbonyl oxygen atom is capable of forming hydrogen bonds with water, the solubility of aldehydes and ketones in water is to be expected for the lower members (*cf.* alcohols).

Formaldehyde is a powerful disinfectant and antiseptic, and so is used for preserving anatomical specimens. Its main uses are in the manufacture of dyes, the hardening of casein and gelatin, and for making plastics.

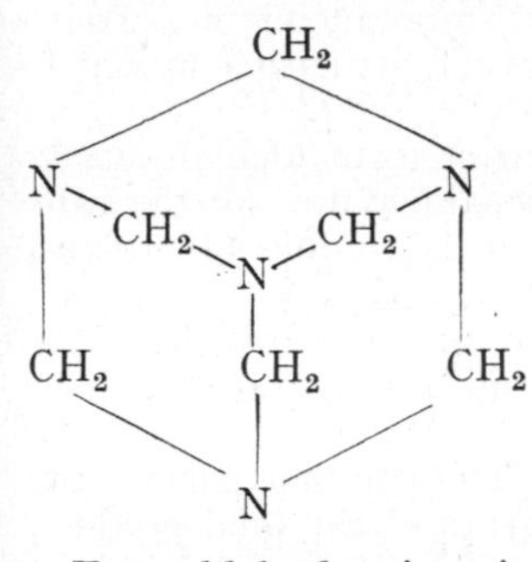

Formaldehyde undergoes many of the general reactions of aldehydes, but differs in certain respects. When treated with ammonia, it does not form an aldehyde-ammonia, but gives instead *hexamethylenetetramine*:

$$6H{\cdot}CHO + 4NH_3 \longrightarrow (CH_2)_6N_4 + 6H_2O \ (80\%)$$

The structure of hexamethylenetetramine appears to be a complicated ring compound. It is a crystalline solid, and has been used in medicine under the name of *urotropine* or *aminoform* as treatment for gout and rheumatism.

Formaldehyde, since it has no α-hydrogen atoms, readily undergoes the Cannizzaro reaction (see p. 148).

Formaldehyde is very useful for methylating primary and secondary amines, *e.g.*, it converts ethylamine into ethylmethylamine:

$$C_2H_5{\cdot}NH_2 + 2H{\cdot}CHO \longrightarrow C_2H_5{\cdot}NH{\cdot}CH_3 + H{\cdot}CO_2H$$

Polymers of formaldehyde. (i) Dilute formaldehyde solutions are stable, and the stability is believed to be due to the formation of methylene glycol:

$$CH_2O + H_2O \rightleftharpoons CH_2(OH)_2$$

On the other hand, polymethylene glycols, $(CH_2O)_n{\cdot}H_2O$, are formed in concentrated solutions of formaldehyde.

The structure of these compounds is believed to be $HOCH_2{\cdot}(CH_2O)_n{\cdot}OH$, and they may possibly be formed as follows:

$$HOCH_2\boxed{OH + H}OCH_2\boxed{OH + H}OCH_2OH + \ldots \longrightarrow HOCH_2{\cdot}(OCH_2)_n{\cdot}OH$$

An alternative mechanism is an ionic one:

$$CH_2{=}O \quad CH_2{=}O \quad CH_2{=}O\cdots \longrightarrow \overset{+}{C}H_2{\cdot}O{\cdot}CH_2{\cdot}O\cdots CH_2O^- \xrightarrow{H-OH} HOCH_2{\cdot}O{\cdot}CH_2{\cdot}O\cdots CH_2OH$$

Cessation of polymerisation is brought about by the intervention of a "foreign" molecule, water in this case.

(ii) When a formaldehyde solution is evaporated to dryness, a white crystalline solid, m.p. 121–123°, is obtained. This is known as *paraformaldehyde*, $(CH_2O)_n{\cdot}H_2O$, and it appears to be a mixture of polymers, n having values between 6 and 50. Paraformaldehyde reforms formaldehyde when heated.

Formaldehyde cannot be separated from methanol (in formalin) by fractionation; pure aqueous formaldehyde may be obtained by refluxing paraformaldehyde with water until solution is complete.

(iii) When a formaldehyde solution is treated with concentrated sulphuric acid, *polyoxymethylenes*, $(CH_2O)_n{\cdot}H_2O$—n is greater than 100—are formed.

Polyoxymethylenes are white solids, insoluble in water, and reform formaldehyde when heated.

(iv) When allowed to stand at room temperature, formaldehyde gas slowly polymerises to a white solid, *trioxymethylene* (*metaformaldehyde, trioxan*), $(CH_2O)_3$, m. p. 61–62°. This trimer is soluble in water, and does not show any reducing properties. Hence it is believed to have a cyclic structure (in which there is no free aldehyde group).

$$\text{cyclic trimer: } CH_2-O-CH_2-O-CH_2-O \text{ (six-membered ring)}$$

Trioxan is very useful for generating formaldehyde since: (*a*) it is an anhydrous form of formaldehyde; (*b*) the rate of depolymerisation can be controlled; and (*c*) it is soluble in organic solvents.

(v) Formaldehyde polymerises in the presence of weak alkalis, *e.g.*, calcium hydroxide, to a mixture of sugars of formula $C_6H_{12}O_6$, which is known as *formose* or α-*acrose*.

Condensation reactions of formaldehyde. Formaldehyde can participate in the "crossed" Cannizzaro reaction, and the nature of the final product depends on the structure of the other aldehyde. Aldehydes with *no* α-hydrogen atoms readily undergo the crossed Cannizzaro reaction; *e.g.*, benzaldehyde forms benzyl alcohol:

$$C_6H_5{\cdot}CHO + H{\cdot}CHO + NaOH \longrightarrow C_6H_5{\cdot}CH_2OH + H{\cdot}CO_2Na$$

Aldehydes with *one* α-hydrogen atom react as follows:

$$RR'CH{\cdot}CHO + H{\cdot}CHO \xrightarrow{NaOH} RR'C\begin{cases}CH_2OH\\CHO\end{cases}$$

This β-hydroxyaldehyde in the presence of excess formaldehyde forms a substituted trimethylene glycol:

$$RR'C\begin{cases}CH_2OH\\CHO\end{cases} + H{\cdot}CHO + NaOH \longrightarrow RR'C\begin{cases}CH_2OH\\CH_2OH\end{cases} + H{\cdot}CO_2Na$$

Thus the first step in the above reaction is the replacement of the α-hydrogen atom by a *hydroxymethyl* group, $\cdot CH_2OH$, and the second step is the crossed Cannizzaro reaction.

In a similar manner, aldehydes with *two* α-hydrogen atoms are converted first into the hydroxymethyl, then into the bishydroxymethyl, and finally into the trishydroxymethyl compound:

$$R{\cdot}CH_2{\cdot}CHO + H{\cdot}CHO \xrightarrow{NaOH} R{\cdot}CH\begin{cases}CHO\\CH_2OH\end{cases} \xrightarrow{H{\cdot}CHO}$$

$$R{\cdot}C\begin{cases}CHO\\CH_2OH\\CH_2OH\end{cases} \xrightarrow[NaOH]{H{\cdot}HCO} R{\cdot}C\begin{cases}CH_2OH\\CH_2OH\\CH_2OH\end{cases} + H{\cdot}CO_2Na$$

A special case is acetaldehyde, which has *three* α-hydrogen atoms. This reaction is best carried out by adding powdered calcium oxide to a suspension of paraformaldehyde in water containing acetaldehyde. Tetrakishydroxymethylmethane (tetramethylolmethane) or *pentaerythritol* is formed:

$$CH_3{\cdot}CHO + 4H{\cdot}CHO \xrightarrow{Ca(OH)_2} C(CH_2OH)_4 + H{\cdot}CO_2Ca/_2 \quad (55\text{–}57\%)$$

Pentaerythritol is important industrially since its tetra-nitrate is a powerful explosive.

Structure of formaldehyde. Analysis and molecular-weight determinations show that the molecular formula of formaldehyde is CH_2O. Assuming the quadrivalency of carbon, the bivalency of oxygen and the univalency of hydrogen, only one structure is possible:

$$\begin{array}{c} \text{H} \\ | \\ \text{H—C=O} \end{array}$$

This structure agrees with all the known properties of formaldehyde, and has been proved by both infra-red and ultra-violet spectra measurements.

Acetaldehyde (*ethanal*), $CH_3 \cdot CHO$, is prepared industrially:

(i) By passing ethanol vapour over copper at 300°:

$$CH_3 \cdot CH_2OH \longrightarrow CH_3 \cdot CHO + H_2$$

(ii) By passing ethanol vapour mixed with air over a silver catalyst at 250°:

$$C_2H_5OH + \tfrac{1}{2}O_2 \longrightarrow CH_3 \cdot CHO + H_2O$$

(iii) From acetylene:

$$C_2H_2 + H_2O \xrightarrow[HgSO_4]{H_2SO_4} CH_3 \cdot CHO$$

(iv) By the hydrolysis of methyl vinyl ether (*q.v.*):

$$CH_3 \cdot O \cdot CH{:}CH_2 + H_2O \longrightarrow CH_3 \cdot CHO + CH_3OH$$

(v) By the oxidation of natural gas.

Acetaldehyde is a colourless, pungent-smelling liquid, b.p. 21°, miscible with water, ethanol and ether in all proportions. It is used in the preparation of acetic acid, ethanol, paraldehyde, rubber accelerators, phenolic resins, synthetic drugs, etc.

Polymers of acetaldehyde. (i) When acetaldehyde is treated with a few drops of concentrated sulphuric acid, a vigorous reaction takes place and the trimer *paraldehyde*, $(CH_3 \cdot CHO)_3$, is formed. This is a pleasant-smelling liquid, b.p. 128°, and is used in medicine as an hypnotic. When paraldehyde is distilled with dilute sulphuric acid, acetaldehyde is regenerated. Paraldehyde has no reducing properties, and its structure is believed to be (I):

$$\begin{array}{ccccc} & & CH_3 & & \\ & & | & & \\ & & CH & & \\ & O\diagup & & \diagdown O & \\ & | & & | & \\ CH_3 \cdot HC & \diagdown & O & \diagup & CH \cdot CH_3 \end{array}$$

(I)

$$\begin{array}{c} CH_3 \cdot CH \cdot O \cdot CH \cdot CH_3 \\ \quad\;\; | \qquad\quad | \\ \quad\;\; O \qquad\quad O \\ \quad\;\; | \qquad\quad | \\ CH_3 \cdot CH \cdot O \cdot CH \cdot CH_3 \end{array}$$

(II)

(ii) When acetaldehyde is treated with a few drops of concentrated sulphuric acid at 0°, the tetramer *metaldehyde*, $(CH_3 \cdot CHO)_4$, is formed. This is a white solid, m.p. 246°, and regenerates acetaldehyde when distilled with dilute sulphuric acid. Its structure may be (II).

Structure of acetaldehyde. Analysis and molecular-weight determinations show that the molecular formula of acetaldehyde is C_2H_4O. Ethanol may be oxidised to acetaldehyde, which, in turn, may be oxidised to acetic acid. Both ethanol and acetic acid (*q.v.*) contain a methyl group, and it is therefore reasonable to suppose that this methyl group remains intact during the oxidation, and is therefore present in acetaldehyde:

$$\mathbf{CH_3}\text{—}CH_2OH \xrightarrow{[O]} \mathbf{CH_3}\text{—}CHO \xrightarrow{[O]} \mathbf{CH_3}\text{—}CO_2H$$

Phosphorus pentachloride reacts with acetaldehyde to form ethylidene chloride, $C_2H_4Cl_2$, and no hydrogen chloride is evolved in the reaction. This implies that there is no hydroxyl group present in acetaldehyde (*cf.* p. 126), and since two univalent chlorine atoms have replaced one bivalent oxygen atom, the inference is that there is a carbonyl group, $>C{=}O$, present.

Thus the structure of acetaldehyde is $CH_3{-}C\genfrac{}{}{0pt}{}{\nearrow O}{\searrow H}$.

Study of the dipole moments of aldehydes and ketones, however, has presented some difficulty in elucidating the structure of carbonyl compounds. It has been suggested that the values of the dipole moments are larger than can be accounted for by the inductive effect of the oxygen atom, and it has therefore been proposed that aldehydes and ketones are resonance hybrids:

$$>C{=}O \longleftrightarrow >\overset{+}{C}{-}\overset{-}{O}$$

Chloral (*trichloroacetaldehyde*), $CCl_3{\cdot}CHO$, is prepared industrially by the chlorination of ethanol. Chlorine is passed into cooled ethanol, and then at 60°, until no further absorption of chlorine takes place. The final product is chloral alcoholate, $CCl_3{\cdot}CH(OH){\cdot}(OC_2H_5)$, which separates out as a crystalline solid which, on distillation with concentrated sulphuric acid, gives chloral.

The mechanism of the reaction is obscure. The following set of equations have been proposed (Fritsch, 1897):

$$CH_3{\cdot}CH_2OH \xrightarrow{Cl_2} CH_3{\cdot}CH\genfrac{}{}{0pt}{}{\nearrow OH}{\searrow Cl} \xrightarrow{C_2H_5OH} [CH_3{\cdot}CH(OH){\cdot}(OC_2H_5)] \xrightarrow{C_2H_5OH}$$

$$[CH_3{\cdot}CH(OC_2H_5)_2] \xrightarrow{Cl_2} CH_2Cl{\cdot}CH(OC_2H_5)_2 \xrightarrow{Cl_2} CHCl_2{\cdot}CH(OC_2H_5)_2$$

$$CH_2Cl{\cdot}CH(OC_2H_5)_2 \xrightarrow{HCl} CH_2Cl{\cdot}CHCl{\cdot}(OC_2H_5); \quad CHCl_2{\cdot}CH(OC_2H_5)_2 \xrightarrow{Cl_2} CHCl_2{\cdot}CHCl{\cdot}(OC_2H_5)$$

$$CH_2Cl{\cdot}CHCl{\cdot}(OC_2H_5) \xrightarrow{Cl_2} CHCl_2{\cdot}CHCl{\cdot}(OC_2H_5) \xrightarrow{H_2O}$$

$$CHCl_2{\cdot}CH(OH){\cdot}(OC_2H_5) \xrightarrow{Cl_2} CCl_3{\cdot}CH(OH){\cdot}(OC_2H_5) \xrightarrow{H_2SO_4} CCl_3{\cdot}CHO$$

Chloral is a colourless, oily, pungent-smelling liquid, b.p. 98°, soluble in water, ethanol and ether. When heated with concentrated potassium hydroxide, it yields pure chloroform:

$$CCl_3{\cdot}CHO + KOH \longrightarrow CHCl_3 + H{\cdot}CO_2K$$

The hydrolysis of chloral has been carried out in alkaline solution containing deuterium, and the results are consistent with the following mechanism (Lauder *et al.*, 1946):

$$CCl_3{\cdot}CHO + OD^- \longrightarrow CCl_3^- + DO{\cdot}C\genfrac{}{}{0pt}{}{\nearrow H}{\searrow O}$$

$$OD^- + H{\cdot}COOD \longrightarrow DOD + H{\cdot}CO_2^-$$

$$CCl_3^- + DOD \longrightarrow DCCl_3 + OD^-$$

Chloral is oxidised by concentrated nitric acid to trichloroacetic acid (I), and is reduced by aluminium ethoxide to trichloroethanol (II).

$$\underset{(I)}{CCl_3{\cdot}CO_2H} \xleftarrow{HNO_3} CCl_3{\cdot}CHO \xrightarrow{Al(OC_2H_5)_3} \underset{(II)}{CCl_3{\cdot}CH_2OH}$$

Chloral undergoes the usual reactions of an aldehyde, but its behaviour towards water and ethanol is unusual. When chloral is treated with water or ethanol, combination takes place with the evolution of heat, and a crystalline solid is formed, chloral hydrate, m.p. 57°, or chloral alcoholate, m.p. 46°, respectively. *These compounds are stable,* and the water or ethanol can only be removed by treatment with concentrated sulphuric acid. It therefore seems likely that in chloral hydrate the water is present as *water of constitution, i.e.,* the structure of chloral hydrate is $CCl_3\cdot CH(OH)_2$; similarly, the structure of chloral alcoholate is $CCl_3\cdot CH(OH)\cdot(OC_2H_5)$. The stability of these compounds is remarkable in view of the fact that the group $>C(OH)_2$ in other compounds very readily eliminates water.

The mechanism of the elimination of water from the $>C(OH)_2$ group is possibly:

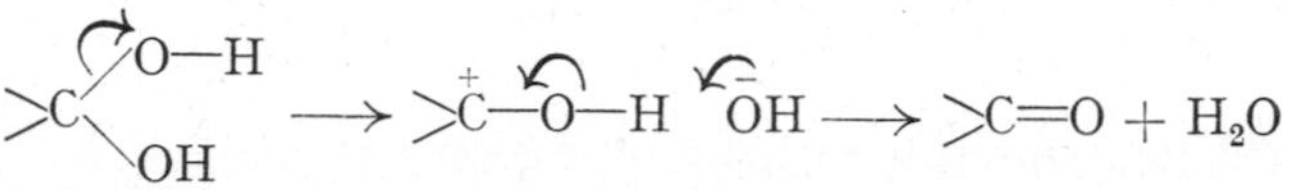

$$>C\begin{matrix}O-H\\OH\end{matrix} \longrightarrow >\overset{+}{C}-O-H \quad \overset{-}{O}H \longrightarrow >C{=}O + H_2O$$

One hydroxyl group is released as the hydroxyl ion; this leaves the carbon atom positively charged, causing it to attract towards itself the shared electron pair of the C—O bond. This causes the oxygen atom to attract towards itself the shared pair of the O—H bond, thus facilitating the release of a proton, the removal of which is completed by the hydroxyl ion.

In chloral (and in all compounds of the type $RCX_2\cdot CHO$), owing to the strong inductive effect of the chlorine atoms, the carbon atom of the aldehyde group acquires a small positive charge which will tend to prevent the release of a hydroxyl ion, *i.e.,* this will prevent the elimination of a molecule of water (III). On the other hand, Davies (1940) has shown by infra-red

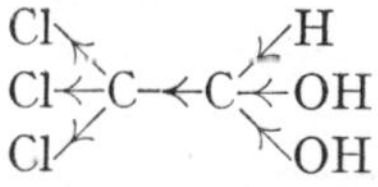

$Cl_3 \leftarrow C \leftarrow C(H)(\leftarrow OH)_2$ (III)

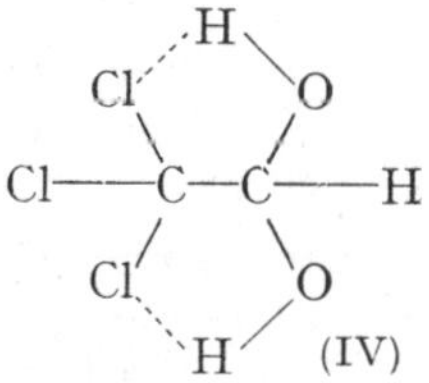

$Cl_3C-CH(O)_2$ with $Cl\cdots H-O$ hydrogen bonds (IV)

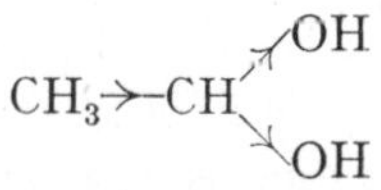

$CH_3 \rightarrow CH(\rightarrow OH)_2$ (V)

studies that chloral hydrate (and related compounds) contains hydrogen bonds, and he suggests that this accounts for the stability of the $>C(OH)_2$ group. It is possible that both hydrogen bonding and the inductive effect operate to stabilise chloral hydrate (IV). In the case of acetaldehyde the corresponding compound ethylidene glycol, $CH_3\cdot CH(OH)_2$, will be very unstable since the methyl group is electron repelling (V). This will displace the shared pair of the C—O bond towards the oxygen atom, thereby facilitating the release of a hydroxyl ion, *i.e.,* the elimination of water will take place readily. At the same time, no hydrogen bonding is possible to stabilise the molecule.

Methylene glycol, $CH_2(OH)_2$, will be more stable than ethylidene glycol since hydrogen is not electron-repelling, and dimethylmethylene glycol, $(CH_3)_2C(OH)_2$—from acetone and water—will be less stable than ethylidene glycol since the electron-repelling effect of two methyl groups must necessarily be more powerful than one.

Propionaldehyde, $CH_3\cdot CH_2\cdot CHO$, b.p. 49°, and ***iso*****butyraldehyde,** $(CH_3)_2CH\cdot CHO$, b.p. 61°, are prepared industrially by the isomerisation of propylene oxide and *iso*butylene oxide, respectively, in the presence of steam and an alumina–silica catalyst.

$$CH_3{\cdot}CH{-}CH_2 \text{ (epoxide, } {-}O{-}\text{ bridge)} \longrightarrow CH_3{\cdot}CH_2{\cdot}CHO$$

$$(CH_3)_2C{-}CH_2 \text{ (epoxide, } {-}O{-}\text{ bridge)} \longrightarrow (CH_3)_2CH{\cdot}CHO$$

Propionaldehyde is also prepared industrially by the *oxo process* by passing a compressed mixture of ethylene, carbon monoxide and hydrogen over the catalyst at 125–145° (p. 115).

Many higher aldehydes occur in nature, *e.g.*, *n*-octaldehyde, $C_8H_{16}O$, and *n*-nonaldehyde, $C_9H_{18}O$, in rose-oil; *n*-decaldehyde, $C_{10}H_{20}O$, in rose-oil and orange-peel oil.

Acetone (*dimethyl ketone, propan-2-one*), $CH_3{\cdot}CO{\cdot}CH_3$, is prepared industrially:

(i) By passing *iso*propanol vapour over copper at 300°:

$$CH_3{\cdot}CH(OH){\cdot}CH_3 \longrightarrow CH_3{\cdot}CO{\cdot}CH_3 + H_2$$

(ii) By passing acetic acid vapour over calcium oxide or manganous oxide at 300–400°:

$$2CH_3{\cdot}CO_2H \longrightarrow CH_3{\cdot}CO{\cdot}CH_3 + CO_2 + H_2O$$

(iii) By passing ethanol vapour mixed with steam over zinc chromite as catalyst, at 500°:

$$2C_2H_5OH + H_2O \longrightarrow CH_3{\cdot}CO{\cdot}CH_3 + CO_2 + 4H_2$$

A newer process is to pass a mixture of acetylene and steam over heated pure zinc oxide as catalyst. Another new process is to heat a mixture of propylene and steam under pressure in the presence of a suitable catalyst (p. 127). Acetone is also manufactured by the oxidation of natural gas.

(iv) By fermentation (see *n*-butanol, p. 128), but this method is being replaced by the above synthetic methods.

Acetone is a colourless, pleasant-smelling liquid, b.p. 56°, miscible with water, ethanol and ether in all proportions. Pure acetone is best prepared by saturating acetone with sodium iodide at 25–30°. The solution is decanted off from the excess solid, cooled to −10°, and the precipitate, $NaI{\cdot}3CH_3{\cdot}CO{\cdot}CH_3$, is warmed to 30°, pure dry acetone thereby being produced. Acetone is used as a solvent for acetylene, cellulose acetate and nitrate, celluloid, lacquers, etc., and for the preparation of keten, sulphonal, etc.

Ketones do not polymerise, but readily undergo condensation reactions. Acetone readily forms mesityl oxide, phorone and diacetone alcohol (p. 223), but in addition to these condensations, acetone forms mesitylene when distilled with concentrated sulphuric acid:

$$3CH_3{\cdot}CO{\cdot}CH_3 \longrightarrow C_6H_3(CH_3)_3 \text{ (1,3,5-trimethylbenzene)} + 3H_2O \quad (25\%)$$

Structure of acetone. Analysis and molecular-weight determinations show that the molecular formula of acetone is C_3H_6O. Acetone reacts with phosphorus pentachloride to form *iso*propylidene chloride, $C_3H_6Cl_2$, and no hydrogen chloride is evolved. This indicates that there is no hydroxyl group present, and since a bivalent oxygen atom has been replaced by two univalent chlorine atoms, this implies that a carbonyl group is present. Assuming the quadrivalency of carbon, the bivalency of oxygen and the univalency of hydrogen, there are two structures possible for acetone:

$$\text{(I)}\quad CH_3{\cdot}CH_2{\cdot}CHO \qquad\qquad CH_3{\cdot}CO{\cdot}CH_3\quad \text{(II)}$$

(I) contains the aldehyde group, but since acetone does not behave like an aldehyde, (II) must be its structure. This is confirmed by all the known reactions of acetone (*cf.* acetaldehyde, for the structure of the carbonyl group).

Ethyl methyl ketone, butan-2-one, $CH_3{\cdot}CO{\cdot}CH_2{\cdot}CH_3$, is prepared industrially:

(i) By passing *sec*-butanol vapour over copper at 300°:

$$CH_3{\cdot}CH(OH){\cdot}CH_2{\cdot}CH_3 \longrightarrow CH_3{\cdot}CO{\cdot}CH_2{\cdot}CH_3 + H_2$$

(ii) By the oxidation of *sec*.-butanol with air, using a silver catalyst at 250°:

$$CH_3{\cdot}CH(OH){\cdot}CH_2{\cdot}CH_3 + \tfrac{1}{2}O_2 \longrightarrow CH_3{\cdot}CO{\cdot}CH_2{\cdot}CH_3 + H_2O$$

Butanone is a pleasant-smelling liquid, b.p. 80°. It is widely used as a solvent for vinyl resins, synthetic rubber, etc.

Methyl *iso*propyl ketone, 3-methylbutan-2-one, $CH_3{\cdot}CO{\cdot}CH(CH_3)_2$, b.p. 94°, may be prepared in several ways, but the best method is by treating *tert*.-pentanol with bromine and hydrolysing the dibromo-derivative, whereupon a molecular rearrangement takes place; the mechanism of the steps involved is still not known:

$$(CH_3)_2C(OH){\cdot}CH_2{\cdot}CH_3 \xrightarrow{Br_2} (CH_3)_2CBr{\cdot}CHBr{\cdot}CH_3 \xrightarrow{H_2O}$$
$$[(CH_3)_2C(OH){\cdot}CH(OH){\cdot}CH_3] \xrightarrow[\text{rearranges}]{-H_2O} (CH_3)_2CH{\cdot}CO{\cdot}CH_3$$

***tert*.-Butyl methyl ketone, pinacolone, pinacone,** $CH_3{\cdot}CO{\cdot}C(CH_3)_3$, may be prepared:

(i) By distilling pinacol or pinacol hydrate with sulphuric acid:

$$(CH_3)_2C(OH){\cdot}C(OH)(CH_3)_2 \xrightarrow{-H_2O} CH_3{\cdot}CO{\cdot}C(CH_3)_3 \quad (65\text{–}72\%)$$

(ii) By passing pinacol dissolved in dioxan over a heated catalyst of silica-gel impregnated with phosphoric acid, a 94 per cent. yield of pinacolone being obtained (Emerson, 1947).

In these reactions a methyl group has migrated from one carbon atom to the other. This rearrangement is known as the *pinacol–pinacolone* rearrangement.

Pinacolone is a colourless liquid, b.p. 119°, with a camphor-like odour. It is oxidised by alkaline sodium hypobromite to trimethylacetic acid:

$$CH_3{\cdot}CO{\cdot}C(CH_3)_3 \xrightarrow{Br_2/NaOH} (CH_3)_3C{\cdot}CO_2H \quad (71\text{–}74\%)$$

Many higher ketones occur in nature, *e.g.*, heptan-2-one, $CH_3{\cdot}CO{\cdot}C_5H_{11}$, in clove-oil, and undecan-2-one, $CH_3{\cdot}CO{\cdot}C_9H_{19}$, in oil of rue.

The mechanism of the pinacol–pinacolone rearrangement is still unsettled, but Whitmore (1932) has offered a very interesting mechanism to account for this and other rearrangements (see below).

Consider the molecule ABX, where A and B represent single atoms and X is an atom or group of atoms which is strongly electron-attracting, *e.g.*, oxygen, halogen, nitrogen, hydroxyl group, and A and B are neither strongly electron-attracting nor repelling, *e.g.*, carbon. Molecules containing this structure can undergo the pinacol–pinacolone, Hofmann, Curtius, Lossen, Beckmann, etc., rearrangements (see text). According to the Whitmore mechanism, when the molecule enters reaction such that X is removed, *then X takes its shared pair of electrons, leaving atom B with 6 electrons (open sextet).* Thus:

$$:\ddot{\underset{\cdot\cdot}{A}}:\ddot{\underset{\cdot\cdot}{B}}:\ddot{\underset{\cdot\cdot}{X}}: \longrightarrow :\ddot{\underset{\cdot\cdot}{A}}:\ddot{\underset{\cdot\cdot}{B}}^{+} + :\ddot{\underset{\cdot\cdot}{X}}:^{-}$$

Three different reactions may now take place, depending on the conditions:

(i) AB combines with the negative ion Y from the reaction mixture, resulting in a normal substitution reaction:

$$:\ddot{\underset{\cdot\cdot}{A}}:\ddot{\underset{\cdot\cdot}{B}}^{+} + :\ddot{\underset{\cdot\cdot}{Y}}:^{-} \longrightarrow :\ddot{\underset{\cdot\cdot}{A}}:\ddot{\underset{\cdot\cdot}{B}}:\ddot{\underset{\cdot\cdot}{Y}}:$$

(ii) If one of the atoms attached to A is hydrogen, then AB can lose a proton, and so the fragment AB is stabilised by olefin formation:

$$H:\ddot{\underset{\cdot\cdot}{A}}:\ddot{\underset{\cdot\cdot}{B}}^{+} \longrightarrow \ddot{\underset{\cdot\cdot}{A}}\vdots\ddot{\underset{\cdot\cdot}{B}} + \overset{+}{H}$$

The loss of a proton is facilitated by the positive charge on B which produces the inductive effect: $H \rightarrow A \rightarrow B^{+}$. An example of this type of reaction is the formation of ethylene from ethanol under the influence of concentrated sulphuric acid:

$$H:\underset{H}{\overset{H}{\ddot{\underset{\cdot\cdot}{C}}}}:\underset{H}{\overset{H}{\ddot{\underset{\cdot\cdot}{C}}}}:\ddot{\underset{\cdot\cdot}{O}}:H + \overset{+}{H} \xrightarrow{H_2SO_4} H:\underset{H}{\overset{H}{\ddot{\underset{\cdot\cdot}{C}}}}:\underset{H}{\overset{H}{\ddot{\underset{\cdot\cdot}{C}}}}:\overset{H}{\ddot{O}}{}^{+}:H \longrightarrow$$

$$H:\underset{H}{\overset{H}{\ddot{\underset{\cdot\cdot}{C}}}}:\underset{H}{\overset{H}{\ddot{\underset{\cdot\cdot}{C}}}}{}^{+} + H_2O \longrightarrow \underset{H}{\overset{H}{\ddot{\underset{\cdot\cdot}{C}}}}\vdots\underset{H}{\overset{H}{\ddot{\underset{\cdot\cdot}{C}}}} + H^{+}$$

(iii) If B has a greater electron-affinity than A, the electrons rearrange as follows:

$$:\ddot{\underset{\cdot\cdot}{A}}:\ddot{\underset{\cdot\cdot}{B}}^{+} \longrightarrow :\overset{+}{\underset{\cdot\cdot}{A}}:\ddot{\underset{\cdot\cdot}{B}}:$$

A now has the open sextet, and the shift of this electron pair also includes the atom or group which it holds. The fragment so formed can now combine with ions X or Y, and the result is the abnormal or rearranged product XAB or YAB, respectively.

The detailed mechanism of the pinacol–pinacolone rearrangement is still not certain, but it is generally accepted that the first stage of the reaction is addition of a proton to one of the hydroxyl groups. Thus, according to Duncan *et al.* (1956), the rearrangement in aqueous acids, *e.g.*, hydrochloric, sulphuric, nitric, etc., is (P = pinacol):

$$P + H^{+} \underset{}{\overset{\text{fast}}{\rightleftharpoons}} HP^{+} \xrightarrow{\text{slow}} \text{products}$$

Thus a possible mechanism, using the Whitmore mechanism, is:

$$CH_3-\underset{CH_3}{\overset{OH}{\underset{|}{\overset{|}{C}}}}-\underset{OH}{\overset{CH_3}{\underset{|}{\overset{|}{C}}}}-CH_3 \overset{H^+}{\rightleftharpoons} CH_3-\underset{CH_3}{\overset{\overset{+}{O}H_2}{\underset{|}{\overset{|}{C}}}}-\underset{OH}{\overset{CH_3}{\underset{|}{\overset{|}{C}}}}-CH_3 \longrightarrow$$

$$H_2O + \begin{matrix} H_3C \\ H_3C \end{matrix}\!\!>C\!-\!\!-\!C\!<\!\!\begin{matrix} CH_3 \\ CH_3 \end{matrix} \text{ (bridged by } \overset{+}{O}\text{–H)} \longrightarrow CH_3\cdot\underset{O}{\underset{\|}{C}}\cdot C\!\!\begin{matrix} CH_3 \\ CH_3 \\ CH_3 \end{matrix} + H^+$$

QUESTIONS

1. Write out the structures and names of the isomeric aldehydes and ketones having the molecular formula $C_5H_{10}O$.
2. What are all the possible oxidation products of: (*a*) *n*-pentanol, (*b*) hexan-2-ol, (*c*) *tert.*-butanol?
3. Give an analytical table to show how you could distinguish between the following alcohols: methanol, ethanol, *iso*propanol and pentan-3-ol.
4. Starting with ethanol, how would you synthesise: (*a*) *iso*butyraldehyde; (*b*) crotyl alcohol?
5. Show, by means of equations, how you would convert acetylene into isoprene.
6. Describe the industrial methods of preparation of:—(*a*) formaldehyde, (*b*) acetaldehyde, (*c*) chloral, (*d*) acetone, (*e*) butanone.
7. Give an account of the evidence for the structure of (*a*) propionaldehyde, (*b*) butanone.
8. Name the compounds and state the conditions under which they are formed when acetaldehyde or acetone, respectively, is treated with:—(*a*) "nascent" hydrogen, (*b*) molecular hydrogen, (*c*) aluminium *iso*propoxide, (*d*) aluminium ethoxide, (*e*) sodium ethoxide, (*f*) NH_3, (*g*) $NaHSO_3$, (*h*) HCN, (*i*) N_2H_4, (*j*) RSH, (*k*) Br_2, (*l*) PBr_5, (*m*) SeO_2, (*n*) NaOH, (*o*) HCl, (*p*) ammoniacal $AgNO_3$, (*q*) $C_6H_5\cdot NH_2$, (*r*) HN_3, (*s*) ROH, (*t*) HNO_2, (*u*) SO_2Cl_2, (*v*) Fehling's solution, (*w*) H·CHO.
9. Define and give examples of:—(*a*) the Oppenauer oxidation, (*b*) the Rosenmund reduction, (*c*) ozonolysis, (*d*) Stephen's aldehyde synthesis, (*e*) the Meerwein–Ponndorf–Verley reduction, (*f*) the Wolff–Kishner reduction, (*g*) the Clemmensen reduction, (*h*) Girard's reagent, (*i*) the aldol condensation, (*j*) the Cannizzaro reaction, (*k*) the Claisen condensation, (*l*) the Claisen reaction, (*m*) the Knoevenagel reaction, (*n*) the Perkin reaction, (*o*) disproportionation, (*p*) the Tischenko reaction, (*q*) the haloform reaction, (*r*) the pinacol–pinacolone rearrangement, (*s*) the Schmidt reaction, (*t*) polymerisation, (*u*) condensation, (*v*) the crossed Cannizzaro reaction, (*w*) Darzens glycidic ester condensation.

READING REFERENCES

Bevington, The Polymerisation of Aldehydes, *Quart. Reviews* (*Chem. Soc.*), 1952, **6**, 141.
Fuson and Bull, The Haloform Reaction, *Chem. Reviews*, 1934, **15**, 275.
Booth and Saunders, The Iodoform Reaction, *Chem. and Ind.*, 1950, 824.
Organic Reactions (Wiley).

(i) Vol. I. (1942), Ch. 7. The Clemmensen Reduction.
(ii) Vol. II. (1944), Ch. 3. The Cannizzaro Reaction.
(iii) Vol. II. (1944), Ch. 5. Reduction with Aluminium Alkoxides.
(iv) Vol. IV. (1948), Ch. 7. The Rosenmund Reduction of Acid Chlorides to Aldehydes.
(v) Vol. IV. (1948), Ch. 8. The Wolff–Kishner Reduction.
(vi) Vol. V. (1949), Ch. 7. The Leuckart Reaction.
(vii) Vol. V. (1949), Ch. 8. Selenium Dioxide Oxidation.
(viii) Vol. V. (1949), Ch. 10. The Darzens Glycidic Ester Condensation.
(ix) Vol. VI. (1951), Ch. 5. The Oppenauer Oxidation.
(x) Vol. III. (1946), Ch. 8. The Schmidt Reaction.
(xi) Vol. VII. (1953), Ch. 6. The Nitrosation of Aliphatic Carbon Atoms.
(xii) Vol. VIII. (1954), Ch. 5. The Synthesis of Aldehydes from Carboxylic Acids.

Whitmore, The Common Basis of Intramolecular Rearrangements, *J. Amer. Chem. Soc.*, 1932, **54**, 3274.
Davies, An Infra-Red Study of Chloral Hydrate and Related Compounds, *Trans. Faraday Soc.*, 1940, **63**, 333, 1114.
Walsh, Remarks on the Strengths of Bonds, *ibid.*, 1947, 46, 60, 158, 342.
Smith, The Schmidt Reaction, *J. Amer. Chem. Soc.*, 1948, **70**, 320.
Angyal *et al.*, The Preparation of Aliphatic Aldehydes, *J.C.S.*, **1953**, 1737.
Duncan and Lynn, The Mechanism of the Pinacol–Pinacone Rearrangement, *ibid.*, **1956**, 3512, 3519, 3674.
Ballester, Mechanisms of the Darzens and Related Condensations, *Chem. Reviews*, 1955, **55**, 283.

CHAPTER IX

FATTY ACIDS

THE fatty acid series was so named because some of the higher members, particularly palmitic and stearic acids, occur in natural fats. The general formula of the fatty acids is $C_nH_{2n}O_2$. As, however, their functional group is the carboxyl group, $-CO_2H$, they are more conveniently expressed as $C_nH_{2n+1}CO_2H$ or $R{\cdot}CO_2H$, since these show the nature of the functional group. Furthermore, since the fatty acids contain only one carboxyl group, they are also known as the *saturated monocarboxylic acids*.

Only the hydrogen atom of the carboxyl group is replaceable by a metal; therefore the fatty acids are monobasic. The structure of the carboxyl group is written as $-C\begin{matrix}\diagup\!\!\diagup O\\ \diagdown OH\end{matrix}$ (or $-COOH$), but, as we shall see later, it does not represent accurately the behaviour of the carboxyl group.

Nomenclature. The fatty acids are commonly known by their trivial names, which have been derived from the source of the particular acid; *e.g.*, formic acid, $H{\cdot}CO_2H$, was so named because it was first obtained by the distillation of ants; the Latin word for ant is *formica*. Acetic acid, $CH_3{\cdot}CO_2H$, is the chief constituent of vinegar, the Latin word for which is *acetum*; etc. (see below).

Another system of nomenclature considers the fatty acids, except formic acid, as derivatives of acetic acid, *e.g.*,

$CH_3{\cdot}CH_2{\cdot}CO_2H$	methylacetic acid
$(CH_3)_3C{\cdot}CO_2H$	trimethylacetic acid
$(CH_3)_2CH{\cdot}CH_2{\cdot}CO_2H$	*iso*propylacetic acid

In the above two systems the positions of substituents in the chain are indicated by Greek letters, the α-carbon atom being the one joined to the carboxyl group, *e.g.*,

$CH_3{\cdot}CH(OH){\cdot}CH_2{\cdot}CH_2{\cdot}CO_2H$	γ-hydroxyvaleric acid
$CH_3{\cdot}CHCl{\cdot}CH(CH_3){\cdot}CO_2H$	β-chloro-α-methylbutyric acid

According to the I.U.C. system of nomenclature, the suffix of the monocarboxylic acids is *-oic*, which is added to the name of the alkane corresponding to the longest carbon chain containing the carboxyl group, *e.g.*,

$H{\cdot}CO_2H$	methanoic acid
$CH_3{\cdot}CH_2{\cdot}CO_2H$	propanoic acid

The positions of side-chains (or substituents) are indicated by numbers, *the carboxyl group always being given number* 1 (see p. 58), *e.g.*,

$CH_3{\cdot}CH(CH_3){\cdot}CH(CH_3){\cdot}CH_2{\cdot}CO_2H$	3 : 4-dimethylpentanoic acid

Alternatively, the carboxyl group is regarded as a substituent, and is denoted by the suffix carboxylic acid, *e.g.*,

$$\overset{4}{C}H_3{\cdot}\overset{3}{C}H_2{\cdot}\overset{2}{C}H(CH_3){\cdot}\overset{1}{C}H_2{\cdot}CO_2H \qquad \text{2-methylbutane-1-carboxylic acid}$$

According to the *British Chemical Abstracts*, when numbering substituents in acids, the carbon atom of the carboxyl group is not assigned a number, number 1 being given to the α-carbon atom. Thus, in this scheme, the Greek letters α, β, etc., are replaced by 1, 2, etc., *e.g.*,

$CH_3{\cdot}CHBr{\cdot}CH_2{\cdot}CO_2H$ 2-bromo-*n*-butyric acid or 2-bromopropane-1-carboxylic acid

In this book the α-carbon atom will be given number 2, but the reader should always ascertain which system of numbering has been used by individual authors.

General methods of preparation. 1. Oxidation of alcohols, aldehydes or ketones with acid dichromate yields acids:

$$R{\cdot}CH_2OH \xrightarrow{[O]} R{\cdot}CHO \xrightarrow{[O]} R{\cdot}CO_2H \qquad (g.\text{–}v.g.)$$

$$R_2CHOH \xrightarrow{[O]} R_2CO \xrightarrow{[O]} R{\cdot}CO_2H + R'{\cdot}CO_2H \qquad (g.)$$

In certain cases the ester, and not the acid, is obtained by the oxidation of alcohols. Part of the alcohol is oxidised, and the acid formed esterifies the rest of the alcohol (see p. 177).

2. A very good synthetic method is the hydrolysis of cyanides with acid or alkali:

$$R{\cdot}C{\equiv}N \xrightarrow{H_2O} \left[R{-}C\begin{matrix}{\diagup}OH\\ {\diagdown\!\!\diagdown}NH\end{matrix}\right] \longrightarrow R{-}C\begin{matrix}{/\!\!/}O\\ {\diagdown}NH_2\end{matrix} \xrightarrow{H_2O} R{\cdot}CO_2H + NH_3 \qquad (g.\text{–}v.g.)$$

The amide, $R{\cdot}CO{\cdot}NH_2$, may be isolated if suitable precautions are taken (p. 190).

3. By the reaction between a Grignard reagent and carbon dioxide:

$$RMgX + CO_2 \longrightarrow R{\cdot}CO_2MgX \xrightarrow{H_2O} R{\cdot}CO_2H$$

4. Many fatty acids may be conveniently synthesised from alkyl halides and ethyl malonate or acetoacetic ester. These syntheses will be discussed in detail later (pp. 215, 218).

5. A number of higher fatty acids may be obtained by the hydrolysis of natural fats, but it is usually difficult to obtain the acids pure from these sources. On the other hand, higher fatty acids may be prepared by the electrolysis of a methanolic solution of a mixture of a monocarboxylic acid and a half-ester of a dicarboxylic acid (Linstead *et al.*, 1950; *cf.* p. 46):

$$R{\cdot}CO_2H + CO_2H{\cdot}(CH_2)_n{\cdot}CO_2CH_3 \longrightarrow H_2 + 2CO_2 + R{\cdot}(CH_2)_n{\cdot}CO_2CH_3$$

6. By the hydrolysis of trihalogen derivatives in which the three halogen atoms are all attached to the same carbon atom:

$$R{\cdot}CX_3 \xrightarrow{KOH} [R{\cdot}C(OH)_3] \longrightarrow R{\cdot}CO_2H + H_2O$$

The above method has very little practical importance, since all trihalogen derivatives, except those of methane, are inaccessible.

7. The sodium salt of a fatty acid may be obtained by heating a sodium alkoxide with carbon monoxide under pressure:

$$RONa + CO \longrightarrow R{\cdot}CO_2Na$$

It has also been found that the acid may be obtained by heating the alcohol with carbon monoxide at 125–180°, under a pressure of 500 atmospheres, in the presence of a catalyst of boron trifluoride and a little water:

$$ROH + CO \longrightarrow R{\cdot}CO_2H$$

The sodium salts of acetic and propionic acids are formed by the interaction of methylsodium or ethylsodium, respectively, and carbon dioxide, *e.g.*,

$$C_2\bar{H}_5\overset{+}{Na} + CO_2 \longrightarrow C_2H_5{\cdot}CO_2Na$$

A recent method of preparing fatty acids is by the catalytic oxidation of long-chain hydrocarbons. The hydrocarbons are obtained from the wax fraction of the Fischer–Tropsch synthesis of hydrocarbons (p. 54), which are oxidised by the passage of air at 120° in the presence of manganous stearate as catalyst; or by oxidising with air in aluminium vessels, the aluminium acting as catalyst. A mixture of fatty acids is obtained, and this has been used for making fats. The actual composition of the mixture of acids has not yet been ascertained.

Another recent method for manufacturing fatty acids is to heat an olefin with carbon monoxide and steam under pressure at 300–400° in the presence of a catalyst, *e.g.*, phosphoric acid:

$$CH_2{=}CH_2 + CO + H_2O \longrightarrow CH_3{\cdot}CH_2{\cdot}CO_2H$$

$$CH_3{\cdot}CH{=}CH_3 + CO + H_2O \longrightarrow (CH_3)_2CH{\cdot}CO_2H$$

General properties of the fatty acids. The first three fatty acids are colourless, pungent-smelling liquids; the acids from butyric, $C_4H_8O_2$, to nonoic, $C_9H_{18}O_2$, are oils which smell like goats' butter; and those higher than decoic acid, $C_{10}H_{20}O_2$, are odourless solids.

The lower members are far less volatile than is to be expected from their molecular weight. A study of the infra-red absorption spectra of carboxylic acids has led to the conclusion that these acids exist as dimers in the liquid and solid states (Sheppard *et al.*, 1953). The existence of these dimers can be explained by hydrogen bonding, and electron diffraction studies (Pauling, 1934) have shown that an eight-membered ring is present. On the other hand, a study of infra-red spectra of formic acid in the liquid and solid states has provided evidence that this acid, unlike most of the other carboxylic acids, is not dimeric in these states, but is associated as a polymer (Chapman, 1956).

$$R{-}C\begin{matrix}{/\!\!/}O\cdots H{-}O\backslash \\ \backslash O{-}H\cdots O{/\!\!/}\end{matrix}C{-}R$$

The melting points of the *n*-fatty acids show alternation or oscillation from one member to the next, the melting point of an " even " acid being higher than that of the " odd " acid immediately below and above it in the series (see the physical constants of the individuals). A number of homologous series follow this oscillation or " saw-tooth " rule; some authors believe this to be connected with the zig-zag nature of the carbon chain.

The first four members are very soluble in water, and the solubility decreases as the molecular weight increases.

General reactions of the fatty acids. 1. The fatty acids are acted upon by the strongly electropositive metals with the liberation of hydrogen and formation of a salt:

$$R{\cdot}CO_2H + Na \longrightarrow R{\cdot}CO_2Na + \tfrac{1}{2}H_2$$

Salts are also formed by the reaction between an acid and an alkali:

$$R{\cdot}CO_2H + NaOH \longrightarrow R{\cdot}CO_2Na + H_2O$$

2. Fatty acids react with alcohols to form *esters*:

$$R\cdot CO_2H + R'OH \rightleftharpoons R\cdot CO_2R' + H_2O$$

3. Phosphorus trichloride, phosphorus pentachloride or thionyl chloride act upon the fatty acids to form *acid chlorides*:

$$3R\cdot CO_2H + PCl_3 \longrightarrow 3R\cdot COCl + H_3PO_3$$
$$R\cdot CO_2H + PCl_5 \longrightarrow R\cdot COCl + HCl + POCl_3$$
$$R\cdot CO_2H + SOCl_2 \longrightarrow R\cdot COCl + HCl + SO_2$$

The acid series may be "stepped up" via the acid chloride, but since the process involves many steps, the yield of the higher acid homologue is usually only *f.–f.g.*:

$$(a)\ R\cdot CO_2H \xrightarrow{PCl_5} R\cdot COCl \xrightarrow[\text{catalyst}]{H_2} R\cdot CHO \xrightarrow[\text{catalyst}]{H_2} R\cdot CH_2OH \xrightarrow{PBr_3} R\cdot CH_2Br \xrightarrow{KCN} R\cdot CH_2\cdot CN \xrightarrow{H_2O} R\cdot CH_2\cdot CO_2H$$

$$(b)\ R\cdot CO_2H \xrightarrow{PCl_5} R\cdot COCl \xrightarrow{KCN} R\cdot CO\cdot CN \xrightarrow{H_2O} R\cdot CO\cdot CO_2H \xrightarrow[\text{reduction}]{\text{Clemmensen}} R\cdot CH_2\cdot CO_2H$$

Although method (*b*) involves fewer steps than (*a*), the final yield of acid by route (*a*) is higher than that by (*b*), since the yields in each step of (*b*) are generally low.

4. When the ammonium salts of the fatty acids are strongly heated, the *acid amide* is formed by the elimination of water:

$$R\cdot CO_2NH_4 \longrightarrow R\cdot CO\cdot NH_2 + H_2O$$

5. When the anhydrous sodium salt of a fatty acid is heated with soda-lime, a paraffin and other products are formed (p. 45).

$$R\cdot CO_2Na + NaOH(CaO) \longrightarrow RH + Na_2CO_3$$

The mechanism of this decarboxylation is uncertain, but there is much evidence to show that *salts* decompose by an S_E1 reaction:

$$R{-}C(=O)O^- \longrightarrow \bar{R}\colon + O{=}C{=}O$$

$$\bar{R}\colon + \overset{+}{H} \longrightarrow R{-}H$$

The decarboxylation of *free* acids may be:

$$R{-}C(=O){-}O{-}H \longrightarrow \overset{+}{H} + R{-}C(=O)O^- \longrightarrow \overset{+}{H} + \bar{R}\colon + CO_2 \longrightarrow R{-}H + CO_2$$

If the calcium, barium, manganous or thorium salt of a fatty acid is strongly heated, a ketone is formed (p. 137). This reaction may be used to "step down" the acid series. The calcium salt of the acid is heated with calcium acetate, and the methyl ketone produced is oxidised with acid dichromate:

$$R\cdot CH_2\cdot CO_2Ca/_2 + CH_3\cdot CO_2\cdot Ca/_2 \longrightarrow R\cdot CH_2\cdot CO\cdot CH_3 \xrightarrow{[O]} R\cdot CO_2H + CH_3CO_2H$$

It should be noted that the second step is based on the general rule that when an unsymmetrical ketone is oxidised, the carbonyl group remains chiefly with the smaller alkyl group.

Since very few fatty acids containing an odd number of carbon atoms occur naturally, this method of descending the series affords a useful means of obtaining " odd " acids from " even ".

When a mixture of the calcium salt (or any of the others mentioned above) and calcium formate is heated, an aldehyde is obtained:

$$R{\cdot}CO_2Ca/_2 + H{\cdot}CO_2Ca/_2 \longrightarrow R{\cdot}CHO + CaCO_3$$

Metallic salts, particularly the silver salts, are converted by bromine into the alkyl bromide. This reaction may also be used to " step down " the acid series (p. 96).

6. When a concentrated aqueous solution of the sodium or potassium salt of a fatty acid is electrolysed, a paraffin is obtained:

$$2R{\cdot}CO_2K + 2H_2O \longrightarrow R{-}R + 2CO_2 + 2KOH + H_2$$

7. Fatty acids may be readily halogenated in the *α-position*, and the reaction is best carried out in the presence of a halogen carrier (see p. 196), *e.g.*,

$$R{\cdot}CH_2{\cdot}CO_2H \xrightarrow{P/Br_2} R{\cdot}CHBr{\cdot}CO_2H \xrightarrow{P/Br_2} R{\cdot}CBr_2{\cdot}CO_2H$$

8. All the fatty acids, except formic acid, are extremely resistant to oxidation, but prolonged heating with oxidising agents ultimately produces carbon dioxide and water.

9. All the fatty acids are resistant to reduction, but prolonged heating under pressure with concentrated hydriodic acid and a small amount of red phosphorus produces a paraffin. Paraffins are also produced when a fatty acid is heated with hydrogen at high temperature and under pressure, in the presence of a nickel catalyst.

$$R{\cdot}CO_2H + 3H_2 \xrightarrow{Ni} R{\cdot}CH_3 + 2H_2O$$

If the hydrogenation is carried out in the presence of a ruthenium or copper–chromium oxide catalyst, carboxylic acids are converted into primary alcohols (Guyer *et al.*, 1955). Lithium aluminium hydride also reduces acids to alcohols.

10. The fatty acids undergo the *Schmidt reaction* (p. 150) to form a primary amine:

$$R{\cdot}CO_2H + HN_3 \xrightarrow{H_2SO_4} R{\cdot}NH_2 + CO_2 + N_2$$

Formic acid (*methanoic acid*), $H{\cdot}CO_2H$, is prepared industrially by heating sodium hydroxide with carbon monoxide at 210°, and at a pressure of 6–10 atmospheres:

$$NaOH + CO \longrightarrow H{\cdot}CO_2Na$$

An aqueous solution of formic acid is obtained by distilling the sodium salt with dilute sulphuric acid:

$$2H{\cdot}CO_2Na + H_2SO_4 \longrightarrow 2H{\cdot}CO_2H + Na_2SO_4$$

Anhydrous formic acid is obtained by warming the sodium salt with concentrated sulphuric acid to which has been added some anhydrous formic acid. Concentrated sulphuric acid dehydrates formic acid to carbon monoxide:

$$H{\cdot}CO_2H \xrightarrow[H_2SO_4]{-H_2O} CO$$

On the other hand, concentrated sulphuric acid diluted with formic acid shows very little tendency to dehydrate formic acid.

Formic acid may be prepared in the laboratory in several ways. One method is to pass methanol vapour or formaldehyde mixed with air over a platinum-black catalyst:

$$CH_3OH + O_2 \xrightarrow{Pt} H \cdot CO_2H + H_2O$$

$$H \cdot CHO + \tfrac{1}{2}O_2 \xrightarrow{Pt} H \cdot CO_2H$$

Another method, which is mainly of academic interest, is the hydrolysis of hydrogen cyanide:

$$HCN + 2H_2O \xrightarrow{acid} H \cdot CO_2H + NH_3$$

Carbon dioxide, when passed into an ethereal solution of lithium borohydride at 0°, is reduced to formic acid (Burr *et al.*, 1950):

$$2CO_2 + 2LiBH_4 \longrightarrow 2H \cdot CO_2Li + B_2H_6 \ (69\text{–}88\%)$$

The most convenient laboratory preparation of formic acid is to heat glycerol with oxalic acid at 100–110°. Glyceryl monoxalate is produced, and decomposes into glyceryl monoformate (monoformin) and carbon dioxide. When the evolution of carbon dioxide ceases, more oxalic acid is added, whereupon formic acid is produced:

$$\begin{array}{l} CH_2OH \\ | \\ CHOH \\ | \\ CH_2OH \end{array} + \begin{array}{l} COOH \\ | \\ COOH \end{array} \longrightarrow \begin{array}{l} CH_2O \cdot CO \cdot COOH \\ | \\ CHOH \\ | \\ CH_2OH \end{array} + H_2O \xrightarrow{100\text{–}110^\circ}$$

$$CO_2 + \begin{array}{l} CH_2O \cdot CO \cdot H \\ | \\ CHOH \\ | \\ CH_2OH \end{array} \xrightarrow{(COOH)_2} \begin{array}{l} CH_2O \cdot CO \cdot COOH \\ | \\ CHOH \\ | \\ CH_2OH \end{array} + H \cdot CO_2H$$

The distillate contains formic acid and water. The aqueous formic acid solution cannot be fractionated to give anhydrous formic acid because the boiling point of the acid is 100·5°. The procedure adopted is to neutralise the aqueous acid solution with lead carbonate, and concentrate the solution until lead formate crystallises out. The precipitate is then recrystallised, dried, and heated at 100° in a current of hydrogen sulphide:

$$(H \cdot CO_2)_2Pb + H_2S \longrightarrow 2H \cdot CO_2H + PbS$$

The anhydrous formic acid which distils over contains a small amount of hydrogen sulphide, and may be freed from the latter by adding some dry lead formate and redistilling.

The above procedure for obtaining the anhydrous acid from its aqueous solution can only be used for volatile acids.

Formic acid is a pungent corrosive liquid, m.p. 8·4°, b.p. 100·5°, miscible in all proportions with water, ethanol and ether. It forms salts which, except for the lead and silver salts, are readily soluble in water. Physico-chemical methods show that formic acid exists as the dimer in the vapour phase, and this is believed to be due to hydrogen bonding (see general properties). In the liquid state the degree of association is much higher, and this accounts for its high boiling point as compared with that of the corresponding paraffin, alcohol or aldehyde. Formic acid is a stronger acid than any of its homologues (see Table III).

TABLE III

Acid	Dissociation Constant, k (at 25°)
Formic	$2 \cdot 4 \times 10^{-4}$
Acetic	$1 \cdot 845 \times 10^{-5}$
Propionic	$1 \cdot 22 \times 10^{-5}$
n-Butyric	$1 \cdot 5 \times 10^{-5}$
*iso*Butyric	$1 \cdot 4 \times 10^{-5}$
n-Valeric	$1 \cdot 56 \times 10^{-5}$
*iso*Valeric	$1 \cdot 68 \times 10^{-5}$
Trimethylacetic	$9 \cdot 6 \times 10^{-5}$
Caproic	$1 \cdot 4 \times 10^{-5}$
n-Heptoic	$1 \cdot 3 \times 10^{-5}$
Chloroacetic	$1 \cdot 55 \times 10^{-3}$
Bromoacetic	$1 \cdot 38 \times 10^{-3}$
Iodoacetic	$7 \cdot 3 \times 10^{-4}$
Dichloroacetic	$5 \cdot 14 \times 10^{-2}$
Trichloroacetic	$1 \cdot 2$

Formic acid is dehydrated to carbon monoxide by concentrated sulphuric acid (see above). When heated under pressure at 160°, formic acid is decomposed into carbon dioxide and hydrogen:

$$H \cdot CO_2H \longrightarrow CO_2 + H_2$$

The same decomposition takes place at room temperature in the presence of a catalyst such as iridium, rhodium, etc.

When metallic formates are heated with an alkali, hydrogen is evolved:

$$H \cdot CO_2Na + NaOH \longrightarrow H_2 + Na_2CO_3$$

When calcium or zinc formate is strongly heated, formaldehyde is produced:

$$(H \cdot CO_2)_2Ca \longrightarrow H \cdot CHO + CaCO_3$$

When sodium or potassium formate is rapidly heated to 360°, hydrogen is evolved and the oxalate is formed:

$$2H \cdot CO_2Na \longrightarrow (COONa)_2 + H_2$$

Formic acid forms esters, but since it is a relatively strong acid it is not necessary to use a catalyst; refluxing 90 per cent. formic acid with the alcohol is usually sufficient.

Formic acid differs from the rest of the members of the fatty acid series in being a powerful reducing agent; it reduces ammoniacal silver nitrate and the salts of many of the heavy metals, *e.g.*, it converts mercuric chloride into mercurous chloride.

Structure of formic acid. Analysis and molecular-weight determinations show that the molecular formula of formic acid is CH_2O_2. Assuming that carbon is quadrivalent, oxygen bivalent and hydrogen univalent, two structures are possible:

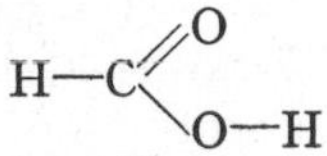

H—C(=O)—O—H (I)

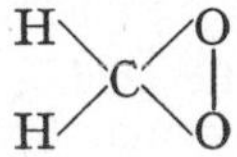

$H_2C<(O—O)$ (II)

Only one of the two hydrogen atoms in formic acid is replaceable by a metal. This suggests that the two hydrogen atoms are not in the same state of combination. Moreover, since hydrogen is evolved when formic acid is treated with sodium, the implication is that a hydroxyl group is present. Structure (I), but not (II), satisfies the above observations, and also indicates the relationship of formic acid to aldehydes, thus accounting for its reducing properties (see also acetic acid, below).

Acetic acid (*ethanoic acid*), $CH_3{\cdot}CO_2H$, is prepared industrially by the oxidation of acetaldehyde with air in the presence of manganous acetate as catalyst:

$$CH_3{\cdot}CHO + \tfrac{1}{2}O_2 \longrightarrow CH_3{\cdot}CO_2H$$

The function of the catalyst appears to be to prevent the formation of peracetic acid (*q.v.*). Acetic acid is also manufactured by the oxidation of natural gas.

One of the earliest methods for preparing acetic acid was by the destructive distillation of wood to give pyroligneous acid. This contains about 10 per cent. acetic acid, and was originally treated by neutralising with lime and then distilling off the volatile compounds (these are mainly methanol and acetone). On distillation with dilute sulphuric acid, the residue gives dilute acetic acid. More recently, the acetic acid is extracted by means of solvents, *e.g.*, *iso*propyl ether.

Vinegar, which is a 6–10 per cent. aqueous solution of acetic acid, may be made in several ways. Malt vinegar is prepared by the oxidation of wort (p. 125) by means of the bacteria *Mycoderma aceti*:

$$CH_3{\cdot}CH_2OH + O_2 \longrightarrow CH_3{\cdot}CO_2H + H_2O$$

In the "quick vinegar process", beech shavings, contained in barrels, are moistened with strong vinegar containing the bacteria. A 10 per cent. aqueous solution of ethanol containing phosphates and inorganic salts (which are necessary for the fermentation) is then poured through the barrels, and the ethanol is thereby oxidised to acetic acid. A plentiful supply of air is necessary, otherwise the oxidation is incomplete and acetaldehyde is produced.

It is only recently that vinegar has been used as a source of acetic acid, and this is entirely due to the introduction of highly efficient methods of fractionation.

Acetic acid is a pungent corrosive liquid, m.p. 16·6°, b.p. 118°, miscible in all proportions with water, ethanol and ether. It is highly associated in the liquid state, and exists as the dimer in the vapour phase. It is stable towards oxidising agents, and so is a useful solvent for chromium trioxide oxidations. Acetic acid is commonly used as a solvent, and in the preparation of acetates, acetone, acetic anhydride, etc.

Most of the normal acetates are soluble in water, whereas most of the basic acetates are insoluble. Calcium and manganese acetates are used in the preparation of acetone. Lead tetra-acetate is a very useful oxidising agent for 1 : 2 glycols. Aluminium acetate, which is known only in solution, is used for waterproofing cloth, and as a mordant.

A solution of a neutral acetate gives a red coloration when treated with ferric chloride. The same coloration is also produced by neutral formates, but acetates and formates may be readily distinguished from one another by the fact that the latter are powerful reducing agents.

Structure of acetic acid. Analysis and molecular-weight determinations show that the molecular formula of acetic acid is $C_2H_4O_2$. The presence of a methyl group in acetic acid is indicated by the following considerations:

(i) Treatment of boiling acetic acid with chlorine gives halogen substituted acids. The highest halogenated acid that can be produced is trichloroacetic acid, $C_2HO_2Cl_3$. Of the four hydrogen atoms in the acetic acid molecule, three have been replaced by chlorine and are, therefore, in a different state of combination from the fourth. This suggests that acetic acid contains a methyl group.

(ii) Methyl chloride may be converted into methyl cyanide, which, on hydrolysis, gives acetic acid. Methyl chloride contains a methyl group, and when it is converted into methyl cyanide the chlorine atom is replaced by the cyano-group. Since there is no reason to suppose that the methyl group in methyl chloride is affected by the substitution, it follows that methyl cyanide contains a methyl group. Similarly, since the hydrolysis of a cyanide affects the cyano-group only, when methyl cyanide is hydrolysed to acetic acid, the methyl group remains intact. Thus the above reactions may be formulated:

$$\mathbf{CH_3}\text{—Cl} \xrightarrow{\text{KCN}} \mathbf{CH_3}\text{—CN} \xrightarrow{H_2O} \mathbf{CH_3}\text{—}CO_2H$$

When acetic acid is treated with phosphorus pentachloride, acetyl chloride, CH_3—COCl, is formed and hydrogen chloride is evolved. This indicates the presence of a hydroxyl group. Thus acetic acid contains a methyl group and a hydroxyl group. Assuming the quadrivalency of carbon, the bivalency of oxygen and univalency of hydrogen, only one structural formula is possible for acetic acid, *viz.*, $CH_3\text{—}\overset{\overset{\displaystyle O}{\|}}{C}\text{—OH}$. The presence of the carbonyl group is supported by the fact that acetyl chloride may be catalytically reduced to acetaldehyde, which has been shown to contain a carbonyl group (p. 156).

Kolbe's synthesis of acetic acid (1845) is interesting in connection with the vital force theory (p. 1). Carbon and sulphur were heated together, and the carbon disulphide produced chlorinated:

$$C + 2S \longrightarrow CS_2$$

$$CS_2 \xrightarrow{Cl_2} CCl_4$$

The carbon tetrachloride was then passed through a red-hot tube, whereupon chlorine and tetrachloroethylene were formed and these, on cooling, combined to form hexachloroethane; but in the presence of a little water and under the influence of direct sunlight, some of the tetrachloroethylene was converted into trichloroacetic acid:

$$CCl_2{=}CCl_2 + Cl_2 + 2H_2O \longrightarrow CCl_3{\cdot}CO_2H + 3HCl$$

Treatment of the trichloroacetic acid in aqueous solution with potassium amalgam, or the electrolysis of the aqueous solution of the trichloroacetic acid between electrodes of amalgamated zinc plates, produced acetic acid:

$$CCl_3{\cdot}CO_2H + 6[H] \longrightarrow CH_3{\cdot}CO_2H + 3HCl$$

The structure of the carboxyl group is still not known with certainty. If its structure were $\text{—C}\genfrac{}{}{0pt}{}{\diagup\!\!\diagup O}{\diagdown OH}$, then the acid strength should be greater than that of alcohols, due to the inductive effect of the carbonyl group which tends to facilitate the release of a proton:

$$R\!\rightarrow\!\overset{\overset{\displaystyle O}{\|}}{C}\!\leftarrow\!O\!\leftarrow\!H$$

The acid strength of the fatty acids is greater than that of alcohols, but it seems unlikely that the inductive effect alone would account for the large difference. It has therefore been suggested that the carboxyl group is a resonance hybrid:

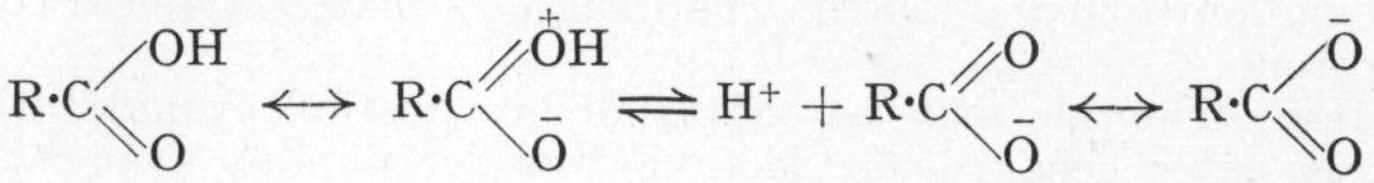

$$\mathrm{R{\cdot}C}\begin{matrix}\diagup\mathrm{OH}\\ \diagdown\!\!\diagdown\mathrm{O}\end{matrix} \longleftrightarrow \mathrm{R{\cdot}C}\begin{matrix}\diagup\!\!\diagup\overset{+}{\mathrm{O}}\mathrm{H}\\ \diagdown\overset{-}{\mathrm{O}}\end{matrix} \rightleftharpoons \mathrm{H^+} + \mathrm{R{\cdot}C}\begin{matrix}\diagup\!\!\diagup\mathrm{O}\\ \diagdown\overset{-}{\mathrm{O}}\end{matrix} \longleftrightarrow \mathrm{R{\cdot}C}\begin{matrix}\diagup\overset{-}{\mathrm{O}}\\ \diagdown\!\!\diagdown\mathrm{O}\end{matrix}$$

Owing to the positive charge on the oxygen atom of the hydroxyl group, the electron pair of the O—H bond is displaced towards the oxygen atom. thereby facilitating the release of a proton. When the proton is released, the two *equivalent* resonating structures contribute to the carboxylate ion formed, and so the resonance energy of the ion will be greater than that of the undissociated acid. Thus the driving force for the dissociation is this tendency to achieve greater stabilisation. Since resonance is not possible in alcohols, proton release is much more difficult than in carboxylic acids.

If acids are resonance hybrids, the C=O bond will have some single-bond character, and its length should therefore be longer than that of a " pure " C=O double bond; similarly, the C—OH bond will have some double-bond character, and should be shorter than a " pure " C—OH single bond. Electron diffraction experiments (Schomaker and O'Gorman, 1947) have shown that the C=O bond length in formic acid monomer is a trifle greater than normal, and that the C—OH bond is considerably less than normal. These results are in keeping with a resonating structure of the carboxyl group.

The treatment of the carboxyl group and the carboxylate ion from the M.O. point of view also leads to the same results as those obtained by the V.B. method, the increased stability now being due to *delocalisation* (*cf.* p. 81). Let us first consider the *undissociated* carboxylic acid (Fig. 1*a*). The carbon atom is linked to the hydroxyl group by a σ-bond, and to the oxygen of the carbonyl group by one σ- and one π-bond. This is shown in (*b*). Now the oxygen atom of the hydroxyl group has two lone pairs, one pair consisting of two $2s$ electrons and the

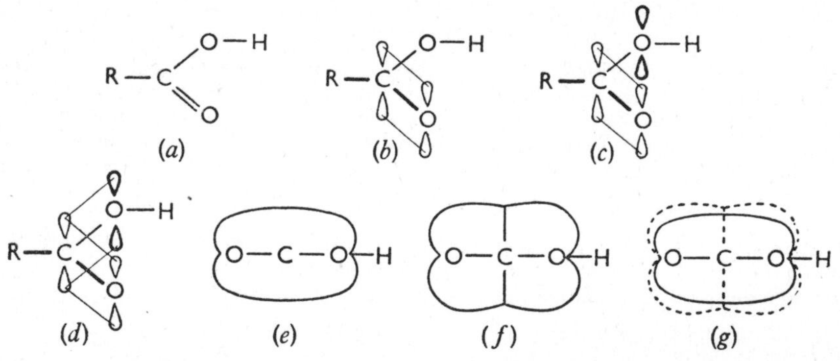

(*a*) (*b*) (*c*) (*d*) (*e*) (*f*) (*g*)

Fig. 9.1.

other of two $2p$ electrons. This oxygen atom can rotate about the single C—OH bond until the axis of the pair of $2p$ electrons is parallel to that of the $2p_z$ electron of the carbon atom (Fig. *c*). These two $2p$ electrons can now *conjugate* with the π-bond of the C=O group (p. 82). The result is an M.O. embracing *three* nuclei (Fig. *d*). Since *four* electrons are involved, they must be accommodated, in the ground state, in the lowest two M.O.s. The M.O. with the lowest energy level has *one* node (Fig. *e*), and the next energy level has *two* nodes (Fig. *f*). Thus (*g*) represents the ground state of the undissociated carboxyl group. Because of delocalisation, this group has become more stable. Since a hydroxyl group is more electron-attracting than an oxygen atom, the delocalisation of the lone pair of $2p$ electrons is not very large, *i.e.*, although this lone pair embraces three nuclei, this pair is far more likely to be found in the region of the donor atom than anywhere else. Since the oxygen atom of the hydroxyl group has lost " full-control " of this lone pair, it will acquire a small positive charge, and since the oxygen atom of the CO group has acquired a small share of this lone pair, this oxygen atom acquires a small negative charge (actually this oxygen atom already has a small negative charge due to the inductive effect). The greater electron-attracting power of oxygen in a hydroxyl group over that of an oxygen atom alone is due to the hydrogen atom sharing one pair of electrons in forming the bond, and thereby decreasing, to some extent, the electron density on that oxygen atom.

Now let us consider the *carboxylate ion* (Fig. 2*a*). The oxygen atom of the original hydroxyl group retains the σ-electrons when the hydrogen atom is removed as a proton. As in the case of the *carboxyl group*, one lone pair enters

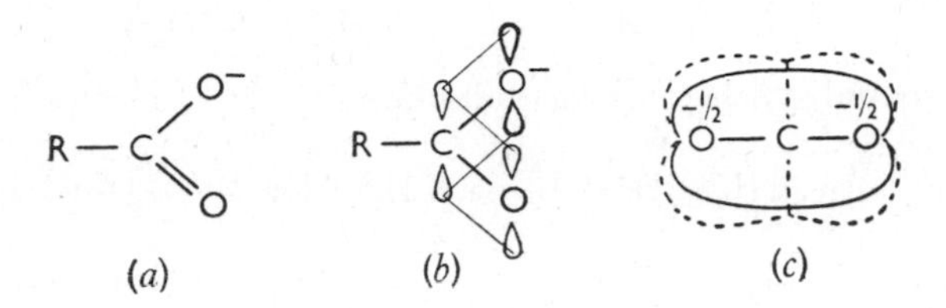

FIG. 9.2.

into conjugation with the π-bond of the C═O group (Fig. *b*). In the latter case, however, delocalisation is complete, *i.e.*, the lone pair is now likely to be found equally well on either oxygen atom (each atom will have a charge of $-\frac{1}{2}$). Since delocalisation is complete, the resonance (delocalisation) energy is much greater than in the case of the undissociated carboxyl group.

In Figs. 1 and 2, the orbitals drawn in thicker type indicate that the atoms concerned contain *two* electrons in these orbitals. This scheme has been used throughout the book.

Peracetic acid, $CH_3{\cdot}C{\overset{\displaystyle O}{\diagup\!\!\diagup}}\atop{\diagdown O{-}OH}$, may be prepared by treating acetic anhydride with concentrated hydrogen peroxide, and then distilling under reduced pressure. It may also be prepared by adding 90 per cent. hydrogen peroxide to cooled glacial acetic acid in the presence of a small amount of sulphuric acid.

Peracetic acid is an unpleasant-smelling liquid, f.p. +0·1°, soluble in water, ethanol and ether. It explodes violently when heated above 110°. It is a powerful oxidising agent; it oxidises the olefinic bond to the oxide.

$$>C{=}C< + CH_3{\cdot}CO{\cdot}O_2H \longrightarrow >\overset{O}{C{-\!\!-}C}< + CH_3{\cdot}CO_2H$$

It also oxidises primary aromatic amines to nitroso-compounds, *e.g.*, aniline is converted into nitrosobenzene:

$$C_6H_5{\cdot}NH_2 + 2CH_3{\cdot}CO{\cdot}O_2H \longrightarrow C_6H_5{\cdot}NO + 2CH_3{\cdot}CO_2H + H_2O$$

Infrared absorption spectra measurements of per-acids show that these acids exist in solution very largely in the monomeric, intramolecularly hydrogen-bonded form (*inter alia*, Minkoff, 1954).

$$CH_3{\cdot}C\begin{matrix}{=}O\cdots H\\ \quad\quad |\\ {-}O{-}O\end{matrix}$$

Propionic acid (*propanoic acid*), $CH_3{\cdot}CH_2{\cdot}CO_2H$, is prepared industrially by the oxidation of *n*-propanol:

$$CH_3{\cdot}CH_2{\cdot}CH_2OH \xrightarrow{[O]} CH_3{\cdot}CH_2{\cdot}CO_2H$$

It is a colourless liquid with an acrid odour, m.p. −22°, b.p. 141°, miscible with water, ethanol and ether in all proportions.

Butyric acids, $C_4H_8O_2$. There are two isomers possible, and both are known.

***n*-Butyric acid,** $CH_3{\cdot}CH_2{\cdot}CH_2{\cdot}CO_2H$, occurs as the glyceryl ester in butter, and as the free acid in perspiration. It is prepared industrially by the oxidation of *n*-butanol, and by the *butyric* fermentation of carbohydrates by means of the micro-organism *Bacillus butyricus*.

n-Butyric acid is a viscous unpleasant-smelling liquid, m.p. −4·7°, b.p. 162°, miscible with water, ethanol and ether. It is the liberation of free *n*-butyric acid that gives stale butter its rancid odour.

***iso*Butyric acid,** $(CH_3)_2CH{\cdot}CO_2H$, occurs in the free state and as its esters in many plants. It is prepared industrially by the oxidation of *iso*butanol:

$$(CH_3)_2CH{\cdot}CH_2OH \xrightarrow{[O]} (CH_3)_2CH{\cdot}CO_2H$$

It may be prepared synthetically as follows:

$$(CH_3)_2CHOH \xrightarrow{PBr_3} (CH_3)_2CHBr \xrightarrow{KCN} (CH_3)_2CH{\cdot}CN \xrightarrow[\text{acid}]{H_2O} (CH_3)_2CH{\cdot}CO_2H$$

*iso*Butyric acid is a liquid, m.p. −47°, b.p. 154°. Its calcium salt is more soluble in hot water than in cold, whereas calcium butyrate is more soluble in cold water than in hot.

Valeric acids, $C_5H_{10}O_2$. There are four isomers possible, and all are known:

***n*-Valeric acid,** $CH_3{\cdot}CH_2{\cdot}CH_2{\cdot}CH_2{\cdot}CO_2H$, m.p. −34·5°, b.p. 187°.
***iso*Valeric acid,** $(CH_3)_2CH{\cdot}CH_2{\cdot}CO_2H$, m.p. −51°, b.p. 175°.
Ethylmethylacetic acid or **active valeric acid,** $CH_3{\cdot}CH_2{\cdot}CH(CH_3){\cdot}CO_2H$, b.p. 175°.
Trimethylacetic acid or **pivalic acid,** $(CH_3)_3C{\cdot}CO_2H$, m.p. 35·5°, b.p. 164°.

The higher fatty acids which occur in nature usually have straight chains, and usually contain an *even* number of carbon atoms. **Caproic** (*hexoic*), $C_6H_{12}O_2$ (m.p. −9·5°, b.p. 205°), **caprylic** (*octoic*), $C_8H_{16}O_2$ (m.p. 16°, b.p. 237°), and **capric** (*decoic*) acid, $C_{10}H_{20}O_2$ (m.p. 31·5°, b.p. 270°), are present as glyceryl esters in goats' butter. **Lauric** (*dodecoic*), $C_{12}H_{24}O_2$ (m.p. 44°), and **myristic** (*tetradecoic*) acid, $C_{14}H_{28}O_2$ (m.p. 58°), occur as their glyceryl esters in certain vegetable oils. The most important higher fatty acids are **palmitic** (*hexadecoic*), $C_{16}H_{32}O_2$ (m.p. 64°), and **stearic** (*octadecoic*), $C_{18}H_{36}O_2$ (m.p. 72°), which are very widely distributed as their glyceryl esters (together with oleic acid) in most animal and vegetable oils and fats. The sodium and potassium salts of palmitic and stearic acids are the constituents of ordinary soaps.

Hansen *et al.* (1952, 1956) have shown the presence of branched-chain acids in a number of animal fats, *e.g.*, 13-methyltetradecanoic acid in butter fat, and 14-methylpentadecanoic acid (*iso*palmitic acid) in hydrogenated sheep fat.

Some still higher acids are found in waxes: **arachidic** (*eicosoic*), $C_{20}H_{40}O_2$ (m.p. 77°), **behenic** (*docosoic*), $C_{22}H_{44}O_2$ (m.p. 82°), **lignoceric** (*tetracosoic*), $C_{24}H_{48}O_2$ (m.p. 83·5°), **cerotic** (*hexacosoic*), $C_{26}H_{52}O_2$ (m.p. 87·7°), and **melissic** acid (*triacontoic*), $C_{30}H_{60}O_2$ (m.p. 90°).

The odd fatty acids may be obtained by degrading an even acid (see below). Two odd acids which may be prepared readily are ***n*-heptoic** or **œnanthylic acid,** $C_7H_{14}O_2$ (m.p. −10°, b.p. 223·5°), and **nonoic** or **pelargonic acid,** $C_9H_{18}O_2$ (m.p. 12°, b.p. 254°). *n*-Heptoic acid is prepared by the oxidation of *n*-heptaldehyde, which is obtained by destructively distilling castor oil which contains ricinoleic acid (*q.v.*):

$$CH_3\cdot(CH_2)_5\cdot CHO + [O] \xrightarrow[H_2SO_4]{KMnO_4} CH_3\cdot(CH_2)_5\cdot CO_2H \quad (68\text{–}70\%)$$

Nonoic acid is obtained by the oxidation of oleic acid (*q.v.*).

Margaric acid (heptadecanoic acid), $C_{16}H_{33}\cdot CO_2H$, m.p. 61°, is prepared by heating a mixture of the calcium salts of stearic and acetic acids, and then oxidising the heptadecyl methyl ketone so produced.

$$C_{17}H_{35}\cdot CO_2ca + CH_3\cdot CO_2ca \longrightarrow CaCO_3 + C_{17}H_{35}\cdot CO\cdot CH_3 \xrightarrow{[O]} C_{16}H_{33}\cdot CO_2H$$

Margaric acid has been used as a source of artificial fats for diabetics. Until recently, margaric acid was considered to be a synthetic compound. In 1954, however, Hansen *et al.* isolated *n*-heptadecanoic and *n*-pentadecanoic acids from mutton fat, and *n*-pentadecanoic and *n*-tridecanoic acids from butter fat, and in 1955 showed the presence of *n*-undecanoic acid in butter fat. Hansen *et al.* (1954) have also shown that ox perenephric fat contains the consecutive series of acids C_2 to C_{10}.

ESTERS

Esters are compounds which are formed when the hydroxylic hydrogen atom in oxygen acids is replaced by an alkyl group; the acid may be organic or inorganic. The most important esters are derived from the carboxylic acids. The general formula of the carboxylic esters is $C_nH_{2n}O_2$, which is the same as that of the carboxylic acids. The structural formula of the esters is $RC(=O)—OR'$, and they are named as the alkyl salts of the acid, *e.g.*,

$CH_3\cdot COOC_2H_5$	ethyl acetate
$(CH_3)_2CH\cdot COOCH(CH_3)_2$	*iso*propyl *iso*butyrate

Carboxylic esters are formed by the action of the acid on an alcohol:

$$\text{acid} + \text{alcohol} \rightleftharpoons \text{ester} + \text{water}$$

The reaction is reversible, the *forward* reaction being known as *esterification*, and the *backward* reaction as *hydrolysis*.

The rate of esterification depends on both the structure of the acid and the alcohol. Generally, branching of the α-carbon atom of the acid causes slower esterification, *e.g.*, trimethylacetic acid is esterified much more slowly than acetic acid. The reason for this behaviour is obscure, but a contributing factor is probably the spatial factor (p. 99). The order of reactivity of alcohols is primary>secondary>tertiary, which may be explained by the fact that since it is the hydrogen of the alcoholic hydroxyl group which is involved in esterification (see below), the more readily the alcohol releases a proton, the faster will the esterification take place; it has been shown previously (p. 118) that the ease of proton release from an alcohol is primary> secondary>tertiary. The spatial effect may also be a contributing factor.

The rate of reaction between alcohols and the halogen acids is the reverse of that with oxygen acids. This is understandable if the reaction mechanisms are different, and this has been shown to be so (see below).

General methods of preparation of the carboxylic esters. 1. The usual method is *esterification*. The reaction is always slow, but is speeded up by the presence of small amounts of inorganic acids as catalysts, *e.g.*, when the acid is refluxed with the alcohol in the presence of 5–10 per cent. concentrated sulphuric acid:

$$R\cdot COOH + R'OH \xrightleftharpoons{H_2SO_4} R\cdot COOR' + H_2O \quad (v.g.)$$

Alternatively, hydrogen chloride is passed into the mixture of alcohol and acid until there is a 3 per cent. increase in weight, and the mixture is refluxed (the yields are very good). This is known as the *Fischer–Speier method* (1895), and is more satisfactory for secondary and tertiary alcohols than the sulphuric acid method, which tends to dehydrate the alcohol to olefin. Klosa (1956) has shown that phosphoryl chloride is a good catalyst in the esterification of acids with alcohols.

Esterification without the use of catalysts, and starting with one molecule of acid and one molecule of alcohol, gives rise to about $\frac{2}{3}$ molecule of ester. The yield of ester may be increased by using excess acid or alcohol, the cheaper usually being the one in excess. Increased yields may also be effected by dehydrating agents, *e.g.*, concentrated sulphuric acid behaves both as a catalyst and a dehydrating agent. The same effect may be obtained by removing the water or ester from the reaction mixture by distillation, which is particularly useful for high-boiling acids and alcohols. On the other hand, the water may be removed from the reaction mixture by the addition of benzene or carbon tetrachloride, each of which forms a binary mixture with water (and may form a ternary mixture with water and the alcohol), the azeotropic mixtures boiling at a lower temperature than any of the components.

The esterification of a carboxylic acid may be formulated in either of two ways:

$$\text{(I)} \qquad R{\cdot}CO\boxed{OH + H}OR' \longrightarrow R{\cdot}COOR' + H_2O$$

$$\text{(II)} \qquad R{\cdot}COO\boxed{H + HO}R' \longrightarrow R{\cdot}COOR' + H_2O$$

The mechanism has been examined by several methods, the most reliable of which involves the use of the isotopic indicator ^{18}O, *e.g.*, Roberts and Urey (1938) esterified benzoic acid with methanol containing an increased amount of ^{18}O. No unusual amount of ^{18}O was found in the water formed in the reaction. Therefore the oxygen of the water must have come from the benzoic acid, *i.e.*, the reaction must have taken place by mechanism (I):

$$C_6H_5{-}\overset{\overset{^{16}O}{\|}}{C}{-}\overset{16}{O}H + CH_3\overset{18}{O}H \longrightarrow C_6H_5{-}\overset{\overset{^{16}O}{\|}}{C}{-}\overset{18}{O}CH_3 + H_2\overset{16}{O}$$

The actual steps involved in esterification are still obscure. Many detailed mechanisms have been suggested, *e.g.*, according to Davies and Evans (1940), acid-catalysed esterification takes place as follows:

$$R{\cdot}\overset{\overset{O\;\; H^+}{\|}}{\underset{\underset{HO\;\;H}{|}}{C}}\;\; OR' \rightleftharpoons R{\cdot}\overset{\overset{O-H}{|}}{\underset{\underset{\overset{+}{O}H_2}{|}}{C}}{-}OR' \rightleftharpoons R{\cdot}\overset{\overset{O}{\|}}{C}{-}OR' + H_2O + H^+$$

When an alcohol reacts with a halogen acid to form an alkyl halide, the hydroxyl group of the *alcohol* must be involved:

$$R\boxed{OH + H}X \longrightarrow RX + H_2O$$

Therefore the mechanism of this reaction must be different from that involving an oxygen acid. The more readily the alcohol releases its hydroxyl group, the faster will be the formation of the alkyl halide. It has been shown previously (p. 118) that the order of the ease of release of the hydroxyl group from an alcohol is tertiary>secondary>primary. Consequently, the rate of reaction of the different classes of alcohols with a halogen acid will be in this order, thus accounting for the reversed rates of reaction of alcohols with halogen acids compared with oxygen acids. The mechanism is possibly:

$$R{-}OH + HX \longrightarrow R{-}\overset{+}{O}H_2 + \overset{-}{X} \longrightarrow \overset{+}{R} + H_2O + \overset{-}{X} \longrightarrow R{-}X + H_2O$$

Many primary alcohols, on oxidation with chromic acid, form esters in addition to acids, *e.g.*, *n*-butanol gives *n*-butyl *n*-butyrate:

$$2C_3H_7{\cdot}CH_2OH \xrightarrow[H_2SO_4]{Na_2Cr_2O_7} C_3H_7{\cdot}CO_2C_4H_9 \quad (41\text{–}47\%)$$

Several mechanisms have been proposed for this reaction, *e.g.*, the direct esterification of unchanged alcohol with acid formed on oxidation, or hemi-acetal formation followed by oxidation to ester. Mosher *et al.* (1953) have obtained evidence for the latter:

$$R{\cdot}CH_2OH \xrightarrow{[O]} R{\cdot}CHO \xrightarrow[H^+]{R{\cdot}CH_2OH} R{\cdot}CH\begin{cases}OH \\ OCH_2{\cdot}R\end{cases} \xrightarrow{[O]} R{\cdot}CO_2CH_2{\cdot}R$$

2. Acid chlorides or anhydrides react rapidly with alcohols to form esters:

$$R{\cdot}COCl + R'OH \longrightarrow R{\cdot}CO_2R' + HCl \qquad (v.g.\text{–}ex.)$$

$$(R{\cdot}CO)_2O + R'OH \longrightarrow R{\cdot}CO_2R' + R{\cdot}CO_2H \qquad (v.g.\text{–}ex.)$$

The reaction with tertiary alcohols is very slow, and is often accompanied by the dehydration of the alcohol to olefin. When the acid chloride is used, there is also a tendency for a tertiary alcohol to form a tertiary alkyl chloride (p. 119). Esters of tertiary alcohols may be conveniently prepared by means of a Grignard reagent (see p. 340).

3. Esters may be prepared by refluxing the silver salt of an acid with an alkyl halide in ethanolic solution:

$$R{\cdot}CO_2Ag + R'Br \longrightarrow R{\cdot}CO_2R' + AgBr \quad (v.g.\text{–}ex.)$$

This method is useful where direct esterification is difficult (*cf.* 2 above).

4. Esters are formed when a mixture of the vapours of an acid and an alcohol is passed over a metallic oxide catalyst at 300°:

$$R{\cdot}CO_2H + R'OH \xrightarrow{ThO_2} R{\cdot}CO_2R' + H_2O$$

5. *Methyl* esters are very conveniently prepared by treating an acid with an ethereal solution of diazomethane (*q.v.*):

$$R{\cdot}CO_2H + CH_2N_2 \longrightarrow R{\cdot}CO_2CH_3 + N_2 \quad (ex.)$$

6. Esters are readily obtained when an acid is treated with an olefin in the presence of boron trifluoride as catalyst (Nieuwland *et al.*, 1934):

$$R{\cdot}CO_2H + C_2H_4 \xrightarrow{BF_3} R{\cdot}CO_2C_2H_5$$

It has been found that the complex $(CH_3{\cdot}CO_2H)_2{\cdot}BF_3$ is a very efficient catalyst in the preparation of esters from acids and alcohols (Smith *et al.*, 1940). Another example of the use of boron trifluoride as a catalyst in organic chemistry is the formation of esters by the interaction between an ether and carbon monoxide at 125–180°, under 500 atmospheres pressure, in the presence of boron trifluoride plus a little water:

$$R_2O + CO \longrightarrow R{\cdot}CO_2R$$

General properties of the esters. The carboxylic esters are pleasant-smelling liquids or solids. The boiling points of the straight-chain isomers are higher than those of the branched-chain isomers. The boiling points of the methyl and ethyl esters are lower than those of the corresponding acid, and this is probably due to the fact that the esters are not associated since they cannot form intermolecular hydrogen bonds. The esters of low molecular weight are fairly soluble in water—hydrogen bonding between ester and water is possible—and the solubility decreases as the series is ascended; all esters are soluble in most organic solvents.

The structure of the esters is usually written as $R-\overset{\overset{O}{\|}}{C}-OR'$, but, as in the case of the acids from which they are derived, there is a certain amount of evidence to show that esters are resonance hybrids (or conjugated, p. 172):

$$R-\overset{\overset{O}{\|}}{C}-OR' \longleftrightarrow R-\overset{\overset{\bar{O}}{|}}{C}=\overset{+}{O}R$$

General reactions of the esters. 1. Esters are hydrolysed by acids or alkalis:

$$R\cdot CO_2R' + H_2O \xrightarrow{\text{acid}} R\cdot CO_2H + R'OH$$
$$R\cdot CO_2R' + NaOH \longrightarrow R\cdot CO_2Na + R'OH$$

When hydrolysis is carried out with alkali, the salt of the acid is obtained, and since the alkali salts of the higher acids are soaps, alkaline hydrolysis is known as *saponification* (derived from Latin word meaning soap); saponification is far more rapid than acid hydrolysis.

Hydrolysis of secondary and particularly tertiary halides is accompanied by the formation of olefin (p. 100). In many cases a better yield of alcohol can be obtained by first converting the alkyl halide into the acetate ester by heating with silver acetate in ethanolic solution, and then saponifying the acetate ester:

$$CH_3\cdot CO_2Ag + RX \longrightarrow CH_3\cdot CO_2R \xrightarrow{\text{NaOH}} CH_3\cdot CO_2Na + ROH$$

Under the above conditions, secondary and tertiary halides show far less tendency to form olefin than when hydrolysed directly by alkali.

The hydrolysis of an ester may be formulated in either of two ways (*cf.* esterification, above):

$$\text{(I)} \qquad R\cdot CO\boxed{\mathbf{OR'} + H}OH \longrightarrow R\cdot COOH + \mathbf{R'O}H$$

$$\text{(II)} \qquad R\cdot COO\boxed{\mathbf{R'} + HO}H \longrightarrow R\cdot COOH + \mathbf{R'}OH$$

(I) is referred to as *acyl-oxygen* fission and (II) as *alkyl-oxygen* fission (Day and Ingold, 1941).

A detailed study of the hydrolysis of esters has shown that in the majority of cases the carboxylic esters undergo hydrolysis by mechanism (I); *e.g.*, Polanyi and Szabo (1934) hydrolysed amyl acetate with sodium hydroxide in water containing an increased proportion of isotope ^{18}O, and showed that the resulting amyl alcohol contained only the normal proportion of ^{18}O. Therefore the O in amyl alcohol must have come from the ester:

$$CH_3\cdot C\overset{16}{O}\boxed{\overset{16}{O}C_5H_{11} + H}\overset{18}{O}H \xrightarrow{\text{NaOH}} CH_3\cdot C\overset{16}{O}\overset{18}{O}H + C_5H_{11}\overset{16}{O}H$$

Ingold *et al.* (1939) hydrolysed methyl hydrogen succinate in acid aqueous solution enriched with ^{18}O, and obtained methanol with the normal proportion of ^{18}O:

$$\begin{array}{l} CH_2\cdot C\overset{16}{O}\overset{16}{O}CH_3 \\ | \\ CH_2\cdot C\overset{16}{O}\overset{16}{O}H \end{array} + H\overset{18}{O}H \xrightarrow{\text{acid}} \begin{array}{l} CH_2\cdot C\overset{16}{O}\overset{18}{O}H \\ | \\ CH_2\cdot C\overset{16}{O}\overset{16}{O}H \end{array} + CH_3\overset{16}{O}H$$

If R′ is an optically active group, then if mechanism (I) operates, the alcohol produced will retain its optical activity since the **R′—O** bond is never broken; various examples of retention of optical activity are known.

The actual steps involved in acid or alkaline hydrolysis of esters are still not certain. It has been shown that both may take place by a bimolecular mechanism involving acyl-oxygen fission. According to Ingold the mechanisms are:

Acid hydrolysis

$$R'\text{—}\overset{\overset{\displaystyle O}{\|}}{C}\text{—}OR + H^+ \rightleftharpoons R'\text{—}\overset{\overset{\displaystyle O}{\|}}{C}\text{—}\overset{\overset{\displaystyle H}{|+}}{O}\text{—}R \overset{H_2O}{\rightleftharpoons} R'\text{—}\underset{\underset{\displaystyle \overset{+}{O}H_2}{|}}{\overset{\overset{\displaystyle \bar{O}}{|}}{C}}\text{—}\overset{\overset{\displaystyle H}{|+}}{O}\text{—}R \rightleftharpoons$$

$$R'\text{—}\underset{\underset{\displaystyle \overset{+}{O}H_2}{|}}{\overset{\overset{\displaystyle O}{\|}}{C}} + ROH \rightleftharpoons R'\text{—}\underset{\underset{\displaystyle OH}{|}}{\overset{\overset{\displaystyle O}{\|}}{C}} + H^+$$

Alkaline hydrolysis

$$HO^- + \underset{\underset{\displaystyle R'}{|}}{\overset{\overset{\displaystyle O}{\|}}{C}}\text{—}OR \rightleftharpoons HO\text{—}\underset{\underset{\displaystyle R'}{|}}{\overset{\overset{\displaystyle \bar{O}}{|}}{C}}\text{—}OR \rightleftharpoons HO\text{—}\underset{\underset{\displaystyle R'}{|}}{\overset{\overset{\displaystyle O}{\|}}{C}} + RO^- \longrightarrow \bar{O}\text{—}\underset{\underset{\displaystyle R'}{|}}{\overset{\overset{\displaystyle O}{\|}}{C}} + ROH$$

It has, however, been found that alkyl-oxygen fission (mechanism (II)) can also occur both in basic and acid media, either (I) or (II) taking place according to circumstances; *e.g.*, experiments on the alkaline hydrolysis of the hydrogen phthalate of dextrorotatory anisylphenylcarbinol have shown that mechanism (I) takes place in ethanolic solution containing only about 2 per cent. water, whereas mechanism (II) takes place when the water content is increased to 20 per cent. (Kenyon *et al.*, 1936). It has also been shown that the presence of electron-releasing groups on the α-alkyl-carbon atom increases the ease of fission of the alkyl-oxygen bond, *e.g.*, triphenylmethyl acetate, $CH_3\cdot CO_2C(C_6H_5)_3$, undergoes hydrolysis by alkyl-oxygen fission in acid, neutral and basic media (Bunton *et al.*, 1955).

2. Esters are converted into alcohols by the Bouveault–Blanc reduction:

$$R\cdot CO_2R' + 4[H] \xrightarrow{C_2H_5OH/Na} R\cdot CH_2OH + R'OH \quad (g)$$

The yield of alcohol from the acid portion of the ester increases with the molecular weight of the alkyl radical R′, *e.g.*, the amyl ester gives a higher yield of alcohol $R\cdot CH_2OH$ than does the ethyl ester. Esters which are difficult to reduce at the boiling point of ethanol are usually satisfactorily reduced in *n*-butanol, which has a higher boiling point than ethanol, and so permits the reduction to be carried out at a higher temperature. Lithium aluminium hydride also reduces esters to alcohols.

Esters may also be reduced by molecular hydrogen at 100–300 atmospheres in the presence of a copper chromite catalyst at 200–300° (the yields are almost quantitative).

The formation of esters affords a convenient method of converting an acid into its corresponding alcohol, and stepping up the acid series:

$$R\cdot CO_2H \xrightarrow{R'OH} R\cdot CO_2R' \xrightarrow{[H]} R\cdot CH_2OH \xrightarrow{PBr_3} R\cdot CH_2Br \xrightarrow{KCN}$$

$$R\cdot CH_2\cdot CN \xrightarrow[acid]{H_2O} R\cdot CH_2\cdot CO_2H$$

3. Esters react with ammonia to form amides. This reaction is an example of *ammonolysis* (which means, literally, splitting by ammonia):

$$R{\cdot}COOR' + NH_3 \longrightarrow R{\cdot}CO{\cdot}NH_2 + R'OH \quad (g.)$$

A possible mechanism for this reaction is:

$$:NH_3 + \underset{R}{\overset{O}{\overset{\|}{C}}}{-}OR' \rightleftharpoons H_3\overset{+}{N}{-}\underset{R}{\overset{\bar{O}}{\overset{|}{C}}}{-}OR' \rightleftharpoons$$

$$H_3\overset{+}{N}{-}\underset{R}{\overset{O}{\overset{\|}{C}}} + OR^- \longrightarrow H_2N{-}\underset{R}{\overset{O}{\overset{\|}{C}}} + R'OH$$

With hydrazine, esters form acid hydrazides:

$$R{\cdot}COOR' + H_2N{\cdot}NH_2 \longrightarrow R{\cdot}CO{\cdot}NH{\cdot}NH_2 + R'OH$$

4. By means of *alcoholysis* (splitting by alcohol), an alcohol residue in a ester can be replaced by another alcohol residue. Alcoholysis is carried out by refluxing the ester with a large excess of an alcohol, preferably in the presence of a small amount of acid or sodium alkoxide as catalyst. Alcoholysis is usually effective in replacing a higher alcohol by a lower one, *e.g.*,

$$CH_3{\cdot}CO_2C_4H_9 + C_2H_5OH \xrightleftharpoons{C_2H_5ONa} CH_3{\cdot}CO_2C_2H_5 + C_4H_9OH$$

In *acidolysis*, the acid residue is displaced from its ester by another acid residue, *e.g.*,

$$CH_3{\cdot}CO_2C_2H_5 + C_5H_{11}{\cdot}CO_2H \rightleftharpoons C_5H_{11}{\cdot}CO_2C_2H_5 + CH_3{\cdot}CO_2H$$

Acidolysis is a useful reaction for converting the neutral ester of a dibasic acid into its acid ester.

5. When an ester—preferably the methyl or ethyl ester—is treated with sodium in an inert solvent, *e.g.*, ether, benzene or toluene, and subsequently with acid, an **acyloin** is formed (50–70 per cent. yield). It is important that the reaction be carried out *in the absence of any free alcohol.* Acyloins are αβ-*keto-alcohols*, and the mechanism of their formation is obscure. According to Kharasch and his co-workers (1939), the formation of acyloins takes place via a free-radical mechanism, *e.g.*, propionin from ethyl propionate:

$$2C_2H_5{\cdot}CO_2C_2H_5 + 2Na \longrightarrow 2C_2H_5{-}\dot{C}\begin{matrix}{\diagup}ONa\\ {\diagdown}OC_2H_5\end{matrix} \rightleftharpoons$$

$$\begin{matrix}C_2H_5{\cdot}C(ONa)(OC_2H_5)\\ |\\ C_2H_5{\cdot}C(ONa)(OC_2H_5)\end{matrix} \rightleftharpoons 2C_2H_5ONa + \begin{matrix}C_2H_5{\cdot}C{=}O\\ |\\ C_2H_5{\cdot}C{=}O\end{matrix} \xrightarrow{2Na} \begin{matrix}C_2H_5{\cdot}C{-}ONa\\ \|\\ C_2H_5{\cdot}C{-}ONa\end{matrix} \xrightarrow{acid}$$

$$\begin{bmatrix}C_2H_5{\cdot}C{-}OH\\ \|\\ C_2H_5{\cdot}C{-}OH\end{bmatrix} \xrightarrow{rearranges} \begin{matrix}C_2H_5{\cdot}CO\\ |\\ C_2H_5{\cdot}CHOH\end{matrix}$$

6. Carboxylic esters which contain α-hydrogen atoms react with sodamide in liquid ammonia solution to form the acid amide and a condensation product involving two molecules of the ester, *e.g.*, ethyl acetate gives acetamide and acetoacetic ester (see also p. 210):

$$CH_3{\cdot}CO_2C_2H_5 + NaNH_2 \longrightarrow CH_3{\cdot}CO{\cdot}NH_2 + C_2H_5ONa$$

$$CH_3{\cdot}CO_2C_2H_5 + NaNH_2 \longrightarrow NH_3 + [\ddot{C}H_2{\cdot}CO_2C_2H_5]^-Na^+ \xrightarrow{CH_3{\cdot}CO_2C_2H_5} CH_3{\cdot}CO{\cdot}CH_2{\cdot}CO_2C_2H_5 + C_2H_5OH$$

Of particular interest is the *carbonation* of esters, *i.e.*, the introduction of the carboxyl group. The ester is treated with sodamide in liquid ammonia solution, the solvent is evaporated off, ether is added, and then solid carbon dioxide:

$$R{\cdot}CH_2{\cdot}CO_2R' + NaNH_2 \xrightarrow{\text{liquid } NH_3} NH_3 + [R{\cdot}\ddot{C}H{\cdot}CO_2R']^-Na^+ \xrightarrow[\text{ether}]{CO_2} \begin{matrix} R{\cdot}CH{\cdot}CO_2R' \\ | \\ CO_2Na \end{matrix}$$

The yields of these *malonic acid derivatives* are 54–60 per cent. with acetates, and become progressively lower as the molecular weight of the acid increases.

Esters are used as solvents for cellulose, oils, gums, resins, etc., and as plasticisers. They are also used for making artificial flavours and essences, *e.g.*, *iso*amyl acetate—banana oil; amyl butyrate—apricot; *iso*amyl *iso*valerate—apple; methyl butyrate—pineapple; etc.

Ortho-esters are compounds of the type $R{\cdot}C(OR')_3$. They are derived from the ortho-acids, $R{\cdot}C(OH)_3$, which have not yet been isolated, but which are possibly present in aqueous solution (*cf.* ethylidene glycol, p. 157):

$$R{-}C{\begin{matrix} {/\!\!/}O \\ \backslash OH \end{matrix}} + H_2O \rightleftharpoons R{\cdot}C(OH)_3$$

The most important ortho-esters are the orthoformic esters, particularly ethyl orthoformate. Ethyl orthoformate may be prepared by running ethanol and chloroform into sodium covered with ether:

$$2CHCl_3 + 6C_2H_5OH + 6Na \longrightarrow 2H{\cdot}C(OC_2H_5)_3 + 6NaCl + 3H_2 \quad (70\%)$$

Another method is to pass dry hydrogen chloride into a solution of hydrogen cyanide and ethanol in ether:

$$H{\cdot}C{\equiv}N + C_2H_5OH + HCl \longrightarrow H{\cdot}C{\begin{matrix} {/\!\!/}NH{\cdot}HCl \\ \backslash OC_2H_5 \end{matrix}}$$

The formidic ester hydrochloride is then allowed to stand in ethanol, whereupon ethyl orthoformate is produced:

$$H{\cdot}C{\begin{matrix} {/\!\!/}NH{\cdot}HCl \\ \backslash OC_2H_5 \end{matrix}} + 2C_2H_5OH \longrightarrow H{\cdot}C(OC_2H_5)_3 + NH_4Cl$$

Ethyl orthoformate may be used for preparing ketals (p. 151), and for preparing aldehydes by means of a Grignard reagent (p. 338).

Esters of the Inorganic Acids

Alkyl halides, which can be prepared by the action of a halogen acid on an alcohol, may be regarded as esters, but are exceptional in that they do not contain oxygen.

Alkyl sulphates, $(RO)_2SO_2$. Only methanol and ethanol give a good yield of the alkyl sulphate by reaction with concentrated sulphuric acid; the higher alcohols give mainly olefins and ethers. On the other hand, all the alcohols give a fair yield of alkyl hydrogen sulphate when a mixture of alcohol and concentrated sulphuric acid is heated on a steam bath.

According to Barkenbus and Owen (1934), the most useful method for preparing alkyl sulphates is by the action of an alkyl chlorosulphonate on an alkyl sulphite:

$$(RO)_2SO + ClSO_2{\cdot}OR \longrightarrow (RO)_2SO_2 + HCl + SO_2 + R'{\cdot}CH{=}CH_2$$
$$(RO)_2SO + ClSO_2{\cdot}OR \longrightarrow (RO)_2SO_2 + SO_2 + RCl$$

Methyl sulphate may be prepared:

(i) By heating methyl iodide with silver sulphate:

$$2CH_3I + Ag_2SO_4 \longrightarrow (CH_3)_2SO_4 + 2AgI$$

(ii) By heating methanol with concentrated sulphuric acid, and then distilling the methyl hydrogen sulphate under reduced pressure:

$$CH_3OH + H_2SO_4 \longrightarrow CH_3HSO_4 + H_2O$$
$$2CH_3HSO_4 \longrightarrow (CH_3)_2SO_4 + H_2SO_4$$

(iii) By treating methanol with sulphur trioxide at low temperatures:

$$2SO_3 + 2CH_3OH \longrightarrow (CH_3)_2SO_4 + H_2SO_4$$

(ii) and (iii) are industrial methods.

Ethyl sulphate may be prepared by the same methods as methyl sulphate, but in addition, there is the industrial preparation by passing ethylene in excess into cold concentrated sulphuric acid:

$$2C_2H_4 + H_2SO_4 \longrightarrow (C_2H_5)_2SO_4$$

Methyl sulphate, b.p. 188°, and ethyl sulphate, b.p. 208°, are heavy poisonous liquids. They are largely used as alkylating agents since the alkyl group will replace the hydrogen atom of the groups —OH, ·NH· or —SH. The alkylation may be carried out by treating the compound with the alkyl sulphate in sodium hydroxide solution. Usually only one of the alkyl groups takes part in the reaction, *e.g.*, methylation of a primary amine:

$$R{\cdot}NH_2 + (CH_3)_2SO_4 + NaOH \longrightarrow R{\cdot}NH{\cdot}CH_3 + CH_3NaSO_4 + H_2O$$

The methyl and ethyl esters of the carboxylic acids may be conveniently prepared by treating the sodium salt of the acid with respectively methyl or ethyl sulphate:

$$R{\cdot}CO_2Na + (C_2H_5)_2SO_4 \longrightarrow R{\cdot}CO_2C_2H_5 + C_2H_5NaSO_4$$

The sodium alkyl sulphates of the higher alcohols are used as detergents, *e.g.*, sodium lauryl sulphate:

Alkyl nitrates, $R{\cdot}O{\cdot}NO_2$. The only important alkyl nitrate is ethyl nitrate, $C_2H_5{\cdot}O{\cdot}NO_2$. This may be prepared by heating ethyl iodide with silver nitrate in ethanolic solution:

$$C_2H_5I + AgNO_3 \longrightarrow C_2H_5{\cdot}O{\cdot}NO_2 + AgI$$

When concentrated nitric acid is added to ethanol, the reaction is usually violent; part of the ethanol is oxidised, and some of the nitric acid is reduced to nitrous acid. Apparently it is the presence of the nitrous acid which produces the violent oxidation of the alcohol by the nitric acid. This danger may be avoided by first boiling the nitric acid with urea, which destroys any nitrous acid present, and then adding this mixture to cool ethanol, any nitrous acid produced being immediately destroyed by the urea:

$$CO(NH_2)_2 + 2HNO_2 \longrightarrow CO_2 + 2N_2 + 3H_2O$$

Ethyl nitrate is a pleasant-smelling liquid, b.p. 87·5°. When reduced with tin and hydrochloric acid, it forms hydroxylamine and ethanol:

$$C_2H_5{\cdot}O{\cdot}NO_2 + 6[H] \xrightarrow{Sn/HCl} C_2H_5OH + NH_2{\cdot}OH + H_2O$$

Alkyl nitrites, R·O·NO. Alkyl nitrites are isomeric with the nitroparaffins (p. 284). The only important alkyl nitrites are the ethyl and amyl nitrites; the latter is actually mainly *iso*amyl nitrite, since the amyl alcohol used is the *iso*pentanol from fusel oil (p. 125). Ethyl and amyl nitrites are prepared by adding, concentrated hydrochloric acid or sulphuric acid to aqueous sodium nitrite and the alcohol, *e.g.*,

$$C_5H_{11}OH + HNO_2 \longrightarrow C_5H_{11}{\cdot}O{\cdot}NO + H_2O \quad (75\text{–}85\%)$$

Ethyl nitrite, b.p. 17°, and amyl nitrite, b.p. 99°, are pleasant-smelling liquids, and are used as a means of preparing nitrous acid in anhydrous media; *e.g.*, an ethanolic solution of nitrous acid may be prepared by passing dry hydrogen chloride into amyl nitrite dissolved in ethanol.

Trialkyl phosphates, $(RO)_3PO$, may be prepared by refluxing an alcohol with phosphoryl chloride in the presence of pyridine:

$$3ROH + POCl_3 + 3C_5H_5N \longrightarrow (RO)_3PO + 3C_5H_5N{\cdot}HCl \quad (g.)$$

Triethyl phosphate, tributyl phosphate and tricesyl phosphate are widely used as plasticisers.

Trialkyl borates, $(RO)_3B$, may be prepared by fractionally distilling a mixture of an alcohol and boric acid (Thomas, 1946):

$$3ROH + H_3BO_3 \longrightarrow (RO)_3B + 3H_2O \quad (ex.)$$

Trialkyl borates may be conveniently prepared in good yield by trans-esterification (alcoholysis) of methyl borate (which is readily available) with the appropriate alcohol (Brown *et al.*, 1956).

$$4(CH_3O)_3B + 3ROH \longrightarrow (RO)_3B + 3[CH_3OH,(CH_3O)_3B].$$

These authors have also shown that the following reaction readily occurs with primary and secondary alcohols:

$$3ROH + NaBH_4 + CH_3{\cdot}CO_2H \longrightarrow (RO)_3B + CH_3{\cdot}CO_2Na + 4H_2$$

With tertiary alcohols the reaction is:

$$2ROH + NaBH_4 + CH_3{\cdot}CO_2H \longrightarrow (RO)_2BH + CH_3{\cdot}CO_2Na + 3H_2$$

Tributyl borate is mainly used as a plasticiser.

ACID OR ACYL CHLORIDES

The general formula of the *acyl* radicals is $R{-}C{\overset{\displaystyle O}{\diagup\!\!\diagup}}{-}$. Acid chlorides, which may be prepared by the replacement of the hydroxyl in the carboxyl group by chlorine, are also known as *acyl chlorides* because they contain the acyl radical. Their general formula may therefore be written $R{-}C\begin{smallmatrix}\diagup\!\!\diagup O\\ \diagdown Cl\end{smallmatrix}$.

Nomenclature. According to the I.U.C. system the class suffix of the acyl chlorides is *-oyl*, and the names may be illustrated by the following examples:

$$CH_3\cdot C\begin{matrix}\diagup O \\ \diagdown Cl\end{matrix} \qquad CH_3\cdot CH_2\cdot C\begin{matrix}\diagup O \\ \diagdown Cl\end{matrix}$$

ethanoyl chloride — propanoyl chloride

This system is rarely used for naming the acyl chlorides. The more common names are formed by changing the suffix *-ic* of the *trivial* name of the acid into *-yl*, *e.g.*,

$$CH_3\cdot C\begin{matrix}\diagup O \\ \diagdown Cl\end{matrix} \qquad (CH_3)_2CH\cdot COCl$$

acetyl chloride — *iso*butyryl chloride

According to the *British Chemical Abstracts*, the nomenclature of all substances containing acyl radicals is in all cases based on the name " carbonyl " for the CO group, *e.g.*,

$CH_3\cdot CH_2\cdot CH_2\cdot COCl$ propane-1-carbonyl chloride

When naming amides (see below), the " yl " is elided before the suffix amide, *e.g.*,

$CH_3\cdot CH_2\cdot CH_2\cdot CONH_2$ propane-1-carbonamide

General methods of preparation. 1. The acid is heated with phosphorus trichloride or pentachloride, *e.g.*,

$$3R\cdot COOH + PCl_3 \longrightarrow 3R\cdot COCl + H_3PO_3 \qquad (g.)$$
$$R\cdot COOH + PCl_5 \longrightarrow R\cdot COCl + HCl + POCl_3 \qquad (v.g.)$$

The reaction with phosphorus trichloride is accompanied by the formation of small amounts of volatile phosphorus compounds, *e.g.*,

$$R\cdot CO_2H + PCl_3 \longrightarrow R\cdot CO_2PCl_2 + HCl$$

In some cases the acid anhydride is also formed due to the following reaction:

$$R\cdot CO_2H + R\cdot COCl \rightleftharpoons (R\cdot CO)_2O + HCl$$

Thionyl chloride may be used instead of the phosphorus chlorides:

$$R\cdot CO_2H + SOCl_2 \longrightarrow R\cdot COCl + SO_2 + HCl \qquad (v.g.)$$

The inorganic chloride is chosen according to the boiling point of the acyl chloride formed. Phosphorous acid decomposes at 200°; the boiling point of phosphoryl chloride is 107°, and that of thionyl chloride is 76°. Since acetyl chloride boils at 52°, any of the three inorganic halides may be used, but it is difficult to separate acetyl chloride from thionyl chloride (which is generally used in excess) by fractionation. *n*-Butyryl chloride boils at 102°, and so phosphorus pentachloride cannot be used. Usually thionyl chloride is the most convenient, but although it may be used with all the monocarboxylic acids, it is not satisfactory for all dicarboxylic acids (p. 359).

2. By distilling the salt of the acid with either phosphorus trichloride, phosphoryl chloride or sulphuryl chloride, *e.g.*,

$$3CH_3\cdot CO_2Na + PCl_3 \longrightarrow 3CH_3\cdot COCl + Na_3PO_3$$
$$2CH_3\cdot CO_2Na + POCl_3 \longrightarrow 2CH_3\cdot COCl + NaCl + NaPO_3$$
$$(CH_3\cdot CO_2)_2Ca + SO_2Cl_2 \longrightarrow 2CH_3\cdot COCl + CaSO_4$$

This method is used industrially since the salts are cheaper than the acid.

Acyl bromides may be prepared by the action of phosphorus tribromide or pentabromide (red phosphorus and bromine), or by the action of excess hydrogen bromide on the acyl chloride:

$$R{\cdot}COCl + HBr \longrightarrow R{\cdot}COBr + HCl$$

Acyl iodides are prepared in the same way as the bromides. *Acyl fluorides* are also known, and may be prepared by the action of hydrogen fluoride on acid anhydrides:

$$(R{\cdot}CO)_2O + HF \longrightarrow R{\cdot}COF + R{\cdot}CO_2H$$

General properties and reactions of the acyl chlorides. The lower acyl chlorides are colourless liquids with irritating odours; the higher members are colourless solids. The chlorine atom is very reactive and so the acid chlorides are important reagents.

1. The acyl chlorides are readily hydrolysed by water, the lower members reacting vigorously:

$$R{\cdot}COCl + H_2O \longrightarrow R{\cdot}CO_2H + HCl$$

Acyl chlorides usually react rapidly with compounds containing " active " hydrogen atoms, *i.e.*, hydrogen attached to oxygen, nitrogen or sulphur; *e.g.*, esters are formed with alcohols:

$$R{\cdot}COCl + R'OH \longrightarrow R{\cdot}COOR' + HCl$$

Amides are formed with ammonia, and *N*-substituted amides with primary and secondary amines:

$$R{\cdot}COCl + 2NH_3 \longrightarrow R{\cdot}CO{\cdot}NH_2 + NH_4Cl$$
$$R{\cdot}COCl + R'{\cdot}NH_2 \longrightarrow R{\cdot}CO{\cdot}NH{\cdot}R' + HCl$$

Hydrazides are formed with hydrazine, and hydroxamic acids with hydroxylamine:

$$R{\cdot}COCl + H_2N{\cdot}NH_2 \longrightarrow R{\cdot}CO{\cdot}NH{\cdot}NH_2 + HCl$$
$$R{\cdot}COCl + NH_2{\cdot}OH \longrightarrow R{\cdot}CO{\cdot}NH{\cdot}OH + HCl$$

The mechanisms of all of these reactions are uncertain. Alcoholysis of acid chlorides has been studied in some detail, and some mechanisms that have been suggested are (i) and (ii), which differ in the nature of the transition states (I) and (II).

(i) $$R{-}C({=}O){-}Cl + R'OH \underset{}{\overset{\text{slow}}{\rightleftharpoons}} R{-}C(O^-)(Cl){-}\overset{+}{O}(H){-}R' \ \text{(I)} \xrightarrow{\text{fast}} R{-}C({=}O){-}OR' + HCl$$

(ii) $$R{-}COCl + R'OH \overset{\text{slow}}{\rightleftharpoons} \overset{\delta+}{R'O}(H)\cdots C({=}O)(R)\cdots \overset{\delta-}{Cl} \ \text{(II)} \xrightarrow{\text{fast}} R{-}C({=}O){-}OR' + HCl$$

According to Hudson *et al.* (1955), the transition state is best represented as intermediate between (I) and (II), and is stabilised by solvation. It is possible that the other reactions—hydrolysis, ammonolysis, etc.—follow similar paths.

2. Acyl chlorides may be reduced catalytically to aldehydes or to alcohols:

$$R{\cdot}COCl \xrightarrow[\text{Pd}]{H_2} R{\cdot}CHO \xrightarrow{H_2} R{\cdot}CH_2OH$$

Acid chlorides are reduced to esters of an enediol by sodium amalgam in an inert solvent, *e.g.*, ether (*cf.* esters, p. 180):

$$4R{\cdot}COCl + 4Na \longrightarrow \begin{matrix} R \\ R{\cdot}CO{\cdot}O \end{matrix}\!\!>C{=}C<\!\!\begin{matrix} R \\ O{\cdot}CO{\cdot}R \end{matrix} + 4NaCl$$

Under suitable conditions, small yields of α-diketones have been obtained. Acid chlorides are reduced to alcohols by lithium aluminium hydride or sodium borohydride, and to aldehydes by lithium hydride.

3. Acyl chlorides react with the sodium salt of the fatty acids to form *acid anhydrides* (*q.v.*):

$$R{\cdot}COCl + R'{\cdot}COONa \longrightarrow R{\cdot}CO{\cdot}O{\cdot}CO{\cdot}R' + NaCl$$

4. Acyl chlorides may be used in the Friedel–Crafts reaction to produce an aromatic ketone; *e.g.*, acetyl chloride reacts with benzene in the presence of anhydrous aluminium chloride to form acetophenone:

$$C_6H_6 + CH_3{\cdot}COCl \xrightarrow{AlCl_3} C_6H_5{\cdot}CO{\cdot}CH_3 + HCl$$

5. Acyl chlorides react with Grignard reagents to produce ketones or tertiary alcohols, according to the conditions (see p. 338); *e.g.*, acetyl chloride forms butanone with ethylmagnesium iodide:

$$CH_3{\cdot}COCl + C_2H_5{\cdot}Mg{\cdot}I \longrightarrow CH_3{\cdot}CO{\cdot}C_2H_5 + Mg{\cdot}ClI$$

6. Acyl chlorides react with carboxylic acids as follows:

$$R{\cdot}COCl + R'{\cdot}CO_2H \rightleftharpoons R{\cdot}CO_2H + R'{\cdot}COCl$$

If the acyl chloride, R′·COCl, has the lowest boiling point, and the apparatus is arranged so as to allow only this to distil, all of R·COCl will be converted into R′·COCl. This reaction may therefore be used to prepare a volatile acyl chloride.

A small amount of acid anhydride is formed as a by-product, due to the reaction :

$$R{\cdot}COCl + R'{\cdot}CO_2H \rightleftharpoons R{\cdot}CO{\cdot}O{\cdot}CO{\cdot}R' + HCl$$

There will also be present the anhydrides $(R{\cdot}CO)_2O$ and $(R'{\cdot}CO)_2O$.

7. Acyl chlorides are readily halogenated in the α-position (see p. 196).

8. Acyl chlorides form esters (and other products) when heated with an ether in the presence of anhydrous zinc chloride as catalyst:

$$R{\cdot}COCl + R'_2O \xrightarrow{ZnCl_2} R{\cdot}CO_2R' + R'Cl$$

9. Acyl chlorides add on to the double bond of an olefin in the presence of a catalyst, *e.g.*, zinc chloride or aluminium chloride, to form a chloroketone which, on heating, eliminates a molecule of hydrogen chloride to form an unsaturated ketone:

$$CH_3{-}\overset{\overset{\displaystyle CH_3}{|}}{C}{=}CH_2 + CH_3{\cdot}COCl \xrightarrow{ZnCl_2} CH_3{-}\overset{\overset{\displaystyle CH_3}{|}}{\underset{\underset{\displaystyle Cl}{|}}{C}}{-}CH_2{\cdot}CO{\cdot}CH_3 \xrightarrow{heat}$$

$$CH_3{-}\overset{\overset{\displaystyle CH_3}{|}}{C}{=}CH{\cdot}CO{\cdot}CH_2 + HCl$$

Formyl chloride, H·COCl, and **formyl fluoride,** H·COF, are said to exist at low temperatures (−80°). There is no evidence of their existence at ordinary temperature, but a mixture of carbon monoxide and hydrogen chloride behaves as if it were formyl chloride in the Gattermann–Koch aldehyde synthesis (p. 618).

Acetyl chloride, $CH_3 \cdot COCl$, is the most important acyl halide. It is a colourless fuming liquid, b.p. 52°, and is soluble in ether and chloroform. It is largely used as an *acetylating* agent, *i.e.*, as a means of introducing the acetyl group, into compounds containing " active " hydrogen atoms. It is also used to detect the presence of hydroxyl groups in organic compounds, and to estimate their number.

Acetyl chloride readily acetylates primary and secondary alchols, but it tends to replace the hydroxyl group of a tertiary alcohol by chlorine (p. 119):

$$R_3COH + CH_3 \cdot COCl \longrightarrow R_3CCl + CH_3 \cdot CO_2H$$

The acetate of a tertiary alcohol may, however, be obtained by carrying out the reaction in the presence of pyridine, the function of which is uncertain:

$$R_3COH + CH_3 \cdot COCl \xrightarrow{\text{pyridine}} CH_3 \cdot CO_2CR_3 + HCl$$

The accepted abbreviation for the acetyl group is Ac; *e.g.*, AcOH is acetic acid; Ac_2O, acetic anhydride; AcCl, acetyl chloride; $C_6H_5 \cdot NH \cdot Ac$, acetanilide; etc.

ACID ANHYDRIDES

The acid anhydrides may be regarded theoretically as being derived from an acid by the removal of one molecule of water from two molecules of the acid:

$$\begin{matrix} R{-}C({=}O){-}O\boxed{H} \\ R{-}C({=}O){-}\boxed{OH} \end{matrix} \xrightarrow{-H_2O} \begin{matrix} R{-}C{=}O \\ \quad\;\; >O \\ R{-}C{=}O \end{matrix}$$

It is possible in practice to prepare many acid anhydrides by the direct dehydration as indicated above, but this method is usually confined to the anhydrides of the higher members of the acid series (see below).

Nomenclature. The acid anhydrides are named as the anhydride of the acid radicals present, the *trivial* name of the acid being used, *e.g.*,

$(CH_3 \cdot CO)_2O$	acetic anhydride
$(CH_3 \cdot CH_2 \cdot CO)_2O$	propionic anhydride

The most important acid anhydride is acetic anhydride, but propionic anhydride is increasing in importance due to its use in preparing cellulose propionate. Formic anhydride is unknown, but mixed anhydrides containing the formic acid radical have been prepared, *e.g.*, acetic formic anhydride, $H \cdot CO \cdot O \cdot CO \cdot CH_3$.

Acetic anhydride, $(CH_3 \cdot CO)_2O$, may be conveniently prepared by distilling a mixture of anhydrous sodium acetate and acetyl chloride:

$$CH_3 \cdot CO_2Na + CH_3 \cdot COCl \longrightarrow (CH_3 \cdot CO)_2O + NaCl \quad (80\%)$$

Acetic anhydride is prepared industrially :

(i) By heating anhydrous sodium acetate with sufficient inorganic chloride —phosphoryl chloride, thionyl chloride or sulphuryl chloride—to convert half of the sodium salt into the acid chloride, which then reacts with unchanged sodium acetate to form acetic anhydride.

(ii) By passing chlorine into a mixture of sodium acetate and sulphur dichloride, and distilling:

$$8CH_3{\cdot}CO_2Na + SCl_2 + 2Cl_2 \longrightarrow 4(CH_3{\cdot}CO)_2O + 6NaCl + Na_4SO_4$$

(iii) By passing acetylene into glacial acetic acid in the presence of mercuric ions as catalyst, and distilling the resulting ethylidene acetate:

$$C_2H_2 + 2CH_3{\cdot}CO_2H \xrightarrow{Hg^{2+}} CH_3{\cdot}CH(O{\cdot}CO{\cdot}CH_3)_2 \xrightarrow{heat} (CH_3{\cdot}CO)_2O + CH_3{\cdot}CHO$$

(iv) By passing keten into glacial acetic acid:

$$CH_2{=}C{=}O + CH_3{\cdot}CO_2H \longrightarrow (CH_3{\cdot}CO)_2O$$

(v) By passing acetic acid vapour over a catalyst consisting of a mixture of sodium ammonium hydrogen phosphate and boron phosphate, at 600–620°:

$$2CH_3{\cdot}CO_2H \xrightarrow{-H_2O} (CH_3{\cdot}CO)_2O$$

Anhydrides of the higher acids may be prepared by heating, and then fractionating, a mixture of the acid and acetic anhydride:

$$2R{\cdot}CO_2H + (CH_3{\cdot}CO)_2O \rightleftharpoons (R{\cdot}CO)_2O + 2CH_3{\cdot}CO_2H$$

This method is only satisfactory for anhydrides which have higher boiling points than acetic acid. A much better method of preparation is to treat the acid chloride with pyridine and benzene, add the acid, and then heat:

$$R{\cdot}COCl + R{\cdot}CO_2H + C_5H_5N \longrightarrow (R{\cdot}CO)_2O + C_5H_5N{\cdot}HCl \quad (g.\text{–}ex.)$$

On the other hand, acid anhydrides may be prepared in very high yield by the action of thionyl chloride on an ethereal solution of a mixture of acid and pyridine (Gerrard *et al.*, 1952):

$$2R{\cdot}CO_2H + SOCl_2 + 2C_5H_5N \longrightarrow (R{\cdot}CO)_2O + C_5H_5N{\cdot}HCl + C_5H_5NH{\cdot}O{\cdot}SOCl$$

Properties of acetic anhydride. Acetic anhydride is a colourless liquid, b.p. 139·5°, with an irritating smell. It is neutral when pure, and is slightly soluble in water, but readily soluble in ether and benzene. It is hydrolysed slowly in water, but rapidly by alkali:

$$(CH_3{\cdot}CO)_2O + H_2O \longrightarrow 2CH_3{\cdot}CO_2H$$

It undergoes reactions similar to those of acetyl chloride, but with less vigour : only half of the acetic anhydride molecule is used in acetylation, the other half being converted into acetic acid:

$$(CH_3{\cdot}CO)_2O + C_2H_5OH \longrightarrow CH_3{\cdot}CO_2C_2H_5 + CH_3{\cdot}CO_2H$$
$$(CH_3{\cdot}CO)_2O + NH_3 \longrightarrow CH_3{\cdot}CO{\cdot}NH_2 + CH_3{\cdot}CO_2H$$

Acetylation with acetic anhydride is usually best carried out in the presence of a small amount of sodium acetate or concentrated sulphuric acid as catalyst. Acetic anhydride reacts with dry hydrogen chloride to form acetyl chloride:

$$(CH_3{\cdot}CO)_2O + HCl \longrightarrow CH_3{\cdot}COCl + CH_3{\cdot}CO_2H$$

It is readily halogenated, and may be used in the Friedel–Crafts reaction. It reacts with aldehydes to form alkylidene acetates; *e.g.*, with acetaldehyde it forms ethylidene acetate:

$$(CH_3{\cdot}CO)_2O + CH_3{\cdot}CHO \longrightarrow CH_3{\cdot}CH(O{\cdot}CO{\cdot}CH_3)_2$$

Acetic anhydride reacts with nitrogen pentoxide to form **acetyl nitrate,** $CH_3{\cdot}CO{\cdot}O{\cdot}NO_2$. This is a colourless fuming liquid, b.p. 22°/70 mm., which explodes violently if heated suddenly. It is hydrolysed by water to acetic and nitric acid:

$$CH_3{\cdot}CO{\cdot}O{\cdot}NO_2 + H_2O \longrightarrow CH_3{\cdot}CO_2H + HNO_3$$

Acetyl nitrate is very useful for preparing certain aromatic nitro-compounds, but it is dangerous to handle (see p. 528).

Acetyl peroxide, $CH_3{\cdot}CO{\cdot}O{\cdot}O{\cdot}CO{\cdot}CH_3$, may be prepared by the action of barium peroxide on acetic anhydride. It is colourless, pungent-smelling liquid, b.p. 63°/21 mm., and tends to explode on warming. It is a powerful oxidising agent.

ACID AMIDES

Acid amides are compounds in which the hydroxyl of the carboxyl group has been replaced by the amino-group, $\cdot NH_2$, to form the *amido-group*:

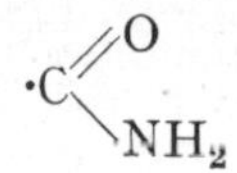

There are three classes of amides: primary, $R{\cdot}CO{\cdot}NH_2$; secondary, $(R{\cdot}CO)_2NH$; and tertiary, $(R{\cdot}CO)_3N$. Only the primary amides are important, and it can be seen from their formulæ that all three classes may be regarded as the acyl derivatives of ammonia.

Nomenclature. According to the I.U.C. system of nomenclature, the suffix *-oic* of the parent acid is replaced by *amide* (see also acid chlorides, above):

$H{\cdot}CO{\cdot}NH_2$	methanamide
$CH_3{\cdot}CO{\cdot}NH_2$	ethanamide

The amides, however, are commonly named by replacing the suffix *-ic* of the trivial name of the parent acid by *amide, e.g.*,

$H{\cdot}CO{\cdot}NH_2$	formamide
$CH_3{\cdot}CO{\cdot}NH_2$	acetamide

General methods of preparation of the amides. 1. By heating the ammonium salt of the acid:

$$R{\cdot}COONH_4 \longrightarrow R{\cdot}CO{\cdot}NH_2 + H_2O \quad (g.\text{–}v.g.)$$

Since the ammonium salts tend to dissociate on heating, the reaction is best carried out in the presence of some free acid $R{\cdot}CO_2H$ which represses the hydrolysis and the dissociation of the ammonium salt.

Amides may also be prepared by heating an acid with urea (Cherbuliez *et al.*, 1946):

$$R{\cdot}CO_2H + CO(NH_2)_2 \longrightarrow R{\cdot}CONH_2 + CO_2 + NH_2 \quad (g.\text{–}v.g.)$$

2. By *ammonolysis, i.e.*, the action of concentrated ammonia solution on acid chlorides, acid anhydrides or esters:

$$R{\cdot}COCl + 2NH_3 \longrightarrow R{\cdot}CO{\cdot}NH_2 + NH_4Cl \quad (v.g.)$$

$$(R{\cdot}CO)_2O + 2NH_3 \longrightarrow R{\cdot}CO{\cdot}NH_2 + R{\cdot}CO_2NH_4 \quad (v.g.)$$

$$R{\cdot}COOR' + NH_3 \longrightarrow R{\cdot}CO{\cdot}NH_2 + R'OH \quad (g.)$$

N-Substituted amides may be prepared by using primary or secondary amines instead of ammonia, *e.g.*,

$$R{\cdot}COCl + R'{\cdot}NH_2 \longrightarrow R{\cdot}CO{\cdot}NH{\cdot}R' + HCl$$

Philbrook (1954) has shown that amides may be readily prepared by adding a benzene solution of an acid chloride dropwise to benzene through which is passed a current of ammonia; for the lower aliphatic amides the yield is 65–95 per cent.

Meyer (1906) found that ammonolysis of esters occurs most readily with esters of strong acids and least readily with esters of weak acids or sterically hindered acids. It has been found that ammonia and aliphatic amines react, in general, more readily than aromatic amines. Stern (1956) has shown that acyl arylamides may be readily prepared as follows (Ar = aryl radical):

$$Ar{\cdot}NH_2 \xrightarrow[NaNH_2]{Na\ or} Ar{\cdot}NHNa$$

$$R{\cdot}CO_2C_2H_5 + Ar{\cdot}NHNa \longrightarrow R{\cdot}CO{\cdot}NH{\cdot}Ar + C_2H_5ONa$$

3. By the *graded* hydrolysis of alkyl cyanides. The hydrolysis must be carried out carefully, since if taken too far, the acid is produced. The hydrolysis may be carried out satisfactorily by dissolving the alkyl cyanide in concentrated sulphuric acid and then pouring the solution into cold water, or by shaking the alkyl cyanide with cold concentrated hydrochloric acid:

$$R{\cdot}C{\equiv}N + H_2O \longrightarrow R{\cdot}CO{\cdot}NH_2 \qquad (g.)$$

A possible mechanism for this hydrolysis is:

$$R{\cdot}C{\equiv}N{:} + \overset{+}{H} \longrightarrow R{\cdot}C{\equiv}\overset{+}{N}{-}H \longleftrightarrow R{\cdot}\overset{+}{C}{=}\ddot{N}{-}H \xrightarrow{H_2O}$$

$$R{\cdot}C(\overset{+}{O}H_2){=}\ddot{N}{-}H \xrightarrow{-H^+} R{\cdot}C(OH){=}\ddot{N}H \rightleftharpoons R{\cdot}C({=}O){-}NH_2$$

Sometimes the conversion of an alkyl cyanide into the amide may be effected by means of alkaline hydrogen peroxide:

$$R{\cdot}CN + 2H_2O_2 \xrightarrow{NaOH} R{\cdot}CO{\cdot}NH_2 + O_2 + H_2O$$

General properties and reactions of the amides. Except for formamide, which is a liquid, all the amides are colourless crystalline solids, and those of low molecular weight are soluble in water (with which they can form hydrogen bonds). The lower amides have much higher melting points and boiling points than are to be expected from their molecular weights; this indicates association (through hydrogen bonding):

$$H_2N{-}C(R){=}O \cdots H{-}NH{-}C(R){=}O \cdots H{-}NH{-}C(R){=}O \cdots$$

Infra-red spectroscopic studies indicate that in dilute solution (dioxan and chloroform) amides are monomeric; in concentrated solution (choroform) and in the liquid state there is some association, and in the solid state association is complete. Furthermore, the spectroscopic evidence appears to indicate that amides are resonance hybrids (Richards and Thomson, 1947):

$$R{-}C({=}O){-}\ddot{N}H_2 \longleftrightarrow R{-}C(O^-){=}\overset{+}{N}H_2$$

1. Amides are hydrolysed slowly by water, rapidly by acids, and far more rapidly by alkalis:

$$R{\cdot}CO{\cdot}NH_2 + H_2O \longrightarrow R{\cdot}CO_2H + NH_3$$

Possible mechanisms are:

Base hydrolysis

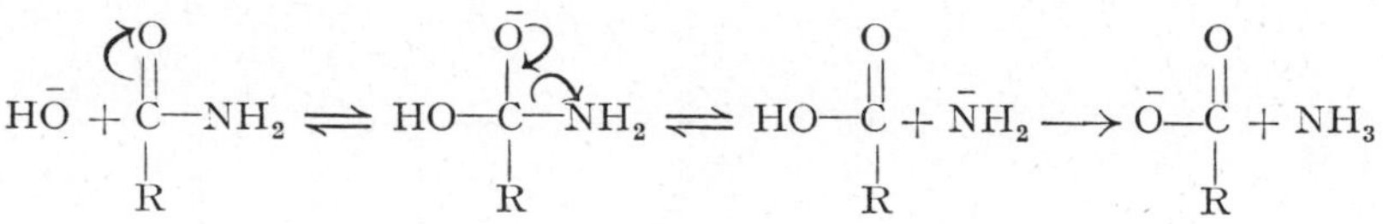

$$H\bar{O} + R{-}C({=}O){-}NH_2 \rightleftharpoons HO{-}C(R)(\bar{O}){-}NH_2 \rightleftharpoons HO{-}C(R){=}O + \bar{N}H_2 \longrightarrow \bar{O}{-}C(R){=}O + NH_3$$

Acid hydrolysis

$$R{-}C({=}O){-}NH_2 + \overset{+}{H} \rightleftharpoons R{-}C({=}O){-}\overset{+}{N}H_3 \overset{H_2O}{\rightleftharpoons} H_2\overset{+}{O}{-}C(R)(\bar{O}){-}\overset{+}{N}H_3 \rightleftharpoons$$

$$H_2\overset{+}{O}{-}C(R){=}O + NH_3 \longrightarrow HO{-}C(R){=}O + NH_4^+$$

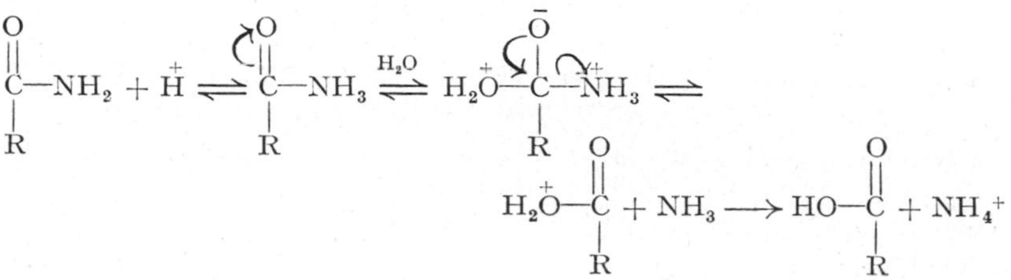

2. Amides are very feebly basic and form unstable salts with strong inorganic acids, *e.g.*, $R{\cdot}CO{\cdot}NH_2{\cdot}HCl$. The structure of these salts may be I or II:

$$\left[R{-}C({=}O{-}H){-}NH_2\right]^+ Cl^- \qquad \left[R{-}C({=}O){-}NH_3\right]^+ Cl^-$$

(I) (II)

In the case of formamide (R=H), infra-red measurements have shown that II is the actual state.

3. Amides are also feebly acidic; *e.g.*, they dissolve mercuric oxide to form covalent mercury compounds in which the mercury is probably linked to the nitrogen:

$$2R{\cdot}CO{\cdot}NH_2 + HgO \longrightarrow (R{\cdot}CO{\cdot}NH)_2Hg + H_2O$$

When amides are treated with sodium or sodamide in ethereal solution, the sodium *salt*, $[R{\cdot}CO{\cdot}NH]^-Na^+$, is formed, and the structure of these salts may be I or II:

$$\left[R{-}C({=}O){-}\ddot{\bar{N}}H\right]Na^+ \qquad \left[R{-}C(O^-){=}NH\right]Na^+$$

(I) (II)

When the dry sodium salt is heated with an alkyl iodide, the *N*-alkyl derivative is obtained; this corresponds to I. When, however, the silver salt is used, the *O*-alkyl derivative is obtained; this corresponds to II. It is possible that I and II are resonating structures.

4. Amides are reduced by sodium and ethanol, catalytically, or by lithium aluminium hydride to a primary amine:

$$R{\cdot}CO{\cdot}NH_2 + 4[H] \xrightarrow{Na/C_2H_5OH} R{\cdot}CH_2{\cdot}NH_2 + H_2O$$

5. When heated with phosphorus pentoxide, amides are dehydrated to alkyl cyanides:

$$R{\cdot}CO{\cdot}NH_2 \xrightarrow[-H_2O]{P_2O_5} R{\cdot}C{\vdots}N$$

Alkyl cyanides are also formed when the amides of the higher fatty acids are heated to a high temperature:

$$2R\cdot CO\cdot NH_2 \longrightarrow R\cdot CN + R\cdot CO_2H + NH_3$$

If this reaction is carried out in the presence of excess of ammonia, then all the amide is converted into alkyl cyanide:

$$R\cdot CO_2H + NH_3 \longrightarrow R\cdot CO_2NH_4 \xrightarrow{-H_2O} R\cdot CO\cdot NH_2 \xrightarrow{-H_2O} R\cdot CN$$

Amides may also be converted into cyanides by phosphorus pentachloride, and according to Wallach (1877), the reaction proceeds via the *amido-chloride* I and then the *imido-chloride* (*imino-chloride*) II.

$$\underset{}{R\cdot CO\cdot NH_2} \xrightarrow{PCl_5} \underset{(I)}{R\cdot CCl_2\cdot NH_2} \xrightarrow{-HCl} \underset{(II)}{R\cdot CCl{=}NH} \xrightarrow{-HCl} R\cdot CN$$

According to Kirsanov (1954), however, the reaction proceeds as follows, the intermediate III being decomposed by heat or by hydrogen chloride.

$$R\cdot CO\cdot NH_2 + PCl_5 \longrightarrow 2HCl + \underset{(III)}{R\cdot CO\cdot N{=}PCl_3} \longrightarrow R\cdot CN + POCl_3$$

Alkyl cyanides may be obtained from amides by treating the amide with the boron trifluoride-amide complex in the presence of a small amount of a carboxylic acid (Nieuwland, 1937), *e.g.*,

$$CH_3\cdot CONH_2\cdot BF_3 + CH_3\cdot CO\cdot NH_2 \xrightarrow{CH_3\cdot CO_2H} CH_3\cdot CN + CH_3\cdot CO_2H + NH_3\cdot BF_3$$

It is also interesting to note that the complex $CH_3\cdot CO\cdot NH_2\cdot BF_3$ has been found to be an effective acetylating agent for alcohols and phenols:

$$CH_3\cdot CO\cdot NH_2\cdot BF_3 + ROH \longrightarrow CH_3\cdot CO_2R + NH_3\cdot BF_3$$

6. When amides are treated with nitrous acid, nitrogen is evolved and the acid is formed:

$$R\cdot CO\cdot NH_2 + HNO_2 \longrightarrow R\cdot CO_2H + N_2 + H_2O$$

7. **Hofmann reaction or Hofmann degradation** (1881). The Hofmann reaction is the conversion of an amide into a primary amine with one carbon atom less by means of bromine (or chlorine) and alkali. The overall equation for the reaction may be written:

$$R\cdot CO\cdot NH_2 + Br_2 + 4KOH \longrightarrow R\cdot NH_2 + 2KBr + K_2CO_3 + 2H_2O$$

A number of intermediates have been isolated, *viz.*, the *bromamide* $R\cdot CO\cdot NH\cdot Br$, the salt of this bromamide $[R\cdot CO\cdot NBr]^-K^+$, and the *iso-cyanate* $R\cdot NCO$. The mechanism of the rearrangement of the salt of the bromamide into the *iso*cyanate is still an open question, but if we assume that it takes place by the Whitmore mechanism (p. 160), the sequence of events may be written:

$$R\cdot C(=O)\cdot \ddot{N}H_2 \xrightarrow{Br_2} R\cdot C(=O)\cdot \ddot{N}(Br)H \xrightarrow[(-H^+)]{KOH} [R\cdot C(=O)\cdot \ddot{N}{-}Br]^-K^+ \xrightarrow{-KBr}$$

$$[R\cdot C(=O)\cdot N\colon] \longrightarrow R{-}N{=}C{=}O \xrightarrow{KOH} R\cdot NH_2$$

The Hofmann reaction can be carried out on all monocarboxylic acids, and the yields are 70–90 per cent. for amides containing up to seven carbon atoms; amides with more than seven carbon atoms in the chain give mainly alkyl cyanide:

$$R\cdot CH_2\cdot CO\cdot NH_2 \xrightarrow{Br_2/KOH} R\cdot CN$$

The alkyl cyanide, however, may readily be reduced to the primary amine $R\cdot CH_2\cdot NH_2$.

It is possible to obtain the amine in good yield from the long-chain amides by modifying the procedure as follows. Bromine is added rapidly to a methanolic solution of the amide containing sodium methoxide:

$$R\cdot CO\cdot NH_2 + 2CH_3ONa + Br_2 \longrightarrow R\cdot NH\cdot CO_2CH_3 + 2NaBr + CH_3OH$$

The *N*-alkyl-urethan, on hydrolysis with alkali, gives the amine:

$$R\cdot NH\cdot CO_2CH_3 + 2NaOH \longrightarrow R\cdot NH_2 + Na_2CO_3 + CH_3OH$$

The Hofmann reaction offers an excellent method of preparing primary amines free from secondary and tertiary amines; it also affords a means of descending a series. A further interesting point about this reaction is that if the amide contains an electronegative group, the product is a bromide, *e.g.*, heptafluorobutyramide gives bromoheptafluoropropane (Haszeldine *et al.*, 1956):

$$C_3F_7\cdot CO\cdot NH_2 \xrightarrow[NaOH]{Br_2} C_3F_7Br \quad (85\%)$$

HYDROXAMIC ACIDS

The hydroxamic acids exhibit tautomerism; the keto form I is known as the *hydroxamic* form, and the enol form II as the *hydroximic* form:

$$\text{(I)}\quad R-\overset{\overset{\displaystyle O}{\|}}{C}-NH\cdot OH \rightleftharpoons R-\overset{\overset{\displaystyle OH}{|}}{C}=N\cdot OH \quad \text{(II)}$$

Hydroxamic acids may be prepared by the action of hydroxylamine on esters or acid chlorides:

$$R-C\begin{matrix}\nearrow O\\ \searrow OC_2H_5\end{matrix} + NH_2\cdot OH \longrightarrow R-\overset{O}{\overset{\|}{C}}-NH\cdot OH + C_2H_5OH$$

$$R\cdot COCl + NH_2\cdot OH \longrightarrow R-\overset{O}{\overset{\|}{C}}-NH\cdot OH + HCl$$

Hydroxamic acids give a red coloration with ferric chloride solution, a reaction which is characteristic of enols. When treated with a strong inorganic acid, hydroxamic acids undergo the **Lossen rearrangement** (1875), which results in the formation of a primary amine. The mechanism of the Lossen rearrangement is closely related to that of the Hofmann reaction, and so may be formulated:

$$R-\underset{\underset{\displaystyle O}{\|}}{C}-\overset{\overset{\displaystyle H}{|}}{\ddot{N}}-OH \xrightarrow{-H_2O} R-\underset{\underset{\displaystyle O}{\|}}{C}-\ddot{N}: \longrightarrow \underset{\underset{\displaystyle O}{\|}}{C}=N-R \xrightarrow{H_2O} R\cdot NH_2$$

The amides of the hydroxamic acids are known as **amidoximes.** These are tautomeric substances:

$$R\cdot C\begin{matrix}\nearrow NH_2\\ \searrow N\cdot OH\end{matrix} \rightleftharpoons R\cdot C\begin{matrix}\nearrow NH\\ \searrow NH\cdot OH\end{matrix}$$

Aliphatic amidoximes are best obtained by the action of hydroxylamine on an alkyl cyanide:

$$R{\cdot}CN + NH_2{\cdot}OH \longrightarrow R{\cdot}C\begin{matrix}\diagup NH_2 \\ \diagdown\!\!\diagdown N{\cdot}OH\end{matrix}$$

IMIDIC ESTERS AND AMIDINES

Imidic esters, which are also known as *imino-ethers,* are best prepared by passing dry hydrogen chloride into a solution of an alkyl cyanide in anhydrous alcohol; the imidic ester hydrochloride is slowly deposited (Pinner, 1877):

$$R{\cdot}C{:}N + R'OH + HCl \longrightarrow R{\cdot}C\begin{matrix}\diagup\!\!\diagup NH{\cdot}HCl \\ \diagdown OR'\end{matrix} \qquad (g.\text{–}v.g.)$$

This reaction is believed to be analogous to the hydrolysis of cyanides to amides:

$$R{\cdot}C{:}N + H_2O \longrightarrow \left[R{-}C\begin{matrix}\diagup\!\!\diagup NH \\ \diagdown OH\end{matrix}\right] \longrightarrow R{-}C\begin{matrix}\diagup NH_2 \\ \diagdown\!\!\diagdown O\end{matrix}$$

There is, however, no evidence for the existence of the enol form in unsubstituted amides.

Imidic esters form ortho-esters when allowed to stand in an alcohol:

$$R{\cdot}C\begin{matrix}\diagup\!\!\diagup NH{\cdot}HCl \\ \diagdown OR'\end{matrix} + 2R'OH \longrightarrow R{\cdot}C(OR')_3 + NH_4Cl$$

Imidic esters are readily hydrolysed to esters:

$$R{\cdot}C\begin{matrix}\diagup\!\!\diagup NH{\cdot}HCl \\ \diagdown OR'\end{matrix} + H_2O \longrightarrow R{-}C\begin{matrix}\diagup\!\!\diagup O \\ \diagdown OR'\end{matrix} + NH_4Cl$$

When an ethereal solution of an imidic ester hydrochloride is treated with potassium carbonate, the free ester $R{\cdot}C\begin{matrix}\lessgtr NH \\ OR'\end{matrix}$, is obtained. When treated with an ethanolic solution of ammonia, the imidic ester hydrochloride forms the **amidine**:

$$R{\cdot}C\begin{matrix}\diagup\!\!\diagup NH{\cdot}HCl \\ \diagdown OR'\end{matrix} + 2NH_3 \longrightarrow R{\cdot}C\begin{matrix}\diagup\!\!\diagup NH \\ \diagdown NH_2\end{matrix} + NH_4Cl$$

Amidines are strong monoacid bases, forming salts with strong acids. Their basic strength may be explained by resonance. In the amidine, two *different* resonating structures contribute to the actual state of the molecule:

$$R{-}C\begin{matrix}\diagup\!\!\diagup NH \\ \diagdown NH_2\end{matrix} \longleftrightarrow R{-}C\begin{matrix}\diagup \bar{N}H \\ \diagdown\!\!\diagdown \overset{+}{N}H_2\end{matrix}$$

In the amidine *ion,* the resonating structures are *equivalent,* and hence the resonance energy is a maximum; the ion will therefore be stable:

$$R{-}C\begin{matrix}\diagup\!\!\diagup \overset{+}{N}H_2 \\ \diagdown NH_2\end{matrix} \longleftrightarrow R{-}C\begin{matrix}\diagup NH_2 \\ \diagdown\!\!\diagdown \overset{+}{N}H_2\end{matrix}$$

Amidines are readily hydrolysed to amides:

$$R{-}C\begin{matrix}\diagup\!\!\diagup NH \\ \diagdown NH_2\end{matrix} + H_2O \longrightarrow R{-}C\begin{matrix}\diagup\!\!\diagup O \\ \diagdown NH_2\end{matrix} + NH_3$$

Amidines or their salts may be reduced to aldehydes by sodium and ethanol in liquid ammonia, or by sodium and ethanol, but in the latter case the yields are lower (Birch *et al.*, 1954).

ACID HYDRAZIDES AND ACID AZIDES

Acid hydrazides may be prepared by the action of hydrazine on esters or acyl chlorides:

$$R{\cdot}COOC_2H_5 + N_2H_4 \longrightarrow R{\cdot}CO{\cdot}NH{\cdot}NH_2 + C_2H_5OH$$
$$R{\cdot}COCl + N_2H_4 \longrightarrow R{\cdot}CO{\cdot}NH{\cdot}NH_2 + HCl$$

Girard's reagent " T " (p. 143) is trimethylaminoacetohydrazide, which may be prepared by interaction between trimethylamine, ethyl chloroacetate and hydrazine:

$$(CH_3)_3N + ClCH_2{\cdot}CO_2C_2H_5 + N_2H_4 \longrightarrow [(CH_3)_3N{\cdot}CH_2{\cdot}CO{\cdot}NH{\cdot}NH_2]^+Cl^- + C_2H_5OH$$

Girard's reagent " P " is formed in a similar manner, except that pyridine is used instead of trimethylamine.

The acid hydrazides resemble the acid amides, but differ in the following ways:

(i) They are much more readily hydrolysed than the amides:

$$R{\cdot}CO{\cdot}NH{\cdot}NH_2 + H_2O \longrightarrow R{\cdot}CO_2H + N_2H_4$$

(ii) They are reducing agents—hydrazine is a powerful reducing agent.

(iii) They form acid azides when treated with nitrous acid; no nitrogen is evolved:

$$R{\cdot}CO{\cdot}NH{\cdot}NH_2 + HNO_2 \longrightarrow R{\cdot}CO{\cdot}N_3 + 2H_2O$$

Acid azides may also be prepared by the reaction between an acyl chloride and sodium azide:

$$R{\cdot}COCl + NaN_3 \longrightarrow R{\cdot}CO{\cdot}N_3 + NaCl$$

The structure of the acid azides is best represented as a resonance hybrid:

$$R{-}\overset{\overset{\displaystyle O}{\|}}{C}{-}\ddot{\underset{\cdot\cdot}{N}}{-}\overset{+}{N}{-}\overset{-}{\ddot{N}}{:} \longleftrightarrow R{-}\overset{\overset{\displaystyle O}{\|}}{C}{-}\overset{-}{\underset{\cdot\cdot}{\ddot{N}}}{-}\overset{+}{N}{\equiv}N{:}$$

When boiled with an alcohol, acid azides undergo rearrangement to form *N*-alkyl-substituted urethans:

$$R{\cdot}CO{\cdot}N_3 + R'OH \longrightarrow R{\cdot}NH{\cdot}CO_2R' + N_2 \qquad (v.g.\text{–}ex.)$$

The mechanism of this rearrangement—the **Curtius rearrangement** (1894)—is similar to that of the Hofmann and Lossen rearrangements (see above), and so may be formulated:

$$R{-}\underset{\underset{\displaystyle O}{\|}}{C}{-}\ddot{\underset{\cdot\cdot}{N}}{-}\overset{+}{N}{\equiv}N{:} \xrightarrow{-N_2} \left[R{-}\underset{\underset{\displaystyle O}{\|}}{C}{-}\ddot{N}{:}\right] \longrightarrow \underset{\underset{\displaystyle O}{\|}}{C}{=}N{-}R \xrightarrow{R'OH} R{\cdot}NH{\cdot}CO_2R'$$

This mechanism is supported by the fact that when the terminal nitrogen atom is ^{15}N in 3 : 5-dinitrobenzazide, all of this tracer is found in the nitrogen eliminated in the reaction (Bothner—By *et al.*, 1951).

The Curtius reaction may be used to step down a series (*cf.* the Hofmann reaction):

$$R{\cdot}CO_2H \xrightarrow{C_2H_5OH} R{\cdot}CO_2C_2H_5 \xrightarrow{N_2H_4} R{\cdot}CO{\cdot}NH{\cdot}NH_2 \xrightarrow{HNO_2} R{\cdot}CO{\cdot}N_3 \xrightarrow{CH_3OH} R{\cdot}NH{\cdot}CO_2CH_3 \xrightarrow{NaOH} R{\cdot}NH_2$$

The Curtius reactions offers a very good method for preparing primary amines free from secondary and tertiary amines, and may also be used for preparing *iso*cyanates and urethans; *e.g.*, when heated in benzene or chloroform solution, an acid azide rearranges to the alkyl *iso*cyanate which can be isolated. If the *iso*cyanate is warmed with an alcohol, an *N*-substituted urethan is formed:

$$R{\cdot}CO{\cdot}N_3 \xrightarrow[\text{solution}]{\text{benzene}} R{\cdot}NCO \xrightarrow{R'OH} R{\cdot}NH{\cdot}CO_2R'$$

HALOGEN DERIVATIVES OF THE FATTY ACIDS

The halogen derivatives of the fatty acids are compounds in which one or more hydrogen atoms in the *carbon chain* have been replaced by halogen.

Nomenclature. The usual method of naming the halogenated fatty acids is to use the trivial names of the acids, and to indicate the positions of the halogens atoms by Greek letters, *e.g.*,

$CH_2Cl{\cdot}CO_2H$	monochloroacetic acid
$CH_3{\cdot}CHCl{\cdot}CO_2H$	α-chloropropionic acid
$(CH_3)_2CCl{\cdot}CHBr{\cdot}CO_2H$	α-bromo-β-chloro*iso*valeric acid

Preparation of the halogenated acids. There are no general methods of preparing the various types of halogenated acids, *i.e.*, the α-, β-, γ-, etc., halogeno-acids; the method depends on the position of the halogen atom.

α-**Halogeno-acids.** Although the fatty acids themselves are not readily halogenated, their acid chlorides and anhydrides may be halogenated very easily. Bromination takes place only at the α-position, but chlorination, although it occurs mainly at the α-position, may also take place further in the chain; *e.g.*, chlorination of propionic acid results in the formation of the α- and β-chloro-derivatives:

$$CH_3{\cdot}CH_2{\cdot}CO_2H \xrightarrow{Cl_2} CH_3{\cdot}CHCl{\cdot}CO_2H + CH_2Cl{\cdot}CH_2{\cdot}CO_2H$$

Fluorination of the fatty acids has not yet been studied in great detail, but the work done so far seems to indicate that fluorine enters the chain somewhat indiscriminately; *e.g.*, fluorination of butyric acid in carbon tetrachloride solution gives the β- and γ-fluoro-derivatives (Bockemüller, 1933).

Iodo-derivatives are prepared from the chloro- or bromo-compound by the action of potassium iodide in methanolic or acetone solution (*cf.* alkyl iodides, p. 96).

The usual method for preparing α-chloro- or bromo-acids is by the **Hell–Volhard–Zelinsky reaction** (**H.V.Z. reaction**), which is carried out by treating the acid with chlorine or bromine in the presence of a small amount of red phosphorus. The reaction possibly takes place as follows:

$$R{\cdot}CH_2{\cdot}CO_2H \xrightarrow{P + Br_2} R{\cdot}CH_2{\cdot}COBr \xrightarrow{Br_2} R{\cdot}CHBr{\cdot}COBr$$

$$R{\cdot}CHBr{\cdot}COBr + R{\cdot}CH_2{\cdot}CO_2H \rightleftharpoons R{\cdot}CHBr{\cdot}CO_2H + R{\cdot}CH_2{\cdot}COBr$$

$$R{\cdot}CH_2{\cdot}COBr \xrightarrow{Br_2} R{\cdot}CHBr{\cdot}COBr, \text{ etc.}$$

The second α-hydrogen atom may be replaced by chlorine or bromine by using excess of the halogen, but whereas bromination ceases when both α-hydrogen atoms have been replaced, chlorination proceeds further in the chain (see above). Since the H.V.Z. reaction with bromine is specific for α-hydrogen atoms, it can be used to detect the presence of α-hydrogen in an acid; *e.g.*, trimethylacetic acid does not undergo the H.V.Z. reaction with bromine.

The H.V.Z. reaction with bromine is applicable to dibasic and polybasic acids, all the α-positions being substituted if sufficient bromine is used.

Sulphuryl chloride, in the presence of a small amount of iodine, chlorinates aliphatic acids in the α-position; but in the presence of organic peroxides, the α-, β-, γ-, etc., positions are substituted.

Another convenient method of preparing α-bromo-acids is by brominating an alkyl-malonic acid and heating the bromo-acid, whereupon it is decarboxylated to the monobasic acid:

$$R{\cdot}CH(CO_2H)_2 \xrightarrow{Br_2} R{\cdot}CBr(CO_2H)_2 \xrightarrow{heat} R{\cdot}CHBr{\cdot}CO_2H + CO_2$$

β-Halogeno-acids may be prepared by treating an αβ-unsaturated acid with halogen acid; *e.g.*, acrylic acid forms β-bromopropionic acid when treated with hydrogen bromide in acetic acid solution:

$$CH_2{=}CH{\cdot}CO_2H + HBr \longrightarrow CH_2Br{\cdot}CH_2{\cdot}CO_2H$$

This addition takes place contrary to Markownikoff's rule, and may be explained by the inductive effect of the carboxyl group (see p. 265).

β-Halogeno-acids may also be prepared by treating an αβ-unsaturated aldehyde with halogen acid, and oxidising the β-chloroaldehyde produced; *e.g.*, acraldehyde gives β-chloropropionic acid when treated with concentrated hydrochloric acid, and the product then oxidised with concentrated nitric acid:

$$CH_2{=}CH{\cdot}CHO + HCl \longrightarrow CH_2Cl{\cdot}CH_2{\cdot}CHO \xrightarrow{[O]} CH_2Cl{\cdot}CH_2{\cdot}CO_2H \quad (60\text{–}65\%)$$

The addition of all the halogen acids to αβ-unsaturated carbonyl compounds takes place very readily, and in a direction contrary to Markownikoff's rule.

When an olefin cyanohydrin is refluxed with 40 per cent. hydrobromic acid, the β-bromoacid is obtained; *e.g.*, ethylene cyanohydrin gives β-bromopropionic acid:

$$CH_2(OH){\cdot}CH_2{\cdot}CN + 2HBr + H_2O \longrightarrow CH_2Br{\cdot}CH_2{\cdot}CO_2H + NH_4Br \quad (82\text{–}83\%)$$

Alternatively, when an olefin halohydrin is oxidised with concentrated nitric acid, the halogeno-acid is produced; *e.g.*, trimethylene chlorohydrin gives β-chloropropionic acid:

$$CH_2Cl{\cdot}CH_2{\cdot}CH_2OH \xrightarrow{[O]} CH_2Cl{\cdot}CH_2{\cdot}CO_2H \quad (78\text{–}79\%)$$

γ-Halogeno-acids may be prepared by the addition of halogen acid to a βγ-unsaturated acid; the addition occurs contrary to Markownikoff's rule (*cf.* above); *e.g.*, pent-3-enoic acid gives γ-bromo-*n*-valeric acid when treated with hydrobromic acid:

$$CH_3{\cdot}CH{=}CH{\cdot}CH_2{\cdot}CO_2H + HBr \longrightarrow CH_3{\cdot}CHBr{\cdot}CH_2{\cdot}CH_2{\cdot}CO_2H$$

γ-Halogeno-acids may also be prepared by heating a γ-hydroxyacid with concentrated halogen acid solution; *e.g.*, γ-hydroxybutyric acid gives γ-chlorobutyric acid when treated with concentrated hydrochloric acid:

$$CH_2OH{\cdot}CH_2{\cdot}CH_2{\cdot}CO_2H + HCl \longrightarrow CH_2Cl{\cdot}CH_2{\cdot}CH_3{\cdot}CO_2H + H_2O$$

δ-Halogeno-acids, etc., are prepared by methods which are usually specific for the particular acid.

Properties of the halogen-acids. The α-halogeno-acids undergo most of the reactions of the alkyl halides, but the halogen atom in the acid is far more reactive than that in the alkyl halide; the enhanced reactivity is due to the adjacent carbonyl group. The reactions of the carboxyl group are unchanged. β-, γ- and δ-Halogeno-acids undergo some of the reactions of the alkyl halides, but tend to eliminate a molecule of hydrogen halide to form an unsaturated acid or a lactone (p. 378). They do not form Grignard reagents, but the halogeno-acid esters react with Grignard reagents to form halogen-substituted tertiary alcohols. The halogeno-acids are reduced to the corresponding fatty acids by sodium amalgam, but the reduction of acids of the type $RR'CCl{\cdot}CO_2H$ with lithium aluminium hydride gives chlorohydrins (I), alcohols (II), aldehydes (III) and glycols (IV).

$$\underset{(I)}{RR'CCl{\cdot}CH_2OH} \quad \underset{(II)}{RR'CH{\cdot}CH_2OH} \quad \underset{(III)}{RR'CH{\cdot}CHO} \quad \underset{(IV)}{RR'C(OH){\cdot}CH_2OH}$$

The amount of each depends on the nature of R and R′, *e.g.*, very little glycol is obtained unless at least one of these radicals is phenyl (Eliel *et al.*, 1956).

The behaviour of an halogeno-acid with alkali depends on the position of the halogen atom relative to the carboxyl group.

(*a*) α-Halogeno-acids are converted into the corresponding α-hydroxy-acid:

$$R{\cdot}CHX{\cdot}CO_2H + H_2O \xrightarrow{NaOH} R{\cdot}CH(OH){\cdot}CO_2H$$

On the other hand, if the α-halogeno-acid ester is heated with a tertiary amine, the αβ-unsaturated acid ester is formed by the elimination of a molecule of hydrogen halide; *e.g.*, ethyl α-bromobutyrate gives ethyl crotonate when heated with dimethylaniline, $C_6H_5{\cdot}N(CH_3)_2$:

$$CH_3{\cdot}CH_2{\cdot}CHBr{\cdot}CO_2C_2H_5 \xrightarrow{-HBr} CH_3{\cdot}CH{=}CH{\cdot}CO_2C_2H_5$$

(*b*) β-Halogeno-acids are converted into the corresponding β-hydroxyacid, which, on continued reflux with alkali, eliminates a molecule of water to form the αβ-unsaturated acid:

$$R{\cdot}CHBr{\cdot}CH_2{\cdot}CO_2H \xrightarrow{NaOH} R{\cdot}CH(OH){\cdot}CH_2{\cdot}CO_2H \xrightarrow[-H_2O]{NaOH} R{\cdot}CH{=}CH{\cdot}CO_2H$$

(*c*) γ- and δ-Halogeno-acids are converted into lactones; *e.g.*, γ-chlorobutyric acid gives γ-butyrolactone:

$$CH_2Cl{\cdot}CH_2{\cdot}CH_2{\cdot}CO_2H \xrightarrow[-HCl]{NaOH} \underbrace{CH_2{\cdot}CH_2{\cdot}CH_2{\cdot}CO}_{O}$$

(*d*) ε-Halogeno-acids, etc., give the corresponding hydroxyacid; *e.g.*, ε-bromocaproic acid gives ε-hydroxycaproic acid:

$$CH_2Br{\cdot}CH_2{\cdot}CH_2{\cdot}CH_2{\cdot}CH_2{\cdot}CO_2H \xrightarrow{NaOH} CH_2OH{\cdot}CH_2{\cdot}CH_2{\cdot}CH_2{\cdot}CH_2{\cdot}CO_2H$$

The most characteristic reaction of the α-halogeno-acid esters is the *Reformatsky reaction* (p. 346).

The halogeno-acids are all stronger acids than the parent acid (see Table III, p. 169), and for a group of isomeric acids, the further the halogen is removed from the carboxyl group the weaker is the acid. The increase in acid strength may be explained by the high electron-affinity of the halogen atom which exerts a strong inductive effect, thereby facilitating the release of proton from the carboxyl group.

$$X{\leftarrow}CH_2{\leftarrow}\overset{\overset{\displaystyle O}{\|}}{C}{\leftarrow}O{\leftarrow}H \qquad CH_3{\rightarrow}\overset{\overset{\displaystyle O}{\|}}{C}{\rightarrow}O{\rightarrow}H$$

$$\begin{matrix}X\searrow \\ \\ X\nearrow\end{matrix}CH{\leftarrow\leftarrow}\overset{\overset{\displaystyle O}{\|}}{C}{\leftarrow\leftarrow}O{\leftarrow\leftarrow}H \qquad \begin{matrix}CH_3\searrow \\ \\ CH_3\nearrow\end{matrix}CH{\rightarrow\rightarrow}\overset{\overset{\displaystyle O}{\|}}{C}{\rightarrow\rightarrow}O{\rightarrow\rightarrow}H$$

$$\begin{array}{l} X \searrow \\ X \leftarrow C - \leftarrow\leftarrow\leftarrow \overset{O}{\overset{\|}{C}} - \leftarrow\leftarrow\leftarrow O - \leftarrow\leftarrow\leftarrow H \\ X \nearrow \end{array} \qquad \begin{array}{l} CH_3 \searrow \\ CH_3 \rightarrow C \rightarrow\rightarrow\rightarrow \overset{O}{\overset{\|}{C}} \rightarrow\rightarrow\rightarrow O \rightarrow\rightarrow\rightarrow H \\ CH_3 \nearrow \end{array}$$

The larger the number of halogen atoms on the α-carbon atom, the stronger is the inductive effect, and consequently the stronger is the acid; also, the further removed the halogen atom is from the carboxyl group, the weaker is the inductive effect at the carboxyl group, and consequently the weaker is the acid. In the same way, since an alkyl group is electron-repelling, increasing their number on the α-carbon atom should *decrease* the strength of the acid since release of the proton will be hindered (see Table III). This explanation, based on the purely inductive effect through the chain of atoms, appears to be too simple. Work by Grob *et al.* (1955) has led them to conclude that the direct (or field) effect (p. 16) is the decisive factor in determining the strengths of the carboxylic acids.

Chloroacetic acid, $CH_2Cl{\cdot}CO_2H$, may be prepared by the H.V.Z. reaction; the reaction can be carried out in direct sunlight, and in the absence of phosphorus. Chloroacetic acid is prepared industrially: (i) by agitating trichloroethylene with 90 per cent. sulphuric acid:

$$CHCl{=\!=}CCl_2 + 2H_2O \xrightarrow{H_2SO_4} CH_2Cl{\cdot}CO_2H + 2HCl$$

(ii) By the oxidation of ethylene chlorohydrin with nitric acid:

$$CH_2Cl{\cdot}CH_2OH \xrightarrow{HNO_3} CH_2Cl{\cdot}CO_2H \quad (84\%)$$

Chloroacetic acid is a deliquescent solid, m.p. 61°, soluble in water and ethanol. It finds many uses in organic syntheses, and is used in the industrial preparation of indigotin (*q.v.*).

Ethyl chloroacetate is converted into chloroacetamide when shaken with aqueous ammonia:

$$CH_2Cl{\cdot}COOC_2H_5 + NH_3 \longrightarrow CH_2Cl{\cdot}CO{\cdot}NH_2 + C_2H_5OH \quad (78\text{–}84\%)$$

Dichloroacetic acid, $CHCl_2{\cdot}CO_2H$, may be prepared in the laboratory and industrially by adding calcium carbonate to a warm aqueous solution of chloral hydrate, then adding an aqueous solution of sodium cyanide, and finally heating the mixture:

$$2CCl_3{\cdot}CH(OH)_2 + 2CaCO_3 \xrightarrow{NaCN} (CHCl_2{\cdot}CO_2)_2Ca + 2CO_2 + CaCl_2 + 2H_2O$$
$$\xrightarrow{HCl} CHCl_2{\cdot}CO_2H \quad (88\text{–}92\%)$$

The action of the sodium cyanide is not understood.

Dichloroacetic acid is a liquid, b.p. 194°. When carefully hydrolysed with dilute alkali, it gives glyoxylic acid (*q.v.*):

$$CHCl_2{\cdot}CO_2H + H_2O \xrightarrow{NaOH} CHO{\cdot}CO_2H + 2HCl$$

Vigorous hydrolysis with concentrated alkali gives oxalate and glycollate, due to the glyoxylic acid undergoing the Cannizzaro reaction (p. 148):

$$2CHO{\cdot}CO_2H + 3NaOH \longrightarrow (CO_2Na)_2 + CH_2(OH){\cdot}CO_2Na + 2H_2O$$

Trichloroacetic acid, $CCl_3{\cdot}CO_2H$, is best prepared by oxidising chloral hydrate with concentrated nitric acid:

$$CCl_3{\cdot}CH(OH)_2 + [O] \xrightarrow{HNO_3} CCl_3{\cdot}CO_2H + H_2O$$

Trichloroacetic acid is a deliquescent solid, m.p. 58°, and is one of the strongest organic acids.

The presence of three chlorine atoms on a carbon atom adjacent to a carbonyl group causes the C—C bond to break very easily. Thus when trichloroacetic acid is boiled with dilute sodium hydroxide, or even water, chloroform is obtained:

$$CCl_3 \cdot CO_2H \longrightarrow CHCl_3 + CO_2$$

When boiled with concentrated alkali, formates are produced, possibly due to the hydrolysis of the chloroform which is formed first.

Trifluoroacetic acid, $CF_3 \cdot CO_2H$, is conveniently prepared by the oxidation of *p*-trifluoromethyltoluidine with chromic acid:

$$CF_3\text{—}C_6H_4\text{—}NH_2 \xrightarrow{[O]} CF_3 \cdot CO_2H$$

Trifluoroacetic acid is a liquid that fumes in the air, and is one of the strongest organic acids known. It does not form fluoroform when heated with alkali, and is reduced to trifluoroacetaldehyde by lithium aluminium hydride. Peroxytrifluoroacetic acid, $CF_3 \cdot CO_3H$, is a useful oxidising agent (Emmons, 1954; *cf.* peracetic acid).

Fluoroacetic acid may be prepared by heating a mixture of carbon monoxide, hydrogen fluoride and formaldehyde under pressure.

$$CO + HF + H \cdot CHO \longrightarrow CH_2F \cdot CO_2H$$

The simplest chloro-acid would be chloroformic acid, $Cl \cdot CO_2H$, but it is unknown; chlorination of formic acid results in the formation of hydrogen chloride and carbon dioxide:

$$H \cdot CO_2H \xrightarrow{Cl_2} 2HCl + CO_2$$

On the other hand, esters of chloroformic acid are known, and they may be prepared by the action of carbonyl chloride on an alcohol in the cold, *e.g.*, ethyl chloroformate from carbonyl chloride and ethanol:

$$COCl_2 + C_2H_5OH \longrightarrow Cl \cdot COOC_2H_5 + HCl$$

QUESTIONS

1. Write out the structures and the names of the isomeric acids having the molecular formula $C_6H_{12}O_2$.

2. Name the compounds and state the conditions under which they are formed when AcOH is treated with: (*a*) EtOH, (*b*) PCl_3, (*c*) PCl_5, (*d*) $SOCl_2$, (*e*) Br_2, (*f*) SO_2Cl_2, (*g*) $KMnO_4$, (*h*) HI/red P, (*i*) $LiAlH_4$, (*i*) H_2O_2, (*k*) CH_2N_2, (*l*) C_2H_4, (*m*) HN_3, (*n*) AcCl.

3. How would you determine the structures of *n*- and *iso*butyric acids?

4. Suggest a synthesis of each of the valeric acids, starting with compounds containing not more than three carbon atoms.

5. Name the compounds and state the conditions under which they are formed when EtOAc, AcCl and Ac_2O, respectively, are treated with:—(*a*) H_2O, (*b*) NaOH, (*c*) HCl, (*d*) nascent hydrogen, (*e*) molecular hydrogen, (*f*) NH_3, (*g*) *n*-BuOH, (*h*) PCl_5, (*i*) Br_2, (*j*) $NaNH_2$, (*k*) Na, (*l*) $NH_2 \cdot OH$, (*m*) N_2H_4, (*o*) benzene, (*p*) Et_2O, (*q*) *iso*butene.

6. Name the compounds and state the conditions under which they are formed when $CH_3 \cdot CO \cdot NH_2$ is treated with:—(*a*) NaOH, (*b*) HCl, (*c*) Na, (*d*) nascent hydrogen, (*e*) molecular hydrogen, (*f*) P_2O_5, (*g*) PCl_5, (*h*) HNO_2, (*i*) BF_3, (*j*) Br_2/KOH.

7. Define and give examples of:—(*a*) acetylation, (*b*) esterification, (*c*) saponification, (*d*) ammonolysis, (*e*) alcoholysis, (*f*) acidolysis, (*g*) acyloin condensation, (*h*) alkylation, (*i*) Hofmann degradation, (*j*) Curtius reaction, (*k*) Lossen rearrangement, (*l*) H.V.Z. reaction, (*m*) Rosenmund's reduction.

8. Describe the industrial preparations of: (*a*) HCO_2H, (*b*) AcOH, (*c*) EtOAc, (*d*) AcCl, (*e*) Ac_2O, (*f*) Me_2SO_4, (*g*) Et_2SO_4, (*h*) $CH_2Cl \cdot CO_2H$, (*i*) $CHCl_2 \cdot CO_2H$, (*j*) $CCl_3 \cdot CO_2H$.

9. Show by means of equations how you would convert acetic acid into propionic acid and vice-versa.

10. Show how you would distinguish between:—(*a*) $CH_2Cl{\cdot}CO_2H$, $CH_3{\cdot}COCl$ and $CH_2Cl{\cdot}COCl$; (*b*) paraffin, olefin, alkyl halide, alcohol, ether, carboxylic acid, carboxylic ester, Ac_2O, AcCl and $AcNH_2$.

11. Discuss the mechanism of:—(*a*) esterification and hydrolysis; (*b*) the Hofmann, Curtius and Lossen rearrangements, (*c*) ammonolysis of esters and acid chlorides, (*d*) hydrolysis of cyanides and amides.

12. Discuss the methods of preparation and the properties of the halogeno-acids.

READING REFERENCES

Reid, Esterification, *Ind. Eng. Chem.*, 1950, **42**, 1667.
Ann. Reports, 1942, **69**, pp. 128–130. Esterification.
Greenspan, Oxidation Reactions with Aliphatic Peracids, *Ind. Eng. Chem.*, 1947, **39**, 847.
Bell, The Use of the Terms "Acid" and "Base", *Quart. Reviews* (*Chem. Soc.*), 1947, **1**, 113.
Organic Reactions, Wiley. Vol. IV (1948), Ch. 4. Acyloins.
Richards and Thomson, Spectroscopic Studies of the Amide Linkage, *J.C.S.*, 1947, 1248.
Organic Reactions. Wiley. Vol. III (1946).

(i) Ch. 7. The Hofmann Reaction.
(ii) Ch. 8. The Schmidt Reaction.
(iii) Ch. 9. The Curtius Reaction.

Sidgwick, *The Organic Chemistry of Nitrogen*, Oxford Press. (Revised Edition by Taylor and Baker, 1937.)

Ch. I. Esters of Nitrous and Nitric Acids.
Ch. V. Amides, etc.

Brown, The Mechanism of Thermal Decarboxylation, *Quart. Reviews* (*Chem. Soc.*), 1951, **5**, 131.
Sonntag, The Reactions of Aliphatic Acid Chlorides, *Chem. Reviews*, 1953, **52**, 237.
Davies and Kenyon, Alkyl-Oxygen Heterolysis in Carboxylic Esters and Related Compounds, *Quart. Reviews* (*Chem. Soc.*), 1955, **9**, 203.
Allen and Caldin, The Association of Carboxylic Acids, *ibid.*, 1953, **7**, 255.
Gunstone, Recent Developments in the Preparation of Natural and Synthetic Straight-Chain Fatty Acids, *ibid.*, 1953, **7**, 175.

CHAPTER X

TAUTOMERISM

Acetoacetic ester or **ethyl acetoacetate** (E.A.A.) is the ethyl ester of acetoacetic acid, $CH_3{\cdot}CO{\cdot}CH_2{\cdot}CO_2H$, a β-ketonic acid. Acetoacetic ester was first discovered by Geuther (1863), who prepared it by the action of sodium on ethyl acetate, and suggested the formula, $CH_3{\cdot}C(OH){:}CH{\cdot}CO_2C_2H_5$ (β-hydroxycrotonic ester). In 1865, Frankland and Duppa, who, independently of Geuther, also prepared acetoacetic ester by the action of sodium on ethyl acetate, proposed the formula $CH_3{\cdot}CO{\cdot}CH_2{\cdot}CO_2C_2H_5$ (β-ketobutyric ester). These two formulæ immediately gave rise to two schools of thought, one upholding the Geuther formula, and the other the Frankland–Duppa formula, each school bringing forward evidence to prove its own claim, *e.g.*,

Evidence in favour of the Geuther formula (*reactions of an unsaturated alcohol*). (i) When acetoacetic ester is treated with sodium, hydrogen is evolved and the sodium derivative is formed. This indicates the presence of a hydroxyl group.

(ii) When acetoacetic ester is treated with an ethanolic solution of bromine, the colour of the latter is immediately discharged. This indicates the presence of an olefinic double bond.

(iii) When acetoacetic ester is treated with ferric chloride, a reddish-violet colour is produced. This is characteristic of compounds containing the group $-C(OH){:}C<$ (*cf.* phenols).

Evidence in favour of the Frankland–Duppa formula (*reactions of a ketone*). (i) Acetoacetic ester forms a bisulphite compound with sodium hydrogen sulphite.

(ii) Acetoacetic ester forms a cyanohydrin with hydrogen cyanide.

(iii) Acetoacetic ester forms a phenylhydrazone with phenylhydrazine.

Thus the remarkable position arose where it was possible to show that a given compound had two different formulæ, each of which was based on a number of *particular* reactions. The controversy continued until about 1910, when chemists were coming to the conclusion that both formulæ were correct, and that the two compounds existed together in equilibrium in solution (or in the liquid state):

$$CH_3{\cdot}CO{\cdot}CH_2{\cdot}CO_2C_2H_5 \rightleftharpoons CH_3{\cdot}\overset{\displaystyle OH}{\overset{|}{C}}{=}CH{\cdot}CO_2C_2H_5$$

When a reagent which reacts with ketones is added to acetoacetic ester, the ketone form is removed. This upsets the equilibrium, and in order to restore the equilibrium mixture, the hydroxy-form of acetoacetic ester changes into the ketone form. Thus, provided sufficient reagent is added, acetoacetic ester reacts completely as the ketone form. Similarly, when a reagent which reacts with olefins or with hydroxy-compounds is added in sufficient quantity, acetoacetic ester reacts completely as the hydroxy-form.

The problem was finally settled by Knorr (1911), who succeeded in isolating both forms. He cooled a solution of acetoacetic ester in light petrol to $-78°$, and obtained crystals which melted at $-39°$. This substance gave no coloration with ferric chloride and did not combine with bromine, and was therefore the pure ketone form corresponding to the Frankland–Duppa formula. Knorr then suspended the sodium derivative of acetoacetic ester in light petrol cooled to $-78°$, and treated this suspension with just enough hydrogen chloride to decompose the sodium salt. He now obtained a product which did not crystallise, but set to a glassy solid when cooled. This substance gave an intense coloration with ferric chloride, and was therefore the pure hydroxy-form corresponding to the Geuther formula.

Thus acetoacetic ester is a substance that does the duty of two structural isomers, each isomer being capable of changing rapidly into the other when the equilibrium is disturbed, *e.g.*, by the addition of certain reagents. This is a case of *dynamic isomerism*, and the name *tautomerism* (Greek: *same parts*) was given to this phenomenon by Laar (1885). The two forms are known as *tautomers* or *tautomerides*, the ketone isomer being called the *keto* form, and the hydroxy isomer the *enol* form. Hence this type of tautomerism is known as *keto-enol* tautomerism. (In the I.U.C. system of nomenclature the suffix *-en* indicates the presence of a double bond, and the suffix *-ol*, a hydroxyl group. The word *enol* is a combination of these suffixes and indicates the structure of this form.)

A simplified version for the occurrence of tautomerism is as follows. Every structure has a certain amount of internal energy, and when dealing with two structural isomers, a definite amount of energy must be supplied in order to overcome the energy of transformation. If this amount of energy is small, then each isomer will change *spontaneously* into the other, resulting in an equilibrium mixture the composition of which depends on various factors (see below).

When one tautomer is more stable than the other under ordinary conditions, the former is known as the *stable* form, and the latter as the *labile* form. In practice, it is generally difficult to say which is the labile form, since very often a slight change in the conditions, *e.g.*, temperature, solvent, shifts the equilibrium from keto to enol or vice-versa (see below). Furthermore, in the solid state one or other form is stable, *i.e.*, tautomerism, is not possible in the solid state (unless the tautomers form a solid solution), but only in the liquid or gaseous state, or in solution.

It has been found that the enol form is more volatile than the keto, and that the change from enol to keto is extremely sensitive to catalysts. Meyer *et al.* (1920, 1921) found that traces of basic compounds were very effective catalysts. Thus they found that soft glass vessels were unsuitable for the separation of the keto and enol forms, since, when fractionated, the more volatile enol form rapidly changed into the original keto-enol mixture under the catalytic influence of the walls of the containing vessel. Meyer, however, succeeded in separating the enol form from the keto by carrying out the fractional distillation under reduced pressure in silica apparatus which had been thoroughly cleaned (freed from dust, moisture, etc.). Distillation under these conditions is known as *aseptic distillation.*

The greater volatility of the enol form is unexpected in view of the fact that alcohols are less volatile than ketones containing the same number of carbon atoms. This anomalous behaviour of the enol form may be explained by assuming that chelation takes place through hydrogen bonding. This is supported by various facts, *e.g.*, (i) the enol form is more soluble in *cyclo*hexane, and less soluble in water, than the keto form. The presence of the hydroxyl group should have made the enol form less soluble in *cyclo*hexane, and more soluble in water, than the keto (*cf.* alcohols). (ii) The formation of the hydrogen bond *intramolecularly* prevents the formation of the hydrogen bond *intermolecularly*, *i.e.*, prevents association which would have raised the boiling point of the enol form.

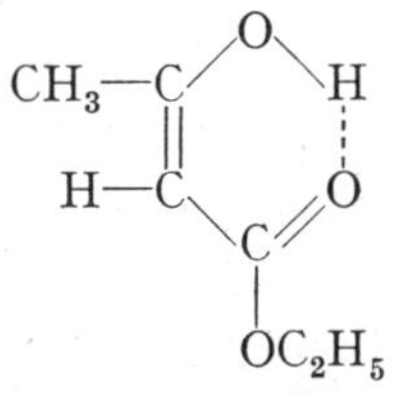

```
           O
          / \
CH3—C       H
        ‖       :
 H—C       O
        \   //
          C
          |
         OC2H5
```

The vibrational spectrum of liquid ethyl acetoacetate shows *intermolecular* bonding between the enol and keto forms. In solvents such as carbon tetrachloride, and in dilute solution, *intramolecular* hydrogen bonding occurs in the enolic form, and the tautomeric equilibrium is displaced in the direction of the enol form (Shigorin, 1950).

In tautomerism in general there may be an equilibrium between two or more forms. One may predominate, or all may be present to about the same extent, the concentration of each form depending on the temperature and the solvent (if in solution). Although it may not be possible to separate tautomers owing to the ease and rapidity of their interconversion or, as in many cases, due to one form being almost completely absent, the presence of more than one compound may be shown by special properties of each isomer. The refractive index of the mixture may be observed directly, and the value obtained compared with those calculated for the various tautomeric structures. Spectral analysis may show the presence of more than one substance, since each structure will have its own characteristic absorption bands. Furthermore, the intensities of the bands change as the temperature changes, thus showing the displacement of the equilibrium. The Raman effect may also be used to show the presence of tautomers; *e.g.*, the equilibrium mixture of acetoacetic esters shows Raman shifts due to both the C=C and C=O groups. Experiments using deuterium exchange reactions have also shown the presence of keto-enol mixtures, *e.g.*, Klar (1934) showed that hydrogen is exchanged slowly by deuterium when acetaldehyde is dissolved in D_2O. Since the C—H bond in paraffins is stable under these conditions, the inference is that a hydroxyl group is present in acetaldehyde, *i.e.*, some enol form is present. Acetone was found to undergo this exchange more rapidly.

The methods used for the quantitative estimation of each form in any tautomeric equilibrium mixture, of which the keto-enol system is only one example, fall into two distinct groups, physical and chemical. Obviously, whatever the method used, it should be one that does not disturb the equilibrium of the mixture during the estimation.

Physical methods Physical methods do not disturb the equilibrium, for they do not depend on the removal of one form, and they should therefore be used wherever possible.

(i) The refractive index of the equilibrium mixture is determined experimentally. The refractive indices of both the keto and enol forms are calculated (from a table of atomic refractions), and from these figures it is then possible to calculate the amount of each form present in the equilibrium mixture. In some cases, the refractive index of each form may be obtained directly by isolating it, *e.g.*, acetoacetic ester.

(ii) If *one* form is an electrolyte, the electrical conductivity of the mixture is determined experimentally, and the amount of this form present may be calculated from the results, *e.g.*, nitromethane (p. 287).

(iii) The composition of the equilibrium mixture may be determined by means of optical rotation measurements (*cf.* mutarotation, p. 429).

(iv) Joshi and Tuli (1951) have introduced a new physical constant which they have named the *refrachor*, and have used it to determine the percentage of tautomers in an equilibrium mixture, *e.g.*, they found that ethyl acetoacetate contains 7·7% enol, and acetylacetone 72·4% enol.

(v) Jarrett *et al.* (1953) have determined keto-enol equilibria in two β-diketones by measurement of proton resonance.

Chemical methods. Since chemical methods cause the removal of one form, it is necessary to use a reagent that reacts with this form faster than the rate of interconversion of the tautomers. Meyer (1911, 1912) found that in the case of keto-enol tautomerism, bromine reacts instantaneously with the enol form, and so slowly with the keto form in comparison with the enol, that the keto reaction may be ignored. Meyer introduced two procedures, the *direct* and the *indirect* method. In the *direct* method a weighed sample of the keto-enol mixture dissolved in ethanol is *rapidly* titrated with a dilute ethanolic solution of bromine at 0° (to slow down the interconversion of the tautomers). The first appearance of excess bromine indicates the end point (see also the bromination of acetone, p. 144).

The titration must be carried out rapidly; otherwise the keto form changes into the enol during the time taken for the titration. In any case, it has been found impossible to carry out the titration sufficiently rapidly to avoid the conversion of some keto into enol, and so this method always results in too high a value for the enol form.

More reliable results may be obtained by the *indirect* method. An *excess* of dilute ethanolic solution of bromine is added rapidly to the weighed sample dissolved in ethanol, and then an excess of 2-naphthol dissolved in ethanol is added *immediately*. By this means, the excess bromine is removed almost instantaneously, and so the keto-enol equilibrium is not given time to be disturbed. Potassium iodide solution and hydrochloric acid are now added, and the liberated iodine is titrated with standard thiosulphate:

$$KI + HCl \longrightarrow KCl + HI$$

$$CH_3{\cdot}CO{\cdot}CHBr{\cdot}CO_2C_2H_5 + KI \longrightarrow CH_3{\cdot}CO{\cdot}CHI{\cdot}CO_2C_2H_5 + KBr$$

$$CH_3{\cdot}CO{\cdot}CHI{\cdot}CO_2C_2H_5 + HI \longrightarrow CH_3{\cdot}CO{\cdot}CH_2{\cdot}CO_2C_2H_5 + I_2$$

Cooper and Barnes (1938) have suggested an improved indirect method using methanol instead of ethanol, and di-*iso*butene instead of 2-naphthol (di-*iso*butene is a mixture of 2 : 4 : 4-trimethylpent-1-ene and 2 : 4 : 4-trimethylpent-2-ene).

Schwarzenbach and Wittwer (1947) have introduced a new technique, the *flow-method*, for the estimation of the enol content. The solution of the keto-enol mixture and an acidified bromide–bromate solution are simultaneously mixed and diluted in a mixing chamber, and the mixture made to flow past a platinum electrode. The relative amounts of the two solutions are adjusted so that the potential measured at the platinum electrode shows a sharp rise—this corresponds to the end-point in the titration of the enol form by the bromine. This method gives good results of enol contents as low as 10^{-5} per cent.; *e.g.*, the enol content of acetone in aqueous solution was found to be $2{\cdot}5 \times 10^{-4}$ per cent.

TABLE IV

Compound	Per cent. enol (in ethanol)
$CH_3{\cdot}CO{\cdot}CH_2{\cdot}CO_2CH_3$	4·8
$CH_3{\cdot}CO{\cdot}CH_2{\cdot}CO_2C_2H_5$	7·5
$CH_3{\cdot}CO{\cdot}CH_2{\cdot}CO{\cdot}CH_3$	76
$CH_3{\cdot}CO{\cdot}CH(CH_3){\cdot}CO{\cdot}CH_3$	31
$C_6H_5{\cdot}CO{\cdot}CH_2{\cdot}CO{\cdot}C_6H_5$	96
$CH_2(CO_2C_2H_5)_2$	trace
Aldehydes of type $R{\cdot}CH_2{\cdot}CHO$	trace
Ketones of type $R{\cdot}CH_2{\cdot}CO{\cdot}CH_2{\cdot}R$	trace

The enol content in keto-enol mixtures (in dipropyl ether) has been determined by means of lithium aluminium hydride; the hydrogen liberated is estimated (Höfling *et al.*, 1952). The values obtained are about 10 per cent. higher than those obtained by the bromine titration or by physical methods.

Enolisation. The phenomenon of enolisation is exhibited by compounds containing either a methylene group, $\cdot CH_2\cdot$, or a methyne group, $>CH-$, adjacent to a carbonyl group. The presence of one carbonyl group does not always give rise to an appreciable amount of enol form, *e.g.*, acetaldehyde, acetone (see Table IV, above). If the compound contains a methylene or methyne group attached to two carbonyl groups the percentage of enol form is usually high, *e.g.*, acetylacetone, $CH_3{\cdot}CO{\cdot}CH_2{\cdot}CO{\cdot}CH_3$. When a methyne group is attached to three carbonyl groups, the compound may exist almost completely as the enol form, *e.g.*, triacetylmethane, $(CH_3{\cdot}CO)_3CH$.

When the methylene or methyne group is attached to two or three carbonyl groups, the hydrogen atom might migrate equally well to one or other carbonyl group. This is not found to be so in practice for unsymmetrical compounds, one enol form being present exclusively, or largely predominating; *e.g.*, in acetoacetic ester the hydrogen atom migrates exclusively to the acetyl carbonyl group (see also below). When two or more enol forms are theoretically possible, ozonolysis may be used to ascertain the structure of the form present; *e.g.*, in hexane-2 : 4-dione, $CH_3{\cdot}CO{\cdot}CH_2{\cdot}CO{\cdot}CH_2{\cdot}CH_3$, the two possible enols are:

$$CH_3{\cdot}\underset{}{\overset{OH}{\overset{|}{C}}}{=}CH{\cdot}CO{\cdot}CH_2{\cdot}CH_3 \quad (I) \qquad CH_3{\cdot}CO{\cdot}CH{=}\overset{OH}{\overset{|}{C}}{\cdot}CH_2{\cdot}CH_3 \quad (II)$$

Ozonolysis of I will give $CH_3{\cdot}CO_2H$ and $CH_3{\cdot}CH_2{\cdot}CO{\cdot}CHO$; II will give $CH_3{\cdot}CO{\cdot}CHO$ and $CH_3{\cdot}CH_2{\cdot}CO_2H$. Identification of these compounds will decide whether the enol is I or II, or both.

The type of tautomerism discussed above is known as the **keto-enol triad system.** In this system a hydrogen atom migrates from atom 1 (*oxygen*) to atom 3 (*carbon*):

$$>\overset{3}{C}H{-}\overset{2}{C}{=}\overset{1}{O} \rightleftharpoons >\overset{3}{C}{=}\overset{2}{C}{-}\overset{1}{O}H$$

Enols resemble phenols in a number of ways; *e.g.*, both form soluble sodium salts; both give characteristic colorations with ferric chloride; and both couple with diazonium salts.

The keto-enol type of tautomerism is only one example of a triad system. The triad system is the most important class of tautomeric systems, and the following, which are exemplified in the text, are the commonest:

(i) *Three-carbon systems*:

$$CH{-}C{=}C \rightleftharpoons C{=}C{-}CH$$

(ii) *Nitro-acinitro* (*pseudonitro*) *system*:

$$CH{-}NO_2 \rightleftharpoons C{=}NO{\cdot}OH$$

(iii) *Nitroso-oximino system*:

$$CH{-}N{=}O \rightleftharpoons C{=}N{\cdot}OH$$

(iv) *Amidine system*:

$$NH{-}C{=}N \rightleftharpoons N{=}C{-}NH$$

(v) *Amido-imidol system*:

$$NH{-}C{=}O \rightleftharpoons N{=}C{-}OH$$

(vi) *Azo-hydrazone system*:

$$N{=}N{-}CH \rightleftharpoons HN{-}N{=}C$$

(vii) *Diazo-amino* (*triazen*) *system*:

$$N{=}N{-}NH \rightleftharpoons NH{-}N{=}N$$

(viii) *Diazo-nitrosamine system*:

$$Ar—N{=}N{\cdot}OH \rightleftharpoons Ar—NH—N{=}O$$

Modern theories of tautomerism. Ingold (1927) suggested the name *cationotropy* for all those cases of tautomerism which involve the separation of a *cation*; and the name *anionotropy* for those cases which involve the separation of an *anion*. Lowry (1923) suggested the name *prototropy* for those cases in which a proton separates, and called such systems *prototropic* systems. Using Ingold's generalised classification of tautomeric systems, it can be seen that prototropy is a special case of cationotropy. Braude and Jones (1944) have proposed the term *oxotropy* for anionotropic rearrangements involving only the migration of a *hydroxyl* group (see allylic rearrangement, p. 256).

Laar (1885) attempted to account for keto-enol tautomerism by postulating that the hydrogen atom occupied a mean position with respect to the final positions it would occupy in the keto and enol forms, and that by a lateral movement in either direction the hydrogen atom formed the keto or enol form. Baly and Desch (1904) extended this theory into the *oscillation theory* (*isorropesis*), according to which the hydrogen atom oscillated continuously between the two positions as shown. This theory soon became untenable, since it did not agree with many of the experimental observations (see below).

$$—CH \xleftarrow{\;H\;} \rightarrow \overset{O}{\overset{\|}{C}}—$$

Jacobson (1887) objected to the use of the word tautomerism to describe the above phenomenon because it involved the view that tautomers have no definite structure, but are continually changing. Jacobson thought that *both* forms were present, and that the change from one into the other was caused by the presence of certain reagents. He therefore proposed the name *desmotropy* or *desmotropism* (Greek: change of bonds). Hantzsch and Hermann (1887) suggested that both the terms tautomerism and desmotropism should be used, the former to denote that a compound exhibited a dual nature, and the latter to indicate those cases of tautomerism where the two forms exist in different physical forms (*i.e.*, those cases of tautomerism in which both forms have been isolated).

Knorr (1896) introduced the term *allelotropic mixture* for equilibrium mixtures whose composition varied with changes in temperature, *i.e.*, an allelotropic mixture is a tautomeric mixture in the liquid state or in solution; a mixture of solid tautomers is not an allelotropic mixture.

The term *pseudomerism* has also been used for those cases of tautomerism in which only one form, the keto or enol, may be shown to be present.

The actual steps involved in keto-enol tautomerism are still the subject of much discussion. According to Hughes and Ingold, base-catalysed enolisation of a ketone proceeds through an enolate anion I whose formation is controlled largely by the inductive effects of the alkyl groups.

$$B + R_2CH{\cdot}CO{\cdot}R \longrightarrow BH^+ + R_2C{=}\overset{O^-}{\overset{|}{C}}{\cdot}R \quad \text{(I)}$$

Acid-catalysed enolisation involves the removal of a proton from the conjugate acid of the ketone, II, and this process is dependent mainly on the hyperconjugation (p. 253) by the alkyl groups in the transition state for the formation of the carbon-carbon double bond.

$$H^+ + R_2\overset{H}{\overset{|}{C}}—\overset{O}{\overset{\|}{C}}—R \longrightarrow R_2\overset{H}{\overset{|}{C}}—\overset{OH}{\overset{|}{\overset{+}{C}}}—R \;\text{(II)} \longrightarrow H^+ + R_2C{=}\overset{OH}{\overset{|}{C}}—R$$

Evidence for these mechanisms is that alkyl groups depress base-catalysed reaction rates.

There is a great deal of evidence, however, to suggest that acid and base catalysis of enolisation take place by a *concerted* or *push-pull* mechanism, *i.e.*, the molecule undergoing change is attacked simultaneously at two places. Thus the enolisation of, *e.g.*, acetone, proceeds by the simultaneous removal of a proton from an α-carbon and the addition of a proton to the oxygen of the carbonyl group. This may be represented as follows (B is a general base, and HA is a general acid):

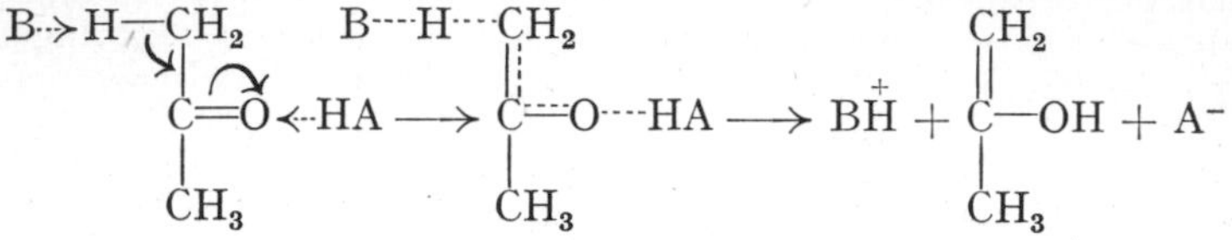

$$B \dashrightarrow H-CH_2-C(CH_3)=O \leftarrow HA \longrightarrow \underset{\text{transition state}}{B\cdots H\cdots CH_2 \cdots C(CH_3) \cdots O\cdots HA} \longrightarrow B\overset{+}{H} + CH_2=C(CH_3)-OH + A^-$$

In this type of mechanism, the solvent water molecules are believed to be involved, one acting as a proton acceptor and the other as a proton donor. Furthermore, the above mechanism is termolecular, and Swain (1950) has presented evidence to show that both the acid- and base-catalysed enolisation of acetone are termolecular reactions. Emmons *et al.* (1956) have obtained evidence supporting Swain's termolecular mechanism for ketone enolisation, but propose that the transition state for both acid- and base-catalysed enolisation may be represented by III.

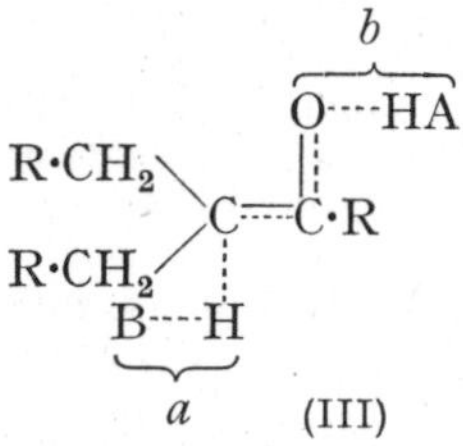

$$(R\cdot CH_2)_2C \overset{\vdots}{\underset{}{=}} C(\cdot R)\cdots O\cdots HA \;[b]; \quad C\cdots H\cdots B \;[a] \qquad \text{(III)}$$

Under these conditions in either acid- or base-catalysed reactions, the transition state will be very close to the enol and hence will be stabilised by hyperconjugation. In the acid-catalysed reaction, bond *b* is relatively tight and bond *a* is relatively loose. Hence in acid-catalysed enolisation, steric hindrance around bond *a* is not observed in most cases, and hyperconjugation is therefore a dominating factor in the enolisation of a ketone. In the base-catalysed reaction, bond *a* is relatively tight and bond *b* is relatively loose. Under these conditions a steric factor becomes important and is probably the reason why alkyl groups depress base-catalysed reaction rates.

The tremendous increase in speed by acid and base catalysts is well illustrated by the fact that the pure keto and enol forms of ethyl acetoacetate change very slowly into the equilibrium mixture (several weeks), whereas the latter is obtained rapidly (several minutes) by the addition of acid or base catalysts (Lowry *et al.*, 1924).

It has been shown that in keto-enol equilibrium mixtures, the enol form reacts extremely rapidly with halogens, is acidic and produces an anion which is reactive both at the oxygen and α-carbon (to the hydroxyl group).

It has been pointed out above (see also Table IV, p. 205) that in keto-enol tautomerism the enol content of the equilibrium mixture varies from compound to compound; but the reason for this is still an open question. It appears to be quite certain that the solvent plays a part, but the nature of the other factors is uncertain. Some authors believe that resonance and hydrogen bonding are involved; *e.g.*, it has been suggested that the enol form of acetylacetone is stabilised by chelation through hydrogen bonding:

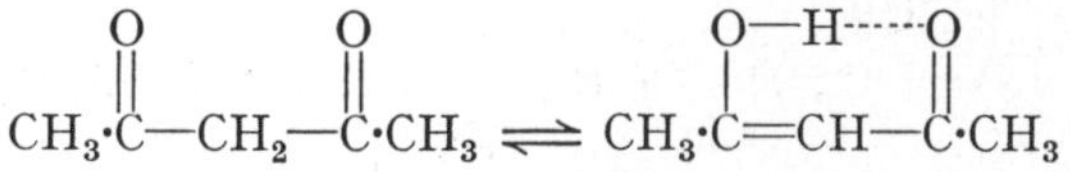

$$CH_3\cdot CO-CH_2-CO\cdot CH_3 \rightleftharpoons CH_3\cdot C(-O-H\cdots O=)=CH-C\cdot CH_3$$

Hydrogen bond formation is not possible in acetaldehyde, acetone, etc., and therefore the enol forms of these compounds cannot be stabilised this way.

Now let us consider the case of ethyl acetoacetate:

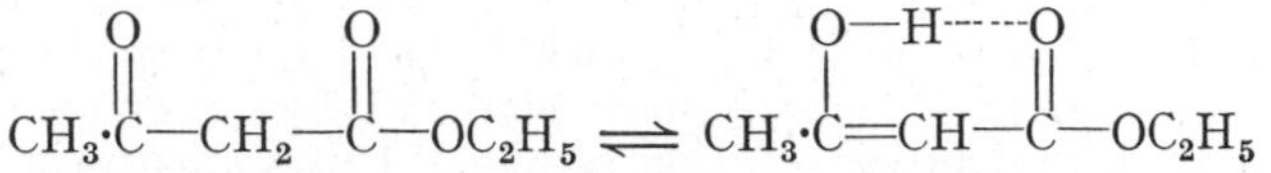

$$CH_3\cdot\overset{\overset{O}{\|}}{C}-CH_2-\overset{\overset{O}{\|}}{C}-OC_2H_5 \rightleftharpoons CH_3\cdot\overset{\overset{O-H\cdots}{|}}{C}=CH-\overset{\overset{O}{\|}}{C}-OC_2H_5$$

The enol form is stabilised by chelation; but ethyl acetoacetate contains 54 per cent. enol form in the vapour state, whereas acetylacetone contains 92 per cent. If chelation were the only factor involved, one might have expected that the enol content of the two compounds would have been about the same. A possible explanation for this difference may be due to the resonating structure of the carbethoxy group:

$$-\overset{\overset{O}{\|}}{C}-OC_2H_5 \longleftrightarrow -\overset{\overset{O^-}{|}}{C}=\overset{+}{O}C_2H_5$$

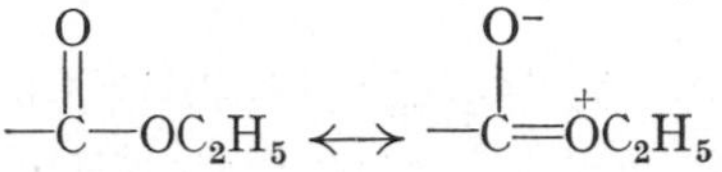

This effect will tend to stabilise the keto form, thereby reducing the tendency to enolise. The large part played by the resonance effect of the carbethoxy group in reducing the enol content may be inferred by considering ethyl malonate. This compound contains only a trace of the enol form. Its structure is IV, and its enol structure will be V.

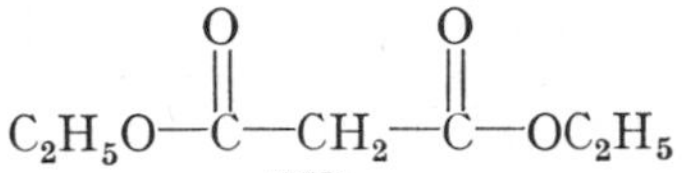

$$\underset{\text{(IV)}}{C_2H_5O-\overset{\overset{O}{\|}}{C}-CH_2-\overset{\overset{O}{\|}}{C}-OC_2H_5} \qquad \underset{\text{(V)}}{C_2H_5O-\overset{\overset{O-H\cdots}{|}}{C}=CH-\overset{\overset{O}{\|}}{C}-OC_2H_5}$$

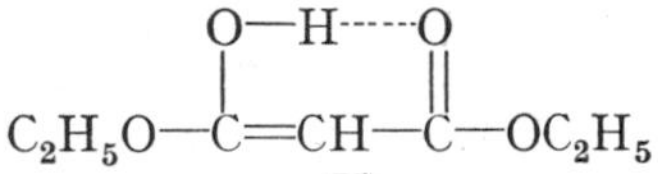

If both carbethoxy groups are affected by resonance, the *keto* form will be stabilised, *i.e.*, there will be very little tendency to enolise.

It was pointed out above that the nature of the solvent also affects the position of equilibrium in keto-enol tautomerism. If we assume (as we have above) that the enol form is, where possible, stabilised by chelation, then solvents that prevent chelation will reduce the enol content. Thus hydroxylic solvents such as water, methanol, ethanol, acetic acid, etc., in which the hydrogen atom of the hydroxyl group can form a hydrogen bond with the oxygen atom of the carbonyl group of the keto form, will tend to reduce the enol content; *e.g.*, ethyl acetoacetate contains 54 per cent. enol in the vapour phase; in ethanol, the enol content is 7·5 per cent. On the other hand, where hydrogen bond formation with the solvent is not possible, *e.g.*, in hexane, benzene, etc., the enol content will be large.

According to Arndt *et al.* (1946), the effect of the solvent on enol content is to be explained as follows. Hydrophilic solvents favour the keto form, whereas hydrophobic and lipophilic solvents favour the enol form. The above authors have shown that the more the hydrophobic groups predominate in a molecule of a tautomeric substance of a given structure, the greater is the enol content in the equilibrium mixture. Thus they found that the enol content of the esters of acetoacetic acid increased in the order methyl, ethyl, propyl, butyl, 2-octyl and benzyl; this is the order in which the whole molecule (ester) becomes more hydrophobic.

The preparation of ethyl acetoacetate. In the preparation of ethyl acetoacetate, condensation is effected between two molecules of the same ester. This is one example of the **Claisen condensation** (1887), in which a keto-ester is formed by the reaction between two molecules of an ester containing α-hydrogen atoms. In certain cases the second ester does not contain an α-hydrogen atom, *e.g.*, ethyl formate, ethyl benzoate and ethyl oxalate (see text for examples of their use). The Claisen condensation may also take place between an ester and a ketone to form a 1 : 3-diketone. The condensation is brought about by sodium ethoxide, sodamide, triphenylmethylsodium, etc. Sodium ethoxide is the reagent usually employed in the preparation of ethyl acetoacetate.

If sodium is added to ethyl acetate which has been very carefully freed from ethanol, very little action takes place. When a small amount of ethanol is added, a vigorous reaction sets in. This seems to indicate that it is probably sodium ethoxide, and not sodium, which is the effective reagent for the condensation (Snell and McElvain, 1931). The product is the sodium enolate of ethyl acetoacetate and this, on treatment with acid, liberates ethyl acetoacetate, which may be purified by distillation *in vacuo*.

Many mechanisms have been proposed for the formation of ethyl acetoacetate. The one most widely accepted at the moment is (*cf.* aldol condensation).

$$CH_3{\cdot}COOC_2H_5 + [OC_2H_5]^- \rightleftharpoons :\bar{C}H_2{\cdot}COOC_2H_5 + C_2H_5OH$$

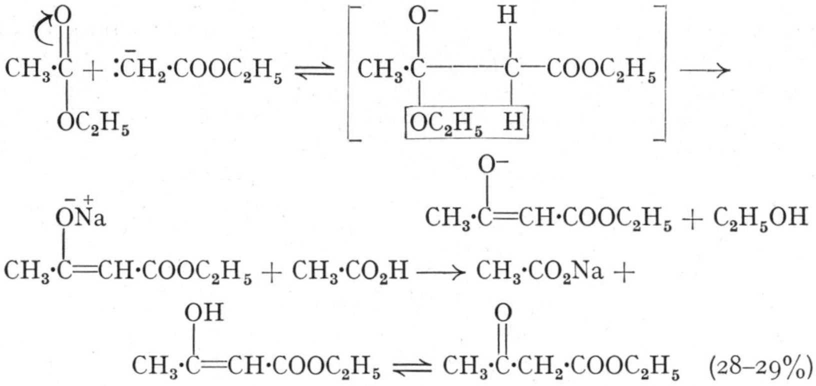

$$CH_3{\cdot}C(=O)(OC_2H_5) + :\bar{C}H_2{\cdot}COOC_2H_5 \rightleftharpoons \left[CH_3{\cdot}C(O^-)(\boxed{OC_2H_5}) - C(H)(\boxed{H}) - COOC_2H_5 \right] \longrightarrow$$

$$CH_3{\cdot}C(O^-){=}CH{\cdot}COOC_2H_5 + C_2H_5OH$$

$$CH_3{\cdot}C(\overset{-}{O}\overset{+}{Na}){=}CH{\cdot}COOC_2H_5 + CH_3{\cdot}CO_2H \longrightarrow CH_3{\cdot}CO_2Na +$$

$$CH_3{\cdot}C(OH){=}CH{\cdot}COOC_2H_5 \rightleftharpoons CH_3{\cdot}C(=O){\cdot}CH_2{\cdot}COOC_2H_5 \quad (28\text{–}29\%)$$

Ethyl acetoacetate is now also being prepared industrially by polymerising keten in acetone solution to diketen, which is then treated with ethanol.

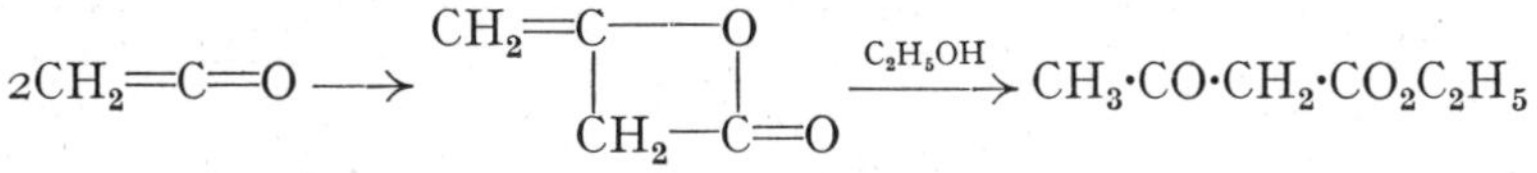

$$2CH_2{=}C{=}O \longrightarrow \begin{matrix} CH_2{=}C - O \\ | \quad\quad | \\ CH_2 - C{=}O \end{matrix} \xrightarrow{C_2H_5OH} CH_3{\cdot}CO{\cdot}CH_2{\cdot}CO_2C_2H_5$$

In " mixed ethyl acetoacetate condensations " between two different esters, a mixture of all four possible products is usually obtained; *e.g.*, with ethyl acetate and ethyl propionate:

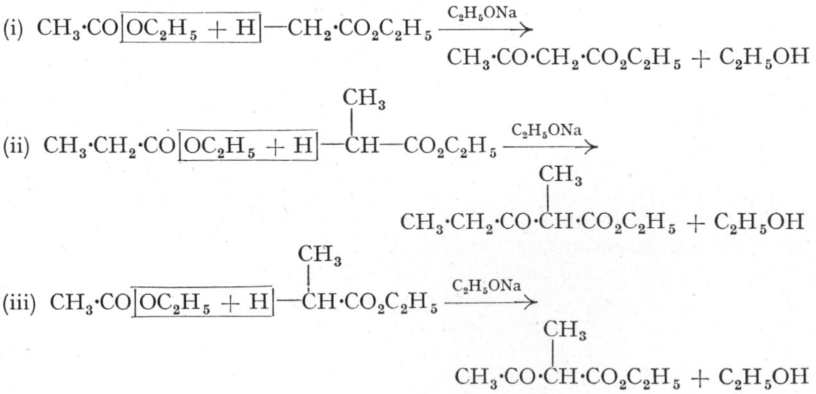

(i) $CH_3{\cdot}CO\boxed{OC_2H_5 + H}{-}CH_2{\cdot}CO_2C_2H_5 \xrightarrow{C_2H_5ONa} CH_3{\cdot}CO{\cdot}CH_2{\cdot}CO_2C_2H_5 + C_2H_5OH$

(ii) $CH_3{\cdot}CH_2{\cdot}CO\boxed{OC_2H_5 + H}{-}CH(CH_3){-}CO_2C_2H_5 \xrightarrow{C_2H_5ONa} CH_3{\cdot}CH_2{\cdot}CO{\cdot}CH(CH_3){\cdot}CO_2C_2H_5 + C_2H_5OH$

(iii) $CH_3{\cdot}CO\boxed{OC_2H_5 + H}{-}CH(CH_3){\cdot}CO_2C_2H_5 \xrightarrow{C_2H_5ONa} CH_3{\cdot}CO{\cdot}CH(CH_3){\cdot}CO_2C_2H_5 + C_2H_5OH$

(iv) $CH_3{\cdot}CH_2{\cdot}CO\boxed{OC_2H_5 + H}{-}CH_2{\cdot}CO_2C_2H_5 \xrightarrow{C_2H_5ONa}$
$CH_3{\cdot}CH_2{\cdot}CO{\cdot}CH_2{\cdot}CO_2C_2H_5 + C_2H_5OH$

These reactions clearly show that only α-hydrogen atoms are involved in the Claisen condensation.

Properties of ethyl acetoacetate. Ethyl acetoacetate is a colourless, pleasant-smelling liquid, b.p. 181° (with slight decomposition), sparingly soluble in water, but miscible with most organic solvents. It is readily reduced by sodium amalgam, or catalytically to β-hydroxybutyric ester:

$$CH_3{\cdot}CO{\cdot}CH_2{\cdot}CO_2C_2H_5 + 2[H] \longrightarrow CH_3{\cdot}CH(OH){\cdot}CH_2{\cdot}CO_2C_2H_5$$

Lithium aluminium hydride reduces ethyl acetoacetate to butane-1 : 3-diol (Buchta *et al.*, 1951).

$$CH_3{\cdot}CO{\cdot}CH_2{\cdot}CO_2C_2H_5 \xrightarrow{LiAlH_4} CH_3{\cdot}CHOH{\cdot}CH_2{\cdot}CH_2OH \quad (30\%)$$

On the other hand, ethyl acetoacetate may be reduced to ethyl butyrate by treating it with methyl mercaptan in the presence of zinc chloride and sodium sulphate, and then reducing the thioketal with Raney nickel in ethanolic solution (Newman *et al.*, 1950; *cf.* p. 317).

Ethyl acetoacetate is neutral to litmus, but is soluble in dilute sodium hydroxide solution: it is the enol form which dissolves to form the sodium salt. When ethyl acetoacetate is hydrolysed in the cold with dilute sodium hydroxide, the solution then acidified, extracted with ether and the ether removed in the cold under reduced pressure, free acetoacetic acid is obtained. Krueger (1952) has prepared acetoacetic acid as a crystalline solid, m.p. 36–37°. As prepared in the usual way it is unstable, readily decomposing into acetone and carbon dioxide:

$$CH_3{\cdot}CO{\cdot}CH_2{\cdot}CO_2H \longrightarrow CH_3{\cdot}CO{\cdot}CH_3 + CO_2$$

All β-ketonic acids readily decompose in this manner, but it is interesting to note that trifluoroacetoacetic acid, $CF_3{\cdot}CO{\cdot}CH_2{\cdot}CO_2H$, is quite stable and can be distilled without much decomposition. Ethyl acetoacetate forms α-oximinoacetoacetate when treated with nitrous acid:

$$CH_3{\cdot}CO{\cdot}CH_2{\cdot}CO_2C_2H_5 \xrightarrow{HNO_2} CH_3{\cdot}CO{\cdot}C({=}NOH){\cdot}CO_2C_2H_5$$

On the other hand, monosubstituted derivatives of ethyl acetoacetate are split by nitrous acid; the nitroso-compound is formed first and then rearranges to the oximino form with fission of the molecule.

$$CH_3{\cdot}CO{\cdot}CHR{\cdot}CO_2C_2H_5 \xrightarrow{HNO_2} CH_3{\cdot}CO{\cdot}\underset{\displaystyle NO}{\underset{|}{C}}R{\cdot}CO_2C_2H_5 \longrightarrow R{\cdot}\underset{\displaystyle NOH}{\underset{\|}{C}}{\cdot}CO_2C_2H_5$$

Ethyl acetoacetate forms a green copper compound which is soluble in organic solvents. This indicates that the copper compound is not an ionic but a chelate compound, and its structure is possibly:

```
  CH3—C—O        O—C—CH3
     //    \    /    \\
   CH        Cu        CH
     \     ↗   ↖      /
C2H5O—C=O         O=C—OC2H5
```

Acetoacetic ester reacts with ammonia (and with primary amines), but the structure of the compound produced is uncertain, there being two possibilities, the *imine* form I, and the *amine* form II:

$$\text{(I)}\quad CH_3{\cdot}C({=}NH){\cdot}CH_2{\cdot}CO_2C_2H_5 \qquad\qquad CH_3{\cdot}C(NH_2){=}CH{\cdot}CO_2C_2H_5\quad\text{(II)}$$

Most of the experimental work favours II. It is possible that the reaction takes places through the enol form:

$$CH_3{\cdot}C(OH){=}CH{\cdot}CO_2C_2H_5 + NH_3 \longrightarrow \left[CH_3{\cdot}C(OH)(NH_2){-}CH(H){\cdot}CO_2C_2H_5\right] \xrightarrow{-H_2O} CH_3{\cdot}C(NH_2){=}CH{\cdot}CO_2C_2H_5$$

Monoalkyl derivatives of acetoacetic ester, $CH_3{\cdot}CO{\cdot}CHR{\cdot}CO_2C_2H_5$, react with ammonia in a similar manner, but the dialkyl derivatives, $CH_3{\cdot}CO{\cdot}CR_2{\cdot}CO_2C_2H_5$, form the amide $CH_3{\cdot}CO{\cdot}CR_2{\cdot}CO{\cdot}NH_2$. This supports the mechanism given above, since the monoalkyl derivatives can enolise, whereas the dialkyl derivatives cannot. Ethyl acetoacetate also reacts with hydroxylamine to form an *iso*-oxazolone.

$$CH_3{\cdot}CO{\cdot}CH_2{\cdot}CO_2C_2H_5 + NH_2OH \longrightarrow CH_3{\cdot}C({=}NOH){\cdot}CH_2{\cdot}CO_2C_2H_5$$

$$\longrightarrow \underbrace{CH_3{\cdot}C{=}N{-}O{-}CO{-}CH_2}_{\text{ring}} + C_2H_5OH$$

With phenylhydrazine, ethyl acetoacetate forms a pyrazolone (p. 724).

Acetoacetic ester undergoes the Knoevenagel reaction due to the presence of an " active " methylene group (p. 145), and also couples with diazonium salts. It reacts with Grignard reagents to form the hydrocarbon, which indicates that it reacts in the enol form, *e.g.*,

$$CH_3{\cdot}C(OH){=}CH{\cdot}CO_2C_2H_5 + CH_3{\cdot}Mg{\cdot}I \longrightarrow CH_3{\cdot}C(OMgI){=}CH{\cdot}CO_2C_2H_5 + CH_4$$

When acetoacetic ester is heated under reflux with a trace of sodium hydrogen carbonate, ethanol is eliminated and **dehydroacetic acid,** m.p. 180°, is obtained:

$$\begin{array}{l} CH_3{-}C(O\boxed{H\;\;C_2H_5O}){=}CH{-}C({=}O){-}\boxed{OC_2H_5H}\;\cdots\;C({=}O){-}CH{\cdot}CO{\cdot}CH_3 \end{array} \xrightarrow{-2C_2H_5OH} \begin{array}{l} CH_3{-}C{=}CH{-}C({=}O){-}CH(CO{\cdot}CH_3){-}C({=}O){-}O \;\text{(ring)} \end{array} \quad (53\%)$$

Dehydroacetic acid may also be prepared by the polymerisation of diketen:

$$2\begin{array}{l}CH_2{=}C{-}O\\ \quad\ \ | \qquad |\\ \ \ CH_2{-}C{=}O\end{array} \longrightarrow \begin{array}{c}\text{(ring: } CH_3{-}C{=}CH{-}C({=}O){-}CH(CO{\cdot}CH_3){-}CO{-}O\text{)}\end{array}$$

(60–80%)

THE USE OF ACETOACETIC ESTER IN THE SYNTHESIS OF KETONES AND FATTY ACIDS

The synthetic use of acetoacetic ester depends on two chemical properties:

1. (*a*) When treated with sodium ethoxide, acetoacetic ester forms sodioacetoacetic ester, *i.e.*, the sodium derivative of the enolic form:

$$CH_3{\cdot}\overset{\overset{OH}{|}}{C}{:}CH{\cdot}CO_2C_2H_5 + C_2H_5ONa \longrightarrow \left[CH_3{\cdot}\overset{\overset{O^-}{|}}{C}{:}CH{\cdot}CO_2C_2H_5\right]\overset{+}{Na} + C_2H_5OH \quad (ex.)$$

(*b*) Sodioacetoacetic ester readily reacts with primary and secondary alkyl halides (vinyl and aryl halides do *not* react) to produce alkyl derivatives of acetoacetic ester in which the alkyl group is attached to carbon. This fact has given rise to considerable speculation regarding the mechanism of the alkylation process. The problem is still not settled, but a highly favoured theory is that the negative ion is a resonance hybrid:

$$\underset{(I)}{CH_3{\cdot}\overset{\overset{O^-}{|}}{C}{:}CH{\cdot}CO_2C_2H_5} \longleftrightarrow \underset{(II)}{CH_3{\cdot}\overset{\overset{O}{\|}}{C}{-}\overset{\cdot\cdot -}{C}H{\cdot}CO_2C_2H_5}$$

Thus in the actual state both the oxygen and carbon atoms have a negative charge; but since a negatively charged carbon atom is more reactive than a negatively charged oxygen atom, it is the carbon atom that is the point of attack. As the actual state of the molecule cannot be represented by a single formula, the process of alkylation may be regarded as involving structure II, *i.e.*, a carbanion. There is also evidence to show that the alkylation occurs by an S_N2 process. Thus:

$$\begin{array}{c}CH_3{-}C{=}O\\ |\\ H\overset{-}{C}{:}\\ |\\ CO_2C_2H_5\end{array}\ R{-}X \longrightarrow \begin{array}{c}CH_3{-}C{=}O\\ |\\ HC{-}R\\ |\\ CO_2C_2H_5\end{array} + X^-$$

For the sake of simplicity the alkylation of sodioacetoacetic ester will, in future, be represented as:

$$[CH_3{\cdot}CO{\cdot}CH{\cdot}CO_2C_2H_5]^-Na^+ + RX \longrightarrow CH_3{\cdot}CO{\cdot}CHR{\cdot}CO_2C_2H_5 + NaX \quad (v.g.)$$

After one alkyl group has been introduced, the whole process may then be repeated to give the dialkyl derivative of acetoacetic ester:

$$CH_3{\cdot}CO{\cdot}CHR{\cdot}CO_2C_2H_5 \xrightarrow{C_2H_5ONa} [CH_3{\cdot}CO{\cdot}CR{\cdot}CO_2C_2H_5]^-Na^+ \xrightarrow{R'X} CH_3{\cdot}CO{\cdot}CRR'{\cdot}CO_2C_2H_5 \quad (g.\text{–}v.g.)$$

Until recently, it was not considered possible to prepare *disubstituted* derivatives of acetoacetic ester in *one* step. Sandberg (1957), however, has now carried out this one-step reaction in the preparation of ethyl β-acetotricarballylate from acetoacetic ester (0·5 mole), ethyl bromoacetate (1·2 mole) and sodium hydride (1·2 mole) in benzene solution.

$$CH_3{\cdot}CO{\cdot}CH_2{\cdot}CO_2C_2H_5 + 2CH_2Br{\cdot}CO_2C_2H_5 \xrightarrow{2NaH} CH_3{\cdot}CO{\cdot}C\begin{cases} CH_2{\cdot}CO_2C_2H_5 \\ CO_2C_2H_5 \\ CH_2{\cdot}CO_2C_2H_5 \end{cases} \quad (77\%)$$

Potassium *tert.*-butoxide is usually best for preparing the metallo-acetoacetic ester compounds, and generally alkyl iodides react faster than alkyl bromides (Renfrow and Renfrow, 1946).

2. Acetoacetic ester and its alkyl derivatives can undergo two types of hydrolysis with potassium hydroxide:

(*a*) **Ketonic hydrolysis.** Ketonic hydrolysis, so called because a ketone is the chief product, is carried out by boiling with *dilute* aqueous or ethanolic potassium hydroxide solution, *e.g.*,

$$CH_3{\cdot}CO{\cdot}CH_2{\cdot}CO_2C_2H_5 + 2KOH \longrightarrow CH_3{\cdot}CO{\cdot}CH_3 + K_2CO_3 + C_2H_5OH \quad (g.)$$

$$CH_3{\cdot}CO{\cdot}CHR{\cdot}CO_2C_2H_5 + 2KOH \longrightarrow CH_3{\cdot}CO{\cdot}CH_2R + K_2CO_3 + C_2H_5OH \quad (g.)$$

The ketone obtained is acetone or its derivatives, and the latter *always contain the group* $CH_3{\cdot}CO$—.

Dehn and Jackson (1933) found that 85 per cent. phosphoric acid was a very good catalyst for the ketonic hydrolysis of acetoacetic ester and its alkyl derivatives, the yield of ketone reaching 95 per cent.

The mechanism of ketonic hydrolysis is uncertain; a possibility is:

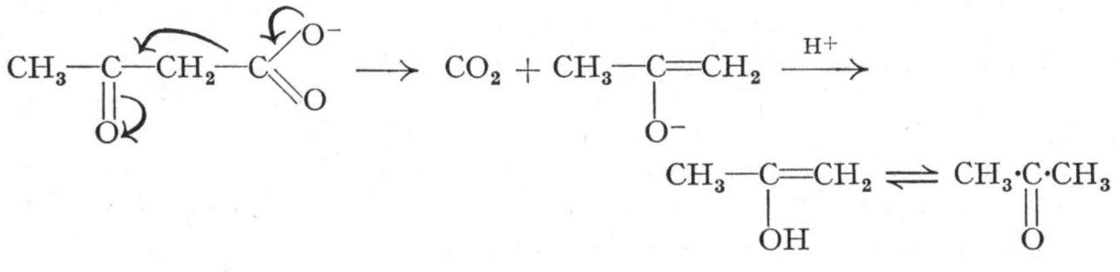

$$CH_3{-}\underset{\underset{O}{\parallel}}{C}{-}CH_2{-}C\begin{matrix}\nearrow O^- \\ \searrow O\end{matrix} \longrightarrow CO_2 + CH_3{-}\underset{\underset{O^-}{|}}{C}{=}CH_2 \xrightarrow{H^+}$$

$$CH_3{-}\underset{\underset{OH}{|}}{C}{=}CH_2 \rightleftharpoons CH_3{\cdot}\underset{\underset{O}{\parallel}}{C}{\cdot}CH_3$$

It is the electron-attracting property of the carbonyl group that facilitates the elimination of carbon dioxide.

(*b*) **Acid hydrolysis.** Acid hydrolysis, so called because an acid is the chief product, is carried out by boiling with *concentrated* ethanolic potassium hydroxide solution, *e.g.*,

$$CH_3{\cdot}CO{\cdot}CH_2{\cdot}CO_2C_2H_5 + 2KOH \longrightarrow CH_3{\cdot}CO_2K + CH_3{\cdot}CO_2K + C_2H_5OH \quad (f.g.)$$

$$CH_3{\cdot}CO{\cdot}CR_2{\cdot}CO_2C_2H_5 + 2KOH \longrightarrow CH_3{\cdot}CO_2K + R_2CH{\cdot}CO_2K + C_2H_5OH \quad (f.g.)$$

The acid obtained is acetic acid or its derivatives as the potassium salt. From this the free acid is readily obtained by treatment with inorganic acid.

The mechanism of acid hydrolysis is possibly a reversal of the Claisen condensation. Only the ester of acetic acid undergoes condensation, and when the condensation is reversed, the ester is converted into the potassium salt which cannot recondense; hence the equilibrium is forced in the reverse direction to that of condensation.

Examples of the synthesis of ketones. The formula of the ketone is written down, and *provided it contains the group* $CH_3 \cdot CO-$, the ketone can be synthesised via acetoacetic ester as follows. The acetone nucleus is picked out, and the alkyl groups attached to it are then introduced into acetoacetic ester one at a time; this is followed by ketonic hydrolysis. It is usually better to introduce the larger group before the smaller (spatial effect):

(i) *Butanone.* $\boxed{CH_3 \cdot CO \cdot CH_2 \cdot} CH_3$

$$CH_3 \cdot CO \cdot CH_2 \cdot CO_2C_2H_5 \xrightarrow{C_2H_5ONa} [CH_3 \cdot CO \cdot CH \cdot CO_2C_2H_5]^- Na^+ \xrightarrow{CH_3I}$$
$$CH_3 \cdot CO \cdot CH(CH_3) \cdot CO_2C_2H_5 \xrightarrow[\text{hydrolysis}]{\text{ketonic}} CH_3 \cdot CO \cdot CH_2 \cdot CH_3$$

(ii) 3-*Methylpentan-2-one.* $\boxed{CH_3 \cdot CO \cdot \underset{}{\overset{CH_3}{\overset{|}{C}H}} \cdot} CH_2 \cdot CH_3$

$$CH_3 \cdot CO \cdot CH_2 \cdot CO_2C_2H_5 \xrightarrow{C_2H_5ONa} [CH_3 \cdot CO \cdot CH \cdot CO_2C_2H_5]^- Na^+ \xrightarrow{C_2H_5I}$$
$$CH_3 \cdot CO \cdot CH(C_2H_5) \cdot CO_2C_2H_5 \xrightarrow{C_2H_5ONa} [CH_3 \cdot CO \cdot C(C_2H_5) \cdot CO_2C_2H_5]^- Na^+$$
$$\xrightarrow{CH_3I} CH_3 \cdot CO \cdot C(CH_3)(C_2H_5) \cdot CO_2C_2H_5 \xrightarrow[\text{hydrolysis}]{\text{ketonic}} CH_3 \cdot CO \cdot \underset{\underset{CH_3}{|}}{C}H \cdot CH_2 \cdot CH_3$$

Examples of the synthesis of fatty acids. The approach is similar to that for ketones except that the acetic acid nucleus is picked out, and the acetoacetic ester derivative is subjected to acid hydrolysis. The acetoacetic ester acid synthesis is usually confined to the preparation of straight-chain acids or branched-chain acids where the branching occurs on the α-carbon atom:

(i) n-*Butyric acid.* $CH_3 \cdot CH_2 \cdot \boxed{CH_2 \cdot CO_2H}$

$$CH_3 \cdot CO \cdot CH_2 \cdot CO_2C_2H_5 \xrightarrow{C_2H_5ONa} [CH_3 \cdot CO \cdot CH \cdot CO_2C_2H_5]^- Na^+ \xrightarrow{C_2H_5I}$$
$$CH_3 \cdot CO \cdot CH(C_2H_5) \cdot CO_2C_2H_5 \xrightarrow[\text{hydrolysis}]{\text{acid}} CH_3 \cdot CH_2 \cdot CH_2 \cdot CO_2H$$

(ii) α-*Methyl*-n-*valeric acid.* $CH_3 \cdot CH_2 \cdot CH_2 \cdot \boxed{\overset{CH_3}{\overset{|}{C}H} \cdot CO_2H}$

$$CH_3 \cdot CO \cdot CH_2 \cdot CO_2C_2H_5 \xrightarrow{C_2H_5ONa} [CH_3 \cdot CO \cdot CH \cdot CO_2C_2H_5]^- Na^+ \xrightarrow{C_3H_7Br}$$
$$CH_3 \cdot CO \cdot CH(C_3H_7) \cdot CO_2C_2H_5 \xrightarrow{C_2H_5ONa} [CH_3 \cdot CO \cdot C(C_3H_7) \cdot CO_2C_2H_5]^- Na^+$$
$$\xrightarrow{CH_3I} CH_3 \cdot CO \cdot C(CH_3)(C_3H_7) \cdot CO_2C_2H_5 \xrightarrow[\text{hydrolysis}]{\text{acid}} CH_3 \cdot CH_2 \cdot CH_2 \cdot \overset{CH_3}{\overset{|}{C}H} \cdot CO_2H$$

It has been found that ketonic hydrolysis and acid hydrolysis of acetoacetic ester *always take place simultaneously,* but one or the other can be made to predominate by adjusting the concentration of the potassium hydroxide. Thus, in the preparation of acids, there will always be some ketone formed as by-product; and vice-versa. For this reason it is better to use ethyl malonate to synthesise acids since the yields are greater.

In addition to the acetoacetic ester ketone synthesis, ketones may be prepared in a somewhat analogous method as follows:

(i) From simpler ketones; *e.g.*, acetone in ether solution is treated with sodamide and the sodioacetone then treated with methyl iodide, whereupon ethyl methyl ketone is produced:

$$CH_3{\cdot}CO{\cdot}CH_3 \xrightarrow[\text{ether}]{NaNH_2} [CH_3{\cdot}CO{\cdot}CH_2]^-Na^+ \xrightarrow{CH_3I} CH_3{\cdot}CO{\cdot}CH_2{\cdot}CH_3$$

Repetition of the process on ethyl methyl ketone gives a mixture of methyl *iso*propyl ketone and diethyl ketone, which can be separated by fractional distillation. By repeating the process hexamethylacetone (di-*tert.*-butyl ketone), $(CH_3)_3C{\cdot}CO{\cdot}C(CH_3)_3$, can finally be obtained.

This synthesis has been modified to prepare *tert.*-carboxylic acids, acetophenone being the ketone used as starting material (Haller *et al.*, 1914). The yields are good for the simpler members of the series (Carter *et al.*, 1946).

$$CH_3{\cdot}CO{\cdot}C_6H_5 \xrightarrow[\text{(ii) RI}]{\text{(i) }NaNH_2} R{\cdot}CH_2{\cdot}CO{\cdot}C_6H_5 \xrightarrow[\text{(ii) R'I}]{\text{(i) }NaNH_2} RR'CH{\cdot}CO{\cdot}C_6H_5$$

$$\xrightarrow[\text{(ii) R''I}]{\text{(i) }NaNH_2} RR'R''C{\cdot}CO{\cdot}C_6H_5 \xrightarrow{NaNH_2} RR'R''C{\cdot}CO{\cdot}NH_2 \xrightarrow{HNO_2} RR'R''C{\cdot}CO_2H$$

(ii) Ketones may also be prepared from certain esters. It has been found that esters of the type $R_2CH{\cdot}CO_2C_2H_5$ do not undergo the normal Claisen condensation with sodium ethoxide. In the presence of triphenylmethylsodium, $(C_6H_5)_3C^-Na^+$, however, they readily form the sodio-salt (Schlenk *et al.*, 1931). These sodium salts react with acid chlorides, and the resulting compounds, which are β-keto-esters, yield ketones on ketonic hydrolysis:

$$R_2CH{\cdot}CO_2C_2H_5 \xrightarrow{(C_6H_5)_3CNa} [R_2C{\cdot}CO_2C_2H_5]^-Na^+ \xrightarrow{R'{\cdot}COCl} R'{\cdot}CO{\cdot}CR_2{\cdot}CO_2C_2H_5 \xrightarrow[\text{hydrolysis}]{\text{ketonic}} R'{\cdot}CO{\cdot}CHR_2$$

Sodioacetoacetic ester reacts with many other halogen compounds besides alkyl halides, and so may be used to synthesise a variety of compounds.

(i) 1 : 3-*Diketones.* In the synthesis of 1 : 3-diketones the halogen compound used is an acid chloride. Since acid chlorides react with ethanol, the reaction cannot be carried out in this solvent in the usual way. The reaction, however, may conveniently be carried out by treating acetoacetic ester in benzene solution with magnesium and the acid chloride; *e.g.*, pentane-2 : 4-dione may be obtained by the ketonic hydrolysis of the intermediate product ethyl diacetylacetate:

$$CH_3{\cdot}CO{\cdot}CH_2{\cdot}CO_2C_2H_5 + CH_3{\cdot}COCl \xrightarrow{Mg} (CH_3{\cdot}CO)_2CH{\cdot}CO_2C_2H_5 \xrightarrow[\text{hydrolysis}]{\text{ketonic}} CH_3{\cdot}CO{\cdot}CH_2{\cdot}CO{\cdot}CH_3$$

If sodioacetoacetic ester or acetoacetic ester itself is treated with acetyl chloride in pyridine as solvent, the *O-acetyl* derivative of acetoacetic ester, acetoxycrotonic ester, is obtained, and not the carbon-linked compound (as above):

$$[CH_3{\cdot}CO{\cdot}CH{\cdot}CO_2C_2H_5]^-Na^+ + CH_3{\cdot}COCl \xrightarrow{\text{pyridine}} CH_3{\cdot}C(O{\cdot}CO{\cdot}CH_3){:}CH{\cdot}CO_2C_2H_5 + NaCl$$

The reason for this unusual reaction is obscure.

(ii) *Dicarboxylic acids.* Dicarboxylic acids may be prepared by interaction of sodioacetoacetic ester and a halogen derivative of an ester, *e.g.*, succinic acid from ethyl chloroacetate:

$$[CH_3 \cdot CO \cdot CH \cdot CO_2C_2H_5]^- Na^+ + ClCH_2 \cdot CO_2C_2H_5 \longrightarrow$$

$$\begin{array}{c} CH_2 \cdot CO_2C_2H_5 \\ | \\ CH_3 \cdot CO \cdot CH \cdot CO_2C_2H_5 \end{array} \xrightarrow[\text{hydrolysis}]{\text{acid}} \begin{array}{c} CH_2 \cdot CO_2H \\ | \\ CH_2 \cdot CO_2H \end{array}$$

Ketonic hydrolysis of this acetoacetic ester derivative gives the γ-keto-acid ester (ethyl ester of lævulic acid):

$$\begin{array}{c} CH_2 \cdot CO_2C_2H_5 \\ | \\ CH_3 \cdot CO \cdot CH \cdot CO_2C_2H_5 \end{array} \xrightarrow[\text{hydrolysis}]{\text{ketonic}} CH_3 \cdot CO \cdot CH_2 \cdot CH_2 \cdot CO_2C_2H_5$$

(iii) *Long-chain fatty acids.* An ingenious method of synthesising long-chain fatty acids via acetoacetic ester involves a combination of methods (i) and (ii) described above (Mrs. Robinson, 1930):

$$[CH_3 \cdot CO \cdot CH \cdot CO_2C_2H_5]^- Na^+ \xrightarrow{Br \cdot (CH_2)_x \cdot CO_2C_2H_5} \begin{array}{c} (CH_2)_x \cdot CO_2C_2H_5 \\ | \\ CH_3 \cdot CO \cdot CH \cdot CO_2C_2H_5 \end{array}$$

$$\xrightarrow[\text{(ii) } CH_3 \cdot (CH_2)_y \cdot COCl]{\text{(i) } C_2H_5ONa} \begin{array}{c} (CH_2)_x \cdot CO_2C_2H_5 \\ | \\ CH_3 \cdot CO \cdot C \cdot CO_2C_2H_5 \\ | \\ CO(CH_2)_y \cdot CH_3 \end{array} \xrightarrow[\text{hydrolysis}]{\text{graded}}$$

$$CH_3 \cdot (CH_2)_y \cdot CO \cdot CH_2 \cdot (CH_2)_x \cdot CO_2H$$

These keto-acids are readily reduced to the corresponding fatty acid by means of the Clemmensen reduction (p. 140). Improved modifications of this method have now been developed (see p. 346).

(iv) *Ring compounds.* (*a*) When sodioacetoacetic ester is treated with certain dihalogen derivatives of the paraffins, carbocyclic compounds are obtained (see p. 448).

(*b*) Acetoacetic ester may be used to prepare a number of heterocyclic compounds (see Ch. XXX).

MALONIC ESTER SYNTHESES

Malonic ester, $CH_2(CO_2C_2H_5)_2$, which is the diethyl ester of malonic acid $CH_2(CO_2H)_2$, is prepared by dissolving potassium cyanoacetate in ethanol, adding concentrated hydrochloric acid, and warming the mixture on the water-bath:

$$NC \cdot CH_2 - CO_2K + 2C_2H_5OH + 2HCl \longrightarrow CH_2(CO_2C_2H_5)_2 + KCl + NH_4Cl \quad (v.g.)$$

Malonic ester may be prepared (yield 82–84 per cent.) by refluxing cyano-acetic acid in ethanol in the presence of chlorosulphonic acid (Dvornik *et al.*, 1953).

It is a pleasant-smelling liquid, b.p. 199°. Its use as a synthetic reagent depends on two chemical properties.

1. With sodium ethoxide it forms a sodium derivative, sodiomalonic ester, which reacts with compounds containing a reactive halogen atom, *e.g.*, alkyl halides, acid chlorides, halogen-substituted esters, etc. (*cf.* aceto-acetic ester). In all cases the yields are *g.–v.g.* The anion of the sodium salt

is probably a resonance hybrid, and when it reacts with a halogen reagent, the entering radical becomes attached to the carbon atom:

$$C_2H_5O{-}\overset{\overset{\displaystyle O}{\|}}{C}{-}CH_2{-}\overset{\overset{\displaystyle O}{\|}}{C}{-}OC_2H_5 \rightleftharpoons C_2H_5O{-}\overset{\overset{\displaystyle OH}{|}}{C}{=}CH{-}\overset{\overset{\displaystyle O}{\|}}{C}{-}OC_2H_5 \xrightarrow{C_2H_5ONa}$$

$$\left[C_2H_5O{-}\overset{\overset{\displaystyle \bar{O}}{|}}{C}{=}CH{-}\overset{\overset{\displaystyle O}{\|}}{C}{-}OC_2H_5\right]\overset{+}{Na} \longleftrightarrow \left[C_2H_5O{-}\overset{\overset{\displaystyle O}{\|}}{C}{-}\bar{C}H{-}\overset{\overset{\displaystyle O}{\|}}{C}{-}OC_2H_5\right]\overset{+}{Na}$$

$$\xrightarrow{RX} C_2H_5O{-}\overset{\overset{\displaystyle O}{\|}}{C}{-}CHR{-}\overset{\overset{\displaystyle O}{\|}}{C}{-}OC_2H_5 + NaX$$

The process may then be repeated to produce the disubstituted derivative of malonic ester:

$$R{\cdot}CH(CO_2C_2H_5)_2 \xrightarrow{C_2H_5ONa} [R{\cdot}C(CO_2C_2H_5)_2]^-Na^+ \xrightarrow{R'X} RR'C(CO_2C_2H_5)_2$$

These disubstituted derivatives of malonic ester can readily be prepared in *one* step by treating the ester with *two* equivalents of sodium ethoxide and then with *two* equivalents of alkyl halide. This procedure is only used if it is required to introduce two identical alkyl groups. The mechanism of this reaction is obscure; it will be represented as follows:

$$CH_2(CO_2C_2H_5)_2 \xrightarrow{2C_2H_5ONa} [C(CO_2C_2H_5)_2]^{2-}2Na^+ \xrightarrow{2RX} R_2C(CO_2C_2H_5)_2 + 2NaX$$

2. Malonic acid and its derivatives eliminate a molecule of carbon dioxide when heated just above the melting point of the acid (usually between 150° and 200°) to form acetic acid or its derivatives (the yields are *v.g.–ex.*):

$$CO_2H{\cdot}CH_2{\cdot}CO_2H \longrightarrow CH_3{\cdot}CO_2H + CO_2$$
$$CO_2H{\cdot}CHR{\cdot}CO_2H \longrightarrow R{\cdot}CH_2{\cdot}CO_2H + CO_2$$

Decarboxylation may also be effected by refluxing malonic acid or its derivatives in sulphuric acid solution.

In a number of cases ethyl cyanoacetate (b.p. 207°) may be used instead of malonic ester in many syntheses. The cyano-group is readily converted into the carboxyl group on hydrolysis.

Synthesis of fatty acids. Malonic ester is preferable to acetoacetic ester in synthesising acids, and should be used wherever possible. The structural formula of the acid required is written down, the acetic acid nucleus picked out, and the required alkyl groups introduced into sodiomalonic ester. The substituted ester is then refluxed with potassium hydroxide solution, acidified with hydrochloric acid, and the precipitated acid dried and then heated just above its melting point. Alternatively, the potassium salt may be refluxed with sulphuric acid:

(i) n-*Valeric acid.* $CH_3{\cdot}CH_2{\cdot}CH_2{\cdot}\boxed{CH_2{\cdot}CO_2H}$

$$CH_2(CO_2C_2H_5)_2 \xrightarrow{C_2H_5ONa} [CH(CO_2C_2H_5)_2]^-Na^+ \xrightarrow{C_3H_7Br}$$
$$C_3H_7{\cdot}CH(CO_2C_2H_5)_2 \xrightarrow{KOH} C_3H_7{\cdot}CH(CO_2K)_2 \xrightarrow{HCl}$$
$$C_3H_7{\cdot}CH(CO_2H)_2 \xrightarrow{150-200^\circ} CH_3{\cdot}CH_2{\cdot}CH_2{\cdot}CH_2{\cdot}CO_2H$$

(ii) *Dimethylacetic acid.* $CH_3 \cdot \boxed{\overset{\overset{CH_3}{|}}{C}H \cdot CO_2H}$

$$CH_2(CO_2C_2H_5)_2 \xrightarrow{C_2H_5ONa} [CH(CO_2C_2H_5)_2]^-Na^+ \xrightarrow{CH_3I} CH_3 \cdot CH(CO_2C_2H_5)_2$$
$$\xrightarrow{C_2H_5ONa} [CH_3 \cdot C(CO_2C_2H_5)_2]^-Na^+ \xrightarrow{CH_3I} (CH_3)_2C(CO_2C_2H_5)_2 \xrightarrow{KOH}$$
$$(CH_3)_2C(CO_2K)_2 \xrightarrow{HCl} (CH_3)_2C(CO_2H)_2 \xrightarrow{150-200^\circ} (CH_3)_2CH \cdot CO_2H$$

Since two methyl groups are required for this synthesis, their introduction can be carried out in one step (see above):

$$CH_2(CO_2C_2H_5)_2 \xrightarrow{2C_2H_5ONa} [C(CO_2C_2H_5)_2]^{2-}2Na^+ \xrightarrow{2CH_3I}$$
$$(CH_3)_2C(CO_2C_2H_5)_2 \xrightarrow{KOH,\ etc.} (CH_3)_2CH \cdot CO_2H$$

Synthesis of dicarboxylic acids. Dicarboxylic acids of the type $RR'C(CO_2H)_2$ are readily prepared from malonic ester as shown above. They are important only in so far as they are intermediates in the preparation of fatty acids.

Dicarboxylic acids of the type $CO_2H \cdot (CH_2)_n \cdot CO_2H$ are very important, and the malonic ester synthesis is particularly useful for their preparation. The actual procedure depends mainly on the value of n, and the following examples illustrate this point:

(i) *Adipic acid.* $\boxed{CO_2H \cdot CH_2 \cdot} CH_2 \cdot CH_2 \boxed{\cdot CH_2 \cdot CO_2H}$

The acetic acid is blocked off at *one* end, and the remaining fragment is considered from the point of view of accessibility. In this example the fragment required is γ-bromobutyric ester. This is not readily accessible, and so the procedure now is to block off the acetic acid nucleus at the *other* end of the adipic acid molecule, and then to use *two* molecules of malonic ester and the *$\alpha\omega$-dihalide* of the polymethylene fragment that joins together the two acetic acid nuclei. In this case it is ethylene bromide, and since this is readily accessible, the synthesis of adipic acid may be carried out as follows:

$$[(C_2H_5O_2C)_2CH]^-Na^+ + BrCH_2 \cdot CH_2Br + Na^+[CH(CO_2C_2H_5)_2]^- \longrightarrow$$
$$(C_2H_5O_2C)_2CH \cdot CH_2 \cdot CH_2 \cdot CH(CO_2C_2H_5)_2 \xrightarrow[(ii)\ HCl]{(i)\ KOH}$$
$$(HO_2C)_2CH \cdot CH_2 \cdot CH_2 \cdot CH(CO_2H)_2 \xrightarrow{150-200^\circ} CO_2H \cdot CH_2 \cdot CH_2 \cdot CH_2 \cdot CH_2 \cdot CO_2H$$

Should the fragments required by either route be inaccessible, then a method not involving the use of malonic ester may be more satisfactory (see p. 362).

(ii) *Succinic acid.* $\boxed{CO_2H \cdot CH_2 \cdot} CH_2 \cdot CO_2H$

If *one* acetic acid nucleus is blocked off, the fragment required is ethyl chloroacetate. This is readily accessible and hence succinic acid may be synthesised from *one* molecule of malonic ester as follows:

$$[CH(CO_2C_2H_5)_2]^-Na^+ + ClCH_2 \cdot CO_2C_2H_5 \longrightarrow (C_2H_5O_2C)_2CH \cdot CH_2 \cdot CO_2C_2H_5$$
$$\xrightarrow[(ii)\ HCl]{(i)\ KOH} (HO_2C)_2CH \cdot CH_2 \cdot CO_2H \xrightarrow{150-200^\circ} CO_2H \cdot CH_2 \cdot CH_2 \cdot CO_2H$$

If the *other* acetic acid nucleus is succinic acid is blocked off, there is no intervening fragment left. Hence if two molecules of malonic ester could be united *directly*, this would offer an alternative route for the synthesis of succinic acid. Actually, the union of two malonic ester molecules may be effected by means of iodine. Thus:

$$[(C_2H_5O_2C)_2CH]^-Na^+ + I_2 + Na^+[CH(CO_2C_2H_5)_2] \longrightarrow$$

$$(C_2H_5O_2C)_2CH{\cdot}CH(CO_2C_2H_5)_2 \xrightarrow[\text{(ii) HCl}]{\text{(i) KOH}} (HO_2C)_2CH{\cdot}CH(CO_2H)_2$$

$$\xrightarrow{150\text{–}200^\circ} CO_2H{\cdot}CH_2{\cdot}CH_2{\cdot}CO_2H$$

Synthesis of ketones. Bowman *et al.* (1952) have introduced the following general synthesis of ketones and β-keto-esters (R′ = tetrahydropyran-2-ol):

$$R{\cdot}CH(CO_2R')_2 \xrightarrow[\text{(ii) R''}{\cdot}\text{COCl}]{\text{(i) Na}} R''{\cdot}CO{\cdot}CR(CO_2R')_2 \xrightarrow[\text{reflux}]{CH_3{\cdot}CO_2H}$$

$$R''{\cdot}CO{\cdot}CH_2{\cdot}R \quad (50\text{–}92\%)$$

Johnson *et al.* (1952) have used *tert.*-butyl esters of malonic acid (R′ = *tert.*-butyl):

$$R{\cdot}CH(CO_2R')_2 \xrightarrow[\text{(ii) R''}{\cdot}\text{COCl}]{\text{(i) NaH}} R''{\cdot}CO{\cdot}CR(CO_2R')_2 \xrightarrow[CH_3{\cdot}CO_2H]{CH_3C_6H_4SO_3H}$$

$$R''{\cdot}CO{\cdot}CH_2{\cdot}R \quad (56\text{–}85\%)$$

Synthesis of higher ketonic acids. Sodiomalonic ester is treated with the acid chloride-ester derivative of a dibasic acid, *e.g.*, ε-ketoheptoic acid:

$$[(C_2H_5O_2C)_2CH]^-Na^+ + COCl{\cdot}(CH_2)_4{\cdot}CO_2C_2H_5 \longrightarrow$$

$$(C_2H_5O_2C)_2CH{\cdot}CO(CH_2)_4{\cdot}CO_2C_2H_5 \xrightarrow[\text{(ii) HCl}]{\text{(i) KOH}} (HO_2C)_2CH{\cdot}CO(CH_2)_4{\cdot}CO_2H$$

$$\xrightarrow{150\text{–}200^\circ} [CO_2H{\cdot}CH_2{\cdot}CO{\cdot}(CH_2)_4{\cdot}CO_2H] \longrightarrow CH_3{\cdot}CO{\cdot}(CH_2)_4{\cdot}CO_2H$$

The intermediate β-keto-dicarboxylic acid is unstable and is readily decarboxylated. This might have been anticipated, since it may be regarded as a derivative of acetoacetic acid, which is readily decarboxylated on warming.

Synthesis of polybasic acids. It has been pointed out previously (p. 197) that the monoalkyl derivatives of malonic acid are readily brominated, and that these bromo-derivatives give α-bromo-fatty acids on decarboxylation. Malonic ester is also readily brominated, and this monobromo-derivative may be used to synthesise polybasic acids, *e.g.*,

$$CH_2(CO_2C_2H_5)_2 \xrightarrow{Br_2} CHBr(CO_2C_2H_5)_2$$

$$CHBr(CO_2C_2H_5)_2 + [CH(CO_2C_2H_5)_2]^-Na^+ \longrightarrow$$

$$NaBr + (C_2H_5O_2C)_2CH{\cdot}CH(CO_2C_2H_5)_2 \xrightarrow{Br_2}$$

$$\begin{matrix}(C_2H_5O_2C)_2C\text{—}Br \\ | \\ (C_2H_5O_2C)_2C\text{—}Br\end{matrix} \xrightarrow{2[CH(CO_2C_2H_5)_2]^-Na^+} \begin{matrix}(C_2H_5O_2C)_2C\text{—}CH(CO_2C_2H_5)_2 \\ | \\ (C_2H_5O_2C)_2C\text{—}CH(CO_2C_2H_5)_2\end{matrix}$$

Malonic ester may also be used for the preparation of unsaturated acids (Knoevenagel reaction, p. 263), alicyclic compounds (p. 447), and heterocyclic compounds (p. 369).

HYDROXYALDEHYDES AND HYDROXYKETONES

When naming a compound which contains more than one functional group, it is necessary to choose one as the principal function. The compound is then named by using the suffix of the principal function and the prefixes of the other functions. The carboxylic and the sulphonic acid group are *always* chosen as principal functions, and the usual order for choosing the principal function is:

Carboxylic, sulphonic, acid halide, amide, imide, aldehyde, cyanide, *iso*cyanide, ketone, alcohol, phenol, thioalcohol, amine, imine.

Examples. Acetoacetic acid contains a ketonic group and a carboxyl group, and since the latter is the principal function, acetoacetic acid is named as a ketone acid, *viz.*, β-ketobutyric acid. Acetoacetic acid may also be named propan-2-one-1-carboxylic acid—each functional group is indicated by its appropriate suffix.

$CH_2OH{\cdot}CH_2{\cdot}CHO$. This is both an alcohol and an aldehyde, so that, bearing in mind the order of preference, the name of the compound will be β-hydroxypropionaldehyde.

Table V indicates the prefixes and suffixes used for designating the functions (in alphabetical order).

TABLE V

Function	Prefix	Suffix
Acid	carboxy	carboxylic or -oic
Alcohol	hydroxy	ol
Aldehyde	oxo, aldo (for aldehydic O) or formyl (for CHO)	al
Amine	amino	amine
Azo-derivative	azo	—
Azoxy-derivative	azoxy	—
Carbonitrile (nitrile)	cyano	carbonitrile
Double bond	—	ene
Ether	alkoxy	—
Ethylene oxide, etc.	epoxy	—
Halogenide (halide)	halogeno (halo)	—
Hydrazine	hydrazino	hydrazine
Ketone	oxo or keto	one
Mercaptan	mercapto	thiol
Nitro-derivative	nitro	—
Nitroso-derivative	nitroso	—
"Quinquevalent" nitrogen	—	onium, inium
Sulphide	alkylthio	—
Sulphinic derivative	sulphino	sulphinic
Sulphone	sulphonyl	—
Sulphonic derivative	sulpho	sulphonic
Sulphoxide	sulphinyl	—
Triple bond	—	yne
Urea	ureido	urea

The simplest hydroxyaldehyde is **glycolaldehyde** (*hydroxyethanal*), $CH_2OH{\cdot}CHO$. It may be prepared by the oxidation of glycol with *Fenton's reagent* (hydrogen peroxide and ferrous sulphate):

$$CH_2OH{\cdot}CH_2OH + H_2O_2 \xrightarrow{FeSO_4} CH_2OH{\cdot}CHO + 2H_2O$$

It may also be prepared by ozonolysis of allyl alcohol:

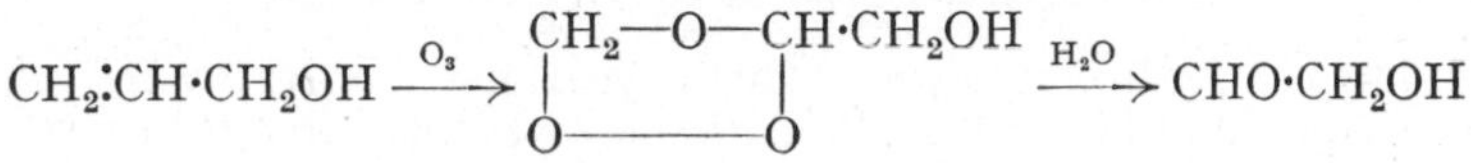

$$CH_2{:}CH{\cdot}CH_2OH \xrightarrow{O_3} \begin{array}{l} CH_2{-}O{-}CH{\cdot}CH_2OH \\ | \qquad\qquad\quad | \\ O{-}{-}{-}{-}{-}{-}O \end{array} \xrightarrow{H_2O} CHO{\cdot}CH_2OH$$

The most convenient means of preparing glycolaldehyde, however, is by heating dihydroxymaleic acid, which is obtained from the oxidation of tartaric acid (*q.v.*):

$$\begin{array}{l} HO_2C-C-OH \\ \quad\quad\;\; \| \\ HO_2C-C-OH \end{array} \longrightarrow 2CO_2 + \left[\begin{array}{l} H-C-OH \\ \quad\;\; \| \\ H-C-OH \end{array}\right] \longrightarrow \begin{array}{l} CHO \\ | \\ CH_2OH \end{array}$$

Glycolaldehyde exists in the solid form as the dimer, m.p. 96°; but in aqueous solution it exists as the monomer which forms the stable hydrate, $CH(OH)_2{\cdot}CH_2OH$ (*cf.* chloral, p. 157). Careful oxidation of glycolaldehyde with bromine water produces glycollic acid:

$$CH_2OH{\cdot}CHO + [O] \longrightarrow CH_2OH{\cdot}CO_2H$$

Glycolaldehyde is a powerful reducing agent, reducing ammoniacal silver nitrate and Fehling's solution at room temperature. With phenylhydrazine it forms the *osazone*. This osazone is identical with that formed from glyoxal, and the mechanism of its formation is still an open question (see carbohydrates, p. 422).

$$\begin{array}{l} CH{:}N{\cdot}NH{\cdot}C_6H_5 \\ | \\ CH{:}N{\cdot}NH{\cdot}C_6H_5 \end{array}$$

Glycolaldehyde undergoes the aldol condensation in the presence of alkali; with sodium hydroxide solution a tetrose sugar is formed, and with sodium carbonate solution, a hexose sugar:

$$2CH_2OH{\cdot}CHO \xrightarrow{NaOH} CH_2OH{\cdot}CHOH{\cdot}CHOH{\cdot}CHO$$

$$3CH_2OH{\cdot}CHO \xrightarrow{Na_2CO_3} CH_2OH{\cdot}CHOH{\cdot}CHOH{\cdot}CHOH{\cdot}CHOH{\cdot}CHO$$

Glycolaldehyde is formed in small amounts when formaldehyde is allowed to stand in the presence of calcium carbonate:

$$2H{\cdot}CHO \xrightarrow{CaCO_3} CH_2OH{\cdot}CHO$$

Glycolaldehyde is a useful starting material in a number of organic syntheses, but since it readily polymerises, the ethyl ether is used in synthetic work. The ethyl ether may be prepared by catalytically dehydrogenating ethyl cellosolve:

$$C_2H_5O{\cdot}CH_2{\cdot}CH_2OH \xrightarrow[250^\circ]{Cu} C_2H_5O\,CH_2{\cdot}CHO + H_2 \quad (43\%)$$

The ethyl group is easily eliminated when necessary by means of concentrated hydriodic acid or hydrobromic acid (p. 132).

Aldol (*acetaldol, β-hydroxybutyraldehyde, 3-hydroxybutanal*), $CH_3{\cdot}CHOH{\cdot}CH_2{\cdot}CHO$, may be prepared by the aldol condensation of acetaldehyde (p. 146):

$$2CH_3{\cdot}CHO \xrightarrow{NaOH} CH_3{\cdot}CHOH{\cdot}CH_2{\cdot}CHO$$

It is a colourless syrupy liquid, b.p. 83°/20 mm., miscible with water and ethanol. When heated, it is dehydrated to crotonaldehyde:

$$CH_3{\cdot}CHOH{\cdot}CH_2{\cdot}CHO \longrightarrow CH_3{\cdot}CH{:}CH{\cdot}CHO + H_2O$$

There is some doubt about the structure of aldol. Recent work suggests it is an equilibrium mixture of β-hydroxybutyraldehyde and the cyclic hemiacetal:

$$CH_3{\cdot}CHOH{\cdot}CH_2{\cdot}CHO \rightleftharpoons CH_3{\cdot}\overset{\lceil\text{———O———}\rceil}{CH{\cdot}CH_2{\cdot}CHOH}$$

The simplest hydroxyketone is **hydroxyacetone** (*acetol, pyruvic alcohol*), $CH_3{\cdot}CO{\cdot}CH_2OH$. The best method of preparation is by heating bromoacetone with potassium hydroxide in methanolic solution, and adding ethyl formate:

$$H{\cdot}CO_2C_2H_5 + KOH \longrightarrow H{\cdot}CO_2K + C_2H_5OH$$

$$CH_3{\cdot}CO{\cdot}CH_2Br + H{\cdot}CO_2K \longrightarrow CH_3{\cdot}CO{\cdot}CH_2{\cdot}OOC{\cdot}H + KBr$$

$$CH_3{\cdot}CO{\cdot}CH_2{\cdot}OOC{\cdot}H + CH_3OH \longrightarrow CH_3{\cdot}CO{\cdot}CH_2OH + H{\cdot}CO_2CH_3 \ (54\text{–}58\%)$$

This is an example of alcoholysis, hydroxyacetone being replaced by methanol.

Hydroxyacetone is a colourless liquid, b.p. 145°, soluble in water, ethanol and ether. It reduces ammoniacal silver nitrate, thereby being oxidised to DL-lactic acid, and reduces Fehling's solution, thereby being oxidised to a mixture of formic and acetic acids. Although ketones do not normally reduce ammoniacal silver nitrate and Fehling's solution, α-hydroxyketones are exceptions. Similarly, ketones form phenylhydrazones with phenylhydrazine, but α-hydroxyketones form osazones; thus hydroxyacetone gives the same osazone as methylglyoxal (*cf.* glycolaldehyde):

$$\begin{matrix} CH_3 \\ | \\ CO \\ | \\ CH_2OH \end{matrix} \xrightarrow{C_6H_5{\cdot}NH{\cdot}NH_2} \begin{matrix} CH_3 \\ | \\ C{:}N{\cdot}NH{\cdot}C_6H_5 \\ | \\ CH{:}N{\cdot}NH{\cdot}C_6H_5 \end{matrix}$$

Hydroxyacetone appears to exist as an equilibrium mixture of hydroxyketone and cyclic hemiacetal forms:

$$CH_3{\cdot}CO{\cdot}CH_2OH \rightleftharpoons CH_3{\cdot}\underset{OH}{C}\overset{\quad O \quad}{\text{——}}CH_2$$

The structure of this cyclic hemiacetal is related to that of ethylene oxide (p. 236), which has the property of reducing ammoniacal silver nitrate. It is therefore possible that the reducing properties of α-hydroxyketones are due to the presence of the oxide-ring form.

Diacetone alcohol (*4-hydroxy-4-methylpentan-2-one*), $(CH_3)_2C(OH){\cdot}CH_2{\cdot}CO{\cdot}CH_3$, may be prepared by the condensation of acetone in the presence of barium hydroxide:

$$2CH_3{\cdot}CO{\cdot}CH_3 \xrightarrow{Ba(OH)_2} (CH_3)_2C(OH){\cdot}CH_2{\cdot}CO{\cdot}CH_3$$

Diacetone alcohol is a colourless liquid, b.p. 164°. When heated with a trace of acid or iodine, it eliminates a molecule of water to form mesityl oxide:

$$(CH_3)_2C(OH){\cdot}CH_2{\cdot}CO{\cdot}CH_3 \xrightarrow{I_2} (CH_3)_2C{=}CH{\cdot}CO{\cdot}CH_3 + H_2O$$

Diacetone alcohol is oxidised by sodium hypobromite to β-hydroxy*iso*valeric acid (*cf.* haloform reaction):

$$(CH_3)_2C(OH){\cdot}CH_2{\cdot}CO{\cdot}CH_3 \xrightarrow{[O]} (CH_3)_2C(OH){\cdot}CH_2{\cdot}CO_2H$$

Diacetone alcohol is a very good solvent for cellulose esters.

DIALDEHYDES AND DIKETONES

Dialdehydes. The simplest dialdehyde is **glyoxal** (*oxaldehyde, ethanedial*), CHO·CHO. It may be obtained by the oxidation of ethanol, acetaldehyde or glycol with nitric acid, but the yields of glyoxal are poor. It is most conveniently prepared, as the bisulphite compound, by refluxing a mixture of paraldehyde, 50 per cent. aqueous acetic acid, dioxan, and selenious acid (yield 72–74 per cent. on the selenious acid):

$$(CH_3{\cdot}CHO)_3 + 3H_2SeO_3 \longrightarrow 3CHO{\cdot}CHO + 3Se + 6H_2O \xrightarrow{NaHSO_3} CHO{\cdot}CHO{\cdot}2NaHSO_3{\cdot}H_2O$$

Glyoxal is manufactured by the vapour-phase oxidation of glycol with air at 250–300° in the presence of copper as catalyst.

Glyoxal exists as a colourless polymer giving, on distillation, the monomer. This is a green vapour, which condenses to yellow crystals (m.p. 15°) which polymerise on standing to a colourless solid of unknown molecular weight. Glyoxal exists in aqueous solution as the dihydrate, $CH(OH)_2{\cdot}CH(OH)_2$, which has been isolated[4] (*cf.* chloral hydrate, p. 157).

Glyoxal undergoes many of the reactions of a dialdehyde; *e.g.*, it reduces ammoniacal silver nitrate, and forms addition compounds with two molecules of hydrogen cyanide and sodium hydrogen sulphite. It does *not* reduce Fehling's solution. Since it has no α-hydrogen atom, glyoxal undergoes the Cannizzaro reaction in the presence of alkali to form glycollic acid, one half of the molecule undergoing disproportionation at the expense of the other half:

$$CHO{\cdot}CHO + NaOH \longrightarrow CH_2OH{\cdot}CO_2Na$$

With phenylhydrazine, glyoxal forms the osazone (this is identical with that from glycolaldehyde, see p. 222):

$$\begin{matrix} CHO \\ | \\ CHO \end{matrix} + 2C_6H_5{\cdot}NH{\cdot}NH_2 \longrightarrow \begin{matrix} CH{:}N{\cdot}NH{\cdot}C_6H_5 \\ | \\ CH{:}N{\cdot}NH{\cdot}C_6H_5 \end{matrix} + 2H_2O$$

It also combines with *o*-phenylenediamines to form *quinoxalines* (heterocyclic compounds); *e.g.*, with *o*-phenylenediamine it forms quinoxaline itself:

$$C_6H_4(NH_2)_2 + \begin{matrix} O{=}CH \\ | \\ O{=}CH \end{matrix} \longrightarrow C_6H_4\begin{matrix} N{=}CH \\ | \\ N{=}CH \end{matrix} + 2H_2O$$

It combines with ammonia to form the heterocyclic compound *glyoxaline* (*iminazole*). The mechanism of this reaction is uncertain; one suggestion is that one molecule of glyoxal breaks down into formic acid and formaldehyde, and the latter reacts as follows:

$$\begin{matrix} CHO \\ | \\ CHO \end{matrix} + \begin{matrix} NH_3 \\ \\ H{\cdot}CHO \\ NH_3 \end{matrix} \longrightarrow \begin{matrix} HC{-}{-}{-}N \\ \| \quad\quad \| \\ HC \quad\quad CH \\ \diagdown NH \diagup \end{matrix} + 3H_2O$$

Glyoxal is one of the simplest coloured organic compounds, and when reduced it forms the colourless compound glycol (see Ch. XXXI).

Methylglyoxal (**pyruvaldehyde**), $CH_3{\cdot}CO{\cdot}CHO$, may be prepared by the oxidation of hydroxyacetone or by the hydrolysis of oximinoacetone:

$$CH_3{\cdot}CO{\cdot}CH_2OH \xrightarrow{[O]} CH_3{\cdot}CO{\cdot}CHO$$

$$CH_3{\cdot}CO{\cdot}CH{:}NOH \xrightarrow{acid} CH_3{\cdot}CO{\cdot}CHO$$

It is manufactured by the vapour-phase oxidation of propylene glycol with air at 250–300° in the presence of copper as catalyst:

$$CH_3{\cdot}CHOH{\cdot}CH_2OH \xrightarrow[Cu]{O_2} CH_3{\cdot}CO{\cdot}CHO + 2H_2O$$

It is a yellow oil with a pungent odour, and begins to boil at 72° to give a light green vapour. The liquid form of methylglyoxal is the dimer, and this slowly polymerises at room temperature to form a glassy mass of unknown molecular weight (*cf.* glyoxal).

Succinaldehyde (succindialdehyde, butanedial), $CHO{\cdot}CH_2{\cdot}CH_2{\cdot}CHO$, may be prepared by the ozonolysis of hexa-1 : 5-diene:

$$CH_2{:}CH{\cdot}CH_2{\cdot}CH_2{\cdot}CH{:}CH_2 \xrightarrow{\text{ozonolysis}} CHO{\cdot}CH_2{\cdot}CH_2{\cdot}CHO$$

Another method of preparation is to allow pyrrole and hydroxylamine to interact, and to treat the succinaldoxime so formed with aqueous nitrous acid:

$$\begin{matrix} CH{=}CH \\ | \\ CH{=}CH \end{matrix}\!\!>\!NH \xrightarrow{NH_2{\cdot}OH} \begin{matrix} CH_2{\cdot}CH{:}N{\cdot}OH \\ | \\ CH_2{\cdot}CH{:}N{\cdot}OH \end{matrix} \xrightarrow{HNO_2} \begin{matrix} CH_2{\cdot}CHO \\ | \\ CH_2{\cdot}CHO \end{matrix}$$

Succinaldehyde is a colourless oil, b.p. 170°, which readily polymerises. It undergoes the usual reactions of a (di)aldehyde; *e.g.*, it reduces ammoniacal silver nitrate and Fehling's solution, forms addition compounds with two equivalents of hydrogen cyanide and sodium hydrogen sulphite; etc. When treated with phosphorus pentoxide, ammonia and phosphorus pentasulphide, it gives respectively furan, pyrrole and thiophen:

$$\begin{matrix} CH_2{\cdot}CHO \\ | \\ CH_2{\cdot}CHO \end{matrix} \rightleftharpoons \begin{matrix} CH{=}CHOH \\ | \\ CH{=}CHOH \end{matrix} \longrightarrow \begin{cases} \xrightarrow{P_2O_5} \begin{matrix} CH{=}CH \\ | \\ CH{=}CH \end{matrix}\!\!>\!O \\ \xrightarrow{NH_3} \begin{matrix} CH{=}CH \\ | \\ CH{=}CH \end{matrix}\!\!>\!NH \\ \xrightarrow{P_2S_5} \begin{matrix} CH{=}CH \\ | \\ CH{=}CH \end{matrix}\!\!>\!S \end{cases}$$

Diketones. These are classified as α, β, γ . . . diketones according as the two carbonyl groups are in the 1 : 2, 1 : 3, 1 : 4, . . . positions respectively.

Butane-2 : 3-dione, dimethylglyoxal (*diacetyl*), $CH_3{\cdot}CO{\cdot}CO{\cdot}CH_3$, is the simplest α-diketone. It may be prepared:

(i) By the hydrolysis of oximinobutan-2-one formed by the action of nitrous acid on the ketone:

$$CH_3{\cdot}CO{\cdot}CH_2{\cdot}CH_3 \xrightarrow{HNO_2} CH_3{\cdot}CO{\cdot}C({:}NOH){\cdot}CH_3 \xrightarrow{HCl} CH_3{\cdot}CO{\cdot}CO{\cdot}CH_3$$

(ii) By the oxidation of butan-2-one with selenium dioxide:

$$CH_3{\cdot}CO{\cdot}CH_2{\cdot}CH_3 + SeO_2 \longrightarrow CH_3{\cdot}CO{\cdot}CO{\cdot}CH_3 + Se + H_2O$$

(iii) By the catalytic dehydrogenation of acetoin:

$$CH_3{\cdot}CO{\cdot}CH(OH){\cdot}CH_3 \xrightarrow[300°]{Cu} CH_3{\cdot}CO{\cdot}CO{\cdot}CH_3 + H_2$$

Acetoin may be readily oxidised by bismuth oxide in acetic acid; the yield of dimethylglyoxal is almost quantitative (Rigby, 1951). Air may be used as the oxidising agent, with a small amount of bismuth oxide as catalyst (Rigby *et al.*, 1951).

Butane-2 : 3-dione is a yellow oil, b.p. 88°. It gives the usual reactions of a diketone; *e.g.*, it forms the monoxime and di-oxime with hydroxylamine, the bisulphite compound with sodium hydrogen sulphite, etc. It is oxidised by hydrogen peroxide to acetic acid:

$$CH_3{\cdot}CO{\cdot}CO{\cdot}CH_3 \xrightarrow{H_2O_2} 2CH_3{\cdot}CO_2H$$

This reaction is unexpected since hydrogen peroxide does not usually break a carbon–carbon bond. Reduction with lithium aluminium hydride produces the corresponding diol.

Butane-2 : 3-dione forms a glyoxaline derivative with ammonia, and a quinoxaline derivative with *o*-phenylenediamine (*cf.* glyoxal, p. 224).

The dioxime of butane-2 : 3-dione, *i.e.*, *dimethylglyoxime*, $CH_3{\cdot}C(\vdots NOH){\cdot}C(\vdots NOH){\cdot}CH_3$, forms chelate compounds with many metals, and is used to estimate nickel, whose salts produce a red precipitate when treated with dimethylglyoxime. According to Brady *et al.* (1930), the structure of bisdimethylglyoxime nickel is I. The planar configuration round the nickel ion has been demonstrated (Sugden *et al.*, 1935), and confirmed by X-ray analysis (Rundle *et al.*, 1953).

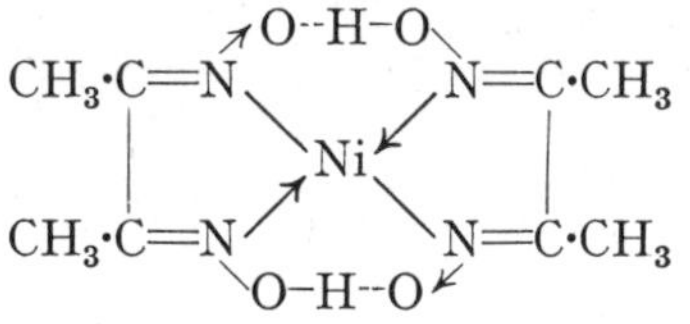

```
           ↗O--H-O↘
CH3·C=N              N=C·CH3
   |      ↘      ↙      |
   |        Ni          |        (I)
   |      ↗      ↘      |
CH3·C=N              N=C·CH3
           ↘O-H--O↙
```

Pentane-2 : 4-dione, acetylacetone, $CH_3{\cdot}CO{\cdot}CH_2{\cdot}CO{\cdot}CH_3$, is the simplest β-diketone. It may be prepared:

(i) By means of the Claisen condensation between ethyl acetate and acetone (yield 38–45 per cent. on the acetone):

$$CH_3{\cdot}CO_2C_2H_5 + CH_3{\cdot}CO{\cdot}CH_3 \xrightarrow{C_2H_5ONa} CH_3{\cdot}CO{\cdot}CH_2{\cdot}CO{\cdot}CH_3$$

(ii) By the ketonic hydrolysis of the acetyl derivative of acetoacetic ester:

$$CH_3{\cdot}CO{\cdot}CH_2{\cdot}CO_2C_2H_5 \xrightarrow[Mg]{CH_3{\cdot}COCl} CH_3{\cdot}CO{\cdot}\underset{\displaystyle}{\overset{\displaystyle CO{\cdot}CH_3 \atop |}{C}}H{\cdot}CO_2C_2H_5 \xrightarrow[\text{hydrolysis}]{\text{ketonic}} CH_3{\cdot}CO{\cdot}CH_2{\cdot}CO{\cdot}CH_3$$

(iii) By the condensation of acetic anhydride with acetone in the presence of boron trifluoride as catalyst (yield 80–85 per cent. on the acetone):

$$CH_3{\cdot}CO{\cdot}CH_3 + (CH_3{\cdot}CO)_2O \xrightarrow{BF_3} CH_3{\cdot}CO{\cdot}CH_2{\cdot}CO{\cdot}CH_3 + CH_3{\cdot}CO_2H$$

Hauser *et al.* (1956) have prepared β-diketones as follows:

$$R{\cdot}CO{\cdot}CH_3 + NaNH_2 \longrightarrow NH_3 + R{\cdot}CO{\cdot}CH_2Na \xrightarrow{R'{\cdot}COCl} R{\cdot}CO{\cdot}CH_2{\cdot}CO{\cdot}R'$$

Pentane-2 : 4-dione is a colourless liquid, b.p. 139°/746 mm. It exhibits tautomerism, *e.g.*, gives a red coloration with ferric chloride (*cf.* acetoacetic ester):

$$CH_3{\cdot}CO{\cdot}CH_2{\cdot}CO{\cdot}CH_3 \rightleftharpoons CH_3{\cdot}CO{\cdot}CH{=}C(OH){\cdot}CH_3$$

It is readily oxidised to acetic acid, and is converted into a mixture of acetone and acetic acid when heated with potassium hydroxide solution (*cf.* acid hydrolysis of acetoacetic ester, p. 214). It forms pyrazoles when treated with hydrazine or its derivatives; *e.g.*, with phenylhydrazine it forms 3 : 5-dimethyl-1-phenylpyrazole:

$$CH_3{\cdot}C(OH){=}CH{-}C(CH_3){=}O + H_2N{\cdot}NH{\cdot}C_6H_5 \longrightarrow \underset{\text{(3:5-dimethyl-1-phenylpyrazole)}}{CH_3{\cdot}C{=}CH{-}C(CH_3){=}N{-}N(C_6H_5)} + 2H_2O$$

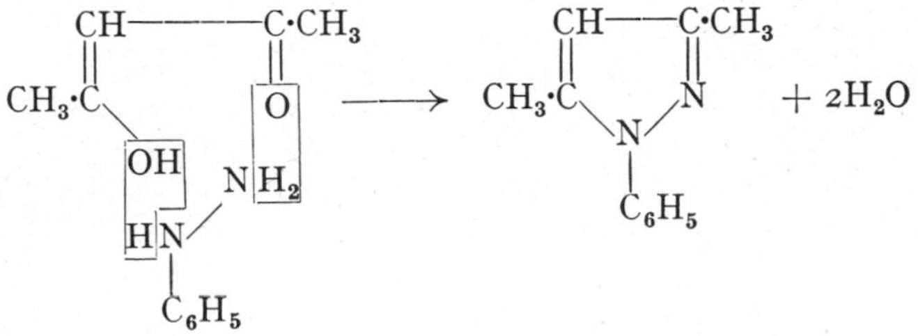

Pentane-2: 4-dione forms chelated compounds with various metals, *e.g.*, iron, aluminium, copper, etc.:

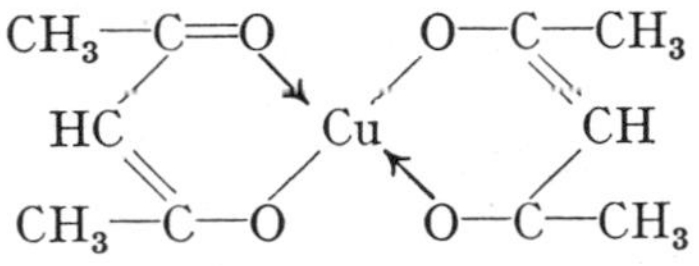

$$(CH_3{-}C{=}O{\rightarrow})(HC{=})(CH_3{-}C{-}O{-})Cu(O{-}C{-}CH_3)({=}CH)(O{\rightarrow}{=}C{-}CH_3)$$

Hexane-2 : 5-dione, acetonylacetone, $CH_3{\cdot}CO{\cdot}CH_2{\cdot}CH_2{\cdot}CO{\cdot}CH_3$, is the simplest γ-diketone. It may be prepared by means of the acetoacetic ester synthesis:

$$[CH_3{\cdot}CO{\cdot}CH{\cdot}CO_2C_2H_5]^-Na^+ + BrCH_2{\cdot}CO{\cdot}CH_3 \longrightarrow$$

$$CH_3{\cdot}CO{\cdot}CH(CH_2{\cdot}CO{\cdot}CH_3){\cdot}CO_2C_2H_5 \xrightarrow[\text{hydrolysis}]{\text{ketonic}} CH_3{\cdot}CO{\cdot}CH_2{\cdot}CH_2{\cdot}CO{\cdot}CH_3$$

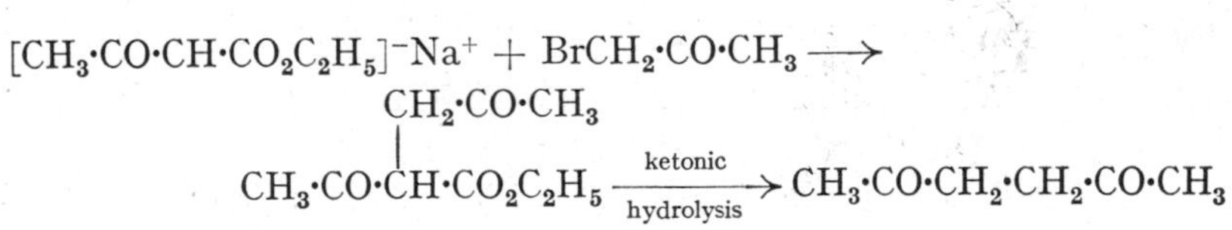

An alternative and more convenient acetoacetic ester synthesis is as follows:

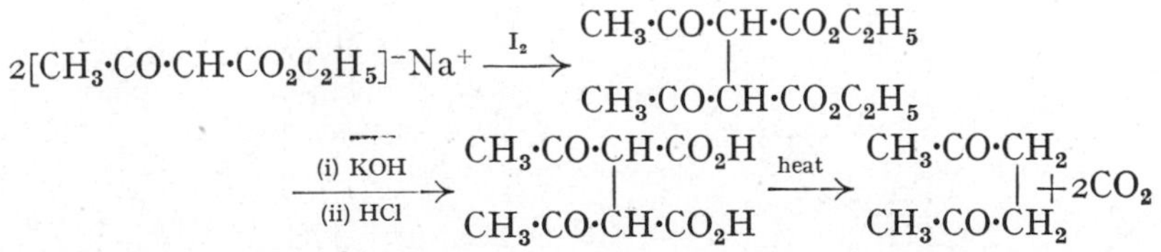

$$2[CH_3{\cdot}CO{\cdot}CH{\cdot}CO_2C_2H_5]^-Na^+ \xrightarrow{I_2} \begin{array}{l} CH_3{\cdot}CO{\cdot}CH{\cdot}CO_2C_2H_5 \\ \quad\quad\quad | \\ CH_3{\cdot}CO{\cdot}CH{\cdot}CO_2C_2H_5 \end{array}$$

$$\xrightarrow[\text{(ii) HCl}]{\text{(i) KOH}} \begin{array}{l} CH_3{\cdot}CO{\cdot}CH{\cdot}CO_2H \\ \quad\quad\quad | \\ CH_3{\cdot}CO{\cdot}CH{\cdot}CO_2H \end{array} \xrightarrow{\text{heat}} \begin{array}{l} CH_3{\cdot}CO{\cdot}CH_2 \\ \quad\quad\quad | \\ CH_3{\cdot}CO{\cdot}CH_2 \end{array} + 2CO_2$$

Hexane-2 : 5-dione is a colourless liquid, b.p. 192–194°. It exhibits tautomerism:

$$CH_3{\cdot}CO{\cdot}CH_2{\cdot}CH_2{\cdot}CO{\cdot}CH_3 \rightleftharpoons CH_3{\cdot}C(OH){=}CH{-}CH{=}C(OH){\cdot}CH_3$$

It readily forms five-membered rings: with phosphorus pentoxide, 2 : 5-dimethylfuran; with ammonia, 2 : 5-dimethylpyrrole; and with phosphorus pentasulphide, 2 : 5-dimethylthiophen (*cf.* succinaldehyde, p. 225):

$$\begin{array}{c} CH_3 \\ | \\ CH_2{\cdot}CO \\ | \\ CH_3{\cdot}CO \\ | \\ CH_3 \end{array} \rightleftharpoons \begin{array}{c} CH_3 \\ | \\ CH{=}C{-}OH \\ | \\ CH{=}C{-}OH \\ | \\ CH_3 \end{array} \longrightarrow \begin{cases} \xrightarrow{P_2O_5} \begin{array}{c} CH_3 \\ \cdot \\ CH{=}C \diagdown \\ | \qquad O \\ CH{=}C \diagup \\ \cdot \\ CH_3 \end{array} \\ \xrightarrow{NH_3} \begin{array}{c} CH_3 \\ \cdot \\ CH{=}C \diagdown \\ | \qquad NH \\ CH{=}C \diagup \\ \cdot \\ CH_3 \end{array} \\ \xrightarrow{P_2S_5} \begin{array}{c} CH_3 \\ \cdot \\ CH{=}C \diagdown \\ | \qquad S \\ CH{=}C \diagup \\ \cdot \\ CH_3 \end{array} \end{cases}$$

1 : 5- and 1 : 7-Diketones do not exist; all attempts to prepare them result in the formation of cyclic compounds. On the other hand, 1 : 6- and 1 : 8-diketones are known.

ALDEHYDIC AND KETONIC ACIDS

Glyoxylic acid (*glyoxalic acid, oxoethanoic acid*), $CHO{\cdot}CO_2H$, is the simplest aldehydic acid. It occurs in unripe fruits, *e.g.*, gooseberries, and disappears during ripening; it also occurs in animal tissues and fluids. It may be prepared by the oxidation of ethanol, glycol or glycollic acid with nitric acid (yields are poor). It may also be prepared by the reduction of oxalic acid either electrolytically or by means of magnesium and sulphuric acid, but it is most conveniently prepared by the hydrolysis of dichloroacetic acid with water:

$$CHCl_2{\cdot}CO_2H + H_2O \longrightarrow CHO{\cdot}CO_2H + 2HCl$$

Glyoxylic acid crystallises from water with one molecule of water which is combined as water of constitution, $CH(OH)_2{\cdot}CO_2H$, *i.e.*, dihydroxy-acetic acid (*cf.* chloral hydrate). The anhydrous acid may be obtained as a thick syrup by evaporating the aqueous solution over phosphorus pentoxide *in vacuo*.

Glyoxylic acid gives all the reactions of an aldehyde and an acid; *e.g.*, it reduces ammoniacal silver nitrate, forms a bisulphite compound, etc. Since it has no α-hydrogen atoms, glyoxylic acid undergoes the Cannizzaro reaction to form glycollic and oxalic acids:

$$2CHO{\cdot}CO_2H \xrightarrow{NaOH} CH_2OH{\cdot}CO_2Na + (CO_2Na)_2$$

When glyoxylic acid is reduced by means of metal and acid, tartaric acid is obtained as well as glycollic acid:

$$CHO{\cdot}CO_2H \xrightarrow{[H]} CH_2OH{\cdot}CO_2H + \begin{array}{l} CH(OH){\cdot}CO_2H \\ | \\ CH(OH){\cdot}CO_2H \end{array}$$

In this respect glyoxylic acid resembles acetone which also gives a bimolecular reduction product, pinacol (see p. 151).

Higher homologues of glyoxylic acid are known, but they are not important.

Pyruvic acid (*acetylformic acid, pyroracemic acid, α-ketopropionic acid, 2-oxopropanoic acid*), $CH_3{\cdot}CO{\cdot}CO_2H$, is the simplest keto-acid. It may be prepared:

(i) By heating tartaric acid alone, or better, with potassium hydrogen sulphate at 210–220°. The reaction is believed to take place via the formation of hydroxymaleic acid, I, which rearranges to oxalacetic acid, II:

$$\begin{matrix} CH(OH){\cdot}CO_2H \\ | \\ CH(OH){\cdot}CO_2H \end{matrix} \xrightarrow{-H_2O} \underset{(I)}{\begin{matrix} CH{\cdot}CO_2H \\ \| \\ C(OH){\cdot}CO_2H \end{matrix}} \longrightarrow \underset{(II)}{\begin{matrix} CH_2{\cdot}CO_2H \\ | \\ CO{\cdot}CO_2H \end{matrix}}$$

$$\longrightarrow CH_3{\cdot}CO{\cdot}CO_2H + CO_2 \quad (50\text{–}55\%)$$

This is the best method for preparing pyruvic acid, and it was this method which gave rise to the name pyroracemic acid.

(ii) By the oxidation of lactic acid with silver oxide suspended in water, or with Fenton's reagent:

$$CH_3{\cdot}CH(OH){\cdot}CO_2H + [O] \longrightarrow CH_3{\cdot}CO{\cdot}CO_2H + H_2O$$

(iii) By the hydrolysis of α : α-dibromopropionic acid with water:

$$CH_3{\cdot}CBr_2{\cdot}CO_2H + H_2O \longrightarrow CH_3{\cdot}CO{\cdot}CO_2H + 2HBr$$

(iv) By the hydrolysis of acetyl cyanide formed by the action of potassium cyanide on acetyl chloride:

$$CH_3{\cdot}COCl \xrightarrow{KCN} CH_3{\cdot}CO{\cdot}CN \xrightarrow[H_2O]{HCl} CH_3{\cdot}CO{\cdot}CO_2H$$

A general method for preparing α-keto-acids is to reflux a mixture of oxalic ester, fatty acid ester and sodium ethoxide in ether for 16 hours, and then boil the oxalo-ester with 10 per cent. sulphuric acid for 6 hours (Adickes and Andresen, 1943):

$$\begin{matrix} COOC_2H_5 \\ | \\ COOC_2H_5 \end{matrix} + H_2\overset{\overset{R}{|}}{C}{\cdot}CO_2C_2H_5 \xrightarrow{C_2H_5ONa} \begin{matrix} CO{\cdot}\overset{\overset{R}{|}}{C}H{\cdot}CO_2C_2H_5 \\ | \\ COOC_2H_5 \end{matrix} \xrightarrow{H_2SO_4} \left[\begin{matrix} CO{\cdot}\overset{\overset{R}{|}}{C}H{\cdot}CO_2H \\ | \\ CO_2H \end{matrix}\right]$$

$$\xrightarrow{-CO_2} R{\cdot}CH_2{\cdot}CO{\cdot}CO_2H \quad (\text{up to } 94\%)$$

Shreiber (1954) has prepared α-keto-acids as follows:

$$R{\cdot}CH_2{\cdot}CO_2C_2H_5 \xrightarrow{(C_6H_5)_3CNa} R{\cdot}CHNa{\cdot}CO_2C_2H_5 \xrightarrow{(CO_2C_2H_5)_2} \left[\bar{O}{-}C\begin{matrix} R{\cdot}CH{\cdot}CO_2C_2H_5 \\ OC_2H_5 \\ CO_2C_2H_5 \end{matrix}\right]Na^+$$

$$\longrightarrow C_2H_5ONa + CO_2C_2H_5{\cdot}CHR{\cdot}CO{\cdot}CO_2C_2H_5$$

$$\xrightarrow{\text{hydrolysis}} 2C_2H_5OH + R{\cdot}CH_2{\cdot}CO{\cdot}CO_2H$$

Another general method for preparing α-keto-esters is by the action of acetic anhydride on a glycidic ester (p. 147), followed by hydrolysis (Vogel *et al.*, 1950):

$$\underset{R'}{\overset{R}{>}}C\overset{O}{—}CH{\cdot}CO_2C_2H_5 \xrightarrow{(CH_3{\cdot}CO)_2O} \underset{R'}{\overset{R}{>}}C(O{\cdot}COCH_3){\cdot}CH(O{\cdot}COCH_3){\cdot}CO_2C_2H_5$$

$$\xrightarrow{-CH_3{\cdot}CO_2H} \underset{R'}{\overset{R}{>}}C{=}C(O{\cdot}COCH_3){\cdot}CO_2C_2H_5 \xrightarrow{H_2O} \underset{R'}{\overset{R}{>}}CH{\cdot}CO{\cdot}CO_2C_2H_5$$

Pyruvic acid is a colourless liquid, b.p. 165° (with slight decomposition), and smells like acetic acid. It is miscible in all proportions with water, ethanol and ether. It behaves as a ketone and as an acid; it forms an oxime, hydrazone, etc. It is reduced by sodium amalgam to lactic acid and dimethyltartaric acid (*cf.* glyoxylic acid, above):

$$3CH_3{\cdot}CO{\cdot}CO_2H \xrightarrow{[H]} CH_3{\cdot}CH(OH){\cdot}CO_2H + \begin{array}{l} CH_3{\cdot}C(OH){\cdot}CO_2H \\ \quad | \\ CH_3{\cdot}C(OH){\cdot}CO_2H \end{array}$$

Pyruvic acid reduces ammoniacal silver nitrate, itself being oxidised to acetic acid:

$$CH_3{\cdot}CO{\cdot}CO_2H + [O] \longrightarrow CH_3{\cdot}CO_2H + CO_2$$

It is oxidised by warm nitric acid to oxalic acid:

$$CH_3{\cdot}CO{\cdot}CO_2H + 4[O] \longrightarrow (CO_2H)_2 + CO_2 + H_2O$$

Pyruvic acid is easily decarboxylated with warm dilute sulphuric acid to give acetaldehyde:

$$CH_3{\cdot}CO{\cdot}CO_2H \longrightarrow CH_3{\cdot}CHO + CO_2$$

On the other hand, when warmed with *concentrated* sulphuric acid, pyruvic acid eliminates a molecule of carbon monoxide to form acetic acid:

$$CH_3{\cdot}CO{\cdot}CO_2H \longrightarrow CH_3{\cdot}CO_2H + CO$$

Both of these reactions with sulphuric acid are characteristic of α-keto-acids.

The methyl group is made reactive by the adjacent carbonyl group, and so pyruvic acid undergoes many condensation reactions characteristic of a compound containing an active methylene group; *e.g.*, in the presence of dry hydrogen chloride, pyruvic acid forms α-keto-γ-valerolactone-γ-carboxylic acid:

$$CH_3{\cdot}\overset{\overset{CO_2H}{|}}{C}{=}O + CH_3{\cdot}CO{\cdot}CO_2H \xrightarrow{HCl} \left[CH_3{\cdot}\underset{\underset{OH}{|}}{\overset{\overset{CO_2H}{|}}{C}}{—}CH_2{—}CO{\cdot}CO_2H \right]$$

$$\xrightarrow{-H_2O} CH_3{\cdot}\overset{\overset{CO_2H}{|}}{C}{—}CH_2{—}CO{\cdot}CO \quad (\text{C and CO joined through } {—}O{—})$$

Pyruvic acid is a very important substance biologically, since it is an intermediate product in the metabolism of carbohydrates and proteins.

Lævulic acid (β-*acetylpropionic acid*, γ-*ketovaleric acid*, *butan*-3-*one*-1-

carboxylic acid), $CH_3{\cdot}CO{\cdot}CH_2{\cdot}CH_2{\cdot}CO_2H$, is the simplest γ-keto-acid. It may be prepared via acetoacetic ester as follows:

$$[CH_3{\cdot}CO{\cdot}CH{\cdot}CO_2C_2H_5]^-Na^+ + ClCH_2{\cdot}CO_2C_2H_5 \longrightarrow$$

$$NaCl + CH_3{\cdot}CO{\cdot}\underset{}{\overset{CH_2\cdot CO_2C_2H_5}{\overset{|}{C}}}H{\cdot}CO_2C_2H_5 \xrightarrow[\text{hydrolysis}]{\text{ketonic}} CH_3{\cdot}CO{\cdot}CH_2{\cdot}CH_2{\cdot}CO_2H$$

It may also be prepared by heating a hexose sugar, particularly lævulose, with concentrated hydrochloric acid:

$$C_6H_{12}O_6 \longrightarrow CH_3{\cdot}CO{\cdot}CH_2{\cdot}CH_2{\cdot}CO_2H + H{\cdot}CO_2H + H_2O$$

In practice it is customary to use cane-sugar as the starting material:

$$C_{12}H_{22}O_{11} \longrightarrow 2CH_3{\cdot}CO{\cdot}CH_2{\cdot}CH_2{\cdot}CO_2H + 2H{\cdot}CO_2H + H_2O \quad (21\text{–}22\%)$$

By heating dilute solutions of sucrose under pressure with hydrochloric acid, the yield is increased to 50 per cent.

Lævulic acid is a crystalline solid; m.p. 34°, very soluble in water, ethanol and ether. It behaves as a ketone (forms oxime, etc.) and as an acid (forms esters, etc.). On the other hand, many of the reactions of lævulic acid indicate that it exists in the *lactol* form, *i.e.*, hydroxylactone:

$$\begin{array}{l} CH_2{\cdot}CO{\cdot}CH_3 \\ | \\ CH_2{\cdot}CO_2H \end{array} \rightleftharpoons \begin{array}{l} \quad\ \ OH \\ \quad\ \ | \\ CH_2{\cdot}C{-}CH_3 \\ |\quad\ \ >O \\ CH_2{\cdot}CO \end{array}$$

When heated for some time, lævulic acid is converted into α- and β-*angelica* lactones:

$$\underset{\alpha\text{-}}{\begin{array}{l} CH{=}C{-}CH_3 \\ |\quad\ \ >O \\ CH_2{-}CO \end{array}} \qquad\qquad \underset{\beta\text{-}}{\begin{array}{l} CH{-}CH{-}CH_3 \\ \|\quad\ \ >O \\ CH{-}CO \end{array}}$$

It should be noted that α- and γ-keto-acids differ from β-keto-acids in that their esters do not form sodio-derivatives, and the acids are not readily decomposed by moderate heating (*cf.* acetoacetic acid).

QUESTIONS

1. Show by means of equations how you would synthesise:—(*a*) hexane-2 : 5-dione, (*b*) methyl *n*-amyl ketone, (*c*) methyl *iso*propyl ketone, (*d*) α-methylsuccinic acid, (*e*) $\alpha : \beta$-dimethylbutyric acid, (*f*) $Et_2CH{\cdot}CO_2H$, (*g*) $Me{\cdot}CO{\cdot}Pr$, (*h*) $CH_3{\cdot}CH(CO_2H){\cdot}CH(Me){\cdot}CO_2H$, (*i*) $CH_3{\cdot}CO{\cdot}CH(Me){\cdot}CH_2{\cdot}CO_2H$, (*j*) $CH_3{\cdot}CH_2{\cdot}CH(Me){\cdot}CO{\cdot}NH_2$, (*k*) $CH_3{\cdot}CO{\cdot}CH_2{\cdot}CH_2{\cdot}CO_2H$, (*l*) $CH_2OH{\cdot}CH_2{\cdot}CH_2{\cdot}CO_2H$, (*m*) $CH_3{\cdot}CH(CO_2H){\cdot}CH(CO_2H){\cdot}CH_2{\cdot}CO_2H$, (*n*) $CH_3{\cdot}CH_2{\cdot}CH(Me){\cdot}CH(Et){\cdot}CO_2H$, (*o*) $Me_2CH{\cdot}CH_2{\cdot}CH_2{\cdot}CH(Me){\cdot}CH_2{\cdot}CO_2H$, (*p*) $Me_2CH{\cdot}CO{\cdot}CHMe_2$, (*q*) $Me_2EtC{\cdot}CO_2H$.

2. Starting with compounds containing three or less carbon atoms, how would you synthesise:—(*a*) $CH_3{\cdot}CO{\cdot}CH_2{\cdot}CHO$, (*b*) $CH_3{\cdot}CO{\cdot}CH_2{\cdot}CO{\cdot}CO_2Et$, (*c*) $CHO{\cdot}CH_2{\cdot}CO_2Et$, (*d*) $CH_3{\cdot}CHOH{\cdot}CH_2{\cdot}CH_2OH$, (*e*) $CH_3{\cdot}CHBr{\cdot}CH_2{\cdot}CO_2H$, (*f*) $Me_2CH{\cdot}CH_2{\cdot}CH_2{\cdot}CH_3$, (*g*) $CH_3{\cdot}CH_2{\cdot}CHCl{\cdot}CH_2{\cdot}CO_2H$, (*h*) $Me_2CBr{\cdot}CH_2{\cdot}CO_2H$?

3. Define and give examples of:—(*a*) tautomerism, (*b*) isomerism, (*c*) desmotropism, (*d*) resonance, (*e*) enolisation, (*f*) cationotropy, (*g*) anionotropy, (*h*) prototropy, (*i*) the Claisen condensation, (*j*) chelate compounds, (*k*) water of constitution.

4. Discuss the methods for determining the composition of keto-enol mixtures, and discuss the relation between structure and enol content.

5. Name the compounds and state the conditions under which they are formed when E.A.A. is treated with:—(*a*) NaOH, (*b*) H_3PO_4, (*c*) HNO_2, (*d*) $CuSO_4$, (*e*) NH_3, (*f*) $MeNH_2$, (*g*) MeMgI, (*h*) $CH_3{\cdot}CHO$, (*i*) AcCl, (*j*) ArN_2Cl, (*k*) O_3, (*l*) heated under reflux.

6. Give *one convenient* method for preparing:—(*a*) glycolaldehyde, (*b*) aldol, (*c*) acetol, (*d*) glyoxal, (*e*) methylglyoxal, (*f*) dimethylglyoxal, (*g*) succinaldehyde, (*h*) acetylacetone, (*i*) acetonylacetone, (*j*) glyoxylic acid, (*k*) pyruvic acid, (*l*) lævulic acid.

7. Which of the compounds in question 6 react with:—(*a*) $NaHSO_3$, (*b*) $C_6H_5{\cdot}NH{\cdot}NH_2$, (*c*) P_2O_5, (*d*) NH_3, (*e*) P_2S_5? Name the compounds and state under what conditions they are formed.

READING REFERENCES

Organic Reactions, Wiley, Vol. I (1942), Ch. 9. The Acetoacetic Ester Condensation and Certain Related Reactions.

Cooper and Barnes, An Improved Kurt Meyer Titration, *Ind. Eng. Chem.* (*Anal. Ed.*), 1938, **10**, 379.

Schwarzenbach and Wittwer, The Bromometric Estimation of Enol Content by Means of a Flow Apparatus, *Helv. Chim. Acta*, 1947, **60**, 657, 653, 663, 669.

Barnes and co-workers, Direction of Enolisation, *J. Amer. Chem. Soc.*, 1945, **37**, 132, 134.

Zuffanti, Enolisation, *J. Chem. Educ.*, 1945, **22**, 230.

Baker, *Tautomerism*, Routledge & Sons (1934).

Wheland, *Advanced Organic Chemistry*, Wiley (1949, 2nd ed.). Ch. 14. Tautomerism.

Braude, Anionotropy, *Quart. Reviews* (*Chem. Soc.*), 1950, **4**, 404.

Dewar, *The Electronic Theory of Organic Chemistry*, Oxford Press (1949). Ch. 5 and 6. The Replacement and Elimination Reactions.

Feigl and Suter, The Inner Complex Salts of Dimethylglyoxime, *J.C.S.*, **1948**, 378.

Joshi and Tuli, Refrachor: A New Physical Constant, *ibid.*, **1951**, 837.

Ingold, *Structure and Mechanism in Organic Chemistry*, Bell and Sons (1953). Ch. X. Unsaturated Rearrangements. Ch. XIV. Carboxyl Reactions.

Organic Reactions, Wiley, Vol. VIII (1954), Ch. 3. The Acylation of Ketones to form β-Diketones or β-Ketoaldehydes. Vol. IX (1957), Ch. 1. The Cleavage of Non-enolisable Ketones with Sodium Amide. Ch. 4. The Alkylation of Esters and Nitriles.

Gunstone, Recent Developments in the Preparation of Natural and Synthetic Straight-Chain Fatty Acids, *Quart. Reviews* (*Chem. Soc.*), 1953, **7**, 175.

Emmons and Hawthorne, Primary and Secondary Isotope Effects in the Enolisation of Ketones, *J. Amer. Chem. Soc.*, 1956, **78**, 5593.

CHAPTER XI

POLYHYDRIC ALCOHOLS

DIHYDRIC ALCOHOLS OR GLYCOLS

DIHYDRIC alcohols are compounds containing two hydroxyl groups. They are classified as α, β, γ . . . glycols, according to the relative positions of the two hydroxyl groups: α is the 1 : 2 glycol; β, 1 : 3; γ, 1 : 4 . . . Although it is unusual to find a compound with two hydroxyl groups attached to the same carbon atom, ether derivatives of these 1 : 1 glycols are stable, *e.g.*, acetals (p. 149). The commonest glycols are the α-glycols.

Nomenclature. The common names of the α-glycols are derived from the corresponding olefin from which they may be prepared by direct hydroxylation, *e.g.*,

$CH_2OH{\cdot}CH_2OH$	ethylene glycol
$CH_3{\cdot}CHOH{\cdot}CH_2OH$	propylene glycol
$(CH_3)_2CHOH{\cdot}CH_2OH$	*iso*butylene glycol

β-, γ- . . . Glycols are named as the corresponding *polymethylene* glycols, *e.g.*,

$CH_2OH{\cdot}CH_2{\cdot}CH_2OH$	trimethylene glycol
$CH_2OH{\cdot}CH_2{\cdot}CH_2{\cdot}CH_2{\cdot}CH_2OH$	pentamethylene glycol

According to the I.U.C. system of nomenclature, the class suffix is *-diol*, and numbers are used to indicate the positions of side-chains and the two hydroxyl groups, *e.g.*,

$CH_3{\cdot}CHOH{\cdot}CH_2OH$ propane-1 : 2-diol

$$\begin{array}{c} \quad CH_3 \qquad CH_3 \\ CH_2OH{\cdot}CH_2{\cdot}\dot{C}H{\cdot}CH_2{\cdot}\dot{C}H{\cdot}CH_2OH \end{array}$$ 2 : 4-dimethylhexane-1 : 6-diol

Ethylene glycol, glycol, (*ethane-1 : 2-diol*), $CH_2OH{\cdot}CH_2OH$, is the simplest glycol, and may be prepared as follows:

(i) By passing ethylene into cold dilute alkaline permanganate solution:

$$CH_2{:}CH_2 + [O] + H_2O \longrightarrow CH_2OH{\cdot}CH_2OH$$

(ii) By passing ethylene into hypochlorous acid, and then hydrolysing the ethylene chlorohydrin by boiling with aqueous sodium hydrogen carbonate:

$$CH_2{:}CH_2 + HOCl \longrightarrow CH_2Cl{\cdot}CH_2OH$$

$$CH_2Cl{\cdot}CH_2OH + NaHCO_3 \longrightarrow CH_2OH{\cdot}CH_2OH + NaCl + CO_2$$

(iii) By boiling ethylene bromide with aqueous sodium carbonate:

$$CH_2Br{\cdot}CH_2Br + Na_2CO_3 + H_2O \longrightarrow CH_2OH{\cdot}CH_2OH + 2NaBr + CO_2 \quad (50\%)$$

The low yield in this reaction is due to the conversion of some ethylene bromide into vinyl bromide:

$$CH_2Br{\cdot}CH_2Br + Na_2CO_3 \longrightarrow CH_2{:}CHBr + NaBr + NaHCO_3$$

If aqueous sodium hydroxide is used instead of sodium carbonate, vinyl bromide is again obtained as a by-product. The best yield of glycol from ethylene bromide is obtained by heating ethylene bromide with potassium acetate in glacial acetic acid, and subsequently hydrolysing the glycol diacetate with hydrogen chloride in methanolic solution:

$$CH_2Br{\cdot}CH_2Br + 2CH_3{\cdot}CO_2K \longrightarrow$$
$$CH_2{\cdot}(O{\cdot}CO{\cdot}CH_3){\cdot}CH_2(O{\cdot}CO{\cdot}CH_3) + 2KBr \xrightarrow{HCl} CH_2OH{\cdot}CH_2OH$$
$$(90\%) \qquad\qquad\qquad (83\text{–}84\%)$$

(iv) By treating ethylene oxide with dilute hydrochloric acid:

$$\begin{matrix} CH_2 \\ | \\ CH_2 \end{matrix}\!\!>\!O + H_2O \xrightarrow{HCl} CH_2OH{\cdot}CH_2OH$$

(v) By the reduction of any of the following compounds:

$$\begin{matrix} CHO \\ | \\ CHO \\ \text{glyoxal} \end{matrix} \qquad \begin{matrix} CHO \\ | \\ CH_2OH \\ \text{glycolaldehyde} \end{matrix} \qquad \begin{matrix} CH_2OH \\ | \\ CO_2CH_3 \\ \text{methyl glycollate} \end{matrix} \qquad \begin{matrix} CO_2C_2H_5 \\ | \\ CO_2C_2H_5 \\ \text{ethyl oxalate} \end{matrix}$$

Glycol is prepared industrially by methods (ii) and (iv), and by the catalytic reduction of methyl glycollate which is produced synthetically (see p. 379).

Glycol is a colourless viscous liquid, b.p. 197°, and has a sweet taste (the prefix *glyc-* indicates that the compound has a sweet taste: Greek *glukus*, sweet). It is miscible in all proportions with water and ethanol, but is insoluble in ether. It is widely used as a solvent and as an antifreeze agent.

The chemical reactions of glycol are those which might have been expected of a monohydric primary alcohol. One hydroxyl group, however, is almost always completely attacked before the other reacts. This is probably due to the fact that the primary alcoholic group is more reactive in glycol itself than in a compound of structure, *e.g.*, $R{\cdot}O{\cdot}CH_2{\cdot}CH_2OH$. Thus one group can be made to undergo one type of reaction and the other group another type of reaction, to give complex products.

(i) When glycol is treated with sodium at 50°, only one alcoholic group is attacked. To obtain the disodium derivative the temperature must be raised to 160°:

$$\begin{matrix} CH_2OH \\ | \\ CH_2OH \end{matrix} \xrightarrow[50^\circ]{Na} \begin{matrix} CH_2ONa \\ | \\ CH_2OH \end{matrix} \xrightarrow[160^\circ]{Na} \begin{matrix} CH_2ONa \\ | \\ CH_2ONa \end{matrix}$$

(ii) Hydrogen chloride converts glycol into ethylene chlorohydrin at 160°. To obtain ethylene chloride it is necessary to raise the temperature to 200°:

$$\begin{matrix} CH_2OH \\ | \\ CH_2OH \end{matrix} \xrightarrow[160^\circ]{HCl} \begin{matrix} CH_2Cl \\ | \\ CH_2OH \end{matrix} \xrightarrow[200^\circ]{HCl} \begin{matrix} CH_2Cl \\ | \\ CH_2Cl \end{matrix}$$

Ethylene chlorohydrin (β-*chloroethyl alcohol, 2-chloroethanol*) is a colourless liquid, b.p. 128·8°. It is very useful in organic syntheses since it contains two different reactive groups; *e.g.*, by heating with aqueous sodium cyanide it may be converted into ethylene cyanohydrin, which, on hydrolysis, gives β-hydroxypropionic acid (p. 389):

$$CH_2OH{\cdot}CH_2Cl + NaCN \longrightarrow CH_2OH{\cdot}CH_2{\cdot}CN + NaCl \quad (79\text{–}80\%)$$

$$CH_2OH{\cdot}CH_2{\cdot}CN \xrightarrow{HCl} CH_2OH{\cdot}CH_2{\cdot}CO_2H$$

(iii) When glycol is treated with phosphorus trichloride or phosphorus tribromide, the corresponding ethylene halide is obtained:

$$\begin{array}{l} CH_2OH \\ | \\ CH_2OH \end{array} \xrightarrow{PBr_3} \begin{array}{l} CH_2Br \\ | \\ CH_2Br \end{array}$$

Phosphorus tri-iodide, however, produces ethylene. Ethylene iodide is formed as an intermediate, but readily eliminates iodine to form the corresponding olefin (see p. 105):

$$\begin{array}{l} CH_2OH \\ | \\ CH_2OH \end{array} \xrightarrow{PI_3} \left[\begin{array}{l} CH_2I \\ | \\ CH_2I \end{array}\right] \longrightarrow I_2 + \begin{array}{l} CH_2 \\ \| \\ CH_2 \end{array}$$

(iv) When glycol is treated with organic acids or inorganic oxygen acids, the mono- or di-esters are obtained, depending on the relative amounts of glycol and acid; *e.g.*, glycol diacetate is obtained by heating glycol with acetic acid in the presence of a small amount of sulphuric acid as catalyst:

$$\begin{array}{l} CH_2OH \\ | \\ CH_2OH \end{array} + 2CH_3{\cdot}CO_2H \xrightarrow{H_2SO_4} \begin{array}{l} CH_2{\cdot}O{\cdot}CO{\cdot}CH_3 \\ | \\ CH_2{\cdot}O{\cdot}CO{\cdot}CH_3 \end{array} + 2H_2O$$

When glycol is heated with dibasic acids, condensation polymers are obtained:

$$HOCH_2{\cdot}CH_2O\boxed{H + HO}OC{\cdot}(CH_2)_n{\cdot}CO\boxed{OH + H}OCH_2{\cdot}CH_2O[H$$
$$+ \boxed{HO}OC{\cdot}(CH_2)_n{\cdot}CO\boxed{OH + ---} \longrightarrow$$
$$HOCH_2{\cdot}CH_2{\cdot}O{\cdot}CO{\cdot}(CH_2)_n{\cdot}CO{\cdot}O{\cdot}CH_2{\cdot}CH_2{\cdot}O{\cdot}CO{\cdot}(CH_2)_n{\cdot}CO{\cdot} ---$$

(v) Glycol condenses with aldehydes or ketones in the presence of acid to yield respectively cyclic acetals or cyclic ketals (1 : 3-*dioxolanes*):

$$\begin{array}{l} CH_2OH \\ | \\ CH_2OH \end{array} + O{=}C\begin{array}{l} \diagup R \\ \diagdown R' \end{array} \longrightarrow \begin{array}{l} CH_2O\diagdown \\ | \\ CH_2O\diagup \end{array} C \begin{array}{l} \diagup R \\ \diagdown R' \end{array} + H_2O$$

Compounds of this type are useful in sugar chemistry (see p. 419).

(vi) When glycol is oxidised with nitric acid, glycollic and oxalic acids may be readily isolated. All theoretically possible oxidation products have been isolated, but since, except for glycollic and oxalic acids, they are more readily oxidised than glycol itself, they have only been obtained in very poor yields.

$$\begin{array}{l} CH_2OH \\ | \\ CH_2OH \end{array} \xrightarrow{[O]} \begin{array}{l} CHO \\ | \\ CH_2OH \end{array} \xrightarrow{[O]} \begin{array}{l} CO_2H \\ | \\ CH_2OH \end{array} \xrightarrow{[O]} \begin{array}{l} CO_2H \\ | \\ CHO \end{array} \xrightarrow{[O]} \begin{array}{l} CO_2H \\ | \\ CO_2H \end{array}$$

$$\begin{array}{l} CHO \\ | \\ CH_2OH \end{array} \xrightarrow{[O]} \begin{array}{l} CHO \\ | \\ CHO \end{array} \xrightarrow{[O]} \begin{array}{l} CO_2H \\ | \\ CHO \end{array}$$

Oxidation of glycol with acid permanganate, acid dichromate, lead tetraacetate or periodic acid results in fission of the carbon–carbon bond (see p. 67).

(vii) Glycol is converted in acetaldehyde when heated with dehydrating agents, *e.g.*,

$$CH_2OH{\cdot}CH_2OH \xrightarrow{ZnCl_2} CH_3{\cdot}CHO + H_2O$$

On the other hand, when glycol is heated with a dehydrating agent such as phosphoric acid, *polyethylene glycols* are obtained, *e.g.*, diethylene glycol:

$$2CH_2OH{\cdot}CH_2OH \xrightarrow{-H_2O} CH_2OH{\cdot}CH_2{\cdot}O{\cdot}CH_2{\cdot}CH_2OH$$

By varying the amount of phosphoric acid and the temperature, the polyethylene glycols up to decaethylene glycol can be obtained. These condensation polymers contain both the alcohol and ether functional groups: they are soluble in water (alcohol function) and are very good solvents (ether function). They are widely used as solvents for gums, resins, cellulose esters, etc.

Ethylene oxide, $\overset{O}{CH_2{-}CH_2}$. According to the I.U.C. system of nomenclature, an oxygen atom linked to two of the carbon atoms in a carbon chain is denoted by the prefix *epoxy* in all cases other than those in which a substance is named as a cyclic compound; thus ethylene oxide is *epoxyethane*. Epoxy-compounds contain the *oxiran* (*oxirane*) ring, and ethylene oxide is also known as *oxiran* (*oxirane*). Oxiran compounds are also referred to as *cyclic ethers* or *alkylene oxides*.

Ethylene oxide may be prepared by distilling ethylene chlorohydrin with a concentrated solution of potassium hydroxide:

$$CH_2OH{\cdot}CH_2Cl + KOH \longrightarrow \overset{O}{CH_2{-}CH_2} + KCl + H_2O$$

This method is used industrially, but the potassium hydroxide is replaced by calcium hydroxide. A recent industrial preparation of ethylene oxide is to pass ethylene and air under pressure over a silver catalyst at 200–400°:

$$C_2H_4 + \tfrac{1}{2}O_2 \longrightarrow \overset{O}{CH_2{-}CH_2}$$

Ethylene oxide is a colourless gas, b.p. 10·7°, soluble in water, ethanol and ether. Ethylene oxide in aqueous solution is slowly converted into glycol; in dilute hydrochloric acid the conversion is rapid:

$$\overset{O}{CH_2{-}CH_2} + H_2O \longrightarrow CH_2OH{\cdot}CH_2OH$$

Ethylene oxide undergoes molecular rearrangement on heating to form acetaldehyde:

$$\overset{O}{CH_2{-}CH_2} \longrightarrow CH_3{\cdot}CHO$$

It reduces ammoniacal silver nitrate solution, and is reduced to ethanol by sodium amalgam.

Epoxides are reduced by lithium aluminium hydride to alcohols, unsymmetrical epoxides giving as main product the more highly substituted alcohol; thus I and III are the main products:

$$R{\cdot}\overset{O}{CH{-}CH_2} \xrightarrow{LiAlH_4} \underset{(I)}{R{\cdot}CHOH{\cdot}CH_3} + \underset{(II)}{R{\cdot}CH_2{\cdot}CH_2OH}$$

$$R_2\overset{O}{C{-}CHR} \xrightarrow{LiAlH_4} \underset{(III)}{R_2C(OH){\cdot}CH_2{\cdot}R} + \underset{(IV)}{R_2CH{\cdot}CHOH{\cdot}R}$$

Eliel *et al.* (1956), however, have shown that the reverse takes place if the reduction with lithium aluminium hydride is carried out in the presence of aluminium chloride or bromide, *i.e.*, II and IV are now the main products.

Ethylene oxide is used as an insecticide and in many laboratory syntheses. Its use as a synthetic reagent is due to its reactions with compounds of the type H—Z as follows:

$$\overset{\frown O \frown}{CH_2—CH_2} + H—Z \longrightarrow CH_2OH{\cdot}CH_2Z$$

where H—Z may be H—OH, H—Cl, H—Br, H—OR, $H—NH_2$. When it is desired to add halogen acid to ethylene oxide, a concentrated solution of the acid must be used since dilute acid catalyses the addition of water; *e.g.*, 46 per cent. hydrobromic acid gives ethylene bromohydrin:

$$\overset{\frown O \frown}{CH_2—CH_2} + HBr \longrightarrow CH_2OH{\cdot}CH_2Br \quad (87–92\%)$$

Of particular interest is the addition of hydrogen cyanide to form ethylene cyanohydrin:

$$\overset{\frown O \frown}{CH_2—CH_2} + HCN \longrightarrow CH_2OH{\cdot}CH_2{\cdot}CN$$

Sekino (1950) has obtained ethylene cyanohydrin (yield: 95–96 per cent.) by reaction between liquefied ethylene oxide and liquefied hydrogen cyanide in the presence of a catalyst such as an alkali-earth oxide.

The structure of ethylene oxide is uncertain; it may contain " bent " bonds. The oxygen bond is about 62°, and p^2 bonding has been assumed with " bent " bonds (see *cyclo*propane, p. 464).

When ethylene oxide is heated with methanol under pressure, the monomethyl ether of glycol is formed:

$$\overset{\frown O \frown}{CH_2—CH_2} + CH_3OH \longrightarrow CH_2OH{\cdot}CH_2{\cdot}O{\cdot}CH_3$$

This is known as *methyl cellosolve*; the corresponding ethyl ether is known as *ethyl cellosolve*. Cellosolves are very useful as solvents since they contain both the alcohol and ether functional groups (*cf.* polyethylene glycols, above).

Ethyl cellosolve may be used to prepare the ethyl ether of glycolaldehyde. The vapour of ethyl cellosolve is dehydrogenated by passing it over copper heated at about 250°:

$$C_2H_5O{\cdot}CH_2{\cdot}CH_2OH \xrightarrow{Cu} C_2H_5O{\cdot}CH_2{\cdot}CHO + H_2$$

This ethyl ether derivative does not polymerise so readily as glycolaldehyde, and so may be used instead of the latter in certain syntheses. The ethyl group is finally removed by means of concentrated hydrogen bromide.

The further action of ethylene oxide on cellosolves produces *carbitols*, *e.g.*,

$$CH_2OH{\cdot}CH_2{\cdot}O{\cdot}CH_3 + \overset{\frown O \frown}{CH_2—CH_2} \longrightarrow CH_2OH{\cdot}CH_2{\cdot}O{\cdot}CH_2{\cdot}CH_2{\cdot}O{\cdot}CH_3$$

When glycol is treated with ethylene oxide, diethylene glycol is formed:

$$CH_2OH{\cdot}CH_2OH + \overset{\frown O \frown}{CH_2—CH_2} \longrightarrow CH_2OH{\cdot}CH_2{\cdot}O{\cdot}CH_2{\cdot}CH_2OH$$

Ethylene oxide reacts with ammonia to form a mixture of three amino-alcohols which are usually referred to as the *ethanolamines*:

$$C_2H_4O + NH_3 \longrightarrow CH_2OH{\cdot}CH_2{\cdot}NH_2 \xrightarrow{C_2H_4O} (CH_2OH{\cdot}CH_2)_2NH \xrightarrow{C_2H_4O} (CH_2OH{\cdot}CH_2)_3N$$

The ethanolamines are widely used as emulsifying agents.

Dioxan (1 : 4-*dioxan, diethylene dioxide*) may be prepared:

(i) By distilling glycol with a little sulphuric acid or concentrated phosphoric acid:

$$2CH_2OH{\cdot}CH_2OH \longrightarrow O\left\langle\begin{array}{l}CH_2-CH_2\\CH_2-CH_2\end{array}\right\rangle O + 2H_2O$$

(ii) By heating 2 : 2′-dichlorodiethyl ether with aqueous potassium hydroxide:

$$CH_2Cl{\cdot}CH_2{\cdot}O{\cdot}CH_2{\cdot}CH_2Cl + 2KOH \longrightarrow O\left\langle\begin{array}{l}CH_2-CH_2\\CH_2-CH_2\end{array}\right\rangle O + 2KCl + H_2O$$

(iii) Dioxan is prepared industrially by distilling glycol with phosphoric acid (method i), and by dimerising ethylene oxide with 4 per cent. sulphuric acid:

$$2C_2H_4O \longrightarrow O\left\langle\begin{array}{l}CH_2-CH_2\\CH_2-CH_2\end{array}\right\rangle O$$

Dioxan is a colourless liquid, b.p. 101·5°, miscible in all proportions with water and most organic solvents. It is a useful solvent for cryoscopic and ebullioscopic work.

General Methods of Preparation of 1 : 2 Glycols Other than Glycol itself

1. By the reduction of ketones with magnesium amalgam, *e.g.*, pinacol may be prepared by adding mercuric chloride in acetone to a mixture of magnesium and benzene, refluxing the mixture, and then adding water to decompose the magnesium " pinacolate " (the yield is 43–50 per cent. based on the magnesium):

$$2CH_3{\cdot}CO{\cdot}CH_3 + Mg \longrightarrow \begin{array}{c}(CH_3)_2C - C(CH_3)_2\\ | \qquad\quad | \\ O \quad\; O \\ \diagdown \; \diagup \\ Mg\end{array} \xrightarrow{H_2O} (CH_3)_2C(OH){\cdot}C(OH)(CH_3)_2 + Mg(OH)_2$$

2. By the action of a Grignard reagent on α-diketones, *e.g.*,

$$CH_3{\cdot}CO{\cdot}CO{\cdot}CH_3 \xrightarrow{2RMgX} CH_3{\cdot}\overset{R}{\underset{XMgO}{C}}-\overset{R}{\underset{OMgX}{C}}{\cdot}CH_3 \xrightarrow{H_2O} CH_3{\cdot}\overset{R}{\underset{HO}{C}}-\overset{R}{\underset{OH}{C}}{\cdot}CH_3$$

3. By the action of a Grignard reagent on α-ketonic esters, *e.g.*,

$$CH_3{\cdot}CO{\cdot}CO_2C_2H_5 \xrightarrow{3RMgX} CH_3{\cdot}\overset{R}{\underset{XMgO}{C}}-\overset{R}{\underset{OMgX}{C}}{\cdot}R \xrightarrow{H_2O} CH_3{\cdot}\overset{R}{\underset{HO}{C}}-\overset{R}{\underset{OH}{C}}{\cdot}R$$

4. By the catalytic reduction of acyloins:

$$R{\cdot}CH(OH){\cdot}CO{\cdot}R \xrightarrow[Ni]{H_2} R{\cdot}CH(OH){\cdot}CH(OH){\cdot}R$$

5. By hydroxylation of unsaturated compounds (see p. 66).

Pinacol (*tetramethylethylene glycol, 2 : 3-dimethylbutane-2 : 3-diol*), $(CH_3)_2C(OH){\cdot}C(OH)(CH_3)_2$, is most conveniently prepared by reducing acetone with magnesium amalgam (see above). It crystallises out of solution as the hexahydrate. The most important reaction of pinacol is the rearrangement it undergoes when distilled with dilute sulphuric acid:

$$(CH_3)_2C(OH){\cdot}C(OH)(CH_3)_2 \xrightarrow{H_2SO_4} CH_3{\cdot}CO{\cdot}C(CH_3)_3 + H_2O$$

The *pinacol–pinacolone rearrangement* (p. 160) is general for pinacols (ditertiary alcohols). If the pinacol contains two different groups, it is generally the *larger* one which migrates, *e.g.*,

$$CH_3{-}\underset{OH}{\overset{C_2H_5}{C}}{-}\underset{OH}{\overset{C_2H_5}{C}}{-}CH_3 \xrightarrow{H_2SO_4} CH_3{\cdot}CO{\cdot}\underset{CH_3}{\overset{C_2H_5}{C}}{-}C_2H_5 + H_2O$$

When sulphuric acid is used as the catalyst, some diene is formed as by-product:

$$CH_3{-}\underset{OH}{\overset{CH_3}{C}}{-}\underset{OH}{\overset{CH_3}{C}}{-}CH_3 \xrightarrow{H_2SO_4} CH_2{=}\overset{CH_3}{C}{-}\overset{CH_3}{C}{=}CH_2 + 2H_2O$$

If pinacol is heated with 48 per cent. hydrobromic acid, 22–25 per cent. of pinacolone and 55–60 per cent. of diene are obtained. The yield of diene is further increased (79 86 per cent.) by passing pinacol over alumina at 420–470°.

Polymethylene Glycols

A general method of preparing polymethylene glycols is to reduce αω-dicarboxylic esters with sodium and ethanol or lithium aluminium hydride, or catalytically, *e.g.*, (i) ethyl sebacate refluxed with sodium in ethanol gives decamethylene glycol:

$$C_2H_5O_2C{\cdot}(CH_2)_8{\cdot}CO_2C_2H_5 \xrightarrow{[H]} CH_2OH{\cdot}(CH_2)_8{\cdot}CH_2OH \quad (73\text{–}75\%)$$

(ii) Ethyl adipate heated with hydrogen under pressure in the presence of copper chromite as catalyst gives hexamethylene glycol:

$$C_2H_5O_2C{\cdot}(CH_2)_4{\cdot}CO_2C_2H_5 \xrightarrow{H_2} CH_2OH{\cdot}(CH_2)_4{\cdot}CH_2OH \quad (85\text{–}90\%)$$

Individual polymethylene glycols are usually prepared by special methods.

Trimethylene glycol (propane-1 : 3-diol), $CH_2OH{\cdot}CH_2{\cdot}CH_2OH$, b.p. 214° (with decomposition), may be prepared by the hydrolysis of trimethylene bromide, or by fermentation of glycerol by *Schizomycetes* (together with *n*-butanol).

Tetramethylene glycol (butane-1 : 4-diol), $CH_2OH{\cdot}(CH_2)_2{\cdot}CH_2OH$, b.p. 230°, and **hexamethylene glycol (hexane-1 : 6-diol)**, $CH_2OH{\cdot}(CH_2)_4{\cdot}CH_2OH$, m.p. 42°, are most conveniently prepared by reducing the corresponding αω-dicarboxylic esters (succinic and adipic, respectively). Tetramethylene glycol is prepared industrially by hydrogenating butynediol. It is used for preparing butadiene, γ-butyrolactone and tetrahydrofuran.

Pentamethylene glycol (pentane-1 : 5-diol), $CH_2OH{\cdot}(CH_2)_3{\cdot}CH_2OH$, b.p. 239°, can be obtained from pentamethylene bromide, which is obtained from piperidine by the *von Braun reaction* (p. 732).

The pentamethylene bromide is converted into the corresponding glycol by heating with potassium acetate in glacial acetic acid, and subsequently hydrolysing the diacetate with alkali (*cf.* glycol):

$$CH_2Br{\cdot}(CH_2)_3{\cdot}CH_2Br \xrightarrow{CH_3{\cdot}CO_2K} CH_3{\cdot}CO{\cdot}O{\cdot}CH_2{\cdot}(CH_2)_3{\cdot}CH_2{\cdot}O{\cdot}OC{\cdot}CH_3 \xrightarrow{NaOH} CH_2OH{\cdot}(CH_2)_3{\cdot}CH_2OH \quad (v.g.)$$

The four $\alpha : \omega$-diols C_{22}, C_{24}, C_{26}, and C_{28} have been isolated from carnauba wax (Murray *et al.*, 1955). These authors have also isolated seven ω-hydroxyacids from the same source: C_{18}, C_{20}, C_{22}, C_{24}, C_{26}, C_{28}, C_{30}.

The polymethylene glycols are readily converted into the corresponding mono- or di-halogen derivative by halogen acid, according to the amount of halogen acid used. These polymethylene halides are useful reagents in organic syntheses since they contain two reactive halogen atoms, one or both of which may be made to undergo reaction. If the synthesis requires reaction with one halogen atom only, the most satisfactory procedure is to "protect" the other halogen atom by ether formation and subsequently decompose the ether with concentrated hydrobromic acid, *e.g.*,

$$C_2H_5ONa + BrCH_2{\cdot}CH_2{\cdot}CH_2Br \longrightarrow NaBr + C_2H_5{\cdot}O{\cdot}CH_2{\cdot}CH_2{\cdot}CH_2Br$$

$$\xrightarrow{AgNO_2} C_2H_5{\cdot}O{\cdot}CH_2{\cdot}CH_2{\cdot}CH_2{\cdot}NO_2 \xrightarrow{HBr} CH_2Br{\cdot}CH_2{\cdot}CH_2{\cdot}NO_2$$

Then, *e.g.*,

$$CH_2Br{\cdot}CH_2{\cdot}CH_2{\cdot}NO_2 \xrightarrow{KCN} CN{\cdot}CH_2{\cdot}CH_2{\cdot}CH_2{\cdot}NO_2$$

TRIHYDRIC ALCOHOLS

The only important trihydric alcohol is **glycerol (propane-1 : 2 : 3-triol)**, $CH_2OH{\cdot}CHOH{\cdot}CH_2OH$. It occurs in almost all animal and vegetable oils and fats as the glyceryl esters of mainly palmitic, stearic and oleic acids (see below).

Glycerol is obtained in large quantities as a by-product in the manufacture of soap, and this is still a commercial source of glycerol (see below). Another method of preparing glycerol is the fermentation of glucose to which sodium sulphite has been added (the yield is 20–25 per cent.). Glycerol is now also prepared synthetically as follows:

$$\underset{}{CH_3{\cdot}CH{:}CH_2} \xrightarrow[480\text{–}500^\circ]{Cl_2} \underset{\text{allyl chloride}}{CH_2Cl{\cdot}CH{:}CH_2} \xrightarrow[150^\circ\,.\,12\text{ atm.}]{aq.\ Na_2CO_3} \underset{\text{allyl alcohol}}{CH_2OH{\cdot}CH{:}CH_2}$$

$$\xrightarrow{HOCl} \underset{\text{glycerol }\beta\text{-monochlorohydrin}}{CH_2OH{\cdot}CHCl{\cdot}CH_2OH} \xrightarrow{NaOH} CH_2OH{\cdot}CHOH{\cdot}CH_2OH$$

An alternative route that is used is:

$$CH_2Cl{\cdot}CH{:}CH_2 \xrightarrow{HOCl} \left.\begin{matrix} CH_2Cl{\cdot}CHOH{\cdot}CH_2Cl \\ + \\ CH_2Cl{\cdot}CHCl{\cdot}CH_2OH \end{matrix}\right\} \xrightarrow{CaO}$$

$$\underset{\text{epichlorohydrin}}{\overset{\;\;O}{CH_2\text{—}CH{\cdot}CH_2Cl}} \xrightarrow{NaOH} CH_2OH{\cdot}CHOH{\cdot}CH_2OH$$

A new process is to add osmium tetroxide and hydrogen peroxide to acraldehyde; this produces glyceraldehyde which is then catalytically hydrogenated to glycerol.

$$CH_2{:}CH{\cdot}CHO \xrightarrow{H_2O_2} CH_2OH{\cdot}CHOH{\cdot}CHO \xrightarrow{H_2} CH_2OH{\cdot}CHOH{\cdot}CH_2OH$$

Glycerol is a colourless, syrupy liquid, b.p. 290° (with some decomposition). It is miscible with water and ethanol in all proportions, but is almost insoluble in ether. It is used as an antifreeze, for making explosives, and, because of its hygroscopic properties, as a moistening agent for tobacco, shaving soaps, etc.

Glycerol contains one secondary and two primary alcoholic groups, and it undergoes many of the reactions to be expected of these types of alcohols. The carbon atoms in glycerol are indicated as shown: $\overset{\alpha}{C}H_2OH{\cdot}\overset{\beta}{C}HOH{\cdot}\overset{\alpha' \text{ or } \gamma}{C}H_2OH$.

(i) When glycerol is treated with sodium, one α-hydroxyl group is readily attacked, and the other α-group less readily; the β-hydroxyl group is not attacked at all:

$$CH_2OH{\cdot}CHOH{\cdot}CH_2OH \xrightarrow{Na} CH_2ONa{\cdot}CHOH{\cdot}CH_2OH \xrightarrow{Na} CH_2ONa{\cdot}CHOH{\cdot}CH_2ONa$$

(ii) On passing hydrogen chloride into glycerol at 110° until there is the theoretical increase in weight corresponding to the esterification of one hydroxyl group, both α- and β-glycerol monochlorohydrin are formed, the former predominating (66 per cent.). Continued action of hydrogen chloride at 110°, using 25 per cent. of acid in excess required by theory for the esterification of two hydroxyl groups, produces glycerol α : α'-dichlorohydrin (α-dichlorohydrin) and glycerol α : β-dichlorohydrin (β-dichlorohydrin), the former predominating (55–57 per cent.); some other products are also formed:

$$CH_2OH{\cdot}CHOH{\cdot}CH_2OH \xrightarrow{HCl} CH_2Cl{\cdot}CHOH{\cdot}CH_2OH + CH_2OH{\cdot}CHCl{\cdot}CH_2OH$$

$$\xrightarrow{HCl} CH_2Cl{\cdot}CHOH{\cdot}CH_2Cl + CH_2Cl{\cdot}CHCl{\cdot}CH_2OH$$

When either of these dichlorohydrins or glycerol itself is treated with phosphorus pentachloride, glycerol trichlorohydrin (1 : 2 : 3-trichloropropane) is obtained. This is a liquid, b.p. 156–158°, which smells like chloroform.

When glycerol α : α'-dichlorohydrin is oxidised with sodium dichromate–sulphuric acid mixture, *s*-dichloroacetone (1 : 3-dichloropropan-2-one) is obtained:

$$CH_2Cl{\cdot}CHOH{\cdot}CH_2Cl \xrightarrow{[O]} CH_2Cl{\cdot}CO{\cdot}CH_2Cl \quad (68\text{–}75)\%$$

It is a solid, m.p. 45°, and is a useful starting material in many syntheses.

When glycerol α : α'-dichlorohydrin is treated with powdered sodium hydroxide in ether solution, **epichlorohydrin** (3-chloro-1 : 2-epoxypropane) is obtained:

$$CH_2Cl{\cdot}CHOH{\cdot}CH_2Cl + NaOH \longrightarrow CH_2Cl{\cdot}\overset{\frown O \frown}{CH{-}CH_2} + NaCl + H_2O \quad (76\text{–}81\%)$$

Epichlorohydrin is also obtained by distilling an alkaline solution of the α-dichlorohydrin under reduced pressure (yield: 90 per cent.). It is a liquid, b.p. 117°, and smells like chloroform.

Hydrogen bromide and the phosphorus bromides react with glycerol in the same way as the corresponding chlorine compounds, but the analogous iodine compounds behave differently, the products depending on the amount of reagent used. When glycerol is heated with a *small* amount of hydrogen iodide or phosphorus tri-iodide, *allyl iodide* is the main product:

$$CH_2OH{\cdot}CHOH{\cdot}CH_2OH \xrightarrow{PI_3} [CH_2I{\cdot}CHI{\cdot}CH_2I] \longrightarrow I_2 + CH_2{:}CH{\cdot}CH_2I$$

When a *large* amount of phosphorus tri-iodide is used, the main product is iso*propyl iodide*, which is formed by the following sequence of reactions from the allyl iodide first formed:

$$CH_2{:}CH{\cdot}CH_2I \xrightarrow{HI} [CH_3{\cdot}CHI{\cdot}CH_2I] \xrightarrow{-I_2} CH_3{\cdot}CH{:}CH_2 \xrightarrow{HI} CH_3{\cdot}CHI{\cdot}CH_3 \quad (80\%)$$

(iii) When glycerol is treated with monocarboxylic acids, esters are obtained which may be mono-, di- or tri-esters, according to the amount of acid used; high temperature and an excess of acid favour the formation of the tri-ester (see the glycerides, below).

Nitroglycerine is manufactured by adding glycerol in a thin stream to a cold mixture of concentrated nitric and sulphuric acids:

$$\begin{array}{l} CH_2OH \\ | \\ CHOH \\ | \\ CH_2OH \end{array} + 3HNO_3 \longrightarrow \begin{array}{l} CH_2{\cdot}O{\cdot}NO_2 \\ | \\ CH{\cdot}O{\cdot}NO_2 \\ | \\ CH_2{\cdot}O{\cdot}NO_2 \end{array} + 3H_2O$$

Nitroglycerine is an ester, not a nitro-compound; it is *glyceryl trinitrate*. The incorrect name appears to have been introduced due to the use of " mixed acid " which is normally used for nitration (see p. 528).

Nitroglycerine is a poisonous, colourless, oily liquid, insoluble in water. It usually burns quietly when ignited, but when heated rapidly, struck or detonated, it explodes violently. Nobel (1867) found that nitroglycerine could be stabilised by absorbing it in kieselguhr. This was *dynamite*, which is now, however, usually manufactured by using sawdust as the absorbent, and adding solid ammonium nitrate. *Blasting gelatin* or *gelignite* is made by mixing nitroglycerine with gun-cotton (cellulose nitrate). The smokeless powder, *cordite*, is a mixture of nitroglycerine, gun-cotton and vaseline.

When heated with formic acid or oxalic acid at 260°, glycerol is converted into allyl alcohol (p. 251). With dibasic acids, glycerol forms condensation polymers known as *alkyd resins*, the commonest of which is glyptal, formed by heating glycerol with phthalic anhydride.

When boric acid is added to an aqueous solution of glycerol, a complex is produced which has a higher electrical conductivity than boric acid itself, *i.e.*, is a stronger acid. This complex is believed to be a borospiranic acid in which the two rings attached to the boron atom are perpendicular to each other (hence name spiran):

$$\left[\begin{array}{c} >C{-}O \\ | \\ >C{-}O \end{array} \!\!> B < \!\! \begin{array}{c} O{-}C< \\ | \\ O{-}C< \end{array}\right]^- H^+$$

Glycol does not increase the conductivity of boric acid. It is therefore believed that the two hydroxyl groups in glycol are in the *trans*-position, whereas the hydroxyl groups in glycerol are in the *cis*-position.

(iv) Glycerol can theoretically give rise to a large variety of oxidation products. The actual product obtained in practice depends on the nature of the oxidising agent used:

$$CH_2OH\cdot CHOH\cdot CH_2OH \rightarrow \underset{\text{glyceraldehyde}}{CH_2OH\cdot CHOH\cdot CHO} \rightarrow \underset{\text{glyceric acid}}{CH_2OH\cdot CHOH\cdot CO_2H} \rightarrow \underset{\text{tartronic acid}}{CO_2H\cdot CHOH\cdot CO_2H}$$

$$CH_2OH\cdot CHOH\cdot CH_2OH \rightarrow \underset{\text{dihydroxyacetone}}{CH_2OH\cdot CO\cdot CH_2OH} \rightarrow \underset{\text{mesoxalic acid}}{CO_2H\cdot CO\cdot CO_2H} \leftarrow \text{tartronic acid}$$

Dilute nitric acid converts glycerol into glyceric and tartronic acids; concentrated nitric acid oxidises it to mainly glyceric acid (80 per cent.); bismuth nitrate produces mainly mesoxalic acid. Bromine water, sodium hypobromite and Fenton's reagent (hydrogen peroxide and ferrous sulphate) oxidise glycerol to a mixture of glyceraldehyde (predominantly) and dihydroxyacetone; this mixture is known as *glycerose*. These two compounds are interconvertible in the presence of anhydrous pyridine, this being known as the *Lobry de Bruyn–van Ekenstein rearrangement* (see also p. 429):

$$CHO\cdot CHOH\cdot CH_2OH \rightleftharpoons [CHOH{=}COH\cdot CH_2OH] \rightleftharpoons CH_2OH\cdot CO\cdot CH_2OH$$

(v) When heated with potassium hydrogen sulphate, glycerol is dehydrated to acraldehyde:

$$CH_2OH\cdot CHOH\cdot CH_2OH \xrightarrow{KHSO_4} CH_2{:}CH\cdot CHO + 2H_2O$$

(vi) The mixed ethers of glycerol may be conveniently prepared by the action of sodium alkoxide on a glycerol chlorohydrin, *e.g.*, *triethylin*, the triethyl ether of glycerol, is prepared by heating 1 : 2 : 3-trichloropropane with sodium ethoxide:

$$CH_2Cl\cdot CHCl\cdot CH_2Cl + 3C_2H_5ONa \rightarrow CH_2\cdot O\cdot C_2H_5\cdot CH\cdot O\cdot C_2H_5\cdot CH_2\cdot O\cdot C_2H_5 + 3NaCl$$

Helferich and co-workers (1923) found that triphenylmethyl chloride, $(C_6H_5)_3CCl$, usually formed ethers only with primary alcoholic groups. Thus the α-mono- and the α : α'-di-triphenylmethyl ethers of glycerol can be prepared, the latter offering a means of preparing β-esters of glycerol, *e.g.*,

$$CH_2OH\cdot CHOH\cdot CH_2OH \xrightarrow{(C_6H_5)_3CCl} CH_2\cdot O\cdot C(C_6H_5)_3\cdot CHOH\cdot CH_2\cdot O\cdot C(C_6H_5)_3 \xrightarrow{RCOCl} CH_2\cdot O\cdot C(C_6H_5)_3\cdot CH\cdot O\cdot CO\cdot R\cdot CH_2\cdot O\cdot C(C_6H_5)_3 \xrightarrow{HBr} CH_2OH\cdot CH\cdot O\cdot CO\cdot R\cdot CH_2OH$$

A better means of obtaining the β-ester is to protect the αα'-hydroxyl groups by cyclic ether formation with benzaldehyde (Bergmann and Carter, 1930). This acetal-like compound is formed when glycerol and benzaldehyde are heated together, or the cool mixture treated with hydrogen chloride:

$$\begin{array}{l} CH_2OH \\ | \\ CHOH \\ | \\ CH_2OH \end{array} + C_6H_5\cdot CHO \xrightarrow{HCl} \begin{array}{l} CH_2O\diagdown \\ | \\ CHOH \\ | \\ CH_2O\diagup \end{array} CH\cdot C_6H_5 + H_2O$$

(vii) Glycerol can be fermented to produce a variety of compounds, *e.g.*, propionic acid, succinic acid, acetic acid, *n*-butanol, trimethylene glycol, lactic acid, *n*-butyric acid, etc. Fermentation by means of a particular micro-organism usually produces more than one compound, *e.g.*, propionic acid bacteria produce propionic acid, succinic acid and acetic acid.

Structure of glycerol. All the chemical reactions of glycerol indicate that its structure is $CH_2OH\cdot CHOH\cdot CH_2OH$, and this is supported by many syntheses, *e.g.*,

(i) From propylene (see above).
(ii) The following absolute synthesis:

$$CaC_2 \xrightarrow{H_2O} C_2H_2 \xrightarrow[HgSO_4]{H_2SO_4} CH_3\cdot CHO \xrightarrow{O_2} CH_3\cdot CO_2H \xrightarrow[salt]{distil\ Ca} CH_3\cdot CO\cdot CH_3$$

$$\xrightarrow{[H]} CH_3\cdot CHOH\cdot CH_3 \xrightarrow[250^\circ]{Al_2O_3} CH_3\cdot CH{:}CH_2 \xrightarrow{Br_2/CCl_4} CH_3\cdot CHBr\cdot CH_2Br$$

$$\xrightarrow{Br_2/Fe} CH_2Br\cdot CHBr\cdot CH_2Br \xrightarrow{CH_3\cdot CO_2K} \begin{array}{l} CH_2\cdot O\cdot CO\cdot CH_3 \\ | \\ CH\cdot O\cdot CO\cdot CH_3 \\ | \\ CH_2\cdot O\cdot CO\cdot CH_3 \end{array} \xrightarrow{NaOH} \begin{array}{l} CH_2OH \\ | \\ CHOH \\ | \\ CH_2OH \end{array}$$

Polyhydric Alcohols

Tetrahydric alcohols. Erythritol, $CH_2OH\cdot CHOH\cdot CHOH\ CH_2OH$, exists in three forms: dextrorotatory erythritol, m.p. 88°; lævorotatory erythritol, m.p. 88°; *meso*-erythritol, m.p. 121·5°. The *meso*-form occurs in certain lichens and seaweeds. All three forms may be oxidised to tartaric acid,

$$CO_2H\cdot CHOH\cdot CHOH\ CO_2H$$

Pentaerythritol, $C(CH_2OH)_4$, is prepared by the condensation of formaldehyde with acetaldehyde (see p. 154).

Pentahydric alcohols (*pentitols*). There are four pentitols with the structure $CH_2OH\cdot(CHOH)_3\cdot CH_2OH$, which may be prepared by reducing the corresponding aldopentoses (see p. 416). Two are optically active, forming a pair of enantiomorphs—D- and L-**arabitol**—and the other two are optically inactive, existing as *meso* forms—**adonitol** and **xylitol.**

Aldopentose	*Pentitol*
D- and L-ribose	adonitol (ribitol)
D- and L-xylose	xylitol
D-arabinose, D-lyxose	D-arabitol (D-lyxitol)
L-arabinose, L-lyxose	L-arabitol (L-lyxitol)

Adonitol and D-arabitol occur naturally.

D-Rhamnitol, $CH_3\cdot(CHOH)_4\cdot CH_2OH$, may be prepared by reducing the corresponding deoxyhexose, D-rhamnose.

Hexahydric Alcohols (*hexitols*). There are ten hexitols with the structure $CH_2OH{\cdot}(CHOH)_4{\cdot}CH_2OH$, which may be prepared by reducing the corresponding aldohexoses (see p. 417). Eight exist as four pairs of enantiomorphs, and the remaining two as *meso* forms.

Aldohexose	*Hexitol*
D-glucose and L-gulose	D-sorbitol (D-glucitol)
L-glucose and D-gulose	L-sorbitol (L-glucitol)
D-mannose	D-mannitol
L-mannose	L-mannitol
D-idose	D-iditol
L-idose	L-iditol
D-talose and D-altrose	D-talitol
L-talose and L-altrose	L-talitol
D- and L-galactose	dulcitol
D- and L-allose	allodulcitol (allitol)

D-*Sorbitol*, D-*mannitol* and *dulcitol* occur naturally.

Rhamnohexitol, $CH_3{\cdot}(CHOH)_5{\cdot}CH_2OH$, is prepared by reducing the corresponding aldose, rhamnohexose.

The polyhydric alcohols chemically resemble glycerol in many ways. When heated with concentrated hydriodic acid or with a mixture of red phosphorus, iodine and water, they are converted into the corresponding 2-iodoparaffin and paraffin; *e.g.*, any hexitol gives a mixture of 2-iodohexane and *n*-hexane when heated with hydriodic acid (see also the sugars, p. 417):

$$CH_2OH{\cdot}(CHOH)_4{\cdot}CH_2OH \xrightarrow{HI} CH_3{\cdot}CH_2{\cdot}CH_2{\cdot}CH_2{\cdot}CHI{\cdot}CH_3 + CH_3{\cdot}(CH_2)_4{\cdot}CH_3$$

OILS, FATS AND WAXES

Oils and fats are compounds of glycerol and various organic acids, *i.e.*, they are glyceryl esters or *glycerides*. Oils, which are liquids at ordinary temperatures, contain a larger proportion of unsaturated acids than do the fats, which are solids at ordinary temperatures. The acids present in the glycerides are almost exclusively straight-chain acids, and almost always contain an even number of carbon atoms. The chief saturated acids are lauric, myristic, palmitic and stearic (see p. 174). The chief unsaturated acids are oleic, linoleic and linolenic (see p. 268). Palmitic acid is the most abundant of the saturated acids, and acids containing less than eighteen carbon atoms are usually present only as minor constituents, but sometimes they are present in appreciable amounts in insect waxes and marine fats.

Glycerides are named according to the nature of the acids present, the suffix-*ic* of the common name of the acid being changed into *-in*. Glycerides are said to be " simple " when all the acids are the same, and " mixed " when the acids are different:

$$\begin{array}{l} CH_2{\cdot}O{\cdot}CO{\cdot}C_{17}H_{35} \\ | \\ CH{\cdot}O{\cdot}CO{\cdot}C_{17}H_{35} \\ | \\ CH_2{\cdot}O{\cdot}CO{\cdot}C_{17}H_{35} \end{array} \qquad \begin{array}{l} CH_2{\cdot}O{\cdot}CO{\cdot}C_{15}H_{31} \\ | \\ CH{\cdot}O{\cdot}CO{\cdot}C_{17}H_{33} \\ | \\ CH_2{\cdot}O{\cdot}CO{\cdot}C_{17}H_{33} \end{array}$$

tristearin (simple glyceride) — α-palmito-α′ : β-diolein (mixed glyceride)

It is still not certain whether simple glycerides occur naturally; if they do, they are definitely not as common as the mixed glycerides.

Synthesis of glycerides. Simple triglycerides are readily prepared from glycerol and an excess of acyl chloride, or from 1 : 2 : 3-tribromopropane and the silver or potassium salts of the fatty acids.

Mixed triglycerides are far more difficult to prepare. A number of methods have been developed, *e.g.*,

(i) The sodium salt of an acid is heated with glycerol monochlorohydrin, and the monoester so formed is acylated:

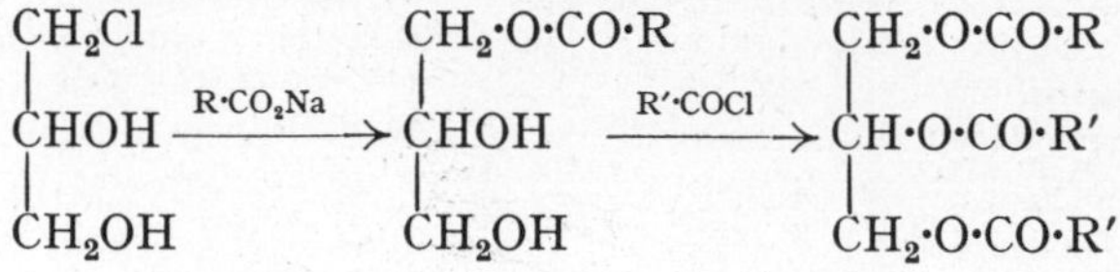

$$\begin{array}{l} CH_2Cl \\ | \\ CHOH \\ | \\ CH_2OH \end{array} \xrightarrow{R\cdot CO_2Na} \begin{array}{l} CH_2\cdot O\cdot CO\cdot R \\ | \\ CHOH \\ | \\ CH_2OH \end{array} \xrightarrow{R'\cdot COCl} \begin{array}{l} CH_2\cdot O\cdot CO\cdot R \\ | \\ CH\cdot O\cdot CO\cdot R' \\ | \\ CH_2\cdot O\cdot CO\cdot R' \end{array}$$

(ii) 1 : 3-Benzylidene-glycerol is treated with an acid chloride, the benzaldehyde residue is removed by hydrolysis, and the monoester so formed is then further acylated:

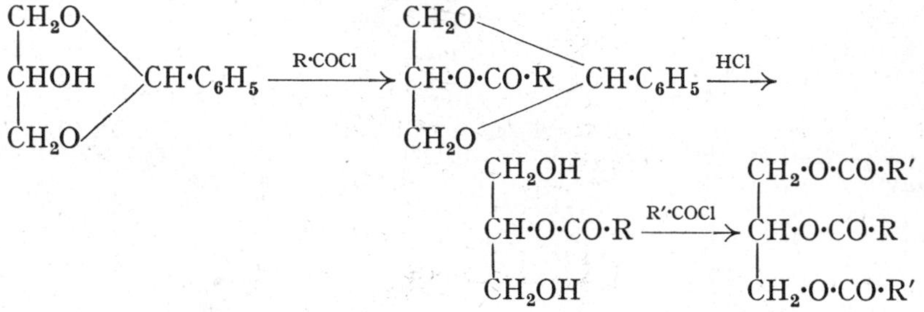

$$\begin{array}{l} CH_2O \\ | \\ CHOH \\ | \\ CH_2O \end{array} \!\!>\! CH\cdot C_6H_5 \xrightarrow{R\cdot COCl} \begin{array}{l} CH_2O \\ | \\ CH\cdot O\cdot CO\cdot R \\ | \\ CH_2O \end{array} \!\!>\! CH\cdot C_6H_5 \xrightarrow{HCl}$$

$$\begin{array}{l} CH_2OH \\ | \\ CH\cdot O\cdot CO\cdot R \\ | \\ CH_2OH \end{array} \xrightarrow{R'\cdot COCl} \begin{array}{l} CH_2\cdot O\cdot CO\cdot R' \\ | \\ CH\cdot O\cdot CO\cdot R \\ | \\ CH_2\cdot O\cdot CO\cdot R' \end{array}$$

In both methods (i) and (ii) there is, however, still difficulty in knowing with certainty the position of the acyl group introduced first, since the acyl group tends to migrate in the monoester, producing the following equilibrium:

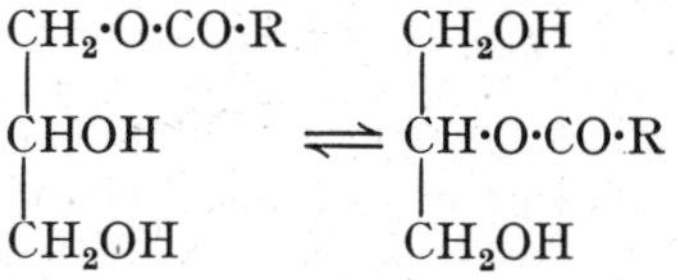

$$\begin{array}{l} CH_2\cdot O\cdot CO\cdot R \\ | \\ CHOH \\ | \\ CH_2OH \end{array} \rightleftharpoons \begin{array}{l} CH_2OH \\ | \\ CH\cdot O\cdot CO\cdot R \\ | \\ CH_2OH \end{array}$$

This isomerisation has been shown to be intramolecular. When 2-palmitin was isomerised to the 1-isomer in alcohol containing glycerol labelled with ^{14}C, no ^{14}C was found in the ester (Doerschuk, 1952). Martin (1953) has shown that perchloric acid rapidly catalyses the change of 1- or 2-monoglycerides to the equilibrium mixture containing 90–92 per cent. of the 1-isomer. Isomerisation of aliphatic 2-monoglycerides to the corresponding 1-isomer may even occur slowly in the solid state (Brokaw *et al.*, 1955).

An interesting difference between the 1- and 2-isomers is that the former form urea inclusion compounds (p. 369) whereas the latter do not (Aylward *et al.*, 1956).

Analysis of oils and fats. Oils and fats are characterised by means of physical as well as chemical tests. The usual physical constants that are determined are melting point, solidifying point, specific gravity and refractive index.

The chemical tests give an indication of the type of fatty acids present in the oil or fat.

The **acid value,** which is the number of milligrams of potassium hydroxide required to neutralise 1 gram of the oil or fat, indicates the amount of free acid present.

The **saponification value** is the number of milligrams of potassium hydroxide required to neutralise the fatty acids resulting from the complete hydrolysis of 1 gram of the oil or fat.

The **iodine value,** which is the number of grams of iodine that combine with 100 grams of oil or fat, gives the degree of unsaturation of the acids in the substance. Several methods are used for determining the iodine value. In *Hubl's method,* a carbon tetrachloride solution of the substance is treated with a solution of iodine and mercuric chloride in ethanol; in *Wijs' method,* iodine monochloride in glacial acetic acid is used. Another method is to use a solution of glacial acetic acid containing pyridine, bromine and concentrated sulphuric acid (*Dam's solution*).

The **Reichert-Meissl value,** which is the number of ml. of 0·1N-potassium hydroxide required to neutralise the distillate of 5 grams of hydrolysed fat, indicates the amount of steam-volatile fatty acids (*i.e.*, acids up to lauric) present in the substance.

The **acetyl value,** which is the number of milligrams of potassium hydroxide required to neutralise the acetic acid obtained when 1 gram of an acetylated oil or fat is hydrolysed, indicates the number of free hydroxyl groups present in the substance.

Preparation of glycerol from oils and fats. When an oil or fat is hydrolysed by superheated steam, glycerol and the free fatty acids are obtained:

$$\begin{array}{l} CH_2{\cdot}O{\cdot}CO{\cdot}R \\ | \\ CH{\cdot}O{\cdot}CO{\cdot}R \\ | \\ CH_2{\cdot}O{\cdot}CO{\cdot}R \end{array} + 3H_2O \longrightarrow \begin{array}{l} CH_2OH \\ | \\ CHOH \\ | \\ CH_2OH \end{array} + 3R{\cdot}CO_2H$$

Alternatively, the hydrolysis may be carried out by means of very dilute sulphuric acid in the presence of a catalyst, *e.g.*, 2-(β-sulphonaphthyl)-stearic acid. This method is rapidly gaining industrial importance. The free fatty acids are used in the manufacture of candles.

$CH_3{\cdot}(CH_2)_{15}{\cdot}CH{\cdot}CO_2H$ (attached to a naphthalene ring bearing SO_3H)

If an oil or fat is saponified, *i.e.*, hydrolysed with alkali, soaps are obtained. Any metallic salt of a fatty acid is a soap, but the term soap is usually applied to the water-soluble salts since only these have detergent properties. The saturated fats give hard soaps whereas the unsaturated fats, *i.e.*, the oils, give soft soaps. Ordinary soap is a mixture of the sodium salts of the even fatty acids from octoic to stearic. The sodium salts of a given oil or fat are harder and less soluble than the corresponding potassium salts. Thus soft soaps are usually the potassium salts, particularly when they are derived from oils.

The preparation of soaps and glycerol is carried out by saponifying the oil or fat with sodium hydroxide solution, and then adding sodium chloride to " salt out " the soap, *i.e.*, help the soap to separate out by causing it to rise to the top of the liquid. The lower aqueous layer is run off and glycerol is obtained from it. The soap is again heated with sodium hydroxide solution to ensure complete saponification, and allowed to separate out to the top. The lower layer is run off, and the soap is then boiled with water and allowed to set.

Glycerol is obtained from the aqueous layer by neutralising the excess of sodium hydroxide with sulphuric acid, and evaporating *in vacuo* until the liquid contains about 50 per cent. glycerol. Sodium chloride (which was added for salting out the soap) is precipitated. The liquid is filtered and the sodium chloride is used again. The filtrate is concentrated further by evaporation *in vacuo* until the glycerol content is about 85 per cent. Glycerol is then obtained in over 99 per cent. purity by steam distillation *in vacuo*. A more recent method of purification of crude glycerol is by means of ion-exchange resins.

Hardening of oils. Glycerides of the unsaturated acids are liquid at room temperature and so are unsuitable for edible fats. By converting the unsaturated acids into saturated acids, oils are changed into fats. This introduction of hydrogen is known as the hydrogenation or *hardening of oils*, and is carried out by the Sabatier–Senderens reduction (p. 33). The oil is heated to 150–200° and hydrogen is passed in, under pressure, in the presence of a finely divided nickel catalyst. The nickel is recovered by filtration. In the hydrogenation process only a proportion of the unsaturated acids are converted into the saturated acids, otherwise a fat as hard as tallow would be obtained; the hydrogenation is carried out until a fat of the desired consistency is obtained.

Synthetic fats. Truly synthetic fats would be those prepared from synthetic glycerol and synthetic fatty acids. The cost of synthetic glycerol is so high that synthetic fats are not, so far, prepared industrially since they cannot compete, in price, with natural fats. During the war (1939–1945), however, synthetic fats were prepared in Germany by three methods:

(i) Glycerol and fatty acids, both of which are obtained as by-products from natural fats, were recombined.

(ii) Fatty acids were esterified with alcohols other than glycerol, *e.g.*, ethanol. These ethyl esters hydrolyse fairly easily, giving rise to an unpleasant taste.

(iii) Acids, obtained by the oxidation of hydrocarbons (p. 165), were esterified with glycerol in the presence of tin or zinc, and under reduced pressure; under these conditions the excess glycerol and the water formed during the reaction were removed.

Phosphatides (phospholipids). These occur in all animal and vegetable cells, and are glycerides in which one organic acid residue, the α- or β-, is replaced by a group containing phosphoric acid and a base. When the base is **cholamine,** $CH_2OH{\cdot}CH_2{\cdot}NH_2$, the phosphatide is known as a **kephalin**; when the base is **choline,** $CH_2OH{\cdot}CH_2{\cdot}\overset{+}{N}(CH_3)_3\}\overset{-}{O}H$, the phosphatide is known as a **lecithin,** *e.g.*,

```
CH2·O·CO·R
|
CH·O·CO·R  O
|          ||
CH2·O──────P·O─CH2·CH2·NH2
           |
           OH
     α-kephalin
```

```
CH2·O·CO·R  O
|           ||                    +        -
CH·O────────P·O─CH2·CH2·N(CH3)3}OH
|           |
CH2·O·CO·R  OH
       β-lecithin
```

α-kephalin

β-lecithin

It is quite likely that both kephalins and lecithins have a betaine structure (see p. 308).

Only a few monocarboxylic acids have been isolated from phosphatides: stearic, oleic, linoleic and arachidonic from kephalins, and palmitic, stearic, oleic, linoleic, linolenic and arachidonic from lecithins.

Drying oils. These are oils which, on exposure to air, change into hard solids, *e.g.*, linseed oil. All drying oils contain a large proportion of the unsaturated acids linoleic and linolenic, and it is this "drying" property which makes these oils valuable in the paint industry. The mechanism of drying is not known. It appears to be a complicated process involving oxidation, polymerisation and colloidal gel formation, and it has been found to be catalysed by various metallic oxides, particularly lead monoxide.

Waxes. These are esters of the higher homologues of both the fatty acids and monohydric alcohols, *e.g.*,

beeswax	myricyl palmitate	$C_{25}H_{31}{\cdot}CO_2C_{30}H_{61}$
spermaceti	cetyl palmitate	$C_{15}H_{31}{\cdot}CO_2C_{16}H_{33}$
carnauba wax	myricyl cerotate	$C_{25}H_{51}{\cdot}CO_2C_{30}H_{61}$

Some waxes are also esters of cholesterol, *e.g.*, cholesteryl esters occur in wool-wax.

QUESTIONS

1. Name the compounds and state the conditions under which they are formed when glycol is treated with:—(*a*) Na, (*b*) HBr, (*c*) PCl_5, (*d*) PI_3, (*e*) AcCl, (*f*) $CH_3{\cdot}CHO$, (*g*) $CH_3{\cdot}CO{\cdot}CH_3$, (*h*) H_3PO_4, (*i*) HNO_3, (*j*) $KMnO_4$, (*k*) $ZnCl_2$, (*l*) $C_6H_5{\cdot}NCO$.

2. Name the compounds and state the conditions under which they are formed when glycerol is treated with:—(*a*) Na, (*b*) HCl, (*c*) PCl_5, (*d*) PI_3, (*e*) Ac_2O, (*f*) HNO_3, (*g*) $H{\cdot}CO_2H$, (*h*) $(CO_2H)_2$, (*i*) H_3BO_3, (*j*) Br_2, (*k*) $KHSO_4$, (*l*) $C_6H_5{\cdot}CHO$.

3. How are glycol and glycerol prepared (i) in the laboratory; (ii) industrially?

4. By means of equations show how you would convert glycerol into:— (*a*) *n*-PrOH, (*b*) dihydroxyacetone, (*c*) diallyl ether, (*d*) epichlorohydrin, (*e*) β-ketoglutaric acid.

5. Show by means of equations how you would prepare:—(*a*) $CH_2OH{\cdot}CH_2{\cdot}OMe$, (*b*) $CH_2{\cdot}(OEt){\cdot}CH_2{\cdot}OEt$, (*c*) $CH_2{\cdot}(OAc){\cdot}CH_2{\cdot}O{\cdot}CO{\cdot}C_2H_5$, (*d*) C_2H_4O,

(*e*) $MeO{\cdot}CH_2{\cdot}CH_2{\cdot}O{\cdot}CH_2{\cdot}CH_2OH$, (*f*) $O\begin{matrix}\diagup CH_2{-}CH_2 \diagdown \\ \diagdown CH_2{-}CH_2 \diagup\end{matrix}O$, (*g*) $Et_2C(OH){\cdot}C(OH)Et_2$,

(*h*) $CH_2OH{\cdot}(CH_2)_n{\cdot}CH_2OH$, where $n = 1, 2, 3$ and 4, respectively,
(*i*) $CH_2OH{\cdot}(CH_2)_6{\cdot}CH_2{\cdot}CO_2H$, (*j*) $CH_2OMe{\cdot}CHOMe{\cdot}CH_2OMe$,
(*k*) $CH_2OH{\cdot}CHOAc{\cdot}CH_2OH$.

6. Define and give examples of:—(*a*) oils, fats and waxes, (*b*) acid value, (*c*) saponification value, (*d*) iodine value, (*e*) Reichert-Meissl value, (*f*) acetyl value, (*g*) soap, (*h*) hardening of oils, (*i*) kephalins, (*j*) lecithins, (*k*) drying oils.

7. Show how you would distinguish between:
   (*a*) a mineral oil and a vegetable oil;
   (*b*) triolein and tristearin.

READING REFERENCE

Davidson, Glycol Ethers, *Ind. Eng. Chem.*, 1926, **18**, 669.
Stempel, Rearrangement of Substituted Benzopinacols, *J. Chem. Educ.*, 1946, **23**, 434.
Duncan and Lynn, The Mechanism of the Pinacol–Pinacone Rearrangement, *J.C.S.*, **1956**, 3512, 3519, 3674.
Snell, Synthetic Detergents and Surface Activity, *J. Chem. Educ.*, 1947, **24**, 505.
The Structure of Cyclopropane and Ethylene Oxide.
  Walsh, *Nature*, 1947, **159**, 165, 712.
  Robinson, *ibid.*, 1947, **159**, 400; 1947, **160**, 162.
  Linnett, *ibid.*, 1947, **160**, 162.
Levey, Synthetic Glycerol, *Ind. Eng. Chem.* (*News Ed.*), 1938, **16**, 326.
Eoff, Linder and Beyer, Glycerol from Sugar Fermentation, *Ind. Eng. Chem.*, 1919, **11**, 842.
Snell, Soap and Glycerol, *J. Chem. Educ.*, 1942, **19**, 172.
Wurster, Hydrogenation of Fats, *Ind. Eng. Chem.*, 1940, **32**, 1193.
Chen and Daubert, Synthetic Triglycerides, *J. Amer. Chem. Soc.*, 1945, **67**, 1256.
Drying Oils.
  Bradley, *Ind. Eng. Chem.*, 1937, **29**, 440; 1942, **34**, 237.
  Frilette, *ibid.*, 1946, **38**, 493.
Williams, Synthetic Fats, *Chem. and Ind.*, 1947, 251.
Hilditch, *Chemical Constitution of Natural Fats*, Wiley (1947, 2nd ed.).
Elderfield (Editor), *Heterocyclic Compounds*, Wiley, Vol. I. (1949). Ch. 1. Ethylene and Trimethylene Oxides.
Mugdan and Young, Catalytic Hydroxylation of Unsaturated Compounds, *J.C.S.*, **1949**, 2988.
Gilman, *Advanced Organic Chemistry*, Wiley (1953). Vol. III, Ch. 3. Lipids.

CHAPTER XII

UNSATURATED ALCOHOLS, ETHERS, CARBONYL COMPOUNDS AND ACIDS

UNSATURATED ALCOHOLS

THE simplest unsaturated alcohol is **vinyl alcohol,** $CH_2{:}CHOH$. This is, however, unknown; all attempts to prepare it result in the formation of acetaldehyde (together with a small amount of ethylene oxide), *e.g.*, vinyl bromide on treatment with silver oxide in boiling water gives acetaldehyde:

$$CH_2{:}CHBr + \text{“ AgOH ”} \longrightarrow AgBr + [CH_2{:}CHOH] \longrightarrow CH_3{\cdot}CHO$$

It thus appears that the group $—CH{:}CHOH$ is unstable. It should, however, be noted that this group is unstable only when the CHOH group is at the end of a chain; when it occurs in the chain, *i.e.*, as $—CH{:}C(OH)—$, it is stable (*cf.* keto-enol tautomerism, p. 206).

Although vinyl alcohol itself is unknown, many of its derivatives have been prepared, and are quite stable. These derivatives may be prepared by the interaction between acetylene and the other reactant in the presence of a suitable catalyst (see also p. 87); *e.g.*, *vinyl chloride*:

$$C_2H_2 + HCl \xrightarrow{Hg^{2+}} CH_2{:}CHCl$$

Vinyl chloride may also be prepared directly by the action of concentrated hydrochloric acid on calcium carbide in the presence of mercuric ions as catalyst:

$$CaC_2 \xrightarrow[Hg^{2+}]{HCl} CH_2{:}CHCl$$

Vinyl chloride is manufactured by the thermal decomposition of ethylene chloride at 600–650°:

$$CH_2Cl{\cdot}CH_2Cl \longrightarrow CH_2{=}CHCl + HCl$$

Vinyl chloride and *bromide* are conveniently prepared in the laboratory by heating ethylene chloride and bromide, respectively, with ethanolic potassium hydroxide:

$$CH_2Br{\cdot}CH_2Br + KOH \xrightarrow{\text{ethanol}} CH_2{:}CHBr + KBr + H_2O$$

Many of the vinyl compounds are used to make plastics. *Vinyon*, which is a thermoplastic, is a copolymer of vinyl chloride and vinyl acetate. Its main use at the moment is the manufacture of industrial filter cloth which is very resistant to the action of acids and alkalis, and which has great strength both wet and dry.

Vinyl cyanide (*acrylonitrile*) is very useful for introducing the cyanoethyl group, $\cdot CH_2{\cdot}CH_2{\cdot}CN$, by reaction with compounds containing an active methylene group. The best catalyst for **cyanoethylation** is benzyltrimethylammonium hydroxide, $C_6H_5{\cdot}CH_2{\cdot}\overset{+}{N}(CH_3)_3\}OH^-$, but in many cases an aqueous or ethanolic solution of alkalis is effective (Bruson, 1942, 1943), *e.g.*,

$$CH_3{\cdot}CO{\cdot}CH_2{\cdot}CH_3 + 2CH_2{:}CH{\cdot}CN \longrightarrow CH_3{\cdot}CO{\cdot}\underset{\textstyle CH_2{\cdot}CH_2{\cdot}CN}{\overset{\textstyle CH_2{\cdot}CH_2{\cdot}CN}{C}}{\cdot}CH_3 \qquad (90\%)$$

This type of reaction offers a means of preparing a variety of compounds. Vinyl cyanide normally causes di- or tri-cyanoethylation of compounds which have an active methylene or methyl group respectively, but Campbell *et al.* (1956) have described conditions for monocyanoethylation. In addition to active methylene and methyl groups, compounds such as primary and secondary amines, alcohols, phenols, etc., can also undergo cyanoethylation.

The halogen atom in vinyl halides is not reactive; vinyl halides do not undergo the usual double decomposition reactions of the alkyl halides and do not form Grignard reagents. They do, however, react with lithium to form lithium compounds which undergo the usual reactions (Braude, 1950–1952; see p. 345), *e.g.*,

$$R_2C{=}CHBr \xrightarrow{Li} R_2C{=}CHLi \xrightarrow{R'{\cdot}CHO} R_2C{=}CH{\cdot}CHOH{\cdot}R'$$

Substituted vinyl halides form Grignard reagents (see p. 343).

The reason for the unreactivity of the halogen atom is not clear. Some believe it to be due to resonance through which the halogen atom acquires some double-bond character, and is thereby more strongly bound to the carbon atom due to the shortening of the C—Cl bond (p. 18):

$$CH_2{=}CH{-}\ddot{\underset{\cdot\cdot}{Cl}}{:} \longleftrightarrow \overset{-}{\ddot{C}}H_2{-}CH{=}\overset{+}{\underset{\cdot\cdot}{Cl}}{:}$$

At the same time, resonance also stabilises the compound, and so the chlorine atom will not be so reactive.

The non-reactivity of the chlorine atom in vinyl chloride may be explained from the M.O. point of view as follows. Chlorine has two lone pairs of $p_n$electrons which can conjugate with the π-bond of the ethylenic link (Fig. 1). The $2p_z$ pair of orbitals of the chlorine atom will produce the greatest overlap. Thus two M.O.s will be required to accommodate these four π-electrons (*cf.* the carboxyl group, p. 172). Furthermore, since chlorine is far more electron-attracting than carbon, the electrons will tend to be found in the vicinity of the chlorine atom. Nevertheless, the chlorine atom has now lost " full control " of the lone pair, and so acquires a small positive charge (or alternatively, it is less negative than it would have been had there been no conjugation). Since two carbon atoms have acquired a share in the lone pair, each carbon atom acquires a small negative charge. Hence, owing to delocalisation of bonds (through conjugation), the vinyl chloride molecule has an increased stability. Before the chlorine atom can be displaced by some other group, the lone pair must be localised again on the chlorine atom. This requires energy, and so the chlorine is more " firmly bound " than had no conjugation occurred.

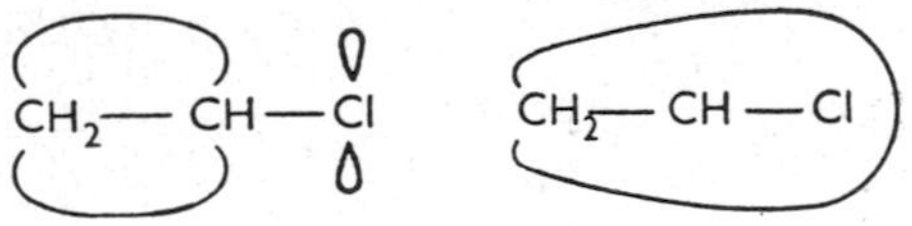

CH₂— CH—Cl   CH₂— CH —Cl

FIG. 12.1.

Allyl alcohol (*prop-2-en-1-ol*), $CH_2{:}CH{\cdot}CH_2OH$, may be prepared as follows:

(i) By boiling allyl chloride with dilute sodium hydroxide solution under pressure (this is a commercial method).

$$CH_2{=}CH{\cdot}CH_2Cl + NaOH \xrightarrow{150^\circ} CH_2{=}CH{\cdot}CH_2OH + NaCl$$

Another commercial method is the isomerisation of propylene oxide in the presence of lithium phosphate as catalyst (*cf.* p. 158).

(ii) By the controlled catalytic reduction of propargyl alcohol:

$$CH\vdots C\cdot CH_2OH \xrightarrow{H_2} CH_2{:}CH\cdot CH_2OH$$

(iii) By heating glycerol with formic acid or oxalic acid at 260°:

$$\begin{array}{l} CH_2OH \\ | \\ CHOH \\ | \\ CH_2OH \end{array} + \begin{array}{l} COOH \\ | \\ COOH \end{array} \longrightarrow \underset{\text{glyceral monoxalate}}{\begin{array}{l} CH_2\cdot O\cdot CO\cdot COOH \\ | \\ CHOH \\ | \\ CH_2OH \end{array}} \xrightarrow{-CO_2} \underset{\text{glyceryl monoformate}}{\begin{array}{l} CH_2\cdot OOC\cdot H \\ | \\ CHOH \\ | \\ CH_2OH \end{array}}$$

$$\text{glyceral monoxalate} \xrightarrow{-H_2O} \underset{\text{dioxalin}}{\begin{array}{l} CH_2\cdot O\cdot CO \\ |\qquad\quad | \\ CH\cdot O\cdot CO \\ | \\ CH_2OH \end{array}} \xrightarrow{-2CO_2} \begin{array}{l} CH_2 \\ \| \\ CH \\ | \\ CH_2OH \end{array}$$

$$\text{glyceryl monoformate} \xrightarrow{-CO_2-H_2O} \begin{array}{l} CH_2 \\ \| \\ CH \\ | \\ CH_2OH \end{array}$$

In practice it is better to use formic acid since this gives a higher yield (45–47 per cent.).

Allyl alcohol is a colourless, pungent-smelling liquid, b.p. 97°, miscible with water in all proportions. The presence of the allyl group produces a pungent smell in compounds containing it, *e.g.*, mustard oils contain allyl *iso*thiocyanate; onions and garlic, allyl sulphide.

Allyl alcohol has the properties of an unsaturated compound and a primary alcohol. It is oxidised to glycerol by dilute alkaline permanganate:

$$CH_2{:}CH\cdot CH_2OH + H_2O + [O] \longrightarrow CH_2OH\cdot CHOH\cdot CH_2OH$$

If it is desired to oxidise the alcoholic group in allyl alcohol, it is necessary to " protect " the double bond since this is also attacked by many of the oxidising agents usually employed for oxidising alcohols. " Protection " of the double bond is conveniently carried out by the addition of bromine which is subsequently removed by zinc dust in methanolic solution; *e.g.*, allyl alcohol may be oxidised to acrylic acid as follows:

$$CH_2{:}CH\cdot CH_2OH \xrightarrow{Br_2} CH_2Br\cdot CHBr\cdot CH_2OH \xrightarrow[HNO_3]{[O]}$$
$$CH_2Br\cdot CHBr\cdot CO_2H \xrightarrow{Zn/CH_3OH} CH_2{:}CH\cdot CO_2H$$

Allyl alcohol adds on chlorine or bromine to form the corresponding 2 : 3-dihalogeno-propan-1-ol. Allyl alcohol also adds on halogen acids and hypohalous acids, but the addition takes place *contrary* to Markownikoff's rule, *e.g.*, glycerol β-monochlorohydrin is formed with hypochlorous acid:

$$CH_2{:}CH\cdot CH_2OH + HOCl \longrightarrow CH_2OH\cdot CHCl\cdot CH_2OH$$

This may be due to the presence of the oxygen atom which exerts a strong inductive effect causing the electromeric effect to take place *towards* the oxygen atom, *i.e.*,

$$CH_2 \overset{\curvearrowright}{=} CH \succ CH_2 \succ OH$$

The allyl halides form an interesting group of compounds because of the high reactivity of the halogen atom.

Allyl chloride (3-*chloropropene*), b.p. 45°, is prepared industrially by the chlorination of propylene at high temperature. It may be conveniently prepared in the laboratory by warming allyl alcohol with hydrochloric acid:

$$CH_2{:}CH{\cdot}CH_2OH + HCl \longrightarrow CH_2{:}CH{\cdot}CH_2Cl + H_2O$$

It is now important as a chemical raw material for the production of drugs, plastics, etc.

Allyl bromide (3-*bromopropene*), b.p. 70°, is best prepared in the laboratory by distilling aqueous allyl alcohol with 48 per cent. hydrobromic acid in the presence of sulphuric acid:

$$CH_2{:}CH{\cdot}CH_2OH + HBr \longrightarrow CH_2{:}CH{\cdot}CH_2Br + H_2O \quad (92\text{–}96\%)$$

Allyl iodide (3-*iodopropene*), b.p. 103·1°, may be prepared by heating glycerol with a small amount of hydriodic acid (p. 242).

The halogen atom in the allyl halides is very reactive, and it has been found experimentally that the position of the double bond with respect to the halogen atom determines the reactivity of the halogen atom. In compounds of the type C:C—X, the halogen atom X is unreactive (see vinyl halides, above). In C:C·C—X, X is more reactive than in the alkyl halides (and the allyl halides also form Grignard reagents). When the halogen atom in an unsaturated compound is further removed from the double bond than in the allyl position, it behaves similarly to the halogen atom in alkyl halides; *e.g.*, 4-chlorobut-1-ene, $CH_2{:}CH{\cdot}CH_2{\cdot}CH_2Cl$, undergoes the usual reactions of the alkyl halides with reagents that do not affect the double bond.

Thus in the compound of the type $CH_2{:}CH{\cdot}CH_2$—Z, *i.e.*, the *allyl type*, the substituent Z is very reactive: Z may be chlorine, bromine, iodine or the hydroxyl group. Z may even be hydrogen, *e.g.*, a hydrogen atom in propylene is replaced by chlorine at 400–600° to form allyl chloride or by bromine at low temperature by means of *N*-bromosuccinimide (Ziegler, 1942) to form allyl bromide (see p. 358).

The allyl halides add on the halogen acids to form a mixture of the 1 : 2- and 1 : 3-dihalides. The addition of hydrogen bromide to allyl bromide has been studied in great detail (Kharasch, 1933):

$$CH_2{:}CH{\cdot}CH_2Br + HBr \longrightarrow \underset{1:3\text{-dibromide}}{CH_2Br{\cdot}CH_2{\cdot}CH_2Br} + \underset{1:2\text{-dibromide}}{CH_3{\cdot}CHBr{\cdot}CH_2Br}$$

In the presence of peroxides, the 1 : 3-dibromide is obtained in 90 per cent. yield. In the absence of peroxides, the 1 : 2-dibromide is obtained in 90 per cent. yield. When allyl bromide, which has not been carefully purified, is treated with hydrogen bromide, without special precautions being taken to exclude all traces of air, a mixture of the 1 : 2- and 1 : 3-dibromides is obtained.

In view of the relatively high electron affinity of the halogen atom, it might have been expected that the addition of halogen acids and hypohalous acids would take place contrary to Markownikoff's rule to produce the 1 : 3-dihalide (*cf.* allyl alcohol, above). It is, however, difficult to explain the formation of the 1 : 2-dihalide. A possible explanation may be obtained from a consideration of *hyperconjugation*. According to Baker and Nathan (1935), the methyl group in propylene (and in certain other compounds) is more electron-releasing than is expected by the inductive effect. They suggested that the methyl group permits additional electron-release by a mechanism exhibited to a very small extent or not at all, in other alkyl groups. *The phenomenon is exhibited when the methyl group is attached to an unsaturated carbon atom* (see also p. 496).

There are various ways of looking at the *Baker–Nathan effect.* According to one view (Mulliken and co-workers, 1941), the methyl group in propylene should be written $H_3{\equiv}C{-}CH{=}CH_2$. This quasi-triple bond is considered to be analogous to an ordinary triple bond, and therefore conjugation is present above the ordinary (as in, *e.g.*, butadiene). Resonance can then be assumed as follows, the two electrons spinning in opposite directions to form a formal bond (p. 81).

$$H_3{\equiv}C{-}CH{=}CH_2 \longleftrightarrow \dot{H}_3{=}C{=}CH{-}\dot{C}H_2 \text{ or } \dot{H}_3{=}C{=}CH{-}\dot{C}H_2$$

It can be seen from the above that hyperconjugation is conjugation between electrons of a *single* bond and those of a *multiple* bond.

The heat of hydrogenation is probably the most reliable method for determining the resonance energy of an unsaturated compound. The observed heat of hydrogenation of propylene is less than the calculated value, *i.e.*, propylene is more stable than anticipated from its structure $CH_3{\cdot}CH{:}CH_2$. This would be explained by the resonance which results from *hyperconjugation* (the name which Mulliken gave the Baker–Nathan effect).

An alternative approach to hyperconjugation is to regard the resonating structures of propylene as follows:

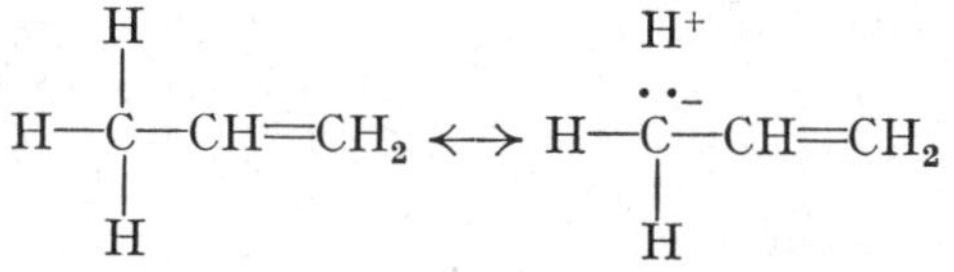

$$H{-}\underset{H}{\overset{H}{C}}{-}CH{=}CH_2 \longleftrightarrow H{-}\underset{H}{\overset{H^+}{\ddot{C}^-}}{-}CH{=}CH_2$$

Looking at it from this point of view, hyperconjugation may be regarded as "*no-bond resonance*". The hydrogen atoms are not *free*; the effect of no-bond resonance is a *weakening* of the C—H bond. This approach may now be used to explain the formation of the mixture of 1 : 2- and 1 : 3-dihalides when halogen acid adds on to allyl chloride. The electromeric effect in allyl halides can take place in two ways. In the first, the electromeric effect takes place *towards* the chlorine atom resulting in the formation of the 1 : 3-dihalide (see above):

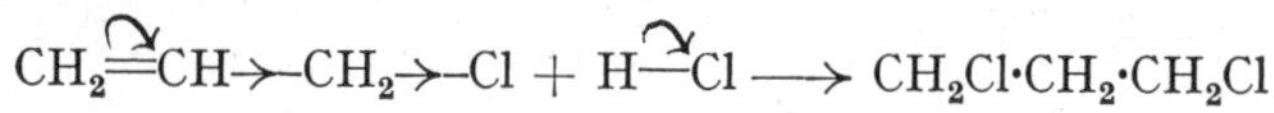

$$CH_2{=}CH{\rightarrow}CH_2{\rightarrow}Cl + H{-}Cl \longrightarrow CH_2Cl{\cdot}CH_2{\cdot}CH_2Cl$$

In the second, the electromeric effect takes place *away* from the chlorine atom because of hyperconjugation which produces a negative charge on the carbon atom of the C—Cl bond, thereby causing this atom to repel electrons; thus the 1 : 2-dihalide is produced:

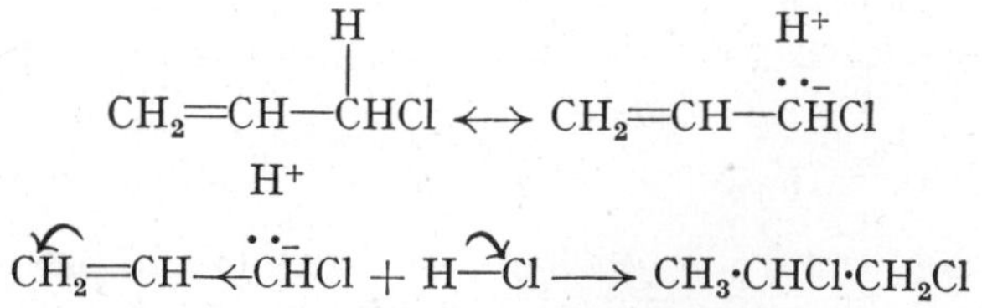

$$CH_2{=}CH{-}\overset{H}{C}HCl \longleftrightarrow CH_2{=}CH{-}\overset{H^+}{\ddot{C}^-}HCl$$

$$CH_2{=}CH{\leftarrow}\overset{H^+}{\ddot{C}^-}HCl + H{-}Cl \longrightarrow CH_3{\cdot}CHCl{\cdot}CH_2Cl$$

It may therefore be imagined that in allyl halides the inductive effect and hyperconjugation both operate, resulting in a mixture of the 1 : 2- and 1 : 3-dihalides. Although this scheme is purely qualitative, it can be appreciated that the extent to which each effect operates will undoubtedly depend on the conditions of the experiment.

It might also be noted, in passing, that hyperconjugation may be used to explain the reactivity of the halogen atom in allyl halides. As shown above, the carbon atom of the C—X group acquires a negative charge. This carbon atom therefore repels the electrons of the C—X bond, thereby facilitating the release of a halide ion.

Hyperconjugation can be used to explain Markownikoff's rule.

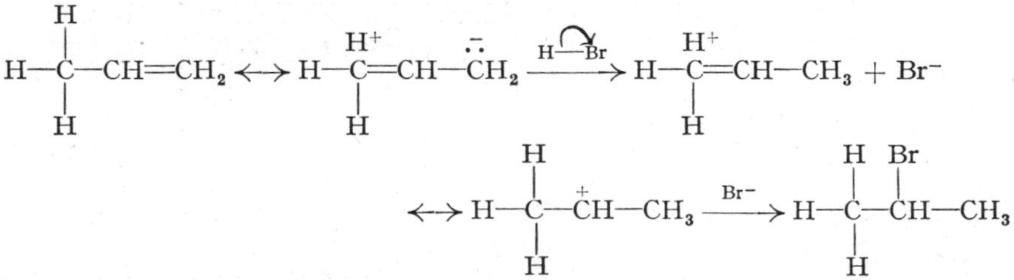

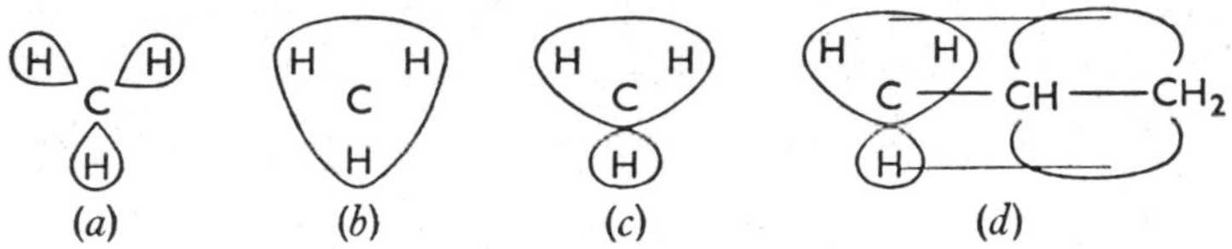

$$H_3C—CH{=}CH_2 \longleftrightarrow H^+\,H_2C{=}CH—\overset{..}{C}H_2^- \xrightarrow{H—Br} H^+\,H_2C{=}CH—CH_3 + Br^-$$

$$\longleftrightarrow H_3C—\overset{+}{C}H—CH_3 \xrightarrow{Br^-} H_3C—CHBr—CH_3$$

(a) (b) (c) (d)

FIG. 12.2.

From the M.O. point of view, hyperconjugation may be explained as follows π-Orbitals can overlap with other π-orbitals to produce conjugation (p. 82). π-Orbitals, however, can also overlap to a certain extent with adjacent σ-orbitals to form extended orbitals. When this occurs we have *hyperconjugation*, and this phenomenon is exhibited mainly by the hydrogen bonds in a *methyl* group when this group is attached to an unsaturated carbon atom. The question is: how does this overlapping occur? Coulson (1942) treats the methyl group (Fig. 2*a*) as a "compound" atom to form a "group" orbital (Fig. *b*). An alternative "group" orbital may also be formed as in (*c*). In this arrangement, the methyl group behaves as a group with a π-orbital, and this can conjugate with an adjacent π-bond in, *e.g.*, propylene (Fig. *d*). Hence, owing to partial delocalisation of bonds (σ and π) in this way, the propylene molecule is more stable than "expected".

The unusual reactivity of the halogen atom in allyl halides may be explained as follows. If the chlorine were to ionise, the carbon atom to which it was attached now has a positive charge and has only *six* electrons. Hence the π-bond covering the other two carbon atoms can extend to embrace this third carbon atom. The net result is an M.O. covering *three* carbon atoms, and so the delocalisation energy will be increased, *i.e.*, the new arrangement is stabilised, and behaves as if the chlorine atom is ionic (Fig. 3).

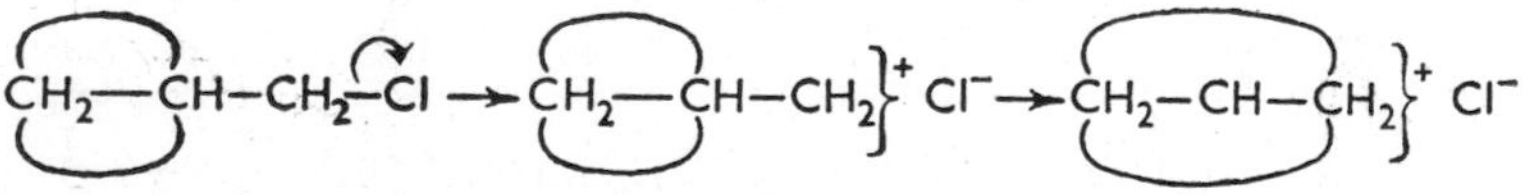

$$CH_2—CH—CH_2—Cl \rightarrow \{CH_2—CH—CH_2\}^+ Cl^- \rightarrow \{CH_2—CH—CH_2\}^+ Cl^-$$

FIG. 12.3.

Crotyl alcohol (*crotonyl alcohol, but-2-en-1-ol*), $CH_3{\cdot}CH{:}CH{\cdot}CH_2OH$, may be prepared by the reduction of crotonaldehyde with aluminium *iso*-propoxide (p. 140):

$$CH_3{\cdot}CH{:}CH{\cdot}CHO \xrightarrow{[(CH_3)_2CHO]_3Al} CH_3{\cdot}CH{:}CH{\cdot}CH_2OH \quad (85\text{–}90\%)$$

Crotyl alcohol is a colourless liquid, b.p. 118°, fairly soluble in water. When treated with hydrogen bromide, crotyl alcohol produces a mixture of crotyl bromide and methylvinylcarbinyl bromide:

$$CH_3{\cdot}CH{:}CH{\cdot}CH_2OH \xrightarrow{HBr} CH_3{\cdot}CH{:}CH{\cdot}CH_2Br + CH_3{\cdot}CHBr{\cdot}CH{:}CH_2$$

Both of these bromides are also obtained when *methylvinylcarbinol*, $CH_3{\cdot}CHOH{\cdot}CH{:}CH_2$, is treated with hydrogen bromide.

When either crotyl bromide or methylvinylcarbinyl bromide is treated with moist silver oxide, a mixture of crotyl alcohol and methylvinylcarbinol is obtained:

$$\left.\begin{array}{l} CH_3{\cdot}CH{:}CH{\cdot}CH_2Br \xrightarrow{\text{"AgOH"}} \\ CH_3{\cdot}CHBr{\cdot}CH{:}CH_2 \xrightarrow{\text{"AgOH"}} \end{array}\right\} CH_3{\cdot}CH{:}CH{\cdot}CH_2OH + CH_3{\cdot}CHOH{\cdot}CH{:}CH_2$$

These rearrangements are examples of the **allylic rearrangement**, and a suggested mechanism is that it takes place via the intermediate formation of a resonating cation (S_N1 reaction):

$$CH_3{\cdot}CH{:}CH{\cdot}CH_2OH \xrightarrow{-OH^-} CH_3{\cdot}CH{:}CH{\cdot}\overset{+}{C}H_2 \longleftrightarrow CH_3{\cdot}\overset{+}{C}H{\cdot}CH{:}CH_2$$

Thus the bromide ion (or the hydroxyl ion) can attach itself to one or other positive carbon atom, resulting in a mixture of bromides (or alcohols). If this be the correct mechanism, then it is to be expected that each alcohol should give the same mixture of bromides. This, however, is not so in practice, each alcohol giving a higher proportion of its corresponding bromide. Thus the reaction proceeds by a different mechanism altogether, or it may proceed partly by the above mechanism and partly (and simultaneously) by a different mechanism in which the hydroxyl ion is directly displaced by the bromide ion, *i.e.*, by an S_N2 reaction (*cf.* the alkyl halides, p. 99). Work by Young and Lane (1938) shows that the rearrangement can be explained by the two independent, simultaneous reactions. The allylic rearrangement is one example of anionotropy (p. 207), and when it occurs by an S_N1 mechanism it is often denoted by S_N1'; similarly, when the rearrangement occurs by an S_N2 mechanism, it is denoted by S_N2'.

A number of unsaturated alcohols occur in *essential oils*. The essential oils are volatile oils with pleasant odours, and are obtained from various plants to which they impart their characteristic odours. They are widely used in the perfume industry. **Citronellol** occurs in citronella oil, rose oil, etc. It appears to be a mixture of the two structural isomers I and II:

$$(CH_3)_2C{:}CH{\cdot}CH_2{\cdot}CH_2{\cdot}CH(CH_3){\cdot}CH_2{\cdot}CH_2OH \quad \text{(I)}$$

$$\text{(II)} \quad CH_2{:}C(CH_3){\cdot}CH_2{\cdot}CH_2{\cdot}CH_2{\cdot}CH(CH_3)\ CH_2{\cdot}CH_2OH$$

Geraniol and **nerol** are *cis-trans* isomers of the following structure (and possibly of the structure corresponding to II above):

$$(CH_3)_2C{:}CH\ CH_2{\cdot}CH_2{\cdot}C(CH_3){:}CH{\cdot}CH_2OH$$

Geraniol is a constituent of geranium oil, rose oil, etc. Nerol occurs in neroli oil, etc. **Linalool,** which is an isomer of geraniol and nerol, occurs in linaloe oil, lavender oil, coriander oil, etc.:

$$(CH_3)_2C{:}CH{\cdot}CH_2{\cdot}CH_2{\cdot}C(OH){\cdot}(CH_3){\cdot}CH{:}CH_2$$

These alcohols are the oxygen derivatives of the group of compounds known as the *open-chain terpenes*. It appears that all of these alcohols are mixtures of structural isomers (see citronellol, above). It is possible, however, that the two structures form a three-carbon tautomeric system:

$$\begin{array}{ccc} \quad\;\; CH_3 & & \quad\;\; CH_3 \\ \quad\;\; | & & \quad\;\; | \\ CH_3{-}C{=}CH\cdots & \rightleftharpoons & CH_2{=}C{-}CH_2\cdots \end{array}$$

Farnesol, a *sesquiterpene* alcohol, occurs in rose oil, the oil from ambrette seeds, etc., and, like the terpene alcohols, is a mixture of two forms, one of which is:

$$(CH_3)_2C{:}CH{\cdot}CH_2{\cdot}CH_2{\cdot}C(CH_3){:}CH{\cdot}CH_2{\cdot}CH_2{\cdot}C(CH_3){:}CH{\cdot}CH_2OH$$

Phytol is an unsaturated alcohol which occurs in chlorophyll (the green colouring matter of leaves and other parts of a plant). Its structure is:

$$\begin{array}{l} (CH_3)_2CH{\cdot}(CH_2)_3{\cdot}\underset{\displaystyle CH_3}{\underset{|}{CH}}{\cdot}(CH_2)_3{\cdot}\underset{\displaystyle CH_3}{\underset{|}{CH}}{\cdot}(CH_2)_3{\cdot}\underset{\displaystyle CH_3}{\underset{|}{C}}{:}CH{\cdot}CH_2OH \end{array}$$

The simplest acetylenic alcohol is **propargyl alcohol** (*prop-2-yn-1-ol*), $CH{:}C{\cdot}CH_2OH$. This may be prepared from 1 : 2 : 3-tribromopropane by the following series of reactions, which clearly show the difference in reactivity of the bromine atoms, and at the same time illustrate the use of aqueous and ethanolic solutions of potassium hydroxide:

$$CH_2Br{\cdot}CHBr{\cdot}CH_2Br \xrightarrow[KOH]{\text{ethanolic}} CH_2{:}CBr{\cdot}CH_2Br \xrightarrow[KOH]{\text{aqueous}}$$

$$CH_2{:}CBr{\cdot}CH_2OH \xrightarrow[KOH]{\text{ethanolic}} CH{:}C{\cdot}CH_2OH$$

Propargyl alcohol (together with butyne-diol) is prepared by the interaction of acetylene and formaldehyde in the presence of silver or cuprous acetylide as catalyst:

$$C_2H_2 + H{\cdot}CHO \xrightarrow{Ag_2C_2} CH{:}C{\cdot}CH_2OH$$

$$C_2H_2 + 2H{\cdot}CHO \xrightarrow{Ag_2C_2} CH_2OH{\cdot}C{:}C{\cdot}CH_2OH$$

Propargyl alcohol is a colourless liquid, b.p. 114°. It behaves in many ways like acetylene, *e.g.*, it adds on two or four bromine atoms, and forms the silver or cuprous compounds when treated with an ammoniacal solution of silver nitrate or cuprous chloride. It may be catalytically reduced to allyl and *n*-propyl alcohols; it is now being used to prepare these two compounds commercially.

UNSATURATED ETHERS

The simplest unsaturated ether is methyl vinyl ether, $CH_3{\cdot}O{\cdot}CH{:}CH_2$, which is prepared industrially by passing acetylene into methanol at 160–200° in the presence of 1–2 per cent. potassium methoxide, and under pressure sufficient to prevent boiling:

$$C_2H_2 + CH_3OH \longrightarrow CH_3{\cdot}O{\cdot}CH{:}CH_2$$

The acetylene is diluted with nitrogen to prevent explosions.

Methyl vinyl ether is a very reactive gas, b.p. 5–6°. It is hydrolysed rapidly by dilute acid at room temperature to give methanol and acetaldehyde (*cf.* the ethers).

$$CH_3{\cdot}O{\cdot}CH{:}CH_2 + H_2O \longrightarrow CH_3OH + CH_3{\cdot}CHO$$

This is a potential industrial method for preparing acetaldehyde. Methyl vinyl ether is stable in alkaline solution. It undergoes many addition reactions at the double bond, *e.g.*,

$$CH_2{:}CH{\cdot}O{\cdot}CH_3 + HCl \xrightarrow{0^\circ} CH_3{\cdot}CHCl{\cdot}O{\cdot}CH_3$$

$$CH_2{:}CH{\cdot}O{\cdot}CH_3 + CH_3OH \xrightarrow[\text{trace of HCl}]{25^\circ} CH_3{\cdot}CH(OCH_3)_2$$

It readily polymerises, and is used for making polyvinyl ether plastics.

Divinyl ether (*vinyl ether*), $CH_2{:}CH{\cdot}O{\cdot}CH{:}CH_2$, may be prepared by heating ethylene chlorohydrin with sulphuric acid, and then passing the product, 2:2′-dichlorodiethyl ether, over potassium hydroxide at 200–240°:

$$2ClCH_2{\cdot}CH_2OH \xrightarrow[(-H_2O)]{H_2SO_4} \underset{(75\%)}{ClCH_2{\cdot}CH_2{\cdot}O{\cdot}CH_2{\cdot}CH_2Cl} \xrightarrow[(-2HCl)]{KOH} \underset{(25\%)}{CH_2{:}CH{\cdot}O{\cdot}CH{:}CH_2}$$

Divinyl ether is a colourless liquid, b.p. 39°. It is used as an anaesthetic, being better for this purpose than diethyl ether.

UNSATURATED ALDEHYDES

The simplest unsaturated aldehyde is **acraldehyde** (*acrolein, prop-2-en-1-al*), $CH_2{:}CH{\cdot}CHO$. This is conveniently prepared by heating glycerol with potassium hydrogen sulphate, which is the most satisfacto.y dehydrating agent for this reaction:

$$CH_2OH{\cdot}CHOH{\cdot}CH_2OH \xrightarrow{-2H_2O} CH_2{:}CH{\cdot}CHO \quad (33\text{–}48\%)$$

Acraldehyde is prepared industrially in many ways, *e.g.*,

(i) by passing a mixture of acetaldehyde and formaldehyde vapour over sodium silicate as catalyst:

$$CH_3{\cdot}CHO + CH_2O \longrightarrow CH_2{=}CH{\cdot}CHO + H_2O$$

(ii) By the direct oxidation of propylene:

$$CH_2{=}CH{\cdot}CH_3 + O_2 \longrightarrow CH_2{=}CH{\cdot}CHO + H_2O.$$

(iii) By the pyrolysis of diallyl ether:

$$(CH_2{=}CH{\cdot}CH_2{-})_2O \longrightarrow CH_2{=}CH{\cdot}CHO + CH_3{\cdot}CH{=}CH_2 + H_2$$

Acraldehyde is a colourless liquid, b.p. 52°, with a pungent, irritating odour. It is unstable, readily polymerising to a white solid. It is an αβ-unsaturated aldehyde, and undergoes many of the usual reactions of an olefin and an aldehyde, *e.g.*, it adds on two halogen atoms or a molecule of halogen acid (contrary to Markownikoff's rule; *cf.* allyl alcohol):

$$CH_2{:}CH{\cdot}CHO + Br_2 \longrightarrow CH_2Br{\cdot}CHBr{\cdot}CHO$$

$$CH_2{:}CH{\cdot}CHO + HCl \longrightarrow CH_2Cl{\cdot}CH_2{\cdot}CHO$$

The addition of hydrogen bromide is unaffected by the presence of peroxides. Acraldehyde reduces ammoniacal silver nitrate, forms a cyanohydrin with hydrogen cyanide, and a phenylhydrazone witn phenylhydrazine:

$$CH_2{:}CH{\cdot}CHO + [O] \xrightarrow{AgNO_3} CH_2{:}CH{\cdot}CO_2H$$

$$CH_2{:}CH{\cdot}CHO + HCN \longrightarrow CH_2{:}CH{\cdot}CH(OH){\cdot}CN$$

$$CH_2{:}CH{\cdot}CHO + C_6H_5{\cdot}NH{\cdot}NH_2 \longrightarrow CH_2{:}CH{\cdot}CH{:}N{\cdot}NH{\cdot}C_6H_5 + H_2O$$

Acraldehyde undergoes the Tischenko reaction (p. 149) to form allyl acrylate:

$$2CH_2{:}CH{\cdot}CHO \xrightarrow{(C_2H_5O)_3Al} CH_2{:}CH{\cdot}CO_2CH_2{\cdot}CH{:}CH_2$$

It does not, however, undergo the normal aldol condensation; instead, in the presence of alkali, cleavage of the molecule takes place:

$$CH_2{:}CH{\cdot}CHO + H_2O \overset{NaOH}{\rightleftharpoons} H{\cdot}CHO + CH_3{\cdot}CHO$$

This reaction is actually the reversal of the aldol condensation, and is characteristic of αβ-unsaturated aldehydes.

When acraldehyde is reduced with metal and acid, there are obtained an unsaturated alcohol, a saturated aldehyde, a saturated alcohol, and a compound formed by bimolecular reduction:

$$CH_2{:}CH{\cdot}CHO \xrightarrow{[H]} CH_2{:}CH{\cdot}CH_2OH + CH_3{\cdot}CH_2{\cdot}CHO + CH_3{\cdot}CH_2{\cdot}CH_2OH + CH_2{:}CH{\cdot}CHOH{\cdot}CHOH{\cdot}CH{:}CH_2$$

A good yield of the bimolecular product is obtained by reducing acraldehyde with magnesium amalgam (*cf.* pinacol, p. 239). Acraldehyde is reduced by sodium amalgam to *n*-propanol and by aluminium *iso*propoxide (Meerwein–Ponndorf–Verley reduction, p. 140) to allyl alcohol. It should be noted that metal and acid do not usually reduce a double bond; it is only when the double bond is in the αβ-position with respect to a carbonyl group that it is reduced in this way (see also below). αβ-Unsaturated aldehydes may be catalytically reduced to unsaturated alcohols by means of a platinum catalyst in the presence of traces of ferrous sulphate and zinc acetate; the former promotes reduction of the aldehyde group and the latter inhibits reduction of the double bond (Adams *et al.*, 1927). When Raney nickel is used as catalyst at fairly low temperatures and pressures, the product is a saturated aldehyde, but at higher temperatures and pressures the product is a saturated alcohol. Goldberg *et al.* (1955) have shown that the double bond of αβ-unsaturated aldehydes may be selectively reduced by catalytic hydrogenation with a Raney nickel catalyst of the Schiff's base (p. 542) formed with 2-aminobutan-1-ol, followed by hydrolysis.

αβ-Unsaturated aldehydes (and ketones) may be reduced to the unsaturated alcohols by lithium aluminium hydride, *e.g.*,

$$CH_3{\cdot}CH{=}CH{\cdot}CHO \xrightarrow{LiAlH_4} CH_3{\cdot}CH{=}CH{\cdot}CH_2OH$$

If, however, a phenyl group is attached to the β-carbon atom, the double bond is also reduced (see cinnamic acid, p. 662).

Acraldehyde adds on to butadiene to form a cyclic compound (see the *Diels–Alder* reaction, p. 450):

$$\begin{matrix} & CH_2 & & & & CH_2 & \\ HC\!\!\nearrow & & CH_2 & & HC & & CH_2 \\ | & + & \| & \longrightarrow & \| & & | \\ HC\!\!\searrow & & CH{\cdot}CHO & & HC & & CH{\cdot}CHO \\ & CH_2 & & & & CH_2 & \end{matrix}$$

Crotonaldehyde (*but-2-en-1-al*), $CH_3{\cdot}CH{:}CH{\cdot}CHO$, may be prepared by heating aldol alone, or better, with a dehydrating agent, *e.g.*, zinc chloride. The best yield is obtained by distilling aldol with acetic acid as catalyst:

$$CH_3{\cdot}CHOH{\cdot}CH_2{\cdot}CHO \xrightarrow{-H_2O} CH_3{\cdot}CH{:}CH{\cdot}CHO$$

Crotonaldehyde is a colourless liquid, b.p. 104°. It closely resembles acraldehyde in its chemical properties. It exists, however, in two geometrical isomeric forms, *cis* and *trans*:

$$\begin{array}{c} H-C-CH_3 \\ \| \\ H-C-CHO \\ \textit{cis} \end{array} \qquad \begin{array}{c} CH_3-C-H \\ \| \\ H-C-CHO \\ \textit{trans} \end{array}$$

Catalytic reduction (Raney nickel) of crotonaldehyde in the presence of chloroform gives butyraldehyde; in the absence of chloroform, butanol is formed (Cornubert *et al.*, 1950).

A number of unsaturated aldehydes occur naturally in the essential oils, many accompanying the corresponding unsaturated alcohol, *e.g.*, citral or geranial, neral, citronellal.

The simplest acetylenic aldehyde is **propargylaldehyde** (propiolaldehyde, propynal), $CH{:}C{\cdot}CHO$. This may be prepared from acraldehyde, the aldehyde group of which must be "protected" by acetal formation:

$$CH_2{:}CH{\cdot}CHO + 2C_2H_5OH \underset{}{\overset{HCl}{\rightleftharpoons}} H_2O + CH_2{:}CH{\cdot}CH(OC_2H_5)_2 \xrightarrow{Br_2}$$

$$CH_2Br{\cdot}CHBr{\cdot}CH(OC_2H_5)_2 \xrightarrow[KOH]{\text{ethanolic}} CH{:}C{\cdot}CH(OC_2H_5)_2 \xrightarrow[HCl]{\text{dilute}} CH{:}C{\cdot}CHO$$

It may also be obtained by the controlled oxidation of propargyl alcohol.

Propargylaldehyde is a liquid, b.p. 60°, which undergoes cleavage when treated with sodium hydroxide (*cf.* acraldehyde, above):

$$CH{:}C{\cdot}CHO + NaOH \longrightarrow CH{:}CH + H{\cdot}CO_2Na$$

UNSATURATED KETONES

The simplest unsaturated ketone is **methyl vinyl ketone** (*but-3-en-2-one*), $CH_3{\cdot}CO{\cdot}CH{:}CH_2$. This may be prepared by means of an aldol condensation between formaldehyde and acetone, the product being dehydrated by heat:

$$H{\cdot}CHO + CH_3{\cdot}CO{\cdot}CH_3 \xrightarrow{NaOH} CH_2OH{\cdot}CH_2{\cdot}CO{\cdot}CH_3 \xrightarrow{-H_2O} CH_2{:}CH{\cdot}CO{\cdot}CH_3$$

It may also be prepared by the action of acetic anhydride on ethylene in the presence of zinc chloride as catalyst:

$$CH_2{:}CH_2 + (CH_3{\cdot}CO)_2O \xrightarrow{ZnCl_2} CH_2{:}CH{\cdot}CO{\cdot}CH_3 + CH_3{\cdot}CO_2H$$

It is manufactured by hydrating vinylacetylene in the presence of dilute sulphuric acid and mercuric sulphate (*cf.* acetaldehyde, p. 155):

$$CH_2{:}CH{\cdot}C{:}CH + H_2O \longrightarrow CH_2{:}CH{\cdot}CO{\cdot}CH_3$$

Methyl vinyl ketone is a liquid, b.p. 79°, which polymerises on standing. It is used commercially as the starting material for plastics.

Mesityl oxide (4-methylpent-3-en-2-one), $(CH_3)_2C{:}CH{\cdot}CO{\cdot}CH_3$, may be prepared by distilling diacetone alcohol (*q.v.*) with a trace of iodine:

$$(CH_3)_2C(OH){\cdot}CH_2{\cdot}CO{\cdot}CH_3 \xrightarrow{-H_2O} (CH_3)_2C{:}CH{\cdot}CO{\cdot}CH_3 \quad (90\%)$$

Stross *et al.* (1947) have shown that mesityl oxide prepared this way is a mixture of mesityl oxide and iso*mesityl oxide*, $CH_2{:}C(CH_3){\cdot}CH_2{\cdot}CO{\cdot}CH_3$.

Mesityl oxide may also be prepared as follows:

$$(CH_3)_2C{:}CH_2 + CH_3{\cdot}COCl \xrightarrow{ZnCl_2} (CH_3)_2CCl{\cdot}CH_2{\cdot}CO{\cdot}CH_3$$

$$\xrightarrow{-HCl} (CH_3)_2C{:}CH{\cdot}CO{\cdot}CH_3$$

Mesityl oxide is a liquid, b.p. 130°, with a peppermint smell. It is used as a solvent for oils, gums, etc.

Phorone (2:6-dimethylhepta-2:5-dien-4-one), $(CH_3)_2C{:}CH{\cdot}CO{\cdot}CH{:}C(CH_3)_2$, may be prepared by the action of hydrochloric acid on acetone:

$$3CH_3{\cdot}CO{\cdot}CH_3 \xrightarrow{HCl} (CH_3)_2C{:}CH{\cdot}CO{\cdot}CH{:}C(CH_3)_2 + 2H_2O$$

Phorone is a yellow, crystalline solid, m.p. 28°, b.p. 198°.

αβ-Unsaturated ketones show very marked additive properties at the olefinic double bond. They may be reduced catalytically (platinum or nickel catalyst) to saturated ketones, since the olefinic linkage is more rapidly reduced than the keto group. If the hydrogenation is carried further, saturated alcohols are produced:

$$R{\cdot}CH{:}CH{\cdot}CO{\cdot}R' \xrightarrow[Pt]{H_2} R{\cdot}CH_2{\cdot}CH_2{\cdot}CO{\cdot}R' \xrightarrow[Pt]{H_2} R{\cdot}CH_2{\cdot}CH_2{\cdot}CHOH{\cdot}R'$$

Cornubert *et al.* (1954) have shown that the double bond may be selectively reduced by catalytic hydrogenation (Raney nickel) if the reaction is carried out in ethylene chloride solution.

Reduction with metal and acid, or better, with magnesium amalgam, gives bimolecular products (*cf.* acraldehyde, above):

$$2(CH_3)_2C{:}CH{\cdot}CO{\cdot}CH_3 \xrightarrow{Mg/Hg} \begin{array}{l} (CH_3)_2C{\cdot}CH_2{\cdot}CO{\cdot}CH_3 \\ \quad\;\; | \\ (CH_3)_2C{\cdot}CH_2{\cdot}CO{\cdot}CH_3 \end{array}$$

αβ-Unsaturated ketones add on halogens in the usual way. The addition of the halogen acids usually takes place by the hydrogen atom becoming attached to the α-carbon atom, and the halogen atom to the β-carbon atom. This is to be expected when we consider the strong inductive effect of the carbonyl group (*cf.* allyl alcohol, above):

$$R{\cdot}CH{=}CH{\rightarrow}CO{\leftarrow}R' + H{-}X \longrightarrow R{\cdot}CHX{\cdot}CH_2{\cdot}CO{\cdot}R'$$

The αβ-unsaturated ketones add on ammonia, primary amines and secondary amines to form β-amino compounds; with ammonia, mesityl oxide forms diacetonamine, and phorone forms triacetonamine:

$$(CH_3)_2C{:}CH{\cdot}CO{\cdot}CH_3 + NH_3 \longrightarrow (CH_3)_2C(NH_2){\cdot}CH_2{\cdot}CO{\cdot}CH_3$$

$$(CH_3)_2C{:}CH{\cdot}CO{\cdot}CH{:}C(CH_3)_2 + 2NH_3 \longrightarrow$$

$$\left[\begin{array}{l}(CH_3)_2C{\cdot}CH_2{\cdot}CO{\cdot}CH_2{\cdot}C(CH_3)_2 \\ \qquad\;\; | \qquad\qquad\qquad\quad\;\; | \\ \qquad NH_2 \qquad\qquad\quad\;\; NH_2\end{array}\right] \xrightarrow{-NH_3} CO\begin{array}{l} \diagup CH_2{-}C(CH_3)_2 \\ \qquad\qquad\quad \searrow NH \\ \diagdown CH_2{-}C(CH_3)_2 \nearrow \end{array}$$

This type of addition may possibly take place through what is known as the 1 : 4-*mechanism*:

$$\underset{\displaystyle R'}{R{-}\overset{4}{C}H{=}\overset{3}{C}H{-}\overset{2}{C}{=}\overset{1}{O}} \longrightarrow R{-}\overset{+}{C}H{-}CH{=}\underset{\displaystyle R'}{C}{-}\overset{-}{O} \xrightarrow{:NH_3} R{-}\underset{\displaystyle H{-}\overset{+}{N}{-}H \atop H}{CH}{-}CH{=}\underset{\displaystyle R'}{C}{-}\overset{-}{O}$$

$$R{-}\underset{\displaystyle NH_2}{CH}{-}CH{=}\underset{\displaystyle R'}{C}{-}OH \longrightarrow R{\cdot}\underset{\displaystyle NH_2}{CH}{\cdot}CH_2{\cdot}\underset{\displaystyle R'}{C}{=}O$$

(enol form) (keto form)

The net result is addition to the αβ-double bond. On the other hand, it is possible that the electromeric effect takes place only at the olefinic bond as follows:

$$R\cdot CH{=}CH\cdot CO\cdot R' \longrightarrow R\cdot\overset{+}{C}H{-}\overset{\cdot\cdot}{\bar{C}}H\cdot CO\cdot R' \xrightarrow{:NH_3} \underset{\overset{+}{N}H_3}{R\cdot CH}{-}\overset{\cdot\cdot}{\bar{C}}H\cdot CO\cdot R' \longrightarrow \underset{NH_2}{R\cdot CH}{-}CH_2\cdot CO\cdot R'$$

Similarly, αβ-unsaturated ketones add on hydrogen cyanide to form β-cyano-compounds, $R\cdot CH(CN)\cdot CH_2\cdot CO\cdot R'$; and sodium hydrogen sulphite to form β-sulphonic acids, $R\cdot CH(SO_3Na)\cdot CH_2\cdot CO\cdot R'$. The reaction with hydroxylamine usually results in a mixture of the oxime, $R\cdot CH{:}CH\cdot C({:}N\cdot OH)\cdot R'$, and the β-hydroxylaminoketone, $R\cdot CH(NH\cdot OH)\cdot CH_2\cdot CO\cdot R'$. In some cases there is also formed the β-hydroxylamino-oxime, $R\cdot CH(NH\cdot OH)\cdot CH_2\cdot C({:}N\cdot OH)\cdot R'$.

One of the most important reactions that αβ-unsaturated ketones undergo is the **Michael condensation** (1887). This is the addition reaction between an αβ-unsaturated keto-compound and a compound with an active methylene group, *e.g.*, malonic ester, acetoacetic ester, etc. The condensation is carried out in the presence of a base, *e.g.*, sodium ethoxide, or secondary amines. The catalyst usually employed is the cyclic secondary base piperidine, $C_5H_{10}NH$.

(i) $$(CH_3)_2C{:}CH\cdot CO\cdot CH_3 + CH_2(CO_2C_2H_5)_2 \xrightarrow{C_5H_{10}NH} (CH_3)_2\underset{CH(CO_2C_2H_5)_2}{C}\cdot CH_2\cdot CO\cdot CH_3$$

(ii) $$(CH_3)_2C{:}CH\cdot CO\cdot CH_3 + CH_3\cdot CO\cdot CH_2\cdot CO_2C_2H_5 \xrightarrow{C_5H_{10}NH} (CH_3)_2\underset{CH_3\cdot CO\cdot CH\cdot CO_2C_2H_5}{C}\cdot CH_2\cdot CO\cdot CH_3$$

By this means it is possible to synthesise a variety of compounds.

The mechanism of the Michael condensation is believed to be as follows (*cf.* the aldol and Claisen condensations):

$$CH_2(CO_2C_2H_5)_2 + B \rightleftharpoons {:}\bar{C}H(CO_2C_2H_5)_2 + BH^+$$

$$(CH_3)_2C{=}CH{-}\overset{O}{\overset{\|}{C}}\cdot CH_3 + {:}\bar{C}H(CO_2C_2H_5)_2 \longrightarrow (CH_3)_2\underset{CH(CO_2C_2H_5)_2}{C}{-}CH{=}\overset{\bar{O}}{\overset{|}{C}}\cdot CH_3 \xrightarrow{BH^+} (CH_3)_2\underset{CH(CO_2C_2H_5)_2}{C}{-}CH_2\cdot CO\cdot CH_3$$

UNSATURATED MONOCARBOXYLIC ACIDS

Nomenclature. The longest carbon chain with the carboxyl group and the double bond is chosen, and the position of the double bond with respect to the carboxyl group is indicated by number, *e.g.*,

$CH_3\cdot CH{:}CH\cdot CH_2\cdot CO_2H$ pent-3-enoic acid

Alternatively, the acid is named as a substitution product of the olefin, *e.g.*,

$$CH_3{\cdot}CH{:}CH{\cdot}CO_2H \text{ prop-1-ene-1-carboxylic acid}$$

In practice the unsaturated acids are usually known by their common names (see text below).

Many methods are available for preparing unsaturated monocarboxylic acids, but each one depends on the position of the double bond in the acid. A general method for preparing αβ-unsaturated acids is by the **Knoevenagel reaction** (1898). This is the reaction between aldehydes and compounds with active methylene groups in the presence of an organic base. The reaction may take place in one of two ways:

$$\text{(i) } R{\cdot}CHO + CH_2(CO_2C_2H_5)_2 \xrightarrow{\text{base}} R{\cdot}CH{:}C(CO_2C_2H_5)_2 + H_2O$$

$$\text{(ii) } R{\cdot}CHO + 2CH_2(CO_2C_2H_5)_2 \xrightarrow{\text{base}} R{\cdot}CH\begin{matrix} \diagup CH(CO_2C_2H_5)_2 \\ \diagdown CH(CO_2C_2H_5)_2 \end{matrix} + H_2O$$

Reaction (i) is favoured by using equivalent amounts of aldehyde and ethyl malonate in the presence of pyridine (Doebner, 1900). Reaction (ii) is favoured by using excess ethyl malonate in the presence of piperidine. Obviously then, to prepare αβ-unsaturated acids, (i) must be used, followed by hydrolysis and heating:

$$R{\cdot}CHO + CH_2(CO_2C_2H_5)_2 \xrightarrow{\text{pyridine}} R{\cdot}CH{:}C(CO_2C_2H_5)_2 \xrightarrow[\text{(ii) HCl}]{\text{(i) KOH}}$$

$$R{\cdot}CH{:}C(CO_2H)_2 \xrightarrow{150-200^\circ} R{\cdot}CH{:}CH{\cdot}CO_2H + CO_2$$

In practice, it is usually sufficient to treat the aldehyde with malonic acid in the presence of pyridine; *e.g.*, acetaldehyde gives crotonic acid:

$$CH_3{\cdot}CHO + CH_2(CO_2H)_2 \xrightarrow{\text{pyridine}} CH_3{\cdot}CH{:}CH{\cdot}CO_2H + CO_2 + H_2O \quad (60\%)$$

The mechanism is possibly as follows (*cf.* the Michael condensation, above):

$$CH_2(CO_2C_2H_5)_2 + B \rightleftharpoons {:}\bar{C}H(CO_2C_2H_5)_2 + BH^+$$

$$R{-}\underset{H}{\underset{|}{C}}{=}O + {:}\bar{C}H(CO_2C_2H_5)_2 \rightleftharpoons R{-}\underset{H}{\underset{|}{\overset{O^-}{\overset{|}{C}}}}{-}CH(CO_2C_2H_5)_2 \underset{}{\overset{BH^+}{\rightleftharpoons}}$$

$$B + R{-}\underset{H}{\underset{|}{\overset{OH}{\overset{|}{C}}}}{-}CH(CO_2C_2H_5)_2 \xrightarrow{-H_2O} R{\cdot}CH{:}C(CO_2C_2H_5)_2$$

Ethyl malonate condenses with aldehydes only. On the other hand, ethyl cyanoacetate condenses with ketones in the presence of acetamide in glacial acetic acid solution, provided the water formed is removed continually by distillation; *e.g.*, acetone forms *iso*propylidenecyanoacetic ester:

$$(CH_3)_2CO + CH_2(CN){\cdot}CO_2C_2H_5 \xrightarrow{-H_2O} (CH_3)_2C{:}C\begin{matrix} \diagup CN \\ \diagdown CO_2C_2H_5 \end{matrix}$$

Since cyano-compounds are readily hydrolysed to the corresponding acid, the above condensation may be used to prepare αβ-unsaturated acids of the type $R_2C{:}CH{\cdot}CO_2H$.

It can be seen from the foregoing that although the methylene group in ethyl malonate will react with aldehydes, it is not sufficiently "active" to react with ketones. Replacement of one carbethoxy group by a cyano-group makes the methylene group (in the cyano-ester) active enough, *i.e.*, increases the tendency for proton release, to react with ketones. Thus the cyano-group is more strongly electron-attracting than the carbethoxy group. Groups with a -I effect are usually known as *negative groups*. It is the presence of a negative group that is the common feature in compounds which tend to undergo condensation reactions, exhibit tautomerism, and show increased strength as an acid and decreased strength as a base.

Many negative groups are characterised by the presence of multiple bonds, *e.g.*, NO_2, CN, CO, etc., and it is these negative groups which give rise to an active methylene group, and to tautomerism. On the other hand, negative groups which do not contain multiple bonds, *e.g.*, F, Cl, Br, I, $\cdot OCH_3$, do not give rise to an active methylene group, or to tautomerism. All the negative groups, however, increase the strength of an acid and decrease the strength of a base (examples of these phenomena will be found in the text).

αβ-Unsaturated acids may also be prepared by heating α-bromo-acids with ethanolic potassium hydroxide, or better still, with potassium *tert.*-butoxide (Cason *et al.*, 1953); or by heating β-hydroxy-acids with aqueous sodium hydroxide:

$$R\cdot CH_2\cdot CHBr\cdot CO_2H + KOH \xrightarrow{\text{ethanol}} R\cdot CH{:}CH\cdot CO_2H + KBr + H_2O$$

$$R\cdot CHOH\cdot CH_2\cdot CO_2H \xrightarrow{\text{NaOH}} R\cdot CH{:}CH\cdot CO_2H + H_2O$$

βγ-Unsaturated acids may be prepared by heating an aldehyde with sodium succinate and acetic anhydride at 100°. The product is a *γ-alkylparaconic acid,* and when this is heated at 150°, it eliminates carbon dioxide to form the βγ-unsaturated acid (Fittig *et al.*, 1885):

$$R\cdot CHO + \begin{array}{l} CH_2\cdot CO_2Na \\ | \\ CH_2\cdot CO_2Na \end{array} \xrightarrow[100^\circ]{(CH_3\cdot CO)_2O} \left[\begin{array}{lll} R\cdot CH & — & CH\cdot CO_2H \\ | & & | \\ OH & & CH_2\cdot CO_2H \end{array}\right] \xrightarrow{-H_2O}$$

$$\begin{array}{lll} R\cdot CH & — & CH\cdot CO_2H \\ | & & | \\ O & & CH_2 \\ & \diagdown CO \diagup & \end{array} \xrightarrow{150^\circ} R\cdot CH{:}CH\cdot CH_2\cdot CO_2H + CO_2$$

This reaction is really an extension of the Perkin reaction (see p. 623).

Unsaturated alcohols may be oxidised to the corresponding unsaturated acid, provided the double bond is protected, *e.g.*, acrylic acid from allyl alcohol:

$$CH_2{:}CH\cdot CH_2OH \xrightarrow{Br_2} CH_2Br\cdot CHBr\cdot CH_2OH \xrightarrow[HNO_3]{[O]}$$

$$CH_2Br\cdot CHBr\cdot CO_2H \xrightarrow{Zn/CH_3OH} CH_2{:}CH\cdot CO_2H$$

Oxidation of unsaturated aldehydes produces unsaturated acids. The oxidation, however, cannot be carried out with the usual oxidising agents, such as acid or alkaline permanganate, acid dichromate, etc., since these will attack the double bond. A useful oxidising agent for unsaturated aldehydes is ammoniacal silver nitrate (see p. 148); *e.g.*, crotonaldehyde is oxidised to crotonic acid:

$$CH_3{\cdot}CH{:}CH{\cdot}CHO + [O] \xrightarrow[AgNO_3]{ammoniacal} CH_3{\cdot}CH{:}CH{\cdot}CO_2H$$

Unsaturated methyl ketones may be oxidised to unsaturated acids by sodium hypochlorite (*cf.* the haloform reaction), *e.g.*,

$$R{\cdot}CH{:}CH{\cdot}CO{\cdot}CH_3 \xrightarrow{NaOCl} R{\cdot}CH{:}CH{\cdot}CO_2H$$

General reactions of the unsaturated acids. The esters of αβ-unsaturated acids undergo the same addition reactions (including the Michael condensation) at the double bond as the αβ-unsaturated ketones. When reduced by the Bouveault–Blanc method, αβ-unsaturated esters are converted into the corresponding saturated alcohol:

$$CH_3{\cdot}CH{:}CH{\cdot}CO_2C_2H_5 \xrightarrow[Na/C_2H_5OH]{[H]} CH_3{\cdot}CH_2{\cdot}CH_2{\cdot}CH_2OH$$

Lithium aluminium hydride, however, generally reduces these esters to the corresponding *unsaturated* alcohols (*cf.* p. 114).

Esters in which the double bond is further removed from the ester group are reduced to the corresponding *unsaturated* alcohol (*cf.* acraldehyde, above); *e.g.*, butyl oleate is reduced to oleyl alcohol:

$$CH_3{\cdot}(CH_2)_7{\cdot}CH{:}CH{\cdot}(CH_2)_7{\cdot}CO_2C_4H_9 \xrightarrow{Na/C_4H_9OH} CH_3{\cdot}(CH_2)_7{\cdot}CH{:}CH{\cdot}(CH_2)_7{\cdot}CH_2OH \quad (82\text{–}84\%)$$

All the unsaturated acids may be reduced catalytically to saturated acids.

αβ- and βγ-Unsaturated acids add on halogen acid, the halogen atom becoming attached to the unsaturated carbon atom which is further from the carboxyl group:

$$CH_2{:}CH{\cdot}CO_2H + HCl \longrightarrow CH_2Cl{\cdot}CH_2{\cdot}CO_2H$$
$$CH_3{\cdot}CH{:}CH{\cdot}CH_2{\cdot}CO_2H + HBr \longrightarrow CH_3{\cdot}CHBr{\cdot}CH_2{\cdot}CH_2{\cdot}CO_2H$$

This mode of addition (which may be contrary to Markownikoff's rule, as in the case of acrylic acid) may be ascribed to the inductive effect of the carboxyl group (*cf.* allyl alcohol, etc.). On the other hand, addition of halogen acid to γδ-unsaturated acids of the type $CH_2{:}CH{\cdot}CH_2{\cdot}CH_2{\cdot}CO_2H$ takes place in accordance with Markownikoff's rule. This must be due to the fact that the inductive effect of the carboxyl group ceases to be felt beyond the β-carbon atom.

When unsaturated acids are boiled with alkali, the double bond tends to move so as to form the αβ-unsaturated acid:

$$CH_3{\cdot}CH{:}CH{\cdot}CH_2{\cdot}CO_2H \xrightarrow{NaOH} CH_3{\cdot}CH_2{\cdot}CH{:}CH{\cdot}CO_2H$$

An interesting example of this migration of the double bond is the hydrolysis of allyl cyanide with boiling alkali to produce *crotonic* acid. But -3-enoic acid is probably formed first, and this then rearranges to crotonic acid:

$$CH_2{:}CH{\cdot}CH_2{\cdot}CN \xrightarrow{NaOH} [CH_2{:}CH{\cdot}CH_2{\cdot}CO_2H] \xrightarrow{NaOH} CH_3{\cdot}CH{:}CH{\cdot}CO_2H$$

When unsaturated acids are fused with alkali, cleavage of the chain takes place with the formation of two acids, one of which is always acetic acid. This again indicates the migration of the double bond to the αβ-position; *e.g.*, oleic acid gives acetic and palmitic acids:

$$CH_3{\cdot}(CH_2)_7{\cdot}CH{:}CH{\cdot}(CH_2)_7{\cdot}CO_2H \xrightarrow{KOH} [CH_3{\cdot}(CH_2)_{14}{\cdot}CH{:}CH{\cdot}CO_2H]$$
$$\xrightarrow{KOH} CH_3{\cdot}(CH_2)_{14}{\cdot}CO_2H + CH_3{\cdot}CO_2H$$

It is therefore obvious that fusion of an unsaturated acid with alkali cannot be used to determine the position of the double bond. If, however, the unsaturated acid is treated with cold dilute alkaline permanganate, or hydrogen peroxide in acetic acid (or formic acid), the double bond is hydroxylated, and the glycol formed under these conditions, *i.e.*, without migration of the double bond, may now be oxidised in the usual way (see p. 67). Alternatively, the position of the double bond may be ascertained by ozonolysis (p. 68).

αβ-Unsaturated esters add on aliphatic diazo-compounds to form *pyrazoline* derivatives; *e.g.*, acrylic ester reacts with diazomethane to give pyrazoline-5-carboxylic ester:

$$CH_2{:}CH{\cdot}CO_2C_2H_5 + CH_2N_2 \longrightarrow \begin{array}{c} CH_2{-}CH{\cdot}CO_2C_2H_5 \\ |\qquad\quad | \\ HC\qquad NH \\ \diagdown\!\!\diagdown\quad\diagup \\ N \end{array}$$

αβ-Unsaturated acids may be degraded by the Hofmann method (p. 192) using a modified procedure. The αβ-unsaturated acid amide in methanol is treated with an alkaline solution of sodium hypochlorite, the urethan produced being hydrolysed in acid solution to give the *aldehyde* in good yield:

$$R{\cdot}CH{:}CH{\cdot}CO{\cdot}NH_2 \xrightarrow[CH_3OH]{NaOCl/NaOH} R{\cdot}CH{:}CH{\cdot}NH{\cdot}CO_2CH_3 \xrightarrow{HCl} R{\cdot}CHO$$

In this case, *two* carbon atoms are eliminated from the acid. On the other hand, βγ- and γδ-unsaturated acid amides eliminate *one* carbon atom to produce the corresponding unsaturated primary amine, but in poor yield:

$$R{\cdot}CH{:}CH{\cdot}CH_2{\cdot}CO{\cdot}NH_2 \longrightarrow R{\cdot}CH{:}CH{\cdot}CH_2{\cdot}NH_2$$

Acrylic acid (*prop-2-enoic acid*), $CH_2{:}CH{\cdot}CO_2H$, may be prepared:

(i) By the oxidation of allyl alcohol or acraldehyde (see p. 252).
(ii) By heating β-hydroxypropionic acid with aqueous sodium hydroxide:

$$CH_2OH{\cdot}CH_2{\cdot}CO_2H \xrightarrow{NaOH} CH_2{:}CH{\cdot}CO_2H + H_2O$$

Alternatively, ethylene cyanohydrin may be heated with sulphuric acid:

$$CH_2OH{\cdot}CH_2{\cdot}CN \xrightarrow{H_2SO_4} [CH_2OH{\cdot}CH_2{\cdot}CO_2H] \xrightarrow{-H_2O} CH_2{:}CH{\cdot}CO_2H$$

Vinyl cyanide also gives acrylic acid on hydrolysis:

$$CH_2{:}CH{\cdot}CN \xrightarrow{H_2O} CH_2{:}CH{\cdot}CO_2H$$

It is therefore possible that the intermediate in the hydrolysis of ethylene cyanohydrin may be vinyl cyanide or β-hydroxypropionic acid, or both. Acrylic acid is prepared industrially with ethylene cyanohydrin (prepared from ethylene oxide and hydrogen cyanide, p. 237) as the starting material.

(iii) A new industrial preparation is by the interaction of acetylene, carbon monoxide and water in the presence of nickel salts as catalyst:

$$CH{:}CH + CO + H_2O \longrightarrow CH_2{:}CH{\cdot}CO_2H$$

If an alcohol is used instead of water, the corresponding acrylic ester is obtained, *e.g.*,

$$CH{:}CH + CO + CH_3OH \longrightarrow CH_2{:}CH{\cdot}CO_2CH_3$$

Another industrial method is by the pyrolysis of an alkyl acetyl-lactate, *e.g.*,

$$CH_3{\cdot}CH(O{\cdot}CO{\cdot}CH_3){\cdot}CO_2CH_3 \longrightarrow CH_2{=}CH{\cdot}CO_2CH_3 + CH_3{\cdot}CO_2H$$

Acrylic acid is a colourless liquid, b.p. 141°, which is miscible with water in all proportions. On standing it slowly polymerises to a solid.

Methacrylic acid (2-methylprop-2-enoic acid), $CH_2{:}C(CH_3){\cdot}CO_2H$, exists as colourless prisms, m.p. 15°. It may be prepared by removing a molecule of hydrogen bromide from α-bromo*iso*butyric acid:

$$CH_3{\cdot}\overset{\overset{CH_3}{|}}{C}Br{\cdot}CO_2H \xrightarrow[-\,HBr]{\text{ethanolic KOH}} CH_2{:}\overset{\overset{CH_3}{|}}{C}{\cdot}CO_2H$$

Methyl methacrylate is very important commercially, since it polymerises to polymethyl methacrylate under the influence of heat. This polymer is tough, transparent, and can be moulded; one of its trade names is *perspex*. One industrial method of preparing methyl methacrylate is as follows:

$$(CH_3)_2CO \xrightarrow{HCN} (CH_3)_2C(OH)(CN) \xrightarrow[H_2SO_4]{CH_3OH} CH_2{:}\overset{\overset{CH_3}{|}}{C}{\cdot}CO_2CH_3 + NH_4HSO_4$$

Methyl acrylate, which may be prepared by heating ethylene cyanohydrin with methanol and sulphuric acid, also polymerises, but this polymer is softer than that from the methacrylate.

Crotonic acid and ***iso*crotonic acid** both have the same structure $CH_3{\cdot}CH{:}CH{\cdot}CO_2H$ (*but-2-enoic acid*), but are geometrical isomers, crotonic acid being the *trans* isomer, and *iso*crotonic the *cis*:

$$\begin{array}{c} H{-}C{-}CH_3 \\ \| \\ HO_2C{-}C{-}H \end{array} \qquad \begin{array}{c} H{-}C{-}CH_3 \\ \| \\ H{-}C{-}CO_2H \end{array}$$

crotonic acid | *iso*crotonic acid

The more stable form is crotonic acid, m.p. 72°. *iso*Crotonic acid, m.p. 15°, slowly changes into crotonic acid when heated at 100°.

Crotonic acid (*trans*-but-2-enoic acid) may be prepared by oxidising crotonaldehyde with ammoniacal silver nitrate; by heating β-hydroxybutyric acid with sodium hydroxide; or by the Knoevenagel reaction (see p. 263);

$$CH_3{\cdot}CHO + CH_2(CO_2H)_2 \xrightarrow[20^\circ]{\text{pyridine}} CH_3{\cdot}CH{:}CH{\cdot}CO_2H + CO_2 + H_2O \quad (60\%)$$

***iso*Crotonic acid** (*cis*-but-2-enoic acid) may be prepared by the action of sodium amalgam on β-chloro*iso*crotonic ester which is obtained from acetoacetic ester by reaction with phosphorus pentachloride:

$$CH_3{\cdot}CO{\cdot}CH_2{\cdot}CO_2C_2H_5 \xrightarrow{PCl_5} CH_3{\cdot}CCl_2{\cdot}CH_2{\cdot}CO_2C_2H_5 \xrightarrow{-HCl}$$
$$CH_3{\cdot}CCl{:}CH{\cdot}CO_2C_2H_5 \xrightarrow{Na/Hg} CH_3{\cdot}CH{:}CH{\cdot}CO_2C_2H_5$$

The action of sodium amalgam is particularly interesting, since it normally reduces a double bond in the αβ-position.

Angelic and **tiglic acids** are geometrical isomers with the structure $CH_3{\cdot}CH{:}C(CH_3){\cdot}CO_2H$ (2-*methylbut*-2-*enoic acid*):

$$\begin{array}{c} CH_3—C—H \\ \| \\ CH_3—C—CO_2H \end{array} \qquad \begin{array}{c} H—C—CH_3 \\ \| \\ CH_3—C—CO_2H \end{array}$$

angelic acid, m.p. 45° tiglic acid, m.p. 64°

Both acids are found in nature as esters.

Undecylenic acid (*dec*-9-*ene*-1-*carboxylic acid*), $CH_2{:}CH{\cdot}(CH_2)_8{\cdot}CO_2H$, may be obtained by the destructive distillation of *ricinoleic acid* (11-*hydroxyheptadec*-8-*ene*-1-*carboxylic acid*), which occurs as the glyceride ester in castor-oil. Heptanal is the other product, 10 per cent. yield of each being obtained:

$$CH_3{\cdot}(CH_2)_5{\cdot}CHOH{\cdot}CH_2{\cdot}CH{:}CH{\cdot}(CH_2)_7{\cdot}CO_2H \longrightarrow CH_3{\cdot}(CH_2)_5{\cdot}CHO + CH_2{:}CH{\cdot}(CH_2)_8{\cdot}CO_2H$$

Undecylenic acid is a solid, m.p. 24·5°, and is said to be a preventive and a cure for athlete's foot.

When ricinoleic acid is heated with sodium hydroxide in air, octan-2-ol and sebacic acid are obtained:

$$CH_3{\cdot}(CH_2)_5{\cdot}CHOH{\cdot}CH_2{\cdot}CH{:}CH{\cdot}(CH_2)_7{\cdot}CO_2H \xrightarrow[\text{air}]{\text{NaOH}} CH_3{\cdot}(CH_2)_5{\cdot}CHOH{\cdot}CH_3 + CO_2H{\cdot}(CH_2)_8{\cdot}CO_2H$$

When ricinoleic acid (castor oil) is treated with concentrated sulphuric acid, it gives a complex mixture consisting of the hydrogen sulphate of ricinoleic acid in which the hydroxyl group is esterified, and a compound in which the sulphuric acid has added to the double bond: esterification and addition do not occur together in the same molecule of ricinoleic acid. The product, which is known as *Turkey-red oil*, is used as a wetting agent.

Oleic acid (*cis-heptadec*-8-*ene*-1-*carboxylic acid*) occurs as the glyceryl ester in oils and fats. It is a colourless oil, m.p. 16°, which is insoluble in water, but soluble in ethanol and ether. Catalytic reduction converts it into stearic acid. Cold dilute alkaline permanganate, or hydrogen peroxide in acetic acid, converts oleic acid into 9 : 10-dihydroxystearic acid, which, on oxidation with, *e.g.*, acid permanganate, gives nonoic acid and azelaic acid:

$$CH_3{\cdot}(CH_2)_7{\cdot}CH{:}CH{\cdot}(CH_2)_7{\cdot}CO_2H \xrightarrow[CH_3{\cdot}CO_2H]{H_2O_2} CH_3{\cdot}(CH_2)_7{\cdot}CHOH{\cdot}CHOH{\cdot}(CH_2)_7{\cdot}CO_2H$$

$$\xrightarrow[KMnO_4]{\text{acid}} CH_3{\cdot}(CH_2)_7{\cdot}CO_2H + CO_2H{\cdot}(CH_2)_7{\cdot}CO_2H$$

This shows that the double bond in oleic acid is in the 9 : 10 position (carboxyl group being 1), and this is confirmed by ozonolysis.

Oleic acid is the *cis* form. The *trans* form is **elaidic acid,** m.p. 51°, which may be obtained by the action of nitrous acid on oleic acid:

$$\begin{array}{c} H—C—(CH_2)_7{\cdot}CH_3 \\ \| \\ H—C—(CH_2)_7{\cdot}CO_2H \end{array} \xrightarrow{HNO_2} \begin{array}{c} CH_3{\cdot}(CH_2)_7{\cdot}C—H \\ \| \\ H—C—(CH_2)_7{\cdot}CO_2H \end{array}$$

Linoleic acid (*heptadeca*-8 : 11-*diene*-1-*carboxylic acid*), $CH_3{\cdot}(CH_2)_4{\cdot}CH{:}CH{\cdot}CH_2{\cdot}CH{:}CH{\cdot}(CH_2)_7{\cdot}CO_2H$, b.p. 228°/14 mm., occurs as the glyceryl ester in linseed oil, hemp oil, etc.; it has been synthesised by Raphael *et al.* (1950).

Linolenic acid (*heptadeca*-8 : 11 : 14-*triene*-1-*carboxylic acid*), $CH_3{\cdot}CH_2{\cdot}CH{:}CH{\cdot}CH_2{\cdot}CH{:}CH{\cdot}CH_2{\cdot}CH{:}CH{\cdot}(CH_2)_7{\cdot}CO_2H$, is a liquid which occurs as the glyceryl ester in, *e.g.*, poppy-seed oil. Oils containing linoleic and linolenic acids are drying oils (p. 248). Linolenic acid is the most abundant and widespread triene acid in Nature; it has been synthesised by Weedon *et al.* (1956).

Erucic acid, m.p. 34°, is the *cis* form of *heneicos-12-ene-1-carboxylic acid,* $CH_3 \cdot (CH_2)_7 \cdot CH{:}CH \cdot (CH_2)_{11} \cdot CO_2H$. It occurs as the glyceryl ester in various oils, *e.g.*, rape oil, cod-liver oil, etc. It is converted into the *trans* isomer **brassidic acid,** m.p. 61·5°, by the action of nitrous acid (*cf.* oleic acid, above):

$$\begin{matrix} H—C—(CH_2)_7 \cdot CH_3 \\ \| \\ H—C—(CH_2)_{11} \cdot CO_2H \end{matrix} \xrightarrow{HNO_2} \begin{matrix} CH_3 \cdot (CH_2)_7—C—H \\ \| \\ H—C—(CH_2)_{11} \cdot CO_2H \end{matrix}$$

Nervonic acid (*tricos-14-ene-1-carboxylic acid*), $CH_3 \cdot (CH_2)_7 \cdot CH{:}CH \cdot (CH_2)_{13} \cdot CO_2H$, occurs in human brain-tissue and in fish oils. Both the *cis* and *trans* forms are known, but it appears to be the *cis* acid, m.p. 43°, which occurs naturally.

Propiolic acid (*propargylic acid, prop-2-ynoic acid*), $CH{\vdots}C \cdot CO_2H$, is the simplest acetylenic carboxylic acid. It is conveniently prepared by the action of dry carbon dioxide on sodium acetylide:

$$CH{\vdots}CNa \xrightarrow{CO_2} CH{\vdots}C \cdot CO_2Na \xrightarrow[H_2SO_4]{\text{dilute}} CH{\vdots}C \cdot CO_2H$$

It is a colourless liquid, m.p. 9°, which smells like acetic acid; it is reduced by sodium amalgam to propionic acid; it adds on halogen acid to give the β-halogeno-acrylic acid. It forms the silver or cuprous salt when treated with an ammoniacal solution of silver nitrate or cuprous chloride, respectively. When exposed to sunlight, it polymerises to *trimesic acid* (benzene 1 : 3 : 5-tricarboxylic acid; *cf.* acetylene):

$$3CH{\vdots}C \cdot CO_2H \longrightarrow C_6H_3(CO_2H)_3$$

αβ-Acetylenic acids are stronger acids than their ethylenic and saturated analogues due to the acetylene bond exerting a strong electron-attracting effect (*cf.* p. 89).

THE PRINCIPLE OF VINYLOGY

According to Fuson (1935), the principle of vinylogy may be described as follows: If E_1 and E_2 represent non-metallic elements, then in the compound of the type $A—E_1{=}E_2$ or $A—E_1{\equiv}E_2$, if a structural unit of the type $(—C{=}C—)_n$ is interposed between A and E_1, the function of E_2 remains qualitatively unchanged, but that of E_1 may be usurped by the carbon atom attached to A. Thus

$$A—(C{=}C)_n—E_1{=}E_2 \text{ or } A—(C{=}C)_n—E_1{\equiv}E_2$$

form vinylogous series. This may be illustrated by the compounds ethyl acetate and ethyl crotonate. These are vinylogues (n being equal to 1):

$$CH_3—C(OC_2H_5){=}O \qquad CH_3—(CH{=}CH)—C(OC_2H_5){=}O$$

A is equivalent to CH_3 and $E_1{=}E_2$ to $—C(OC_2H_5){=}O$

Ethyl acetate condenses with ethyl oxalate to form *oxalacetic ester* (this, of course, is an example of the Claisen condensation):

$$C_2H_5OOC \cdot COOC_2H_5 + CH_3 \cdot COOC_2H_5 \xrightarrow[\text{ether}]{Na} C_2H_5OOC \cdot CO \cdot CH_2 \cdot COOC_2H_5 + C_2H_5OH$$

In the same way, ethyl crotonate also condenses with ethyl oxalate:

$$C_2H_5OOC{\cdot}COOC_2H_5 + CH_3{\cdot}(CH{=}CH){\cdot}COOC_2H_5 \xrightarrow[\text{ether}]{\text{Na}}$$

$$C_2H_5OOC{\cdot}CO{\cdot}CH_2{\cdot}(CH{=}CH){\cdot}COOC_2H_5 + C_2H_5OH$$

Several other examples of the application of vinylogy will be found in the text.

KETENS (KETENES)

Ketens are compounds which are characterised by the presence of the grouping $>C{=}C{=}O$. If the compound is of the type $R{\cdot}CH{:}C{:}O$, it is known as an *aldoketen*; and if $R_2C{:}C{:}O$, then a *ketoketen*.

The most general method of preparing a keten is by debrominating an α-bromoacyl bromide with zinc, *e.g.*, dimethylketen from α-bromo*iso*butyryl bromide:

$$(CH_3)_2CBr{\cdot}COBr + Zn \longrightarrow (CH_3)_2C{:}C{:}O + ZnBr_2$$

The simplest member of the keten series is **keten** (*ketene*), $CH_2{:}C{:}O$. Keten may be prepared by debrominating bromoacetyl bromide with zinc:

$$CH_2Br{\cdot}COBr + Zn \longrightarrow CH_2{:}C{:}O + ZnBr_2$$

It is, however, usually prepared by the thermal decomposition of acetone (ethyl acetate or acetic anhydride may also be used as the starting material):

$$CH_3{\cdot}CO{\cdot}CH_3 \longrightarrow CH_2{:}C{:}O + CH_4$$

In practice, acetone vapour is passed over an electrically heated metal filament at 700–750°; the filament is made of chromel wire (an alloy of 80 per cent. nickel and 20 per cent. chromium). The yield of keten is high, being usually between 90 and 95 per cent. An alternative procedure, which gives a much lower yield (25–29 per cent.), is to pass acetone vapour through a long combustion tube filled with broken porcelain heated to redness.

The thermal decomposition of acetone has been shown to be a free-radical chain reaction. The exact details are not known with certainty; Rice and Walters (1941) have suggested the following:

$$CH_3{\cdot}CO{\cdot}CH_3 \longrightarrow CH_3{\cdot} + CH_3{\cdot}CO{\cdot} \longrightarrow 2CH_3{\cdot} + CO$$

$$CH_3{\cdot}CO{\cdot}CH_3 + CH_3{\cdot} \longrightarrow CH_3{\cdot}CO{\cdot}CH_2{\cdot} + CH_4$$

$$CH_3{\cdot}CO{\cdot}CH_2{\cdot} \longrightarrow CH_2{:}C{:}O + CH_3{\cdot}, \text{ etc.}$$

Keten is prepared industrially by passing acetone vapour through a copper tube at 700–850°, and by the decomposition of acetic acid in the presence of phosphoric acid or ethyl phosphate as catalyst:

$$CH_3{\cdot}CO_2H \xrightarrow[\text{cat.}]{700^\circ} CH_2{=}C{=}O + H_2O$$

Keten is a colourless, poisonous, pungent gas, b.p. −41°, which oxidises in air to the unstable peroxide, the structure of which may be as shown.

```
CH2—C=O
|   |
O———O
```

Keten is a very reactive compound, and so is important as a synthetic reagent. It rapidly polymerises to *diketen*, and because of this tendency to polymerise, keten is usually used immediately when prepared.

The reactions of keten are generally those of an acid anhydride; it acetylates most compounds with an active hydrogen atom (p. 185), provided the compound can be dissolved in some solvent inert to the action of keten. The yield of acetyl derivative is almost 100 per cent. (based on keten). The following reactions clearly show the acetylating property of keten:

(i) When keten is passed into water, acetic acid is formed:

$$CH_2{:}CO + H_2O \longrightarrow CH_3{\cdot}CO_2H$$

(ii) When keten is passed into glacial acetic acid, acetic anhydride is formed:

$$CH_2{:}CO + CH_3{\cdot}CO_2H \longrightarrow (CH_3{\cdot}CO)_2O$$

By means of this reaction a mixed anhydride may be obtained, one radical of which, of course, must be the acetyl group:

$$R{\cdot}CO_2H + CH_2{:}CO \longrightarrow R{\cdot}CO{\cdot}O{\cdot}CO{\cdot}CH_3$$

(iii) Keten reacts with aliphatic or aromatic hydroxy-compounds:

$$CH_2{=}CO + ROH \longrightarrow CH_3{\cdot}CO_2R$$

It also acetylates enolisable compounds, *e.g.*,

$$CH_3{\cdot}CO{\cdot}CH_2{\cdot}CO_2C_2H_5 \xrightarrow[H_2SO_4]{CH_2=CO} \underset{\displaystyle O{\cdot}CO{\cdot}CH_3}{CH_3{\cdot}\overset{}{C}}{=}CH{\cdot}CO_2C_2H_5 + \underset{\displaystyle O{\cdot}CO{\cdot}CH_3}{CH_2{=}C}{\cdot}CH_2{\cdot}CO_2C_2H_5$$

(iv) Keten reacts with ammonia to form acetamide, and with primary or secondary amines to form *N*-alkyl-acetamides:

$$CH_2{:}CO + NH_3 \longrightarrow CH_3{\cdot}CO{\cdot}NH_2$$
$$CH_2{:}CO + R{\cdot}NH_2 \longrightarrow CH_3{\cdot}CO{\cdot}NH{\cdot}R$$

Primary amino-groups are acetylated extremely readily, and hence it is possible to acetylate this group selectively in compounds containing both an amino and hydroxyl group, *e.g.*, *p*-aminophenol (*cf.* p. 576):

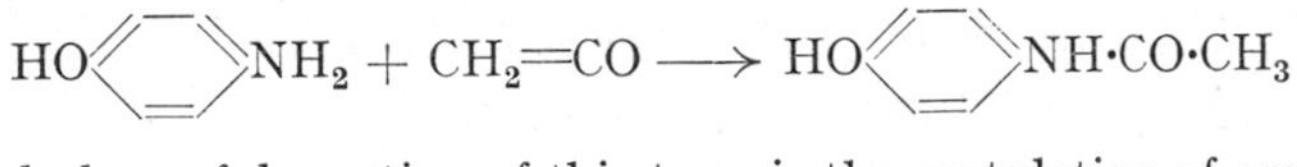

$$HO{\cdot}C_6H_4{\cdot}NH_2 + CH_2{=}CO \longrightarrow HO{\cdot}C_6H_4{\cdot}NH{\cdot}CO{\cdot}CH_3$$

A particularly useful reaction of this type is the acetylation of amino-acids:

$$R{\cdot}CH(NH_2){\cdot}CO_2H + CH_2{:}CO \longrightarrow R{\cdot}CH(NH{\cdot}CO{\cdot}CH_3){\cdot}CO_2H$$

Amides are also acetylated by keten in the presence of sulphuric acid, but at elevated temperatures (in the absence of sulphuric acid) the cyanide is formed.

$$R{\cdot}CO{\cdot}NH_2 + CH_2{=}CO \longrightarrow R{\cdot}CN + CH_3{\cdot}CO_2H$$

(v) Thiols are acetylated:

$$R{\cdot}SH + CH_2{=}CO \longrightarrow R{\cdot}S{\cdot}CO{\cdot}CH_3$$

(vi) Keten reacts with Grignard reagents to form methyl ketones:

$$RMgX + CH_2{=}CO \longrightarrow R{\cdot}CO{\cdot}CH_3$$

In addition to behaving as an acetylating reagent, keten behaves as an unsaturated compound, the carbonyl group showing no reactivity, *e.g.*,

(i) Keten adds on bromine to form bromoacetyl bromide:

$$CH_2{:}CO + Br_2 \longrightarrow CH_2Br{\cdot}COBr$$

The halogeno-acetyl halide is also formed by the interaction of keten and phosphorus pentahalides:

$$CH_2{:}CO + PCl_5 \longrightarrow CH_2Cl{\cdot}COCl + PCl_3$$

(ii) Keten adds on halogen acid to form the acetyl halide:

$$CH_2{:}CO + HX \longrightarrow CH_3{\cdot}COX$$

Alkyl halides also react with the keten in the presence of charcoal at 100° to form acid chlorides:

$$RX + CH_2{=}CO \longrightarrow R{\cdot}CH_2{\cdot}COX$$

This offers a means of stepping up a series.

(iii) A particularly interesting addition reaction of keten is that with aldehydes to form β-lactones; *e.g.*, with formaldehyde, β-*propiolactone* is formed:

$$CH_2{:}CO + H{\cdot}CHO \longrightarrow \underbrace{CH_2{\cdot}CH_2{\cdot}CO}_{\text{—O—}}$$

Diketen is readily formed by passing keten into acetone cooled in solid carbon dioxide (yield: 50–55 per cent.). Diketen is a pungent-smelling liquid, b.p. 127°, which, when strongly heated (550–600°), is depolymerised to keten.

The structure of diketen is still uncertain. Various structures have been suggested, *e.g.*,

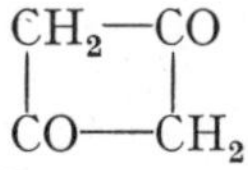

$$\begin{array}{ccc} \begin{array}{l} CH_2\text{—}CO \\ |\quad\quad | \\ CO\text{—}CH_2 \end{array} & \begin{array}{l} CH_2\text{—}C{\cdot}OH \\ |\quad\quad \| \\ CO\text{—}CH \end{array} & \begin{array}{l} CH_2{=}C\text{—}O \\ \quad\quad |\quad | \\ \quad CH_2\text{—}C{=}O \end{array} \end{array}$$

*cyclo*butane-1 : 3-dione (I) mono-enol of I (II) vinylaceto-β-lactone (III)

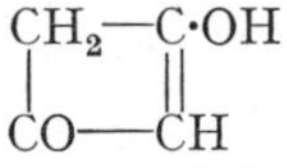

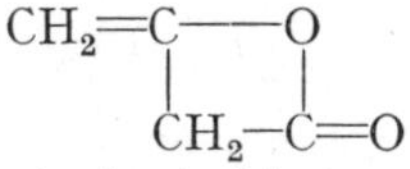

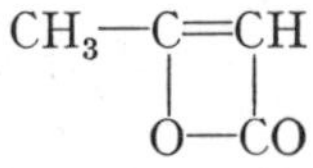

$$\begin{array}{cc} \begin{array}{l} CH_3\text{—}C{=}CH \\ \quad\quad |\quad | \\ \quad\quad O\text{—}CO \end{array} & CH_3\text{—}\overset{\overset{O}{\|}}{C}\text{—}CH{=}C{=}O \end{array}$$

β-crotonolactone (IV) acetylketen (V)

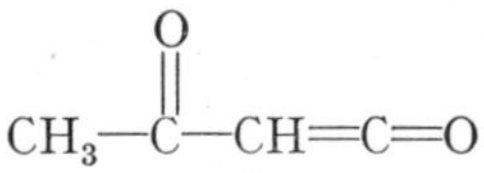

According to Whiffen and Thompson (1946), based on their work of infra-red measurements, the structure of diketen is most likely III or IV, or a mixture of both. These authors also point out that the evidence seems to favour III. This formula is also favoured by Blomquist and Baldwin (1948), who treated diketen with *N*-bromosuccimide and showed that the resulting products agree with structure III (and not with IV). Structure III is also supported by mass spectra studies of Long *et al.* (1953). Structure I has been excluded by work with isotope ^{14}C (Roberts *et al.*, 1949). It is interesting to note, however, that the structure of dimethylketen dimer is 2 : 2 : 4 : 4-tetramethyl*cyclo*buta-1 : 3-dione (*i.e.*, it corresponds to I), and the ring is planar (Robertson *et al.*, 1956).

Diketen may be further polymerised to dehydroacetic acid (p. 212).

Diketen reacts with alcohols to form esters of acetoacetic acid, and this reaction is now being used to prepare acetoacetic ester industrially (see p. 210). It also reacts with primary amines to form *N*-substituted acetoacetamides, *e.g.*, with aniline:

$$\begin{array}{l} CH_2{=}C{-}{-}O \\ \quad\;\; | \qquad | \\ \quad CH_2{-}CO \end{array} + C_6H_5{\cdot}NH_2 \longrightarrow CH_3{\cdot}CO{\cdot}CH_2{\cdot}CO{\cdot}NH{\cdot}C_6H_5$$

Diketen also undergoes the Friedel–Crafts reaction with benzene to form benzoylacetone:

$$\begin{array}{l} CH_2{=}C{-}{-}O \\ \quad\;\; | \qquad | \\ \quad CH_2{-}CO \end{array} + C_6H_6 \xrightarrow{AlCl_3} C_6H_5{\cdot}CO{\cdot}CH_2{\cdot}CO{\cdot}CH_3$$

QUESTIONS

1. Using acetone or glycerol as the starting material, show how you would prepare:—(*a*) 3-methylbut-2-enoic acid, (*b*) $\beta:\beta$-dimethylacrylic acid, (*c*) β-hydroxypropionic acid, (*d*) $\alpha:\alpha$-dimethylsuccinic acid, (*e*) $\alpha:\beta$-dibromopropionic acid, (*f*) glyceraldehyde.

2. Name the following compounds and suggest one synthesis for each:

(*a*) $CH_2{:}CH{\cdot}CH_2{\cdot}CH(CH_3){\cdot}CO_2H$

(*b*) $\begin{array}{l} Me_2C{\cdot}CH_2{\cdot}CO_2H \\ \quad\; | \\ Me_2C{\cdot}CH_2{\cdot}CO_2H \end{array}$

(*c*) $\begin{array}{l} CH_2{\cdot}CH_2{\cdot}CO{\cdot}CH_3 \\ | \\ CH(CO_2H)_2 \end{array}$

(*d*) $Me_2C(CH_2{\cdot}CO_2H)_2$

(*e*) $CH_3{\cdot}CO{\cdot}CH_2{\cdot}CHMe{\cdot}CH_2{\cdot}O{\cdot}CH_3$

(*f*) $Me_2C(CH_2{\cdot}CH_2{\cdot}CO_2H)_2$.

3. How would you distinguish between allyl alcohol and propargyl alcohol?

4. Describe the preparation and the more important properties of:—(*a*) allyl alcohol, (*b*) allyl halides, (*c*) crotyl alcohol, (*d*) propargyl alcohol, (*e*) methyl vinyl ether, (*f*) divinyl ether, (*g*) crotonaldehyde, (*h*) propargylaldehyde, (*i*) methyl vinyl ketone, (*j*) crotonic acid, (*k*) propiolic acid.

5. How may acraldehyde, mesityl oxide, phorone and acrylic acid be prepared? Name the compounds and state the conditions under which they are formed when the above substances, respectively, are treated with:—(*a*) Br_2, (*b*) HBr, (*c*) HCN, (*d*) NaOH, (*e*) NH_3, (*f*) H_2, (*g*) $NaHSO_3$, (*h*) $NH_2{\cdot}OH$, (*i*) $CH_2(CO_2Et)_2$, (*j*) E.A.A., (*k*) CH_2N_2.

6. Define and give examples of:—(*a*) hyperconjugation, (*b*) the allylic rearrangement, (*c*) the 1 : 4 mechanism, (*d*) Michael condensation, (*e*) Knoevenagel reaction, (*f*) negative groups, (*g*) geometrical isomerism, (*h*) vinylogy, (*i*) halochromic salt, (*j*) cyanoethylation.

7. Discuss the general methods of preparation and the more important properties of the unsaturated monocarboxylic acids. Give an account of the methods that can be used for determining the position of the double bond in an unsaturated acid.

8. Write an account of the preparation and properties of keten and diketen, including in your answer a discussion of the structure of diketen.

9. Write an account of the reduction of $\alpha\beta$-unsaturated carbonyl compounds.

READING REFERENCES

Reactions Involving the Allyl Position, *Ann. Reports*, 1943, **40**, 101; 1944, **41**, 191.
Walsh, Remarks on the Strengths of Bonds, *Trans. Faraday Soc.*, 1947, **46**, 60, 158, 342.
Organic Reactions, Wiley. Vol. V. (1949), Ch. 2. Cyanoethylation.
The Michael Condensation.
(i) Connor and McClellan, *J. Org. Chem.*, 1939, **3**, 570.
(ii) Hauser and Abramovitch, *J. Amer. Chem. Soc.*, 1940, **62**, 1763.
(iii) Samuel *et al.*, *J.C.S.*, **1955**, 1288.
Unsaturated Acids, *Ann. Reports*, 1940, **37**, 211.
Boxer and Linstead, The Knoevenagel Reaction, *J.C.S.*, 1931, 740.
Fuson, The Principle of Vinylogy, *Chem. Reviews*, 1935, **16**, 1.
Clara Deasy, Hyperconjugation, *ibid.*, 1945, **36**, 145.
Crawford, Hyperconjugation, *Quart. Reviews* (*Chem. Soc.*), 1949, **3**, 226.
Organic Reactions, Wiley. Vol. III (1946), Ch. 3. Preparation of Ketenes and Ketene Dimers.
Johnson, Lecture on Some Applications of Acetylenic Compounds in Organic Synthesis, *Royal Institute of Chemistry* (1948).

Gilman, *Advanced Organic Chemistry*, Wiley (1942, 2nd ed.).
(i) Vol. I, Ch. 7. Unsaturation and Conjugation.
(ii) Vol. I, Ch. 9. Catalytic Hydrogenation and Hydrogenolysis.
Raphael, *Acetylenic Compounds in Organic Synthesis*, Butterworth (1955).
Gunstone, Recent Developments in the Preparation of Natural Straight-Chain Fatty Acids, *Quart. Reviews (Chem. Soc.)*, 1953, **7**, 175.
Baker, *Hyperconjugation*, Oxford Press (1952).
Quadbeck, Keten in der präparativen organischen Chemie, *Angew. Chem.*, 1956, **68**, 361.
DeWolfe and Young, Substitution and Rearrangement Reactions of Allylic Compounds, *Chem. Reviews*, 1956, **56**, 753.
Friedlander and Robertson, The Crystal Structure of Dimethylketen Dimer, *J.C.S.*, **1956**, 3083.

CHAPTER XIII

NITROGEN COMPOUNDS

SOME compounds containing nitrogen have been described in Chapter IX, since these were regarded primarily as acid derivatives. It is now proposed to deal with many other nitrogen compounds, most of which may be regarded as alkyl nitrogen compounds.

Hydrocyanic acid, hydrogen cyanide (*prussic acid*), HCN, was discovered by Scheele (1782), who obtained it from bitter almonds which contain the glycoside *amygdalin*. Amygdalin, on hydrolysis with dilute acid, yields hydrogen cyanide, benzaldehyde and glucose:

$$C_{20}H_{27}O_{11}N + 2H_2O \xrightarrow{\text{acid}} HCN + C_6H_5{\cdot}CHO + 2C_6H_{12}O_6$$

Hydrogen cyanide also occurs in the leaves of certain plants, *e.g.*, laurel. It may be prepared by heating sodium cyanide with concentrated sulphuric acid, the gas being dried over calcium chloride:

$$NaCN + H_2SO_4 \longrightarrow HCN + NaHSO_4 \quad (93\text{–}97\%)$$

Hydrogen cyanide is prepared industrially:

(i) By passing a mixture of ammonia, air and methane over a platinum–rhodium gauze catalyst at 1000°:

$$2NH_3 + 3O_2 + 2CH_4 \longrightarrow 2HCN + 6H_2O$$

(ii) By passing a mixture of carbon monoxide and ammonia over an alumina catalyst at 500–700°:

$$CO + NH_3 \longrightarrow HCN + H_2O$$

Hydrogen cyanide is a colourless, poisonous liquid, b.p. 26°. It is a very weak acid, and is miscible in all proportions with water, ethanol and ether. It hydrolyses slowly in aqueous solution, and more rapidly in the presence of inorganic acids to form first formamide, and then ammonium formate:

$$HCN \xrightarrow{H_2O} H{\cdot}CO{\cdot}NH_2 \xrightarrow{H_2O} H{\cdot}CO_2NH_4$$

Hydrogen cyanide is reduced by nascent hydrogen to methylamine:

$$HCN + 4[H] \xrightarrow{Zn/HCl} CH_3{\cdot}NH_2$$

It is a useful reagent for certain syntheses, *e.g.*, cyanohydrins by combination with carbonyl compounds (p. 141), and in the Gattermann aldehyde synthesis (p. 618).

Structure of hydrogen cyanide. Hydrogen cyanide is believed to exist in two forms because it gives rise to two kinds of alkyl derivatives: the *alkyl cyanides*, R·CN, which are derivatives of *hydrogen cyanide*, HCN; and the *alkyl* iso*cyanides*, R·NC, which are derivatives of *hydrogen* iso*cyanide*, HNC.

The structures of HCN and R·CN, respectively, were originally believed to be H·C⋮N and R·C⋮N, but recent determinations of the dipole moments of the alkyl cyanides indicate that they are resonance hybrids of structures I and II, the contribution of II being about 57 per cent.:

$$\underset{\text{(I)}}{\mathrm{R{-}C{\equiv}N}\colon} \longleftrightarrow \underset{\text{(II)}}{\mathrm{R{-}\overset{+}{C}{=}\overset{..}{\bar{N}}}\colon}$$

On the other hand, infra-red studies strongly favour I.

The structures of HNC and R·NC proved more difficult to elucidate. Originally, the formula of the alkyl *iso*cyanides was written R—N≡C (nitrogen with a valency of five and carbon, four). This, however, was inconsistent with the chemical properties of *iso*cyanides, and was soon considered unlikely. It is now known, according to the electronic theory of valency, that four bonds between nitrogen and carbon is impossible on theoretical grounds.

Normally, on addition to unsaturated compounds, the addendum adds to each atom joined by the double bond; this does not occur with *iso*cyanides, the addendum adding only to the carbon atom:

$$\mathrm{R{\cdot}NCS} \xleftarrow{\mathrm{S}} \mathrm{R{\cdot}NC} \xrightarrow{\mathrm{Br_2}} \mathrm{R{\cdot}NCBr_2}$$

These facts led Nef (1891–1892) to suggest that *iso*cyanides did not contain quadrivalent carbon but bivalent carbon. He therefore wrote their formula as R—N=C<, with two "free" valencies by means of which *iso*cyanides add on the addendum to the carbon atom alone (as shown in the above examples).

Study of the dipole moments and Raman spectra of *iso*cyanides indicated that bivalent carbon did not represent the true state of affairs, and led to the suggestion that the bond between the nitrogen and carbon atoms was a triple bond. If we use the electronic formula of Nef's structure, we can introduce a triple bond between the nitrogen and carbon atoms by rearranging the lone pair of the nitrogen atom to act as a donor to the carbon atom, *i.e.*,

$$\mathrm{R{-}\overset{..}{N}{=}C}\colon \longrightarrow \mathrm{R{-}N{\stackrel{\rightarrow}{\equiv}}C}$$

Raman spectra of cyanides and *iso*cyanides show the presence of the C≡N group. This is satisfied by the N$\stackrel{\rightarrow}{\equiv}$C group. On the other hand, more recent work indicates that alkyl *iso*cyanides are resonance hybrids of III and IV:

$$\underset{\text{(III)}}{\mathrm{R{-}\overset{..}{N}{=}C}\colon} \longleftrightarrow \underset{\text{(IV)}}{\mathrm{R{-}\overset{+}{N}{\equiv}\bar{C}}}$$

Furthermore, the value of the C—N—C valency bond angle has been found to be 180°, *i.e.*, these three atoms form a linear arrangement, which shows that IV makes a very large contribution to the actual state (see Ch. 11).

Thus, in view of the existence of alkyl cyanides and *iso*cyanides, hydrogen cyanide is believed to be tautomeric, giving rise to the *nitrile-*iso*nitrile diad system*:

$$\mathrm{H{-}C{\equiv}N} \rightleftharpoons \mathrm{C{\stackrel{\leftarrow}{\equiv}}N{-}H}$$

The position, however, cannot be regarded as being completely satisfactory. It appears that only one form of acid is known, *viz.*, hydrogen cyanide; all its reaction indicate the structure H—C≡N, *e.g.*, its hydrolysis to formic acid.

ALKYL CYANIDES

These are also known as **nitriles** or **carbonitriles.**

Nomenclature. This group of compounds is usually named either as the *alkyl cyanides* (*i.e.*, the alkyl derivatives of hydrogen cyanide), or as the *nitrile* of the acid which is produced on hydrolysis, the suffix *-ic* of the trivial name being replaced by *-onitrile*. The following examples illustrate both systems of nomenclature:

HCN	hydrogen cyanide or formonitrile
$CH_3{\cdot}CN$	methyl cyanide or acetonitrile
$(CH_3)_2CH{\cdot}CN$	*iso*propyl cyanide or *iso*butyronitrile

General methods of preparation. 1. By the dehydration of acid amides with phosphorus pentoxide:

$$R{\cdot}CO{\cdot}NH_2 \xrightarrow[-H_2O]{P_2O_5} R{\cdot}CN \quad (g.)$$

Amides may also be converted into cyanides by heating with phosphorus pentachloride or thionyl chloride. Dehydration of the amide to cyanide is also very conveniently effected by heating with sulphamic acid (Kirsanov *et al.*, 1950):

$$R{\cdot}CO{\cdot}NH_2 + NH_2{\cdot}SO_3H \longrightarrow R{\cdot}CN + NH_4HSO_4$$

Stephens *et al.* (1955) have shown that *p*-toluenesulphonyl chloride in pyridine readily dehydrates amides to cyanides (yield: 58–76%).

High molecular weight acid amides are dehydrated to the corresponding cyanide by heat alone (p. 192).

An acid amide may be converted into the cyanide by heating it with the amide–boron trifluoride complex in the presence of a small amount of carboxylic acid (Nieuwland, 1937), *e.g.*,

$$CH_3{\cdot}CO{\cdot}NH_2{\cdot}BF_3 + CH_3{\cdot}CO{\cdot}NH_2 \xrightarrow{CH_3CO_2H} CH_3{\cdot}CN + CH_3{\cdot}CO_2H + H_3N{\cdot}BF_3$$

Cyanides are prepared industrially by passing a mixture of carboxylic acid and ammonia over alumina at 500°. This reaction probably occurs as follows:

$$R{\cdot}CO_2H + NH_3 \longrightarrow R{\cdot}CO_2NH_4 \xrightarrow{Al_2O_3} H_2O + R{\cdot}CO{\cdot}NH_2 \xrightarrow{Al_2O_3} H_2O + R{\cdot}CN$$

2. By the dehydration of aldoximes with phosphorus pentoxide, or better, with acetic anhydride:

$$R{\cdot}CH{:}N{\cdot}OH \xrightarrow[-H_2O]{(CH_3CO)_2O} R{\cdot}CN \quad (g.)$$

3. The most convenient method is to heat an alkyl iodide with potassium cyanide in aqueous ethanolic solution; a small amount of *iso*cyanide is also obtained:

$$RI + KCN \longrightarrow R{\cdot}CN + KI \quad (g.)$$

This method is satisfactory only if R is a primary or secondary alkyl radical. If it is a tertiary radical, very little cyanide is obtained, the tertiary iodide being converted into the corresponding olefin (*cf.* p. 99). Tertiary alkyl cyanides are best prepared by method 4 below.

Many cyanides, particularly the lower members, may be readily prepared by warming the potassium alkyl sulphate with potassium cyanide (some *iso*cyanide is also obtained):

$$RO{\cdot}SO_2{\cdot}OK + KCN \longrightarrow R{\cdot}CN + K_2SO_4 \quad (g.\text{–}v.g.)$$

The cyanide may be freed from *iso*cyanide by shaking with dilute hydrochloric acid, which hydrolyses the latter, but does not affect the former:

$$R{\cdot}NC + 2H_2O \xrightarrow{HCl} R{\cdot}NH_2 + H{\cdot}CO_2H$$

4. By the interaction of a Grignard reagent and cyanogen chloride:

$$RMgCl + ClCN \longrightarrow R{\cdot}CN + MgCl_2$$

This is the best method of preparing tertiary alkyl cyanides.

Methyl cyanide may be formed by passing a mixture of acetylene and ammonia over zirconia at 400–500°, the yield reaching as high as 99 per cent. (Amiel and Nomine, 1947.)

General properties. The alkyl cyanides are stable neutral substances with fairly pleasant smells, and are not as poisonous as hydrogen cyanide. The lower members are liquids which are soluble in water (with which they can form hydrogen bonds), but the solubility diminishes as the molecular weight increases. They are all readily soluble in organic solvents.

Reactions. 1. The alkyl cyanides are hydrolysed by acids or alkalis to the corresponding acid via the intermediate formation of an amide (see also p. 190):

$$R{\cdot}C{\equiv}N \xrightarrow{H_2O} \left[R{-}C\begin{matrix}\diagup OH \\ \diagdown\!\!\diagdown NH\end{matrix}\right] \longrightarrow R{\cdot}CO{\cdot}NH_2 \xrightarrow{H_2O} R{\cdot}CO_2H + NH_3 \; (g.\text{–}v.g.)$$

When a solution of alkyl cyanide in an alcohol is heated with concentrated sulphuric acid or hydrochloric acid, the *ester* is obtained:

$$R{\cdot}CN + R'OH + H_2O \longrightarrow R{\cdot}CO_2R' + NH_3$$

On the other hand, if dry hydrogen chloride is passed into the solution of an alkyl cyanide in anhydrous alcohol, the *imidic ester hydrochloride* is formed:

$$R{\cdot}CN + R'OH + HCl \longrightarrow R{\cdot}C\begin{matrix}\diagup\!\!\diagup NH{\cdot}HCl \\ \diagdown OR'\end{matrix}$$

When an alkyl cyanide is treated with *dry* hydrogen chloride, the *imidochloride* is formed:

$$R{\cdot}C{\equiv}N + 2HCl \longrightarrow R{\cdot}C\begin{matrix}\diagup\!\!\diagup NH{\cdot}HCl \\ \diagdown Cl\end{matrix}$$

2. Alkyl cyanides combine with dry ammonia to form *amidines*:

$$R{\cdot}CN + NH_3 \longrightarrow R{\cdot}C\begin{matrix}\diagup\!\!\diagup NH \\ \diagdown NH_2\end{matrix}$$

3. Alkyl cyanides combine with acid anhydrides on heating to form *tertiary acid amides*:

$$R{\cdot}CN + (R{\cdot}CO)_2O \longrightarrow (R{\cdot}CO)_3N$$

4. Alkyl cyanides undergo *Stephen's reaction* to form aldehydes:

$$R{\cdot}CN \xrightarrow[\text{(ii) } H_2O]{\text{(i) } SnCl_2\text{–}HCl} R{\cdot}CHO$$

This, as we have seen (p. 139), is a general method for preparing aldehydes.

5. Alkyl cyanides are reduced by nascent hydrogen (sodium and ethanol) to give primary amines (the *Mendius reaction*, 1862):

$$R{\cdot}CN + 4[H] \xrightarrow{Na/C_2H_5OH} R{\cdot}CH_2{\cdot}NH_2$$

Some secondary amine, $(R{\cdot}CH_2)_2NH$, is also formed. Catalytic reduction of an alkyl cyanide also produces a primary amine accompanied by the secondary amine, but in this case the amount of the latter is greater than when the reduction is carried out with nascent hydrogen. Von Braun and co-workers (1933) suggested that the mechanism of the formation of secondary amine is:

$$R{\cdot}C{\equiv}N \xrightarrow[Ni]{H_2} R{\cdot}CH{:}NH \xrightarrow{H_2} R{\cdot}CH_2{\cdot}NH_2$$

$$R{\cdot}CH{:}NH + R{\cdot}CH_2{\cdot}NH_2 \longrightarrow R{\cdot}\underset{\substack{|\\NH_2}}{CH}{\cdot}NH{\cdot}CH_2{\cdot}R \longrightarrow$$

$$NH_3 + R{\cdot}CH{:}N{\cdot}CH_2{\cdot}R \xrightarrow{H_2} R{\cdot}CH_2{\cdot}NH{\cdot}CH_2{\cdot}R$$

Support for this mechanism is to be found in the fact that the formation of secondary amine is prevented if the reduction is carried out with a Raney nickel catalyst *in the presence of ammonia*.

Alternatively, the formation of secondary amine may be prevented by carrying out the reduction in acetic anhydride solution, using the Adams' platinum catalyst (p. 60). Under these conditions, the primary amine formed is acetylated; this acetyl derivative cannot react with the imine, $R{\cdot}CH{:}NH$. Reduction of alkyl cyanides with lithium aluminium hydride produces primary amine only.

It should be noted that the above reactions 1 to 5 clearly indicate that the alkyl group in alkyl cyanides is attached to the *carbon* atom of the CN group.

6. Alkyl cyanides (except methyl cyanide) react with Grignard reagents to form ketones:

$$R{\cdot}C{\vdots}N + R'MgX \longrightarrow R{-}\overset{\substack{R'\\|}}{C}{=}N{\cdot}MgX \xrightarrow{H_2O} R{\cdot}CO{\cdot}R'$$

7. Alkyl cyanides undergo condensation reactions in the presence of sodium, only the α-hydrogen atoms being involved. These condensations are to be expected in view of the fact that the cyano-group is a very strong negative group (p. 264). When the reaction is carried out in a solvent, *e.g.*, ether, two molecules of cyanide condense (*cf.* Thorpe's reaction, p. 449):

$$CH_3{\cdot}CH_2{\cdot}C{\equiv}N + CH_3{\cdot}CH_2{\cdot}CN \xrightarrow[\text{ether}]{Na} CH_3{\cdot}CH_2{\cdot}\overset{\substack{NH\\\|}}{C}{-}\overset{\substack{CH_3\\|}}{CH}{-}CN$$

If, however, the reaction is carried out at 150° in the absence of a solvent, three molecules condense to form a heterocyclic compound (a *pyrimidine* derivative):

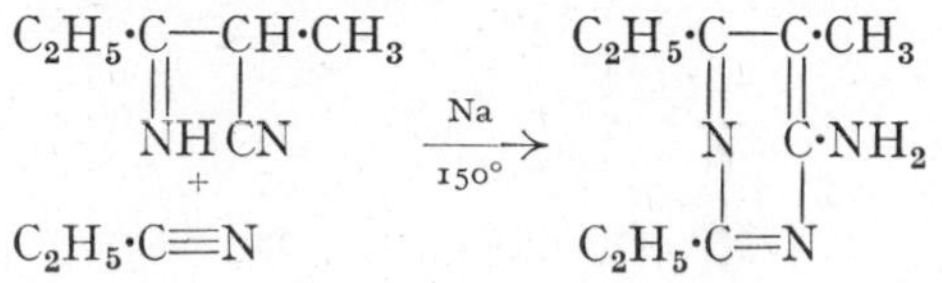

$$\begin{array}{l} C_2H_5{\cdot}C{-}CH{\cdot}CH_3 \\ \quad\;\; \| \quad\;\; | \\ \quad\;\, NH \;\; CN \\ \qquad\;\; + \\ C_2H_5{\cdot}C{\equiv}N \end{array} \xrightarrow[150^\circ]{Na} \begin{array}{l} C_2H_5{\cdot}C{-}C{\cdot}CH_3 \\ \qquad\;\; \| \quad \| \\ \qquad\;\; N \quad C{\cdot}NH_2 \\ \qquad\;\; | \quad\; | \\ C_2H_5{\cdot}C{=}N \end{array}$$

On the other hand, alkyl cyanides with α-hydrogen atoms can condense with esters if the reaction is carried out in ether solution in the presence of sodamide (Levine and Hauser, 1946); *e.g.*, methyl cyanide condenses with ethyl propionate to form propionylmethyl cyanide:

$$CH_3\cdot CN + NaNH_2 \longrightarrow [:\bar{C}H_2\cdot CN]Na^+ + NH_3$$
$$\xrightarrow{CH_3\cdot CH_2\cdot CO_2C_2H_5} CH_3\cdot CH_2\cdot CO\cdot CH_2\cdot CN + C_2H_5OH \quad (40\%)$$

ALKYL *iso*CYANIDES

These are also known as ***iso*nitriles** or **carbylamines.**

General methods of preparation. 1. By heating an alkyl iodide with silver cyanide in aqueous ethanolic solution; a small amount of cyanide is also formed:

$$RI + AgCN \longrightarrow R\cdot NC + AgI$$

2. By heating a mixture of a primary amine and chloroform with ethanolic potassium hydroxide:

$$R\cdot NH_2 + CHCl_3 + 3KOH \longrightarrow R\cdot NC + 3KCl + 3H_2O$$

It has been argued that by analogy with this reaction, replacement of a primary amine by ammonia would lead to the formation of hydrogen *iso*cyanide:

$$H—NH_2 + CHCl_3 + 3KOH \longrightarrow H—NC + KCl + 3H_2O$$

General properties. The alkyl *iso*cyanides are poisonous, most unpleasant-smelling liquids, with lower boiling points than the isomeric cyanides. They are not very soluble in water, the nitrogen atom not having a lone pair of electrons available for hydrogen bonding.

Reactions. 1. Alkyl *iso*cyanides are hydrolysed to an amine and formic acid by dilute acids, *but are not hydrolysed by alkalis*:

$$R\cdot NC + 2H_2O \xrightarrow{acid} R\cdot NH_2 + H\cdot CO_2H$$

2. Alkyl *iso*cyanides are reduced to secondary amines either by nascent hydrogen or by catalytic reduction:

$$R\cdot NC + 4[H] \longrightarrow R\cdot NH\cdot CH_3$$

Both reactions 1 and 2 clearly indicate that the alkyl group in alkyl *iso*cyanides is attached to the *nitrogen* atom of the CN group (*cf.* cyanides, above).

3. Alkyl *iso*cyanides add on halogen to form *alkyliminocarbonyl halides*, sulphur to form *alkyl* iso*thiocyanates*, and are readily oxidised by mercuric oxide to *alkyl* iso*cyanates*:

$$R\cdot NC + X_2 \longrightarrow R\cdot NCX_2$$
$$R\cdot NC + S \longrightarrow R\cdot NCS$$
$$R\cdot NC + HgO \longrightarrow R\cdot NCO + Hg$$

4. When alkyl *iso*cyanides are heated for a long time, they rearrange to the cyanide:

$$R\cdot NC \longrightarrow R\cdot CN$$

Cyanogen (*ethanedinitrile*), C_2N_2, may be prepared by heating the cyanides of mercury or silver:

$$Hg(CN)_2 \longrightarrow C_2N_2 + Hg$$

It may also be prepared by adding sodium cyanide to copper sulphate solution and heating. The cupric cyanide first formed is unstable, decomposing into cuprous cyanide and cyanogen:

$$2CuSO_4 + 4NaCN \longrightarrow 2CuCN + C_2N_2 + 2Na_2SO_4$$

When heated with phosphorus pentoxide, oxamide is dehydrated to cyanogen:

$$\begin{matrix} CO{\cdot}NH_2 \\ | \\ CO{\cdot}NH_2 \end{matrix} \xrightarrow[-2H_2O]{P_2O_5} \begin{matrix} CN \\ | \\ CN \end{matrix}$$

Cyanogen is a poisonous, colourless gas, b.p. $-21°$, very soluble in water. It burns with a violet flame to give carbon dioxide and nitrogen:

$$C_2N_2 + 2O_2 \longrightarrow 2CO_2 + N_2$$

Its aqueous solution slowly decomposes to give a brown precipitate of *azulmic acid*, $C_4H_5ON_5$, and the solution contains ammonium oxalate, hydrogen cyanide, formic acid and urea. When cyanogen is heated at 400°, it polymerises to *paracyanogen*, which, at 800°, regenerates cyanogen. The structure of cyanogen is probably best represented as a resonance hybrid, I being the most important:

$$\underset{(I)}{:N{\equiv}C{-}C{\equiv}N:} \longleftrightarrow \underset{(II)}{:\overset{+}{N}{=}C{=}C{=}\overset{-}{\ddot{N}}:} \longleftrightarrow \underset{(III)}{:\overset{-}{\ddot{N}}{=}C{=}C{=}\overset{+}{N}:}$$

Cyanogen chloride, ClCN, may be prepared by passing chlorine into a cooled solution of sodium cyanide:

$$NaCN + Cl_2 \longrightarrow ClCN + NaCl$$

It is a poisonous, colourless gas, b.p. 12°, which is very soluble in water, ethanol and ether. It readily polymerises to *cyanuric chloride*, $Cl_3C_3N_3$. This is a crystalline solid, m.p. 154°, which is decomposed by heating with water under pressure at 125° to give *cyanuric acid*:

$$Cl_3C_3N_3 + 3H_2O \longrightarrow H_3O_3C_3N_3 + 3HCl$$

Cyanogen bromide, BrCN, may be prepared by adding sodium cyanide to well-cooled bromine water:

$$NaCN + Br_2 \longrightarrow BrCN + NaBr \quad (73–85\%)$$

It is a colourless, crystalline solid, m.p. 52°, which polymerises to *cyanuric bromide*, $Br_3C_3N_3$. Cyanogen bromide is a useful reagent for converting tertiary amines into secondary amines (see p. 301).

Cyanic acid, HOCN. Urea, on dry distillation, gives *cyanuric acid*:

$$3CO(NH_2)_2 \longrightarrow H_3O_3C_3N_3 + 3NH_3$$

The yield is improved by heating urea with zinc chloride. Cyanuric acid is a colourless, crystalline solid, not very soluble in water, and is strongly acid, reacting as a mono-, di- and tribasic acid. It has a cyclic structure (a *triazine* derivative) and is believed to be tautomeric (*amido-imidol triad system*):

[Structures: cyclic keto form (ring of C=O carbons and NH groups) ⇌ enol form (ring of C–OH carbons and N atoms)]

On the other hand, X-ray analysis of cyanuric acid in the solid state indicates that the acid is best represented as a resonance hybrid of the carbonyl form (amido-form). Furthermore, absorption spectra studies in neutral solution show that the same forms are present as in the solid state (Koltz and Askounis, 1947).

When cyanuric acid is heated, it does not melt but decomposes into cyanic acid vapour which, when condensed below 0°, gives a colourless condensate:

$$H_3O_3C_3N_3 \longrightarrow 3HOCN$$

Cyanic acid is a colourless, volatile, strongly acid liquid which, above 0°, readily polymerises to cyanuric acid and *cyamelide,* which is a white solid isomeric with cyanuric acid. The structure of cyamelide is believed to be

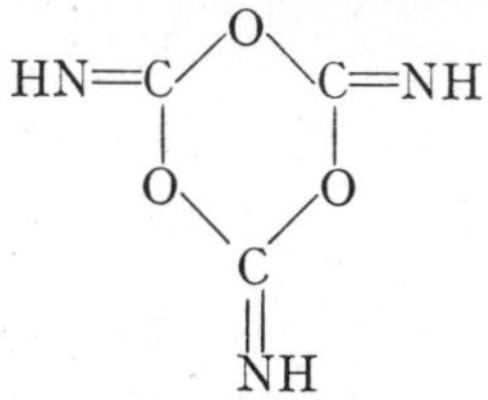

```
            O
          /   \
HN=C           C=NH
     |          |
     O          O
       \      /
          C
          ||
          NH
```

Aqueous solutions of cyanic acid rapidly hydrolyse to give carbon dioxide and ammonia:

$$HOCN + H_2O \longrightarrow CO_2 + NH_3$$

Cyanic acid was believed to be a tautomeric mixture of cyanic acid, IV, and *iso*cyanic acid, V (amido-imidol triad system):

$$\underset{(IV)}{H-O-C\equiv N} \rightleftharpoons \underset{(V)}{O=C=N-H}$$

Infra-red studies, however, have indicated that cyanic acid is V; only derivatives of V are known, *e.g.*, alkyl *iso*cyanates, R·NCO.

When a solution of potassium *iso*cyanate (usually called potassium cyanate) and ammonium sulphate is evaporated to dryness, urea and potassium sulphate are obtained, the urea being formed by the molecular rearrangement of the intermediate product ammonium *iso*cyanate:

$$NH_4NCO \longrightarrow CO(NH_2)_2$$

Cyanic acid reacts with alcohols to form *urethans*; excess of cyanic acid converts urethans into *allophanates*, which are esters of the unknown acid, *allophanic acid*, $NH_2{\cdot}CO{\cdot}NH{\cdot}CO_2H$:

$$ROH + HNCO \longrightarrow NH_2{\cdot}CO_2R \xrightarrow{HNCO} NH_2{\cdot}CO{\cdot}NH{\cdot}CO_2R$$

According to Close *et al.* (1953), the formation of urethan is, if it is truly the intermediate step, not the important one in the usual preparation of allophanates. These authors suggest that allophanate formation occurs via a concerted attack of two molecules of cyanic acid to form a chelate intermediate.

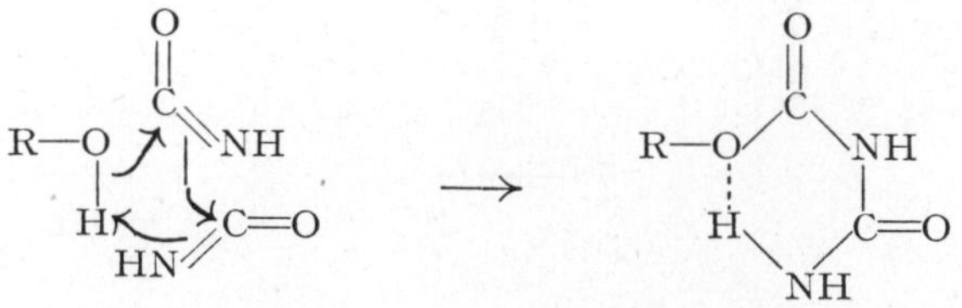

```
          O                                 O
          ||                                ||
          C                                 C
R—O ↗  |  \NH                  R—O      \NH
  |       |           →            :          |
  H↖    ↘C=O                      H        C=O
   HN                                  \  /
                                        NH
```

N-substituted urethans are formed by the reaction between alkyl or aryl *iso*cyanates and an alcohol. These are well-defined crystalline solids, and so are used to characterise alcohols, phenyl and 1-naphthyl *iso*cyanates being the *iso*cyanates used for this purpose:

$$C_6H_5\cdot NCO + ROH \longrightarrow C_6H_5\cdot NH\cdot CO_2R$$

Phenyl *iso*cyanate is also used to characterise primary and secondary amines, with which it forms substituted ureas (see p. 298).

Phenyl *iso*cyanate is usually prepared by the action of carbonyl chloride on aniline:

$$C_6H_5\cdot NH_2 + COCl_2 \longrightarrow HCl + C_2H_5\cdot NH\cdot COCl \xrightarrow{\text{heat}} HCl + C_6H_5\cdot NCO$$

This is a general method for preparing *iso*cyanates; another general method is the Curtius reaction (p. 195).

Di-*iso*cyanates, *e.g.*, hexamethylene di-*iso*cyanate, $OCN\cdot(CH_2)_6\cdot NCO$, are used to prepare polyurethan plastics by reaction with di- and polyhydroxyalcohols, *e.g.*, tetramethylene glycol:

$$HO\cdot(CH_2)_4\cdot OH + OCN\cdot(CH_2)_6\cdot NCO + HO\cdot(CH_2)_4\cdot OH + \ldots \longrightarrow$$
$$HO\cdot(CH_2)_4\cdot O\cdot CO\cdot NH\cdot(CH_2)_6\cdot NH\cdot CO\cdot O\cdot(CH_2)_4\cdot O\cdot \ldots$$

Fulminic acid. $HO\cdot N \rightleftharpoons C$, may be prepared by decomposition of its salts with acid. Mercury fulminate, $[(CNO)_2Hg]_2H_2O$, which is used as a detonator, may be prepared by dissolving mercury in nitric acid, and then adding ethanol. Free fulminic acid is unstable. It is soluble in ether, the ethereal solution also being unstable, the acid readily polymerising.

Cyanamide, $NH_2\cdot CN$, may be prepared by the action of ammonia on cyanogen chloride:

$$ClCN + NH_3 \longrightarrow NH_2\cdot CN + HCl$$

It may also be prepared by heating urea with thionyl chloride:

$$CO(NH_2)_2 + SOCl_2 \longrightarrow NH_2\cdot CN + SO_2 + 2HCl$$

It is also readily prepared by the action of water and carbon dioxide on calcium cyanamide (see below).

Cyanamide is a colourless, crystalline solid, m.p. 42°, very soluble in water, ethanol and ether. It is converted into *guanidine* (*q.v.*) by ammonia, and into *thiourea* (*q.v.*) by hydrogen sulphide. When cyanamide is melted it forms the dimer *dicyanodiamide,* $(NH_2)_2C{:}N\cdot CN$, and the trimer *melamine,* which is a cyclic compound (and tautomeric):

```
          NH2                              NH
          |                                ||
          C                                C
        /   \\                           /   \
       N      N                        HN     NH
       ||     |          <=>           |       |
  NH2·C       C·NH2               HN=C        C=NH
        \\   /                          \    /
          N                               NH
```

Melamine is used for making melamine–formaldehyde plastics.

Cyanamide itself is a tautomeric compound (amidine system), and Raman spectra investigations have shown that two forms are present in equilibrium in the solid or fused state, or in solution:

$$H_2N{-}C{\equiv}N \rightleftharpoons HN{=}C{=}NH$$

Cyanamide forms salts, the most important of which is the calcium salt. This is manufactured by heating calcium carbide mixed with 10 per cent. its weight of calcium chloride in a stream of nitrogen at 800°:

$$CaC_2 + N_2 \longrightarrow CaN\cdot CN + C$$

The calcium cyanamide–carbon mixture is used as a fertiliser; it is hydrolysed in the soil to cyanamide, which is then hydrolysed to urea, which, in turn, is converted into ammonium carbonate by bacteria in the soil:

$$CaN{\cdot}CN + 2H_2O \longrightarrow NH_2{\cdot}CN + Ca(OH)_2$$

$$NH_2{\cdot}CN + H_2O \longrightarrow CO(NH_2)_2$$

$$CO(NH_2)_2 + 2H_2O \longrightarrow (NH_4)_2CO_3$$

Calcium cyanamide is also used to prepare urea industrially.

NITROPARAFFINS

Nomenclature. The nitroparaffins are named as the nitro-derivative of the corresponding paraffin, the positions of the nitro-groups being indicated by numbers (using the rule of least numbers, p. 41), *e.g.*,

$CH_3{\cdot}NO_2$ nitromethane

$CH_3{\cdot}CH(NO_2){\cdot}CH_3$ 2-nitropropane

$CH_3{\cdot}CH(NO_2){\cdot}CH_2{\cdot}CH(NO_2){\cdot}CH_2{\cdot}CH_3$ 2 : 4-dinitrohexane

The nitroparaffins, the structure of which is $R{\cdot}NO_2$, are isomeric with the alkyl nitrites, R·O·NO. The evidence that may be adduced for these respective formulæ is to be found in the study of the reactions of these two groups of compounds. The reactions of the nitrites have already been described (p. 183), and those of the nitroparaffins are described below. It is, however, worth while at this stage to mention the reaction which most clearly indicates their respective structures, *viz.*, reduction. When alkyl nitrites are reduced by nascent hydrogen, an alcohol and ammonia or hydroxylamine are formed. This shows that the alkyl group in nitrites is attached to an oxygen atom:

$$R{-}O{\cdot}NO \xrightarrow{[H]} ROH + NH_3 + H_2O$$

On the other hand, when nitroparaffins are reduced, a primary amine is formed. This shows that the alkyl group is attached to the nitrogen atom, since the structure of a primary amine is known to be $R{-}NH_2$ from its method of preparation (see below):

$$R{\cdot}NO_2 \xrightarrow{[H]} R{\cdot}NH_2 + 2H_2O$$

The structure of the nitro-compounds was originally written $R{-}N\begin{smallmatrix}{/\!\!/}O\\ \searrow O\end{smallmatrix}$,

but work on the dipole moments indicates that they are resonance hybrids:

$$R{-}N\begin{smallmatrix}{/\!\!/}O\\ \searrow O\end{smallmatrix} \longleftrightarrow R{-}N\begin{smallmatrix}\nearrow O\\ {\backslash\!\!\backslash}O\end{smallmatrix} \quad \text{or} \quad R{-}\overset{+}{N}\begin{smallmatrix}{/\!\!/}O\\ \backslash \bar{O}\end{smallmatrix} \longleftrightarrow R{-}\overset{+}{N}\begin{smallmatrix}/\bar{O}\\ {\backslash\!\!\backslash}O\end{smallmatrix}$$

For most purposes, however, the original formula $R{-}N\begin{smallmatrix}{/\!\!/}O\\ \searrow O\end{smallmatrix}$ or the non-committal formula $R{\cdot}NO_2$, is satisfactory.

From the M.O. point of view, the nitro-group is conjugated (Fig. 1), and delocalisation of bonds increases its stability (the two oxygen atoms are equivalent; *cf.* the carboxylate ion, p. 172).

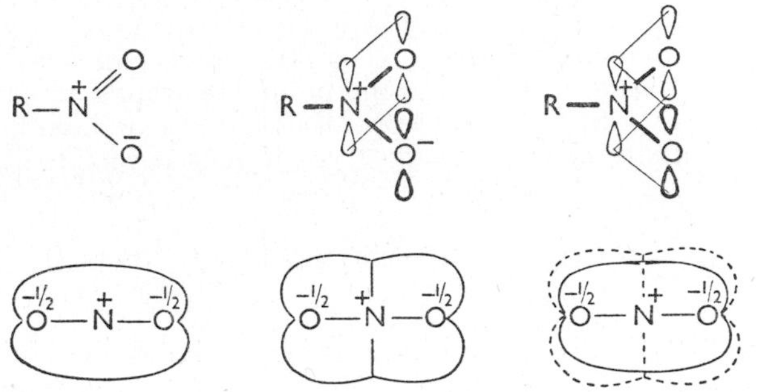

FIG. 13.1.

General methods of preparation. 1. By heating an alkyl halide with silver nitrite in aqueous ethanolic solution:

$$RX + AgONO \longrightarrow R{\cdot}NO_2 + RONO + AgX$$

This method is only useful for the preparation of primary nitroparaffins. With *sec.*-halides the yield is about 15 per cent., and with *tert.*-halides 0–5 per cent.; the yield of nitrite increases from primary to tertiary halides (Kornblum *et al.*, 1954, 1955). Kornblum *et al.* (1956) have now described a simple new synthesis of primary and secondary nitro-compounds. These authors have shown that, contrary to general opinion, sodium nitrite reacts with alkyl halides to give good yields of nitroparaffin (55–62%), together with alkyl nitrites (25–33%). The success of the reaction depends on the use of dimethylformamide as solvent, and the addition of urea increases the solubility of sodium nitrite. Alkyl bromides and iodides are most satisfactory; the chlorides react too slowly to be useful.

The mechanism of the reaction between alkyl halides and silver nitrite is uncertain. Kornblum *et al.* (1955) believe that the reaction proceeds via a transition state which has both S_N1 and S_N2 character in proportions that vary gradually with the structure of the alkyl halide.

2. Nitromethane may be prepared by boiling an aqueous solution of sodium nitrite with a halogeno-acetic acid, *e.g.*,

$$CH_2Cl{\cdot}CO_2Na + NaNO_2 \longrightarrow NaCl + [CH_2(NO_2){\cdot}CO_2H] \longrightarrow CH_3{\cdot}NO_2 + CO_2 \quad (35\text{–}38\%)$$

This method has no value for preparing higher nitroparaffins (Treibs *et al.*, 1954).

The ready decarboxylation of the intermediate nitroacetic acid may be explained on the assumption that the electron-attracting nitro-group facilitates the loss of carbon dioxide (*cf.* p. 166):

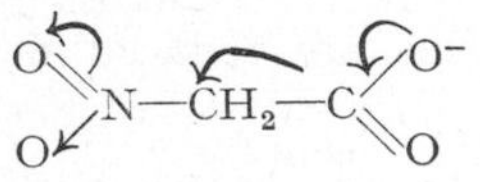

3. Until fairly recently, the preparation of nitro-compounds by direct nitration was of academic interest only, but mainly from the work of Hass and his co-workers direct nitration is now an important industrial

process. Two techniques have been evolved: liquid-phase nitration and vapour-phase nitration.

In *liquid-phase nitration*, the hydrocarbon is heated with concentrated nitric acid under pressure at 140°. Nitration under these conditions is always slow, and a large amount of polynitro-compounds is produced. It is interesting to note that a mixture of nitric and sulphuric acids is not suitable for nitrating paraffins (*cf.* aromatic hydrocarbons, p. 528).

In *vapour-phase nitration*, the hydrocarbon is heated with nitric acid (or with oxides of nitrogen) at 150–475°; each hydrocarbon has its optimum temperature, *e.g.*,

$$CH_3{\cdot}CH_2{\cdot}CH_3 \xrightarrow[400^\circ]{HNO_3} CH_3{\cdot}CH_2{\cdot}CH_2{\cdot}NO_2 + CH_3{\cdot}CH(NO_2){\cdot}CH_3 + CH_3{\cdot}CH_2{\cdot}NO_2 + CH_3{\cdot}NO_2$$

Vapour-phase nitration is more satisfactory than liquid-phase nitration.

Hass and Shechter (1947) have formulated general rules of vapour-phase nitration of paraffins (and *cyclo*paraffins).

(i) Polynitro-compounds are formed only from paraffins of fairly high molecular weight.

(ii) Any hydrogen atom in the hydrocarbon is capable of replacement by a nitro-group, and the ease of replacement is tertiary hydrogen > secondary > primary. As the temperature rises, however, the ease of replacement tends to become equal.

(iii) Any alkyl group present in the paraffin can be replaced by a nitro-group, *i.e.*, chain fission takes place; *e.g.*, *iso*pentane yields nine nitroparaffins. The fission reaction increases as the temperature rises.

(iv) Oxidation always accompanies nitration, resulting in the formation of nitro-compounds and a mixture of acids, aldehydes, ketones, alcohols, nitrites, nitroso-compounds, nitro-olefins, polymers, carbon monoxide and carbon dioxide. Catalysts such as copper, iron, platinum oxide, etc., accelerate oxidation rather than nitration.

4. Another recent method for preparing nitro-compounds is the hydrolysis of α-nitro-olefins with water, acid or alkali; *e.g.*, 2-methyl-1-nitroprop-1-ene gives acetone and nitromethane in almost quantitative yield (Levy and Scaife, 1947):

$$(CH_3)_2C{:}CH{\cdot}NO_2 + H_2O \longrightarrow (CH_3)_2CO + CH_3{\cdot}NO_2$$

5. Kornblum *et al.* (1956) have introduced a practical synthesis of *tert.*-nitro-compounds by the oxidation of *tert.*-carbinamines with potassium permanganate:

$$R_3C{\cdot}NH_2 \xrightarrow{KMnO_4} R_3C{\cdot}NO_2 \quad (70\text{–}80\%)$$

General properties. The nitroparaffins are colourless (when pure), pleasant-smelling liquids which are sparingly soluble in water. Most of them can be distilled at atmospheric pressure.

The nitroparaffins in commercial use at the moment are the lowest four members of the series: nitromethane, nitroethane and 1- and 2-nitropropanes. These are prepared by the vapour-phase nitration of propane, and are used as solvents for oils, fats, cellulose esters, resins and dyes.

Reactions. 1. Nitroparaffins are reduced in *acid* solution to primary amines:

$$R{\cdot}NO_2 + 6[H] \xrightarrow{metal/acid} R{\cdot}NH_2 + 2H_2O$$

Catalytic reduction also produces a primary amine, the yield with a Raney nickel catalyst being 90–100 per cent. When the reduction is carried out in *neutral* solution, *e.g.*, with zinc dust and ammonium chloride solution, nitro-compounds are converted into hydroxylamine derivatives:

$$R{\cdot}NO_2 + 4[H] \xrightarrow{Zn/NH_4Cl} R{\cdot}NH{\cdot}OH + H_2O$$

When stannous chloride and hydrochloric acid are used as the reducing agent, nitro-compounds are converted into a mixture of hydroxylamine derivative and oxime:

$$R{\cdot}CH_2{\cdot}NO_2 \xrightarrow{SnCl_2/HCl} R{\cdot}CH_2{\cdot}NH{\cdot}OH + R{\cdot}CH{:}N{\cdot}OH$$

Since hydroxylamine can give rise to two types of derivatives, *e.g.*, R·NH·OH and $NH_2{\cdot}OR$, it is necessary to distinguish one from the other. A common method is to name the former as the *N*-alkylhydroxylamine, and the latter as the *O*-alkylhydroxylamine, the capital letters *N* and *O*, respectively, indicating where the alkyl group is attached in the molecule.

2. Primary nitro-compounds are hydrolysed by boiling hydrochloric acid or by 85 per cent. sulphuric acid to a carboxylic acid and hydroxylamine:

$$R{\cdot}CH_2{\cdot}NO_2 + H_2O \xrightarrow{HCl} R{\cdot}CO_2H + NH_2{\cdot}OH$$

This reaction is now used for manufacturing hydroxylamine, and may become a commercial source of propionic acid (using 1-nitropropane).

Secondary nitro-compounds are hydrolysed by boiling hydrochloric acid to ketones and nitrous oxide:

$$2R_2CH{\cdot}NO_2 \xrightarrow{HCl} 2R_2CO + N_2O + H_2O$$

Tertiary nitro-compounds are generally unaffected by hydrochloric acid.

3. Primary and secondary nitro-compounds, *i.e.*, those containing α-hydrogen atoms, are acidic in character due to tautomerism (the nitro-group is a very strong negative group and contains multiple bonds):

$$\underset{\text{(I)}}{R{\cdot}CH_2{\cdot}N\begin{matrix}{=}O\\ \rightarrow O\end{matrix}} \rightleftharpoons \underset{\text{(II)}}{R{\cdot}CH{=}N\begin{matrix}{-}OH\\ \rightarrow O\end{matrix}}$$

The nitro-form I is often called the *pseudo-acid* form; II is known as the *aci*-form or *nitronic acid*. This is an example of a triad system, the *nitro-acinitro* system; the equilibrium is almost completely on the left, and this may be due to the nitro-form being stabilised by resonance (of the nitro-group).

These nitronic acids do not dissolve in aqueous sodium carbonate, but do in aqueous sodium hydroxide, which disturbs the nitro-acinitro equilibrium by removing the latter form. Thus nitro-compounds behave as acids in the presence of strong alkalis, but not in their absence; hence they are said to be *pseudo-acids*:

$$R_2CH{\cdot}NO_2 \rightleftharpoons R_2C{:}NO_2H \xrightarrow{NaOH} R_2C{:}NO_2Na$$

These sodium compounds are true salts, *i.e.*, they exist as ions: $[R_2C{:}NO_2]^-Na^+$. When the sodium salt is acidified at low temperature, there is not always an immediate separation of oily drops (of the nitro-form). On standing, however, the acidified solution slowly deposits oily drops due to the slow tautomeric change of the nitronic acid into the nitro-compound. Furthermore, when the sodium salt is carefully neutralised with hydrochloric acid, the resulting solution has a conductivity which is greater than that calculated for the sodium chloride content. Hence, in addition to the sodium and chloride ions, there must be present other ions which must be those from the nitronic acid. Thus the following changes probably take place:

$$[R_2C{:}NO_2]^-Na^+ + HCl \longrightarrow Na^+Cl^- + [R_2C{:}NO_2]^-H^+ \longrightarrow R_2C{:}NO_2H \rightleftharpoons R_2CH{\cdot}NO_2$$

This is evidence for the existence of the nitronic acid; actually Hantzsch and Schultze (1896) isolated both forms of phenylnitromethane, $C_6H_5{\cdot}CH_2{\cdot}NO_2$, thus confirming the existence of the nitro-acinitro tautomeric system.

When the sodium salt solution of the nitronic acid is acidified with 50 per cent. sulphuric acid at room temperature, an aldehyde (from a primary nitro-compound) and a ketone (from a secondary nitro-compound) is obtained, *e.g.*, (R′ is either an alkyl radical or a hydrogen atom):

$$2RR'C{:}NO_2Na + 2H_2SO_4 \longrightarrow 2RR'CO + N_2O + 2NaHSO_4 + H_2O \quad (85\%)$$

When treated with stannous chloride and hydrochloric acid, the sodium salt of the nitronic acid is reduced to the aldoxime or ketoxime:

$$RR'C{:}NO_2Na \xrightarrow{SnCl_2/HCl} RR'C{:}N{\cdot}OH$$

These oximes are readily converted into the parent carbonyl compound by steam distillation or by direct hydrolysis with acid.

4. Primary and secondary nitro-compounds are readily halogenated in alkaline solution in the α-position only:

$$R_2C{:}NO_2Na + Br_2 \xrightarrow{NaOH} R_2CBr{\cdot}NO_2 + NaBr$$

Primary nitro-compounds can form the mono- and dibromo-derivatives, whereas secondary form only the monobromo-derivative: nitromethane is exceptional in that it can form the tribromo-derivative. *Chloropicrin* (p. 107) is manufactured by the reaction between nitromethane, chlorine and sodium hydroxide.

When liquid or gaseous nitro-compounds are treated with halogen *in the absence of alkali*, indiscriminate substitution takes place resulting in the formation of the α-, β-, γ-, halogeno-compounds, *e.g.*,

$$CH_3{\cdot}CH_2{\cdot}NO_2 \xrightarrow{Cl_2} CH_3{\cdot}CHCl{\cdot}NO_2 + CH_2Cl{\cdot}CH_2{\cdot}NO_2$$

5. Nitro-compounds react with nitrous acid, the product formed depending on the nature of the alkyl group.

Primary nitro-compounds form *nitrolic acids*; these are crystalline substances which dissolve in sodium hydroxide to give red solutions:

$$R{-}C(H)(H)(NO_2) + O{=}NOH \longrightarrow R{-}C({=}NOH)(NO_2) + H_2O$$

Secondary nitro-compounds form *pseudonitroles* (ψ-*nitroles*); these are colourless crystalline substances which dissolve in sodium hydroxide to give blue solutions (the blue colour is probably due to the presence of the nitroso-group; see below):

$$R_2C(H)(NO_2) + NO{-}NO \longrightarrow R_2C(NO)(NO_2) + H_2O$$

Tertiary nitro-compounds do not react with nitrous acid since they have no α-hydrogen atom.

These reactions with nitrous acid are the basis of the "red, white and blue" test for the nature of monohydric alcohols (Victor Meyer *et al.*, 1874). The alcohol under investigation is treated as follows:

$$ROH \xrightarrow{PBr_3} RBr \xrightarrow{AgONO} R{\cdot}NO_2$$

The nitro-compound is now treated with an alkaline solution of sodium nitrite, acidified with hydrochloric acid, and finally made alkaline with sodium hydroxide. The development of a red colour indicates a primary alcohol, blue colour a secondary, and the solution remaining colourless ("white"), a tertiary alcohol. This test is now only historically important.

6. Owing to the presence of active α-hydrogen atoms, primary and secondary nitro-compounds undergo condensation with aldehydes; *e.g.*, (i) nitro-methane condenses with benzaldehyde in the presence of ethanolic potassium hydroxide to form *ω-nitrostyrene*:

$$C_6H_5{\cdot}CHO + CH_3{\cdot}NO_2 \xrightarrow{KOH} C_6H_5{\cdot}CH{:}CH{\cdot}NO_2 + H_2O$$

(ii) Nitroethane condenses with formaldehyde in the presence of aqueous potassium hydrogen carbonate to form the bishydroxymethyl compound, 2-methyl-2-nitropropane-1 : 3-diol (*cf.* p. 154).

$$CH_3{\cdot}CH_2{\cdot}NO_2 + 2HCHO \xrightarrow{KHCO_3} CH_3{\cdot}C(NO_2)(CH_2OH)_2$$

These condensations are similar to the aldol condensations, the active methylene or methyne group being produced by the adjacent nitro-group.

The sodium salts of the nitronic acids condense with αβ-unsaturated ketones, a reaction which is similar to the Michael condensation (p. 262); *e.g.*, with mesityl oxide nitromethane forms 4 : 4-dimethyl-5-nitropentan-2-one:

$$(CH_3)_2C{:}CH{\cdot}CO{\cdot}CH_3 + CH_2{:}NO_2Na \longrightarrow (CH_3)_2C(CH{:}NO_2Na){-}CH_2{\cdot}CO{\cdot}CH_3 \xrightarrow{HCl} (CH_3)_2C(CH_2{\cdot}NO_2){-}CH_2{\cdot}CO{\cdot}CH_3$$

Primary and secondary nitro-compounds also undergo the **Mannich reaction** (1917). This is the condensation between formaldehyde, ammonia or a primary or secondary amine (preferably as the hydrochloride), and a compound containing at least one active hydrogen atom. In this reaction, the active hydrogen atom is replaced by an aminoethyl group or substituted aminoethyl group:

$$R_2CH{\cdot}NO_2 + H{\cdot}CHO + NH_4Cl \longrightarrow R_2C(NO_2){-}CH_2{\cdot}NH_2{\cdot}HCl + H_2O$$

The Mannich reaction offers a means of preparing a large variety of compounds, *e.g.*, nitro-amines, diamines, etc.

NITROSO-PARAFFINS

The nitroso-paraffins contain a nitroso-group, —N=O, directly attached to a carbon atom. They are named as the nitroso-derivatives of the corresponding paraffin, *e.g.*,

$(CH_3)_3C{\cdot}NO$ 2-methyl-2-nitrosopropane

General methods of preparation. 1. By the addition of "nitrous fumes" to olefins. The compound formed depends on the nature of the olefin; usually a mixture is obtained, *e.g.*, Michael and Carlson (1940) treated *iso*butene with dinitrogen tetroxide under various conditions, and believed that the following compounds were formed (see also p. 65):

$$\left[\begin{array}{cc}(CH_3)_2C & -CH_2 \\ | & | \\ O{\cdot}NO_2 & NO\end{array}\right]_2 \qquad \left[\begin{array}{cc}(CH_3)_2C & -CH_2 \\ | & | \\ O{\cdot}NO & NO\end{array}\right]_2$$

nitrosate — nitrosite

$$\begin{array}{cc}(CH_3)_2C & -CH_2 \\ | & | \\ NO_2 & NO_2\end{array} \qquad (CH_3)_2C{:}CH{\cdot}NO_2$$

dinitro-compound — nitro-compound

2. By the addition of nitrosyl chloride or bromide to olefins, whereby olefin nitrosohalides are formed (p. 65):

$$CH_2{=}CH_2 + NOCl \longrightarrow \begin{array}{cc}CH_2 & -CH_2 \\ | & | \\ NO & Cl\end{array} \xrightarrow{\text{2 molecules}} \left[\begin{array}{cc}CH_2 & -CH_2 \\ | & | \\ NO & Cl\end{array}\right]_2$$

Thorne (1956) has shown that, in general, structures which increase the availability of electrons at the double bond favour the formation of nitroso-chlorides and nitrosates. Thus it was found that a carboxyl group fairly close to the double bond prevents formation of adducts, *e.g.*, 4-phenylbut-3-enoic and 5-phenylpent-4-enoic acid do not form nitrosochlorides or nitrosates; oleic acid, however, forms a nitrosochloride. Furthermore, the position of a double bond in an olefin determines whether an adduct is formed, *e.g.*, hex-1-ene does not form a nitrosochloride whereas hex-2-ene does.

3. By the action of nitrous acid on certain types of compounds, *e.g.*, secondary nitro-paraffins (see p. 288).

4. By the oxidation of primary amines containing a tertiary alkyl group with *e.g.*, Caro's acid (peroxy(mono)sulphuric acid):

$$R_3C{\cdot}NH_2 + 2[O] \xrightarrow{H_2SO_5} R_3C{\cdot}NO + H_2O$$

5. Gowenlock *et al.* (1956) have prepared nitrosoparaffins ($C_1 - C_4$) by the pyrolysis of alkyl nitrites, and have proposed the following mechanism (*e.g.*, for ethyl nitrite):

$$CH_3{\cdot}CH_2{\cdot}O{\cdot}NO \longrightarrow NO + CH_3{\cdot}CH_2{\cdot}O{\cdot} \longrightarrow NO + CH_3{\cdot} + CH_2O \longrightarrow CH_3{\cdot}NO + CH_2O$$

General properties. Nitroso-compounds, which are usually blue or green liquids, tend to associate to give colourless solids (smelling like camphor) which are dimers. These bimolecular solids regenerate the monomer when fused or when dissolved in solution. The structure of these dimers is not certain; according to Hammick *et al.* (1934), their structure is best represented as a resonance hybrid:

$$\begin{array}{c}R \\ O\end{array}\!\!\rangle \ddot{N}{\rightarrow}N\langle\!\!\begin{array}{c}{\nearrow}O \\ R\end{array} \quad \longleftrightarrow \quad \begin{array}{c}R \\ O{\swarrow}\end{array}\!\!\rangle \ddot{N}{\leftarrow}N\langle\!\!\begin{array}{c}{=}O \\ R\end{array}$$

On the other hand, Chilton *et al.* (1955) and Gowenlock *et al.* (1955) have examined the absorption spectrum of the two solid forms of nitrosomethane, and have concluded that they are geometrical isomers (*N.B.*, a *double-bond* is

$$\begin{array}{c}CH_3 \\ O{\swarrow}\end{array}\!\!\rangle N{=}N\langle\!\!\begin{array}{c}CH_3 \\ {\searrow}O\end{array} \qquad \begin{array}{c}CH_3 \\ O{\swarrow}\end{array}\!\!\rangle N{=}N\langle\!\!\begin{array}{c}{\nearrow}O \\ CH_3\end{array}$$

cis — *trans*

necessary for this molecule to exhibit geometrical isomerism).

Nitroso-compounds exist as such only when the nitroso-group is attached to a carbon atom not joined to hydrogen, *i.e.*, to a tertiary carbon atom. If the nitroso-group is attached to a primary or secondary carbon atom, the nitroso-compound is generally unstable, tending to rearrange to the oxime:

$$R_2CH—NO \longrightarrow R_2C{:}N{\cdot}OH$$

blue and unstable — colourless and stable

This is known as the *nitroso-oximino* triad system. This system is *potentially* tautomeric, but no example is known of the isomerisation of the oxime directly to the nitroso-compound. On the other hand, when an aldoxime is treated with bromine, the bromonitroso compound is formed; this, on fusion, is converted into the isomeric bromo-oxime:

$$R{\cdot}CH{:}N{\cdot}OH \xrightarrow{Br_2} R{\cdot}C(H)(NO)(Br) \xrightarrow{fuse} R{\cdot}CBr{:}N{\cdot}OH$$

It has also been found that the bimolecular nitroso-chlorides rearrange, if possible, to the oxime when treated with sodium hydroxide:

$$\begin{bmatrix} CH_2Cl \\ | \\ CH_2{\cdot}NO \end{bmatrix}_2 \xrightarrow{NaOH} 2 \begin{matrix} CH_2Cl \\ | \\ CH{:}N{\cdot}OH \end{matrix}$$

The so-called *iso*nitroso-compounds (oximino-compounds) are actually the oximes, *e.g.*, *iso*nitrosoacetone, $CH_3{\cdot}CO{\cdot}CH{:}N{\cdot}OH$, formed by the action of nitrous acid on acetone, is really the half oxime of methylglyoxal (*q.v.*).

Nitroso-compounds may be oxidised to the nitro-compound by nitric acid, and reduced to the primary amine by, *e.g.*, tin and hydrochloric acid:

$$R_3C{\cdot}NO_2 \xleftarrow{HNO_3} R_3C{\cdot}NO \xrightarrow{Sn/HCl} R_3C{\cdot}NH_2$$

MONOAMINES

Amines are derivatives of ammonia in which one or more hydrogen atoms have been replaced by alkyl groups. The amines are classified as primary, secondary or tertiary amines according as one, two or three hydrogen atoms in the ammonia molecule have been replaced by alkyl groups. Thus the general formulæ of primary, secondary and tertiary amines may be written $R{\cdot}NH_2$, R_2NH and R_3N, and each is characterised by the presence of the *amino-group* $—NH_2$, the *imino-group* $>NH$, and the *tertiary nitrogen atom* $>N—$, respectively.

In addition to the amines the tetra-alkyl derivatives of ammonium hydroxide, $[R_4N]^+ OH^-$, are known; these are called the *quaternary ammonium hydroxides*.

Nomenclature. The suffix of the series is *amine*, and each member is named according to the alkyl groups attached to the nitrogen atom, *e.g.*,

$CH_3{\cdot}NH_2$	methylamine
$(CH_3)_2NH$	dimethylamine
$(CH_3)_3N$	trimethylamine
$(C_2H_5)_2N{\cdot}CH(CH_3)_2$	diethyl*iso*propylamine

The amines are said to be " simple " when all the alkyl groups are the same, and " mixed " when the alkyl groups are different.

The method of naming a quaternary ammonium hydroxide is illustrated by the following examples:

$(CH_3)_4NOH$	tetramethylammonium hydroxide
$(CH_3)_3N{\cdot}C_2H_5\}OH$	ethyltrimethylammonium hydroxide

General methods of preparation. Many methods are available for preparing amines, but it is instructive to consider them in the following groups:

Methods for the three classes of amines. 1. **Hofmann's method** (1850). This is by means of *ammonolysis*, an alkyl halide and an ethanolic solution of ammonia being heated in a sealed tube at 100°. A mixture of all three classes of amines is obtained, together with some quaternary ammonium compound (see p. 297 for the structure of amine salts):

$$RX + NH_3 \longrightarrow R\cdot NH_2 + HX \longrightarrow R\cdot NH_2\cdot HX$$
$$R\cdot NH_2\cdot HX + NH_3 \rightleftharpoons R\cdot NH_2 + NH_4X$$
$$R\cdot NH_2 + RX \longrightarrow R_2NH + HX \longrightarrow R_2NH\cdot HX$$
$$R_2NH + RX \longrightarrow R_3N + HX \longrightarrow R_3N\cdot HX$$
$$R_3N + RX \longrightarrow [R_4N]^+X^-$$

In many cases a good yield of primary amine may be obtained by using a large excess of ammonia, and a good yield of tertiary amine by using alkyl halide in slight excess required by the equation:

$$3RX + NH_3 \longrightarrow R_3N + 3HX$$

Carrying out the reaction in liquid ammonia (in excess) gives a better yield of primary amine than by using aqueous or ethanolic ammonia; *e.g.*, Watt and Otto (1947) found that ammonolysis of ethyl iodide by liquid ammonia in excess at 0° was complete in less than 15 minutes, and gave 46 per cent. ethylamine, 31 per cent. diethylamine and 17 per cent. triethylamine.

The order of reactivity of the alkyl halides in ammonolysis is alkyl iodide>bromide>chloride, and the method is limited to primary alkyl halides and the secondary halide, *iso*propyl bromide. All other secondary halides and tertiary halides eliminate a molecule of halogen acid to form the olefin and no amine when heated with ethanolic ammonia. Amines of the type $R_3C\cdot NH_2$ are best prepared by means of a Grignard reagent (p. 341).

2. A mixture of the three types of amines may be prepared by the ammonolysis of alcohols; the alcohol and ammonia are heated under pressure in the presence of a catalyst, *e.g.*, copper chromite or alumina:

$$ROH + NH_3 \longrightarrow R\cdot NH_2 + H_2O$$
$$R\cdot NH_2 + ROH \longrightarrow R_2NH + H_2O$$
$$R_2NH + ROH \longrightarrow R_3N + H_2O$$

The primary amine may be obtained as the main product by using a large excess of ammonia (*cf.* method 1).

Separation of amine mixtures. When the mixture contains the three amine salts and the quaternary salt, it is distilled with potassium hydroxide solution. The three amines distil, leaving the quaternary salt unchanged in solution, *e.g.*,

$$R_2NH\cdot HX + KOH \longrightarrow R_2NH + KX + H_2O$$

The distillate of mixed amines may now be separated into the individual amines as follows:

Fractional distillation. This is the most satisfactory method and is now used industrially, its success being due to the high efficiency of industrial fractionation apparatus.

Hinsberg's method (1890). The mixture of amines is treated with an aromatic sulphonyl chloride. Benzenesulphonyl chloride, $C_6H_5\cdot SO_2Cl$, was used originally, but has now been replaced by *p*-toluenesulphonyl chloride, $CH_3\cdot C_6H_4\cdot SO_2Cl$. After treatment with this acid chloride, the solution is made alkaline with potassium hydroxide. Primary amines form the alkyl sulphonamide, *e.g.*, ethylamine forms ethyl *p*-toluenesulphonamide:

$$CH_3{\cdot}C_6H_4{\cdot}SO_2Cl + C_2H_5{\cdot}NH_2 \longrightarrow CH_3{\cdot}C_6H_4{\cdot}SO_2{\cdot}NH{\cdot}C_2H_5 + HCl$$

These sulphonamides are soluble in potassium hydroxide solution, possibly due to the formation of the soluble potassium salt of the enol form of the sulphonamide:

$$CH_3{\cdot}C_6H_4{\cdot}\overset{\overset{O}{\|}}{\underset{\underset{O}{\|}}{S}}-\overset{\overset{H}{|}}{N}-C_2H_5 \rightleftharpoons CH_3{\cdot}C_6H_4{\cdot}\overset{\overset{OH}{|}}{\underset{\underset{O}{\|}}{S}}{=}N{\cdot}C_2H_5 \xrightarrow{KOH} CH_3{\cdot}C_6H_4{\cdot}\overset{\overset{\bar{O}K^+}{|}}{\underset{\underset{O}{\|}}{S}}{=}N{\cdot}C_2H_5$$

Secondary amines form dialkyl sulphonamides, which are insoluble in potassium hydroxide solution because these sulphonamides are incapable of tautomerism (there is no α-hydrogen atom adjacent to the negative group); *e.g.*, diethylamine forms diethyl *p*-toluenesulphonamide:

$$CH_3{\cdot}C_6H_4{\cdot}SO_2Cl + (C_2H_5)_2NH \longrightarrow CH_3{\cdot}C_6H_4{\cdot}SO_2{\cdot}N(C_2H_5)_2 + HCl$$

Tertiary amines do not react with *p*-toluenesulphonyl chloride.

The alkaline solution is distilled, and the tertiary amine thereupon distils off. The residual liquid is filtered: the filtrate contains the primary amine derivative which, on acidification, gives the alkyl sulphonamide; the residual solid is the dialkyl sulphonamide. The amines are regenerated from the sulphonamides by refluxing with 70 per cent. sulphuric acid or 25 per cent. hydrochloric acid.

Preparation of primary amines. 1. By the reduction of nitro-compounds with metal and acid, or with hydrogen and a nickel catalyst:

$$R{\cdot}NO_2 + 3H_2 \xrightarrow{Ni} R{\cdot}NH_2 + 2H_2O \quad (ex.)$$

This method is becoming increasingly important since more aliphatic nitro-compounds are becoming available and is particularly useful for preparing amino-alcohols from the starting materials obtained by the condensation between formaldehyde and nitro-compounds (see p. 289).

2. (i) By the reduction of alkyl cyanides:

$$R{\cdot}CN + 4[H] \xrightarrow{Na/C_2H_5OH} R{\cdot}CH_2{\cdot}NH_2$$

This method is particularly useful for the preparation of high molecular weight amines, since the cyanides are readily prepared from the long-chain fatty acids.

(ii) By the reduction of oximes with sodium and ethanol, or catalytically:

$$R{\cdot}CH{:}N{\cdot}OH + 4[H] \longrightarrow R{\cdot}CH_2{\cdot}NH_2 + H_2O \quad (g.)$$
$$R_2C{:}N{\cdot}OH + 4[H] \longrightarrow R_2CH{\cdot}NH_2 + H_2O \quad (g.)$$

(iii) By the reduction of amides with sodium and ethanol, or catalytically:

$$R{\cdot}CO{\cdot}NH_2 + 4[H] \longrightarrow R{\cdot}CH_2{\cdot}NH_2 + H_2O \quad (f.g.–g.)$$

In all cases there are also obtained varying amounts of secondary amine as by-products, which increase in quantity when the reduction is carried out catalytically (see alkyl cyanides, p. 279). Reeve *et al.* (1956), however, have found that Raney cobalt (and Raney nickel) generally gives a primary amine in high purity by the reduction of oximes. On the other hand, nitro-compounds, cyanides, oximes and amides may be reduced by lithium aluminium hydride to primary amines unaccompanied by secondary amines.

3. By passing a mixture of aldehyde or ketone and a *large excess* of ammonia and hydrogen under pressure (20–150 atm.) over Raney nickel at 40–150°. The reaction may also be carried out at 3 atmospheres in the presence of excess ammonium chloride and Adams' platinum catalyst:

$$R{\cdot}CO{\cdot}R' + NH_3 + H_2 \longrightarrow RR'CH{\cdot}NH_2 + H_2O$$

Small amounts of secondary and tertiary amines are obtained as by-products. This process of introducing alkyl groups into ammonia or primary or secondary amines by means of an aldehyde or ketone in the presence of a reducing agent is known as *reductive alkylation*.

4. By the *Leuckart reaction* (p. 145):

$$R{\cdot}CO{\cdot}R' + 2H{\cdot}CO_2NH_4 \longrightarrow RR'CH{\cdot}NH{\cdot}CHO + 2H_2O + CO_2 + NH_3 \xrightarrow{\text{acid}} RR'CH{\cdot}NH_2$$

5. By the hydrolysis of alkyl *iso*cyanates with boiling alkali (Wurtz, 1849):

$$R{\cdot}NCO + 2KOH \longrightarrow R{\cdot}NH_2 + K_2CO_3$$

This method is not very useful in practice owing to the inaccessibility of the *iso*cyanates. It is, however, historically important because Wurtz discovered amines by this reaction. He at first thought he had obtained ammonia, but subsequently found the gas was inflammable.

6. *By Hofmann's degradation method* (p. 192):

$$R{\cdot}CO{\cdot}NH_2 + Br_2 + 4KOH \longrightarrow R{\cdot}NH_2 + 2KBr + K_2CO_3 + 2H_2O$$

This is generally the most convenient method of preparing primary amines.

7. By the *Curtius reaction* (p. 195):

$$R{\cdot}CO{\cdot}N_3 \xrightarrow{CH_3OH} R{\cdot}NCO \xrightarrow{CH_3OH} R{\cdot}NH{\cdot}CO_2CH_3 \xrightarrow{NaOH} R{\cdot}NH_2$$

This method of preparing primary amines works well for all members of the series.

8. By the *Lossen rearrangement* (p. 193):

$$R{\cdot}CO{\cdot}NH{\cdot}OH \xrightarrow{\text{acid}} H_2O + R{\cdot}NCO \xrightarrow{\text{acid}} R{\cdot}NH_2$$

This has very little importance as a practical method.

9. The *Schmidt reaction* (1923). This reaction is carried out by shaking a solution of a carboxylic acid in concentrated sulphuric acid with a chloroform solution of hydrozoic acid (*cf.* p. 150):

$$R{\cdot}CO_2H + HN_3 \xrightarrow{H_2SO_4} R{\cdot}NH_2 + CO_2 \quad (v.g.)$$

This method generally gives better yields of primary amines than the Hofmann or Curtius reaction, but it is somewhat dangerous because of the explosive and poisonous character of the hydrazoic acid.

Many mechanisms have been proposed for the Schmidt reaction, but none is certain (see p. 150).

10. **Gabriel's phthalimide synthesis** (1887). In this method phthalimide is converted, by means of ethanolic potassium hydroxide, into its salt potassiophthalimide, which, on heating with an alkyl halide, gives the *N*-alkylphthalimide. This is then hydrolysed to phthalic acid and a primary amine by heating with 20 per cent. hydrochloric acid under pressure, or by refluxing with potassium hydroxide solution:

$$C_6H_4\begin{matrix}CO\\CO\end{matrix}>NH \xrightarrow{KOH} C_6H_4\begin{matrix}CO\\CO\end{matrix}>NK \xrightarrow{RI} C_6H_4\begin{matrix}CO\\CO\end{matrix}>N{\cdot}R \xrightarrow{H_2O}$$

$$C_6H_4\begin{matrix}CO_2H\\CO_2H\end{matrix} + R{\cdot}NH_2$$

When hydrolysis is difficult, the alkylphthalimide can be treated with hydrazine to give the amine (Ing, 1926):

$$C_6H_4\begin{matrix}CO\\CO\end{matrix}>N{\cdot}R + \begin{matrix}H_2N\\|\\H_2N\end{matrix} \longrightarrow C_6H_4\begin{matrix}CO{\cdot}NH\\|\\CO{\cdot}NH\end{matrix} + R{\cdot}NH_2$$

Gabriel's synthesis is a very useful method since it gives a pure primary amine.

11. *Decarboxylation of amino-acids.* This is carried out by distilling the amino-acid with barium hydroxide; *e.g.*, glycine gives methylamine:

$$CH_2(NH_2){\cdot}CO_2H \xrightarrow{Ba(OH)_2} CH_3{\cdot}NH_2 + CO_2$$

Decarboxylation of amino-acids may also be effected by bacteria, especially putrefying bacteria (many of which occur in the intestines).

12. By means of a Grignard reagent and chloramine. The product is pure:

$$RMgX + ClNH_2 \longrightarrow R{\cdot}NH_2 + MgXCl$$

Alternatively, a primary amine may be prepared by interaction of a Grignard reagent and *O*-methylhydroxylamine (see p. 341).

13. A good method for preparing primary amines containing a *tert.*-alkyl group is to add a *tert.*-alcohol (or an alkene) to acetic acid in which is dissolved sodium cyanide, and then add sulphuric acid (Ritter *et al.*, 1948):

$$R_3COH \xrightarrow{H_2SO_4} R_3C{\cdot}OSO_3H \xrightarrow{HCN} R_3C{\cdot}N{=}CH{\cdot}OSO_3H$$

$$\xrightarrow{H_2O} H_2SO_4 + R_3C{\cdot}NH{\cdot}CHO \xrightarrow{NaOH} R_3C{\cdot}NH_2 \quad (40\%)$$

The *N*-alkylformamide produced is hydrolysed with sodium hydroxide.

Preparation of secondary amines 1. By the reduction of an alkyl *iso*-cyanide:

$$R{\cdot}NC + 4[H] \longrightarrow R{\cdot}NH{\cdot}CH_3$$

The amine produced always contains a methyl group as one radical; the method is of academic interest only.

2. By heating a primary amine with the calculated quantity of alkyl halide:

$$R{\cdot}NH_2 + R'X \longrightarrow R{\cdot}NH{\cdot}R' + HX$$

3. Aniline is heated with an alkyl halide, and the product, dialkylaniline, is treated with nitrous acid; the *p*-nitroso-dialkylaniline so formed is then boiled with sodium hydroxide solution. A pure secondary amine and *p*-nitrosophenol are produced:

$$C_6H_5NH_2 \xrightarrow{RX} C_6H_5NR_2 \xrightarrow{HNO_2} p\text{-}ON{\cdot}C_6H_4{\cdot}NR_2 \xrightarrow{NaOH} p\text{-}ON{\cdot}C_6H_4{\cdot}OH + R_2NH$$

This is one of the best methods of preparing pure secondary amines.

4. By the catalytic reduction of a Schiff's base, which is formed by interaction of a primary amine and an aldehyde (Henze and Humphreys, 1942; *cf.* primary amines, method 3):

$$R{\cdot}NH_2 + R'{\cdot}CHO \longrightarrow H_2O + R{\cdot}N{:}CH{\cdot}R' \xrightarrow[H_2]{\text{Raney Ni}} R{\cdot}NH{\cdot}CH_2{\cdot}R'$$

Secondary amines prepared this way usually contain an aromatic group as one of the radicals (R is generally the phenyl radical, $C_6H_5{\cdot}$).

5. By the hydrolysis of a dialkyl cyanamide with acid or alkali:

$$CaN{\cdot}CN \xrightarrow{\text{NaOH}} Na_2N{\cdot}CN \xrightarrow{RX} R_2N{\cdot}CN \xrightarrow{H_2O} R_2NH + CO_2 + NH_3$$

Preparation of tertiary amines. 1. The best method of preparation is to heat an ethanolic solution of ammonia with alkyl halide which is used in slight excess required by the equation:

$$3RX + NH_3 \longrightarrow R_3N + 2HX$$

When the reaction mixture is made alkaline and distilled, the tertiary amine is obtained. The residual quaternary compound may be distilled *in vacuo* to yield more tertiary amine (see quaternary compounds, p. 301).

2 By the reduction of a carbonyl compound (in excess) in the presence of hydrogen, ammonia or a primary or secondary amine, with Raney nickel as catalyst (*cf.* primary amines, method 3), *e.g.*,

$$R_2NH + R'{\cdot}CHO + H_2 \xrightarrow{Ni} R_2N{\cdot}CH_2{\cdot}R' + H_2O$$

Preparation of quaternary compounds. There is only one satisfactory method of preparing quaternary compounds, *viz.*, by heating ammonia with a very large excess of alkyl halide; a primary, secondary or tertiary amine may be used instead of ammonia. The starting materials will depend on the nature of the desired quaternary compound, *e.g.*, ethyltrimethylammonium iodide may be prepared by heating trimethylamine with ethyl iodide:

$$(CH_3)_3N + C_2H_5I \longrightarrow [(CH_3)_3N{\cdot}C_2H_5]^+I^-$$

General properties of the amines. The lower members are gases, soluble in water (with which they can form hydrogen bonds). These are followed by members which are liquids, and finally by members which are solids. The solubility in water decreases as their molecular weight increases. All the volatile members have a powerful fishy smell, and are combustible.

The reactions of an amine depend very largely on the class of that amine.

Reactions given by all three classes of amines. 1. All the amines are basic; they are stronger bases than ammonia, their strength increasing with the number of alkyl groups. Even so, all the amines are actually weak bases except the quaternary base, which is a strong electrolyte. Difficulty now arises in formulating the structure of the amine hydroxide. Originally, the following equilibria were suggested (R = H or alkyl), the stronger the base, the greater being the dissociation into ions:

$$R_3N + H_2O \rightleftharpoons R_3NH{\cdot}OH \rightleftharpoons [R_3NH]^+ + OH^-$$

According to the electronic theory of valency, nitrogen cannot be quinquevalent. Thus the formula $R_3NH{\cdot}OH$ is unsatisfactory for the unionised amine hydroxide. The above equilibria were then modified as follows:

$$R_3N + H_2O \rightleftharpoons [R_3NH]^+ + OH^-$$

This also is not satisfactory, since it does not explain the abrupt change in strength from the tertiary amine, a weak base, to the quaternary base, a strong electrolyte. This abrupt change occurs when the last hydrogen atom attached to the nitrogen atom is replaced by an alkyl group. Thus it appears that the hydrogen atom in the amine plays a part in the strength of the base. The explanation is now believed to be due to hydrogen bonding (Moore and Winmill, 1912; Latimer and Rodebush, 1920). According to this scheme, the formula of the *unionised* amine hydroxide is $R_3N—H\cdots OH$. If there is no hydrogen atom attached to the nitrogen, no hydrogen bonding is possible, and so the compound will have the ionic structure $[R_4N]^+OH^-$, and consequently is a strong electrolyte.

The increase in strength as a base as the number of the alkyl groups in the amine increases, may be due to the inductive (+I) effect of the alkyl groups. The more alkyl groups attached to the nitrogen, the greater is the displacement in the N→H bond. This displacement gives the hydrogen atom a negative charge which tends to inhibit hydrogen bonding. Obviously, the greater the negative charge on the hydrogen atom, the less is the tendency for hydrogen bonding, *i.e.*, the smaller is the amount of the unionised form.

```
      R
      ↓
R→—N→—H···OH
      ↑
      R
```

2. All the amines combine with acids to form salts, *e.g.*, methylamine combines with hydrochloric acid to form *methylammonium chloride*:

$$CH_3\cdot NH_2 + HCl \longrightarrow [CH_3\cdot NH_3]^+Cl^-$$

The nitrogen is quadricovalent unielectrovalent in amine salts; but to show their relationship to the amines, their salts are often written as, *e.g.*, $CH_3\cdot NH_2\cdot HCl$, methylamine hydrochloride; $[(C_2H_5)_2NH]_2\cdot H_2SO_4$, diethylamine sulphate.

Amine salts of certain complex acids, particularly chloroplatinic acid, are used for the determination of the molecular weights of amines (see p. 5).

3. All the amines combine with alkyl halides to form alkyl-substituted ammonium halides with more alkyl groups than the amine used.

4. When an amine salt is heated at high temperature, a molecule of alkyl halide is eliminated (*i.e.*, reverse of reaction 3, above):

$$R_3N\cdot HCl \longrightarrow RCl + R_2NH \xrightarrow{HCl} RCl + R\cdot NH_2 \xrightarrow{HCl} RCl + NH_4Cl$$

If the tertiary amine is a mixed amine, it is the smallest alkyl group that is eliminated first:

$$(C_2H_5)_2N\cdot CH_3 \xrightarrow{HCl} (C_2H_5)_2NH + CH_3Cl$$

This is the basis of estimating the *methylimino-group*, $>N\cdot CH_3$, in natural substances such as alkaloids.

The compound under investigation is heated with concentrated hydriodic acid; at 100° the methoxyl group is converted into methyl iodide (*cf.* p. 132):

$$Ar\cdot O\cdot CH_3 + HI \xrightarrow{100^\circ} ArOH + CH_3I$$

This is the **Zeisel method** for the quantitative estimation of methoxyl groups (p. 610).

When the temperature is raised to 150°, *N*-methyl groups are converted into methyl iodide:

$$Ar\cdot NH\cdot CH_3 + HI \xrightarrow{150^\circ} Ar\cdot NH_2 + CH_3I$$

This is the **Herzig–Meyer method** for the quantitative estimation of methylimino-groups. Thus methoxyl and methylimino-groups can be estimated separately when both are present in the same compound.

Reactions given by primary and secondary amines. 1. Primary and secondary amines react with acid chlorides or anhydrides to form the *N*-alkyl acid amide, *e.g.*,

$$R\cdot NH_2 + (CH_3\cdot CO)_2O \longrightarrow CH_3\cdot CO\cdot NH\cdot R + CH_3\cdot CO_2H$$

These monoacetyl derivatives are easily prepared and, since they are usually well-defined crystalline solids, are used to characterise primary amines.

It is difficult to prepare the diacetyl derivative; excess of the acetylating agent and high temperature, however, often yields the diacetyl derivative:

$$R\cdot NH\cdot CO\cdot CH_3 + (CH_3\cdot CO)_2O \longrightarrow R\cdot N(CO\cdot CH_3)_2 + CH_3\cdot CO_2H$$

Secondary amines, obviously, can form only the monoacyl derivative:

$$R_2NH + CH_3\cdot COCl \longrightarrow CH_3\cdot CO\cdot NR_2 + HCl$$

The acetylated amines are neutral substances which do not form salts with inorganic acids. It is the presence of the acetyl group, a negative group, which decreases the basic strength of the amine (see p. 543).

Sulphonyl chlorides also react with primary and secondary amines to form *N*-alkyl sulphonamides (see the Hinsberg separation, above).

2. Halogens, in the presence of alkali, react with primary and secondary amines to form halogeno-amines. Primary amines form the mono- or dihalogeno-derivative according to the amount of halogen used:

$$R\cdot NH_2 \xrightarrow{X_2/NaOH} R\cdot NHX + R\cdot NX_2$$

$$R_2NH \xrightarrow{X_2/NaOH} R_2NX$$

3. Primary amines react with nitrosyl chloride to form an alkyl chloride; secondary amines are converted into a nitrosamine:

$$R\cdot NH_2 + NOCl \longrightarrow RCl + N_2 + H_2O$$
$$R_2NH + NOCl \longrightarrow R_2N\cdot NO + HCl$$

4. Primary and secondary amines form sodium salts when heated with sodium:

$$R\cdot NH_2 + Na \longrightarrow [R\cdot NH]^-Na^+ + \tfrac{1}{2}H_2$$
$$R_2NH + Na \longrightarrow [R_2N]^-Na^+ + \tfrac{1}{2}H_2$$

5. Primary amines react in two stages with Grignard reagents, the first stage taking place at room temperature, the second only at high temperature:

$$R\cdot NH_2 + CH_3\cdot Mg\cdot I \longrightarrow CH_4 + R\cdot NH\cdot MgI$$
$$R\cdot NH\cdot MgI + CH_3\cdot Mg\cdot I \longrightarrow CH_4 + R\cdot N(MgI)_2$$

Secondary amines, since they contain only one active hydrogen atom, can only react with one molecule of a Grignard reagent:

$$R_2NH + CH_3\cdot Mg\cdot I \longrightarrow CH_4 + R_2N\cdot MgI$$

6. Primary and secondary amines form substituted ureas with phenyl *iso*cyanate, and may be characterised by these derivatives:

$$R\cdot NH_2 + C_6H_5\cdot NCO \longrightarrow R\cdot NH\cdot CO\cdot NH\cdot C_6H_5$$
$$R_2NH + C_6H_5\cdot NCO \longrightarrow R_2N\cdot CO\cdot NH\cdot C_6H_5$$

7. Primary and secondary amines can participate in the Mannich reaction (p. 289), *e.g.*,

$$C_6H_5\cdot CO\cdot CH_3 + H\cdot CHO + R\cdot NH_2\cdot HCl \longrightarrow$$
$$C_6H_5\cdot CO\cdot CH_2\cdot CH_2\cdot NHR\cdot HCl + H_2O$$

Reactions given by primary amines. 1. Primary amines form *iso*cyanides when heated with chloroform and ethanolic potassium hydroxide:

$$R \cdot NH_2 + CHCl_3 + 3KOH \longrightarrow R \cdot NC + 3KCl + 3H_2O$$

This reaction is used as a test for primary amines (or for chloroform).

2. When warmed with carbon disulphide, primary amines form a *dithiocarbamic acid*, which is decomposed by mercuric chloride to the *alkyl* iso*thiocyanate*:

$$R \cdot NH_2 + CS_2 \longrightarrow S{=}C\begin{matrix} \diagup NH \cdot R \\ \diagdown SH \end{matrix} \xrightarrow{HgCl_2} R \cdot NCS + HgS + 2HCl$$

This is known as the *Hofmann mustard oil reaction*, and may be used as a test for primary amines.

3. Primary amines combine with aromatic aldehydes to form *Schiff bases*:

$$C_6H_5 \cdot CHO + R \cdot NH_2 \longrightarrow C_6H_5 \cdot CH{:}NR + H_2O$$

4. Primary amines react with nitrous acid with the evolution of nitrogen. The equation is usually written:

$$R \cdot NH_2 + HNO_2 \longrightarrow ROH + N_2 + H_2O$$

The reaction, however, is far more complicated than this equation indicates. The yield of nitrogen is quantitative, but the yield of alcohol depends on the nature of the alkyl group. According to Whitmore (1941), methylamine does not form any methanol at all when treated with nitrous acid; dimethyl ether is produced. Ethylamine gives 60 per cent. of ethanol, and *n*-propylamine 7 per cent. of *n*-propanol, 32 per cent. of *iso*propanol and 28 per cent. of propylene.

Hughes, Ingold *et al.* (1950) have shown that simple acyclic primary amines undergo deamination via the formation of a diazonium ion (p. 556) which then decomposes by an S_N1 process to alcohol and olefin:

$$R \cdot NH_2 \xrightarrow{HNO_2} R \cdot NH \cdot NO \longrightarrow R \cdot \overset{+}{N}{\equiv}N \longrightarrow N_2 + R^+ \longrightarrow ROH + \text{olefin}$$

The products from *n*-propylamine may thus be explained as follows:

$$CH_3 \cdot CH_2 \cdot CH_2^+$$

$$\xrightarrow{\text{isom.}} CH_3 \cdot \overset{+}{C}H \cdot CH_3 \xrightarrow{OH^-} CH_3 \cdot CHOH \cdot CH_3$$

$$\xrightarrow{-H^+} CH_3 \cdot CH{=}CH_2$$

$$\xrightarrow{OH^-} CH_3 \cdot CH_2 \cdot CH_2OH$$

Whatever are the products formed by the action of nitrous acid on a primary amine, nitrogen is always evolved. Thus this reaction may be used as a test for primary amines, since none of the other classes of amines liberates nitrogen.

Primary amines may be converted into the corresponding alcohols in good yields by means of the von Braun method (see also p. 732):

$$R \cdot CH_2 \cdot NH_2 \xrightarrow{C_6H_5 \cdot COCl} R \cdot CH_2 \cdot NH \cdot CO \cdot C_6H_5 \xrightarrow{PCl_5}$$

$$C_6H_5 \cdot CN + POCl_3 + R \cdot CH_2Cl \xrightarrow{NaOH} R \cdot CH_2OH$$

White (1954) has introduced a new method for the deamination of aliphatic amines:

$$R{\cdot}NH_2 \xrightarrow{R'{\cdot}COCl} R{\cdot}NH{\cdot}CO{\cdot}R' \xrightarrow[CH_3{\cdot}CO_2Na]{N_2O_4} R{\cdot}N(NO){\cdot}CO{\cdot}R' \xrightarrow{heat}$$

$$N_2 + R{\cdot}O{\cdot}CO{\cdot}R' \xrightarrow{NaOH} ROH \quad (v.g.)$$

5. *Oxidation of primary amines.* The products obtained depend on the oxidising agent used, and on the nature of the alkyl group, *e.g.*, (i) with potassium permanganate:

$$R{\cdot}CH_2{\cdot}NH_2 \xrightarrow{[O]} \underset{\text{aldimine}}{R{\cdot}CH{:}NH} \xrightarrow{H_2O} R{\cdot}CHO + NH_3$$

$$R_2CH{\cdot}NH_2 \xrightarrow{[O]} \underset{\text{ketimine}}{R_2C{:}NH} \xrightarrow{H_2O} R_2CO + NH_3$$

$$R_3C{\cdot}NH_2 \xrightarrow{[O]} R_3C{\cdot}NO_2$$

(ii) with Caro's acid (H_2SO_5):

$$R{\cdot}CH_2{\cdot}NH_2 \xrightarrow{[O]} \underset{\substack{N\text{-alkyl}\\ \text{hydroxylamine}}}{R{\cdot}CH_2{-}NH{\cdot}OH} + \underset{\text{aldoxime}}{R{\cdot}CH{:}N{\cdot}OH} + \underset{\substack{\text{hydroxamic}\\ \text{acid}}}{R{\cdot}C{\Large\substack{\diagup OH\\ \diagdown\!\!\diagdown N{\cdot}OH}}}$$

$$R_2CH{\cdot}NH_2 \xrightarrow{[O]} R_2C{:}NOH$$

$$R_3C{\cdot}NH_2 \xrightarrow{[O]} R_3C{\cdot}NO$$

Reactions given by secondary amines. 1. Secondary amines react with nitrous acid to form insoluble oily *nitrosamines*; *nitrogen is not evolved*:

$$R_2NH + HNO_2 \longrightarrow R_2N{\cdot}NO + H_2O$$

Nitrosamines are yellow neutral oils which are steam-volatile. When warmed with a crystal of phenol and a few drops of concentrated sulphuric acid, nitrosamines form a green solution which, when made alkaline with aqueous sodium hydroxide, turns deep blue. This procedure may be used as a test for secondary amines; it is known as *Liebermann's nitroso reaction.*

Nitrosamines are readily hydrolysed to the amine by boiling with dilute hydrochloric acid:

$$R_2N{\cdot}NO + H_2O \xrightarrow{HCl} R_2NH + HNO_2$$

Peroxytrifluoroacetic acid converts secondary nitrosamines into nitramines (Emmons, 1954):

$$R_2N{\cdot}NO \xrightarrow{CF_3{\cdot}CO_3H} R_2N{\cdot}NO_2 \quad (73\text{–}95\%)$$

2. When warmed with carbon disulphide, secondary amines form a *dithiocarbamic acid*, which is *not* decomposed by mercuric chloride to the alkyl *iso*thiocyanate (*cf.* primary amines):

$$S{=}C{=}S + R_2NH \longrightarrow S{=}C{\Large\substack{\diagup NR_2\\ \diagdown SH}}$$

3. Secondary amines may be oxidised, the product depending on the oxidising agent used, *e.g.*,

$$R_2NH \xrightarrow{KMnO_4} \underset{\text{tetra-alkylhydrazine}}{R_2N{-}NR_2} \qquad R_2NH \xrightarrow{H_2SO_5} R_2N{\cdot}OH$$

Reactions given by tertiary amines. 1. Tertiary amines dissolve in *cold* nitrous acid to form the nitrite salt, $R_3N{\cdot}HNO_2$ or $[R_3NH]^+NO_2^-$. When this solution is warmed, the nitrite decomposes to form a nitrosamine and alcohol:

$$[R_3NH]^+NO_2^- \longrightarrow R_2N{\cdot}NO + ROH$$

2. Tertiary amines are not affected by potassium permanganate, but are oxidised to the *amine oxide* by Caro's acid or by Fenton's reagent:

$$R_3N + [O] \longrightarrow R_3N \rightarrow O$$

These amine oxides are basic and exist as $[R_3N{\cdot}OH]^+OH^-$ in solution. When the solution is evaporated to dryness, the dihydrate, $R_3NO.2H_2O$, is obtained as crystals. These, when carefully heated *in vacuo*, are converted into the anhydrous amine oxide, R_3NO. Amine oxides form addition compounds with gaseous hydrogen halide, *e.g.*, $[R_3N{\cdot}OH]^+Cl^-$, and with alkyl halides, *e.g.*, $[R_3N{\cdot}OR]^+Cl^-$.

3. Tertiary amines react with cyanogen bromide to form a *dialkyl cyanamide*:

$$R_3N + BrCN \longrightarrow [R_3N{\cdot}CN]^+Br^- \longrightarrow R_2N{\cdot}CN + RBr$$

The dialkyl cyanamides are readily hydrolysed by acid or alkali to a secondary amine:

$$R_2N{\cdot}CN \xrightarrow{H_2O} R_2N{\cdot}CO_2H \longrightarrow R_2NH + CO_2$$

This method therefore offers a means of converting a tertiary amine into a secondary, but is mainly used to open the ring of a cyclic amine containing a tertiary nitrogen atom (see p. 732).

QUATERNARY AMMONIUM COMPOUNDS

The quaternary ammonium salts are white crystalline solids, soluble in water, and completely dissociated in solution (the nitrogen is quadricovalent unielectrovalent). When a quaternary ammonium halide is heated *in vacuo*, it gives the tertiary amine:

$$[R_4N]^+X^- \longrightarrow R_3N + RX \quad (g.\text{–}v.g.)$$

When a quaternary ammonium halide is treated with moist silver oxide, the quaternary ammonium hydroxide is produced:

$$[R_4N]^+X^- + \text{‘AgOH’} \longrightarrow [R_4N]^+OH^- + AgX$$

This change may also be effected by treating the quaternary ammonium halide with a methanolic solution of potassium hydroxide. Potassium halide, which is precipitated, is removed by filtration, and the solvent then evaporated from the filtrate. It is important to note that the quaternary ammonium hydroxide is not liberated by *aqueous* potassium hydroxide.

The quaternary ammonium hydroxides are white deliquescent crystalline solids which are as strongly basic as sodium and potassium hydroxides (all exist as ions in the solid state). Their solutions absorb carbon dioxide, and will liberate ammonia from its salts.

The thermal decomposition of quaternary ammonium hydroxides is a very important reaction. Only tetramethylammonium hydroxide decomposes to give an alcohol:

$$[(CH_3)_4N]^+OH^- \longrightarrow (CH_3)_3N + CH_3OH$$

All other quaternary ammonium hydroxides give an olefin and water, *e.g.*,

$$[(C_2H_5)_4N]^+OH^- \longrightarrow (C_2H_5)_3N + C_2H_4 + H_2O$$

If the quaternary ammonium hydroxide contains different alkyl groups of which one is methyl, then the methyl group is *always* retained by the nitrogen, and an olefin and water are formed. Furthermore, if the ethyl group is one of the radicals, then ethylene is formed preferentially to any other olefin (*Hofmann's rule*). Water is always eliminated by the combination of the hydroxyl ion with a β-*hydrogen atom* of one of the alkyl groups (preferably ethyl):

$$[(CH_3)_2(C_3H_7)N{\cdot}\overset{\alpha}{C}H_2{\cdot}\overset{\beta}{C}H_3]^+OH^- \longrightarrow (CH_3)_2N{\cdot}C_3H_7 + C_2H_4 + H_2O$$

If there is no β-hydrogen in the quaternary hydroxide, *e.g.*, tetramethylammonium hydroxide, then no olefin is formed.

The above reaction is the basis of the *Hofmann exhaustive methylation method* (1851). In certain cases it is used to prepare unsaturated compounds of known structure, *e.g.*, benzene (see p. 483), but it is generally used to ascertain the nature of the carbon skeleton of cyclic compounds containing a nitrogen atom in the ring (see p. 732).

According to Ingold *et al.* (1927, 1933), the reaction proceeds by a bimolecular elimination (E2) mechanism:

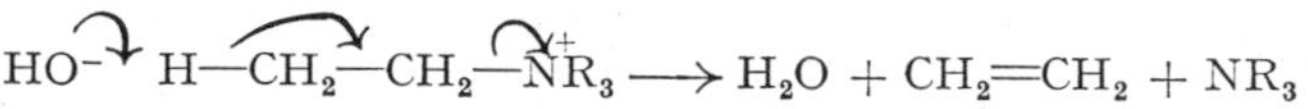

$$HO^- \; H—CH_2—CH_2—\overset{+}{N}R_3 \longrightarrow H_2O + CH_2{=}CH_2 + NR_3$$

The reason for the preferential elimination of ethylene has been explained as follows (Ingold *et al.*, 1927). The positive charge on the nitrogen atom produces an inductive effect which causes positive charges to be produced on neighbouring carbon atoms. This weakens the C—H bonds sufficiently for a β-proton to be eliminated by the E2 mechanism.

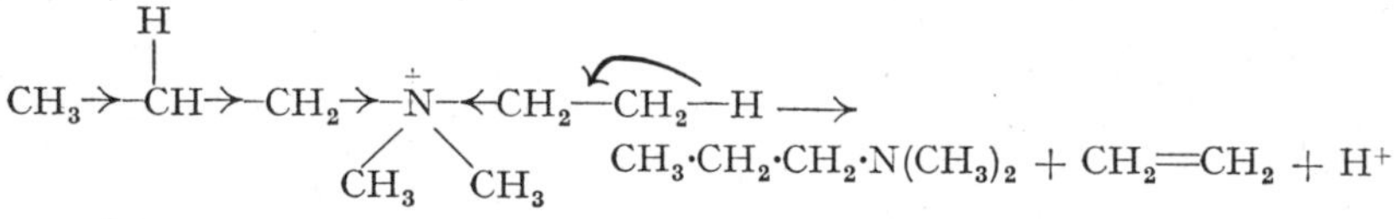

$$CH_3{\rightarrow}\underset{}{\overset{H}{\overset{|}{C}}}H{\rightarrow}CH_2{\rightarrow}\underset{CH_3\;\;CH_3}{\overset{+}{N}}{\leftarrow}CH_2—CH_2—H \longrightarrow$$

$$CH_3{\cdot}CH_2{\cdot}CH_2{\cdot}N(CH_3)_2 + CH_2{=}CH_2 + H^+$$

Since the terminal methyl group of the *n*-propyl radical is electron-releasing, the positive charge induced on the β-carbon atom (of the propyl group) is partially neutralised. This "tightens" the bonding of these β-hydrogen atoms, and so a less tightly bound β-hydrogen atom in the ethyl radical is eliminated preferentially with the formation of ethylene.

As can be seen from the foregoing account, the formation of ethylene (and, in general, the least branched olefin) is attributed to the polar factor. Brown *et al.* (1956), however, have concluded from their work that the Hofmann type of elimination must be attributed to the large steric requirements of the group undergoing elimination and not to the positive charge on the 'onium group (*cf.* Saytzeff's rule, p. 101).

Another interesting application of the method of exhaustive methylation is the preparation of methyl esters of acids which are difficult to esterify by the usual methods. The acid is converted into the quaternary methylammonium salt by titration with tetramethylammonium hydroxide in methanolic solution; the salt, on heating at 200–300°, is decomposed into the methyl ester and trimethylamine (Prelog and Piantanida, 1936):

$$[(CH_3)_4N]^+[O{\cdot}CO{\cdot}R]^- \longrightarrow R{\cdot}CO_2CH_3 + (CH_3)_3N \quad (v.g.)$$

Methylamine, dimethylamine and *trimethylamine* may be prepared by any of the general methods, but are conveniently prepared by special methods.

Methylamine: By heating ammonium chloride with two equivalents of formaldehyde (in formalin soln); the yield is 45–51 per cent. based on the ammonium chloride:

$$2H{\cdot}CHO + NH_4Cl \longrightarrow CH_3{\cdot}NH_2{\cdot}HCl + H{\cdot}CO_2H$$

It is prepared industrially by passing a mixture of methanol and ammonia over a catalyst, and separating the mixture by fractional distillation (see p. 292).

Methylamine is a gas, b.p. −7·6°, which is used as a refrigerant.

Dimethylamine: By heating ammonium chloride with about four equivalents of formaldehyde (in formalin solution):

$$NH_4Cl + 4H{\cdot}CHO \longrightarrow (CH_3)_2NH{\cdot}HCl + 2H{\cdot}CO_2H$$

It is a gas, b.p. 7°.

Trimethylamine: By heating a solid mixture of ammonium chloride and paraformaldehyde:

$$2NH_4Cl + 9H{\cdot}CHO \longrightarrow 2(CH_3)_3N{\cdot}HCl + 3CO_2 \quad (89\%)$$

It is a gas, b.p. 3·5°. It occurs in sugar residues, and is used as a source of methyl chloride:

$$(CH_3)_3N + 4HCl \xrightarrow[\text{pressure}]{\text{heat}} 3CH_3Cl + NH_4Cl$$

N-methylation of primary and secondary amines can readily be effected by formaldehyde (formalin solution); the mechanism may be:

$$>NH + CH_2O \longrightarrow >N{\cdot}CH_2OH \xrightarrow{2[H]} >N{\cdot}CH_3 + H_2O$$

The 2[H] is produced according to the following reactions:

$$2CH_2O + H_2O \longrightarrow CH_3OH + H{\cdot}CO_2H$$
$$H{\cdot}CO_2H \longrightarrow CO_2 + 2[H]$$

Carbon dioxide is always evolved in these reactions.

The long-chain amines, prepared by the catalytic reduction of alkyl cyanides (from fatty acids and ammonia), are used as antioxidants, sterilising agents and flotation agents.

DIAMINES

Diamines may be prepared by methods similar to those for the monoamines, using alkylene halides instead of alkyl halides.

Ethylenediamine, $NH_2{\cdot}CH_2{\cdot}CH_2{\cdot}NH_2$, may be prepared by heating, under pressure, ethylene bromide with a large excess of ammonia:

$$CH_2Br{\cdot}CH_2Br + 2NH_3 \longrightarrow NH_2{\cdot}CH_2{\cdot}CH_2{\cdot}NH_2 + 2HBr$$

It is a colourless liquid, b.p. 118°, soluble in water. It forms *piperazine* when its hydrochloride is heated:

$$\begin{matrix} HCl{\cdot}NH_2{\cdot}CH_2{\cdot}CH_2{\cdot}NH_2{\cdot}HCl \\ + \\ HCl{\cdot}NH_2{\cdot}CH_2{\cdot}CH_2{\cdot}NH_2{\cdot}HCl \end{matrix} \longrightarrow HCl{\cdot}HN\begin{matrix} \diagup CH_2{\cdot}CH_2 \diagdown \\ \diagdown CH_2{\cdot}CH_2 \diagup \end{matrix}NH{\cdot}HCl + 2NH_4Cl$$

Ethylenediamine forms chelate compounds with many metals, *e.g.*, cobalt.

Putrescine, *tetramethylenediamine,* $NH_2{\cdot}(CH_2)_4{\cdot}NH_2$, is formed by the putrefaction of proteins (in flesh). It may be prepared as follows:

$$CH_2Br{\cdot}CH_2Br \xrightarrow{KCN} NC{\cdot}CH_2{\cdot}CH_2{\cdot}CN \xrightarrow{Na/C_2H_5OH} NH_2{\cdot}(CH_2)_4{\cdot}NH_2$$

It is a poisonous solid, m.p. 27°, with a disagreeable odour, and is soluble in water. When its hydrochloride is heated, *pyrrolidine* is formed:

$$\begin{array}{l} CH_2{\cdot}CH_2{\cdot}NH_2{\cdot}HCl \\ | \\ CH_2{\cdot}CH_2{\cdot}NH_2{\cdot}HCl \end{array} \longrightarrow \begin{array}{l} CH_2{-}CH_2\diagdown \\ | \qquad\qquad\quad NH{\cdot}HCl + NH_4Cl \\ CH_2{-}CH_2\diagup \end{array}$$

Cadaverine, *pentamethylenediamine,* $NH_2{\cdot}(CH_2)_5{\cdot}NH_2$, is formed by the putrefaction of proteins (in flesh). It may be prepared by an analogous method to that used for putrescine:

$$Br{\cdot}(CH_2)_3{\cdot}Br \xrightarrow{KCN} NC{\cdot}(CH_2)_3{\cdot}CN \xrightarrow{Na/C_2H_5OH} NH_2{\cdot}(CH_2)_5{\cdot}NH_2$$

It is, however, prepared more conveniently by heating pentamethylene bromide with an excess of ammonia:

$$Br{\cdot}(CH_2)_5{\cdot}Br + 2NH_3 \longrightarrow NH_2{\cdot}(CH_2)_5{\cdot}NH_2 + 2HBr$$

The starting material pentamethylene bromide is readily obtained from piperidine (see p. 731).

Cadaverine is a poisonous, syrupy, fuming liquid, b.p. 178–180°, with a disagreeable odour, and is soluble in water. When its hydrochloride is heated, piperidine is formed:

$$CH_2\begin{array}{l}\diagup CH_2{\cdot}CH_2{\cdot}NH_2{\cdot}HCl \\ \diagdown CH_2{\cdot}CH_2{\cdot}NH_2{\cdot}HCl\end{array} \longrightarrow CH_2\begin{array}{l}\diagup CH_2{-}CH_2\diagdown \\ \diagdown CH_2{-}CH_2\diagup\end{array}NH{\cdot}HCl + NH_4Cl$$

Spermine, a deliquescent crystalline solid which is isolated from human sperm, is a tetramine: $NH_2{\cdot}(CH_2)_3{\cdot}NH{\cdot}(CH_2)_4{\cdot}NH{\cdot}(CH_2)_3{\cdot}NH_2$.

Diamines with two amino-groups attached to the same carbon atom are unknown (*cf.* the group $C(OH)_2$, p. 157). On the other hand, *N*-substituted derivatives have been prepared, *e.g.*, tetraethylmethylenediamine:

$$(C_2H_5)_2NH + CH_2O + NH(C_2H_5)_2 \longrightarrow (C_2H_5)_2N{\cdot}CH_2{\cdot}N(C_2H_5)_2 + H_2O$$

UNSATURATED AMINES

The simplest unsaturated amine is **vinylamine** (ethenylamine); this may be prepared by heating ethylene bromide with ammonia sufficient to bring about ammonolysis of *one* bromine atom, and subsequently heating the product, 2-bromoethylamine, with ethanolic potassium hydroxide:

$$CH_2Br{\cdot}CH_2Br \xrightarrow{NH_3} CH_2Br{\cdot}CH_2{\cdot}NH_2 \xrightarrow[KOH]{ethanolic} CH_2{:}CH{\cdot}NH_2$$

The open-chain structure is doubtful; vinylamine appears to exist as the ring compound, *ethylene-imine*:

$$CH_2{:}CH{\cdot}NH_2 \rightleftharpoons \begin{array}{c} CH_2{-}CH_2 \\ \diagdown\ \diagup \\ NH \end{array}$$

Vinylamine is a syrupy liquid, b.p. 56°, with a strong ammoniacal odour; it is miscible with water, and is strongly basic. It combines with sulphurous acid to form *taurine* (2-aminoethanesulphonic acid), which occurs in human bile:

$$\begin{array}{c} CH_2{-}CH_2 \\ \diagdown\ \diagup \\ NH \end{array} + H_2SO_3 \longrightarrow NH_2{\cdot}CH_2{\cdot}CH_2{\cdot}SO_3H \text{ or } \overset{+}{N}H_3{\cdot}CH_2{\cdot}CH_2{\cdot}SO_3^-$$

Neurine (*trimethylvinylammonium hydroxide*), $[(CH_3)_3N{\cdot}CH{:}CH_2]^+OH^-$, is found in the brain. It may be prepared:

(i) By boiling choline with barium hydroxide solution:

$$[(CH_3)_3N{\cdot}CH_2{\cdot}CH_2OH]^+OH^- \xrightarrow{Ba(OH)_2} [(CH_3)_3N{\cdot}CH{:}CH_2]^+OH^- + H_2O$$

(ii) By heating trimethylamine and ethylene bromide (one molecule of each), and subsequently heating the product with silver oxide in water:

$$(CH_3)_3N + BrCH_2{\cdot}CH_2Br \longrightarrow [(CH_3)_3N{\cdot}CH_2{\cdot}CH_2Br]^+Br^- \xrightarrow{\text{“AgOH”}} [(CH_3)_3N{\cdot}CH{:}CH_2]^+OH^-$$

(iii) A very interesting synthesis is by the interaction of acetylene and trimethylamine under pressure, in the presence of water at 60°:

$$C_2H_2 + (CH_3)_3N + H_2O \longrightarrow [(CH_3)_3N{\cdot}CH{:}CH_2]^+OH^-$$

Neurine is a very poisonous syrupy liquid.

Allylamine (2-*propenylamine*), $CH_2{:}CH{\cdot}CH_2{\cdot}NH_2$, may be prepared by heating allyl iodide with ammonia:

$$CH_2{:}CH{\cdot}CH_2I + NH_3 \longrightarrow CH_2{:}CH{\cdot}CH_2{\cdot}NH_2 + HI$$

It is more conveniently prepared by boiling allyl *iso*thiocyanate with dilute hydrochloric acid:

$$CH_2{:}CH{\cdot}CH_2{\cdot}NCS + H_2O \xrightarrow{HCl} CH_2{:}CH{\cdot}CH_2{\cdot}NH_2 + COS \quad (70\text{–}73\%)$$

It is a colourless liquid, b.p. 53°, with an ammoniacal smell, and is miscible with water.

AMINOALCOHOLS

The simplest aminoalcohol is 2-**aminoethanol,** $NH_2{\cdot}CH_2{\cdot}CH_2OH$ (*cholamine, ethanolamine, 2-hydroxyethylamine*). It occurs in kephalins (p. 248), and is best prepared by the action of ethylene oxide on excess of ammonia.

$$\underset{\text{(ethylene oxide, O bridging)}}{CH_2\text{—}CH_2} + NH_3 \longrightarrow NH_2{\cdot}CH_2{\cdot}CH_2OH$$

It is a viscous liquid, b.p. 171°, miscible with water, and is strongly basic.

Choline (2-*hydroxyethyltrimethylammonium hydroxide*) occurs in lecithins (p. 248); it is best prepared by the action of ethylene oxide on trimethylamine in aqueous solution:

$$\underset{\text{(ethylene oxide, O bridging)}}{CH_2\text{—}CH_2} + (CH_3)_3N + H_2O \longrightarrow [(CH_3)_3N{\cdot}CH_2{\cdot}CH_2OH]^+OH^-$$

It is a colourless viscous liquid, soluble in water, and is strongly basic. It forms neurine when boiled with barium hydroxide solution (see above). It is present in the vitamin B complex; it is a growth factor in chicks.

AMINO-ACIDS

Amino-acids are derivatives of the carboxylic acids in which a hydrogen atom in the carbon chain has been replaced by an amino-group. The amino-group may occupy the α- or β- or γ- . . . position; there may also be two or more amino-groups present in the chain.

The three basic classes of foods are: proteins, fats and carbohydrates. The proteins are nitrogenous substances which occur in most cells of the animal body; they also occur in plants. When hydrolysed by strong inorganic acids or by enzymes, proteins yield a mixture of amino-acids, all of which are α-amino-acids. The number of amino-acids so far obtained appears to be about twenty-five, of which about ten are essential, *i.e.*, a deficiency in any one prevents growth in young animals, and may even cause death.

The amino-acids are classified in several ways; Table VI shows a convenient classification; the letters *g*, *l* and *e* which follow the name of the acid indicate that the acid is respectively of general occurrence, lesser occurrence, and essential (in man).

In this book we shall consider in detail only the simplest amino-acid, **glycine** (*aminoacetic acid, glycocoll*), $CH_2(NH_2)\cdot CO_2H$. This acid is found in many proteins, and occurs in certain animal excretions, usually in combination, *e.g.*, *hippuric acid* (in horses' urine), $C_6H_5\cdot CO\cdot NH\cdot CH_2\cdot CO_2H$. Glycine may be readily prepared by the action of concentrated ammonium hydroxide solution on chloroacetic acid:

$$CH_2Cl\cdot CO_2H + 2NH_3 \longrightarrow CH_2(NH_2)\cdot CO_2H + NH_4Cl \quad (64\text{–}65\%)$$

It may also be prepared pure by Gabriel's phthalimide synthesis (p. 294):

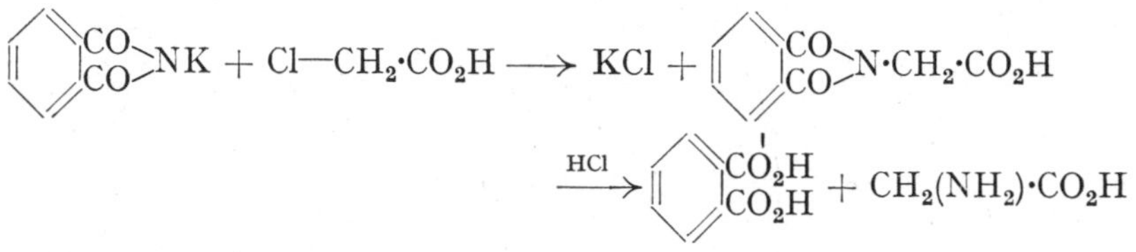

$$C_6H_4\begin{matrix}CO\\CO\end{matrix}\!\!>\!NK + Cl\text{—}CH_2\cdot CO_2H \longrightarrow KCl + C_6H_4\begin{matrix}CO\\CO\end{matrix}\!\!>\!N\cdot CH_2\cdot CO_2H$$

$$\xrightarrow{HCl} C_6H_4\begin{matrix}CO_2H\\CO_2H\end{matrix} + CH_2(NH_2)\cdot CO_2H$$

Glycine exists as white prisms which melt, with decomposition, at 289–292°. It has a sweet taste, and is soluble in water but insoluble in ethanol and ether. Since it contains an amino-group and a carboxyl group, it combines the properties of a base and an acid, *i.e.*, it is *amphoteric*. The following reactions are typical of all α-amino-acids.

Reactions characteristic of the amino-group. 1. Glycine forms salts with strong inorganic acids, *e.g.*, $\overset{-}{Cl}\{H_3\overset{+}{N}\cdot CH_2\cdot CO_2H$.

2. Glycine reacts with acetyl chloride or acetic anhydride to give the acetyl derivative:

$$H_2N\cdot CH_2\cdot CO_2H + (CH_3\cdot CO)_2O \longrightarrow CH_3\cdot CO\cdot NH\cdot CH_2\cdot CO_2H + CH_3\cdot CO_2H$$

Similarly, with benzoyl chloride, it forms benzoylglycine (hippuric acid; see above).

These acylated derivatives are acidic, the basic character of the amino-group being effectively eliminated by the presence of the negative group attached to the nitrogen (see p. 543).

3. When glycine is treated with nitrous acid, nitrogen is evolved and glycollic acid is formed:

$$CH_2(NH_2)\cdot CO_2H + HNO_2 \longrightarrow CH_2OH\cdot CO_2H + N_2 + H_2O$$

4. Nitrosyl chloride (or bromide) reacts with glycine to form chloro- (or bromo-)acetic acid:

$$CH_2(NH_2)\cdot CO_2H + NOCl \longrightarrow CH_2Cl\cdot CO_2H + N_2 + H_2O$$

Reactions characteristic of the carboxyl group. 1. Glycine may be esterified by an alcohol in the presence of inorganic acid, *e.g.*,

$$CH_2(NH_2)\cdot CO_2H + C_2H_5OH \xrightarrow{HCl} HCl\cdot H_2N\cdot CH_2\cdot CO_2C_2H_5 + H_2O$$

The ester is liberated from its hydrochloride by alkali.

TABLE VI

Name	Formula
Neutral Amino-acids (one amino-group and one carboxyl group)	
1. Glycine (*g*)	$CH_2(NH_2)\cdot CO_2H$
2. Alanine (*g*)	$CH_3\cdot CH(NH_2)\cdot CO_2H$
3. Valine (*g*, *e*)	$(CH_3)_2CH\cdot CH(NH_2)\cdot CO_2H$
4. Leucine (*g*, *e*)	$(CH_3)_2CH\cdot CH_2\cdot CH(NH_2)\cdot CO_2H$
5. *iso*Leucine (*g*, *e*)	$(C_2H_5)(CH_3)CH\cdot CH(NH_2)\cdot CO_2H$
6. Norleucine (*l*)	$CH_3\cdot (CH_2)_3\cdot CH(NH_2)\cdot CO_2H$
7. Phenylalanine (*g*, *e*)	$C_6H_5\cdot CH_2\cdot CH(NH_2)\cdot CO_2H$ (benzene ring)
8. Tyrosine (*g*)	$HO\cdot C_6H_4\cdot CH_2\cdot CH(NH_2)\cdot CO_2H$ (benzene ring)
9. Serine (*g*)	$HOCH_2\cdot CH(NH_2)\cdot CO_2H$
10. Cysteine (*g*)	$HS\cdot CH_2\cdot CH(NH_2)\cdot CO_2H$
11. Cystine (*g*)	$(-S\cdot CH_2\cdot CH(NH_2)\cdot CO_2H)_2$
12. Threonine (*g*, *e*)	$CH_3\cdot CHOH\cdot CH(NH_2)\cdot CO_2H$
13. Methionine (*g*, *e*)	$CH_3\cdot S\cdot CH_2\cdot CH_2\cdot CH(NH_2)\cdot CO_2H$
14. Di-iodotyrosine or iodogorgic acid (*l*)	I HO⟨ring⟩$CH_2\cdot CH(NH_2)\cdot CO_2H$ I
15. Thyroxine (*l*)	I I HO⟨ring⟩—O—⟨ring⟩—$CH_2\cdot CH(NH_2)\cdot CO_2H$ I I
16. Dibromotyrosine (*l*)	Br HO⟨ring⟩—$CH_2\cdot CH(NH_2)\cdot CO_2H$ Br
17. Tryptophan (*g*, *e*)	⟨indole ring⟩$CH_2\cdot CH(NH_2)\cdot CO_2H$ NH
18. Proline (*g*)	CH_2—CH_2 CH_2 $CH\cdot CO_2H$ NH
19. Hydroxyproline (*l*)	HOCH—CH_2 CH_2 $CH\cdot CO_2H$ NH
Acidic Amino-acids (one amino-group and two carboxyl groups)	
20. Aspartic acid (*g*)	$CO_2H\cdot CH_2\cdot CH(NH_2)\cdot CO_2H$
21. Glutamic acid (*g*)	$CO_2H\cdot CH_2\cdot CH_2\cdot CH(NH_2)\cdot CO_2H$
22. β-Hydroxyglutamic acid (*l*) [1]	$CO_2H\cdot CH_2\cdot CHOH\cdot CH(NH_2)\cdot CO_2H$
Basic Amino-acids (two amino-groups and one carboxyl group)	
23. Ornithine *	$NH_2\cdot CH_2\cdot CH_2\cdot CH_2\cdot CH(NH_2)\cdot CO_2H$
24. Arginine (*g*, *e*)	NH_2 $HN{=}C{-}NH\cdot CH_2\cdot CH_2\cdot CH_2\cdot CH(NH_2)\cdot CO_2H$
25. Lysine (*g*, *e*)	$NH_2\cdot CH_2\cdot CH_2\cdot CH_2\cdot CH_2\cdot CH(NH_2)\cdot CO_2H$
26. Histidine (*g*, *e*)	⟨ring⟩$CH_2\cdot CH(NH_2)\cdot CO_2H$ HN N

* Ornithine is probably not present in proteins, but is formed by the hydrolysis of arginine.

[1] Occurrence in proteins uncertain.

2. Glycine forms metallic salts when its aqueous solution is warmed with a metallic oxide or hydroxide. These salts are chelate compounds, *e.g.*, the copper salt (deep blue needles) is:

$$\begin{array}{ccc} O{=}C{-}O & & H_2N{\cdot}CH_2 \\ | & \searrow Cu \swarrow & | \\ CH_2{\cdot}NH_2 & \nearrow \quad \nwarrow & O{-}C{=}O \end{array}$$

3. Amino-acids may be reduced to aminoalcohols by lithium aluminium hydride (Vogel *et al.*, 1952).

$$R{\cdot}CH(NH_2){\cdot}CO_2H \xrightarrow{LiAlH_4} R{\cdot}CH(NH_2){\cdot}CH_2OH$$

Reactions due to both the amino- and carboxyl groups. 1. When measured in aqueous solution, the dipole moment of glycine is found to have a large value. To account for this large value it has been suggested that glycine exists, in solution, as an *inner salt*:

$$H_2N{\cdot}CH_2{\cdot}CO_2H + H_2O \rightleftharpoons H_3\overset{+}{N}{\cdot}CH_2{\cdot}CO_2^- + H_2O$$

Such a double charged ion is known, in addition to an inner salt, as a *zwitter-ion, ampholyte,* or a *dipolar ion.* This dipolar ion structure also accounts for the absence of acidic and basic properties of an amino-acid (the carboxyl and amino-groups of the *same* molecule neutralising each other to form a salt). The properties of crystalline glycine, *e.g.*, its high melting point and its insolubility in hydrocarbon solvents, also indicate that it exists as the inner salt in the solid state.

Owing to its amphoteric character, glycine cannot be titrated directly with alkali. When formalin solution is added to glycine, methyleneglycine is formed (reaction probably more complex):

$$H_2N{\cdot}CH_2{\cdot}CO_2H + H{\cdot}CHO \longrightarrow CH_2{:}N{\cdot}CH_2{\cdot}CO_2H + H_2O$$

This is a strong acid (the basic character of the amino-group being now suppressed), and can be titrated with sodium hydroxide. This method is known as the *Sörensen titration.*

2. When heated, glycine forms *diketopiperazine*; glycine esters give a better yield:

$$\begin{array}{l} CH_2{\cdot}CO\boxed{OC_2H_5 \quad H}NH \\ \; | \qquad\qquad\qquad\qquad\quad | \\ HN\boxed{H \quad C_2H_5O}OC{\cdot}CH_2 \end{array} \longrightarrow NH\begin{array}{c} \diagup CH_2{-}CO \diagdown \\ \diagdown CO{-}CH_2 \diagup \end{array}NH + 2C_2H_5O$$

Betaines. These are the trialkyl derivatives of glycine, which exist as dipolar ions of formula $R_3\overset{+}{N}{\cdot}\overset{-}{CO_2}$. Betaine itself is the trimethyl derivative, and may be prepared by heating glycine with methyl iodide in methanolic solution:

$$H_3\overset{+}{N}{\cdot}CH_2{\cdot}\overset{-}{CO_2} + 3CH_3I \longrightarrow (CH_3)_3\overset{+}{N}{\cdot}CH_2{\cdot}\overset{-}{CO_2} + 3HI$$

It is more conveniently prepared by warming an aqueous solution of chloro-acetic acid with trimethylamine:

$$(CH_3)_3N + CH_2Cl{\cdot}CO_2H \longrightarrow (CH_3)_3\overset{+}{N}{\cdot}CH_2{\cdot}\overset{-}{CO_2} + HCl$$

Betaine is a solid, m.p. 300° (with decomposition). It occurs in nature, especially in plant juices. It behaves as a base, *e.g.*, with hydrochloric acid it forms the stable crystalline hydrochloride, $Cl^-(CH_3)_3\overset{+}{N}{\cdot}CH_2{\cdot}CO_2H$.

ALIPHATIC DIAZO-COMPOUNDS

The aliphatic diazo-compounds are characterised by the presence of the group $>CN_2$.

Diazomethane, CH_2N_2, may be prepared in various ways; the first is of historical importance, and the others are very convenient methods.

Method of Von Pechmann (1894). Methylamine is treated with ethyl chloroformate to give *N*-methylurethan which, on treatment with nitrous acid in ethereal solution, forms *N*-methyl-*N*-nitroso-urethan. This, on warming with methanolic potassium hydroxide, decomposes into diazomethane, which is collected on cooled ether:

$$CH_3{\cdot}NH_2 + Cl{\cdot}CO_2C_2H_5 \longrightarrow CH_3{\cdot}NH{\cdot}CO_2C_2H_5 \xrightarrow{HNO_2}$$
$$CH_3{\cdot}N(NO){\cdot}CO_2C_2H_5 \xrightarrow{KOH} CH_2N_2 + CO_2 + C_2H_5OH$$

Method of McKay (1948). Methylamine hydrochloride and nitroguanidine are allowed to react in potassium hydroxide solution, the product *N*-methyl-*N'*-nitroguanidine treated with nitrous acid, and the *N*-methyl-*N*-nitroso-*N'*-nitroguanidine so produced is then warmed with potassium hydroxide:

$$CH_3{\cdot}NH_2{\cdot}HCl + NH_2{\cdot}\overset{\overset{NH}{\|}}{C}{\cdot}NH{\cdot}NO_2 + KOH \longrightarrow$$
$$NH_3 + KCl + CH_3{\cdot}NH{\cdot}\overset{\overset{NH}{\|}}{C}{\cdot}NH{\cdot}NO_2 \xrightarrow{HNO_2}$$
$$CH_3{\cdot}N(NO){\cdot}\overset{\overset{NH}{\|}}{C}{\cdot}NH{\cdot}NO_2 \xrightarrow{KOH} CH_2N_2$$

Method of Backer et al. (1951). The nitroso-derivative of *p*-toluene-*N*-methylsulphonamide is distilled with ethanolic potassium hydroxide:

$$CH_3{\cdot}C_6H_4{\cdot}SO_2N(CH_3){\cdot}NO + KOH \longrightarrow CH_2N_2$$
$$+ CH_3{\cdot}C_6H_4{\cdot}SO_3K + H_2O \quad (80\text{–}90\%)$$

Method of Müller et al. (1955). Nitrous oxide is passed into an ethereal solution of methyl-lithium, and the precipitate decomposed in ether with aqueous potassium hydroxide:

$$N_2O + CH_3Li \longrightarrow CH_3{\cdot}N{=}N{\cdot}OLi \longrightarrow LiOH + CH_2N_2$$
$$\xrightarrow{CH_3Li} CH_4 + CHN_2Li \xrightarrow{H_2O} LiOH + CH{\equiv}N{\cdot}NH \xrightarrow{OH^-} CH_2N_2$$

Diazomethane is a yellow, poisonous gas; liquid diazomethane, b.p. $-24°$, is explosive. The gas is soluble in ether, and since the ethereal solution is fairly safe to handle, reactions with diazomethane are usually carried out in ethereal solution. Diazomethane is neutral; it is reduced by sodium amalgam to methylhydrazine $CH_3{\cdot}NH{\cdot}NH_2$.

Reactions. 1. Diazomethane is widely used as a methylating agent for hydroxyl groups. In these reactions nitrogen is always liberated.

It reacts with halogen acid to form a methyl halide, *e.g.*,

$$CH_2N_2 + HCl \longrightarrow CH_3Cl + N_2$$

Diazomethane methylates *acidic* hydroxyl groups very readily: carboxylic acids, sulphonic acids, phenols, and enols, *e.g.*,

$$R{\cdot}CO_2H + CH_2N_2 \longrightarrow R{\cdot}CO_2CH_3 + N_2$$

Alcohols can also be methylated by diazomethane in the presence of a suitable catalyst, *e.g.*, an aluminium alkoxide.

$$ROH + Al(OR')_3 \rightleftharpoons \begin{matrix} R \\ H \end{matrix}\!\!>\overset{+}{O}-\overset{-}{Al}(OR')_3 \xrightarrow{CH_2N_2}$$

$$N_2 + \begin{matrix} R \\ H_3C \end{matrix}\!\!>\overset{+}{O}-\overset{-}{Al}(OR')_3 \rightleftharpoons R{\cdot}O{\cdot}CH_3 + Al\,(OR')_3$$

Alcohols may, however, be attacked directly by certain diazo-compounds, *e.g.*, diphenyldiazomethane:

$$(C_6H_5)_2CN_2 + C_2H_5OH \xrightarrow{\text{boil}} (C_6H_5)_2CH{\cdot}O{\cdot}C_2H_5$$

Diazomethane also reacts with aldehydes, converting them into methyl ketones; but in some cases the ethylene oxide derivative is formed, particularly when R is a negative group.

$$R{\cdot}CHO + CH_2N_2 \begin{cases} \longrightarrow R{\cdot}CO{\cdot}CH_3 \\ \longrightarrow R{\cdot}CH\!-\!CH_2 \text{ (with O bridging the two carbons)} \end{cases}$$

Ketones also react in a similar manner, but only in the presence of water as catalyst; *e.g.*, acetone forms both the higher ketone and the ethylene oxide derivative:

$$CH_3{\cdot}CO{\cdot}CH_3 \xrightarrow{CH_2N_2} CH_3{\cdot}CO{\cdot}CH_2{\cdot}CH_3 + (CH_3)_2C\!-\!CH_2 \text{ (with O bridging the two carbons)}$$

Certain cyclic ketones undergo ring expansion when treated with diazomethane (p. 456).

2. Diazomethane adds on to ethylenic compounds to form *pyrazoline* derivatives (*cf.* αβ-unsaturated esters, p. 266); with ethylene, *pyrazoline* is formed:

$$\begin{matrix} CH_2 \\ \| \\ CH_2 \end{matrix} + CH_2N_2 \longrightarrow \begin{matrix} CH_2-CH \\ | \quad\quad \| \\ CH_2 \quad N \\ \diagdown \;\; \diagup \\ NH \end{matrix}$$

Diazomethane also adds on to acetylenic compounds, in this case to form *pyrazole* derivatives; with acetylene, *pyrazole* is formed:

$$\begin{matrix} CH \\ ||| \\ CH \end{matrix} + CH_2N_2 \longrightarrow \begin{matrix} CH-CH \\ \| \quad\quad \| \\ CH \quad N \\ \diagdown \;\; \diagup \\ NH \end{matrix}$$

3. Diazomethane is used in the **Arndt–Eistert synthesis** (1935). This is a means of converting an acid (aliphatic, aromatic, alicyclic, or heterocyclic) into the next higher homologue. The acid chloride is treated with diazo-

methane (2 molecules), and the resulting *diazoketone* is warmed with water in the presence of silver oxide as catalyst:

$$R\cdot COCl + 2CH_2N_2 \longrightarrow R\cdot CO\cdot CHN_2 + CH_3Cl + N_2$$

$$R\cdot CO\cdot CHN_2 + H_2O \xrightarrow{Ag_2O} R\cdot CH_2\cdot CO_2H + N_2 \quad (50\text{–}80\%)$$

This rearrangement of the diazoketone is usually referred to as the **Wolff rearrangement.**

Diazoketones react with alcohols and ammonia in the presence of silver oxide as catalyst to form esters and amides, respectively:

$$R\cdot CH_2\cdot CO_2R' \xleftarrow{R'OH} R\cdot CO\cdot CHN_2 \xrightarrow{NH_3} R\cdot CH_2\cdot CONH_2$$

In the absence of a catalyst and in the presence of water and formic acid, diazoketones form hydroxymethyl ketones:

$$R\cdot CO\cdot CHN_2 + H_2O \xrightarrow{H\cdot CO_2H} R\cdot CO\cdot CH_2OH + N_2$$

The mechanism of the Wolff rearrangement is uncertain; a possibility is (*cf.* Whitmore mechanism):

$$O{=}\overset{R}{\overset{|}{C}}{-}\overset{..}{\bar{C}}H{-}\overset{+}{N}{\equiv}N: \xrightarrow{-N_2} O{=}\overset{R}{\overset{|}{C}}{-}\overset{..}{\underset{}{C}}H \longrightarrow O{=}\overset{+}{C}{-}\overset{..}{\bar{C}}HR \xrightarrow{OH^-} O{=}\overset{OH}{\overset{|}{C}}{-}\overset{..}{\bar{C}}HR \xrightarrow{H^+} O{=}\overset{OH}{\overset{|}{C}}{-}CH_2R \text{ (acid)}$$

$$O{=}\overset{+}{C}{-}\overset{..}{\bar{C}}HR \longleftrightarrow O{=}C{=}CHR \text{ (aldoketen)}$$

Now ketens react with water to form acids, with alcohols to form esters, and with ammonia to form amides (p. 271). This mechanism via a keten is supported by the fact that ketens have actually been isolated during this rearrangement (*e.g.*, by Staudinger *et al.*, 1916). Further support is given by the experiments of Huggett *et al.* (1942) who showed by means of isotope ^{13}C that the CO group of the diazoketone is converted into the acid group:

$$C_6H_5MgBr + \overset{*}{C}O_2 \longrightarrow C_6H_5\cdot\overset{*}{C}O_2H \xrightarrow[\text{(ii) } CH_2N_2]{\text{(i) } SOCl_2} C_6H_5\cdot\overset{*}{C}O\cdot CHN_2 \xrightarrow[H_2O]{Ag_2O}$$

$$C_6H_5\cdot CH_2\cdot\overset{*}{C}O_2H \xrightarrow{CuCr_2O_4} C_6H_5\cdot CO_2H + \overset{*}{C}O_2$$

4. A particularly interesting reaction is the formation of the β-lactam of *N*-phenyl-β-alanine when diazomethane reacts with phenyl *iso*cyanate (Sheehan and Izzo, 1948):

$$C_6H_5\cdot NCO + 2CH_2N_2 \longrightarrow \begin{array}{c} C_6H_5\cdot N{-}{-}CO \\ |\qquad\quad | \\ CH_2{-}CH_2 \end{array} + 2N_2$$

Structure of diazomethane. Curtius (1889), working with diazoacetic ester (see below), proposed the ring structure $>C\Big\langle\begin{array}{c}N\\ \|\\ N\end{array}$ for the $>CN_2$ group. Thus diazomethane would be $CH_2\Big\langle\begin{array}{c}N\\ \|\\ N\end{array}$. Angeli (1907) suggested that the structure of diazomethane was linear, and proposed the formula $CH_2{=}N{\equiv}N$. This contains a quinquecovalent nitrogen atom, and therefore, if it is going to be accepted, requires modification. Three modifications are possible: $CH_2{=}\overset{+}{N}{=}\overset{-}{\ddot{N}}\colon$, $CH_2^{-}{-}\overset{+}{N}{\equiv}N\colon$, and $\overset{+}{C}H_2{-}\ddot{N}{=}\overset{-}{\ddot{N}}\colon$. Chemical evidence, however, is insufficient to show whether one of these formulæ or the cyclic formula of Curtius is correct. Measurement of the dipole moment of diazomethane shows that its value is small; each linear structure should have a large dipole moment. It would therefore appear that the linear formula is untenable. On the other hand, Boersch (1935) showed by electron diffraction studies that the diazomethane molecule is linear; this is supported by infrared spectra measurements. If we assume that diazomethane is a resonance hybrid of all three linear structures, we can then account for the small dipole moment, *i.e.*, diazomethane is best represented as a resonance hybrid:

$$CH_2{=}\overset{+}{N}{=}\overset{-}{\ddot{N}}\colon \longleftrightarrow \overset{-}{\ddot{C}}H_2{-}\overset{+}{N}{\equiv}N\colon \longleftrightarrow \overset{+}{C}H_2{-}\ddot{N}{=}\overset{-}{\ddot{N}}\colon$$

The structure of diazomethane from the M.O. point of view is shown in Fig. 2.

Diazoacetic ester (*ethyl diazoacetate*), $CHN_2{\cdot}CO_2C_2H_5$, may be readily prepared by treating a cooled solution of the hydrochloride of ethyl glycine ester with cold sodium nitrite solution:

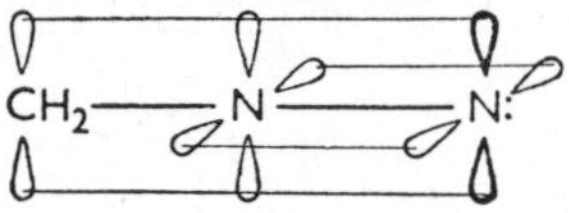

$$Cl^{-}H_3\overset{+}{N}{\cdot}CH_2{\cdot}CO_2C_2H_5 + NaNO_2 \longrightarrow CHN_2{\cdot}CO_2C_2H_5 + NaCl + 2H_2O \quad (85\%)$$

FIG. 13.2.

It is a yellow oil, b.p. 141°/720 mm., insoluble in water, soluble in ethanol and ether.

The reactions of diazoacetic ester are similar to those of diazomethane. It is reduced by zinc dust and acetic acid to ammonia and glycine. When boiled with dilute halogen acid, it eliminates nitrogen to form glycollic ester:

$$CHN_2{\cdot}CO_2C_2H_5 + H_2O \longrightarrow CH_2OH{\cdot}CO_2C_2H_5 + N_2$$

When, however, diazoacetic ester is warmed with *concentrated* halogen acid, ethyl halogeno-acetate is formed, *e.g.*,

$$CHN_2{\cdot}CO_2C_2H_5 + HCl \longrightarrow CH_2Cl{\cdot}CO_2C_2H_5 + N_2$$

Diazoacetic ester reacts with compounds containing an active hydrogen atom, *e.g.*, it forms acetylglycollic ester with acetic acid, and the ethyl ether of glycollic ester with ethanol:

$$CH_3{\cdot}CO_2H + CHN_2{\cdot}CO_2C_2H_5 \longrightarrow CH_3{\cdot}CO{\cdot}O{\cdot}CH_2{\cdot}CO_2C_2H_5 + N_2$$
$$C_2H_5OH + CHN_2{\cdot}CO_2C_2H_5 \longrightarrow CH_2(OC_2H_5){\cdot}CO_2C_2H_5 + N_2$$

It reacts with ethylenic compounds to form *pyrazoline* derivatives, *e.g.*, with ethylene it forms pyrazoline-3-carboxylic ester:

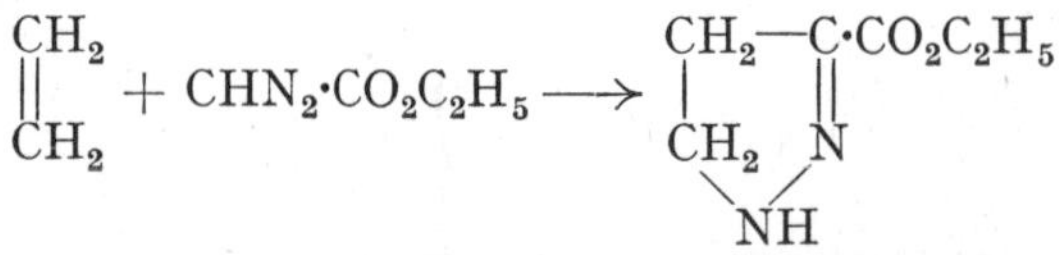

$$\begin{matrix} CH_2 \\ \| \\ CH_2 \end{matrix} + CHN_2{\cdot}CO_2C_2H_5 \longrightarrow \begin{matrix} CH_2{-}C{\cdot}CO_2C_2H_5 \\ | \quad\quad \| \\ CH_2 \quad N \\ \diagdown \; \diagup \\ NH \end{matrix}$$

With acetylenic compounds, it forms *pyrazole* derivatives, *e.g.*, with acetylene, it gives pyrazole-3-carboxylic ester:

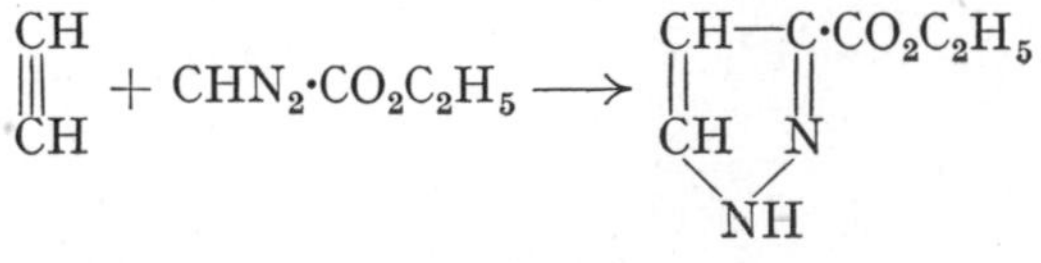

$$\begin{matrix} CH \\ \||| \\ CH \end{matrix} + CHN_2{\cdot}CO_2C_2H_5 \longrightarrow \begin{matrix} CH{-}C{\cdot}CO_2C_2H_5 \\ \| \quad\quad \| \\ CH \quad N \\ \diagdown \; \diagup \\ NH \end{matrix}$$

QUESTIONS

1. Draw up an analytical table to show how you would distinguish between aqueous solutions of $AcNH_2\cdot HCl$, $MeNH_2\cdot HCl$, $Me_2NH\cdot HCl$, $Me_3N\cdot HCl$, Me_4NCl.
2. Write out the structures and names of the isomeric amines of formula $C_4H_{11}N$.
3. Discuss the problem of hydrogen cyanide as a tautomeric mixture, including in your answer an account of the structures of the alkyl cyanides and *iso*cyanides.
4. Describe the methods for preparing MeCN. Name the compounds and state the conditions under which they are formed when MeCN is treated with: (*a*) NaOH, (*b*) HCl, (*c*) ROH + HCl, (*d*) NH_3, (*e*) Ac_2O, (*f*) $SnCl_2$, (*g*) H, (*h*) RMgBr, (*i*) Na, (*j*) AcOEt.
5. Write an account of the preparation and properties of cyanic acid and its related compounds.
6. How may $EtNO_2$ be prepared? Name the compounds and state the conditions under which they are formed when $MeNO_2$ is treated with:—(*a*) H, (*b*) HCl, (*c*) NaOH, (*d*) NaOH followed by H_2SO_4, (*e*) NaOH followed by $SnCl_2$/HCl, (*f*) Br_2, (*g*) HNO_2, (*h*) H·CHO, (*i*) $C_6H_5\cdot CHO$, (*j*) $CH_2{:}CH\cdot CO\cdot CH_3$.
7. Suggest as many methods as you can:—(*a*) for separating the three classes of amines, (*b*) for distinguishing between the three classes of nitro-compounds.
8. Discuss the various methods whereby:—(*a*) a primary amine may be converted into a secondary, and vice-versa, (*b*) a secondary amine into a tertiary, and vice-versa, (*c*) EtOH into *n*-PrOH, and vice-versa.
9. Write an account of the general methods for preparing amines. Name the compounds and state the conditions under which they are formed when $Et\cdot NH_2$, Et_2NH Et_3N, respectively, are treated with:—(*a*) H_2O, (*b*) H_2SO_4, (*c*) MeI, (*d*) AcCl, (*e*) Br_2, (*f*) NOCl, (*g*) Na, (*h*) MeMgI, (*i*) $C_6H_5\cdot NCO$, (*j*) CS_2, (*k*) $C_6H_5\cdot CHO$, (*l*) HNO_2, (*m*) $KMnO_4$, (*n*) H_2SO_5, (*o*) BrCN.
10. Write an account of the preparation and properties of the quaternary ammonium hydroxides.
11. Describe the preparation and properties of:—(*a*) ethylenediamine, (*b*) putrescine, (*c*) cadaverine, (*d*) vinylamine, (*e*) neurine, (*f*) allylamine, (*g*) cholamine, (*h*) choline.
12. Suggest one synthesis for each of the following:—(*a*) $CH_3\cdot CH(NH_2)\cdot CH_2\cdot NH_2$, (*b*) $Me_2C(NH_2)\cdot CH_2OH$, (*c*) $NH_2\cdot (CH_2)_3\cdot CHOH\cdot CH_3$, (*d*) $Me_2N\cdot NH_2$, (*e*) $Me_2N\cdot OH$, (*f*) spermine.
13. Describe the preparation and properties of glycine. What are betaines?
14. Describe the preparation of:—(*a*) CH_2N_2, (*b*) $CHN_2\cdot CO_2Et$. Discuss their structures. Name the compounds and state the conditions under which they are formed when CH_2N_2 and $CHN_2\cdot CO_2Et$, respectively, are treated with:—(*a*) HBr, (*b*) AcOH, (*c*) $Et\cdot SO_3H$, (*d*) EtOH, (*e*) $Et\cdot NH_2$, (*f*) $AcNH_2$, (*g*) $CH_3\cdot CHO$, (*h*) Me_2CO, (*i*) C_2H_4, (*j*) C_2H_2, (*k*) $EtO_2C\cdot CH = CH\cdot CO_2Et$.
15. Define and give examples of:—(*a*) tautomerism, (*b*) pseudo-acids, (*c*) Mannich reaction, (*d*) Schmidt's reaction, (*e*) Gabriel's synthesis, (*f*) Zeisel method, (*g*) Herzig–Meyer method, (*h*) Liebermann's nitroso-reaction, (*i*) Hofmann's exhaustive methylation method, (*j*) Sörensen titration, (*k*) Arndt–Eistert synthesis, (*l*) reductive alkylation.

READING REFERENCES

Sidgwick, *The Organic Chemistry of Nitrogen* (New Edition by Taylor and Baker, 1937), Oxford Press.

Mowry, The Preparation of Nitriles, *Chem. Reviews*, 1948, **42**, 189.

Levy and Rose, The Aliphatic Nitro-Compounds, *Quart. Reviews* (*Chem. Soc.*), 1948, **1**, 358.

Hass and Shechter, The Vapour-Phase Nitration of Saturated Hydrocarbons, *Ind. Eng. Chem.*, 1947, **39**, 817.

Whitmore and Mosher, Aliphatic Amines and Nitrous Acid, *J. Amer. Chem. Soc.*, 1941, **63**, 1118.

Newman and Gildenhorn, The Mechanism of the Schmidt Reactions and Observations on the Curtius Rearrangement, *ibid.*, 1948, **70**, 317.

Smith, The Schmidt Reaction, *ibid.*, 1948, **70**, 320.

Webers and Bruce, The Leuckart Reaction: A Study of the Mechanism, *ibid.*, 1948, **70**, 1422.

Organic Reactions, Wiley. Vol. I (1942), Ch. 10. The Mannich Reaction.

ibid., Vol. I (1942), Ch. 2. The Arndt–Eistert Synthesis.

ibid., Vol. III (1946), Ch. 8. The Schmidt Reaction.

ibid., Vol. IV (1948), Ch. 3. The Preparation of Amines by Reductive Alkylation.

ibid., Vol. VII (1953), Ch. 3. Carbon–Carbon Alkylations with Amines and Ammonium salts, Ch. 6. The Nitrosation of Aliphatic Carbon Atoms.

ibid., Vol. VII (1954), Ch. 8. The Reaction of Diazomethane and its Derivatives with Aldehydes and Ketones.

Smith, Aliphatic Diazo-Compounds, *Chem. Reviews*, 1938, **23**, 193.
Huisgen, Altes und Neues über aliphatische Diazoverbindungen, *Angew. Chem.*, 1955, **67**, 439.
Ingold, *Structure and Mechanism in Organic Chemistry*, Bell and Sons (1953). Ch. 8. Olefin-forming Eliminations.
Thorne, The Formation of Nitrosochlorides and Nitrosates, *J.C.S.*, **1956**, 4271.
Kornblum *et al.*, The Mechanism of the Reaction of Silver Nitrite with Alkyl Halides, *J. Amer. Chem. Soc.*, 1955, **77**, 6269.
Kornblum *et al.*, A New Method for the Synthesis of Aliphatic Nitro Compounds, *ibid.*, 1956, **78**, 1497.
Finar, *Organic Chemistry*, Vol. II, Longmans, Green (1956). Ch. XIII. Amino-Acids and Proteins.

CHAPTER XIV

ALIPHATIC COMPOUNDS OF SULPHUR, PHOSPHORUS, ARSENIC AND SILICON

SULPHUR COMPOUNDS

Mercaptans or **thioalcohols,** RSH. These compounds occur in petroleum and give rise to " sour petrol ".

Nomenclature. One method is to name them as alkyl *mercaptans*, the —*SH* group being known as the *mercapto* or *sulph-hydryl group*. On the other hand, according to the I.U.C. system of nomenclature, the —SH group is known as the *thiol* group, and the suffix of the series is *thiol*. This method of naming the mercaptans arises from the fact that they are the sulphur analogues of the alcohols, the usual procedure of showing that an oxygen atom has been replaced by a sulphur atom being indicated by the prefix *thio*.

$CH_3\cdot SH$	methyl mercaptan	methanethiol
$C_2H_5\cdot SH$	ethyl mercaptan	ethanethiol
$(CH_3)_2CH\cdot CH_2\cdot SH$	*iso*butyl mercaptan	2-methylpropanethiol

General methods of preparation. One method is to heat an alkyl halide with potassium hydrogen sulphide in ethanolic solution:

$$RX + KSH \longrightarrow RSH + KX \quad (g.)$$

Alternatively, a potassium alkyl sulphate may be distilled with potassium hydrogen sulphide (the yield of thioalcohol is variable):

$$RO\cdot SO_2\cdot OK + KSH \longrightarrow RSH + K_2SO_4$$

Another method depends on the direct replacement of oxygen in an alcohol by sulphur. This may be carried out by heating the alcohol with phosphorus pentasulphide:

$$5ROH + P_2S_5 \longrightarrow 5RSH + P_2O_5 \quad (p.)$$

A more satisfactory method of replacing the oxygen by sulphur is to pass a mixture of alcohol vapour and hydrogen sulphide over a thoria catalyst at 400°:

$$ROH + H_2S \xrightarrow{ThO_2} RSH + H_2O \quad (f.–g.)$$

The best method for preparing thioalcohols is to decompose an S-*alkyl*iso-*thiouronium salt* with alkali; these salts may be prepared by interaction of an alkyl halide (preferably the bromide or iodide) and thiourea:

$$RBr + S{=}C\begin{matrix}\diagup NH_2\\ \diagdown NH_2\end{matrix} \longrightarrow R{-}S{-}C\begin{matrix}\diagup\!\!\diagup NH\\ \diagdown NH_2\end{matrix}\cdot HBr \xrightarrow{NaOH} RSH \quad (80\text{–}90\%)$$

On the other hand, Frank and Smith (1946) have found that the *S*-alkyl*iso*-thiouronium salt may be prepared by heating an alcohol and thiourea with 48 per cent. hydrobromic acid (for 7 hours):

$$ROH + S{=}C(NH_2)_2 + HBr \longrightarrow R{-}S{-}C\begin{matrix}\diagup\!\!\diagup NH\\ \diagdown NH_2\end{matrix}\cdot HBr + H_2O$$

The yields are as good as those when the alkyl bromide is used, and so eliminate the step of converting the alcohol into the alkyl bromide.

General properties. The thiols, except methanethiol, which is a gas, are colourless volatile liquids with disagreeable smells. Their boiling points are lower than those of the corresponding alcohols; this is probably due to the fact that they are very little associated, hydrogen bonding not readily taking place between hydrogen and sulphur. The thiols are also less soluble in water than the corresponding alcohols, again, no doubt, due to their inability to form hydrogen bonds with water. They are more strongly acidic than the alcohols; this is to be expected, since the thiols are the alkyl derivatives of hydrogen sulphide, which is a stronger acid than water, of which the alcohols may be regarded as alkyl derivatives.

Reactions. The thioalcohols resemble the alcohols in many ways (sulphur and oxygen occur in the same periodic group); the main difference is their behaviour towards oxidising agents.

1. Thiols form mercaptides with the evolution of hydrogen when treated with alkali metals:

$$2RSH + 2Na \longrightarrow 2RSNa + H_2$$

These alkali mercaptides are salts: $[RS]^-Na^+$, and are decomposed by water:

$$RSNa + H_2O \longrightarrow RSH + NaOH$$

This reaction is reversible for the low-molecular-weight thiols, since these dissolve in aqueous alkali, *e.g.*,

$$C_2H_5SH + NaOH \longrightarrow C_2H_5SNa + H_2O$$

2. Thiols precipitate mercaptides when treated with an aqueous solution of the salt of a heavy metal, *e.g.*,

$$2RSH + (CH_3{\cdot}CO_2)_2Pb \longrightarrow (RS)_2Pb + 2CH_3{\cdot}CO_2H$$

Thiols also attack mercuric oxide in aqueous solution to form the mercury mercaptide:

$$2RSH + HgO \longrightarrow (RS)_2Hg + H_2O$$

It is this reaction which is the origin of the name mercaptans (*mercurius*, mercury; *captans*, seizing). These heavy metals mercaptides are *covalent* compounds.

An aqueous solution of cupric chloride or an alkaline solution of sodium plumbite containing sulphur ("doctor solution") converts thiols into disulphides:

$$2RSH + 2CuCl_2 \longrightarrow R{-}S{-}S{-}R + 2CuCl + 2HCl$$

$$2RSH + Na_2PbO_2 + S \longrightarrow R{-}S{-}S{-}R + PbS + 2NaOH$$

3. Thiols react with carboxylic acids, preferably in the presence of an inorganic acid, to form a *thiolester*:

$$R{\cdot}CO_2H + R'SH \overset{H^+}{\rightleftharpoons} R{\cdot}CO{\cdot}SR + H_2O$$

This reaction suggests that esterification involves the hydroxyl of the carboxyl group, and, as we have seen (p. 176), this has been shown to be the case.

4. Thiols may be oxidised, the nature of the product depending on the oxidising agent used. Mild oxidation with, *e.g.*, air, hydrogen peroxide, cupric chloride or sodium hypochlorite results in the formation of *dialkyldisulphides*:

$$2RSH + H_2O_2 \longrightarrow R{-}S{-}S{-}R + 2H_2O$$

Dialkyl-disulphides may also be prepared by the action of iodine on sodium mercaptides:

$$2RSNa + I_2 \longrightarrow R_2S_2 + 2NaI$$

These disulphides have an unpleasant smell (not as unpleasant as that of thiols), and their formation by the oxidation of thiols is known as " sweetening " (p. 52). Allyl disulphide, $(CH_2{:}CH{\cdot}CH_2{-})_2S_2$, occurs in garlic. Disulphides are reduced to thiols by lithium aluminium hydride.

When oxidised with vigorous oxidising agents, *e.g.*, nitric acid, thiols are converted into *sulphonic acids*:

$$RSH + 3[O] \xrightarrow{HNO_3} R{\cdot}SO_3H$$

5. Thiols readily combine with aldehydes and ketones, in the presence by hydrochloric acid, to form *mercaptals* and *mercaptols* respectively; *e.g.*, ethanethiol forms diethylmethyl mercaptal with acetaldehyde, and diethyldimethyl mercaptal with acetone (see also sulphones, below):

$$CH_3{\cdot}CHO + 2C_2H_5SH \xrightarrow{HCl} CH_3{\cdot}CH(SC_2H_5)_2 + H_2O$$

$$(CH_3)_2CO + 2C_2H_5SH \xrightarrow{HCl} (CH_3)_2C(SC_2H_5)_2 + H_2O$$

Refluxing mercaptals (and mercaptols) with ethanol in the presence of freshly prepared Raney nickel replaces the thiol group by hydrogen (Wolfrom *et al.*, 1944):

$$\gt C(SR)_2 + 4[H] \longrightarrow \gt CH_2 + 2RSH$$

Thus a carbonyl group can be converted into a methylene group (*cf.* the Clemmensen and Wolff–Kishner reductions).

The aldehyde group may be " protected " in *acid* solution by conversion into a mercaptal, and can be regenerated by treatment of the latter with mercuric chloride in the presence of cadmium carbonate (*cf.* acetals, p. 149).

Thioethers or **alkyl sulphides,** R_2S. These are the sulphur analogues of the ethers, from which they differ considerably in a number of ways.

General methods of preparation. 1. By heating potassium sulphide with an alkyl halide or a potassium alkyl sulphate:

$$2RX + K_2S \longrightarrow R_2S + 2KX \quad (f.g.\text{–}g.)$$

$$2RO{\cdot}SO_2{\cdot}OK + K_2S \longrightarrow R_2S + 2K_2SO_4 \quad (g.)$$

2. Heating an ether with phosphorus pentasulphide:

$$5R_2O + P_2S_5 \longrightarrow 5R_2S + P_2O_5 \quad (p.)$$

3. By heating an alkyl halide with a sodium mercaptide (*cf.* Williamson's synthesis, p. 131):

$$RX + R'SNa \longrightarrow R{-}S{-}R' + NaX \quad (g.\text{–}v.g.)$$

4. By passing a thiol over a mixture of alumina and zinc sulphide at 300°:

$$2RSH \longrightarrow R_2S + H_2S$$

5. By the addition of a thiol to an olefin in the presence of peroxides; in the absence of the latter very little reaction occurs (Kharasch *et al.*, 1939):

$$R{\cdot}CH{=}CH_2 + R'SH \longrightarrow R{\cdot}CH_2{\cdot}CH_2{\cdot}SR'$$

General properties and reactions. The thioethers are unpleasant-smelling oils, insoluble in water but soluble in organic solvents. Chemically they are comparatively inert. They may be oxidised to *sulphoxides* which, on further oxidation, are converted into *sulphones*: *e.g.*, ethyl sulphide, on oxidation with hydrogen peroxide in glacial acetic acid, gives first diethyl sulphoxide and then diethyl sulphone:

$$(C_2H_5)_2S \xrightarrow{H_2O_2} (C_2H_5)_2S{=}O \xrightarrow{H_2O_2} (C_2H_5)_2S{\genfrac{}{}{0pt}{}{\nearrow O}{\searrow O}}$$

Other oxidising agents which bring about the same changes are potassium permanganate, nitric acid, perbenzoic acid, etc.

The valency of sulphur in sulphoxides and sulphones is an interesting problem. Originally sulphur was thought to be quadrivalent in the former compounds, and sexavalent in the latter. Then, to conform with the " octet " theory (p. 10), the valencies were changed to 3 and 4, respectively, the formulæ being written with co-ordinate bonds, *viz.*,

$$R_2S \rightarrow O \quad \text{and} \quad R_2S{\genfrac{}{}{0pt}{}{\nearrow O}{\searrow O}}$$

Phillips *et al.* (1945) regard the S—O bond as being primarily a double bond. Moffitt (1950), from M.O. calculations, has shown that the S—O bond is largely double in character and that the 3*d* orbitals of the sulphur atom are involved in the formation of this bond. Bond length measurements of the S—O bond in sulphoxides and sulphones indicate that they are almost all double bonds.

The alkyl sulphides form various addition products, *e.g.*, with bromine the alkyl sulphide dibromide is formed, R_2SBr_2. Alkyl sulphides also combine with a molecule of alkyl halide to form *sulphonium salts*, in which the sulphur is tercovalent uni-electrovalent, *e.g.*, the formula of triethylsulphonium iodide is $(C_2H_5)_3\overset{+}{S}\!:\!\}\overset{-}{I}$. When a sulphonium salt is heated, it decomposes into alkyl sulphide and alkyl halide (*cf.* quaternary ammonium salts, p. 301):

$$[R_3S]^+I^- \longrightarrow R_2S + RI$$

When they are treated with moist silver oxide, the *sulphonium hydroxide* is formed:

$$[R_3S]^+I^- + \text{" AgOH "} \longrightarrow [R_3S]^+OH^- + AgI$$

Sulphonium hydroxides are strongly basic, and on heating form alkyl sulphide and olefin, *e.g.*,

$$[(C_2H_5)_3S]^+OH^- \longrightarrow (C_2H_5)_2S + C_2H_4 + H_2O$$

This is believed to occur by an E2 mechanism (*cf.* p. 302):

$$HO^- \; H{-}CH_2{-}CH_2{-}\overset{+}{S}(C_2H_5)_2 \longrightarrow H_2O + CH_2{=}CH_2 + (C_2H_5)_2S$$

Challenger *et al.* (1948) have isolated dimethyl-β-carboxyethylsulphonium chloride, $[(CH_3)_2\overset{+}{S}\cdot CH_2\cdot CH_2\cdot CO_2H]\overset{-}{Cl}$, from natural sources.

Mustard gas, 2 : 2′-*dichlorodiethyl sulphide, bis*(2-*chloroethyl*)-*sulphide*, $(ClCH_2\cdot CH_2\text{-})_2S$, may be prepared by the action of sulphur monochloride on ethylene:

$$2C_2H_4 + S_2Cl_2 \longrightarrow (ClCH_2\cdot CH_2{-})_2S + S$$

It may also be prepared, in a purer state, by heating ethylene chlorohydrin with sodium sulphide, and treating the product with hydrochloric acid:

$$2HOCH_2\cdot CH_2Cl + Na_2S \longrightarrow 2NaCl + (HOCH_2\cdot CH_2{-})_2S \xrightarrow{HCl} (ClCH_2\cdot CH_2{-})_2S$$

Mustard gas is an oily liquid, b.p. 215–217°, with a mustard-like smell. It is almost insoluble in water, but soluble in most organic solvents. It is a poison, and a vesicant.

Thiocyanic acid, *iso*thiocyanic acid and their derivatives. Thiocyanic acid appears to be a tautomeric substance, the equilibrium mixture of thiocyanic acid, HSCN, and *iso*thiocyanic acid, HNCS. Spectroscopic studies of thiocyanic acid indicate the structure HNCS (Beard *et al.*, 1947):

$$H{-}S{-}C{\equiv}N \rightleftharpoons S{=}C{=}N{-}H$$

Salts and esters of both forms are known (*cf.* cyanic acid, p. 282).

Thiocyanic acid may be prepared by heating a mixture of potassium thiocyanate and potassium hydrogen sulphate:

$$KSCN + KHSO_4 \longrightarrow HSCN + K_2SO_4$$

Thiocyanic acid distils over as a colourless liquid, m.p. 5°. It is soluble in water, ethanol and ether in all proportions. Its dilute aqueous solutions are fairly stable, the concentrated solutions decomposing to form carbonyl sulphide and ammonia:

$$HSCN + H_2O \longrightarrow COS + NH_3$$

Alkyl thiocyanates, R·SCN, may be prepared by heating potassium thiocyanate with an alkyl halide:

$$RI + KSCN \longrightarrow R{\cdot}SCN + KI$$

They may also be prepared by the action of cyanogen chloride on a lead mercaptide:

$$(RS)_2Pb + 2ClCN \longrightarrow 2R{\cdot}SCN + PbCl_2$$

The alkyl thiocyanates are fairly stable volatile oils, with a slight odour of garlic. They are oxidised to sulphonic acids by concentrated nitric acid, and reduced to thiols by, *e.g.*, zinc and sulphuric acid; both of these reactions show that the alkyl radical in alkyl thiocyanates is directly attached to sulphur:

$$R{\cdot}SO_3H \xleftarrow{HNO_3} R{\cdot}SCN \xrightarrow{Zn/H_2SO_4} RSH$$

They are converted into sulphonyl chlorides by chlorine water.

$$R{\cdot}SCN + Cl_2 \xrightarrow{H_2O} R{\cdot}SO_2Cl + ClCN$$

When heated at 180°, alkyl thiocyanates rearrange to the alkyl *iso*thiocyanate:

$$R{\cdot}SCN \xrightarrow{180^\circ} R{\cdot}NCS$$

Alkyl *iso*thiocyanates or **mustard oils,** R·NCS, may be prepared by heating alkyl thiocyanates at 180°, but a much more satisfactory method is the **Hofmann mustard-oil reaction** (1868), which is carried out by heating a mixture of a primary amine, carbon disulphide and mercuric chloride. The mechanism is uncertain; it may be via the formation of a *dithiocarbamic acid salt* (see p. 373 for further details):

$$R{\cdot}NH_2 + S{=}C{=}S \longrightarrow S{=}C\begin{matrix}\diagup NH{\cdot}R \\ \diagdown SH\end{matrix} \xrightarrow{HgCl_2} R{\cdot}NCS + HgS + 2HCl$$

Another convenient method is to add an aqueous solution of a primary amine to carbon disulphide in sodium hydroxide solution, and then ethyl chloroformate:

$$R{\cdot}NH_2 + CS_2 + NaOH \longrightarrow R{\cdot}NH{\cdot}CS_2Na + H_2O \xrightarrow{Cl{\cdot}CO_2C_2H_5}$$
$$NaCl + R{\cdot}NH{\cdot}CS_2CO_2C_2H_5 \longrightarrow R{\cdot}NCS + COS + C_2H_5OH \quad (60\text{–}70\%)$$

The alkyl *iso*thiocyanates are liquids with a powerful mustard smell; they are lachrymatory and vesicatory. They are hydrolysed to primary amines when heated with hydrochloric acid, and reduced to primary amines and thioformaldehyde by, *e.g.*, zinc and sulphuric acid; both of these reactions show that the alkyl radical in alkyl *iso*thiocyanates is directly attached to nitrogen:

$$R{\cdot}NCS + 2H_2O \xrightarrow{HCl} R{\cdot}NH_2 + CO_2 + H_2S$$
$$R{\cdot}NCS + 4[H] \xrightarrow{Zn/H_2SO_4} R{\cdot}NH_2 + H{\cdot}CHS$$

Allyl *iso*thiocyanate (*allyl mustard oil*), $CH_2{:}CH{\cdot}CH_2{\cdot}NCS$, occurs in mustard seed as the glucoside *sinigrin*, which, on hydrolysis by acid or by the enzyme *myrosin* (which is found in mustard seeds), gives allyl *iso*thiocyanate, glucose and potassium hydrogen sulphate. Allyl *iso*thiocyanate is a colourless oil, b.p. 151°, and is the substance which gives mustard its characteristic odour and taste. It is lachrymatory and vesicatory, and is a convenient starting material for the preparation of allylamine.

Gmelin *et al.* (1955) have isolated $CH_3{\cdot}S{\cdot}(CH_2)_4{\cdot}NCS$ and $CH_3{\cdot}S{\cdot}(CH_2)_3{\cdot}NCS$ from natural sources.

Thiocyanogen, $(\text{—}SCN)_2$, may be prepared by treating lead thiocyanate with bromine in ethereal solution at 0°.

$$Pb(SCN)_2 + Br_2 \longrightarrow (\text{—}SCN)_2 + PbBr_2$$

Thiocyanogen is a gas and resembles the halogens in that it adds on to double bonds (*thiocyanation*).

Alkyl sulphoxides, $R_2S{=}O$, may be prepared by oxidising alkyl sulphides with the *theoretical* amount of hydrogen peroxide (in acetic acid) or with *dilute* nitric acid:

$$R_2S + [O] \longrightarrow R_2S{=}O$$

The state of oxidation depends largely on the conditions, and usually a mixture of sulphoxide and sulphone is obtained. Chromium trioxide in acetic acid appears to be specific for oxidation to sulphoxide (Knoll, 1926), and Edwards *et al.* (1954) have shown that saturated (and unsaturated) aliphatic sulphides may be oxidised to sulphoxides by chromium trioxide in pyridine or with manganese dioxide in light petroleum (yield: 49–74%). Alkyl sulphides are also readily oxidised by liquid dinitrogen tetroxide to sulphoxides, and there is no further oxidation to sulphone (yield: 90%; Addison *et al.*, 1956).

The sulphoxides are odourless, relatively unstable solids, soluble in water, ethanol and ether, and are feebly basic, *e.g.*, they form salts with hydrochloric acid. The structure of these salts is uncertain; it may be $[R_2S\text{—}OH]^+Cl^-$. Sulphoxides are reduced to sulphides by zinc and acetic acid:

$$R_2SO + 2[H] \xrightarrow{Zn/CH_3{\cdot}CO_2H} R_2S + H_2O$$

Alkyl sulphones, $R_2S{\lessgtr}^{O}_{O}$, may be prepared by oxidising alkyl sulphides with hydrogen peroxide *in excess* (in acetic acid) or with *concentrated* nitric acid:

$$R_2S + 2[O] \longrightarrow R_2SO_2$$

They are colourless, odourless, very stable solids, soluble in water; they are very resistant to reduction, but some sulphones (and sulphoxides) are reduced to sulphide by lithium aluminium hydride. Many sulphones produce sulphinic acids when fused with potassium hydroxide at 200°, *e.g.*,

$$(C_2H_5)_2SO_2 + KOH \longrightarrow C_2H_4 + C_2H_5{\cdot}SO_2K + H_2O \quad (60\%)$$

This reaction may be used to prepare aliphatic sulphinic acids.

A very important sulphone is **sulphonal** [2 : 2-bis(ethylsulphonyl)-propane], which may be prepared by the oxidation of dimethyldiethyl mercaptol with potassium permanganate:

$$(CH_3)_2C(SC_2H_5)_2 + 4[O] \longrightarrow (CH_3)_2C(SO_2{\cdot}C_2H_5)_2$$

Sulphonal is a colourless solid, m.p. 126°, stable to acids and alkalis. It has been used as an hypnotic. The corresponding 2 : 2-bis(methylsulphonyl)propane has no hypnotic action at all, but as the number of ethyl groups increases, so the hypnotic action increases (see Table VII).

TABLE VII

Name	Formula	Hypnotic action
2 : 2-bis(methylsulphonyl)-propane	$(CH_3)_2C(SO_2{\cdot}CH_3)_2$	O
2-methylsulphonyl-2-ethyl-sulphonylpropane	$(CH_3)_2C(SO_2{\cdot}CH_3)(SO_2{\cdot}C_2H_5)$	+
sulphonal	$(CH_3)_2C(SO_2{\cdot}C_2H_5)_2$	++
trional	$(CH_3)(C_2H_5)C(SO_2{\cdot}C_2H_5)_2$	+++
tetronal	$(C_2H_5)_2C(SO_2{\cdot}C_2H_5)_2$	++++

Sulphur dioxide adds on to unsaturated compounds to form long linear polymers known as *polysulphones*, the valency of the sulphur changing from 4 to 6:

$$>C=C< + SO_2 \longrightarrow \left(-\overset{|}{\underset{|}{C}}-\overset{|}{\underset{|}{C}}-\overset{O}{\underset{O}{\overset{\|}{\underset{\|}{S}}}}- \right)_n$$

The reaction takes place in the liquid phase at room temperature under the influence of light, or in the presence of a catalyst such as silver nitrate or peracetic acid. The properties of the polysulphones depend on the nature of the olefin used; all polysulphones, however, are thermoplastic, resinous substances which are insoluble in water, acids and most organic solvents.

Sulphonic acids, $R{\cdot}SO_3H$. The aliphatic sulphonic acids are named either as alkylsulphonic acids or as alkanesulphonic acids; in the latter case the sulphonic acid group is considered as a substituent group, *e.g.*,

$CH_3{\cdot}SO_3H$	methylsulphonic acid or methanesulphonic acid
$CH_3{\cdot}CH_2{\cdot}CH_2{\cdot}SO_3H$	*n*-propylsulphonic acid or propane-1-sulphonic acid
$(CH_3)_2CH{\cdot}SO_3H$	*iso*propylsulphonic acid or propane-2-sulphonic acid

General methods of preparation. 1. By the action of fuming sulphuric acid or chlorosulphonic acid on a paraffin. The sulphonic acid group enters the chain, probably at the second carbon atom, *e.g.*,

$$CH_3\cdot(CH_2)_4\cdot CH_3 + SO_3 \xrightarrow{H_2SO_4} CH_3\cdot(CH_2)_3\cdot CH(SO_3H)\cdot CH_3$$

Sulphuric acid itself has no action; it is the free sulphur trioxide that is the sulphonating reagent.

2. By the action of sulphuryl chloride on a hydrocarbon in the presence of light and a catalyst, *e.g.*, pyridine, at 40–60°. The sulphonyl chloride is obtained, often in high yield; the sulphonyl chloride group appears to enter mainly at the second carbon atom, but varying amounts of product with this group at the first carbon are also obtained:

$$RH + SO_2Cl_2 \longrightarrow R\cdot SO_2Cl + HCl$$

3. By the oxidation of a lead mercaptide with concentrated nitric acid, the lead sulphonate produced being converted into the free acid by hydrogen sulphide:

$$(RS)_2Pb + 6[O] \xrightarrow{HNO_3} (R\cdot SO_3)_2Pb \xrightarrow{H_2S} 2R\cdot SO_3H \quad (g.)$$

In practice it is usually more convenient to use a thiol or a thiocyanate as the starting material, *e.g.*,

$$RSH + 3[O] \xrightarrow{HNO_3} R\cdot SO_3H \quad (g.\text{–}v.g.)$$

This method is most satisfactory, in that the position of the sulphonic acid group is known with certainty (the position of the mercapto or thiocyanate group being determined by the nature of the alkyl halide used in the preparation of the thiol or thiocyanate).

4. The **Strecker reaction** (1868). This reaction is carried out by heating an alkyl halide with sodium sulphite; the sodium salt of the sulphonic acid is produced:

$$RX + Na_2SO_3 \longrightarrow R\cdot SO_3Na + NaX \quad (g.\text{–}v.g.)$$

5. Sodium hydrogen sulphite adds on to olefins in the presence of peroxides to form sulphonic acids (Kharasch *et al.*, 1939).

$$R\cdot CH{=}CH_2 + NaHSO_3 \longrightarrow R\cdot CH_2\cdot CH_2\cdot SO_3Na$$

6. By the oxidation of *S*-alkyl*iso*thiouronium salts (p. 373).

General properties and reactions. The sulphonic acids are generally thick liquids, soluble in water. They are isomeric with the alkyl hydrogen sulphites:

$$R{-}\overset{\overset{\displaystyle O}{\|}}{\underset{\underset{\displaystyle O}{\|}}{S}}{-}OH \qquad\qquad R{-}O{-}\overset{\overset{\displaystyle O}{\|}}{S}{-}OH$$

alkylsulphonic acid — alkyl hydrogen sulphite

The alkyl hydrogen sulphites are esters readily hydrolysed by alkali; the sulphonic acids are not hydrolysed, but form salts with alkali. Many of the reactions of the sulphonic acids and their methods of preparation show that in these acids the sulphur is directly attached to the alkyl group.

The sulphonic acids are strong acids, forming salts with metallic hydroxides or carbonates; the lead and barium salts are very soluble in water. They form the acid chloride, the sulphonyl chloride, when treated with phosphorus pentachloride or thionyl chloride:

$$R{\cdot}SO_3H + PCl_5 \longrightarrow R{\cdot}SO_2Cl + HCl + POCl_3$$

These sulphonyl chlorides are only very slowly hydrolysed by water (*cf.* acyl chlorides); they react readily with concentrated aqueous ammonia to form *sulphonamides*:

$$R{\cdot}SO_2Cl + 2NH_3 \longrightarrow R{\cdot}SO_2{\cdot}NH_2 + NH_4Cl$$

Sulphonyl chlorides also react with alcohols to form esters:

$$R{\cdot}SO_2Cl + R'OH \longrightarrow R{\cdot}SO_3R' + HCl$$

Alkyl sulphonates *cannot* be produced by heating a mixture of sulphonic acid and alcohol; *no esterification takes place.* Sulphonyl chlorides are reduced by lithium aluminium hydride to thiols (Marvel *et al.*, 1950).

The sulphonic acids undergo many double-decomposition reactions (see the aromatic sulphonic acids, p. 583). There are, however, two important differences between aliphatic and aromatic sulphonic acids. In the former, the sulphonic acid group (*a*) is not eliminated by heating with hydrochloric acid, and (*b*) is hardly replaced, if at all, by hydroxyl when fused with alkali.

Thioaldehydes and thioketones. These readily polymerise to the trimer and the isolation of the monomer is difficult, and impossible in some cases, *e.g.*, thioformaldehyde.

Thioaldehydes and thioketones may be prepared by the action of hydrogen sulphide on an aldehyde or ketone in the presence of hydrochloric acid, *e.g.*, (R′ = H or alkyl):

$$R{\cdot}CO{\cdot}R' + H_2S \xrightarrow{HCl} H_2O + [R{\cdot}CS{\cdot}R'] \xrightarrow{\text{polymerises}} [R{\cdot}CS{\cdot}R']_3$$

These trimers are cyclic compounds (1 : 3 : 5-*trithians*), and many of those of the thioaldehydes have been isolated in two forms. Baumann and Fromm (1891) suggested that the two forms were geometrical isomers, the *cis* form being the one with the three hydrogen atoms all on the same side of the plane:

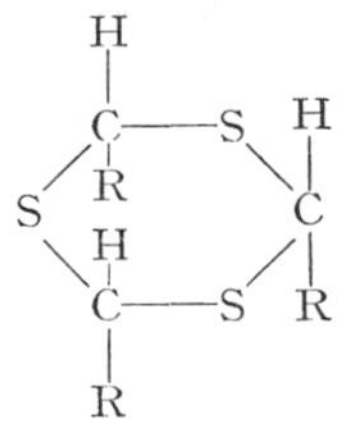

```
      H                        H
      |                        |
      C——S  H                  C——S  R
    / |    \ |               / |    \ |
   S  R     C               S  R     C
    \ H    / |               \ H    / |
      C——S  R                  C——S  H
      |                        |
      R                        R
       cis                      trans
```

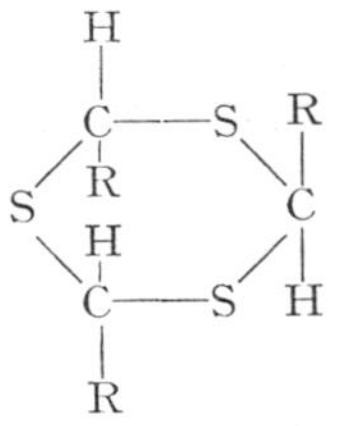

Schönberg and Barakat (1947), however, believe that the ring is not planar, but puckered, and that the two forms are related to each other as "chair" and "boat" forms (*cf. cyclo*hexane, p. 465). Hassell and Viervoll (1947) have shown by electron diffraction studies that the ring is puckered and that it is of the "chair" type. If this is so, then the existence of the two forms can be explained by *cis-trans* isomerism.

Thioacids, R·CO·SH, may be prepared by the action of phosphorus pentasulphide on a carboxylic acid:

$$5R{\cdot}CO_2H + P_2S_5 \longrightarrow 5R{\cdot}CO{\cdot}SH + P_2O_5$$

The thioacids have a most disagreeable odour, and slowly decompose in air. They have lower boiling points and are less soluble in water than the corresponding oxygen compounds; they are soluble in most organic solvents.

In most of their reactions the thioacids and their salts behave as if they contained the mercapto-group, but in a few reactions they behave as if they contained a hydroxyl group. This may be accounted for by tautomerism for the acid and resonance for the salts:

$$\textit{thioacid}\quad R{-}C\begin{matrix}{/\!\!/}O\\ \backslash S{-}H\end{matrix} \rightleftharpoons R{-}C\begin{matrix}/O{-}H\\ \backslash\!\!\backslash S\end{matrix}$$

$$\textit{salts}\quad R{-}C\begin{matrix}{/\!\!/}O\\ \backslash \bar{S}:\end{matrix} \longleftrightarrow R{-}C\begin{matrix}/O^-\\ \backslash\!\!\backslash S\end{matrix}$$

The existence of the acid as a tautomeric mixture is supported by the preparation of both the *O*- and *S*-esters.

Nomenclature. The methods of nomenclature are illustrated by the following example:

$$\underset{\text{(I)}}{CH_3{\cdot}CO{\cdot}SH} \qquad\qquad \underset{\text{(II)}}{CH_3{\cdot}CS{\cdot}OH}$$

According to the trivial system of nomenclature, both I and II are named as thioacetic acid. According to the I.U.C. rules, the suffix *-oic* of the corresponding oxygen acid is changed to *thioic*. Thus both I and II are named either as ethanethioic acid or methanecarbothioic acid. On the other hand, the suffix *-thiolic* is used if it is certain that the oxygen of the hydroxyl group is replaced by sulphur, and the suffix *thionic* if it is the oxygen of the carbonyl group. Thus I is ethanethiolic acid or methanecarbothiolic acid, and II is ethanethionic or methanecarbothionic acid.

The most characteristic reaction of the thioacids is their extreme readiness to acylate alcohols and amines:

$$R{\cdot}CO{\cdot}SH + R'OH \longrightarrow R{\cdot}COOR' + H_2S$$

$$R{\cdot}CO{\cdot}SH + R'{\cdot}NH_2 \longrightarrow R{\cdot}CO{\cdot}NH{\cdot}R' + H_2S$$

Dithioacids, $R{\cdot}CS_2H$, may be prepared by the action of a Grignard reagent on carbon disulphide:

$$RMgX + C\begin{matrix}{/\!\!/}S\\ \backslash\!\!\backslash S\end{matrix} \longrightarrow R{-}C\begin{matrix}{/\!\!/}S\\ \backslash S{\cdot}MgX\end{matrix} \xrightarrow{\text{acid}} R{\cdot}CS_2H$$

Nomenclature. The methods of nomenclature are illustrated by the following example:

$CH_3{\cdot}CS_2H$ is named as dithioacetic acid, ethanethionthiolic acid or methanecarbodithioic acid.

A very important dithioacid is **dithiocarbonic acid,** $HO{\cdot}CS_2H$. The free acid is unknown, but many of its derivatives have been prepared, *e.g., potassium xanthate* may be prepared by the reaction between potassium hydroxide, ethanol and carbon disulphide:

$$KOH + CS_2 + C_2H_5OH \longrightarrow C_2H_5O{\cdot}CS_2K + H_2O$$

The name **xanthate** is derived from the property of these compounds, giving a *yellow* precipitate of copper xanthate with copper salt (Greek: *xanthos*, yellow).

Vulcanisation of rubber. This process is carried out by heating crude rubber with 4–5 per cent. sulphur and certain organic compounds which accelerate the reaction between the rubber and sulphur. These organic compounds are known as *accelerators*, and all contain sulphur or nitrogen, or both. Vulcanising rubber causes the rubber to lose its stickiness, makes it no longer sensitive to temperature changes, causes it to retain its elasticity over a wide temperature range, and increases its tensile strength. The function of the sulphur appears to be to cross-link the long hydrocarbon chains in crude rubber.

PHOSPHORUS COMPOUNDS

Alkyl-phosphines. All three classes of phosphines are known, the tertiary phosphines being the commonest; the quaternary phosphonium compounds are also known.

General methods of preparation. 1. Primary and secondary phosphines are produced when phosphonium iodide is heated with alkyl halide in the presence of zinc oxide, *e.g.*, ethyl and diethylphosphine:

$$2PH_4I + 2C_2H_5I + ZnO \longrightarrow 2C_2H_5{\cdot}PH_2{\cdot}HI + ZnI_2 + H_2O$$
$$PH_4I + 2C_2H_5I + ZnO \longrightarrow (C_2H_5)_2PH{\cdot}HI + ZnI_2 + H_2O$$

If the reaction is carried out in the *absence* of zinc oxide, the tertiary phosphines and quaternary phosphonium compounds are produced, *e.g.*, triethylphosphine and tetraethylphosphonium iodide:

$$PH_4I + 3C_2H_5I \longrightarrow (C_2H_5)_3P{\cdot}HI + 3HI$$
$$(C_2H_5)_3P + C_2H_5I \longrightarrow [(C_2H_5)_4P]^+I^-$$

Secondary phosphines may be prepared by heating a primary phosphine with the calculated amount of alkyl halide:

$$R{\cdot}PH_2 + R'I \longrightarrow RR'PH{\cdot}HI$$

Tertiary phosphines may be prepared from secondary in a similar manner:

$$R_2PH + R'I \longrightarrow R_2R'P{\cdot}HI$$

2. A mixture of tertiary phosphine and quaternary phosphonium compound is produced when phosphonium iodide is heated with one of the lower alcohols or lower ethers, *e.g.*,

$$PH_4I + CH_3OH \longrightarrow PH_3 + CH_3I + H_2O$$
$$PH_4I + 3CH_3I \longrightarrow (CH_3)_3P{\cdot}HI + 3HI \quad (v.p.)$$
$$(CH_3)_3P + CH_3I \longrightarrow [(CH_3)_4P]^+I^- \quad (v.p.)$$

A small amount of tertiary phosphine is produced when a metallic phosphide is heated with alkyl halide, *e.g.*,

$$Ca_3P_2 + 6C_2H_5Br \longrightarrow 2(C_2H_5)_3P + 3CaBr_2$$

A very small amount of quaternary phosphonium compound is produced when phosphorus is heated with an alkyl halide or an alcohol.

3. Tertiary phosphines are prepared most conveniently by the action of excess Grignard reagent on phosphorus trihalide:

$$3R{\cdot}MgBr + PCl_3 \longrightarrow R_3P + 3MgClBr \quad (g.–v.g.)$$

General properties and reactions. Except for methylphosphine (a gas), all the alkyl-phosphines are colourless, unpleasant-smelling liquids. They resemble the corresponding nitrogen compounds in many ways, but differ in being less basic and more easily oxidised, *e.g.*,

$$C_2H_5{\cdot}PH_2 + 3[O] \xrightarrow{HNO_3} C_2H_5{\cdot}P(=O)(OH)_2$$
ethylphosphonic acid

$$(C_2H_5)_2PH + 2[O] \xrightarrow{HNO_3} (C_2H_5)_2P(=O){\cdot}OH$$
diethylphosphonic acid

$$(C_2H_5)_3P + [O] \xrightarrow{HNO_3} (C_2H_5)_3P{=}O$$
triethylphosphonoxide

In naming organic acids and oxides derived from phosphorus, arsenic or antimony, the syllable -on denotes the quinquevalent and -in the tervalent state of the central atom (*British Chemical Abstracts*, 1948).

When quaternary phosphonium halides are treated with moist silver oxide, the quaternary phosphonium hydroxide is produced:

$$[(C_2H_5)_4P]^+I^- + \text{' AgOH '} \longrightarrow [(C_2H_5)_4P]^+OH^- + AgI$$

The quaternary phosphonium hydroxides are strongly basic, comparable in strength with the quaternary ammonium hydroxides and sodium hydroxide. When heated they form the trialkyl-phosphonoxide and a hydrocarbon (*cf.* R_4NOH, p. 301).

$$[R_4P]^+OH^- \longrightarrow R_3P{=}O + RH$$

Phosphorus differs from nitrogen in being able to expand its valency shell to form a decet; compounds of the type R_3PX_2 have been prepared (*cf.* phosphorus pentahalides). Arsenic also forms compounds of this type. Wittig *et al.* (1948) have prepared pentaphenylphosphorus, $(C_6H_5)_5P$.

ARSENIC COMPOUNDS

Alkyl-arsines. There are primary, secondary and tertiary arsines, and quaternary arsonium compounds. Primary arsines may be prepared by the action of dialkyl-mercury on arsenic trichloride and reducing the product, alkyl-dichloroarsine, with zinc and sulphuric acid:

$$AsCl_3 + R_2Hg \longrightarrow RHgCl + R{\cdot}AsCl_2 \xrightarrow{Zn/H_2SO_4} R{\cdot}AsH_2$$

Alternatively, they may be prepared by reducing an alkyl-arsonic acid with zinc and sulphuric acid:

$$R{\cdot}AsO_3H \xrightarrow{Zn/H_2SO_4} R{\cdot}AsH_2$$

Secondary arsines may be prepared by the reduction of dialkyl-chloroarsine:

$$R_2AsCl \xrightarrow{Zn/H_2SO_4} R_2AsH$$

Tertiary arsines may be prepared by the action of excess Grignard reagent on arsenic tribromide:

$$3R{\cdot}MgX + AsBr_3 \longrightarrow R_3As + 3MgClX$$

Quaternary arsonium halides may be prepared by the addition of alkyl halide to a tertiary arsine:

$$R_3As + R'I \longrightarrow [R_3R'As]^+I^-$$

General properties and reactions. Except for methylarsine (a gas), the alkyl-arsines are colourless poisonous liquids with a garlic smell. They have practically no basic properties, and do not form salts with inorganic acids. They are readily oxidised when exposed to air:

$$CH_3{\cdot}AsH_2 \xrightarrow{O_2} CH_3{\cdot}\overset{\overset{\displaystyle O}{\|}}{As}{-}(OH)_2$$

methylarsonic acid

$$(CH_3)_2AsH \xrightarrow{O_2} (CH_3)_2\overset{\overset{\displaystyle O}{\|}}{As}{\cdot}(OH)$$

dimethylarsonic acid

$$(CH_3)_3As \xrightarrow{O_2} (CH_3)_3As{=}O$$
trimethylarsenoxide

Quaternary arsonium halides form the corresponding hydroxide when treated with moist silver oxide. These hydroxides are strongly basic and, on heating, decompose into the trialkyl-arsonoxide and hydrocarbon (*cf.* R_4POH):

$$[R_4As]^+OH^- \longrightarrow R_3As{=}O + RH$$

Cacodyl oxide (*dimethylarsinoxide*), $(CH_3)_2As{-}O{-}As(CH_3)_2$. Cadet (1760) distilled a mixture of equal parts of arsenious oxide and potassium acetate, and obtained a vile-smelling, spontaneously inflammable oil, which subsequently became known as *Cadet's liquid*:

$$As_4O_6 + 8CH_3{\cdot}CO_2K \longrightarrow 2[(CH_3)_2As{-}]_2O + 4K_2CO_3 + 4CO_2 \quad (17\%)$$

This reaction was later investigated by Bunsen (1837–1843), who showed that Cadet's liquid was a mixture of *cacodyl oxide* and *cacodyl*, $(CH_3)_2As{-}As(CH_3)_2$. It was Berzelius who proposed the name *cacodyl* (Greek: *kakodes*, stinking).

A better method for preparing cacodyl oxide is to pass a mixture of the vapours of arsenious oxide and acetic acid over an alkali metal acetate catalyst at 300–400° (yield: 66 per cent., Fuson and Shive, 1947).

Cacodyl oxide is an extremely poisonous liquid, b.p. 150°, insoluble in ethanol and ether. It is not spontaneously inflammable when pure; its inflammability is due to the presence of cacodyl. Cacodyl oxide is feebly basic, reacting with hydrochloric acid to form **cacodyl chloride** (*dimethylchloroarsine*), b.p. 109°:

$$[(CH_3)_2As{-}]_2O + 2HCl \longrightarrow 2(CH_3)_2AsCl + H_2O$$

Pure cacodyl oxide may be prepared by heating cacodyl chloride with potassium hydroxide:

$$2(CH_3)_2AsCl + 2KOH \longrightarrow [(CH_3)_2As]_2O + 2KCl + H_2O$$

Cacodyl (*tetramethyldiarsine*), $[(CH_3)_2As{-}]_2$, may be prepared by heating cacodyl chloride with zinc in an atmosphere of carbon dioxide (*cf.* Wurtz reaction):

$$2(CH_3)_2AsCl + Zn \longrightarrow (CH_3)_2As{-}As(CH_3)_2 + ZnCl_2$$

It is a colourless poisonous liquid, b.p. 170°, spontaneously inflammable in air, giving carbon dioxide, water and arsenious oxide.

Cacodylic acid (*dimethylarsonic acid*), $(CH_3)_2AsO{\cdot}(OH)$, is formed when cacodyl oxide is oxidised with moist mercuric oxide:

$$[(CH_3)_2As{-}]_2O + 2HgO + H_2O \longrightarrow 2(CH_3)_2AsO(OH) + 2Hg$$

It is a crystalline odourless substance, m.p. 200°, soluble in water, the aqueous solution being acid to phenolphthalein. Cacodylic acid reacts with hydrogen sulphide to form *cacodyl sulphide*, $[(CH_3)_2As{-}]_2S$.

Lewisite (*dichloro-β-chlorovinylarsine*), $ClCH{:}CH{\cdot}AsCl_2$, may be prepared by passing acetylene into arsenic trichloride in the presence of anhydrous aluminium chloride:

$$CH{\vdots}CH + AsCl_3 \longrightarrow ClCH{:}CH{\cdot}AsCl_2$$

Continued action of acetylene produces bis(β-chlorovinyl)chloroarsine and finally tris(β-chlorovinyl)-arsine:

$$ClCH{:}CH{\cdot}AsCl_2 \xrightarrow{C_2H_2} (ClCH{:}CH{-})_2AsCl \xrightarrow{C_2H_2} (ClCH{:}CH{-})_3As$$

Lewisite is a liquid, b.p. 190° (with decomposition), and is a powerful vesicant.

Antimony compounds. Antimony forms only tertiary stibines and quaternary stibonium compounds. Tertiary stibines may be prepared by the action of a Grignard reagent on antimony trichloride, *e.g.*, trimethylstibine:

$$3CH_3{\cdot}MgI + SbCl_3 \longrightarrow (CH_3)_3Sb + 3MgClI$$

Trimethylstibine slowly adds on methyl iodide to form tetramethylstibonium iodide, $[(CH_3)_4Sb]^+I^-$, which, on treatment with moist silver oxide, forms tetramethylstibonium hydroxide, $[(CH_3)_4Sb]^+OH^-$. The quaternary stibonium compounds closely resemble the corresponding arsenic compounds.

Bismuth compounds. The organo-bismuth compounds resemble the organo-compounds of mercury, lead and tin in reactivity, *i.e.*, they are true organo-metallic compounds (p. 331). Only tertiary bismuthines are known, and these are best prepared by the action of a Grignard reagent on bismuth trichloride:

$$3R{\cdot}MgX + BiCl_3 \longrightarrow R_3Bi + 3MgClX$$

Tertiary bismuthines do *not* add on a molecule of alkyl halide; generally, they react to form an alkyl-halogeno-bismuthine, *e.g.*, trimethylbismuthine, when heated with methyl iodide at 200°, forms methyl-di-iodo-bismuthine and ethane:

$$(CH_3)_3Bi + 2CH_3I \xrightarrow{200^\circ} CH_3BiI_2 + C_2H_6$$

Pentaphenylbismuth, $(C_6H_5)_5Bi$, has now been prepared by Wittig *et al.* (1952); it is an unstable solid.

SILICON COMPOUNDS

The organo compounds of silicon have come into prominence in recent years due to the discovery that resins could be prepared from them.

Alkyl-silanes. These are silicon hydrides (silanes) in which one or more hydrogen atoms have been replaced by an alkyl group, *e.g.*, $C_2H_5SiH_3$, ethylsilane; $(CH_3)_4Si$, tetramethylsilane.

General methods of preparation. 1. By the action of a dialkyl-zinc on silicon tetrachloride (Friedel and Crafts, 1863):

$$2SiCl_4 + 2(C_2H_5)_2Zn \longrightarrow \underset{\text{ethyltrichlorosilane}}{2C_2H_5SiCl_3} + ZnCl_2$$

$$SiCl_4 + 2(CH_3)_2Zn \longrightarrow (CH_3)_4Si + 2ZnCl_2$$

2. By the action of a Grignard reagent on silicon tetrachloride (Kipping, 1904):

$$SiCl_4 + 2CH_3{\cdot}MgI \longrightarrow \underset{\text{dimethyldichlorosilane}}{(CH_3)_2SiCl_2} + 2MgClI$$

$$SiCl_4 + 4CH_3{\cdot}MgI \longrightarrow (CH_3)_4Si + 4MgClI$$

3. By heating a mixture of silicon tetrachloride and alkyl bromide with sodium (*cf.* Wurtz reaction):

$$SiCl_4 + 4C_2H_5Br + 8Na \longrightarrow (C_2H_5)_4Si + 4NaCl + 4NaBr$$

4. By passing alkyl halide vapour over a mixture of silicon and copper at 350° (Patnode and Rochow, 1945); *e.g.*, methyl chloride gives a mixture of methyltrichlorosilane, dimethyldichlorosilane, trimethylchlorosilane and methyldichlorosilane, of which the first two predominate. This reaction has been shown to take place via the formation of methylcopper, which then undergoes homolytic fission to give a methyl free radical (Hurd and Rochow, 1945):

$$2Cu + CH_3Cl \longrightarrow Cu{-}CH_3 + CuCl$$

$$Cu{-}CH_3 \longrightarrow Cu + CH_3{\cdot}$$

$$CuCl + Si \longrightarrow {\equiv}SiCl + Cu$$

$${\equiv}SiCl + 3CH_3{\cdot} \longrightarrow (CH_3)_3SiCl$$

5. By passing a mixture of alkyl halide vapour and silicon tetrachloride over an aluminium or zinc catalyst at 400°. The same mixture is obtained as in method 4; and probably the mechanism is the same.

Methods 1, 4 and 5 are used on a large scale for preparing the intermediates required for the preparation of silicones (see below).

General properties and reactions. The alkylsilanes are colourless oils, stable in air, and are not affected by acids or alkalis. The alkyl groups in tetra-alkylsilanes may be chlorinated, and these chlorinated compounds undergo many of the reactions characteristic of the alkyl halides, *e.g.*,

$$(C_2H_5)_4Si + Cl_2 \longrightarrow (C_2H_5)_3Si{\cdot}C_2H_4Cl + HCl$$

$$(C_2H_5)_3Si{\cdot}C_2H_4Cl + RONa \longrightarrow (C_2H_5)_3Si{\cdot}C_2H_4{\cdot}OR + NaCl$$

Alkyl-halogenosilanes may be prepared by any of the above methods (1–5). They are usually colourless oily liquids that fume in the air due to their ready hydrolysis to silanols.

Silanols. Hydrolysis of trialkyl-chlorosilanes, dialkyldichlorosilanes and alkyl-trichlorosilanes gives the *silanols*, R_3SiOH, *silanediols*, $R_2Si(OH)_2$, and *silanetriols*, $RSi(OH)_3$, respectively.

Trialkyl silanols are colourless stable liquids, many of which have a camphor-like odour. On the other hand, the silanediols and silanetriols are unstable, eliminating water to form polymers. Hydrolysis is carried out by dissolving the alkyl-chlorosilane in a solvent, and mixing with another solvent containing water. Under these conditions hydrolysis is slow: rapid hydrolysis leads to gel formation. The hydroxy-compounds are polymerised by heating.

Hydrolysis of dimethyldichlorosilane produces cyclic polymers containing 3–9 oxygen atoms in the ring, *e.g.*, the trimer, $(CH_3)_2Si\langle\begin{smallmatrix}O{-}Si(CH_3)_2\\ \quad >O\\ O{-}Si(CH_3)_2\end{smallmatrix}$; linear polymers, $HOSi(CH_3)_2{\cdot}[OSi(CH_3)_2]_n{\cdot}OH$, are also obtained, and the value of n may be increased by treating with sulphuric acid, resulting in higher polymers which are viscous liquids or soft plastics. Hydrolysis of methyltrichlorosilane results in the formation of amorphous powders or hard brittle solids. These polymers consist of linear, cyclic and cross-linked structures, depending on the conditions of the hydrolysis; *e.g.*, the end product of the dehydration process is cross-linked:

```
          |                               |
          O                               O
          |                               |
····O—Si(CH3)—O—Si(CH3)—O—Si(CH3)—O····
                   |
                   O
                   |
····O—Si(CH3)—O—Si(CH3)—O—Si(CH3)—O····
          |                               |
          O                               O
          |                               |
```

Thus by controlling the conditions of hydrolysis, and using mixtures of intermediates, polymers with different properties can be obtained. These polymers are known as the **silicones**. Silicones may be roughly classified as follows:

(i) *Silicone fluids*: used in high-temperature baths and diffusion pumps, as hydraulic fluids, and form water-repellent surfaces.
(ii) *Silicone rubbers*: used as electrical insulators.
(iii) *Silicone greases*: used as lubricants at high and low temperatures.
(iv) *Silicone resins*: used as electrical insulators.

QUESTIONS

1. How may EtSH be prepared? Name the compounds and state the conditions under which they are formed when EtSH is treated with:—(*a*) Na, (*b*) KOH, (*c*) $(AcO)_2Pb$, (*d*) HgO, (*e*) Na_2PbO_2, (*f*) AcOH, (*g*) H_2O_2, (*h*) NaOCl, (*i*) HNO_3, (*j*) $CH_3 \cdot CHO$ (*l*) Me_2CO.
2. Describe the preparation and properties of:—(*a*) Et_2S, (*b*) $(ClCH_2 \cdot CH_2-)_2S$, (*c*) Me·SCN, (*d*) $CH_2{:}CH \cdot CH_2 \cdot NCS$, (*e*) Et_2SO, (*f*) Me_2SO_2, (*g*) $Me_2C(SO_2Et)_2$.
3. Discuss the structures of the sulphoxides, sulphones, sulphonium salts, trimeric thioaldehydes and thioacids.
4. Suggest one synthesis for each of the following:—(*a*) Me·NH·CS·OEt, (*b*) Me·NH·CS·NH·Et, (*c*) $Et \cdot NH \cdot CS_2Me$. What would each of these give on vigorous hydrolysis?
5. Compare and contrast the methods of preparation and the properties of the *onium* compounds of N, S, P and As.
6. How may $Et \cdot SO_3H$ be prepared? How may this be distinguished from $EtO \cdot SO_2H$? How may $Et \cdot SO_3H$ be converted into:—(*a*) $Et \cdot SO_2Cl$, (*b*) $Et \cdot SO_3Na$, (*c*) $(Et \cdot SO_3)_2Pb$, (*d*) $Et \cdot SO_3Et$, (*e*) $Et \cdot SO_2 \cdot NH_2$, (*f*) $Et \cdot SO_2 \cdot NH \cdot Et$?
7. Compare and contrast the methods of preparation and the properties of the phosphines and arsines.
8. Write an account of the preparation and properties of the cacodyl compounds, and discuss the part played by these compounds in the history of organic chemistry.
9. Write an account of the preparation and properties of the tetra-alkyl-silanes and the alkyl-chlorosilanes, and discuss the use of organo-silicon compounds in industry.

READING REFERENCES

Gilman, *Advanced Organic Chemistry*, Wiley (1942, 2nd ed.). Vol. I, Ch. 10. Organic Sulphur Compounds.

Schönberg and Barakat, The Stereochemistry of Trimeric Thioaldehydes, *J.C.S.*, 1947, 693.

Snell, Surface Active Agents, *Ind. Eng. Chem.*, 1943, **35**, 107.

Ann. Reports, 1930, **27**, 143. The Decomposition of the Quaternary Compounds of Nitrogen and Phosphorus.

ibid., 1945, **42**, 103. Phosphorylation.

ibid., 1948, **45**, 198. Recent Work on the Reactions of Organic Sulphur Compounds.

Newton Friend's Inorganic Chemistry:
(i) Vol. XI, Part I (1928), pp. 246–291. Silicon Compounds.
(ii) Vol. XI, Part II (1930), pp. 3–61. Arsenic Compounds.
(iii) Vol. XI, Part III (1936), pp. 3–46. Phosphorus Compounds.

Gilman and Yale, Organo Bismuth Compounds, *Chem. Reviews*, 1942, **30**, 281.

Emblem and Sos, Silicon Organic Compounds, *Chem. and Ind.*, 1946, **51**, 450.

Burkhard *et al.*, The Present State of Organo-Silicon Chemistry, *Chem. Reviews*, 1947, **41**, 97.

Hardy and Megson, The Chemistry of Silicon Polymers, *Quart. Reviews* (*Chem. Soc.*), 1948, **2**, 25.

Jeffes, Some Aspects of the Industrial Development of Silicones, *Chem. and Ind.*, **1954**, 498.

Atherton, Some Aspects of the Organic Chemistry of Derivatives of Phosphorus Oxyacids, *Quart. Reviews* (*Chem. Soc.*), 1949, **3**, 146.

Abrahams, The Stereochemistry of Sub-group VIB of the Periodic Table, *ibid.*, 1956, **10**, 407.

MacDiarmid, Silyl Compounds, *ibid.*, 1956, **10**, 208.

CHAPTER XV

ORGANO-METALLIC COMPOUNDS

GENERALLY speaking, organo-metallic compounds are those organic compounds in which a metal is directly joined to carbon (see, however, alkali metals, p. 344). The most widely studied and the most useful are the magnesium compounds, but in recent years the organo-compounds of sodium and lithium have been studied in great detail; the lithium compounds in particular are becoming increasingly important in synthetic work.

THE GRIGNARD REAGENTS

The alkyl-magnesium halides, R—Mg—X, or Grignard reagents, introduced by Grignard in 1900, are extremely valuable in laboratory organic syntheses, and recently are being used on a large scale (*cf.* silicon compounds, p. 328). A Grignard reagent is generally prepared by reaction between magnesium (1 atom) and alkyl halide (1 molecule) in dry, alcohol-free ether.

$$RX + Mg \longrightarrow RMgX \quad (v.g.\text{–}ex.)$$

The mechanism of the formation of a Grignard reagent is still not clear. A free radical mechanism has been suggested (Gomberg and Bachmann, 1927; *cf.* triphenylmethyl bromide, p. 674). The reaction starts by the formation of a trace of magnesium halide (Wurtz reaction) and then proceeds as follows:

$$2RX + Mg \longrightarrow R\text{—}R + MgX_2$$
$$Mg + MgX_2 \rightleftharpoons 2\cdot MgX$$
$$RX + \cdot MgX \longrightarrow MgX_2 + R\cdot$$
$$R\cdot + \cdot MgX \longrightarrow RMgX$$

The ethereal solution of the Grignard reagent is generally used in all reactions. Other solvents besides ether may be used, *e.g.*, tertiary amines, tetrahydrofuran and the dimethyl ether of ethylene glycol. It is also possible to prepare a Grignard reagent by heating an alkyl chloride with magnesium under pressure (Schorigin, 1931).

The ease with which an alkyl halide forms a Grignard reagent depends on a number of factors. It has been found that for a given alkyl radical the ease of formation is alkyl iodide>bromide>chloride. It has also been found that the formation of a Grignard reagent becomes increasingly difficult as the number of carbon atoms in the alkyl group increases, *i.e.*, the ease of formation is $CH_3X > C_2H_5X > C_3H_7X > \cdots$. Since tertiary alkyl iodides readily eliminate hydrogen iodide with the formation of an olefin, tertiary alkyl chlorides are used.

Structure of Grignard reagents. The structure of the Grignard reagent in ethereal solution has been the subject of much research. Grignard *et al.* (1901), in their attempt to isolate the Grignard reagent, showed that the compound contained ether (which they called "ether of crystallisation"). This led Meisenheimer *et al.* (1928) to suggest I as the structure. Evans *et al.* (1942) showed from the electrolysis of ethereal solutions of Grignard reagents that magnesium is present in both the anions and cations, and therefore suggested the following equilibrium:

$$R_2Mg_2X_2 \rightleftharpoons [RMg]^+ + [RMgX_2]^-$$

Ubbelohde *et al.* (1949), however, examined the behaviour of an ethereal solution of a mixture of methylmagnesium iodide and magnesium iodide, and obtained no evidence for the above equilibrium. These authors suggested that when methylmagnesium iodide is dissolved in ether the complex II is present. This

$$\underset{(I)}{\begin{matrix} R \\ X \end{matrix}\!\!>\!Mg\!\begin{matrix} \swarrow O(C_2H_5)_2 \\ \nwarrow O(C_2H_5)_2 \end{matrix}} \qquad \underset{(II)}{Mg^{2+}\left[\begin{matrix} CH_3 \\ CH_3 \end{matrix}\!\!>\!\overset{2-}{Mg}\!\!<\!\begin{matrix} \overset{+}{I} \\ \underset{+}{I} \end{matrix}\!\!>\!\overset{2-}{Mg}\!\!<\!\begin{matrix} CH_3 \\ CH_3 \end{matrix}\right]}$$

would also account for the electrolysis experiments of Evans *et al.* On the other hand, determinations of the molecular weight of various Grignard reagents in ether have shown that the compounds exist approximately as dimers (*inter alia*, Ubbelohde *et al.*, 1955).

From the foregoing it would appear that the function of the ether is to keep all the substances in solution, but it is still uncertain what these substances are. It appears likely that the more important complexes are I and III.

$$\underset{(I)}{\begin{matrix} R \\ X \end{matrix}\!\!>\!\overset{2-}{Mg}\!\!<\!\begin{matrix} \overset{+}{O}(C_2H_5)_2 \\ \overset{+}{O}(C_2H_5)_2 \end{matrix}} \qquad \underset{(III)}{\begin{matrix} R \\ (C_2H_5)_2\overset{+}{O} \end{matrix}\!\!>\!\overset{2-}{Mg}\!\!<\!\begin{matrix} \overset{+}{X} \\ \overset{+}{X} \end{matrix}\!\!>\!\overset{2-}{Mg}\!\!<\!\begin{matrix} \overset{+}{O}(C_2H_5)_2 \\ R \end{matrix}}$$

In this book the formula RMgX will be used to designate a Grignard reagent.

Reactions of the Grignard reagents. When working with Grignard reagents, it is usual to add the other reactant (often in ethereal solution) slowly to the Grignard solution or vice-versa, and after a short time, decompose the magnesium complex with water or dilute acid; the yields are usually *g.–v.g.*

The majority of Grignard reactions fall into two groups.

(i) *Addition of the Grignard reagent to a compound containing any of the following groups* (*containing multiple bonds*):

$$>C{=}O;\quad -C{\equiv}N;\quad >C{=}S;\quad -N{=}O;\quad -N\overset{\rightarrow}{=}C;\quad >S{=}O$$

In each case the alkyl group of RMgX adds on to the atom with the lower electron-affinity, and the fragment MgX to the atom with the higher. It is important to note that a Grignard reagent does *not* add on to two carbon atoms joined by a double or triple bond.

The addition of a Grignard reagent to an *iso*cyanide is exceptional in that both R and MgX add on to some extent to the carbon atom:

$$R{-}N\overset{\rightarrow}{=}C \xrightarrow{RMgX} R{-}\overset{\overset{MgX}{|}}{N}\overset{\rightarrow}{=}C{-}R + R{-}N{=}C\!\begin{matrix} \nearrow R \\ \searrow MgX \end{matrix}$$

In the case of the *azo-group*, —N=N—, the fragment MgX adds on to each nitrogen atom and the alkyl group, R or C_nH_{2n+1}—, is eliminated as R—R, C_nH_{2n} and C_nH_{2n+2}.

The most important group is the carbonyl group, and kinetic studies have shown that the rate-determining step in the addition of Grignard reagents to this group (and the cyano group) proceeds via a complex (Swain *et al.*, 1950).

$$\begin{matrix} \overset{\delta-}{R}{-}\overset{\delta+}{Mg}X \\ + \\ >C{=}O \end{matrix} \longrightarrow \begin{matrix} R \cdots MgX \\ \vdots \qquad \vdots \\ >C{=}{=}O \end{matrix} \longrightarrow \begin{matrix} R \quad MgX \\ | \qquad | \\ >C{-}O \end{matrix}$$

Kharasch *et al.* (1941, 1944) have shown that in the presence of a small amount of cobaltous chloride the Grignard reaction takes place by a free-radical mechanism. It appears that traces of metal impurities may bring about a free-radical mechanism and thereby lead to an abnormal reaction of the Grignard reagent; even a trace of free magnesium may be sufficient (see diphenyl, p. 670).

(ii) *Double decomposition with compounds containing an active hydrogen atom or a reactive halogen atom.* We shall consider only the former at this stage (see p. 337 for an example of the latter). As we have seen, an active hydrogen atom is one joined to oxygen, nitrogen or sulphur. When such compounds react with a Grignard reagent, the alkyl group is converted into the paraffin, *e.g.*,

$$RMgX + H_2O \longrightarrow RH + Mg(OH){\cdot}Br$$
$$RMgX + R'OH \longrightarrow RH + Mg(OR'){\cdot}X$$
$$RMgX + NH_3 \longrightarrow RH + Mg(NH_2){\cdot}X$$

All reactions with compounds containing an active hydrogen atom result in the quantitative yield of hydrocarbon. Thus this type of reaction is valuable for the determination of the number of active hydrogen atoms in a compound. The procedure is known as the **Zerewitinoff active hydrogen determination** (1907), and methylmagnesium iodide is normally used as the Grignard reagent. The methane which is liberated is measured (by volume), one molecule of methane being equivalent to one active hydrogen atom, *e.g.*,

$$R{\cdot}NH_2 + CH_3MgI \longrightarrow CH_4 + R{\cdot}NH{\cdot}MgI$$
$$R_2NH + CH_3MgI \longrightarrow CH_4 + R_2N{\cdot}MgI$$

Only one hydrogen atom in a primary amine reacts at room temperature. At a sufficiently high temperature, the active hydrogen atom in the magnesium derivative of the primary amine will react with a further molecule of methylmagnesium iodide:

$$R{\cdot}NH{\cdot}MgI + CH_3MgI \longrightarrow CH_4 + R{\cdot}N(MgI)_2$$

It is therefore possible to estimate the number of amino- and imino-groups in compounds containing both. It is not possible to get a high enough temperature for the second reaction with ether; a satisfactory solvent for the complete Zerewitinoff determination is pyridine (Lehman and Basch, 1945).

The Zerewitinoff determination can be used to distinguish between primary, secondary and tertiary amines:

$$R{\cdot}NH_2 + CH_3MgI \xrightarrow{\text{room temperature}} CH_4 + R{\cdot}NH{\cdot}MgI$$
$$R{\cdot}NH{\cdot}MgI + CH_3MgI \xrightarrow{\text{high temperature}} CH_4 + R{\cdot}N(MgI)_2$$
$$R_2NH + CH_3MgI \xrightarrow{\text{room temperature}} CH_4 + R_2N{\cdot}MgI$$

Thus a primary amine ultimately gives two molecules of methane, a secondary one, and a tertiary none (no reaction).

Lithium aluminium hydride also reacts with compounds containing active hydrogen, and so may be used for analytical determinations, *e.g.*,

$$LiAlH_4 + 4ROH \longrightarrow (RO)_4LiAl + 4H_2$$
$$LiAlH_4 + 4R{\cdot}NH_2 \longrightarrow 4H_2 + (R{\cdot}NH)_4LiAl$$
$$\xrightarrow{LiAlH_4} 2(R{\cdot}N)_2LiAl + 4H_2$$

The enolic form of a compound, since it contains an active hydrogen atom, reacts with a Grignard reagent, *e.g.*, acetoacetic ester and nitroethane:

$$CH_3\cdot CO\cdot CH_2\cdot CO_2C_2H_5 \rightleftharpoons CH_3\cdot \underset{}{\overset{OH}{|}}{C}{=}CH\cdot CO_2C_2H_5 \xrightarrow{CH_3MgI} CH_3\cdot \overset{OMgI}{\overset{|}{C}}{=}CH\cdot CO_2C_2H_5 + CH_4$$

$$CH_3\cdot CH_2\cdot NO_2 \rightleftharpoons CH_3\cdot CH{:}NO_2H \xrightarrow{CH_3MgI} CH_3\cdot CH{:}NO_2MgI + CH_4$$

In both cases the methane will not be liberated immediately, but at a rate depending on the speed of the conversion of keto into enol.

The hydrogen atom in the $\equiv$CH group is also active with respect to a Grignard reagent (to be expected, since it is acidic, p. 89):

$$R\cdot C{\vdots}CH + CH_3MgI \longrightarrow R\cdot C{\vdots}CMgI + CH_4$$

This reaction is useful for preparing a Grignard reagent containing an acetylenic radical.

Order of reactivity of functional groups. In most cases of syntheses in which a Grignard reagent is used, the other compound has only one functional group, and consequently the reaction takes place in one direction only. Occasionally it is necessary to carry out a synthesis with a compound containing two (or possibly more) functional groups. If an excess of Grignard reagent is used, then both groups react as would be expected. It has been found experimentally that the reactivity of different groups is not equal, and hence when one equivalent of Grignard reagent is added, two competitive reactions take place simultaneously, but at different rates, resulting in two products in unequal amounts. Experiments have shown that an active hydrogen reacts very much faster than any other group; so much so, in fact, that a compound containing an active hydrogen and another group, reacts with one equivalent of a Grignard reagent as if it had only one reactive group, the active hydrogen.

Experiments have also shown that the reactivity of the carbonyl group in aldehydes is somewhat greater than in ketones. The carbonyl group in both aldehydes and ketones, however, is much more reactive than in acyl chlorides and esters, the latter being less reactive than the former. Finally, the carbonyl group in all the types of compounds named above is more reactive than a halogen atom of the alkyl halide type (which is not to be confused with the halogen in an acyl chloride; see p. 338). The foregoing general rules may be illustrated with the compound:

$$CH_2OH\cdot CH_2\cdot CO\cdot CH_2\cdot CH_2\cdot CO_2C_2H_5$$

One molecule of RMgX would react exclusively with the hydroxyl group; a second molecule of RMgX with the keto-group; and a third molecule with the carbethoxy group.

SYNTHETIC USES OF THE GRIGNARD REAGENTS

Hydrocarbons. When a Grignard reagent is treated with any compound containing active hydrogen, a hydrocarbon is produced; in practice, water or dilute acid is used:

$$R{-}Mg{-}Br + H_2O \longrightarrow RH + Mg(OH)\cdot Br$$

Since alkyl halides are readily prepared from alcohols, it becomes a relatively simple matter to convert an alcohol (saturated or unsaturated) into the corresponding hydrocarbon.

The alkyl group of a Grignard reagent may also be converted into the parent paraffin by reducing the Grignard reagent catalytically:

$$2RMgX + 2H_2 \xrightarrow{Ni} 2RH + MgH_2 + MgX_2$$

Hydrocarbons containing more carbon atoms than the Grignard reagent may be prepared by treating the latter with an alkyl halide. This is an example of the reaction between a Grignard reagent and a compound containing a reactive halogen atom:

$$RMgI + R'I \longrightarrow R{-}R' + MgI_2$$

The yield of R—R′ is very good only if R′ is the allyl radical. On the other hand, a good yield of R—R′, where R′ is an alkyl radical, may be obtained by using *p*-toluenesulphonic esters as the alkylating agent:

$$RMgI + CH_3C_6H_4SO_3R' \longrightarrow R{-}R' + CH_3C_6H_4SO_3MgI$$

When R′ is either a methyl or ethyl group, methyl or ethyl sulphate, respectively, may be used:

$$RMgBr + 2(CH_3)_2SO_4 \longrightarrow R{-}CH_3 + CH_3Br + (CH_3{\cdot}O{\cdot}SO_2{\cdot}O{-})_2Mg$$

Primary alcohols. A Grignard reagent may be used to synthesise an alcohol by treating it with dry oxygen and decomposing the product with water:

$$RMgX \xrightarrow{O_2} RO_2MgX \xrightarrow{RMgX} 2ROMgX \xrightarrow{H_2O} 2ROH \quad (g.\text{–}v.g.)$$

This method (which can be used for all three classes of alcohols) is little used in practice since an alkyl halide may be converted into the corresponding alcohol by simpler means (p. 98). The method, however, is useful for converting aryl halides into phenols.

Walling *et al.* (1955) have isolated peroxides (yield: 30–90%) by the slow addition of a Grignard reagent to oxygen-saturated solvents at $-70°$. This supports the above mechanism (suggested by Porter *et al.*, 1920). Peroxides have not been isolated from aromatic Grignard reagents, but their presence has, however, been detected.

When a Grignard reagent (in ethereal solution) is treated with formaldehyde gas, or when a Grignard reagent in, *e.g.*, di-*n*-butyl ether (b.p. 141°), is refluxed with paraformaldehyde, a primary alcohol is obtained by decomposing the magnesium complex with dilute acid:

$$H_2C{=}O + RMgI \longrightarrow H_2C\begin{cases}OMgI\\R\end{cases} \xrightarrow{H_2O} R{\cdot}CH_2OH \quad (g.)$$

On the other hand, a primary alcohol containing *two* carbon atoms more than the Grignard alkyl radical can be prepared by adding one molecule of ethylene chlorohydrin to two molecules of Grignard reagent.

$$RMgBr + CH_2Cl{\cdot}CH_2OH \longrightarrow RH + CH_2Cl{\cdot}CH_2OMgBr \xrightarrow{RMgBr}$$

$$R{\cdot}CH_2{\cdot}CH_2OMgBr \xrightarrow{H_2O} R{\cdot}CH_2{\cdot}CH_2OH \quad (g.\text{–}v.g.)$$

Two molecules of Grignard reagent are not necessary if ethylene oxide is used instead of ethylene chlorohydrin. Ethylene oxide is added to the well-cooled Grignard solution, the mixture allowed to stand for several hours, the ether then distilled off and the residue treated with ice-cold water:

$$\begin{matrix} CH_2 \\ | \\ CH_2 \end{matrix}\!\!>O + RMgX \longrightarrow \left[\begin{matrix} CH_2 \\ \\ CH_2 \end{matrix}\!\!>O\!<\!\begin{matrix} R \\ \\ MgX \end{matrix}\right] \longrightarrow R\cdot CH_2\cdot CH_2OMgX \xrightarrow{H_2O} R\cdot CH_2\cdot CH_2\cdot OH \quad (g.)$$

Care must be taken in carrying out this reaction since, when all the ether has been distilled, a vigorous reaction often occurs apparently due to the rearrangement of the intermediate complex (an oxonium salt). This vigorous reaction may be avoided by distilling off some of the ether, adding benzene, and then distilling until the temperature of the vapour reaches 65°.

Secondary alcohols. When a Grignard reagent is treated with any aldehyde other than formaldehyde, a secondary alcohol is formed:

$$R\cdot CHO + R'MgX \longrightarrow R\cdot CH\!<\!\begin{matrix} OMgX \\ R' \end{matrix} \xrightarrow{H_2O} R\cdot CHOH\cdot R' \quad (f.g.\text{–}g.)$$

It can be seen that the secondary alcohol R·CHOH·R′, is obtained whether we start with R·CHO and R′MgX, or R′·CHO and RMgX. Which pair we use is generally a matter of their relative accessibility.

Secondary alcohols may also be prepared by interaction of a Grignard reagent (2 molecules) and ethyl formate (1 molecule). The mechanism of the reaction is still not certain; one which is widely accepted is that an aldehyde is formed as an intermediate product, and subsequently reacts with another molecule of Grignard reagent to form the secondary alcohol (see aldehydes, below):

$$H{-}C\!\begin{matrix} \nearrow O \\ \searrow OC_2H_5 \end{matrix} + RMgX \longrightarrow \left[\begin{matrix} & OMgX \\ H{-}C\!<\! & \\ | & OC_2H_5 \\ R & \end{matrix}\right] \longrightarrow$$

$$Mg(OC_2H_5)\cdot X + R\cdot CHO \xrightarrow{RMgX} R\cdot CH\!<\!\begin{matrix} OMgX \\ R \end{matrix} \xrightarrow{H_2O} R\cdot CHOH\cdot R \quad (g.)$$

Tertiary alcohols. A tertiary alcohol may be prepared by the action of a Grignard reagent on a ketone:

$$\begin{matrix} R \\ R' \end{matrix}\!\!>C{=}O + R''MgX \longrightarrow \begin{matrix} R \\ R' \end{matrix}\!\!>C\!<\!\begin{matrix} OMgX \\ R'' \end{matrix} \xrightarrow{H_2O} \begin{matrix} R \\ R' \end{matrix}\!\!>C\!<\!\begin{matrix} OH \\ R'' \end{matrix} \quad (g.)$$

By this means a tertiary alcohol with three different alkyl groups may be prepared, and the starting materials may be any of the following pairs of compounds: R·CO·R′ and R″MgX; R·CO·R″ and R′MgX, or R′·CO·R″ and RMgX (*cf.* secondary alcohols).

Tertiary alcohols containing at least two identical alkyl groups may be prepared by the reaction between a Grignard reagent (2 molecules) and any ester (1 molecule) other than formic ester (*cf.* secondary alcohols):

$$R-C\begin{matrix}\nearrow O \\ \searrow OC_2H_5\end{matrix} + R'MgX \longrightarrow \left[R-\underset{R'}{\overset{OMgX}{C}}-OC_2H_5\right] \longrightarrow$$

$$Mg(OC_2H_5)\cdot X + R\cdot CO\cdot R' \xrightarrow{R'MgX} R-\underset{R'}{\overset{R'}{C}}-OMgX \xrightarrow{H_2O} \begin{matrix}R & & OH \\ & C & \\ R' & & R'\end{matrix} \quad (g.)$$

Similar results may be achieved by using an acid and a slight excess of Grignard reagent, *i.e.*, more than three molecules (Huston *et al.*, 1946):

$$R-C\begin{matrix}\nearrow O \\ \searrow OH\end{matrix} \xrightarrow{R'MgI} R'H + R\cdot C\begin{matrix}\nearrow O \\ \searrow OMgI\end{matrix} \xrightarrow{R'MgI}$$

$$R\cdot C\begin{matrix}\nearrow OMgI \\ -R' \\ \searrow OMgI\end{matrix} \xrightarrow{R'MgI} R\cdot C\begin{matrix}\nearrow OMgI \\ -R' \\ \searrow R'\end{matrix} \xrightarrow{H_2O} RR'_2COH$$

Tertiary alcohols containing three identical alkyl groups may be prepared by the reaction between a Grignard reagent (3 molecules) and ethyl carbonate (1 molecule):

$$3RMgX + (C_2H_5O)_2CO \longrightarrow R_3COMgX + 2Mg(OC_2H_5)\cdot X$$
$$\xrightarrow{H_2O} R_3COH \quad (f.g.\text{–}g.)$$

Ethers. The preparation of an ether using a Grignard reagent is another example of the reaction between the latter and a compound containing a reactive halogen atom (*cf.* hydrocarbons); the method consists in adding an α-monochloroether to a Grignard reagent, *e.g.*,

$$R\cdot O\cdot CH_2Cl + R'MgX \longrightarrow R\cdot O\cdot CH_2\cdot R' + MgClX \quad (g.)$$

Chloroethers of the type $R\cdot O\cdot CH_2Cl$ are readily prepared by passing hydrogen chloride into a cooled mixture of formalin solution and an alcohol:

$$ROH + H\cdot CHO + HCl \longrightarrow R\cdot O\cdot CH_2Cl + H_2O \quad (v.g.)$$

A particularly useful chloroether is monochlorodimethyl ether, by means of which it is possible to ascend both the ether and alcohol series.

The following equations illustrate how it may be used:

$$CH_3OH + H\cdot CHO + HCl \longrightarrow CH_3\cdot O\cdot CH_2Cl + H_2O$$
$$ROH + HBr \longrightarrow RBr + H_2O$$
$$RBr + Mg \longrightarrow RMgBr$$
$$RMgBr + CH_2Cl\cdot O\cdot CH_3 \longrightarrow R\cdot CH_2\cdot O\cdot CH_3 + MgClBr$$

When refluxed with constant-boiling hydrobromic acid, this ether gives the alkyl bromide $R\cdot CH_2Br$ and methyl bromide (see p. 132). The alkyl bromide may be hydrolysed to the corresponding alcohol, $R\cdot CH_2OH$, or may be converted into the ether $R\cdot CH_2\cdot CH_2\cdot O\cdot CH_3$:

$$R\cdot CH_2Br \xrightarrow{Mg} R\cdot CH_2MgBr \xrightarrow{ClCH_2\cdot O\cdot CH_3} R\cdot CH_2.CH_2\cdot O\cdot CH_3$$

Aldehydes. An aldehyde may be prepared by the reaction between a Grignard reagent (1 molecule) and ethyl formate (1 molecule). If the

Grignard reagent is in excess, a secondary alcohol is formed (see above). Hence, to avoid this as much as possible, *the Grignard reagent is added to the ester*:

$$H{-}C\begin{smallmatrix}{/\!\!/}O\\ \diagdown OC_2H_5\end{smallmatrix} + RMgX \longrightarrow \left[H{-}\underset{\displaystyle R}{\underset{|}{C}}\begin{smallmatrix}\diagup OMgX\\ \diagdown OC_2H_5\end{smallmatrix}\right] \longrightarrow R{\cdot}CHO + Mg(OC_2H_5){\cdot}X$$

Isolation of the aldehyde supports the mechanism given for the formation of a secondary alcohol when the Grignard reagent is in excess (see secondary alcohols).

In the preparation of an aldehyde by this method it is impossible to avoid the formation of some secondary alcohol as well. If, however, ethyl orthoformate is used instead of ethyl formate, a better yield of aldehyde is obtained, since the formation of secondary alcohol is prevented by the formation of an acetal:

$$H{\cdot}C(OC_2H_5)_3 + RMgX \longrightarrow R{\cdot}CH(OC_2H_5)_2 + Mg(OC_2H_5){\cdot}X \xrightarrow{\text{acid}} R{\cdot}CHO + 2C_2H_5OH$$

Aldehydes may also be prepared by the reaction between a Grignard reagent and hydrogen cyanide or formamide (see ketones, below).

Ketones. Ketones *cannot* be prepared by the reaction between a Grignard reagent (1 molecule) and any ester (1 molecule) other than formic ester, since it is rarely possible to stop the reaction at the first stage (as can be done for the preparation of an aldehyde using ethyl formate). It is possible, however, to prepare a ketone (as its ketal) by using any orthoester other than orthoformic ester (*cf.* aldehydes):

$$R{\cdot}C(OC_2H_5)_3 + R'MgX \longrightarrow RR'C(OC_2H_5)_2 + Mg(OC_2H_5){\cdot}X \xrightarrow{\text{acid}} R{\cdot}CO{\cdot}R'$$

Ketones may be prepared by adding an alkyl cyanide to a Grignard reagent, and decomposing the complex with dilute acid; methyl cyanide is the only alkyl cyanide which does not form a ketone:

$$R{\cdot}C{\equiv}N + R'MgX \longrightarrow R{-}\overset{\displaystyle R'}{\overset{|}{C}}{=}N{\cdot}MgX \xrightarrow{H_2O} \underset{\text{ketimine}}{RR'C{=}NH} \xrightarrow{H_2O} R{\cdot}CO{\cdot}R' + NH_3$$

The starting materials may be either R·CN and R'MgX, or R'·CN and RMgX. If hydrogen cyanide is used instead of an alkyl cyanide (R=H), an aldehyde is formed.

Acyl chlorides (1 molecule) react rapidly with Grignard reagents (1 molecule) to form ketones:

$$R{\cdot}COCl + R'MgX \longrightarrow R{\cdot}CO{\cdot}R' + MgClX \quad (f.g.)$$

Tertiary alcohol is also formed, due to the action of the Grignard reagent on the ketone produced. The best conditions for the preparation of straight-chain ketones is the addition of one molecule of Grignard reagent to one or more molecules of acyl chloride at $-65°$ in the presence of a small amount of ferric chloride. For branched-chain ketones the temperature can be about $5°$ (Percival *et al.*, 1953).

The mechanism of the reaction is not certain, but it appears to be additive and not double decomposition, since the reactivity of acyl halides with a Grignard reagent is acyl fluoride > chloride > bromide > iodide (Entemann and Johnson, 1933); this order is opposite to that of the reactivity of the halogen atom in acyl halides. Thus the reaction may be formulated:

$$R{-}C{\begin{smallmatrix}{/\!\!/}O\\ \diagdown Cl\end{smallmatrix}} + R'MgX \longrightarrow \left[R{-}\overset{OMgX}{\underset{R'}{C}}{-}Cl \right] \longrightarrow R{\cdot}CO{\cdot}R' + MgClX$$

On the other hand, Morrison *et al.* (1954) propose the following mechanism, a second molecule attacking the Grignard-acyl halide complex:

$$\begin{matrix}Cl\\R\end{matrix}\!\!>\!C{=}O + RMgX \longrightarrow \begin{matrix}Cl\\R\end{matrix}\!\!>\!\overset{+}{C}{-}O{-}\overset{-}{Mg}\!<\!\begin{matrix}X\\R\end{matrix} \;\; (R{-}Mg{-}X) \longrightarrow$$

$$\begin{matrix}Cl\\R\end{matrix}\!\!>\!C\!<\!\begin{matrix}OMgX\\R\end{matrix} + \underset{X}{Mg}{-}R \longrightarrow R_2CO + MgClX + RMgX$$

Acid anhydrides also form ketones, the reaction being best carried out at about $-70°$:

$$(R{\cdot}CO)_2O + R'MgX \xrightarrow{-70°} R{\cdot}CO{\cdot}R' + R{\cdot}CO_2MgX \quad (g.\text{–}v.g.)$$

Amides and *N*-substituted amides react with Grignard reagents to form ketones:

$$R{-}C{\begin{smallmatrix}{/\!\!/}O\\ \diagdown NH_2\end{smallmatrix}} + R'MgX \longrightarrow R'H + R{-}C{\begin{smallmatrix}{/\!\!/}O\\ \diagdown NH{\cdot}MgX\end{smallmatrix}} \xrightarrow{R'MgX}$$

$$R{-}\underset{R'}{C}{\begin{smallmatrix}\diagup OMgX\\ \diagdown NH{\cdot}MgX\end{smallmatrix}} \xrightarrow{H_2O} R{\cdot}CO{\cdot}R' + 2Mg(OH){\cdot}X + NH_3$$

This reaction necessitates the use of two molecules of Grignard reagent, and is therefore of very little practical importance. Formamide gives rise to the formation of an aldehyde.

Acids. When a Grignard reagent is treated with solid carbon dioxide and the complex decomposed with dilute acid, a monocarboxylic acid is obtained:

$$RMgX + C{\begin{smallmatrix}{/\!\!/}O\\ {\diagdown\!\!\diagdown} O\end{smallmatrix}} \longrightarrow R{-}C{\begin{smallmatrix}{/\!\!/}O\\ \diagdown OMgX\end{smallmatrix}} \xrightarrow{H_2O} R{\cdot}CO_2H \quad (f.g.\text{–}g.)$$

Solid carbon dioxide is used in order to attain a low temperature ($-70°$); if the reaction is carried out with carbon dioxide at room temperature, the product is mainly a mixture of ketone and tertiary alcohol. High yields of acid are also obtained by the addition of the Grignard reagent to powdered solid carbon dioxide in ether (Hussey, 1951). On the other hand, a good yield of acid may also be obtained by passing carbon dioxide into the Grignard solution cooled to 0°.

The above method is particularly useful for preparing acids of the type $R_3C{\cdot}CO_2H$, which usually cannot be prepared by the cyanide synthesis using a tertiary alkyl halide (p. 277). It may also be noted that this method offers a means of ascending the acid series.

Esters. When a Grignard reagent (1 molecule) reacts with ethyl chloroformate (1 molecule) an ester is formed. Since chloroformic ester is the half-acid chloride of carbonic acid, the reaction probably takes place by an additive mechanism (see ketones):

$$O{=}\underset{\displaystyle OC_2H_5}{\underset{|}{C}}{-}Cl + RMgX \longrightarrow \left[XMgO{-}\overset{\displaystyle Cl}{\overset{|}{\underset{\displaystyle OC_2H_5}{\underset{|}{C}}}}{-}R \right] \longrightarrow R{\cdot}CO_2C_2H_5 + MgClX$$

To avoid as far as possible reaction of the Grignard reagent with the carbethoxy group of the carboxylic ester produced, the ethyl chloroformate is kept in excess by adding to it the Grignard reagent.

Chloroformic ester is an acid chloride; ethyl chloroacetate is not. When the latter is treated with a Grignard reagent (2 molecules), a chloro-tertiary alcohol is produced, the carbonyl group of the carbethoxy being more reactive than the chlorine atom of the alkyl halide type:

$$ClCH_2{\cdot}C\begin{cases}{=}O\\ {-}OC_2H_5\end{cases} + 2RMgX \longrightarrow$$

$$ClCH_2{\cdot}\underset{\displaystyle R}{\underset{|}{C}}\begin{cases}{-}OMgX\\ {-}R\end{cases} + Mg(OC_2H_5){\cdot}X \xrightarrow{H_2O} R_2C\begin{cases}{-}OH\\ {-}CH_2Cl\end{cases}$$

A very useful method for preparing esters of tertiary alcohols is to treat the tertiary alcohol with a Grignard reagent, and then add an acyl chloride, which reacts with the alkoxy-magnesium halide left in the solution:

$$ROH + CH_3MgI \longrightarrow CH_4 + ROMgI$$
$$R'{\cdot}COCl + ROMgI \longrightarrow R'{\cdot}CO_2R + MgClI$$

Alkyl cyanides. Cyanogen (1 molecule) reacts with a Grignard reagent (1 molecule) to form an alkyl cyanide:

$$RMgX + C_2N_2 \longrightarrow R{\cdot}CN + Mg(CN){\cdot}X$$

Alkyl cyanides are also formed, together with alkyl chloride, when a Grignard reagent (1 molecule) is added to an ethereal solution of cyanogen chloride (1 molecule); the latter should always be in excess, since the alkyl cyanide produced tends to react with the Grignard reagent (*cf.* aldehydes and esters):

$$RMgCl + ClCN \longrightarrow R{\cdot}CN + MgCl_2$$
$$RMgCl + ClCN \longrightarrow RCl + Mg(CN){\cdot}Cl$$

This reaction is probably the best method for preparing tertiary alkyl cyanides.

Only cyanogen chloride reacts to form an alkyl cyanide, and the best yield is obtained when the halogen atom in the Grignard reagent is chlorine. Cyanogen bromide and iodide react with Grignard reagents to form the alkyl bromide and iodide, respectively; no alkyl cyanide is formed at all (Coleman *et al.*, 1928, 1929).

Primary amines. A primary amine is formed by the reaction between a Grignard reagent and chloramine:

$$RMgX + ClNH_2 \longrightarrow R{\cdot}NH_2 + MgClX$$

This is one of the best methods for preparing primary amines containing a tertiary alkyl group. The yields are usually low. This is not unexpected when we consider the very great reactivity of active hydrogen; in fact, it is surprising that we get any amine at all.

A much more satisfactory method for preparing pure primary amines is the reaction between *O*-methylhydroxylamine and a Grignard reagent which may be either the alkyl-magnesium chloride or bromide, but *not* iodide (Brown and Jones, 1946):

$$2RMgCl + CH_3{\cdot}O{\cdot}NH_2 \longrightarrow R{\cdot}NH{\cdot}MgCl + RH + Mg(OCH_3){\cdot}Cl$$

$$\xrightarrow{HCl} R{\cdot}NH_2 \quad (40\text{–}90\%)$$

This reaction is also applicable to the preparation of certain diamines (see also p. 343), *e.g.*, cadaverine:

$$BrCH_2{\cdot}(CH_2)_3{\cdot}CH_2Br \xrightarrow{2Mg} BrMgCH_2{\cdot}(CH_2)_3{\cdot}CH_2MgBr \xrightarrow[\text{(ii) HCl}]{\text{(i) } CH_3{\cdot}O{\cdot}NH_2}$$

$$NH_2{\cdot}CH_2{\cdot}(CH_2)_3{\cdot}CH_2{\cdot}NH_2$$

Primary amines may also be prepared by reducing the adducts formed between cyanides and Grignard reagents with lithium aluminium hydride (Pohland *et al.*, 1953).

$$R{\cdot}CN + R'MgX \longrightarrow RR'C{=}NMgX \xrightarrow[\text{(ii) } H_2O]{\text{(i) } LiAlH_4} RR'CH{\cdot}NH_2 \quad (g.)$$

Organo-metallic and organo non-metallic compounds. These compounds may be prepared by interaction of a Grignard reagent and an inorganic halide, the former acting as an alkylating reagent. Some examples have already been mentioned, *e.g.*, the alkyl phosphines, arsines and silanes; these are regarded as organic compounds of non-metallic elements. Examples of the formation of organo-metallic compounds are diethyl-mercury (from mercuric chloride) and the ethyl-tin compounds (from stannic bromide):

$$HgCl_2 + 2C_2H_5MgI \longrightarrow (C_2H_5)_2Hg + 2MgClI$$

$$SnBr_4 \xrightarrow{C_2H_5MgI} C_2H_5SnBr_3 \xrightarrow{C_2H_5MgI} (C_2H_5)_2SnBr_2 \xrightarrow{C_2H_5MgI}$$

$$(C_2H_5)_3SnBr \xrightarrow{C_2H_5MgI} (C_2H_5)_4Sn$$

A particularly interesting example is the formation of *tetraethyl-lead* from *lead dichloride*:

$$2PbCl_2 + 4C_2H_5MgI \longrightarrow (C_2H_5)_4Pb + Pb + 4MgClI$$

Alkyl iodides. Alkyl iodides are formed when a Grignard reagent—the alkyl-magnesium chloride or bromide—is treated with iodine:

$$RMgX + I_2 \longrightarrow RI + MgXI$$

This reaction provides a good method for preparing alkyl iodides from the corresponding chloride or bromide.

Thioalcohols. These may be prepared by the action of sulphur on a Grignard reagent:

$$RMgX + S \longrightarrow RSMgX \xrightarrow{H_2O} RSH$$

Sulphinic acids. When sulphur dioxide is passed into a well-cooled Grignard solution, a sulphinic acid (as its magnesium complex) is formed:

$$RMgX + S\begin{matrix}\nearrow O \\ \searrow O\end{matrix} \longrightarrow R{-}S\begin{matrix}\nearrow O \\ \searrow OMgX\end{matrix} \xrightarrow{H_2O} R{\cdot}SO_2H$$

Dithioic acids. These may be prepared by the action of carbon disulphide on a Grignard reagent (*cf.* carboxylic and sulphinic acids):

$$RMgX + C\begin{matrix}\nearrow S \\ \searrow S\end{matrix} \longrightarrow R{-}C\begin{matrix}\nearrow S \\ \searrow SMgX\end{matrix} \xrightarrow{H_2O} R{\cdot}CS_2H$$

Union of radicals. Some examples of joining two alkyl radicals together have been considered when dealing with the synthesis of hydrocarbons (p. 335). It has already been pointed out (p. 333) that the addition of a small amount of cobaltous chloride changes the reaction from ionic to free radical, and thereby leads to an abnormal reaction. This abnormal reaction, however, may be used with advantage to join together identical alkyl (or aryl) groups. Many metallic halides may be used, *e.g.*, those of Cu, Ag, Co, Ni, Fe, etc. (see pp. 458, 670).

ABNORMAL BEHAVIOUR OF GRIGNARD REAGENTS

In certain cases a Grignard reagent does not react with compounds containing a functional group which is normally capable of reaction. Generally, branching of the carbon chain near the functional group prevents reaction; the cause is probably the spatial effect, *e.g.*, methylmagnesium bromide or iodide does not react with hexamethylacetone, $(CH_3)_3C{\cdot}CO{\cdot}C(CH_3)_3$. It has also been found that if the Grignard reagent contains large alkyl groups, reaction may be *prevented*; *e.g.*, methyl *iso*propyl ketone reacts with methylmagnesium iodide but not with *tert.*-butylmagnesium chloride. In other cases, *abnormal reaction* may take place, *e.g.*, when *iso*propylmagnesium bromide is added to di-*iso*propyl ketone, the expected tertiary alcohol is *not* formed; instead, the secondary alcohol, di-*iso*propylcarbinol, is obtained, resulting from the *reduction* of the ketone:

$$(CH_3)_2CH{\cdot}CO{\cdot}CH(CH_3)_2 \xrightarrow{(CH_3)_2CHMgBr} (CH_3)_2CH{\cdot}CHOH{\cdot}CH(CH_3)_2 + CH_3{\cdot}CH{:}CH_2$$

This abnormal reaction of a Grignard reagent may be explained by a free-radical mechanism; we have seen (p. 46) that one of the properties of a free radical is disproportionation. The reaction may therefore be formulated:

$$[(CH_3)_2CH{-}]_2C{=}O + (CH_3)_2CHMgBr \longrightarrow [(CH_3)_2CH{-}]_2\dot{C}{-}OMgBr + (CH_3)_2\dot{C}H \longrightarrow [(CH_3)_2CH{-}]_2CHOMgBr + CH_3{\cdot}CH{:}CH_2$$

From the foregoing it can be seen that it is not possible to prepare a tertiary alcohol with more than two branched-chain alkyl groups by means of a Grignard reagent. On the other hand, tertiary alcohols containing three branched-chain alkyl groups may be prepared by means of alkyl-lithium compounds (Vavou and Colin, 1946), *e.g.*,

$$(CH_3)_2CH{\cdot}CO{\cdot}CH(CH_3)_2 + (CH_3)_2CHLi \longrightarrow [(CH_3)_2CH{-}]_3COLi \xrightarrow{H_2O} [(CH_3)_2CH{-}]_3COH + LiOH \quad (53\%)$$

αβ-Unsaturated carbonyl compounds react with a Grignard reagent in the 1 : 2- or 1 : 4-positions (*cf.* p. 261):

1 : 2-addition

$$\overset{4}{\mathrm{R—CH}}=\overset{3}{\mathrm{CH}}—\underset{\mathrm{R'}}{\overset{2}{\mathrm{C}}}=\overset{1}{\mathrm{O}} + \mathrm{R''MgX} \longrightarrow$$

$$\mathrm{R—CH{=}CH—}\underset{\mathrm{R'}}{\overset{\mathrm{R''}}{\mathrm{C}}}\mathrm{—OMgX} \xrightarrow{H_2O} \mathrm{R—CH{=}CH—}\underset{\mathrm{R'}}{\overset{\mathrm{R''}}{\mathrm{C}}}\mathrm{—OH}$$

The 1 : 2-addition takes place by the carbonyl group undergoing the electromeric effect in the usual way:

$$\mathrm{—CH{=}CH—}\underset{|}{\mathrm{C}}\mathrm{{=}O} \longrightarrow \mathrm{—CH{=}CH—}\underset{|}{\overset{+}{\mathrm{C}}}\mathrm{—}\overset{-}{\mathrm{O}}$$

1 : 4-addition

$$\overset{4}{\mathrm{R—CH}}=\overset{3}{\mathrm{CH}}—\underset{\mathrm{R'}}{\overset{2}{\mathrm{C}}}=\overset{1}{\mathrm{O}} + \mathrm{R''MgX} \longrightarrow$$

$$\mathrm{R—}\overset{\mathrm{R''}}{\mathrm{CH}}\mathrm{—CH{=}}\overset{\mathrm{R'}}{\mathrm{C}}\mathrm{—OMgX} \xrightarrow{H_2O} \mathrm{R—}\overset{\mathrm{R''}}{\mathrm{CH}}\mathrm{—CH{=}}\overset{\mathrm{R'}}{\mathrm{C}}\mathrm{—OH}$$

If R′ is a hydrogen atom, then this compound rearranges to the aldehyde $RR''CH—CH_2{\cdot}CHO$ (*cf.* vinyl alcohol). The 1 : 4-addition occurs due to the electromeric effect taking place in the *conjugated chain*:

$$\mathrm{—CH{=}CH—}\underset{|}{\mathrm{C}}\mathrm{{=}O} \longrightarrow \mathrm{—}\overset{+}{\mathrm{C}}\mathrm{H—CH{=}}\underset{|}{\mathrm{C}}\mathrm{—}\overset{-}{\mathrm{O}}$$

Experiments have shown that the addition which takes place depends on the nature of the groups R, R′ and R″.

It appears that vinyl halides do not form Grignard reagents, but apparently substituted vinyl halides do, *e.g.*, styryl bromide, $C_6H_5{\cdot}CH{=}CHBr$. On the other hand, halides with halogen in the allyl position are very reactive, so much so, that coupling usually takes place; *e.g.*, when allyl bromide is treated with magnesium in the presence of ether (the usual procedure for preparing a Grignard reagent), the main product is *diallyl* (*hexa*-1 : 5-*diene*):

$$CH_2{:}CH{\cdot}CH_2Br + Mg \longrightarrow CH_2{:}CH{\cdot}CH_2MgBr$$

$$CH_2{:}CH{\cdot}CH_2MgBr + CH_2{:}CH{\cdot}CH_2Br \longrightarrow CH_2{:}CH{\cdot}CH_2{\cdot}CH_2{\cdot}CH{:}CH_2 + MgBr_2$$

It is possible, however, to prepare allylmagnesium bromide (in 95 per cent. yield) by adding a *very dilute* ethereal solution of allyl bromide or magnesium turnings.

If the halogen atom and the double bond are in positions other than the vinyl or allyl, the halide reacts normally to form the Grignard reagent.

In dihalides of the type $XCH_2{\cdot}(CH_2)_n{\cdot}CH_2X$, if $n = 0$ (*i.e.*, 1 : 2-dihalide) and $n = 1$ (*i.e.*, 1 : 3-dihalide), no Grignard reagent is formed when treated with magnesium; instead, an "internal" Wurtz reaction takes place, *e.g.*, ethylene bromide gives ethylene, and trimethylene bromide *cyclo*-propane:

$$CH_2Br{\cdot}CH_2Br + Mg \longrightarrow CH_2{:}CH_2 + MgBr_2$$

$$CH_2Br{\cdot}CH_2{\cdot}CH_2Br + Mg \longrightarrow \underset{\diagdown\ \diagup \atop CH_2}{CH_2—CH_2} + MgBr_2$$

If $n = 2$ or more, the di-magnesium compound is obtained, but the yields are usually of the order of about 30 per cent., *e.g.*, $n = 3$:

$$BrCH_2{\cdot}(CH_2)_3{\cdot}CH_2Br + 2Mg \longrightarrow BrMgCH_2{\cdot}(CH_2)_3{\cdot}CH_2MgBr$$

ALKYL-METALLIC COMPOUNDS

Alkyl derivatives of practically all the metals have been prepared. The organo-metallic compounds are named as the alkyl metal, *e.g.*, $(CH_3)_2Hg$, dimethylmercury; $(C_2H_5)_4Pb$, tetraethyl-lead. They are not generally isolated, but are used directly as intermediates, and their preparation is usually carried out in an atmosphere of nitrogen.

General methods of preparation. 1. By heating an alkyl halide with an alloy, *e.g.*, diethylmercury from ethyl iodide and sodium amalgam:

$$2C_2H_5I + Na_2/Hg \longrightarrow (C_2H_5)_2Hg + 2NaI$$

2. By the reaction between a Grignard reagent and a metallic halide, *e.g.*,

$$SnCl_4 + 4RMgX \longrightarrow R_4Sn + 4MgClX$$

This method may be used to prepare the organo-compounds of those metals which have a lower electrode potential than magnesium. Generally, an organo-metallic compound may be prepared by the reaction between a dialkyl-metal of *higher* electrode potential and the chloride of a metal of *lower* electrode potential.

3. A metal of *higher* electrode potential generally reacts with the dialkyl-metal of *lower* electrode potential, *e.g.*,

$$(C_2H_5)_2Hg + 2Na \longrightarrow 2C_2\overset{-}{H}_5\overset{+}{Na} + Hg$$

Alkali group of metals. The organo-alkali compounds are generally best prepared by the action of the alkali metal on a dialkyl-mercury or zinc compound (method 3, above), *e.g.*,

$$(CH_3)_2Zn + 2K \longrightarrow 2C\overset{-}{H}_3\overset{+}{K} + Zn$$

Lithium compounds, however, are best prepared by heating an alkyl halide with lithium (Ziegler, 1930):

$$RX + 2Li \longrightarrow RLi + LiX$$

Alkyl chlorides are generally the most satisfactory; the iodides usually undergo the Wurtz reaction. On the other hand, aryl bromides and iodides give good yields of the lithium compound. Many organo-lithium compounds, however, cannot be prepared by this method, but may readily be prepared by the following exchange reaction (" indirect metalation "):

$$RLi + R'X \longrightarrow R'Li + RX$$

The most satisfactory radical (R) for this purpose is *n*-butyl. Another important method is by metalation (see p. 512).

The alkyl sodium and potassium compounds are insoluble, colourless, highly reactive solids. They are electrovalent compounds, *i.e.*, salts. The lithium compounds are colourless liquids or readily fusible solids, and are covalent, *e.g.*, $CH_3{\cdot}Li$, but, according to the nature of the alkyl group, they may have partial ionic character, *e.g.*, *n*-butyl-lithium. Owing to their covalent nature, lithium compounds are more stable and less reactive than those of sodium and potassium.

An important organo-sodium compound is triphenylmethylsodium, $(C_6H_5)_3C\}Na$, which may be prepared by the action of sodamide on triphenylmethane in liquid ammonia solution:

$$(C_6H_5)_3CH + NaNH_2 \longrightarrow (C_6H_5)_3\bar{C}\}\overset{+}{Na} + NH_3$$

It is a very good reagent for bringing about condensation reactions (see, *e.g.*, p. 216).

From the practical point of view, lithium compounds are the most satisfactory to use in organic synthesis, since they are very easily prepared and, being covalent, dissolve in organic solvents. Generally speaking the lithium compounds (and those of sodium and potassium) behave like the Grignard reagents, but the lithium compounds are usually more reactive; *e.g.*,

$$C_2H_5Li + H_2O \longrightarrow C_2H_6 + LiOH$$
$$3CH_3Li + AuBr_3 \longrightarrow (CH_3)_3Au + 3LiBr$$

With carbon dioxide a good yield of ketone is obtained:

$$RLi + CO_2 \longrightarrow R{\cdot}C\begin{cases}{=}O\\ OLi\end{cases} \xrightarrow{RLi} R_2C\begin{cases}OLi\\ OLi\end{cases} \xrightarrow{H_2O} R_2CO$$

A ketone is also the main product when a carboxylic acid is used as starting material:

$$R{\cdot}C\begin{cases}{=}O\\ OH\end{cases} \xrightarrow{R'Li} R{\cdot}C\begin{cases}{=}O\\ OLi\end{cases} \xrightarrow{R'Li} R{\cdot}C\begin{cases}OLi\\ R'\\ OLi\end{cases} \xrightarrow{H_2O} R{\cdot}CO{\cdot}R'$$

Lithium compounds also react with aldehydes and ketones to give alcohols in better yields than with Grignard reagents.

The main difference between lithium compounds and Grignard reagents is that the former can add on to the C=C grouping, *e.g.*, Ziegler *et al.* (1950) have shown that *n*-butyl-lithium adds on to ethylene under high pressure, and that after the addition of formaldehyde a mixture of alcohols (C_7—C_{13}) is obtained, *e.g.*,

$$C_4H_9Li \xrightarrow{C_2H_4} C_4H_9{\cdot}(CH_2)_2{\cdot}Li \xrightarrow{C_2H_4} C_4H_9{\cdot}(CH_2)_4{\cdot}Li$$
$$C_4H_9{\cdot}(CH_2)_2{\cdot}Li \xrightarrow{CH_2O} C_4H_9{\cdot}(CH_2)_2{\cdot}CH_2OH \qquad C_4H_9{\cdot}(CH_2)_4{\cdot}Li \xrightarrow{CH_2O} C_4H_9{\cdot}(CH_2)_4{\cdot}CH_2OH$$

This offers a means of stepping up a series.

It should also be noted that lithium forms lithium alkenyls with various vinyl halides. This offers a means of preparing unsaturated compounds such as alcohols, ketones and acids. Lithium acetylides may also be prepared and used in synthetic work.

Copper group of metals (*copper, silver and gold*). The alkyl derivatives of the copper group are best prepared by the reaction between a Grignard reagent and the metal halide, *e.g.*,

$$RMgX + CuI \longrightarrow R{-}Cu + MgXI$$

Their most characteristic reaction is their ready decomposition, which possibly takes place via the formation of free radicals, *e.g.*,

$$CH_3{-}Cu \longrightarrow CH_3{\cdot} + Cu$$
$$2CH_3{\cdot} \longrightarrow C_2H_6$$

Organo-zinc compounds. The dialkyl-zinc compounds were the first organo-metallic compounds to be prepared; they were discovered by Frankland (1849) in an attempt to prepare the ethyl radical by removing iodine from ethyl iodide by means of zinc. The alkyl iodide is heated with zinc in an atmosphere of carbon dioxide, and the product, alkyl-zinc iodide, is distilled in an atmosphere of carbon dioxide:

$$RI + Zn \longrightarrow R{-}Zn{-}I$$
$$2RZnI \longrightarrow R_2Zn + ZnI_2$$

The yield of dialkyl-zinc may be increased by carrying out the distillation *in vacuo* (50–90 per cent.). Krug *et al.* (1954) have shown that the dialkylzincs are best prepared by reaction between an alkyl bromide or iodide and a zinc–copper couple prepared by heating a mixture of zinc dust and cupric acetate.

The alkyl-zinc compounds are volatile liquids, spontaneously inflammable in air (hence the necessity to use an atmosphere of carbon dioxide in their preparation). They have an unpleasant smell, and burn the skin. The alkyl-zinc compounds have been used in various synthetic reactions (they behave like the Grignard reagents), but owing to the difficulty in handling them, and because better synthetic reagents are known, *e.g.*, the Grignard reagent, the use of the alkyl-zinc compounds is restricted to three synthetic preparations:

(i) *Preparation of hydrocarbons containing a quaternary carbon atom*; *e.g.*, *neo*pentane may be prepared by the action of dimethylzinc on *tert.*-butyl chloride:

$$(CH_3)_3CCl + (CH_3)_2Zn \longrightarrow (CH_3)_4C + CH_3ZnCl \quad (25\text{–}51\%)$$

Apparently dialkyl-zinc compounds do not react with primary or secondary alkyl halides.

(ii) *Preparation of ketones.* Alkyl-zinc compounds react with acyl chlorides to form ketones:

$$R{\cdot}COCl + R_2'Zn \longrightarrow R{\cdot}CO{\cdot}R' + R'ZnCl \quad (g.\text{–}v.g.)$$

The success of this method depends on the fact that the ketone can be isolated in good yield because dialkyl-zinc compounds react very slowly with ketones (*cf.* Grignard reagent, p. 338). Even so, the dialkyl cadmium compounds are replacing the zinc compounds in the preparation of ketones (see below). An alkyl-zinc chloride may be prepared by reaction between a Grignard reagent and zinc chloride:

$$RMgX + ZnCl_2 \longrightarrow RZnCl + MgClX$$

Jones (1947) used these compounds to prepare long-chain fatty acids (*cf.* p. 217). He prepared a keto-ester by reaction between an alkyl-zinc chloride and the acid chloride-ester derivative of a dicarboxylic acid, and reduced the keto-ester by the Clemmensen method:

$$CH_3{\cdot}(CH_2)_xZnCl + Cl{\cdot}CO{\cdot}(CH_2)_y{\cdot}CO_2C_2H_5 \longrightarrow$$
$$CH_3{\cdot}(CH_2)_x{\cdot}CO{\cdot}(CH_2)_y{\cdot}CO_2C_2H_5 + ZnCl_2 \xrightarrow[HCl]{Zn/Hg}$$
$$CH_3{\cdot}(CH_2)_x{\cdot}CH_2{\cdot}(CH_2)_y{\cdot}CO_2C_2H_5 \quad (76\text{–}92\%)$$

(iii) The **Reformatsky reaction** (1887). The Reformatsky reaction is the reaction between an α-bromoacid ester and a carbonyl compound (aldehyde, ketone or ester) in the presence of zinc to form a β-hydroxy-ester. The reaction is best carried out by adding zinc to a mixture of bromoacid ester and carbonyl compound, and then warming. According to Dippy *et al.* (1951), the Reformatsky reaction proceeds as follows:

$$R{\cdot}CHBr{\cdot}CO_2C_2H_5 + Zn \rightleftharpoons Br{\cdot}Zn{\cdot}CHR{\cdot}CO_2C_2H_5$$

$$\text{(i)}\quad R'_2C{=}O + Br{\cdot}Zn{\cdot}CHR{\cdot}CO_2C_2H_5 \longrightarrow R'_2C(OZnBr){\cdot}CHR{\cdot}CO_2C_2H_5$$

$$\xrightarrow[\text{acid}]{\text{dilute}} \underset{\beta\text{-hydroxy-ester}}{R'_2C(OH){\cdot}CHR{\cdot}CO_2C_2H_5} + ZnBrX$$

$$\text{(ii)}\quad Br{\cdot}Zn{\cdot}CHR{\cdot}\overset{OC_2H_5}{\underset{O}{C}} + Br{\cdot}Zn{\cdot}CHR{\cdot}CO_2C_2H_5 \longrightarrow Br{\cdot}Zn{\cdot}CHR{\cdot}\overset{OC_2H_5}{\underset{OZnBr}{C}}{\cdot}CHR{\cdot}CO_2C_2H_5$$

$$\xrightarrow[\text{acid}]{\text{dilute}} \underset{\beta\text{-keto-ester}}{R{\cdot}CH_2{\cdot}CO{\cdot}CHR{\cdot}CO_2C_2H_5} + C_2H_5OH + 2ZnBrX$$

Which of the two reactions predominates depends on the structure of the carbonyl compound. If this is a ketone and the two R′ groups are very large, *i.e.*, the carbonyl group is sterically hindered, the main reaction proceeds via (ii). When the carbonyl compound is an aldehyde (one R′=H), the main reaction proceeds via (i).

A few cases of β-haloesters undergoing the Reformatsky reaction are known, but the yields are low.

The preparation of a Grignard reagent from a bromoacid ester is not practical, since the organo-magnesium compound formed immediately reacts with the ester group of a second molecule.

Organo-cadmium compounds. Dialkyl-cadmium compounds may be prepared by the action of a Grignard reagent on cadmium chloride:

$$2RMgX + CdCl_2 \longrightarrow R_2Cd + 2MgClX$$

These compounds may be used to prepare simple ketones or polyfunctional compounds containing a keto-group. The reaction is carried out by treating an acyl chloride with dialkyl-cadmium, the yield being as high as 98 per cent. (better than with dialkyl-zinc). The high yields of ketone are due to the fact that dialkyl-cadmium compounds show very little tendency to react with a carbonyl group:

$$2R{\cdot}COCl + R'_2Cd \longrightarrow 2R{\cdot}CO{\cdot}R' + CdCl_2$$

This ketone synthesis may be used to synthesise long-chain fatty acids as follows:

$$R{\cdot}(CH_2)_xOH \xrightarrow[\text{(ii) Mg; (iii) CdCl}_2]{\text{(i) HBr}} [R{\cdot}(CH_2)_x]_2Cd \xrightarrow{COCl{\cdot}(CH_2)_y{\cdot}CO_2C_2H_5}$$

$$R{\cdot}(CH_2)_x{\cdot}CO{\cdot}(CH_2)_y{\cdot}CO_2C_2H_5 \xrightarrow[\text{HCl}]{\text{Zn/Hg}} R{\cdot}(CH_2)_x{\cdot}CH_2{\cdot}(CH_2)_y{\cdot}CO_2H$$

Organo-mercury compounds. Dialkyl-mercury compounds are best prepared by the reaction between a Grignard reagent and mercuric chloride:

$$2RMgX + HgCl_2 \longrightarrow R_2Hg + 2MgClX$$

They are poisonous liquids, *not* spontaneously inflammable in air; they are *not* decomposed by water, but are by dilute acids (*cf.* magnesium and zinc compounds).

An important reaction involving the use of mercury is **mercuration.** This process is the introduction of a *mercuri-acid group*, of which the commonest is the *acetoxy-mercuri* group, $-HgO{\cdot}CO{\cdot}CH_3$. Mercuration has some interesting applications in aromatic chemistry, and will be discussed later (p. 513).

Organo-lead compounds. The only organo-lead compound which is important is tetraethyl-lead. This is prepared industrially by heating ethyl chloride with a sodium alloy under pressure:

$$4C_2H_5Cl + 4Na/Pb \longrightarrow (C_2H_5)_4Pb + 3Pb + 4NaCl$$

Tetraethyl-lead is a liquid, b.p. about 200°, insoluble in water but soluble in ether. It is used for raising the octane number of petrol (see p. 52). To prevent lead being deposited in the cylinder head when such " doped " petrol is used (1 part tetraethyl-lead per thousand parts petrol), a small amount of ethylene bromide is added. The lead is thereby converted into lead dibromide, which is sufficiently volatile to be removed with the exhaust gases.

Tetramethyl- and tetraethyl-lead have been used by Paneth and his co-workers (1929, 1931) to prepare *free methyl* and *ethyl radicals*. The vapour of the tetra-alkyl-lead in a stream of hydrogen or nitrogen, under reduced pressure (1–2 mm.), was carried through a tube (gas velocity about 10–15 metres per sec.) heated at a point A (Fig. 1) to 600–800°:

$$R_4Pb \longrightarrow 4R\cdot + Pb$$

The decomposition into lead was shown by the deposition of a lead mirror at point A. The presence of free methyl or ethyl radicals was shown by the disappearance of a lead mirror previously deposited at a point B farther along the tube and kept at room temperature; hydrocarbons do not attack lead. If the distance between A and B was greater than 32 cm., the mirror at B did not disappear. This showed that the free alkyl radicals have a very short life; calculations based on experiment have shown that their half life period is about 0·006 sec.

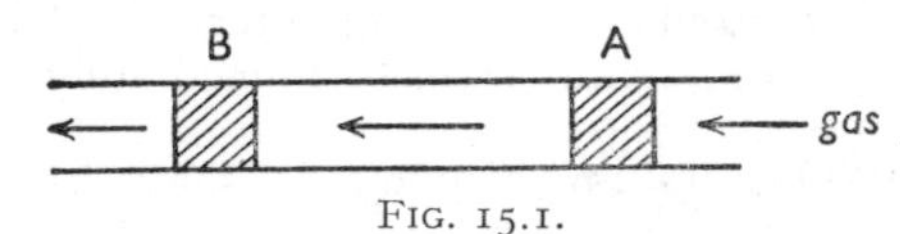

FIG. 15.1.

Paneth and his co-workers were the first to prepare a free alkyl radical, the existence of which had been suspected for a long time. Free radicals higher than methyl and ethyl are difficult to detect (see later).

The removal of metallic mirrors is now a well-established technique for the detection and identification of free radicals produced in the decomposition of organic compounds. The rate of removal of the mirrors is usually followed photometrically, the opacity of the mirror being matched against that of a standard. This procedure has been modified by measuring the electrical conductivity of the mirror (Whittingham, 1947).

Thermal decomposition is a general method for producing free radicals in the gaseous phase. Another general method (for producing free radicals in the gaseous phase or in solution) is photochemical decomposition. Thus photolysis of tetramethyl-lead, dimethylmercury, and dimethylzinc gives rise to free methyl radicals; *e.g.*, Leighton and Mortensen (1936) showed that a mirror of radioactive lead was attacked by a stream of tetramethyl-lead vapour which had been irradiated. Photolysis of alkyl iodides produces free alkyl radicals and iodine atoms, *e.g.*, West (1935) showed that the photochemical decomposition products of methyl iodide converted *para* hydrogen (the two nuclei have opposite spins) into *ortho* hydrogen (parallel spins). Free radicals can often be detected by the conversion of *para* hydrogen into *ortho*. They may also often be detected by combination with nitric oxide (see p. 675). The method of paramagnetic resonance is also being used to detect and measure free-radical concentrations (*inter alia*, Ingram *et al.*, 1954).

Other methods for preparing free radicals (in the gaseous phase or in solution) are by the action of a metal on a halide (see, *e.g.*, p. 674), or the catalytic effect of certain compounds, notably organic peroxides (see, *e.g.*, p. 64). Free radicals may also be *formed* in solution during electrolysis (p. 47); their formation has been used to explain the course of electrolysis in many cases.

When free alkyl radicals are prepared in any *thermal* reaction, recombination, decomposition and disproportionation may all occur simultaneously. The tendency for a free alkyl radical to decompose into a smaller radical and an olefin increases with increase in chain-length. The free methyl radical is stable up to 1000°. The free ethyl radical is not so stable and tends to combine to form butane, and also to disproportionate into ethane and ethylene. Radicals higher than ethyl readily decompose into methyl or ethyl radicals and an olefin, *e.g.*,

$$CH_3—CH_2—CH_2\cdot \longrightarrow CH_3\cdot + CH_2{=}CH_2$$

$$CH_3—CH_2—CH_2—CH_2\cdot \longrightarrow CH_3—CH_2\cdot + CH_2{=}CH_2$$

QUESTIONS

1. Write an account of the preparation of Grignard reagents and discuss their structure.

2. Give examples of the use of a Grignard reagent in preparing:—(*a*) a saturated hydrocarbon, (*b*) an unsaturated hydrocarbon, (*c*) a primary alcohol, (*d*) a secondary alcohol, (*e*) a tertiary alcohol, (*f*) an ether, (*g*) an aldehyde, (*h*) a ketone, (*i*) a carboxylic acid, (*j*) an ester, (*k*) a cyanide, (*l*) a primary amine, (*m*) an organo-metallic compound.

3. Show, by means of equations, how you would convert *n*-BuOH into:—(*a*) *n*-AmOH, (*b*) hexan-2-ol, (*c*) heptan-1-ol, (*d*) di-*n*-Bu carbinol, (*e*) 3-methylheptan-3-ol.

4. Suggest a synthesis for each of the following:—(*a*) $Me_2CBr\cdot CH_2Br$, (*b*) $Et_2CCl\cdot Me$, (*c*) $Me_2\cdot CH\cdot CH_2\cdot CH_3$, (*d*) $CH_3\cdot CH_2\cdot CHBr\cdot CH_2\cdot CH_3$, (*e*) $Me_2CH\cdot CHOH\cdot CH_2\cdot Me$, (*f*) MeEt*iso*PrCOH, (*g*) $(Me_2CH)_3COH$.

5. Starting with AcOH, MeOH and EtOH and any inorganic material you think necessary, show how you would synthesise:—(*a*) $Me_2CH\cdot C(OH)Me_2$, (*b*) $EtCHMe\cdot CHBr\cdot Me$, (*c*) $Me_3C\cdot CO_2H$, (*d*) $Et_2C(OH)\cdot CH_2OH$, (*e*) $CH_3\cdot CHOH\cdot CH_2\cdot CH_2\cdot CO_2Et$, (*f*) $CH_2Cl\cdot CH_2\cdot CO\cdot CH_3$.

6. Describe the preparation and properties of :—(*a*) EtNa, (*b*) $(C_6H_5)_3CNa$, (*c*) EtLi, (*d*) Me_2Zn, (*e*) Et_2Cd, (*f*) Me_2Hg, (*g*) Et_4Pb.

7. Define and give examples of :—(*a*) The Zerewitinoff active hydrogen determination, (*b*) the spatial effect, (*c*) the Reformatsky reaction, (*d*) mercuration.

8. Write an account of the preparation and properties of the free alkyl radicals.

READING REFERENCES

Gilman, *Advanced Organic Chemistry*, Wiley (1942, 2nd ed.). Vol. I, Ch. 5. Organo-metallic Compounds.

Ann. Reports, 1937, **34**, 243. Organo-alkali Compounds.

ibid., 1941, **38**, 136. Organo-metallic Compounds.

ibid., 1944, **41**, 195. Grignard Reactions.

Coates, Organometallic Compounds of the First Three Periodic Groups, *Quart. Reviews (Chem. Soc.)*, 1950, **4**, 217.

Lehman and Basch, The Determination of Active Hydrogen, *Ind. Eng. Chem.* (*Anal. Ed.*), 1945, **17**, 428.

Organic Reactions, Wiley (i) Vol. I (1942), Ch. 1. The Reformatsky Reaction.
(ii) Vol. VI (1951), Ch. 7. The Halogen-Metal Interconversion with Organolithium Compounds.
(iii) Vol. VIII (1954), Ch. 2. The Synthesis of Ketones from Acid Halides and Organo-metallic Compounds of Magnesium, Zinc, and Cadmium.
(iv) Vol. VIII (1954), Ch. 6. The Metalation Reaction with Organo-lithium Compounds.

Cook (Ed.), *Progress in Organic Chemistry*, Butterworth. Vol. III (1955), Ch. 4. Organic Compounds of Lithium.

Cason, The Use of Organo-Cadmium Reagents for the Preparation of Ketones, *Chem. Reviews*, 1947, **40**, 15.

Waters, *The Chemistry of the Free Radicals*, Oxford Press (1946).
Bawn, The Structure and Reactivity of Free Radicals, *J.C.S.*, **1949**, 1042.
Dippy and Parkins, An Investigation of the Course of the Reformatsky Reaction, *ibid.*, **1951**, 1570.
Kharasch and Reinmuth, *Grignard Reactions of Non-metallic Substances*, Constable (1954).
Coates, *Organo-Metallic Compounds*, Methuen (1956).
Leeper, Organo-Lead Compounds, *Chem. Reviews*, 1954, **54**, 101.
Jones, Methods of Preparation of Organo-Metallic Compounds, *ibid.*, 1954, **54**, 835.
Millar and Heaney, Grignard and Organolithium Reagents Derived from Dihalogen Compounds, *Quart. Reviews* (*Chem. Soc.*), 1957, **11**, 109.
Long, The Fate of Methyl Radicals in the Mechanism of Thermal Decomposition of Metal Alkyls, *J.C.S.*, **1956**, 3410.
Rochow, Hurd and Lewis, *The Chemistry of Organometallic Compounds*, Wiley (1957).

CHAPTER XVI

SATURATED DICARBOXYLIC ACIDS

THE general formula of the saturated dicarboxylic acids is $C_nH_{2n}(CO_2H_2)_2$ ($n = 0$ for oxalic acid), and the best-known examples are those which have the two carboxyl groups at the opposite ends of the carbon chain.

Nomenclature. The dicarboxylic acids are commonly known by names which indicate their source, *e.g.*, $CO_2H{\cdot}CO_2H$ oxalic acid; this occurs in plants of the *oxalis* group (for further examples, see the individual acids).

In this trivial system of nomenclature, the positions of side-chains or substituents are indicated by Greek letters, *e.g.*,
$CO_2H{\cdot}CH(CH_3){\cdot}CH_2{\cdot}CH_2{\cdot}CHCl{\cdot}CO_2H$ α-chloro-α′-methyladipic acid.

According to the I.U.C. system of nomenclature, the class suffix is *-dioic, e.g.*,

$CO_2H{\cdot}CO_2H$ ethanedioic acid
$CO_2H{\cdot}CH_2{\cdot}CO_2H$ propanedioic acid
$CO_2H{\cdot}CH(CH_3){\cdot}CH(CH_3){\cdot}CH_2{\cdot}CO_2H$ 2 : 3-dimethylpentanedioic acid

When this method leads to cumbrous names, the alternative scheme is to regard the carboxyl group as a substituent, and the name of the acid is then obtained by adding the suffix *carboxylic acid, e.g.*,

$CO_2H{\cdot}CH_2{\cdot}CH_2{\cdot}CO_2H$ 1 : 2-ethanedicarboxylic acid or ethane-1 : 2-dicarboxylic acid

General methods of preparation. 1. By the oxidation of diprimary glycols, *e.g.*, ethylene glycol gives oxalic acid:

$$CH_2OH{\cdot}CH_2OH \xrightarrow{[O]} CO_2H{\cdot}CO_2H$$

This method is not important, since the higher polymethylene glycols are inaccessible; in fact they are usually prepared from dicarboxylic acids (see p. 239).

2. By treating halogen derivatives of monocarboxylic acid esters with silver or zinc, *e.g.*, ethyl bromoacetate gives ethyl succinate:

$$2CH_2Br{\cdot}CO_2C_2H_5 + 2Ag \longrightarrow C_2H_5O_2C{\cdot}CH_2{\cdot}CH_2{\cdot}CO_2C_2H_5 + 2AgBr \quad (p.)$$

3. The *cyanide synthesis* of dicarboxylic acids is a very useful method; the starting material may be either a halogeno-acid or a polymethylene dibromide:

$$\text{(i)}\ CH_2Cl{\cdot}CO_2H \xrightarrow{KCN} CH_2CN{\cdot}CO_2H \xrightarrow{H_2O} CH_2(CO_2H)_2$$

$$\text{(ii)}\ \begin{matrix} CH_2Br \\ | \\ CH_2Br \end{matrix} \xrightarrow{KCN} \begin{matrix} CH_2{\cdot}CN \\ | \\ CH_2{\cdot}CN \end{matrix} \xrightarrow{H_2O} \begin{matrix} CH_2{\cdot}CO_2H \\ | \\ CH_2{\cdot}CO_2H \end{matrix}$$

4. The **Crum-Brown and Walker electrolytic method** (1891, 1893). This is the electrolysis of an aqueous solution of the potassium alkyl esters of the dicarboxylic acids (*cf.* Kolbe's method):

$$\begin{matrix} K\text{—}\vdots\text{—}O_2C\text{—}\vdots\text{—}(CH_2)_n\text{—}CO_2C_2H_5 \\ \\ K\text{—}\vdots\text{—}O_2C\text{—}\vdots\text{—}(CH_2)_n\text{—}CO_2C_2H_5 \end{matrix} + 2H_2O \longrightarrow$$

$$\begin{matrix} (CH_2)_n{\cdot}CO_2C_2H_5 \\ | \\ (CH_2)_n{\cdot}CO_2C_2H_5 \end{matrix} + 2CO_2 + 2KOH + H_2 \quad (f.g.\text{–}g.)$$

It is obvious that this method can be used to prepare only *even* homologues.

5. Dicarboxylic acids may be prepared by the acetoacetic ester synthesis (p. 216) and better, by the malonic ester synthesis (p. 219).

6. Several dicarboxylic acids may be prepared by the oxidation of unsaturated acids which occur in natural oils and fats, *e.g.*, oleic acid gives nonoic and azelaic acids:

$$CH_3\cdot(CH_2)_7\cdot CH{:}CH\cdot(CH_2)_7\cdot CO_2H \xrightarrow{HNO_3} CH_3\cdot(CH_2)_7\cdot CO_2H + CO_2H\cdot(CH_2)_7\cdot CO_2H$$

7. Cyclic ketones may be oxidised to dicarboxylic acids, *e.g.*, *cyclo*hexanone gives adipic acid:

$$H_2C\begin{matrix} \diagup CH_2—CH_2 \diagdown \\ \diagdown CH_2—CH_2 \diagup \end{matrix}CO \xrightarrow{HNO_3} CO_2H\cdot(CH_2)_4\cdot CO_2H$$

8. The preparation of higher homologues from lower homologues may be carried out in several ways; which method is used depends on the homologue desired. Many *even* higher homologues can be prepared by the Crum-Brown and Walker method (method 4). Any dicarboxylic acid can be "stepped up" by two carbon atoms as follows:

$$(CH_2)_n(CO_2C_2H_5)_2 \xrightarrow{Na/C_2H_5OH} (CH_2)_n(CH_2OH)_2 \xrightarrow{HBr}$$

$$(CH_2)_n(CH_2Br)_2 \xrightarrow{KCN} (CH_2)_n(CH_2\cdot CN)_2 \xrightarrow{H_2O} (CH_2)_n(CH_2\cdot CO_2H)_2$$

By using malonic ester instead of potassium cyanide, the acid may be "stepped up" by four carbon atoms:

$$(CH_2)_n(CH_2Br)_2 + 2[CH(CO_2C_2H_5)_2]^-Na^+ \longrightarrow$$

$$2NaBr + (CH_2)_n[CH_2\cdot CH(CO_2C_2H_5)_2]_2 \xrightarrow[(ii)\ HCl]{(i)\ KOH}$$

$$(CH_2)_n[CH_2\cdot CH(CO_2H)_2]_2 \xrightarrow{150-200^\circ} (CH_2)_n(CH_2\cdot CH_2\cdot CO_2H)_2 + 2CO_2$$

These higher homologues are used to prepare large carbon-ring compounds (p. 469).

General properties. All the dicarboxylic acids are crystalline solids, the lower members being soluble in water, the solubility decreasing with increase in molecular weight; the odd acids are more soluble than the even. None is steam volatile, and the solubility in ether increases with increase in molecular weight. Except for oxalic acid, the dicarboxylic acids are stable towards oxidising agents. Their melting points follow the oscillation rule (p. 165), the even acids having higher melting points than the odd. They dissociate in two steps, the dissociation constant of the first being much greater than that of the second. Furthermore, the acid strength of the dicarboxylic acids decreases as the series is ascended.

The reactions of the dicarboxylic acids depend, to a large extent, on the length of the carbon chain. The dicarboxylic acids, therefore, will be described individually.

Oxalic acid (*ethanedioic acid*), $CO_2H\cdot CO_2H$, is one of the most important dicarboxylic acids. It occurs in rhubarb, in sorrel and other plants of the *oxalis* group (hence its name). Oxalic acid is one of the final products of oxidation of many organic compounds, *e.g.*, sugars, starch, etc., give oxalic acid when oxidised with concentrated nitric acid.

Preparation. (i) An industrial method which is now almost obsolete is to heat saw-dust with a mixture of sodium and potassium hydroxides in iron pans at 200–220° in air. On cooling, the mass is extracted with water and the aqueous solution treated with a calcium hydroxide solution. The calcium oxalate, which is precipitated, is collected by filtration and then decomposed by the calculated quantity of dilute sulphuric acid. The precipitated calcium sulphate is filtered off, and the filtrate evaporated to crystallisation; oxalic acid dihydrate crystallises out.

(ii) Oxalic acid is now prepared industrially by heating sodium formate rapidly to 360°.

$$2H{\cdot}CO_2Na \longrightarrow (CO_2Na)_2 + H_2$$

The free acid is obtained from its sodium salt by the procedure described in method (i).

(iii) The usual laboratory method for preparing oxalic acid is to oxidise sucrose with concentrated nitric acid in the presence of vanadium pentoxide as catalyst:

$$C_{12}H_{22}O_{11} + 18[O] \xrightarrow[V_2O_5]{HNO_3} 6(CO_2H)_2 + 5H_2O \quad (25\%)$$

(iv) Oxalic acid may be prepared by the hydrolysis of cyanogen, the hydrolysis being best carried out with concentrated hydrochloric acid:

$$C_2N_2 + 4H_2O + 2HCl \longrightarrow (CO_2H)_2 + 2NH_4Cl$$

(v) An interesting synthesis of oxalic acid is to heat sodium in a stream of carbon dioxide at 360°:

$$2CO_2 + 2Na \longrightarrow (CO_2Na)_2$$

Properties and reactions. Oxalic acid crystallises from water as colourless crystals with two molecules of water of crystallisation; the melting point of the hydrate is 101·5°; that of the anhydrous acid is 189·5°. Oxalic acid is poisonous, soluble in water and ethanol but almost insoluble in ether. The dihydrate loses water when heated at 100–105°, and when heated at about 200°, oxalic acid decomposes into carbon dioxide, carbon monoxide, formic acid and water:

$$(CO_2H)_2 \longrightarrow CO_2 + H{\cdot}CO_2H$$
$$(CO_2H)_2 \longrightarrow CO_2 + CO + H_2O$$

The anhydrous acid is conveniently obtained by heating the hydrate with carbon tetrachloride.

When heated with concentrated sulphuric acid at 90°, oxalic acid is decomposed:

$$(CO_2H)_2 \xrightarrow{H_2SO_4} CO + CO_2 + H_2O$$

It is oxidised by permanganate to carbon dioxide:

$$(CO_2H)_2 + [O] \longrightarrow 2CO_2 + H_2O$$

It is only very slowly oxidised by concentrated nitric acid. When fused with potassium hydroxide, it evolves hydrogen:

$$(CO_2K)_2 + 2KOH \longrightarrow 2K_2CO_3 + H_2$$

The anhydride of oxalic acid is unknown. When *anhydrous* oxalic acid is refluxed with ethanol, ethyl oxalate is formed:

$$(CO_2H)_2 + 2C_2H_5OH \longrightarrow (CO_2C_2H_5)_2 + 2H_2O \quad (80\text{–}90\%)$$

A more general method for preparing diesters is to heat a mixture of the dicarboxylic acid, alcohol, toluene and concentrated sulphuric acid. Sulphuric acid is the catalyst, and the toluene removes the water by forming a ternary azeotrope of alcohol, water and toluene; the yield of diester is 94–98 per cent. from oxalic to sebacic acid. The esterification may be carried out in the absence of toluene; a larger amount of sulphuric acid is required and the yields are lower (70–90 per cent.).

The ethyl and propyl esters of oxalic acid are liquid; the methyl ester is solid, and hence has been used to prepare pure methanol by hydrolysis with sodium hydroxide solution. Ethyl oxalate undergoes the Claisen condensation with esters containing two α-hydrogen atoms to form keto-esters, *e.g.*, with ethyl acetate, *oxalacetic ester* is formed:

$$C_2H_5O_2C{\cdot}CO_2C_2H_5 + CH_3{\cdot}CO_2C_2H_5 \xrightarrow[\text{ethanol}]{C_2H_5ONa \text{ in}}$$

$$\begin{matrix} CH{\cdot}CO_2C_2H_5 \\ \| \\ C(ONa){\cdot}CO_2C_2H_5 \end{matrix} \xrightarrow{CH_3{\cdot}CO_2H} \begin{matrix} CH_2{\cdot}CO_2C_2H_5 \\ | \\ CO{\cdot}CO_2C_2H_5 \end{matrix} \quad (60\text{–}70\%)$$

When oxalic acid is heated with ethylene glycol, the *cyclic* compound, *ethylene oxalate*, is obtained:

$$HOCH_2{\cdot}CH_2OH + HO_2C{\cdot}CO_2H \longrightarrow O\begin{matrix} \diagup CH_2{-}CH_2 \diagdown \\ \diagdown CO{-}{-}CO \diagup \end{matrix}O + 2H_2O$$

This reaction is characteristic of oxalic acid; the other dicarboxylic acids usually react with glycol to form polyesters (see p. 356). When oxalic acid is heated with glycerol, formic acid (p. 168) or allyl alcohol (p. 252) is obtained according to the conditions.

Oxalic acid forms the diamide, *oxamide*. This may be prepared by shaking ethyl oxalate with concentrated ammonium hydroxide solution:

$$C_2H_5O_2C{\cdot}CO_2C_2H_5 + 2NH_3 \longrightarrow NH_2{\cdot}CO{\cdot}CO{\cdot}NH_2 + 2C_2H_5OH$$

It may also be prepared by passing cyanogen into *cold* concentrated hydrochloric acid:

$$C_2N_2 + 2H_2O \xrightarrow{HCl} (CO{\cdot}NH_2)_2 \quad (50\%)$$

Oxamide exists as white needles, almost insoluble in water. In aqueous solution it slowly changes into ammonium oxalate, a change which is brought about rapidly by hydrochloric acid (on warming):

$$\begin{matrix} CO{\cdot}NH_2 \\ | \\ CO{\cdot}NH_2 \end{matrix} + 2H_2O \longrightarrow \begin{matrix} CO_2NH_4 \\ | \\ CO_2NH_4 \end{matrix}$$

When heated with phosphorus pentoxide, oxamide is dehydrated to cyanogen:

$$(CO{\cdot}NH_2)_2 \xrightarrow{P_2O_5} C_2N_2 + 2H_2O$$

The monoamide of oxalic acid is also known. It is called *oxamic acid*; the suffix of the names of all the monoamides of the dicarboxylic acids is *-amic*. Oxamic acid, m.p. 210°, may be prepared by the action of concentrated ammonium hydroxide solution on ethyl hydrogen oxalate, or by heating ammonium hydrogen oxalate.

When reduced with zinc and sulphuric acid, oxalic acid forms *glycollic acid*, $CH_2OH{\cdot}CO_2H$. Electrolytic reduction with a lead cathode gives glycollic and glyoxylic acids, the latter being obtained in better yield by reducing oxalic acid with magnesium and sulphuric acid.

When oxalic acid is treated with *excess* phosphorus pentachloride, *oxalyl chloride*, b.p. 64°, is formed:

$$(CO_2H)_2 \xrightarrow{PCl_5} (COCl)_2 \quad (\textit{f.-g.})$$

If an excess of phosphorus pentachloride is not used, oxalic acid is decomposed, possibly via the intermediate formation of the half acid chloride:

$$(CO_2H)_2 \xrightarrow{PCl_5} [CO_2H\cdot COCl] \longrightarrow CO_2 + CO + HCl$$

Paraffins can be carboxylated by oxalyl chloride under the influence of light (Kharasch and Brown, 1942):

$$RH + (COCl)_2 \longrightarrow R\cdot COCl + CO + HCl$$

Oxalic acid forms two series of salts, the normal, $(CO_2M)_2$, and the acid, $CO_2H\cdot CO_2M$ (M = univalent metal). Some acid salts crystallise with a molecule of free oxalic acid, *e.g.*, $CO_2K\cdot CO_2H\cdot (CO_2H)_2\cdot 2H_2O$; these are known as *tetroxalates*, and the potassium compound is used as a standard for bases and oxidising agents, since it can be prepared pure and does not deteriorate on standing. The heavy metal oxalates are insoluble in water but soluble in solutions of alkali oxalates due to the formation of complex compounds, *e.g.*, potassium oxalo-chromate, $[Cr(C_2O_4)_3]^{3-}H_3^{3+}$. These complexes are chelate compounds, and are optically active.

Oxalic acid is used for the manufacture of ink and for bleaching straw. Its antimony salts are used as mordants in printing and dyeing.

Malonic acid (*propanedioic acid*) $CO_2H\cdot CH_2\cdot CO_2H$, was first obtained by the oxidation of malic acid (hence its name):

$$CO_2H\cdot CHOH\cdot CH_2\cdot CO_2H + [O] \xrightarrow{K_2Cr_2O_7/H_2SO_4}$$

$$\underset{\text{oxalacetic acid}}{CO_2H\cdot CO\cdot CH_2\cdot CO_2H} \xrightarrow{[O]} CO_2H\cdot CH_2\cdot CO_2H + CO_2$$

Malonic acid may be prepared by heating potassium chloroacetate with aqueous potassium cyanide and hydrolysing the product, potassium cyanoacetate, with hydrochloric acid:

$$CH_2Cl\cdot CO_2K \xrightarrow{KCN} CH_2CN\cdot CO_2K \xrightarrow{H_2O} CH_2(CO_2H)_2 \quad (84\%)$$

Malonic acid is a crystalline solid, m.p. 135·6°, soluble in water and ethanol but only slightly soluble in ether. When heated to 140–150°, or when refluxed in sulphuric acid solution, it eliminates carbon dioxide:

$$CO_2H\cdot CH_2\cdot CO_2H \longrightarrow CH_3\cdot CO_2H + CO_2$$

All dicarboxylic acids which have both carboxyl groups attached to the same carbon atom are decomposed in a similar manner. When malonic acid is heated with phosphorus pentoxide, a small amount of *carbon suboxide* is obtained:

$$CO_2H\cdot CH_2\cdot CO_2H \xrightarrow{P_2O_5} O{:}C{:}C{:}C{:}O + 2H_2O$$

Carbon suboxide, b.p. 7°, may be regarded as a diketen; it combines with water to form malonic acid. Malonic acid does not form a cyclic anhydride, but dimethylmalonic acid does (*cf.* p. 464).

When malonic acid is treated with nitrous acid and the product hydrolysed, **mesoxalic acid** (*ketomalonic acid*) is obtained:

$$(HO_2C)_2CH_2 \xrightarrow{HNO_2} (HO_2C)_2C{:}N\cdot OH \xrightarrow{H_2O} CO_2H\cdot CO\cdot CO_2H$$

Mesoxalic acid crystallises from water with one molecule of water which is held firmly, and hence is believed to be water of constitution: $\begin{matrix}HO\\HO\end{matrix}\!\!>\!C(CO_2H)_2$ (*cf.*

glyoxylic acid). Ethyl malonate may be oxidised directly to ethyl mesoxalate by selenium dioxide (yield: 23 per cent.).

Ethyl malonate is far more important than the acid because of its synthetic uses; the acid contains an active methylene group, the reactivity of which is more pronounced in the ester. Both the acid and ester may be readily brominated, *e.g.*, monobromomalonic acid, $CHBr(CO_2H)_2$, is formed when a suspension of malonic acid in ether is treated with bromine; owing to the high reactivity of the methylene group, no red phosphorus is required as catalyst (*cf.* p. 196).

Ethyl malonate, curiously enough, does not form the diamide, *malonamide*, when shaken with concentrated ammonium hydroxide solution; the dimethyl ester, however, gives a good yield of malonamide. Ethyl malonate forms *barbituric acid* when heated with urea in the presence of sodium ethoxide (see p. 369).

Succinic acid (*butanedioic acid*), $CO_2H{\cdot}CH_2{\cdot}CH_2{\cdot}CO_2H$, was originally obtained by the distillation of amber (Latin: *succinum*, amber). It is also formed during the fermentation of sugar and other substances. Succinic acid may be synthesised by the following methods:

(i) From ethylene bromide:

$$\begin{array}{l}CH_2Br\\|\\CH_2Br\end{array}\xrightarrow{KCN}\begin{array}{l}CH_2{\cdot}CN\\|\\CH_2{\cdot}CN\end{array}\xrightarrow{H_2O}\begin{array}{l}CH_2{\cdot}CO_2H\\|\\CH_2{\cdot}CO_2H\end{array}\quad(80\%)$$

(ii) By the reaction between malonic ester (1 molecule) and ethyl chloroacetate, or between malonic ester (2 molecules) and iodine (see p. 220).

Alkyl-substituted succinic acids may be prepared by using monoalkyl-malonic ester and α-halogeno-acid esters or iodine. Alternatively, they may be prepared by the addition of hydrogen cyanide to αβ-unsaturated esters and hydrolysing the β-cyano-complex produced (see p. 262).

(iii) By heating malic acid, in a sealed tube, with constant boiling hydriodic acid and red phosphorus:

$$\begin{array}{l}CHOH{\cdot}CO_2H\\|\\CH_2{\cdot}CO_2H\end{array}+2HI\longrightarrow\begin{array}{l}CH_2{\cdot}CO_2H\\|\\CH_2{\cdot}CO_2H\end{array}+I_2+H_2O\quad(60\%)$$

Succinic acid is prepared industrially by the catalytic (or by the electrolytic) reduction of maleic acid:

$$\begin{array}{l}CH{\cdot}CO_2H\\||\\CH{\cdot}CO_2H\end{array}+H_2\xrightarrow{Ni}\begin{array}{l}CH_2{\cdot}CO_2H\\|\\CH_2{\cdot}CO_2H\end{array}$$

Succinic acid is a crystalline solid, m.p. 185°, moderately soluble in water and ethanol, but sparingly soluble in ether. When heated, a large amount sublimes, the rest being converted into the *inner* anhydride, succinic anhydride:

$$\begin{array}{l}CH_2{\cdot}CO_2H\\|\\CH_2{\cdot}CO_2H\end{array}\longrightarrow\begin{array}{l}CH_2{\cdot}CO\\|\\CH_2{\cdot}CO\end{array}\!\!\!>O+H_2O$$

When heated with excess of glycol, succinic acid forms high-polymer esters (*polyesters*, which belong to the group known as the *alkyd resins*—see p. 242). These esters are acidic, the end groups being succinic acid residues:

$$CO_2H{\cdot}(CH_2)_2{\cdot}CO_2H+HOCH_2{\cdot}CH_2OH+$$
$$HO_2C{\cdot}(CH_2)_2CO_2H+HOCH_2{\cdot}CH_2OH+\ldots$$
$$\longrightarrow CO_2H{\cdot}(CH_2)_2{\cdot}CO{-}[{-}O{\cdot}(CH_2)_2{\cdot}O{\cdot}CO{\cdot}(CH_2)_2{\cdot}CO{-}]{-}OH$$

The apparent molecular weight of this ester is about 3000 (Carothers, 1930). It has been found that the dicarboxylic acids from malonic to adipic acid form these polyesters with ethylene glycol. These esters are linear polymers, but if glycerol is used instead of glycol, three dimensional polymeric esters are obtained.

Succinic acid condenses with aldehydes; if both methylene groups are involved, *polyenes* are obtained by elimination of carbon dioxide:

$$\begin{matrix} R{\cdot}CHO \\ R{\cdot}CHO \end{matrix} + \begin{matrix} CH_2{\cdot}CO_2H \\ | \\ CH_2{\cdot}CO_2H \end{matrix} \longrightarrow \left[\begin{matrix} R{\cdot}CH{=}C{\cdot}CO_2H \\ | \\ R{\cdot}CH{=}C{\cdot}CO_2H \end{matrix}\right] \xrightarrow{-2CO_2} \begin{matrix} R{\cdot}CH{=}CH \\ | \\ R{\cdot}CH{=}CH \end{matrix}$$

Polyenes have the general formula $R{\cdot}(CH{:}CH)_n{\cdot}R$, and by using conjugated aldehydes the value of n can be made fairly large.

If only one methylene group in succinic acid reacts with the aldehyde, a *paraconic acid* is obtained:

$$R{\cdot}CHO + \begin{matrix} CH_2{\cdot}CO_2H \\ | \\ CH_2{\cdot}CO_2H \end{matrix} \longrightarrow \left[\begin{matrix} R{\cdot}CH{-}CH{\cdot}CO_2H \\ | \quad\quad | \\ OH \quad CH_2{\cdot}CO_2H \end{matrix}\right] \xrightarrow{-H_2O} \begin{matrix} R{\cdot}CH{-}{-}CH{\cdot}CO_2H \\ | \quad\quad | \\ O{-}{-}CO{\cdot}CH_2 \end{matrix}$$

When these paraconic acids are heated, $\beta\gamma$-unsaturated acids are obtained (see p. 264).

Succinic anhydride (*butanedioic anhydride*) is obtained in excellent yield by distilling succinic acid with acetic anhydride, acetyl chloride, or phosphoryl chloride. The anhydride, and not the acid chloride, is obtained when succinic acid is heated with thionyl chloride (see later).

Succinic anhydride is a white crystalline solid, m.p. 119°, and when boiled with water or alkalis, is converted into succinic acid:

$$\begin{matrix} CH_2{\cdot}CO \\ | \\ CH_2{\cdot}CO \end{matrix}\!\!>\!O + H_2O \longrightarrow \begin{matrix} CH_2{\cdot}CO_2H \\ | \\ CH_2{\cdot}CO_2H \end{matrix}$$

When reduced with sodium and ethanol, succinic anhydride is converted first into *γ-butyrolactone*, and finally into tetramethylene glycol:

$$\begin{matrix} CH_2{\cdot}CO \\ | \\ CH_2{\cdot}CO \end{matrix}\!\!>\!O \xrightarrow{[H]} \begin{matrix} CH_2{\cdot}CH_2 \\ | \\ CH_2{\cdot}CO \end{matrix}\!\!>\!O \xrightarrow{[H]} \begin{matrix} CH_2{\cdot}CH_2OH \\ | \\ CH_2{\cdot}CH_2OH \end{matrix}$$

If the reduction is carried out with sodium amalgam in *acid* solution, the lactone is obtained in good yield; some butyric acid is also formed.

Succinic anhydride is very useful for preparing the "half-derivatives" of succinic acid, *e.g.*, with alcohols it forms the acid-ester:

$$\begin{matrix} CH_2{\cdot}CO \\ | \\ CH_2{\cdot}CO \end{matrix}\!\!>\!O + ROH \longrightarrow \begin{matrix} CH_2{\cdot}CO_2R \\ | \\ CH_2{\cdot}CO_2H \end{matrix}$$

Succinimide (*butanimide*) is formed when succinic anhydride is heated in a current of dry ammonia:

$$\begin{matrix} CH_2{\cdot}CO \\ | \\ CH_2{\cdot}CO \end{matrix}\!\!>\!O + NH_3 \longrightarrow \begin{matrix} CH_2{\cdot}CO \\ | \\ CH_2{\cdot}CO \end{matrix}\!\!>\!NH + H_2O \quad (v.g.)$$

Succinamic acid (m.p. 157°), I, and *succinamide* (m.p. 243°), II, are both readily converted into succinimide when heated:

$$\underset{(I)}{\begin{matrix} CH_2{\cdot}CO{\cdot}NH_2 \\ | \\ CH_2{\cdot}CO_2H \end{matrix}} \xrightarrow{-H_2O} \begin{matrix} CH_2{\cdot}CO \\ | \\ CH_2{\cdot}CO \end{matrix}\!\!>\!NH \xleftarrow{-NH_3} \underset{(II)}{\begin{matrix} NH_2{\cdot}CO{\cdot}CH_2 \\ | \\ NH_2{\cdot}CO{\cdot}CH_2 \end{matrix}}$$

Succinimide is a white crystalline solid, m.p. 125°, readily soluble in water, and when boiled with water or alkalis is converted into succinic acid:

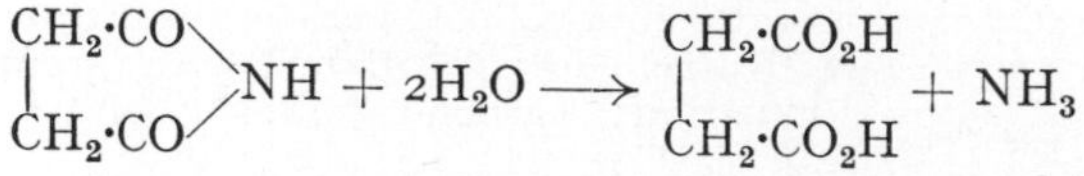

$$\begin{matrix} CH_2\cdot CO \\ | \\ CH_2\cdot CO \end{matrix}\Big\rangle NH + 2H_2O \longrightarrow \begin{matrix} CH_2\cdot CO_2H \\ | \\ CH_2\cdot CO_2H \end{matrix} + NH_3$$

When succinimide is distilled with zinc dust, *pyrrole*, (III), is obtained. When reduced with sodium and ethanol, succinimide forms *pyrrolidine*, (IV), and when reduced electrolytically, it forms *pyrrolidone*, (V):

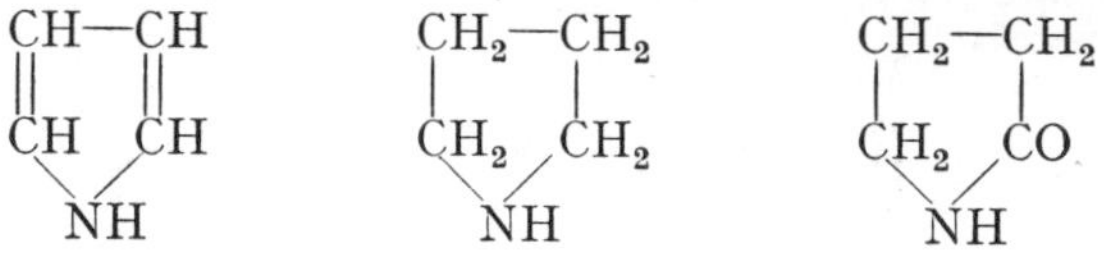

$$\begin{matrix} CH{-}CH \\ \| \quad \| \\ CH \quad CH \\ \diagdown \diagup \\ NH \\ \text{(III)} \end{matrix} \qquad \begin{matrix} CH_2{-}CH_2 \\ | \quad | \\ CH_2 \quad CH_2 \\ \diagdown \diagup \\ NH \\ \text{(IV)} \end{matrix} \qquad \begin{matrix} CH_2{-}CH_2 \\ | \quad | \\ CH_2 \quad CO \\ \diagdown \diagup \\ NH \\ \text{(V)} \end{matrix}$$

Succinimide is acidic, *e.g.*, it reacts with potassium hydroxide to form potassiosuccinimide, the formula of which may be (VI) or (VII):

$$\left[\begin{matrix} CH_2\cdot CO \\ | \\ CH_2\cdot CO \end{matrix}\Big\rangle \bar{N}\right]\overset{+}{K} \quad \text{(VI)} \qquad \left[\begin{matrix} CH_2\cdot C{-}\bar{O} \\ | \qquad \diagdown\!\!=N \\ CH_2\cdot CO \end{matrix}\right]\overset{+}{K} \quad \text{(VII)}$$

Succinimide, however, is only very weakly acidic; the potassium salt is decomposed by carbon dioxide, the imide being regenerated.

A very important derivative of succinimide is N-*bromosuccinimide*, which may be prepared by the action of bromine on succinimide at 0° in the presence of sodium hydroxide:

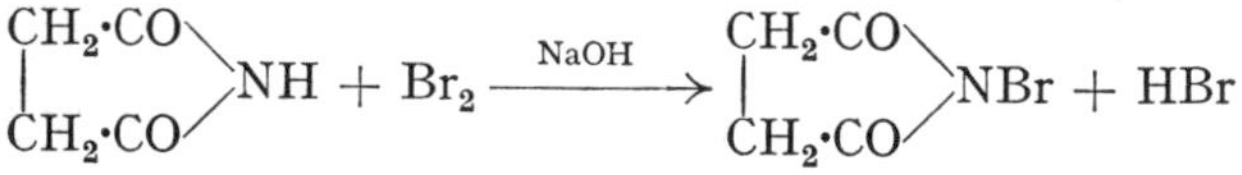

$$\begin{matrix} CH_2\cdot CO \\ | \\ CH_2\cdot CO \end{matrix}\Big\rangle NH + Br_2 \xrightarrow{\text{NaOH}} \begin{matrix} CH_2\cdot CO \\ | \\ CH_2\cdot CO \end{matrix}\Big\rangle NBr + HBr$$

N-bromosuccinimide is a valuable reagent for brominating olefinic compounds in the *allyl* position (Ziegler, 1942).

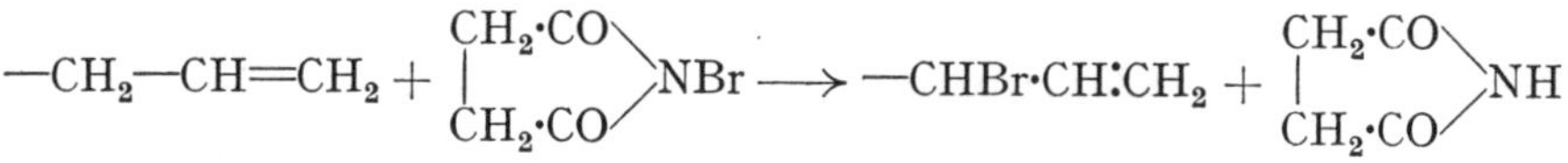

$$-CH_2{-}CH{=}CH_2 + \begin{matrix} CH_2\cdot CO \\ | \\ CH_2\cdot CO \end{matrix}\Big\rangle NBr \longrightarrow -CHBr\cdot CH{:}CH_2 + \begin{matrix} CH_2\cdot CO \\ | \\ CH_2\cdot CO \end{matrix}\Big\rangle NH$$

This reaction offers a means of splitting off *three* carbon atoms from a compound by oxidative degradation, provided the compound contains one double bond or can have one produced, *e.g.*,

$$R\cdot CH_2\cdot CH_2\cdot CH_2\cdot CH_2OH \xrightarrow[350^\circ]{Al_2O_3} R\cdot CH_2\cdot CH_2\cdot CH{:}CH_2 \xrightarrow{N\text{-bromosuccinimide}}$$

$$R\cdot CH_2\cdot CHBr\cdot CH{:}CH_2 \xrightarrow[\text{ethanol}]{\text{KOH}} R\cdot CH{:}CH\cdot CH{:}CH_2 \xrightarrow{\text{ozonolysis}} R\cdot CHO$$

This method has found great use in steroid chemistry.

Normally, *N*-bromosuccinimide *substitutes* olefins in the allyl position, and this reaction is believed to take place by a free-radical mechanism; it is catalysed by peroxides and is promoted by light (both are free-radical producing agents). Bloomfield (1944) proposed the following chain-reaction:

$$>N—Br \longrightarrow >N\cdot + Br\cdot$$

$$>CH—CH{=}CH_2 + >N\cdot \longrightarrow >\dot{C}—CH{=}CH_2 + >NH$$

$$>\dot{C}—CH{=}CH_2 + >N—Br \longrightarrow >CBr—CH{=}CH_2 + >N\cdot, \text{ etc.}$$

N-Bromosuccinimide also brominates unsaturated esters, *e.g.*,

$$CH_3\cdot CH{=}CH\cdot CO_2CH_3 \xrightarrow{>N—Br} CH_2Br\cdot CH{=}CH\cdot CO_2CH_3$$

In addition to substitution, *N*-bromosuccinimide may also produce *addition* compounds, but these are usually formed only in small amount. Braude *et al.* (1952), however, have shown that the *addition* reaction is catalysed by tetra-alkylammonium salts, *e.g.*, *N*-bromosuccinimide and *cyclo*hexene give 3-bromo*cyclo*hexene (Ziegler *et al.*, 1942), but in the presence of, *e.g.*, tetraethylammonium bromide, 1 : 2-dibromo*cyclo*hexane is the main product.

(80–90%) [3-bromocyclohexene: ring CHBr, CH, CH, CH_2, H_2C, H_2C] $\xleftarrow{\text{substitution}}$ [cyclohexene: ring CH_2, CH=CH, CH_2, H_2C, H_2C] $\xrightarrow{\text{addition}}$ [1:2-dibromocyclohexane: ring CH_2, CHBr, CHBr, CH_2, H_2C, H_2C] (74%)

The addition reaction probably involves heterolytic fission:

$$>N—Br + >C{=}C< \longrightarrow >\overset{-}{N} + Br—\overset{|}{C}—\overset{|}{C}+ \xrightarrow{>N—Br} Br—\overset{|}{C}—\overset{|}{C}—Br + >\overset{-}{N} + >\overset{+}{N}$$

$$\longrightarrow 2>N\cdot \xrightarrow[\text{donor}]{\text{hydrogen}} 2>N—H$$

N-Bromosuccinimide can also behave as an oxidising agent; it will oxidise primary alcohols (and primary amines) to aldehydes, and secondary alcohols to ketones (Barakat *et al.*, 1952), *e.g.*,

$$C_2H_5OH + >NBr \longrightarrow CH_3\cdot CHO + >NH + HBr$$

$$(CH_3)_2CHOH + >NBr \longrightarrow (CH_3)_2CO + >NH + HBr$$

Succinyl chloride (butanedioyl chloride). When succinic acid is treated with a *large excess* of phosphorus pentachloride, a good yield of the *symmetrical acid chloride*, $(CH_2\cdot COCl)_2$, is obtained. This is also obtained by heating succinic acid with thionyl chloride *in the presence of a small amount of zinc chloride* (*cf.* succinic anhydride). On the other hand, when succinic acid is heated with phosphorus pentachloride *not in excess*, a small amount of the *s*-acid chloride is obtained; the main product is the *as*-acid chloride. The evidence for the structures of these acid chlorides is shown by the products formed by their reaction with benzene in the presence of anhydrous aluminium chloride. One (the *s*-) gives $C_6H_5\cdot CO\cdot CH_2\cdot CH_2\cdot CO\cdot C_6H_5$ and the other (the *as*-), $(C_6H_5)_2\overset{|}{C}\cdot CH_2\cdot CH_2\cdot \overset{|}{C}O$ (ring closed through —O—).

$$\begin{array}{l} CH_2\cdot CCl_2 \\ | \qquad\quad >O \\ CH_2\cdot CO \end{array}$$

Isomeric with succinic acid is methylmalonic acid or iso*succinic acid*, $CO_2H{\cdot}CH(CH_3){\cdot}CO_2H$, m.p. 130°. It may be readily prepared from sodiomalonic ester and methyl iodide, or as follows:

$$CH_3{\cdot}CH_2{\cdot}CO_2H \xrightarrow{Br_2/P} CH_3{\cdot}CHBr{\cdot}CO_2H \xrightarrow{KCN}$$
$$CH_3{\cdot}CH(CN){\cdot}CO_2H \xrightarrow{H_2O} CH_3{\cdot}CH(CO_2H)_2$$

Oxalacetic ester, $C_2H_5O_2C{\cdot}CO{\cdot}CH_2{\cdot}CO_2C_2H_5$, is the diethyl ester of ketosuccinic acid, and may be prepared by the Claisen condensation between ethyl oxalate and ethyl acetate (see p. 354). It is a colourless liquid which can be distilled under reduced pressure (b.p. 132°/24 mm.), but at atmospheric pressure it eliminates a molecule of carbon monoxide to form malonic ester:

$$C_2H_5O_2C{\cdot}CO{\cdot}CH_2{\cdot}CO_2C_2H_5 \longrightarrow CH_2(CO_2C_2H_5)_2 + CO$$

Hydrogen of the methylene group adjacent to the carbonyl group may be replaced by alkyl groups by reactions similar to those used for acetoacetic ester, *e.g.*,

$$C_2H_5O_2C{\cdot}CO{\cdot}CH_2{\cdot}CO_2C_2H_5 \xrightarrow{C_2H_5ONa} [C_2H_5O_2C{\cdot}CO{\cdot}CH{\cdot}CO_2C_2H_5]^-Na^+ \xrightarrow{CH_3I}$$
$$C_2H_5O_2C{\cdot}CO{\cdot}CH(CH_3){\cdot}CO_2C_2H_5 \xrightarrow[\text{(ii) } C_2H_5I]{\text{(i) } C_2H_5ONa} C_2H_5O_2C{\cdot}CO{\cdot}C(CH_3)(C_2H_5){\cdot}CO_2C_2H_5$$

Oxalacetic ester and its alkyl derivatives undergo " acid hydrolysis " when boiled with alkalis, and " ketonic hydrolysis " when boiled with dilute sulphuric acid.

Acid hydrolysis

$$C_2H_5O_2C{\cdot}CO{\cdot}CHR{\cdot}CO_2C_2H_5 \xrightarrow{NaOH} (CO_2H)_2 + R{\cdot}CH_2{\cdot}CO_2H + 2C_2H_5OH$$

Ketonic hydrolysis

$$C_2H_5O_2C{\cdot}CO{\cdot}CHR{\cdot}CO_2C_2H_5 \xrightarrow{H_2SO_4} [CO_2H{\cdot}CO{\cdot}CHR{\cdot}CO_2H] \longrightarrow$$
$$CO_2 + R{\cdot}CH_2{\cdot}CO{\cdot}CO_2H$$

Oxalacetic ester may be used to prepare citric acid by means of the Reformatsky reaction (see p. 401).

Hydrolysis of oxalacetic ester with concentrated hydrochloric acid in the cold gives *oxalacetic acid* (*ketosuccinic acid*):

$$C_2H_5O_2C{\cdot}CO{\cdot}CH_2{\cdot}CO_2C_2H_5 + 2H_2O \xrightarrow{HCl} CO_2H{\cdot}CO{\cdot}CH_2{\cdot}CO_2H + 2C_2H_5OH$$

A simpler preparation of oxalacetic acid is to oxidise maleic acid with Fenton's reagent.

Oxalacetic acid is a fairly stable substance, soluble in water, the aqueous solution giving a red coloration with ferric chloride, thus indicating the existence of an enolic form. Oxalacetic acid exists in two forms, one with m.p. 155° and the other 184°. These two forms are actually *hydroxymaleic acid*, I, and *hydroxyfumaric acid*, II, respectively:

$$\begin{array}{c} H{-}C{-}CO_2H \\ \| \\ HO{-}C{-}CO_2H \\ \text{(I)} \end{array} \qquad\qquad \begin{array}{c} HO_2C{-}C{-}H \\ \| \\ HO{-}C{-}CO_2H \\ \text{(II)} \end{array}$$

I is convertible into II by 30 per cent. sulphuric acid, and the salts of II give I on treatment with dilute acid. It is doubtful whether oxalacetic acid exists in the keto form.

Glutaric acid (*pentanedioic acid*), $CO_2H{\cdot}(CH_2)_3{\cdot}CO_2H$ (relationship to *glu*tamic acid and tar*taric* acid gave rise to its name), may be prepared by a number of methods, *e.g.*,

(i) By refluxing trimethylene cyanide with concentrated hydrochloric acid:

$$NC{\cdot}(CH_2)_3{\cdot}CN + 4H_2O \xrightarrow{HCl} CO_2H{\cdot}(CH_2)_3{\cdot}CO_2H + 2NH_3 \quad (83\text{–}85\%)$$

(ii) By the action of methylene iodide on sodiomalonic ester:

$$2[CH(CO_2C_2H_5)_2]^-Na^+ + CH_2I_2 \longrightarrow 2NaI + CH_2[CH(CO_2C_2H_5)_2]_2$$

$$\xrightarrow[\text{(ii) HCl}]{\text{(i) KOH}} CH_2[CH(CO_2H)_2]_2 \xrightarrow{150-200^\circ} CO_2H\cdot(CH_2)_3\cdot CO_2H + 2CO_2$$

(iii) By condensing formaldehyde with malonic ester in the presence of diethylamine:

$$(C_2H_5O_2C)_2CH_2 + \overset{CH_2}{\overset{\|}{O}} + CH_2(CO_2C_2H_5)_2 \xrightarrow[\text{reflux}]{(C_2H_5)_2NH} (C_2H_5O_2C)_2CH\cdot CH_2\cdot CH(CO_2C_2H_5)_2 \quad (61\%)$$

This tetracarboxylic ester may now be treated as in (ii), or may be converted into glutaric acid directly by refluxing with concentrated hydrochloric acid:

$$(C_2H_5O_2C)_2CH\cdot CH_2\cdot CH(CO_2C_2H_5)_2 \xrightarrow{HCl} CO_2H\cdot(CH_2)_3\cdot CO_2H \quad (76-80\%)$$

Glutaric acid is a crystalline solid, m.p. 97°. When heated with acetic anhydride or thionyl chloride, it is converted into glutaric anhydride:

$$CH_2\begin{cases} CH_2\cdot CO_2H \\ CH_2\cdot CO_2H \end{cases} \longrightarrow CH_2\begin{cases} CH_2-CO \\ CH_2-CO \end{cases}\!\!\!>O + H_2O$$

Succinic and glutaric acids differ from their higher homologues in that they readily form the cyclic anhydride when heated with acetic anhydride.

Adipic acid (*hexanedioic acid*), $CO_2H\cdot(CH_2)_4\cdot CO_2H$, received its name from the fact that it was first obtained by the oxidation of fats (Latin: *adeps*, fat). It may be synthesised from sodiomalonic ester and ethylene bromide (see p. 219), but is prepared industrially by the oxidation of *cyclo*hexanol with concentrated nitric acid, preferably in the presence of ammonium vanadate as catalyst:

$$\text{cyclohexanol (CHOH; } H_2C, CH_2, H_2C, CH_2, CH_2) \xrightarrow{[O]} \text{cyclohexanone (CO; } H_2C, CH_2, H_2C, CH_2, CH_2) \xrightarrow{[O]} CO_2H\cdot(CH_2)_4\cdot CO_2H \quad (58-60\%)$$

If selenium dioxide is used as catalyst instead of ammonium vanadate, the yield of adipic acid is 74 per cent. (Putnik, 1947).

A potential commercial source of adipic acid is the reaction between tetrahydrofuran, carbon monoxide and water:

$$\begin{matrix} CH_2\cdot CH_2 \\ | \\ CH_2\cdot CH_2 \end{matrix}\!\!>O + 2CO + H_2O \longrightarrow \begin{matrix} CH_2\cdot CH_2\cdot CO_2H \\ | \\ CH_2\cdot CH_2\cdot CO_2H \end{matrix}$$

Adipic acid is a crystalline solid, m.p. 150°. When heated with acetic anhydride, it forms a *linear polymeric anhydride*:

$$CO_2H\cdot(CH_2)_4\cdot CO_2H + CO_2H\cdot(CH_2)_4\cdot CO_2H + \cdots \longrightarrow$$

$$CO_2H\cdot(CH_2)_4\cdot\overset{O}{\overset{\|}{C}}-O-\left[-\overset{O}{\overset{\|}{C}}-(CH_2)_4-\overset{O}{\overset{\|}{C}}-O-\right]_n-\overset{O}{\overset{\|}{C}}-(CH_2)_4\cdot CO_2H$$

When this polymer is distilled *under reduced pressure*, the monomeric adipic anhydride, $(CH_2)_4\langle{CO \atop CO}\rangle O$, is obtained; this monomer very readily polymerises on heating. If the polymeric anhydride is heated in a *molecular still*, a " super-polymer ", *i.e.*, a polymer of very high molecular weight, is obtained as the residue, the distillate being the cyclic monomer or dimer.

All the dicarboxylic acids, $CO_2H{\cdot}(CH_2)_n{\cdot}CO_2H$, where n has a value 4 to 12, behave as adipic acid (Hill and Carothers, 1933).

On the other hand, when adipic and pimelic acids are heated with acetic anhydride and the product distilled at 300°, a cyclic *ketone* is obtained in each case:

$$(CH_2)_4\langle{CO_2H \atop CO_2H} \xrightarrow{300^\circ} {CH_2{\cdot}CH_2 \atop CH_2{\cdot}CH_2}\rangle CO$$

*cyclo*pentanone

$$(CH_2)_5\langle{CO_2H \atop CO_2H} \xrightarrow{300^\circ} CH_2\langle{CH_2{-}CH_2 \atop CH_2{-}CH_2}\rangle CO$$

*cyclo*hexanone

Adipic acid is used for the preparation of resins (polyesters), and is an intermediate in the manufacture of *nylon*. Nylon is used as the generic name for all synthetic fibre-forming polymeric amides having a protein-like structure. Nylon yarns and fabrics are practically non-inflammable. The most important example of a polyamide is that formed from adipic acid and hexamethylenediamine:

$$CO_2H{\cdot}(CH_2)_4{\cdot}CO_2H + H_2N{\cdot}(CH_2)_6{\cdot}NH_2 + HO_2C{\cdot}(CH_2)_4{\cdot}CO_2H + H_2N{-}{-}{-}{-}\longrightarrow$$
$$CO_2H{\cdot}(CH_2)_4{\cdot}CO{-}[{-}NH{\cdot}(CH_2)_6{\cdot}NH{\cdot}CO{\cdot}(CH_2)_4{\cdot}CO{-}]_n{-}NH{\cdot}(CH_2)_6{\cdot}NH_2$$

Pimelic acid (*heptanedioic acid*), $CO_2H{\cdot}(CH_2)_5{\cdot}CO_2H$, m.p. 104°, received its name from the fact that it was obtained originally from the oxidation of fats (Greek: *pimele*, fat). It may be prepared by the hydrolysis of pentamethylene cyanide (formed by the action of potassium cyanide on pentamethylene bromide), or by the malonic ester synthesis, using trimethylene bromide (cf. adipic acid). A most remarkable method of preparing pimelic acid is the reduction of salicylic acid with sodium and *iso*pentanol, followed by the addition of water and then hydrochloric acid; the mechanism of this reaction is obscure (see p. 653):

$$C_6H_4(OH)CO_2H + H_2O + 4[H] \longrightarrow CO_2H{\cdot}(CH_2)_5{\cdot}CO_2H \quad (43\text{–}50\%)$$

Suberic acid (*octanedioic acid*), $CO_2H{\cdot}(CH_2)_6{\cdot}CO_2H$, m.p. 144°, may be synthesised by the electrolysis of potassium ethyl glutarate (*cf.* p. 351). It is prepared industrially by the oxidation of cork (Latin: *suber*, cork) with concentrated nitric acid. A potential commercial source is the oxidation of *cyclo*-octane obtained by the catalytic reduction of *cyclo*-octatetraene (see p. 461).

Azelaic acid (*nonanedioic acid*), $CO_2H{\cdot}(CH_2)_7{\cdot}CO_2H$, m.p. 107°, may be synthesised from malonic ester and pentamethylene bromide. It may be obtained in the laboratory by refluxing castor oil with ethanolic potassium hydroxide, acidifying with sulphuric acid, and oxidising the crude ricinoleic acid so obtained with alkaline permanganate:

$$CH_3{\cdot}(CH_2)_5{\cdot}CHOH{\cdot}CH_2{\cdot}CH{=}CH{\cdot}(CH_2)_7{\cdot}CO_2H \xrightarrow{[O]} CO_2H{\cdot}(CH_2)_7{\cdot}CO_2H \quad (32\text{–}36\%)$$

Azelaic acid is prepared industrially by the oxidation of oleic acid with concentrated nitric acid (p. 268).

Sebacic acid (*decanedioic acid*), $CO_2H{\cdot}(CH_2)_8{\cdot}CO_2H$, m.p. 133°, is prepared industrially by heating castor oil with sodium hydroxide.

$$CH_3{\cdot}(CH_2)_5{\cdot}CHOH{\cdot}CH_2{\cdot}CH{=}CH{\cdot}(CH_2)_7{\cdot}CO_2Na \xrightarrow{NaOH} CO_2Na{\cdot}(CH_2)_8{\cdot}CO_2Na + C_6H_{13}{\cdot}CHOH{\cdot}CH_3$$

Many higher dicarboxylic acids are known.

The acid esters of the dicarboxylic acids may be prepared by refluxing a mixture of the acid with half its equivalent of the di-ester in the presence of concentrated hydrochloric acid. This is an example of acidolysis (p. 180). Alternatively, the acid ester may be obtained by the half saponification of the di-ester. In either case the di-ester is separated from the acid ester by fractional distillation.

When the calcium, barium, or better still, the thorium salts of the carboxylic acids from adipic to nonadecanedioic are distilled, varying yields of cyclic ketones are obtained; *e.g.*, adipic acid gives *cyclo*pentanone:

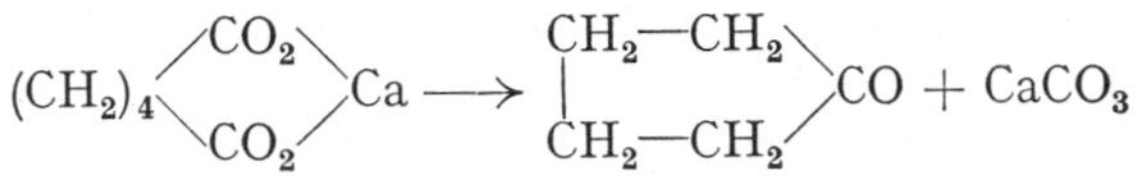

$$(CH_2)_4\begin{matrix} CO_2 \\ CO_2 \end{matrix}Ca \longrightarrow \begin{matrix} CH_2{-}CH_2 \\ | \\ CH_2{-}CH_2 \end{matrix}CO + CaCO_3$$

The best yields of cyclic ketones are obtained for the five- and six-membered rings, *i.e.*, from adipic and pimelic acids respectively. This has some bearing on the problem of *Baeyer's Strain Theory* (p. 463).

Based on the experimental results of the ease of formation of cyclic anhydrides and cyclic ketones, is **Blanc's rule** (1905). Blanc found that dicarboxylic acids, on heating with acetic anhydride, and then distilling at 300° (or distilling directly at 300°), gave cyclic anhydrides or cyclic ketones according to the relative positions of the two carboxyl groups. 1 : 4- and 1 : 5-dicarboxylic acids gave cyclic anhydrides; 1 : 6- and 1 : 7- gave cyclic ketones: this is Blanc's rule. By using Blanc's rule it is possible to determine the size of rings. A double bond is introduced into the ring, and the ring opened by oxidation to the corresponding dicarboxylic acid. This is then heated with acetic anhydride and distilled. If a cyclic anhydride is obtained, the acid is either 1 : 4- or 1 : 5-; if a cyclic ketone, either 1 : 6- or 1 : 7-; if there is no change, the acid is 1 : 8- or more. In naturally occurring compounds the rings are usually five- or six-membered. Hence the formation of the anhydride is taken to mean a five-membered ring, and of the ketone a six-membered ring.

In certain cases, however, Blanc's rule is misleading, *e.g.*, in the investigation of sterols, wrong information on the structure was obtained because of the abnormal Blanc reaction in these compounds. It has been found that substituents in the chain bring about ring closure much more easily; *e.g.*, substituted adipic acids may give rise to the anhydride and not to the cyclic ketone. Hence in polynuclear compounds such as sterols (which have the skeleton shown), if ring B is opened, the resulting dicarboxylic acid is, in effect, a substituted adipic acid:

A B C D ⟶ A C D CO_2H CO_2H

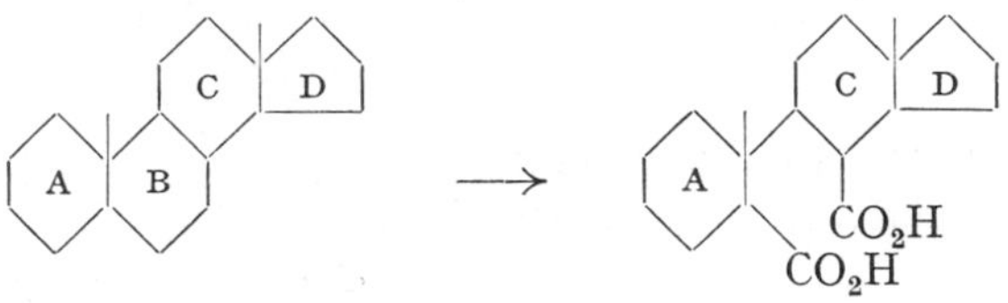

This, when distilled, gives the anhydride and not the expected ketone. Thus, in sterols, one of the rings (B) was thought to be five-membered when

Blanc's rule was used. Further work showed it was six-membered. Blanc's rule is only satisfactory for simple cyclic compounds (see pp. 463–465).

CARBONIC ACID AND ITS DERIVATIVES

Orthocarbonic acid, $C(OH)_4$, is unknown in the free state, but its esters have been prepared. They may be obtained by the reaction between sodium alkoxide and nitrochloroform:

$$4RONa + CCl_3 \cdot NO_2 \longrightarrow C(OR)_4 + 3NaCl + NaNO_2$$

The alkyl orthocarbonates are ethereal smelling liquids.

Carbonic acid (*metacarbonic acid*), $O{:}C(OH)_2$, is unknown in the free state, but its salts and esters have been prepared. Alkyl carbonates may be readily formed by heating alcohols with carbonyl chloride:

$$COCl_2 + 2ROH \longrightarrow CO(OR)_2 + 2HCl$$

They may also be prepared by heating silver carbonate with alkyl iodide:

$$Ag_2CO_3 + 2RI \longrightarrow CO(OR)_2 + 2AgI$$

The alkyl carbonates are ethereal smelling liquids, readily soluble in water. In recent years they have found various uses in organic synthesis, *e.g.*,

(i) They may be used to introduce the carbalkoxy group, CO_2R, into ketones to produce β-ketoesters. The reaction is carried out by heating a ketone with sodium or sodium alkoxide in the presence of a large excess of alkyl carbonate:

$$R' \cdot CO \cdot CH_3 + (RO)_2CO + NaOR \longrightarrow$$
$$[R' \cdot CO \cdot CH \cdot CO_2R]^- Na^+ + 2ROH \xrightarrow{H_2O} R' \cdot CO \cdot CH_2 \cdot CO_2R$$

(ii) Alkyl carbonates react with primary alkyl cyanides in the presence of sodium alkoxide to form α-cyanoesters:

$$R' \cdot CH_2 \cdot CN + (RO)_2CO + NaOR \longrightarrow$$
$$[R' \cdot C(CN) \cdot CO_2R]^- Na^+ + 2ROH \xrightarrow{H_2O} R' \cdot CH(CN) \cdot CO_2R$$

(iii) Alkyl carbonates may be used to alkylate sodiomalonic esters:

$$[R'C(CO_2C_2H_5)_2]^- Na^+ + (RO)_2CO \longrightarrow RR'C(CO_2C_2H_5)_2 + RO \cdot CO \cdot ONa$$

The acid chloride of carbonic acid is *carbonyl chloride* (*phosgene*), $COCl_2$. It may be obtained by the action of chlorine on carbon monoxide under the influence of sunlight, or in the presence of heated charcoal (200°) as catalyst; the latter is the commercial method. Carbonyl chloride may also be obtained by the action of oleum containing 45 per cent. free sulphur trioxide on carbon tetrachloride at 78°:

$$2SO_3 + CCl_4 \longrightarrow COCl_2 + \underset{\text{pyrosulphuryl chloride}}{S_2O_5Cl_2}$$

Carbonyl chloride is a colourless liquid, b.p. 8°, and has been used as a toxic gas in warfare. It is used in various organic syntheses, behaving as an acid chloride, but is not so reactive as might have been expected (*cf.* *gem*-dihalides, p. 105). It is very slowly decomposed by water:

$$COCl_2 + H_2O \longrightarrow CO_2 + 2HCl$$

When treated with slight excess of one equivalent of alcohol in the cold, carbonyl chloride forms chloroformic esters:

$$COCl_2 + ROH \longrightarrow Cl{\cdot}CO_2R + HCl$$

When treated with an excess of alcohol in the presence of pyridine, alkyl carbonates are formed:

$$COCl_2 + 2ROH \longrightarrow CO(OR)_2 + 2HCl$$

Carbonyl chloride reacts with ammonia to form urea:

$$COCl_2 + 2NH_3 \longrightarrow CO(NH_2)_2 + 2HCl$$

With primary or secondary amines, substituted ureas are formed, *e.g.*,

$$COCl_2 + 2R{\cdot}NH_2 \longrightarrow CO(NH{\cdot}R)_2 + 2HCl$$

Chloroformic acid (*chlorocarbonic acid*), $Cl{\cdot}CO_2H$, is not known in the free state, but its esters have been prepared. These may be readily obtained by treating carbonyl chloride with slight excess of one equivalent of alcohol in the cold (see above). Chloroformic esters are acid-chloride esters, and the chlorine atom reacts with compounds containing active hydrogen; thus ethyl chloroformate, b.p. 94°, reacts with water, alcohols, ammonia, primary and secondary amines; *e.g.*, urethan is formed with ammonia:

$$Cl{\cdot}CO_2C_2H_5 + NH_3 \longrightarrow NH_2{\cdot}CO_2C_2H_5 + HCl$$

Ethyl chloroformate is useful for introducing the carbethoxy group on a nitrogen atom; *e.g.*, ethyl-*N*-tricarboxylate is formed when ethyl chloroformate is added to a mixture of urethan, ether and sodium, this mixture having been previously heated:

$$NH_2{\cdot}CO_2C_2H_5 + 2Cl{\cdot}CO_2C_2H_5 + 2Na \longrightarrow N(CO_2C_2H_5)_3 + 2NaCl + H_2 \quad (51\text{–}57\%)$$

Ethyl chloroformate may also be used to prepare ethyl esters by reaction with Grignard reagents (p. 340).

Amides of carbonic acid. Since carbonic acid is dibasic, two amides are possible: the mono- and diamide. These are known, respectively, as *carbamic acid*, (I), and *urea*, (II):

$$O{=}C\begin{matrix}\diagup NH_2\\ \diagdown OH\end{matrix} \qquad\qquad O{=}C\begin{matrix}\diagup NH_2\\ \diagdown NH_2\end{matrix}$$

(I) (II)

Carbamic acid, $NH_2{\cdot}CO_2H$, is not known in the free state, but its salts and esters have been prepared. Ammonium carbamate is formed when dry ammonia reacts with dry carbon dioxide:

$$2NH_3 + CO_2 \longrightarrow NH_2{\cdot}CO{\cdot}ONH_4$$

It is a white crystalline solid, very soluble in water. When its aqueous solution is warmed to 60°, ammonium carbamate is hydrolysed to ammonium carbonate:

$$NH_2{\cdot}CO{\cdot}ONH_4 + H_2O \longrightarrow CO(ONH_4)_2$$

Esters of carbamic acid are known as **urethans.** These may be prepared:

(i) By treating a chloroformic ester with ammonia, *e.g.*, ethyl chloroformate produces ethyl carbamate:

$$Cl{\cdot}CO_2C_2H_5 + NH_3 \longrightarrow NH_2{\cdot}CO_2C_2H_5 + HCl$$

(ii) By refluxing urea in an alcohol, *e.g.*, *n*-butanol gives *n*-butyl carbamate when refluxed for 30 hours:

$$CO(NH_2)_2 \longrightarrow NH_3 + HNCO$$

$$HNCO + CH_3{\cdot}CH_2{\cdot}CH_2{\cdot}CH_2OH \longrightarrow NH_2{\cdot}CO_2CH_2{\cdot}CH_2{\cdot}CH_2{\cdot}CH_3 \quad (75\text{–}76\%)$$

(iii) *N*-substituted urethans may be prepared by the Curtius reaction (p. 195). The acid azide is refluxed in benzene solution and then an alcohol is added:

$$R{\cdot}CO{\cdot}N_3 \longrightarrow N_2 + R{\cdot}NCO \xrightarrow{R'OH} R{\cdot}NH{\cdot}CO_2R'$$

N-phenyl urethans may be prepared by reaction between phenyl *iso*cyanate and alcohol:

$$C_6H_5{\cdot}NCO + ROH \longrightarrow C_6H_5{\cdot}NH{\cdot}CO_2R$$

These are crystalline solids and may be used to characterise the alcohols.

Ethyl carbamate, usually known as *urethan*, is a crystalline solid, m.p. 50°. It reacts with ammonia to form urea:

$$NH_2{\cdot}CO_2C_2H_5 + NH_3 \longrightarrow CO(NH_2)_2 + C_2H_5OH$$

It is decomposed by aqueous sodium hydroxide on warming:

$$NH_2{\cdot}CO_2C_2H_5 + 2NaOH \longrightarrow Na_2CO_3 + NH_3 + C_2H_5OH$$

Ethyl carbamate has hypnotic properties; many urethans are valuable hypnotics, *e.g.*, *aponal* (*tert.*-amyl carbamate, *tert.*-amyl urethan), $NH_2{\cdot}COOC(CH_3)_2(C_2H_5)$

Urea (*carbamide*), $NH_2{\cdot}CO{\cdot}NH_2$, is very important physiologically. It is the chief nitrogenous product of protein metabolism; adults excrete about 30 g. per day in the urine, from which it can be extracted by evaporating the urine to small bulk and adding nitric acid, whereupon the slightly soluble urea nitrate, $CO(NH_2)_2{\cdot}HNO_3$, is precipitated. Urea is historically very important because Wöhler (1828) synthesised it by evaporating a solution containing potassium *iso*cyanate and ammonium sulphate; ammonium *iso*cyanate, which is formed first, undergoes molecular rearrangement:

$$NH_4{\cdot}NCO \rightleftharpoons CO(NH_2)_2$$

The reaction is reversible; the solution contains about 5 per cent. ammonium *iso*cyanate.

Urea may be prepared in the laboratory by the action of ammonia on carbonyl chloride, alkyl carbonates, chloroformates or urethans, *e.g.*,

$$COCl_2 + 2NH_3 \longrightarrow CO(NH_2)_2 + 2HCl \quad (f.)$$

$$(C_2H_5O)_2CO + 2NH_3 \longrightarrow CO(NH_2)_2 + 2C_2H_5OH \quad (f.)$$

Industrially, urea is prepared:

(i) By the partial hydrolysis of cyanamide in feebly acid solution:

$$H_2N{\cdot}CN + H_2O \longrightarrow CO(NH_2)_2$$

(ii) By allowing liquid carbon dioxide and liquid ammonia to interact, and heating the ammonium carbamate so formed to 130–150° under about 35 atm. pressure:

$$2NH_3 + CO_2 \longrightarrow NH_2{\cdot}CO{\cdot}ONH_4 \longrightarrow CO(NH_2)_2 + H_2O$$

Structure of urea. Although urea appears to be a simple molecule, it is only recently that its structure has been ascertained with any degree of certainty. The diamide structure, $CO(NH_2)_2$, seems to be indicated by its synthesis from carbonyl chloride and ammonia:

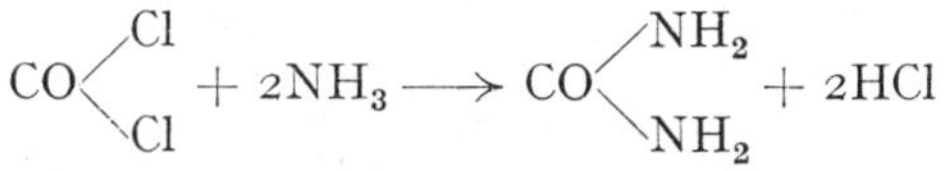

$$CO\begin{matrix}\diagup Cl\\ \diagdown Cl\end{matrix} + 2NH_3 \longrightarrow CO\begin{matrix}\diagup NH_2\\ \diagdown NH_2\end{matrix} + 2HCl$$

In some respects urea appears to behave as a diamide, but not in others, *e.g.*, it forms *stable* salts with strong inorganic acids—*amides* do not form stable salts. Furthermore, a peculiar feature of urea salts is that only *one* molecule of monobasic acid is present, *e.g.*, $CO(NH_2)_2 \cdot HCl$. This was explained by assuming that urea was tautomeric, (I) being the neutral amide (urea) and (II) the basic amidine (*iso*urea):

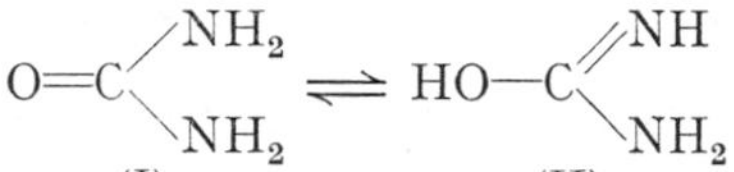

$$\underset{\text{(I)}}{O{=}C\begin{matrix}\diagup NH_2\\ \diagdown NH_2\end{matrix}} \rightleftharpoons \underset{\text{(II)}}{HO{-}C\begin{matrix}{/\!\!/} NH\\ \diagdown NH_2\end{matrix}}$$

The amidine structure is not possible with other amides; also amidines are much stronger bases than amides, and it was believed that it was the amidine form that produced the salts, *e.g.*, (III). Still another structure was suggested by Werner (1913), *viz.*, (IV).

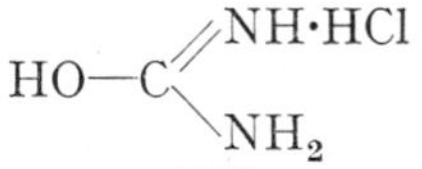

$$\underset{\text{(III)}}{HO{-}C\begin{matrix}{/\!\!/} NH \cdot HCl\\ \diagdown NH_2\end{matrix}} \qquad \underset{\text{(IV)}}{HN{=}C\begin{matrix}\diagup NH_3\\ \diagdown O\end{matrix}}$$

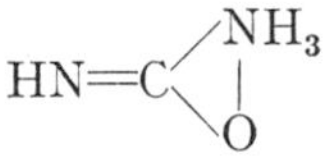

(IV) was proposed to explain the ease with which urea loses ammonia to form cyanic acid:

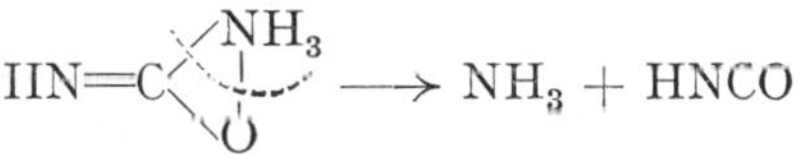

$$HN{=}C\begin{matrix}\diagup NH_3\\ \diagdown O\end{matrix} \longrightarrow NH_3 + HNCO$$

At the same time this formula explained the addition of one molecule of hydrochloric acid, since it has the strongly basic imido group, =NH. Werner's formula contains quinquevalent nitrogen, but rewritten according to modern electronic theory, it will be (V). Thus there is now the possibility of the following equilibria:

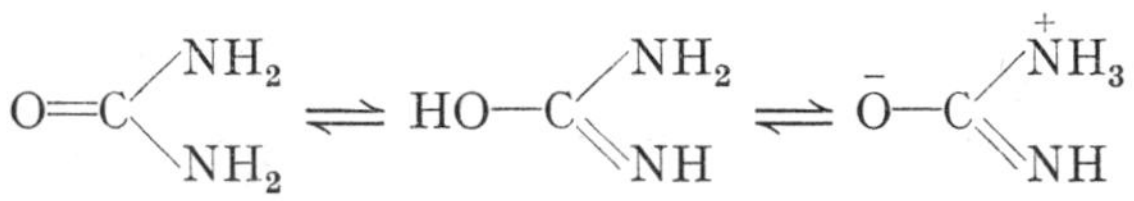

$$\underset{\text{(I)}}{O{=}C\begin{matrix}\diagup NH_2\\ \diagdown NH_2\end{matrix}} \rightleftharpoons \underset{\text{(II)}}{HO{-}C\begin{matrix}\diagup NH_2\\ {\diagdown\!\!\diagdown} NH\end{matrix}} \rightleftharpoons \underset{\text{(V)}}{\bar{O}{-}C\begin{matrix}\diagup \overset{+}{N}H_3\\ {\diagdown\!\!\diagdown} NH\end{matrix}}$$

On the other hand, experience shows that compounds containing the group $>C(OH) \cdot NH_2$ readily eliminate ammonia to form the carbonyl group (*cf.* the group $>C(OH)_2$, p. 157). Thus structure (V) is unnecessary (although it is possible that the elimination of ammonia for (II) takes place through the intermediate formation of (V). Hence structure (II) has been favoured by many, since it explained the " monoacidic " properties of urea and the elimination of ammonia.

Crystal structure studies have shown that in solid urea both nitrogen atoms are identical. This indicates structure (I), and not (II) or (V). Bond-length measurements in urea give the C—N distance as 1·37 A. In aliphatic amines the C—N bond length is 1·47 A. This indicates that the

C—N bond in urea has some double bond character (about 28 per cent.); this can be explained by resonance:

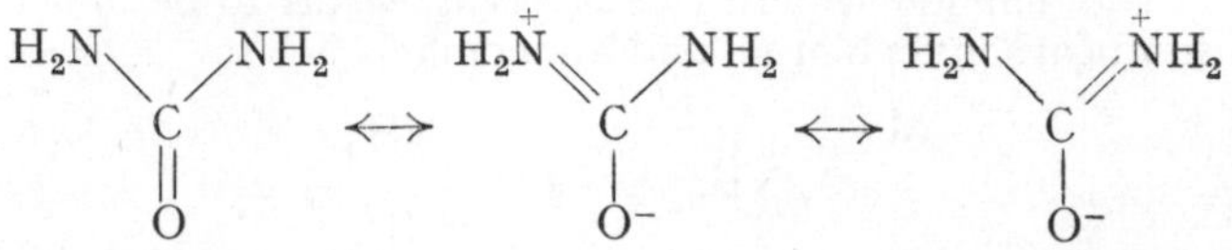

$$H_2N{-}\underset{\underset{\displaystyle O}{\|}}{C}{-}NH_2 \longleftrightarrow H_2\overset{+}{N}{=}\underset{\underset{\displaystyle O^-}{|}}{C}{-}NH_2 \longleftrightarrow H_2N{-}\underset{\underset{\displaystyle O^-}{|}}{C}{=}\overset{+}{N}H_2$$

Both the nitrogen atoms are identical in the hybrid molecule. Furthermore, the negatively charged oxygen atom is capable of co-ordinating with *one* proton (therefore urea will be a "monoacidic" base), and thus the salt may be formulated as a resonance hybrid:

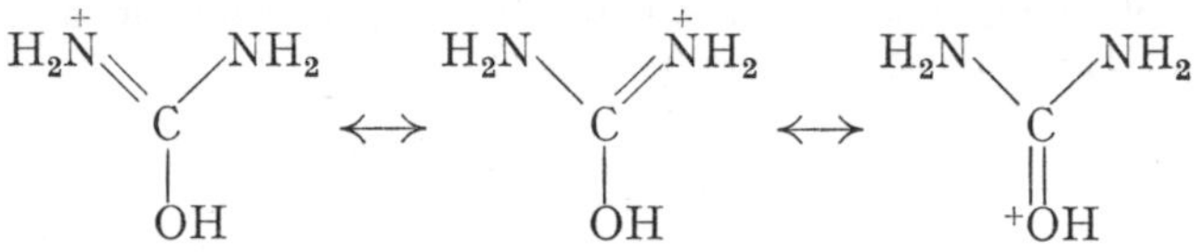

$$H_2\overset{+}{N}{=}\underset{\underset{\displaystyle OH}{|}}{C}{-}NH_2 \longleftrightarrow H_2N{-}\underset{\underset{\displaystyle OH}{|}}{C}{=}\overset{+}{N}H_2 \longleftrightarrow H_2N{-}\underset{\underset{\displaystyle {}^{+}OH}{\|}}{C}{-}NH_2$$

Dipole moment work on urea also indicates that it is a resonance hybrid with charged forms contributing 20–30 per cent.

Properties and reactions of urea. Urea is a white crystalline solid, m.p. 132°, soluble in water and ethanol, but insoluble in ether. It is used for preparing formaldehyde-urea plastics, barbiturates, as a fertiliser, etc. A most recent use is for the manufacture of hydrazine; urea is treated with alkaline sodium hypochlorite (in effect, the Hofmann degradation is applied to urea):

$$NH_2{\cdot}CO{\cdot}NH_2 + NaOCl + 2NaOH \longrightarrow N_2H_4 + NaCl + Na_2CO_3 + H_2O$$

(i) Urea behaves as a "monoacidic" base; the nitrate and oxalate are the most important, since neither is very soluble in water.

When urea nitrate is added to cold concentrated sulphuric acid, *nitrourea* is formed:

$$NH_2{\cdot}CO{\cdot}NH_2{\cdot}HNO_3 \xrightarrow{H_2SO_4} NH_2{\cdot}CO{\cdot}NH{\cdot}NO_2 + H_2O \quad (70\text{–}87\%)$$

(ii) Urea is hydrolysed by boiling with acids or alkalis:

$$CO(NH_2)_2 + H_2O \longrightarrow CO_2 + 2NH_3$$

The enzyme urease (which occurs in soyabeans) produces the same change.

(iii) When gently heated, urea loses ammonia to form *biuret*:

$$2NH_2{\cdot}CO{\cdot}NH_2 \longrightarrow NH_2{\cdot}CO{\cdot}NH{\cdot}CO{\cdot}NH_2 + NH_3$$

When an aqueous biuret solution is treated with sodium hydroxide solution and a drop of copper sulphate solution, a violet coloration is produced. This is known as the *biuret reaction,* which is characteristic of all compounds containing the grouping —CO·NH—, *e.g.*, proteins.

When urea is heated with thionyl chloride, biuret and triuret, $CO(NH{\cdot}CO{\cdot}NH_2)_2$, are obtained (Haworth and Mann, 1943). Thionyl chloride has no action on thiourea (q.v.). When heated rapidly, urea evolves ammonia and forms cyanic acid which rapidly polymerises to cyanuric acid (p. 281). When refluxed with alcohols, urea forms urethans (see above).

(iv) Nitrous acid reacts with urea with the liberation of nitrogen which, however, is not evolved quantitatively:

$$CO(NH_2)_2 + 2HNO_2 \longrightarrow CO_2 + 3H_2O + 2N_2$$

Nitrogen is also evolved, again not quantitatively, when urea is treated with *excess* alkaline hypobromite:

$$CO(NH_2)_2 + 3NaOBr + 2NaOH \longrightarrow N_2 + Na_2CO_3 + 3NaBr + 3H_2O$$

(v) Acid chlorides and acid anhydrides react with urea to form *ureides*, *e.g.*, acetyl chloride forms acetylurea:

$$CH_3{\cdot}COCl + NH_2{\cdot}CO{\cdot}NH_2 \longrightarrow CH_3{\cdot}CO{\cdot}NH{\cdot}CO{\cdot}NH_2 + HCl$$

Many of these ureides are useful drugs, particularly when the acid radical has a branched chain, *e.g.*, bromural (α-bromo*iso*valerylurea), $(CH_3)_2CH{\cdot}CHBr{\cdot}CO{\cdot}NH{\cdot}CO{\cdot}NH_2$.

Dicarboxylic acids react with urea in the presence of phosphoryl chloride to form *cyclic* ureides; *e.g.*, oxalic acid forms *parabanic acid* (oxalylurea):

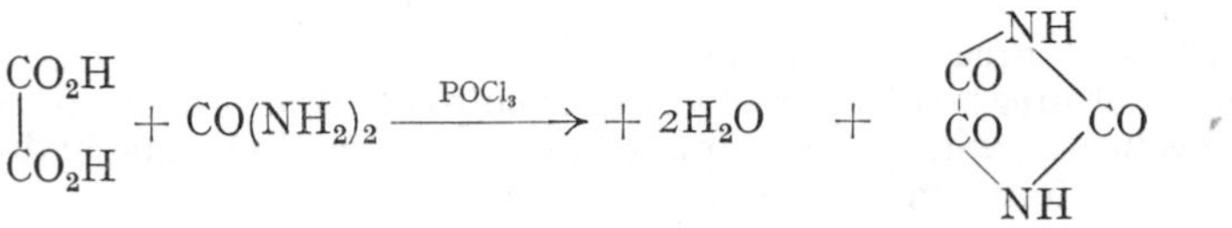

```
                                            NH
CO2H                                      CO  \
 |    + CO(NH2)2 ---POCl3---> + 2H2O  +   CO    CO
CO2H                                        \  /
                                             NH
```

Cyclic ureides may also be prepared by refluxing a diester with urea in ethanolic solution containing sodium ethoxide; *e.g.*, malonic ester forms *barbituric acid* (*malonylurea*):

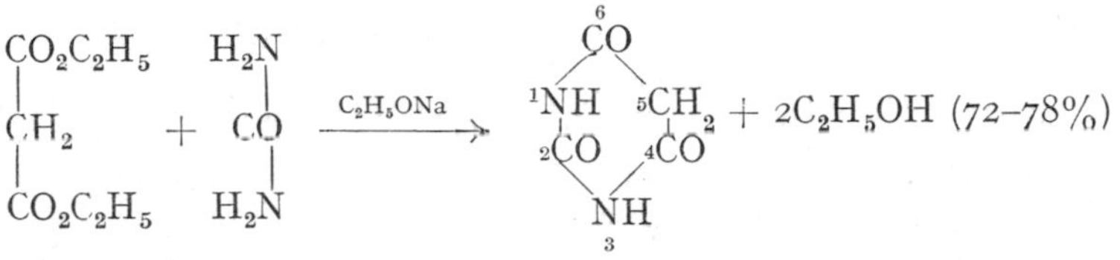

```
                                         6
CO2C2H5    H2N                           CO
 |          |                           /  \
CH2     +  CO   ---C2H5ONa--->      1NH    5CH2  + 2C2H5OH (72-78%)
 |          |                       2CO    4CO
CO2C2H5    H2N                          \  /
                                         NH
                                         3
```

Barbituric acid and its 5- or 5 : 5-derivatives are used in medicine as hypnotics and sedatives, *e.g.*, *barbitone* (5 : 5-diethylbarbituric acid), and *phenobarbitone* (5-phenyl-5-ethylbarbituric acid).

A very important group of cyclic diureides is the *purine* group, *e.g.*, uric acid, caffeine, etc.:

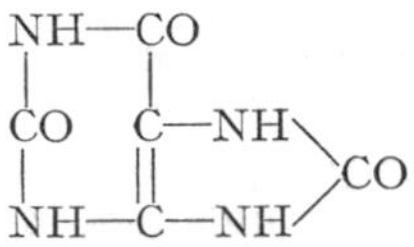

```
NH—CO                      CH3·N——CO
|   |                         |    |
CO  C—NH\                     CO   C—N·CH3
|   ||   CO                   |    ||    >CH
NH—C—NH/                   CH3·N——C—N
 uric acid                    caffeine
```

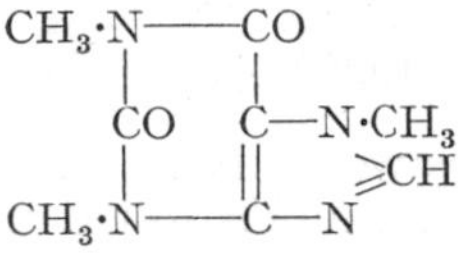

Inclusion complexes. Several types of inclusion complexes are known, and in all of them molecules of one component are physically imprisoned in the cavities of the crystalline structure of the second component. Two important types of inclusion complexes are the *channel* (*canal*) *complexes* and the *clathrate* (*cage*) *complexes* (see p. 608 for a discussion of the latter).

Channel complexes are those cases where one component crystallises in a form with parallel, approximately cylindrical channels in which molecules of a second component are enclosed lengthwise. Urea normally forms a crystal structure which is closely packed, but in the presence of various *straight-chain* molecules, *e.g.*, *n*-paraffins, *n*-alcohols, *n*-acids, *n*-esters, etc., the urea crystallises in a more open structure which contains long channels enclosing molecules of the second component. These channels contain a number of molecules of the second component and, in general, the number is inversely proportional to the length of the enclosed molecule. Branched-chain and cyclic structures cannot " fit " into these channels, and so this property affords a means of separating straight-chain from branched-chain compounds. The complexes are decomposed by melting or by dissolving away the urea with water. The formula of the channel complexes is usually $A_n B$ (A is urea) where n, usually not a whole number, has values of 4 or more and increases as the length of B increases. Furthermore, since channel complexes are characterised by the fact that molecules of the second component bear some structural resemblance to each other, it is not possible to separate homologues by channel complexes. For each homologous series there is a certain minimum chain-length for channel complex formation, *e.g.*, six carbons for paraffins, seven for alcohols, five for acids, etc.

Channel complex formation has been used to resolve racemic modifications (p. 394).

Substituted ureas may be prepared by a reaction similar to Wöhler's synthesis of urea; the hydrochloride or sulphate of a primary or secondary amine is heated with potassium *iso*cyanate, *e.g.*, methylamine hydrochloride (1 molecule) forms methylurea:

$$CH_3{\cdot}NH_2{\cdot}HCl + KNCO \longrightarrow KCl + CH_3{\cdot}NH_2{\cdot}HNCO \longrightarrow CH_3{\cdot}NH{\cdot}CO{\cdot}NH_2$$

If *excess* amine salt is used, *s*-disubstituted ureas are obtained, *e.g.*, excess aniline hydrochloride forms *s*-diphenylurea:

$$C_6H_5{\cdot}NH_2{\cdot}HCl + KNCO \longrightarrow KCl + C_6H_5{\cdot}NH_2{\cdot}HNCO \longrightarrow$$

$$C_6H_5{\cdot}NH{\cdot}CO{\cdot}NH_2 \xrightarrow{C_6H_5{\cdot}NH_2{\cdot}HCl} C_6H_5{\cdot}NH{\cdot}CO{\cdot}NH{\cdot}C_6H_5 + NH_4Cl$$

Alternatively, *s*-diphenylurea may be obtained by refluxing an aqueous solution of aniline hydrochloride with urea:

$$C_6H_5{\cdot}NH_2{\cdot}HCl + NH_2{\cdot}CO{\cdot}NH_2 \longrightarrow C_6H_5{\cdot}NH{\cdot}CO{\cdot}NH_2 + NH_4Cl$$
$$C_6H_5{\cdot}NH{\cdot}CO{\cdot}NH_2 + C_6H_5{\cdot}NH_2{\cdot}HCl \longrightarrow C_6H_5{\cdot}NH{\cdot}CO{\cdot}NH{\cdot}C_6H_5 + NH_4Cl$$

Both phenylurea (38–40 per cent.) and *s*-diphenylurea (52–55 per cent.) may be isolated.

s-Substituted ureas may be obtained by the action of carbonyl chloride on a primary or secondary amine:

$$COCl_2 + 2R{\cdot}NH_2 \longrightarrow CO(NH{\cdot}R)_2 + 2HCl$$

The reaction between phenyl *iso*cyanate and a primary or secondary amine also produces a *s*-disubstituted urea, *e.g.*, with ethylamine, *s*-ethylphenyl-urea is formed:

$$C_6H_5{\cdot}NCO + C_2H_5{\cdot}NH_2 \longrightarrow C_6H_5{\cdot}NH{\cdot}CO{\cdot}NH{\cdot}C_2H_5$$

This reaction is used to characterise amines.

A very convenient method of preparing alkyl-ureas is to evaporate an aqueous or ethanolic solution of an amine and nitrourea (see above); the latter decomposes into cyanic acid and nitroamide, $NH_2{\cdot}NO_2$, which readily decomposes into nitrous oxide:

$$NH_2{\cdot}CO{\cdot}NH{\cdot}NO_2 \longrightarrow HNCO + NH_2{\cdot}NO_2$$
$$HNCO + R_2NH \longrightarrow R_2N{\cdot}CO{\cdot}NH_2$$
$$NH_2{\cdot}NO_2 \longrightarrow N_2O + H_2O$$

When urea is treated with methyl sulphate in faintly alkaline solution, *methyl*iso*urea* is obtained:

$$NH_2\text{—}\overset{\overset{\displaystyle NH_2}{|}}{C}\text{=}O \rightleftharpoons NH_2\text{—}\overset{\overset{\displaystyle NH}{\|}}{C}\text{—}OH \xrightarrow{(CH_3)_2SO_4} NH_2\text{—}\overset{\overset{\displaystyle NH}{\|}}{C}\text{—}OCH_3$$

COMPOUNDS RELATED TO UREA

Semicarbazide (*aminourea*), $NH_2{\cdot}CO{\cdot}NH{\cdot}NH_2$, may be prepared by treating hydrazine sulphate with potassium cyanate:

$$H_2N{\cdot}NH_2{\cdot}HNCO \longrightarrow NH_2{\cdot}CO{\cdot}NH{\cdot}NH_2$$

It may also be prepared by heating urea with hydrazine hydrate.

$$NH_2{\cdot}CO{\cdot}NH_2 + N_2H_4,H_2O \longrightarrow NH_2{\cdot}CO{\cdot}NH{\cdot}NH_2 + NH_3 + H_2O$$

A more recent method is the electrolytic reduction of nitrourea in sulphuric acid solution using a lead anode:

$$NH_2{\cdot}CO{\cdot}NH{\cdot}NO_2 + 6[H] \longrightarrow NH_2{\cdot}CO{\cdot}NH{\cdot}NH_2 + 2H_2O \quad (61\text{–}69\%)$$

Semicarbazide is a white crystalline solid, m.p. 96°. It is an important reagent for the identification of carbonyl compounds, with which it forms *semicarbazones*; it is also used in the Wolff–Kishner reduction (p. 143).

Guanidine (*aminomethanamidine*), $NH{:}C(NH_2)_2$, is found in beet juice, and is one of the degradation products of the purines. It may be prepared:

(i) By heating cyanamide with ammonium chloride:

$$NH_2{\cdot}CN + NH_4Cl \longrightarrow (NH_2)_2C{:}NH{\cdot}HCl$$

(ii) By *prolonged* heating of ammonium thiocyanate at 180° (see also thiourea, below):

$$NH_4SCN \longrightarrow S{:}C(NH_2)_2 \xrightarrow{H_2S} NH_2{\cdot}CN \xrightarrow{NH_4SCN} (NH_2)_2C{:}NH{\cdot}HSCN$$

(iii) By heating ethyl orthocarbonate with ammonia at 160°:

$$C(OC_2H_5)_4 + 3NH_3 \longrightarrow (NH_2)_2C{:}NH + 4C_2H_5OH$$

Guanidine is a white hygroscopic crystalline solid, and is a *strong* " mono-acid " base, even forming a carbonate. Its strength as a base may be explained by resonance.

Neutral molecule

$$NH_2\text{—}\overset{\overset{\displaystyle NH}{\|}}{C}\text{—}NH_2 \longleftrightarrow NH_2\text{—}\overset{\overset{\displaystyle \bar{N}H}{|}}{C}\text{=}\overset{+}{N}H_2 \longleftrightarrow \overset{+}{N}H_2\text{=}\overset{\overset{\displaystyle \bar{N}H}{|}}{C}\text{—}NH_2$$

Ion

$$NH_2\text{—}\overset{\overset{\displaystyle \overset{+}{N}H_2}{\|}}{C}\text{—}NH_2 \longleftrightarrow NH_2\text{—}\overset{\overset{\displaystyle NH_2}{|}}{C}\text{=}\overset{+}{N}H_2 \longleftrightarrow \overset{+}{N}H_2\text{=}\overset{\overset{\displaystyle NH_2}{|}}{C}\text{—}NH_2$$

In the ion, the resonating structures are equivalent. Hence the ion is more stable than the neutral molecule. Thus the neutral molecule tends to form the ion, *i.e.*, it is strongly basic (more so than urea, the ions of which are not all equivalent). X-Ray analysis of guanidinium iodide shows that the three nitrogen atoms are symmetrically placed round the carbon atom. Furthermore, the C—N distance has been found to be 1·18 A (Theilacker,

1935; *cf.* urea). These facts are in keeping with the assumption that the guanidinium ion is a resonance hybrid.

Careful hydrolysis with barium hydroxide solution converts guanidine into urea:

$$(NH_2)_2C{:}NH + H_2O \longrightarrow (NH_2)_2C{:}O + NH_3$$

Guanidine nitrate may be prepared by heating dicyanodiamide with ammonium nitrate:

$$NH_2-\overset{\overset{\displaystyle NH}{\|}}{C}-NH{\cdot}CN + 2NH_4NO_3 \longrightarrow 2NH_2-\overset{\overset{\displaystyle NH_2}{|}}{C}{:}NH{\cdot}HNO_3 \quad (85\%)$$

When treated with concentrated sulphuric acid, guanidine nitrate is converted into nitroguanidine, $NH_2{\cdot}C({:}NH){\cdot}NH{\cdot}NO_2$ (*cf.* urea nitrate, p. 368). Nitroguanidine is used for making flashless powders.

A number of derivatives of guanidine are important, *e.g.*, **creatine** (N-*methylguanidinoacetic acid*), which is found in muscle fluids; **creatinine,** which is found in beef extract and human urine, and is the anhydride (lactam) of creatine; and **arginine** (α-amino-δ-guanidinovaleric acid), which is present in many proteins:

$$NH_2-\underset{\underset{\displaystyle NH}{\|}}{C}-\underset{\underset{\displaystyle CH_3}{|}}{N}{\cdot}CH_2{\cdot}CO_2H$$

creatine

$$\overbrace{NH-\underset{\underset{\displaystyle NH}{\|}}{C}-\underset{\underset{\displaystyle CH_3}{|}}{N}{\cdot}CH_2{\cdot}CO}^{O}$$

creatinine

$$NH{=}\underset{\underset{\displaystyle NH_2}{|}}{C}-NH{\cdot}CH_2{\cdot}CH_2{\cdot}CH_2{\cdot}\underset{\underset{\displaystyle NH_2}{|}}{CH}{\cdot}CO_2H$$

arginine

Thiourea (*thiocarbamide*), $S{:}C(NH_2)_2$, may be prepared by heating ammonium thiocyanate at 170° for some time:

$$NH_4SCN \longrightarrow S{:}C(NH_2)_2 \quad (14\text{–}16\%)$$

It is a white crystalline solid, m.p. 180°, and behaves as a " monoacidic " base. Dipole moment studies show that thiourea is a resonance hybrid. When heated with alkalis, thiourea is hydrolysed:

$$S{:}C(NH_2)_2 + 2H_2O \xrightarrow{NaOH} CO_2 + H_2S + 2NH_3$$

Oxidation with *alkaline* permanganate converts thiourea into urea:

$$S{:}C(NH_2)_2 + [O] \longrightarrow O{:}C(NH_2)_2 + S$$

On the other hand, oxidation with *acid* permanganate converts it into *formamidine disulphide*, $NH_2{\cdot}C({:}NH){\cdot}S{\cdot}S{\cdot}C({:}NH){\cdot}NH_2$. This reaction is characteristic of all compounds containing the mercapto-group, and therefore suggests that in acid solution thiourea exists as

$$\begin{matrix} H_2N \diagdown \\ \quad C-SH \\ H_2\overset{+}{N} \diagup\!\!\diagup \end{matrix}$$

Oxides of lead, silver or mercury remove a molecule of hydrogen sulphide from thiourea at room temperature to form cyanamide:

$$(NH_2)_2CS + HgO \longrightarrow NH_2{\cdot}CN + HgS + H_2O$$

When treated with alkyl halide, thiourea forms S-*alkyl-ψ-thiouronium salts* (S-*alkyl-iso*thiouronium salts*):

$$CH_3I + S{:}C(NH_2)_2 \longrightarrow \left\{CH_3{\cdot}S{\cdot}C\begin{matrix}\overset{+}{N}H_2 \\ NH_2\end{matrix}\right\}I^-$$

These compounds are used to characterise sulphonic acids, with which they form insoluble salts. They may also be used to prepare thioalcohols (p. 315), and also to prepare sulphonyl chlorides by oxidation with chlorine-water.

$$R{\cdot}S{\cdot}C\begin{matrix}NH \\ NH_2\end{matrix}{\cdot}HCl \xrightarrow[H_2O]{Cl_2} R{\cdot}SO_2Cl$$

Thiourea is used to protect furs and clothing against insects.

s-*Diphenylthiourea* or *diphenylthiocarbanilide*, $(C_6H_5{\cdot}NH)_2CS$, which is used as a rubber accelerator, may be prepared by heating aniline with carbon disulphide in an ethanolic solution containing potassium hydroxide.

Dithiocarbamic acid, $S{:}C(NH_2){\cdot}SH$, although unstable in the free state, gives rise to stable salts. These may be prepared by heating a primary or secondary amine with carbon disulphide. This reaction is complicated and the mechanism is uncertain. A possibility is via the formation of the unstable *N*-alkyldithiocarbamic acid which forms the stable dithiocarbamic acid salt with another molecule of amine:

$$R{\cdot}NH_2 + CS_2 \longrightarrow \left[R{\cdot}NH{-}\overset{\overset{S}{\|}}{C}{-}SH\right] \xrightarrow{R{\cdot}NH_2} \left[R{\cdot}NH{-}\overset{\overset{S}{\|}}{C}{-}S\right]^- R{\cdot}NH_3^+$$

The *Hofmann mustard oil reaction* (p. 319) is believed to take place via the formation of a dithiocarbamic acid salt, which is then decomposed by the mercuric chloride, possibly as follows:

$$\left[R{\cdot}NH{-}\overset{\overset{S}{\|}}{C}{-}S\right]^- R{\cdot}NH_3^+ + HgCl_2 \longrightarrow$$

$$[R{\cdot}NH_3]^+Cl^- + \left[R{\cdot}NH{-}\overset{\overset{S}{\|}}{C}{-}S{-}Hg{\cdot}Cl\right] \longrightarrow R{\cdot}NCS + HgS + HCl$$

On the other hand, when heated alone, dithiocarbamic acid salts form thioureas:

$$\left[R{\cdot}NH{\cdot}\overset{\overset{S}{\|}}{C}{\cdot}S\right]^- R{\cdot}NH_3^+ \longrightarrow R{\cdot}NCS + R{\cdot}NH_2 + H_2S$$

$$R{\cdot}NCS + R{\cdot}NH_2 \longrightarrow R{\cdot}NH{\cdot}CS{\cdot}NH{\cdot}R$$

QUESTIONS

1. How may oxalic acid be prepared? Name the compounds and state the conditions under which they are formed when oxalic acid is treated with:—(*a*) H_2SO_4, (*b*) KOH, (*c*) $KMnO_4$, (*d*) EtOH, (*e*) EtOAc, (*f*) $(CH_2OH)_2$, (*g*) H_2, (*h*) PCl_5, (*i*) $CH_2OH{\cdot}CHOH{\cdot}CH_2OH$, (*j*) when it is heated.

2. Describe the more important methods of preparing each of the following acids:—(*a*) malonic, (*b*) succinic, (*c*) glutaric, (*d*) adipic, (*e*) pimelic, (*f*) suberic, (*g*) azelaic, (*h*) sebacic.

Name the compounds and state the conditions under which they are formed when the calcium salt of each of the above acids is heated, and when each is treated with:—(*a*) H_2SO_4, (*b*) EtOH, (*c*) P_2O_5, (*d*) $(CH_2OH)_2$, (*e*) Ac_2O.

3. Describe the preparation and properties of the following compounds:—(*a*) mesoxalic acid, (*b*) oxamide, (*c*) oxamic acid, (*d*) malonamide, (*e*) Et_2 bromomalonate, (*f*) succinic anhydride, (*g*) succinamic acid, (*h*) succinimide, (*i*) succinamide, (*j*) succinyl chloride, (*k*) urethan, (*l*) carbonyl chloride, (*m*) acid ester of pimelic acid, (*n*) ethyl

chloroformate, (*o*) nitrourea, (*p*) barbituric acid, (*q*) semicarbazide, (*r*) guanidine, (*s*) thiourea.

4. Suggest a *complete* synthesis for :—(*a*) succinic acid, (*b*) glutaric acid.

5. By means of equations show how you would synthesise:—

(*a*) $Me \cdot CH \cdot CO_2Et$ | $Et \cdot CH \cdot CO_2Et$ (*b*) $Et \cdot CH(CN) \cdot CO_2Et$

(*c*) $Et \cdot CH \cdot CO_2H$ | $CH_2 \cdot CO_2H$ (*d*) $CH_3 \cdot CH_2 \cdot CO \cdot CH_2 \cdot CO_2Et$ (*e*) $Et \cdot N(CO_2Et)_2$

6. Show, by means of equations, how you would convert succinic acid into:—(*a*) glutaric acid, (*b*) adipic acid, (*c*) suberic acid, (*d*) malonic acid.

7. How could you prepare:—(*a*) *N* : *N*-dimethylurethan, (*b*) *s*-dimethylurea, (*c*) methylthiourea, (*d*) methyl*iso*thiourea, (*e*) barbitone?

8. Define and give examples of:—(*a*) The Crum-Brown and Walker electrolytic method, (*b*) oxidative degradation, (*c*) the Baeyer Strain Theory, (*d*) Blanc's rule, (*e*) the biuret reaction.

9. Discuss the preparation and uses of:—(*a*) *N*-bromosuccinimide, (*b*) oxalacetic ester, (*c*) ethyl carbonate.

10. Write an account of the preparation of urea and discuss its structure. Also give an account of the methods for preparing substituted ureas.

Name the compounds and state the conditions under which they are formed when urea is treated with:—(*a*) $H \cdot CHO$, (*b*) NaOCl, (*c*) HCl, (*d*) NaOH, (*e*) HNO_2, (*f*) HNO_3, (*g*) gentle heating, (*h*) rapid heating, (*i*) $SOCl_2$, (*j*) ROH, (*k*) AcCl, (*l*) $(CO_2H)_2$, (*m*) $CH_2(CO_2Et)_2$, (*n*) Me_2SO_4, (*o*) $C_6H_5 \cdot NH_2 \cdot HCl$.

READING REFERENCES

Hill, Adipic Anhydride, *J. Amer. Chem. Soc.*, 1930, **52**, 4110.
Hill and Carothers, Many-Membered Cyclic Anhydrides, *ibid.*, 1933, **55**, 5023.
Carothers, Polymerisation, *Chem. Reviews*, 1931, **8**, 353.
Hoff, Nylon as a Textile Fibre, *Ind. Eng. Chem.*, 1940, **32**, 1560.
Bolton, Development of Nylon, *ibid.*, 1942, **34**, 53.
Wallingford *et al.*, Alkyl Carbonates in Synthetic Chemistry, *J. Amer. Chem. Soc.*, 1941, **63**, 2252; 1942, **64**, 576, 578, 580.
Kumler and Fohlen, Dipole Moments and Structure of Urea and Thiourea, *ibid.*, 1942, **64**, 1944.
Sidgwick, *The Organic Chemistry of Nitrogen.* (New Edition by Taylor and Baker, 1937), Oxford Press. Ch. IX. Carbonic Acid Derivatives.
Haworth and Mann, Some Properties of Urea, Biuret and Triuret, *J.C.S.*, **1943**, 603.
Linstead and Walpole, The Blanc Rule, *ibid.*, **1939**, 850.
Byrkit and Michalek, Hydrazine in Organic Chemistry, *Ind. Eng. Chem.*, 1950, **42**, 1862.
Braude and Waight, Some Observations on the Course of the Reaction between Ethylenic Compounds and *N*-Bromosuccinimide, *J.C.S.*, **1952**, 1116.
Djerassi, Brominations with *N*-Bromosuccinimide and Related Compounds, *Chem. Reviews*, 1948, **43**, 271.
Weedon, Anodic Syntheses with Carboxylic Acids, *Quart. Reviews* (*Chem. Soc.*), 1952, **6**, 380.
Schroeder, Thioureas, *Chem. Reviews*, 1955, **55**, 181.
Truter, Sorting Molecules by Size and Shape, *Research*, 1953, **6**, 320.

CHAPTER XVII

HYDROXYACIDS. STEREOCHEMISTRY. UNSATURATED DICARBOXYLIC ACIDS

MONOBASIC HYDROXYACIDS

MONOBASIC hydroxyacids are fatty acids which contain one or more hydroxyl groups in the carbon chain.

Nomenclature. The usual method is to name the hydroxyacid as a derivative of the parent fatty acid (named according to the trivial system), the position of the hydroxyl group being indicated by a Greek letter, *e.g.*,

$$CH_3{\cdot}CHOH{\cdot}CH_2{\cdot}CO_2H \qquad \beta\text{-hydroxybutyric acid}$$

According to the I.U.C. system of nomenclature, the position of the hydroxyl group is indicated by a number, *e.g.*,

$CH_3{\cdot}CH_2{\cdot}CHOH{\cdot}CO_2H$ 2-hydroxybutanoic acid or 1-hydroxypropane-1-carboxylic acid

Many hydroxyacids which occur in nature are given special names indicating the source, *e.g.*, $CH_3{\cdot}CHOH{\cdot}CO_2H$, lactic acid, occurs in sour milk (Latin: *lac*, milk).

General methods of preparation. 1. By the controlled oxidation of glycols using dilute nitric acid (the yields are usually poor); *e.g.*, propylene glycol gives lactic acid:

$$CH_3{\cdot}CHOH{\cdot}CH_2OH + 2[O] \xrightarrow{HNO_3} CH_3{\cdot}CHOH{\cdot}CO_2H + H_2O$$

2. By the hydrolysis of halogeno-acids with moist silver oxide, sodium hydroxide, or sodium carbonate solution, *e.g.*,

$$CH_2Cl{\cdot}CO_2H + H_2O \longrightarrow CH_2OH{\cdot}CO_2H + HCl \quad (v.g.\text{–}ex.)$$

This is a very good method for α-hydroxyacids, since the starting materials, α-halogeno-acids, are readily prepared (p. 196).

3. By the reduction of aldehydic, ketonic or dicarboxylic acids under suitable conditions, *e.g.*,

$$CH_3{\cdot}CO{\cdot}CO_2H + 2[H] \xrightarrow[H_2O]{Na/Hg} CH_3{\cdot}CHOH{\cdot}CO_2H$$

In practice only the reduction of dicarboxylic acids is important, since aldehydic and ketonic acids are usually inaccessible:

$$CO_2H{\cdot}(CH_2)_n{\cdot}CO_2H \xrightarrow{C_2H_5OH} C_2H_5O_2C{\cdot}(CH_2)_n{\cdot}CO_2H \xrightarrow{Na/C_2H_5OH} CH_2OH{\cdot}(CH_2)_n{\cdot}CO_2H$$

4. By the action of nitrous acid on aminoacids, *e.g.*,

$$NH_2{\cdot}CH_2{\cdot}CO_2H + HNO_2 \longrightarrow CH_2OH{\cdot}CO_2H + N_2 + H_2O \quad (g.)$$

This method is mainly confined to preparing α-hydroxyacids, since naturally occurring aminoacids are α-derivatives.

5. By hydrolysing the cyanohydrins formed from aldehydes or ketones and hydrogen cyanide, *e.g.*,

$$CH_3{\cdot}CHO + HCN \longrightarrow CH_3{\cdot}CHOH{\cdot}CN \xrightarrow{H_2O} CH_3{\cdot}CHOH{\cdot}CO_2H \quad (g.\text{–}v.g.)$$

6. β-Hydroxyacids may be prepared by the hydrolysis of cyanohydrins prepared from chlorohydrins, *e.g.*,

$$CH_2OH{\cdot}CH_2Cl \xrightarrow{KCN} CH_2OH{\cdot}CH_2{\cdot}CN \xrightarrow{H_2O} CH_2OH{\cdot}CH_2{\cdot}CO_2H \quad (g.)$$

7. β-Hydroxyacids may be prepared by the Reformatsky reaction (p. 346).

8. Weygand *et al.* (1955) have introduced the following method for synthesising α-hydroxyacids. A diazoketone is treated with a sulphenyl chloride and the product hydrolysed with sodium hydroxide or better, first treated with sodium acetate and the resulting compound then treated with sodium hydroxide.

$$R{\cdot}CO_2H \xrightarrow{SOCl_2} R{\cdot}COCl \xrightarrow{CH_2N_2} R{\cdot}CO{\cdot}CHN_2$$

$$\xrightarrow{R'{\cdot}SCl} R{\cdot}CO{\cdot}CHCl{\cdot}SR' \xrightarrow{NaOH} R{\cdot}CHOH{\cdot}CO_2H$$

$$R{\cdot}CO{\cdot}CHCl{\cdot}SR' \xrightarrow{CH_3{\cdot}CO_2Na} R{\cdot}CO{\cdot}CH(O{\cdot}CO{\cdot}CH_3){\cdot}SR' \xrightarrow{NaOH} R{\cdot}CHOH{\cdot}CO_2H$$

General properties and reactions. *Glycollic acid*, the first member of the series, is a solid; the higher members are liquids. All are soluble in water, generally more so than are either the corresponding fatty acid or alcohol. This is to be expected, since hydroxyacids have *two* functional groups which can form hydrogen bonds with water.

1. Hydroxyacids behave both as acids and alcohols; in many reactions the hydroxyl and carboxyl groups do not interfere with each other, particularly when they are far apart. Furthermore, by esterifying the carboxyl group, the ester then behaves predominantly as a hydroxy-compound, *i.e.*, esterification masks, to a large extent, the presence of the carboxyl group. The carboxyl group may be converted into the ester, amide, nitrile, acyl chloride, etc. The hydroxyl group (when the carboxyl group has been esterified) may be converted into the ester, ether, etc.; *e.g.*, glycollic acid reacts with acetyl chloride to form acetylglycollic acid (behaving as a hydroxy-compound):

$$CH_2OH{\cdot}CO_2H + CH_3{\cdot}COCl \longrightarrow CH_3{\cdot}CO{\cdot}O{\cdot}CH_2{\cdot}CO_2H + HCl$$

Glycollic acid reacts with phosphorus pentachloride to form chloroacetyl chloride (behaving both as an alcohol and an acid); the chloroacetyl chloride is readily hydrolysed by water to chloroacetic acid:

$$CH_2OH{\cdot}CO_2H \xrightarrow{PCl_5} CH_2Cl{\cdot}COCl \xrightarrow{H_2O} CH_2Cl{\cdot}CO_2H$$

2. When hydroxyacids are oxidised under suitable conditions, a primary alcoholic group is converted into an aldehyde group, and a secondary into ketonic. The presence of a tertiary alcoholic group leads to the breakdown of the carbon chain (*cf.* alcohols, p. 122):

$$CH_2OH{\cdot}CO_2H \xrightarrow{[O]} CHO{\cdot}CO_2H$$

$$CH_3{\cdot}CHOH{\cdot}CO_2H \xrightarrow{[O]} CH_3{\cdot}CO{\cdot}CO_2H$$

$$(CH_3)_2C(OH){\cdot}CO_2H \xrightarrow{[O]} (CH_3)_2CO + CO_2 + H_2O$$

Various oxidising agents may be used, *e.g.*, dilute nitric acid, Fenton's reagent, permanganate; which is used generally depends on the hydroxyacid involved.

3. When heated with dilute sulphuric acid or dilute permanganate, α-hydroxyacids are converted into aldehydes or ketones:

$$R{\cdot}CHOH{\cdot}CO_2H \xrightarrow{H_2SO_4} R{\cdot}CHO + H{\cdot}CO_2H \quad (v.g.)$$

$$R_2C(OH){\cdot}CO_2H + [O] \xrightarrow{KMnO_4} R_2CO + CO_2 + H_2O \quad (v.g.)$$

These reactions offer a very good means of stepping down the fatty acid series (via the H.V.Z. reaction), one carbon atom at a time.

4. When heated with concentrated hydriodic acid, hydroxyacids are reduced to the corresponding fatty acid:

$$CH_3{\cdot}CHOH{\cdot}CO_2H + 2HI \longrightarrow CH_3{\cdot}CH_2{\cdot}CO_2H + H_2O + I_2$$

5. When hydroxyacids are heated, the product formed depends on the relative positions of the hydroxyl and carboxyl groups.

(i) α-Hydroxyacids form **lactides**; these are six-membered ring compounds formed by reaction between *two* molecules of the hydroxy-acid, and are named systematically as 3 : 6 dialkyl-1 : 4-dioxan-2 : 5-dione:

$$\begin{array}{l} R{\cdot}CHO\boxed{H \quad HO}OC \\ \;| \qquad\qquad\qquad\; | \\ CO\boxed{OH \qquad H}OCH{\cdot}R \end{array} \longrightarrow \begin{array}{l} R{\cdot}CH{-}O{-}CO \\ \;| \qquad\qquad\; | \\ CO{-}O{-}CH{\cdot}R \end{array} + 2H_2O$$

The tendency to form lactides is very pronounced, in many cases the lactide being formed by allowing the α-hydroxyacid to stand in a desiccator over concentrated sulphuric acid. Lactides are readily hydrolysed to the acid by alkali.

The distillation of α-hydroxyacids produces aldehydes via the lactide:

$$2R{\cdot}CHOH{\cdot}CO_2H \longrightarrow \begin{array}{l} R{\cdot}CH{\cdot}O{\cdot}CO \\ \;| \qquad\quad | \\ CO{\cdot}O{\cdot}CH{\cdot}R \end{array} \longrightarrow 2R{\cdot}CHO + 2CO$$

When heated with a trace of zinc chloride, lactides are converted into linear polyesters, HO—(—CHR·COO—)$_n$—H, which regenerate the lactide on distillation under reduced pressure.

(ii) When β-hydroxyacids are heated, they eliminate a molecule of water to form mainly the αβ-unsaturated acid and a very small amount of the βγ-unsaturated acid. The reaction is best carried out by refluxing the β-hydroxyacid with 10 per cent. sodium hydroxide solution:

$$R{\cdot}CHOH{\cdot}CH_2{\cdot}CO_2H \longrightarrow R{\cdot}CH{:}CH{\cdot}CO_2H + H_2O$$

(iii) On heating, γ- and δ-hydroxyacids readily form *internal* esters known as **lactones**:

$$\underset{\gamma\text{-acid}}{\begin{array}{l} \quad OH \qquad\qquad HO \\ \quad | \qquad\qquad\quad | \\ R{\cdot}CH{\cdot}CH_2{\cdot}CH_2{\cdot}CO \end{array}} \longrightarrow \underset{\gamma\text{-lactone}}{\begin{array}{l} \quad\;\ulcorner\!\!-\!\!-\!\!-O-\!\!-\!\!-\!\!\urcorner \\ R{\cdot}CH{\cdot}CH_2{\cdot}CH_2{\cdot}CO \end{array}} + H_2O$$

$$\underset{\delta\text{-acid}}{\begin{array}{l} \quad OH \qquad\qquad\qquad HO \\ \quad | \qquad\qquad\qquad\quad | \\ R{\cdot}CH{\cdot}CH_2{\cdot}CH_2{\cdot}CH_2{\cdot}CO \end{array}} \longrightarrow \underset{\delta\text{-lactone}}{\begin{array}{l} \quad\;\ulcorner\!\!-\!\!-\!\!-\!\!-O-\!\!-\!\!-\!\!-\!\!\urcorner \\ R{\cdot}CH{\cdot}CH_2{\cdot}CH_2{\cdot}CH_2{\cdot}CO \end{array}} + H_2O$$

β-Lactones from β-hydroxyacids can only be obtained under special conditions; in practice β-lactones may be prepared by shaking an aqueous solution of the sodium salt of the β-chloroacid with chloroform:

$$R\cdot CHCl\cdot CH_2\cdot CO_2Na \longrightarrow R\cdot\overbrace{CH\cdot CH_2\cdot CO}^{O} + NaCl$$

They may, however, be prepared more readily by reaction between keten and a carbonyl compound; *e.g.*, β-propiolactone, which promises to be an important intermediate, is prepared from keten and formaldehyde:

$$CH_2{:}C{:}O + H\cdot CHO \longrightarrow \overbrace{CH_2\cdot CH_2\cdot CO}^{O}$$

According to the Geneva system of nomenclature, lactones are known as *-olides*, *e.g.*, $\overbrace{CH_2\cdot CH_2\cdot CH_2\cdot CH_2\cdot CO}^{O}$, δ-valerolactone or 1 : 5-pentanolide. The systematic name of this lactone is 4-*hydroxybutane*-1-*carboxylic acid lactone*.

Lactone formation takes place very readily, particularly with γ-hydroxy-acids, which often form the lactone on standing at room temperature, or even in aqueous solution when the sodium salt is acidified.

γ-Lactones may be prepared by the rearrangement of unsaturated acids by heating with concentrated sulphuric acid, *e.g.*, oleic acid forms γ-stearo-lactone:

$$CH_3\cdot(CH_2)_7\cdot CH{:}CH\cdot(CH_2)_7\cdot CO_2H \xrightarrow{H_2SO_4} CH_3\cdot(CH_2)_{13}\cdot\overbrace{CH\cdot CH_2\cdot CH_2\cdot CO}^{O}$$

γ-Butyrolactone is manufactured by the oxidation of tetramethylene glycol over a copper catalyst:

$$CH_2OH\cdot CH_2\cdot CH_2\cdot CH_2OH \xrightarrow[Cu]{O_2} \overbrace{CH_2\cdot CH_2\cdot CH_2\cdot CO}^{O}$$

It is an important intermediate in the preparation of polyamides.

Lactones are converted into alkali salts when refluxed with excess alkali:

$$R\cdot\overbrace{CH\cdot CH_2\cdot CH_2\cdot CO}^{O} + NaOH \longrightarrow R\cdot CHOH\cdot CH_2\cdot CH_2\cdot CO_2Na$$

Lactones are reduced by sodium amalgam in acid solution to the corresponding fatty acid:

$$R\cdot\overbrace{CH\cdot CH_2\cdot CH_2\cdot CH_2\cdot CO}^{O} + 2[H] \longrightarrow R\cdot CH_2\cdot CH_2\cdot CH_2\cdot CH_2\cdot CO_2H$$

On the other hand, lactones of polyhydroxyacids are reduced, under these conditions, to polyhydroxyaldehydes (see p. 425). Lithium aluminium hydride reduces lactones to diols, *e.g.*, γ-valerolactone forms pentane-1 : 4-diol.

When treated with concentrated halogen acid, lactones form the corresponding halogen-acid:

$$R\cdot\overbrace{CH\cdot CH_2\cdot CH_2\cdot CO}^{O} + HX \rightleftarrows R\cdot CHX\cdot CH_2\cdot CH_2\cdot CO_2H$$

With concentrated ammonium hydroxide solution, the hydroxyamide is formed:

$$R\cdot\overbrace{CH\cdot CH_2\cdot CH_2\cdot CO}^{O} + NH_3 \rightleftarrows R\cdot CHOH\cdot CH_2\cdot CH_2\cdot CO\cdot NH_2$$

δ-Lactones can change spontaneously into linear polyesters:

$$HO{-}(CHR\cdot CH_2\cdot CH_2\cdot CH_2\cdot COO{-})_n{-}H$$

(iv) ε-Hydroxyacids, in certain cases, may form the lactone on heating. Usually they either eliminate a molecule of water to form two unsaturated acids, δε- and εζ- or form linear polyesters.

(v) Hydroxyacids with the hydroxyl group further removed than the ε-position, on heating, either eliminate a molecule of water to form unsaturated acids (of two types; *cf.* ε-hydroxyacids), or form linear esters.

Large ring lactones (fourteen- to eighteen-membered rings) have been prepared by the oxidation of cyclic ketones with Caro's acid (Ruzicka and Stoll, 1928):

$$CH_2\begin{matrix}\diagup(CH_2)_n\diagdown \\ \diagdown(CH_2)_n\diagup\end{matrix}CO + [O] \xrightarrow{H_2SO_5} CH_2\begin{matrix}\diagup(CH_2)_n-CO \\ | \\ \diagdown(CH_2)_n-O\end{matrix}$$

By using the high principle of Ruggli (1912), large ring lactones have also been prepared from hydroxyacids in which the hydroxyl group is far removed from the carboxyl group. According to this principle, by using sufficiently dilute solutions of a hydroxyacid, the distance between *different* molecules can be made greater than the distance between the hydroxyl and carboxyl groups of the *same* molecule. Thus the cyclic compound (lactone) is formed instead of linear condensation taking place; *e.g.*, Stoll and his coworkers (1934) found that ω-hydroxypentadecoic acid gave a high yield of lactone in very dilute solution.

Hunsdiecker and Erlbach (1947) have also prepared large ring lactones by the dilution principle. These workers cyclised ω-bromo-aliphatic acids by boiling dilute solutions in butanone with excess potassium carbonate; they obtained lactones in yields varying from 56·3 to 96·8 per cent., the yield increasing with the size of the ring.

Some large ring lactones occur naturally, *e.g.*, *ambrettolide* (in musk):

$$\begin{matrix}CH\cdot(CH_2)_7\cdot CH_2 \\ \| \qquad\qquad \diagdown O \\ CH\cdot(CH_2)_5\cdot CO\end{matrix}$$

Glycollic acid (*hydroxyacetic acid, hydroxyethanoic acid*), $CH_2OH\cdot CO_2H$, is the simplest hydroxyacid, and occurs in the juice of beet and sugar-cane, and in unripe grapes. It may be prepared by refluxing an aqueous solution of potassium chloroacetate with sodium carbonate and then acidifying with hydrochloric acid:

$$CH_2Cl\cdot CO_2K + H_2O \longrightarrow CH_2OH\cdot CO_2H + KCl \quad (80\%)$$

Glycollic acid may also be prepared by warming a solution of formalin with potassium cyanide, and then acidifying with hydrochloric acid:

$$H\cdot CHO + 2KCN + 2H_2O \longrightarrow CH_2OH\cdot CO_2K + NH_3 \xrightarrow{HCl} CH_2OH\cdot CO_2H \quad (70\%)$$

Glycollic acid is prepared industrially by the electrolytic reduction of oxalic acid. A more recent method of manufacture is to heat, at 160–170° and under pressure, a mixture of formaldehyde, carbon monoxide and water in acetic acid with sulphuric acid as catalyst:

$$H\cdot CHO + CO + H_2O \longrightarrow CH_2OH\cdot CO_2H$$

If methanol is used instead of water, methyl glycollate is obtained.

Glycollic acid is a crystalline solid, m.p. 80°, readily soluble in water, ethanol and ether. It is oxidised to oxalic acid by nitric acid. Its lactide is known as *glycollide*.

Lactic acid (*α-hydroxypropionic acid, 2-hydroxypropanoic acid*), $CH_3\cdot CHOH\cdot CO_2H$, may be prepared:

(i) By oxidising propylene glycol with dilute nitric acid:

$$CH_3\cdot CHOH\cdot CH_2OH + 2[O] \longrightarrow CH_3\cdot CHOH\cdot CO_2H + H_2O \quad (p.\text{–}f.)$$

(ii) By heating α-chloro- or α-bromopropionic acid with silver oxide in water, or with sodium hydroxide solution:

$$CH_3\cdot CHBr\cdot CO_2H + H_2O \longrightarrow CH_3\cdot CHOH\cdot CO_2H + HBr \quad (g.\text{–}v.g.)$$

(iii) By the hydrolysis of acetaldehyde cyanohydrin:

$$CH_3\cdot CHO + HCN \longrightarrow CH_3\cdot CHOH\cdot CN \xrightarrow{H_2O} CH_3\cdot CHOH\cdot CO_2H$$

(iv) By the action of nitrous acid on alanine:

$$CH_3\cdot CH(NH_2)\cdot CO_2H + HNO_2 \longrightarrow CH_3\cdot CHOH\cdot CO_2H + N_2 + H_2O$$

(v) Milk contains the sugar lactose, which is fermented by the *Bacillus acidi lactiti*:

$$C_{12}H_{22}O_{11} + H_2O \longrightarrow 4CH_3\cdot CHOH\cdot CO_2H$$

This is the basis of the industrial preparation of lactic acid. A little sour milk is added to a solution of cane-sugar or glucose in the presence of excess chalk, and the temperature is maintained at 35°. As the lactic acid is produced, it is neutralised by the chalk, being precipitated as the insoluble calcium salt. The solution must be kept neutral, since the micro-organism ceases to function if the concentration of the lactic acid exceeds 1 per cent. The calcium lactate is filtered off and decomposed with the calculated quantity of dilute sulphuric acid. Lactic acid is also prepared by the fermentation of sucrose by *Rhizopus oryzae*.

Lactic acid is a colourless syrup, m.p. 18°, b.p. 122°/15 mm. It has a sour taste and smell, is hygroscopic, and is very soluble in water. It undergoes all the general reactions of α-hydroxyacids; oxidation with Fenton's reagent converts it into pyruvic acid:

$$CH_3\cdot CHOH\cdot CO_2H \xrightarrow{H_2O_2/Fe^{2+}} CH_3\cdot CO\cdot CO_2H$$

It is oxidised to acetic acid by permanganate. Lactic acid is used in the tanning industry to remove lime from the hides; it is used in the dyeing industry, and ethyl lactate is used as a solvent for cellulose nitrate.

Lactic acid exists in three distinct forms, all of which have been shown to possess the *same* chemical structure. The three kinds of lactic acids are: (i) dextrorotatory lactic acid; (ii) lævorotatory lactic acid; (iii) DL-lactic acid. The lactic acid prepared by the above methods is the DL-. Dextrorotatory lactic acid may be obtained from meat extract; this acid is also known as *sarcolactic acid* (Greek: *sarkos*, flesh). Lævorotatory lactic acid may be obtained by the fermentation of sucrose by *Bacillus acidi lævolactiti*.

The chemical properties of these isomeric lactic acids are identical in all respects, except in their behaviour towards other optically active compounds (see later). The differences appear only in certain physical properties. The dextrorotatory and lævorotatory lactic acids both melt at 26°; the DL- melts at 18°. The main difference between dextrorotatory and lævorotatory lactic acid is their respective action on polarised light. This is due to *stereochemical* differences in structure.

STEREOCHEMISTRY

Isomerism consists of three types:

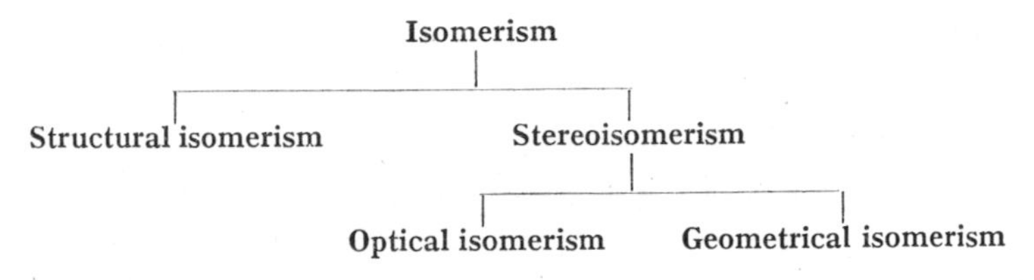

Structural isomerism is due to the difference in structure, and is exhibited in three different ways.

(i) *Chain* or *nuclear isomerism* is exhibited by compounds which differ in the arrangement of the *carbon atoms, e.g., n-* and *iso*butane.

(ii) *Position isomerism* is exhibited by compounds having the *same* carbon skeleton but differing in the position occupied by a substituent group, *e.g., n-* and *iso*propyl alcohols; α-, β- and γ-hydroxybutyric acids; *ortho-, meta-* and *para*-nitrophenols.

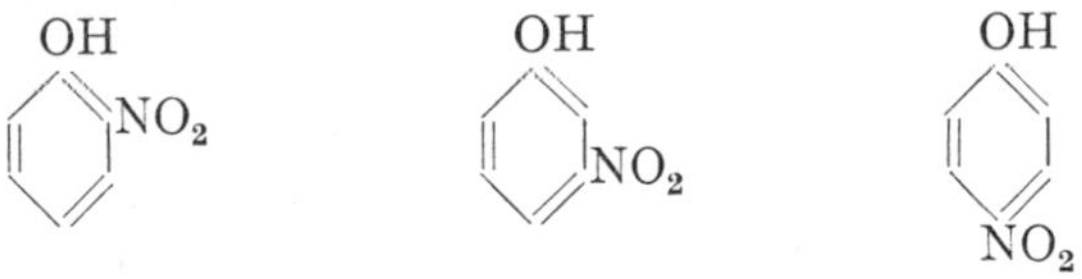

OH, NO_2 — *ortho-*   OH, NO_2 — *meta-*   OH, NO_2 — *para-*

(iii) *Functional group isomerism* is exhibited by compounds having different functional groups, *i.e.*, compounds with the same molecular formula but belonging to different homologous series, *e.g.*, ethanol and dimethyl ether; acetone and propionaldehyde.

This type of isomerism was originally called *metamerism* by Berzelius, but he also included under this heading compounds in the same homologous series, *e.g.*, diethyl ether, methyl *n*-propyl ether and methyl *iso*propyl ether. The name metamerism is now reserved only for the latter type of isomerism (p. 134).

Tautomerism may be regarded as a special case of functional group isomerism.

Stereoisomerism is exhibited by isomers having the *same* structure but differing in their *spatial* arrangement, *i.e.*, having different *configurations*. Different configurations are possible because carbon forms mainly covalent bonds and these have direction in space.

Optical isomerism is characterised by compounds having the *same* structure but different configurations, and because of their *molecular asymmetry* these compounds rotate the plane of polarisation of plane-polarised light. Optical isomers have similar physical and chemical properties; the most marked difference between them is their action on polarised light (see below).

Geometrical isomerism or *cis-trans isomerism* is characterised by compounds having the *same structure but different configurations*, and because of their *molecular symmetry* these compounds do *not* rotate the plane of polarisation of plane-polarised light. Geometrical isomers differ in all their physical and in many of their chemical properties. They can also exhibit optical isomerism if the structure of the molecule, apart from giving rise to geometrical isomerism, also satisfies the requirements for optical isomerism.

Optical activity is the name given to the phenomenon exhibited by compounds which, when placed in the path of a beam of polarised light, are capable of rotating the plane of polarisation to the left or right; such compounds are said to be optically active. The instrument used for measuring the rotatory power of a substance is the *polarimeter*.* Essentially it consists of two Nicol prisms, one the polariser (P) and the other, the analyser (A), and between them a tube (T) which contains the substance (a liquid or a solution) to be examined (Fig. 1). S is a source of monochromatic light.

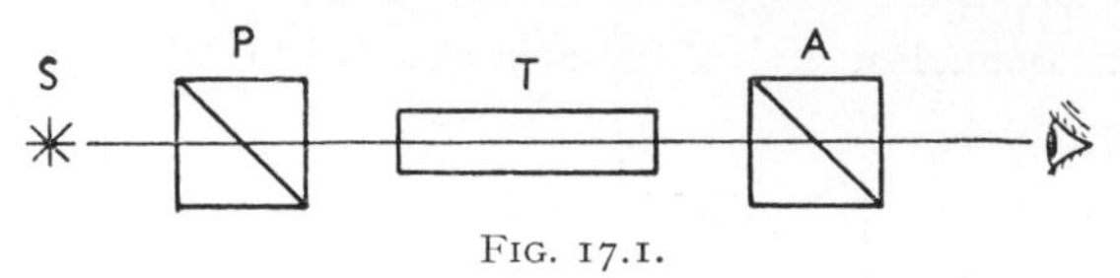

FIG. 17.1.

If the substance rotates the plane of polarisation to the right, *i.e.*, if the analyser has to be turned to the right (clockwise) to restore the original field, the substance is said to be *dextrorotatory*; if to the left (anticlockwise), *lævorotatory*.

It has been found that the amount of the rotation depends, for a given substance, on a number of factors, *e.g.*, (i) the thickness of the layer traversed, (ii) the nature of the solvent (if in solution), (iii) the temperature, and (iv) the wavelength of the light used. If $[\alpha]$ represents the *specific rotation*, l the thickness of the layer in decimetres, d the density of the liquid (if a solution is being examined, d is equal to the number of grams of substance per millilitre of solution), and the determination is carried out at temperature $t°$ using sodium light (the D line), then if α is the *observed* rotation (+ or −),

$$[\alpha]^t_D = \frac{\alpha^t_D}{l \times d}$$

Since the value of the rotation depends on the solvent, this should also be stated.

The original method of indicating optical isomers was to prefix each isomer by *d* or *l* according as it was dextrorotatory or lævorotatory. Van't Hoff (1874) introduced a + and − notation for designating the configuration of an asymmetric carbon atom. He used mechanical models (built of tetrahedra), and the + and − signs were given by observing the tetrahedra of the mechanical model from the centre of the model. Thus a molecule of the type C*abd*–C*abd* may be designated ++, −−, and +− (see also p. 390). E. Fischer (1891) pointed out that this + and − notation can lead to wrong interpretations when applied to molecules containing more than two asymmetric carbon atoms (the signs given depend on the point of observation in the molecule.) Fischer therefore proposed the use of plane projection diagrams of the mechanical models instead of the + and − system.

Fischer, working on the configurations of the sugars, obtained the plane formulæ (I) and (II) for the enantiomorphs of saccharic acid, and *arbitrarily* chose (I) for dextrorotatory saccharic acid, and called it *d*-saccharic acid. He then, *from this*, deduced formula (III) for *d*-glucose. Furthermore, Fischer thought it was more important to indicate stereochemical relationships than merely to indicate the actual direction of rotation. He therefore proposed that **the prefixes *d* and *l* should refer to stereochemical relationships and not to the direction of rotation of the compound.** The question now is: Is it possible to choose a standard to which all sugars may be referred? Fischer apparently intended to use the scheme whereby the compounds derived from a *given aldehyde sugar* should be designated according to the *direction of rotation of the parent aldose*.

* All standard text-books of Practical Physical Chemistry describe the construction and operation of polarimeters.

Natural mannose is dextrorotatory. Hence natural mannose will be *d*-mannose, and all derivatives of *d*-mannose, *e.g.*, mannonic acid, mannose phenylhydrazone, etc., will thus belong to the *d*-series. Natural glucose is dextrorotary. Hence natural glucose will be *d*-glucose, and all its derivatives

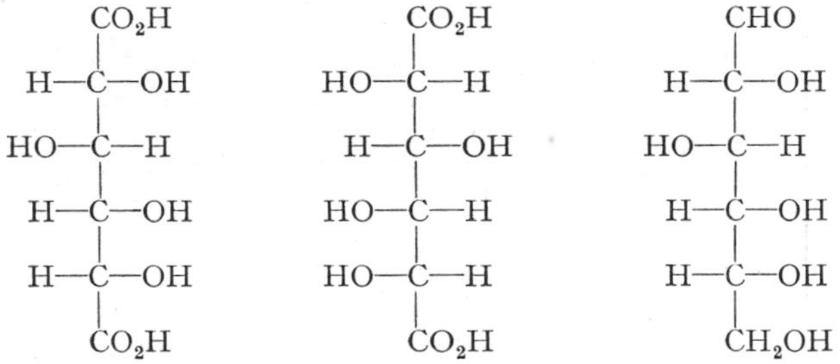

$$
\begin{array}{ccc}
\begin{array}{c} CO_2H \\ H-C-OH \\ HO-C-H \\ H-C-OH \\ H-C-OH \\ CO_2H \\ \text{(I)} \end{array}
&
\begin{array}{c} CO_2H \\ HO-C-H \\ H-C-OH \\ HO-C-H \\ HO-C-H \\ CO_2H \\ \text{(II)} \end{array}
&
\begin{array}{c} CHO \\ H-C-OH \\ HO-C-H \\ H-C-OH \\ H-C-OH \\ CH_2OH \\ \text{(III)} \end{array}
\end{array}
$$

will belong to the *d*-series. Furthermore, Fischer (1890) was able to convert natural mannose into natural glucose, and since the latter is *d*-glucose (according to Fischer's scheme), the prefix *d* for natural glucose *happens* to agree with its dextrorotation (with *d*-mannose as standard). Now natural fructose can also be prepared from natural mannose (or natural glucose), and so will be *d*-fructose. Natural fructose, however, is lævorotatory, and so is written as *d*(—)-fructose, the symbol *d* indicating its *stereochemical* relationship to the parent aldose glucose, and the symbol — placed in parentheses before the name indicating the *actual direction of rotation*.

More recently, the symbols *d* and *l* have been replaced by D and L for configurational relationships, *e.g.*, L(+)-lactic acid. Also, when dealing with compounds that cannot be referred to sugars, (+)- and (—)- are used to indicate the sign of rotation. The prefixes *dextro* and *lævo* (without hyphens) are also used.

Fischer's proposal to use *each aldose* as the arbitrary standard for its derivatives leads to some difficulties, *e.g.*, natural arabinose is dextrorotatory, and so is to be designated D-arabinose. Now this D-arabinose can be converted into mannonic acid, which, if D-arabinose is the parent aldose, will therefore be D-mannonic acid. This same acid, however, can also be obtained from L-mannose, and so should be L-mannonic acid. Thus in cases such as this the use of the symbol D or L will depend on the *historical order* in which the stereochemical relationships were established!

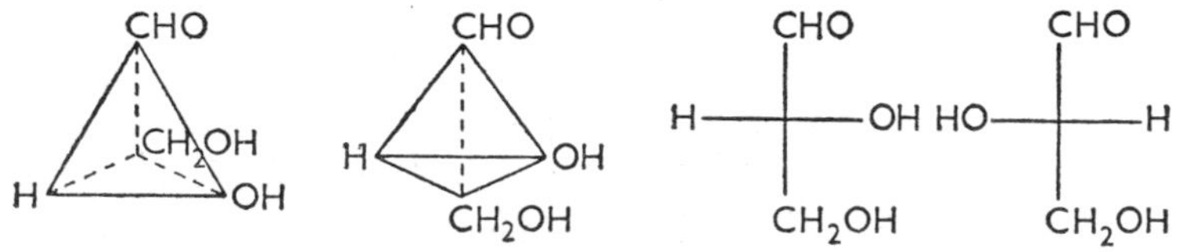

$$
\begin{array}{cc}
\begin{array}{c} CHO \\ H-C-OH \\ CH_2OH \\ (c) \end{array}
&
\begin{array}{c} CHO \\ HO-C-H \\ CH_2OH \\ (d) \end{array}
\end{array}
$$

(*a*) (*b*) (*c*) (*d*)

FIG. 17.2.

Rosanoff (1906) showed that if the enantiomorphs of glyceraldehyde (a molecule which contains only *one* asymmetric carbon atom) are chosen as the (arbitrary) standard, then a satisfactory system for correlating stereochemical relationships can be developed. He also proposed that the formula of dextrorotatory glyceraldehyde should be written as in Fig. 2 (*c*), in order that the arrangement of its asymmetric carbon atom should agree with the arrangement of C_5 (C_1 is the carbon of the CHO group) in Fischer's projection formula for natural glucose (see formula (III) above).

It is of great interest to note in this connection that in 1906 the active forms of glyceraldehyde had not been isolated, but in 1914 Wohl and Momber separated DL-glyceraldehyde into its enantiomorphs, and in 1917 they showed that dextrorotary glyceraldehyde was stereochemically related to natural glucose (*i.e.*, with D(+)-glyceraldehyde as arbitrary standard, natural glucose is D(+)-glucose).

The accepted convention for drawing D(+)-glyceraldehyde—the agreed (*arbitrary*) standard—is shown in Fig. 2 (*a*). The tetrahedron is drawn so that three corners are imagined to be *above* the plane of the paper, and the fourth *below* this plane. Furthermore, the spatial arrangement of the four groups joined to the central carbon atom *must be placed as shown in* (*a*), *i.e.*, the accepted convention for drawing D(+)-glyceraldehyde places the *hydrogen atom at the left and the hydroxyl group at the right, with the aldehyde group at the top corner.* Now imagine the tetrahedron to rotate about the horizontal line joining H and OH until it takes up position (*b*). This is the conventional position for a tetrahedron, groups joined to *full horizontal* lines being *above* the plane of the paper, and those joined to *broken vertical* lines being *below* the plane of the paper. The *conventional plane-diagram* is obtained by drawing the full horizontal and broken vertical lines of (*b*) as full lines, placing the groups as they appear in (*b*), and taking the asymmetric carbon atom to be at the point where the lines cross. Although (*c*) is a plane-diagram, it is most important to remember that horizontal lines represent groups above the plane, and vertical lines groups below the plane of the paper. Fig. (*d*) represents the plane-diagram formula of L(—)-glyceraldehyde; here *the hydrogen atom is to the right and the hydroxyl group to the left.* Another way of drawing (*c*) and (*d*) is to use *broken vertical* lines (instead of the full lines shown). Thus any compound that can be prepared from, or converted into, D(+)-glyceraldehyde will belong to the D-series. Similarly, any compound that can be prepared from, or converted into, L(—)-glyceraldehyde will belong to the L-series. When representing relative configurational relationships of molecules containing more than one asymmetric carbon atom, *the asymmetric carbon atom of glyceraldehyde is always drawn at the bottom,* the rest of the molecule being built up from this unit.

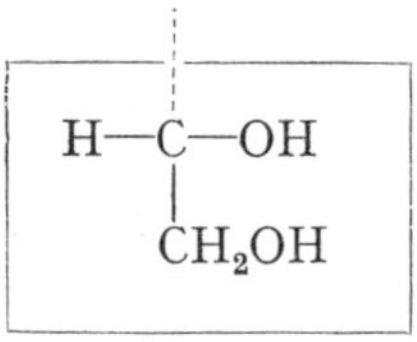

```
      ¦                     ¦                   CO2H
  H—C—OH               HO—C—H             H—|—OH
      |                     |                HO—|—H
      CH2OH                 CH2OH              CO2H
```

D-series 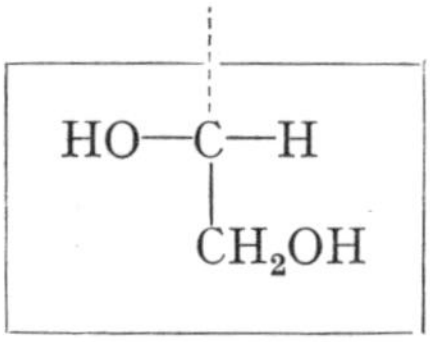 L-series 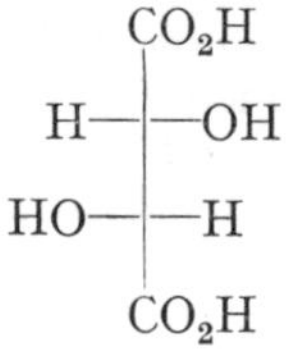 D(+)-tartaric acid

Thus we have a scheme of classification of *relative* configurations based on D(+)-glyceraldehyde as *arbitrary* standard. Until recently there was no way of determining, with certainty, the *absolute* configuration of molecules. *Arbitrary choice* makes the configuration of D(+)-glyceraldehyde have the hydrogen to the left and the hydroxyl to the right. Bijvoet *et al.* (1951), however, have shown by X-ray analysis that dextrorotatory tartaric acid has the configuration assigned to it by E. Fischer. Hence tartaric acid can be used as an *absolute* standard (see p. 398).

In 1848, Pasteur separated sodium ammonium racemate (p. 400) into two kinds of crystals by hand, and found that the specific rotation of each kind of crystal was the same, but one was dextrorotatory and the other, lævorotatory. Pasteur was able to separate the crystals by hand because he observed that they had hemihedral facets, one set of crystals being the mirror images of the other set. Such crystals, one being the mirror image of the other, are said to be *enantiomorphous*.

It has been found that only those structures, crystalline or molecular, which are *not* superimposable on their mirror images, are optically active. Such structures may be *asymmetric*, or *dissymmetric*. Asymmetric means completely devoid of the elements of symmetry. Dissymmetric means not completely devoid of symmetry, but possessing so few elements of symmetry as still to be capable of existing in two forms (one the mirror image of the other) which are not superimposable. To avoid unnecessary complications, we shall use the term asymmetric to cover both cases (of asymmetry and dissymmetry). If a compound is asymmetric, then it is to be expected that the original molecule and its mirror image might differ in some properties although their structures are identical. Experience shows that the most marked difference is their action on polarised light.

Optical activity may be due entirely to the *crystal structure being asymmetric, e.g.*, quartz. In such cases the substance is optically active only so long as it remains solid, the optical activity being lost when the solid is fused or dissolved in a solvent. Quartz crystals exist in hemihedral forms. Hemihedral faces are those faces not symmetrically placed with respect to other faces; they occur only in *half* the positions where they might be expected to occur, and thus give the crystal an asymmetric structure (actually dissymmetric). The (+)- and (—)-forms of quartz are mirror images; but it should be noticed that many optically active crystals do not possess hemihedral faces.

On the other hand, optical activity may be due entirely to *molecular* structure. In this case the *molecular structure is asymmetric, i.e.*, the compounds have molecules in which the *atoms* are arranged spatially so that the original molecule is not superimposable on its mirror image. Such compounds are optically active in the solid, fused, dissolved or gaseous state, *e.g.*, sucrose, lactic acid, limonene, etc.

A molecule and its mirror image, when they are not superimposable, are known as *enantiomorphs* (this name taken from crystallography) or *optical antipodes*. It appears that enantiomorphs are identical physically except in their manner of rotating polarised light; the rotations are equal but opposite. The crystal forms of enantiomorphs may be mirror images of each other, *i.e.*, the crystals themselves may be enantiomorphous, but this is unusual. Enantiomorphs are similar chemically, but their rates of reaction with other optically active substances are usually different. They may also be different physiologically, *e.g.*, (+)-histidine is sweet, (—)-tasteless; (—)-nicotine is more poisonous than (+)-; D(—) ascorbic acid (vitamin C) is more efficient than L(+)-.

In 1874, van't Hoff and Le Bel, independently, gave the solution to the problem of optical isomerism. Van't Hoff proposed the theory that if the four valencies of the carbon atom are arranged tetrahedrally with the carbon atom at the centre, then all the cases of isomerism known are accounted for. Le Bel's theory is substantially the same as van't Hoff's, but differs in that whereas van't Hoff believed that the valency distribution was definitely tetrahedral and fixed as such, Le Bel believed that the valency directions were not rigidly fixed, and did not specify the tetrahedral arrangement, but thought that *whatever* the spatial arrangement, the molecule C*abde* would be *asymmetric* Van't Hoff's theory is more in keeping with later work, *e.g.*, in recent years physico-chemical evidence—X-ray and dipole moment studies—has shown that saturated carbon compounds exhibit a tetrahedral structure and that the carbon atom is situated inside the tetrahedron at the centre. Before the tetrahedral theory was suggested, it was believed that the four valencies of carbon were planar.

Two postulates underlie the tetrahedral theory.

(i) *The principle of constancy of the valency angle.* Mathematical calculation of the angle subtended by each side of a regular tetrahedron at the central carbon atom (Fig. 3) gives a value of 109° 28′. Originally it was postulated (van't Hoff) that the valency angle was fixed at this value. It is now known, however, that the valency angle may deviate from this value, *e.g.*, in various ring structures; even so, great deviations lead to instability (see p. 463).

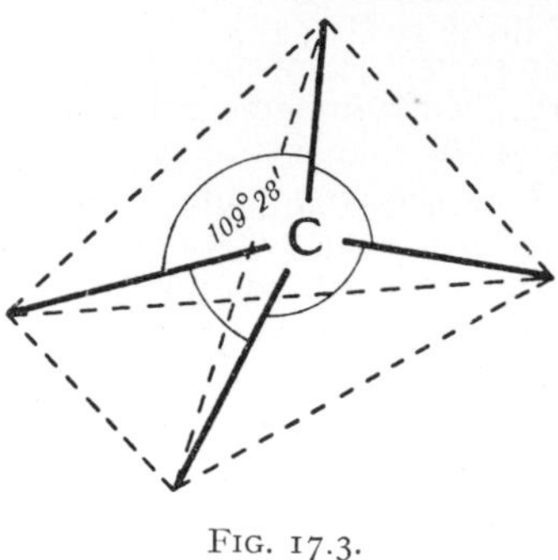

FIG. 17.3.

Quantum mechanical calculations show that the four valencies of carbon (in saturated compounds) are equivalent and directed towards the four corners of a regular tetrahedron; these four valencies are formed by the hybridisation of $2s$ and $2p^3$ electrons (p. 23). Furthermore, quantum mechanical calculation require the carbon bond angles to be close to the tetrahedral value, since change from this value is associated with loss in bond strength and consequently decrease in stability (see also p. 464).

(ii) *The principle of free rotation about a single bond.* Consider the ethane molecule, $CH_3—CH_3$, and let us imagine that one methyl group is rotated about the C—C bond as axis with the other group at rest. The energy content, E, of the molecule will undergo the regular changes shown in Fig. 4 (*a*). Had there been complete free rotation, the graph would have been a horizontal straight line. Fig. (*b*) [the *projection formula*, obtained by viewing

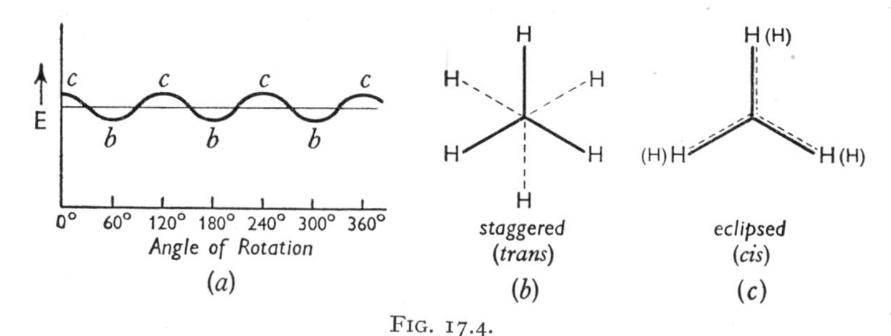

FIG. 17.4.

the molecule along the bonding line of the two carbon atoms] represents the *trans* or *staggered* form in which the hydrogen atoms (on the two carbon atoms) are as far apart as possible. To change from this form to the *cis* or *eclipsed* form in which the hydrogen atoms are as close together as possible (Fig. *c*), energy must be supplied to overcome, among other things, the repulsion between hydrogen atoms. Thus the energy content of the molecule in the eclipsed conformation is greater than that in the staggered conformation. The actual energy difference is 2·75 kg. cal./mole. This is much too small for either form to remain stable, *i.e.*, the eclipsed and staggered forms are readily interconvertible, and so only one form of ethane can be isolated. Even so, the staggered conformation is the preferred form (see below).

Now let us consider ethylene chloride. Here the energy changes are larger because (among other things) of the strong electrostatic repulsion between the chlorine atoms. According to Bernstein (1949), the potential energy of ethylene chloride undergoes the changes shown in Fig. 5. There are two positions of minimum energy, but the staggered conformation is the more preferred one, *i.e.*, the one in which the molecule largely remains. Dipole moment studies show that this is so in practice, and according to

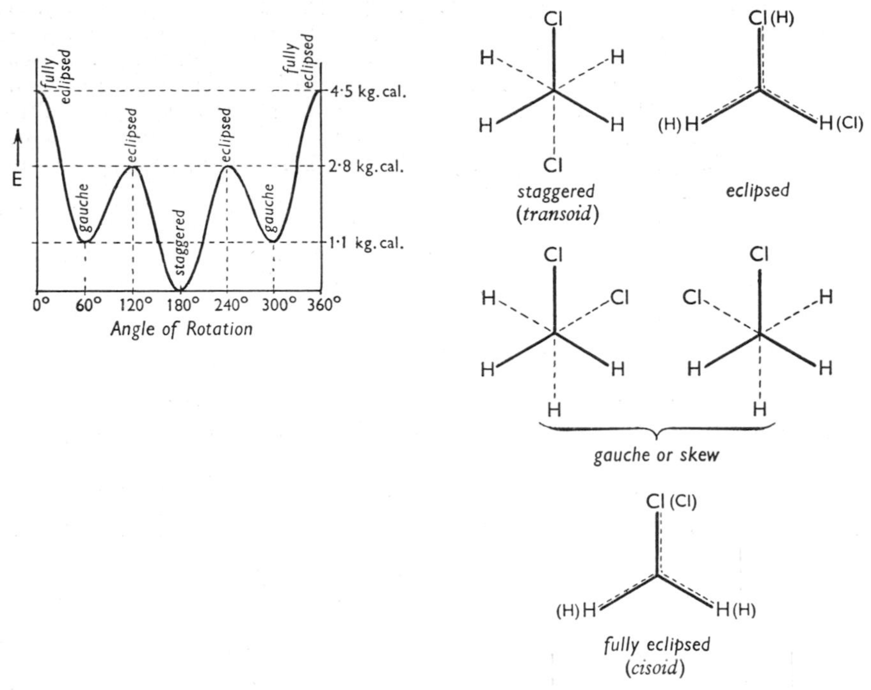

FIG. 17.5.

Mizushima *et al.* (1938), only the staggered form is present at low temperatures.

Thus, in theory, there is no free rotation about a single bond, but in practice it may occur if the various forms do not differ very much in energy content (usually between 1 and 10 kg. cal./mole). Molecules which can form isomers by rotation about single bonds are called **flexible molecules,** and the different forms taken up are different **conformations** (see also p. 465) or **rotational isomers.** Usually. the staggered conformation is the most stable one, and the eclipsed form is always avoided where possible.

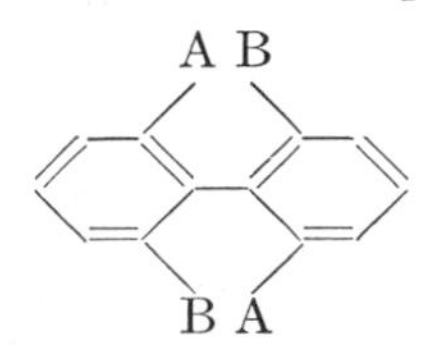

Free rotation about a single bond is generally accepted in *simple* molecules. *Restricted rotation* about a single bond, however, may take place when the molecule contains groups large enough to impede free rotation, *e.g.*, in *ortho*-substituted diphenyls (p. 672), if groups A and B are sufficiently large, the two benzene rings cannot rotate through 360° about the single bond joining the two rings. In some cases, resonance may give rise to restricted rotation about a single bond (see, *e.g.*, p. 659).

It has been pointed out in the foregoing account that the basis of optical activity is that the molecule should be asymmetric. The simplest type of asymmetric structure is that which contains one carbon atom joined to four different atoms or groups, *i.e.*, a molecule of the type C*abde*, in which the groups, *a*, *b*, *d* or *e* may or may not contain carbon. The carbon atom in C*abde* is said to be asymmetric (actually, of course, it is the *group* which is asymmetric; a *carbon atom* cannot be asymmetric). Up to the present time, compounds of the type Ca_4 (*e.g.*, CCl_4), Ca_3b (*e.g.*, $CHCl_3$), Ca_2b_2 (*e.g.*, CH_2Cl_2), Ca_2bd (*e.g.*, $CH_2OH{\cdot}CO_2H$) have never been observed to exist as optical isomers. Only one form of each is known. This agrees with the tetrahedral configuration, *e.g.*, Ca_2bd (Fig. 6). (II), the mirror image of (I), is superimposable on (I); however the four groups are arranged in the tetrahedron, (II) is always superimposable on (I) (see footnote, p. 36). Thus there is only one form of Ca_2bd. Similarly, there is only one form of Ca_4, Ca_3b or Ca_2b_2. On the other hand, the tetrahedral structure of $Cabde$ gives two forms (no more), one related to the other as object and mirror image, which are *not* superimposable (Fig. 7). Thus a molecule of the type $Cabde$

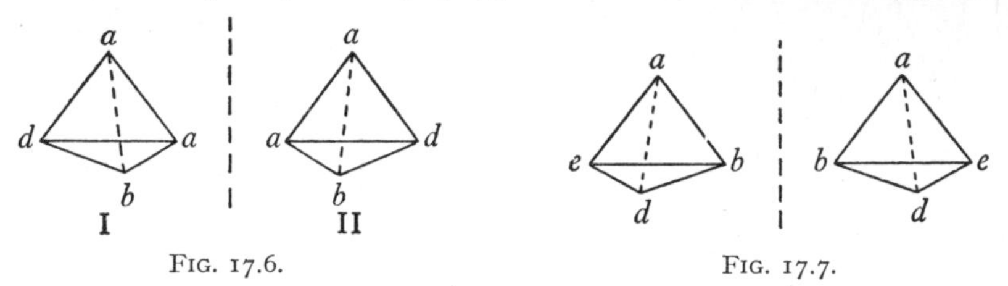

FIG. 17.6.

FIG. 17.7.

should exist in two forms; and these should be detectable if the difference between them (physical or chemical) is sufficiently great. This would account for the structural identity and optical activity of molecules of the type $Cabde$, *e.g.*, the lactic acids, $CH_3{\cdot}CHOH{\cdot}CO_2H$ (Fig. 8). (III) and (IV)

FIG. 17.8.

are mirror images and cannot be superimposed. Further evidence that optical activity is due to this arrangement is shown by the fact that if lactic acid is reduced to propionic acid, optical activity disappears; propionic acid, $CH_3{\cdot}CH_2{\cdot}CO_2H$, is a molecule of the type Ca_2bd, which is superimposable on its mirror image.

Groups *a, b, d, e* are all different, but two or more may be *structural* isomers, *e.g.*, propyl*iso*propylmethanol is optically active. The substitution of hydrogen by deuterium has also been investigated in recent years to ascertain whether these two atoms are sufficiently different to give rise to optical isomerism. The earlier work gave conflicting results, but later work appears to be conclusive in favour of optical activity, *e.g.*, Eliel (1949) prepared optically active methylphenyldeuteromethane, $CH_3{\cdot}CHD{\cdot}C_6H_5$, by reducing optically active methylphenylmethyl chloride with lithium aluminium deuteride.

Lactic acid obtained from sour milk (and by any of the other methods described on p. 380) is *not* optically active. If we examine an equimolecular mixture of the dextrorotatory and lævorotatory lactic acids, we shall find that the mixture is optically inactive. This is to be expected, since optical isomers have equal but opposite rotatory power. Such a mixture (of equimolecular amounts) is said to be **optically inactive by external compensation,** and is known as a **racemic modification.** A racemic modification may be a purely mechanical mixture, a compound, or a solid solution; for this reason it is better to use the term *racemic modification* than *racemic* *mixture.* Lactic acid, which is optically inactive by external compensation, is known as racemic (*r*-) or DL-lactic acid.

We can now therefore account for the existence of three lactic acids:

(i) L(+)-lactic acid, m.p. 26°; prepared from meat extract (sarcolactic acid).
(ii) D(—)-lactic acid, m.p. 26°; prepared by the fermentation of sucrose by *Bacillus acidi lævolactiti.*
(iii) DL-lactic acid, m.p. 18°; prepared from *e.g.*, sour milk.

Thus a compound with *one* asymmetric carbon atom exists in three forms: D, L, and DL (or *r*-).

Isomeric with lactic acid is **hydracrylic acid** or **β-hydroxypropionic acid,** $CH_2OH{\cdot}CH_2{\cdot}CO_2H$. β-Hydroxypropionic acid may be prepared in a number of ways, *e.g.*, by the hydrolysis of ethylene cyanohydrin:

$$CH_2OH{\cdot}CH_2Cl \xrightarrow{KCN} CH_2OH{\cdot}CH_2{\cdot}CN \xrightarrow{NaOH} CH_2OH{\cdot}CH_2{\cdot}CO_2H \quad (28\text{–}31\%)$$

It may also be prepared by the action of silver oxide in boiling water on β-halogeno-propionic acid:

$$CH_2Br{\cdot}CH_2{\cdot}CO_2H + \text{“ AgOH ”} \longrightarrow CH_2OH{\cdot}CH_2{\cdot}CO_2H + AgBr$$

β-Hydroxypropionic acid is a sour, syrupy liquid. It is *not* optically active (it does not contain an asymmetric carbon atom). When heated, it loses a molecule of water to form acrylic acid.

$$CH_2OH{\cdot}CH_2{\cdot}CO_2H \longrightarrow CH_2{:}CH{\cdot}CO_2H + H_2O$$

When oxidised, β-hydroxypropionic acid forms malonic acid:

$$CH_2OH{\cdot}CH_2{\cdot}CO_2H \xrightarrow{[O]} CO_2H{\cdot}CH_2{\cdot}CO_2H$$

β-**Hydroxybutyric acid** (3-*hydroxybutanoic acid*), $CH_3{\cdot}CHOH{\cdot}CH_2{\cdot}CO_2H$, may be prepared by oxidising aldol with ammoniacal silver nitrate:

$$CH_3{\cdot}CHOH{\cdot}CH_2{\cdot}CHO + Ag_2O \longrightarrow CH_3{\cdot}CHOH{\cdot}CH_2{\cdot}CO_2H + 2Ag$$

It may also be prepared by reducing acetoacetic ester, and hydrolysing the product:

$$CH_3{\cdot}CO{\cdot}CH_2{\cdot}CO_2C_2H_5 \xrightarrow{[H]} CH_3{\cdot}CHOH{\cdot}CH_2{\cdot}CO_2C_2H_5 \xrightarrow[\text{(ii) HCl}]{\text{(i) KOH}} CH_3{\cdot}CHOH{\cdot}CH_2{\cdot}CO_2H$$

β-Hydroxybutyric acid can exist in D- and L-forms (it contains one asymmetric carbon atom). It occurs, together with acetoacetic acid, in diabetic urine; the acid found in urine is lævorotatory. When heated with sodium hydroxide solution, β-hydroxybutyric acid forms crotonic acid:

$$CH_3{\cdot}CHOH{\cdot}CH_2{\cdot}CO_2H \longrightarrow CH_3{\cdot}CH{:}CH{\cdot}CO_2H + H_2O$$

HYDROXY-DIBASIC AND POLYBASIC ACIDS

Before describing the individual acids, let us consider the stereochemistry of a molecule containing two asymmetric carbon atoms. First let us consider the case of a compound containing two structurally dissimilar carbon atoms, *i.e.*, compounds of the type *Cabd·Cabe*, *e.g.*, $CH_3{\cdot}\mathbf{C}HBr{\cdot}\mathbf{C}HBr{\cdot}CO_2H$. Investigation shows that there are four possible spatial arrangements for this type of structure (Fig. 9). (I) and (II) are enantiomorphs, and an equimolecular mixture of them forms a racemic modification; similarly for (III) and (IV). Thus there are four optically active forms. In general, a compound containing n different asymmetric carbon atoms exists in 2^n-optically active forms.

(I) and (III) are not identical in configuration and are not mirror images;

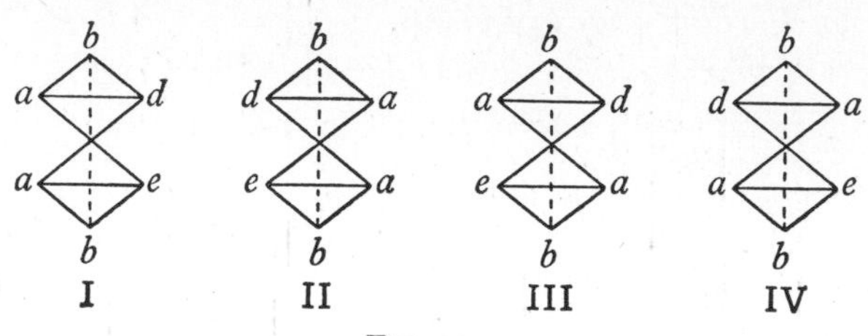

FIG. 17.9.

they are known as **diastereoisomers,** *i.e.*, they are optical isomers but not mirror images (not enantiomorphs). Thus a compound of the type *Cabd*·*Cabe* exists in six forms: two pairs of enantiomorphs, and two racemic modifications. Diastereoisomers differ in physical properties, such as melting point, solubility, specific rotation, etc. Chemically they are similar, but their rates of reaction with other optically active compounds are different.

The plane-diagrams of the molecules (I–IV) in Fig. 9 will be (V–VIII), respectively, as shown below:

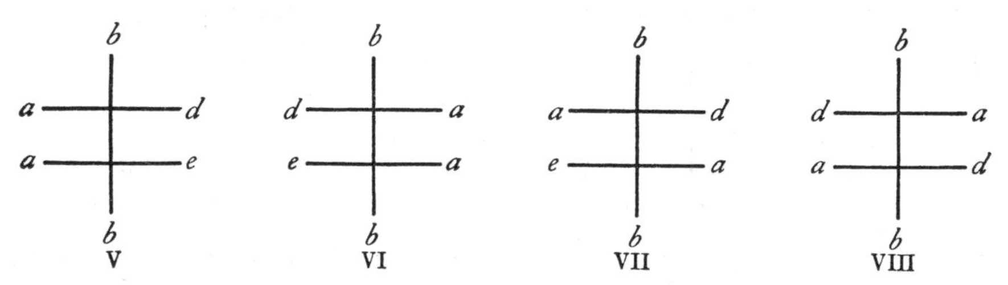

When the formulæ are written as plane-diagrams, it is not always easy to see whether the mirror image is superimposable on the original molecule. A test for non-superimposability of plane-diagrams is to rotate the formula of the mirror image through 180° in the plane of the paper; if the result is the *same* formula as the original molecule, then the two molecules (original and image) are superimposable, and consequently not optically active (see also plane of symmetry, below).

Instead of writing down all the possible configurations, the number of optical isomers for a compound of the type *Cabd*·*Cabe* may be obtained by indicating the *configuration* of each asymmetric carbon atom by the symbol + or —, or by D or L; thus:

Cabd	+ —	+ —	D_1 L_1	D_1 L_1
|				
Cabe	+ —	— +	D_2 L_2	L_2 D_2
	(±)	(±)	DL	DL

Now let us consider the case of a compound containing two asymmetric carbon atoms which are structurally the same, *i.e.*, compounds of the type

C*abd*·C*abd*, *e.g.*, tartaric acid, $CO_2H{\cdot}CHOH{\cdot}CHOH{\cdot}CO_2H$. In compounds of this type, it is obvious that $D_1 = D_2$.

C*abd*	D	L	D	L
|				
C*abd*	D	L	L	D
	(IX)	(X)	(XI)	(XII)

In molecules (IX) and (X), the upper and lower halves reinforce each other; hence (IX), as a whole, has the dextro-, and (X), the lævo-configuration, *i.e.*, (IX) and (X) are optically active, and enantiomorphous. On the other hand, in (XI) the two equal halves are in opposition, and hence the molecule, *as a whole,* will not show optical activity. It is also obvious that (XI) and (XII) are identical, *i.e.*, there is only *one* optically inactive form of C*abd*·C*abd*. Molecule (XI) is said to be **optically inactive by internal compensation**; it is known as the ***meso*-form,** and is a disastereoisomer of (IX) and (X). Thus there are four possible forms: D-, L-, DL- and *meso*-. The *meso*-form is also known as the *inactive* form and is represented as the *i*-form. **The *meso*-form cannot be resolved.**

Molecule (XI) is an example of a *compound having two asymmetric carbon atoms, but is optically inactive* (by internal compensation). It is therefore obvious that inspection of the usual structural formula, which contains two (or more) asymmetric carbon atoms, is not sufficient to decide whether the molecule is optically active or not. *The molecule as a whole must be asymmetric.* The test of superimposing the original formula (tetrahedral) on its mirror image definitely indicates whether the molecule is symmetrical or not. The only satisfactory way in which superimposability may be ascertained is to build up models of the molecule and its mirror image. Uusally, this is not convenient. Alternatively, superimposability may be determined by rotation of the plane-formula in the plane of the paper (see above). A much simpler device to decide whether a molecule is symmetrical or not is to ascertain whether it contains a *plane of symmetry*, a *centre of symmetry*, or an *alternating axis of symmetry*. If any one of these is present the molecule is symmetrical, *i.e.*, superimposable on its mirror image.

A **plane of symmetry** divides a molecule in such a way that points (atoms or groups of atoms) on the one side of the plane form mirror images of those on the other side. This test may be applied to both solid and plane-formulæ, *e.g.*, the plane-formula of the *meso* form of C*abd*·C*abd* possesses a plane of symmetry; the other two, D- and L, do not:

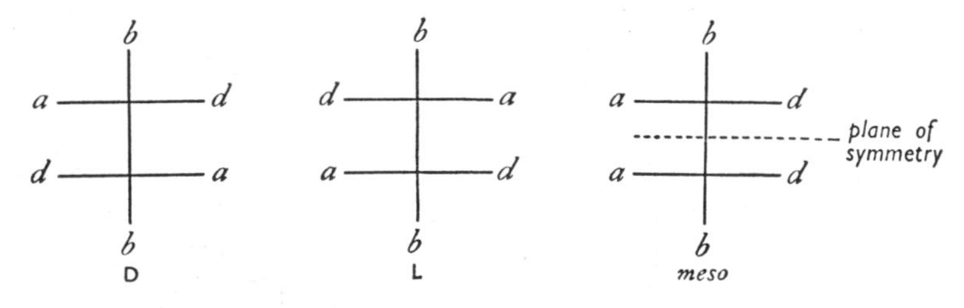

It should also be observed that rotation of the formula of the mirror image of the *meso* form through 180° in the plane of the paper produces the formula of the original molecule. Similar treatment of the L-formula does not produce the D-formula.

A **centre of symmetry** is a point from which lines, when drawn on one side and produced an equal distance on the other side, will meet exactly similar points in the molecule. This test can be satisfactorily applied only to three-dimensional formulæ, particularly those of ring systems, *e.g.*,

(i)

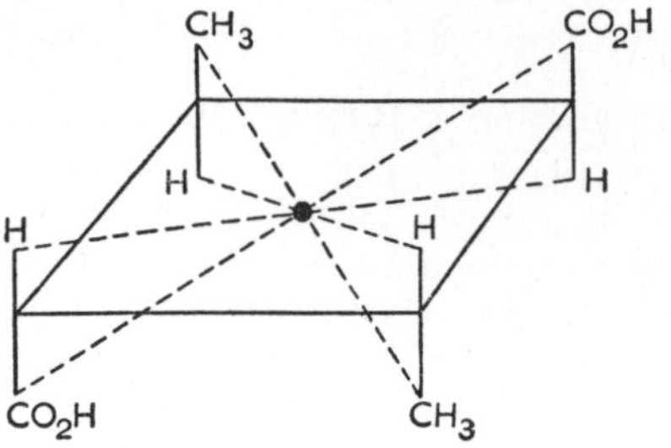

2 : 4-dimethyl*cyclo*butane-1 : 3-dicarboxylic acid. The form shown possesses a centre of symmetry which is the centre of the ring. This form is therefore optically inactive.

(ii) Dimethyldiketopiperazine exists in two geometrical isomeric forms, *cis* and *trans*:

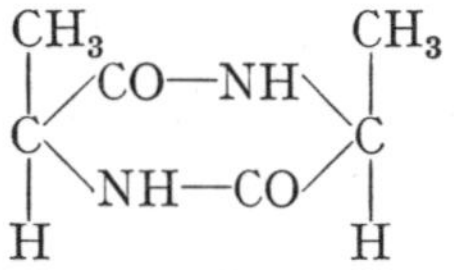

cis 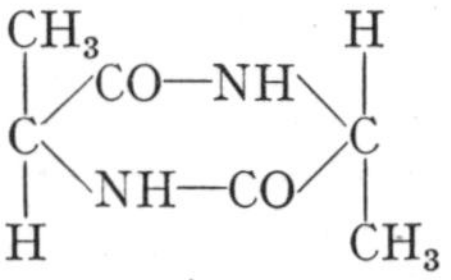 *trans*

The *cis* isomer has neither a plane nor a centre of symmetry. It can therefore exist in two enantiomorphous forms; both are known. The *trans* isomer has a centre of symmetry and is therefore optically inactive.

It is important to note that only *even-numbered* rings can possibly possess a centre of symmetry.

Up to the present, all optically active *natural* compounds have been found to consist of molecules which owe their asymmetry to the absence of both a plane and centre of symmetry. It is possible, however, for these elements of symmetry to be *absent* and the molecule to be superimposable on its mirror image and hence not be optically active. Such a molecule will possess an **alternating axis of symmetry.** This may be defined as follows: a molecule possesses an n-fold alternating axis of symmetry if, when rotated through an angle of $360°/n$ about this axis and then followed by reflection in a plane perpendicular to the axis, the molecule is the same as it was in the starting position.

McCasland and Proskow (1956) have now synthesised, for the first time, a compound which owes its symmetry to the presence of an alternating axis of symmetry only (this compound possesses neither a plane nor a centre of

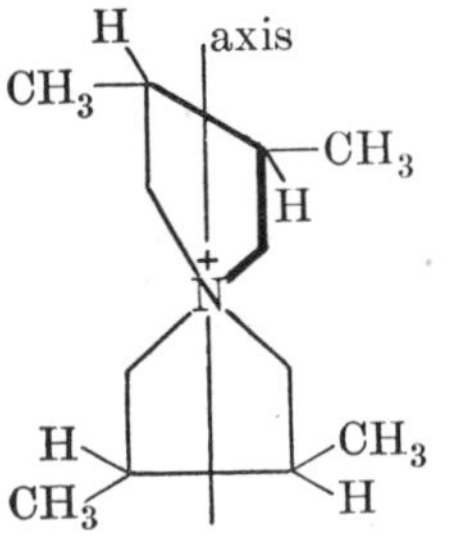

(XIII) 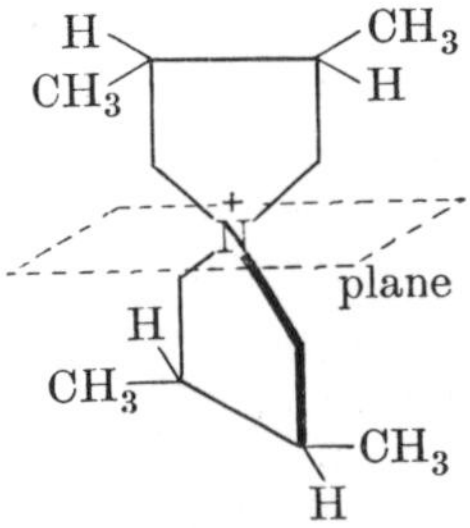 (XIV)

symmetry). It is the *N*-spiro-compound (XIII) (as the *p*-toluenesulphonate). If (XIII) is rotated through 90° about the co-axis of the two rings, (XIV) is obtained. Reflection of (XIV) through a central plane perpendicular to this axis gives a molecule identical and coincident with (XIII).

Resolution of Racemic Modifications

When optically active compounds are prepared by synthetic methods, the usual result is a racemic modification; *e.g.*, bromination of propionic acid results in the formation of DL-α-bromopropionic acid:

$$CH_3{\cdot}CH_2{\cdot}CO_2H \xrightarrow{Br_2/P} CH_3{\cdot}CHBr{\cdot}CO_2H$$

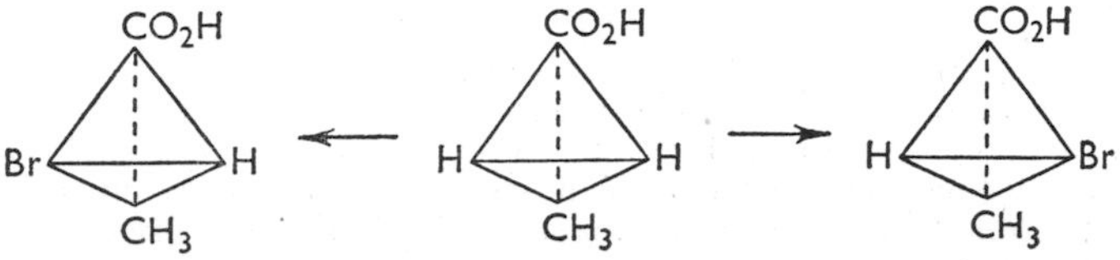

CO₂H / Br, H / CH₃ — II ← CO₂H / H, H / CH₃ — I → CO₂H / H, Br / CH₃ — III

FIG. 17.10.

(II) and (III) (Fig. 10) are enantiomorphs, and since molecule (I) is symmetrical about its vertical axis, it can be anticipated from the theory of probability that either hydrogen atom should be replaced equally well to give DL-α-bromopropionic acid. This actually does occur in practice.

The process of separating a racemic modification into its enantiomorphs is known as *resolution*. Various methods have been introduced.

1. **Mechanical separation** (Pasteur, 1848). In this method the crystals are, if sufficiently well defined, actually separated by hand; the crystals must be enantiomorphous. This method is applicable only to racemic *mixtures*, and is mainly of historical interest. This method of resolution is also known as **spontaneous resolution.**

2. **Biochemical separation** (Pasteur, 1858). Certain bacteria and moulds, when they grow in a dilute solution of a racemic modification, destroy one optical isomer more rapidly than the other; *e.g.*, *Penicillium glaucum* (a mould), when grown in a solution of ammonium racemate, attacks the D-form leaving the L-.

3. **By means of salt-formation** (Pasteur, 1858). This method, which is the best of all the methods of resolution, consists in converting the optical isomers in a racemic modification into *diastereoisomers*; *e.g.*, if an optically active base is combined with a racemic acid, two diastereoisomers are obtained:

$$(D_{acid} + L_{acid}) + 2D_{base} \longrightarrow (D_{acid}D_{base}) + (L_{acid}D_{base})$$

Because of their different solubilities, these diastereoisomers may be separated by fractional crystallisation. After separation, the acids may be regenerated by hydrolysis with inorganic acids or with alkalis.

Bases which are used for the resolution of racemic acids are mainly alkaloids, *e.g.*, quinine, strychnine, brucine, cinchonine, morphine, etc.

Acids which are used for the resolution of racemic bases are, *e.g.*, tartaric acid, camphorsulphonic acid, bromocamphorsulphonic acid.

The method of salt-formation has been extended to compounds other than acids and bases, *e.g.*, (i) Racemic alcohols are converted into the acid ester derivative with phthalic anhydride:

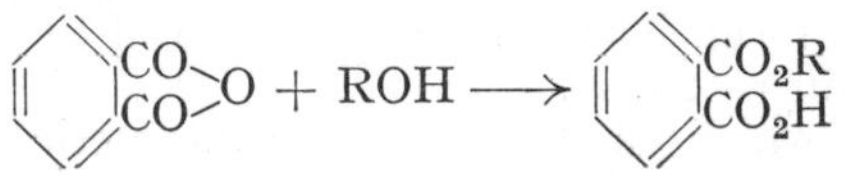

$$C_6H_4\begin{matrix}CO\\CO\end{matrix}\!\!>\!O + ROH \longrightarrow C_6H_4\begin{matrix}CO_2R\\CO_2H\end{matrix}$$

The acid ester, consisting of equimolecular amounts of the D- and L-forms, may now be resolved by the method used for acids.

(ii) Racemic aldehydes and racemic ketones may be resolved by means of optically active derivatives of hydrazine, *e.g.*, (—)-menthylhydrazine.

Resolution of racemic modifications by means of salt formation may be complicated by the phenomenon of *asymmetric transformation*. This phenomenon is exhibited by compounds that are optically unstable, *i.e.*, the enantiomorphs are readily interconvertible:

$$(+)\text{-C} \rightleftharpoons (-)\text{-C}$$

It is possible to get *complete* conversion of C into the form (as salt) that crystallises from solution. The form may be (+) or (—), depending on the nature of the base (used for resolving acids) and the solvent.

4. **Selective adsorption.** Optically active substances may be selectively adsorbed by some optically active adsorbent, *e.g.*, Henderson and Rule (1939) resolved a racemic modification of a camphor derivative on D-lactose as adsorbent; Prelog and Wieland (1944) resolved Tröger's base on D-lactose (p. 412).

5. **Channel complex formation.** This method is possible because the complexes of each enantiomorph have different solubilities; *e.g.*, Schlenk (1952) has resolved (±)-2-chloro-octane by means of channel complex formation with urea (see p. 369).

Racemisation

By using suitable conditions, it is possible to cause most optically active compounds to lose their optical activity without changing their structure. This means that the (+)- and (—)-forms of most optically active compounds are convertible one into the other, the final result being a racemic modification. Such a transformation is known as *racemisation*. The method of effecting racemisation depends on the nature of the compound in question; generally, heat, light or chemical reagents may be used. Thus, if the starting material is the (+)-form, then after treatment half will have been converted into the (—)-form; similarly, when starting with the (—)-form, half will be converted into the (+)-form, *e.g.*, when (+)- or (—)-lactic acid is warmed with sodium hydroxide solution, the result is (±)-lactic acid.

In some cases racemisation occurs spontaneously at room temperature; it is then known as *autoracemisation*, *e.g.*, dimethyl bromosuccinate autoracemises.

Many different types of compounds can racemise, and a number of mechanisms have been developed, each mechanism applying to a particular type of compound. One important type of compound that readily racemises is that in which the asymmetric carbon atom is joined to a hydrogen atom and a negative group. Since this type of compound can undergo tautomeric change, the mechanism proposed for this racemisation is one via enolisation, *e.g.*,

$$\underset{(+)\text{-acid}}{R\text{—}\overset{\overset{\large H}{|}}{\underset{\underset{\large R'}{|}}{C}}\text{—}\overset{\overset{\large O}{\|}}{C}\text{—OH}} \rightleftharpoons \underset{\text{loss of asymmetry}}{\left[R\text{—}\underset{\underset{\large R'}{|}}{C}\text{=}\overset{\overset{\large OH}{|}}{C}\text{—OH}\right]} \rightleftharpoons (\pm)\text{-acid}$$

Clearly, when the intermediate enol form, which is no longer asymmetrical, reverts to the stable form, it can do so equally well to produce the (+)- or (—)-forms, *i.e.*, it will racemise.

Some compounds which cannot undergo tautomeric change can, nevertheless, be racemised, *e.g.*, (—)-limonene, some diphenyl compounds. The mechanism of these racemisations is uncertain.

The Walden Inversion (Optical Inversion)

By a series of reactions, Walden (1893) was able to transform an optically active compound into its optical isomer. In some cases the product is 100 per cent. pure, *i.e.*, the *inversion* is quantitative; in other cases the product is a mixture of the (+)- and (—)-forms, but in unequal quantities, *i.e.*, a partial inversion has taken place.

The phenomenon was first discovered by Walden with the following reactions:

$$\begin{matrix} CHOH{\cdot}CO_2H \\ | \\ CH_2{\cdot}CO_2H \end{matrix} \underset{KOH}{\overset{PCl_5}{\rightleftarrows}} \begin{matrix} CHCl{\cdot}CO_2H \\ | \\ CH_2{\cdot}CO_2H \end{matrix} \xrightarrow{\text{"AgOH"}} \begin{matrix} CHOH{\cdot}CO_2H \\ | \\ CH_2{\cdot}CO_2H \end{matrix}$$

L-malic acid (I) D-chlorosuccinic acid (II) D-malic acid (III)

The change: L-malic acid to D-chlorosuccinic acid to D-malic acid, constitutes a Walden inversion. The Walden inversion may be defined as the conversion of the L-form into the D-, or vice versa, *without recourse to resolution.* In one of the two reactions there must be an interchange of position between two groups; *e.g.*, if the configuration of (I) corresponds with that of (II), the inversion must have taken place between (II) and (III). It is important to note that change in the sign of rotation does not necessarily indicate an inversion of configuration; *e.g.*, when D(+)-glyceraldehyde is oxidised to glyceric acid, the acid obtained is D(—)-glyceric acid. The sign of rotation has changed, but the asymmetric carbon atom is not affected by the reaction, *i.e.*, both compounds have the *same relative configurations.*

$$\begin{matrix} CHO \\ H-\!\!|\!\!-OH \\ CH_2OH \end{matrix} \xrightarrow{[O]} \begin{matrix} CO_2H \\ H-\!\!|\!\!-OH \\ CH_2OH \end{matrix}$$

D(+)-glyceraldehyde D(—)-glyceric acid

The outcome of much investigation has shown that many factors play a part in the Walden inversion, *e.g.*, the nature of the reagent, solvent and compound. Many theories have been suggested to account for the Walden inversion, but none is certain. According to the theory of Hughes and Ingold, nucleophilic substitution reactions may take place by either of the following mechanisms:

(i) The formation of a transition complex. In this case the reaction should proceed by the S_N2 mechanism, leading to inversion, since the replacing group attacks from the position farthest from the group being replaced (see also p. 30):

$$HO^- \; R-X \longrightarrow \overset{\delta-}{HO} \text{- - -} R \text{- - -} \overset{\delta-}{X} \longrightarrow HO-R + X^-$$

In the transition state, the groups OH and X are collinear and on opposite sides of the attacked carbon atom. Furthermore, the line joining OH and X is perpendicular to the plane containing the other three groups *a*, *b* and *d*. In the original molecule C*abd*X, the four groups are arranged tetrahedrally. Hence to achieve a planar configuration of C*abd* in the transition state, the carbon atom changes from tetrahedral to trigonal hybridisation, the remaining p_z orbital being used (by means of its two lobes) to hold the groups OH and X by " half bonds ". When X is ejected, the carbon atom returns to its state of tetrahedral hybridisation (see diagram on p. 396).

The above reaction is a three-centre reaction, proceeding by an end-on approach. Four-centre reactions, which proceed by a side-approach, do not occur with inversion (p. 30).

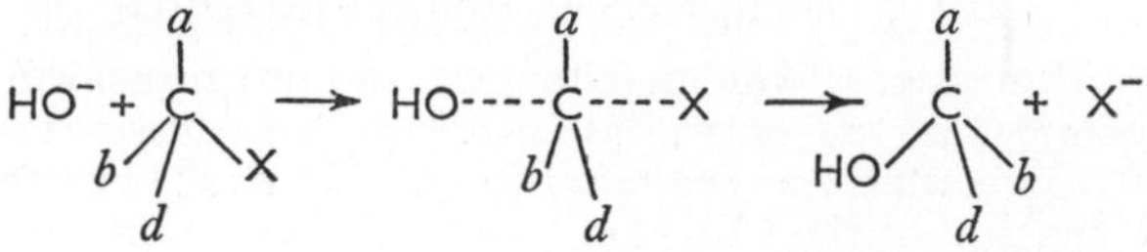

$$HO^- + \underset{d}{\overset{a}{C}}(b)(X) \longrightarrow HO{-}{-}{-}\underset{d}{\overset{a}{C}}(b){-}{-}{-}X \longrightarrow \underset{d}{\overset{a}{C}}(HO)(b) + X^-$$

(ii) The reacting molecule may ionise slowly, and the carbonium ion then undergoes rapid reaction with the reagent:

$$R{-}X \underset{}{\overset{\text{slow}}{\rightleftharpoons}} X^- + R^+ \underset{\text{fast}}{\overset{OH^-}{\longrightarrow}} ROH$$

In this case the reaction should proceed by the S_N1 mechanism, which may result in retention, inversion or racemisation.

In general, the nature of the compound to be substituted, attacking reagent and solvent determine which mechanism (S_N1 or S_N2) will take place (see also p. 98).

Asymmetric Synthesis

In ordinary laboratory preparations of optically active compounds, the racemic modification is always obtained. By special means, however, it is possible to prepare optically active compounds from symmetrical compounds (*i.e.*, not optically active) without the necessity of resolution. The method involves the use of optically active compounds, and is known as *asymmetric synthesis*. The first asymmetric synthesis was carried out by Marckwald (1904), who prepared an active (—)-valeric acid (lævorotatory to the extent of about 10 per cent. of the pure compound) by heating the half brucine salt of ethylmethylmalonic acid at 170°:

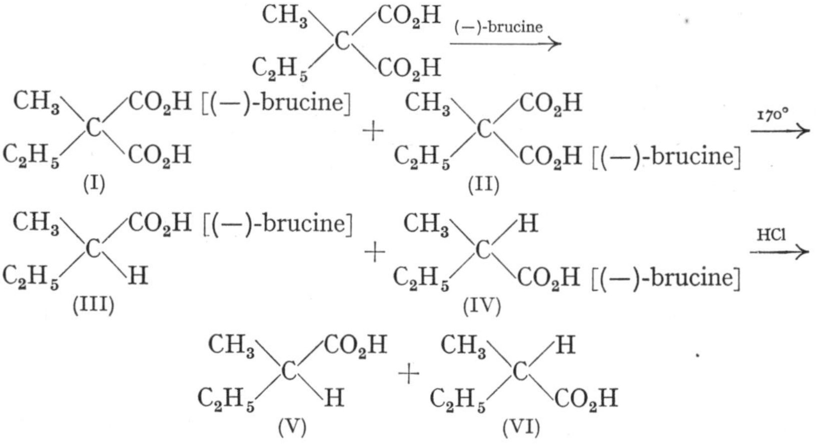

$$(CH_3)(C_2H_5)C(CO_2H)_2 \xrightarrow{(-)\text{-brucine}}$$

$$\underset{(I)}{(CH_3)(C_2H_5)C(CO_2H[(-)\text{-brucine}])(CO_2H)} + \underset{(II)}{(CH_3)(C_2H_5)C(CO_2H)(CO_2H[(-)\text{-brucine}])} \xrightarrow{170^\circ}$$

$$\underset{(III)}{(CH_3)(C_2H_5)C(CO_2H[(-)\text{-brucine}])(H)} + \underset{(IV)}{(CH_3)(C_2H_5)C(H)(CO_2H[(-)\text{-brucine}])} \xrightarrow{HCl}$$

$$\underset{(V)}{(CH_3)(C_2H_5)C(CO_2H)(H)} + \underset{(VI)}{(CH_3)(C_2H_5)C(H)(CO_2H)}$$

(I) and (II) are diastereoisomers; so are (III) and (IV). (V) and (VI) are enantiomorphs, and since the mixture is optically active, they must be present in unequal amounts. This was believed to be due to the different rates of decomposition of diastereoisomers (I) and (II).

This reaction was reinvestigated by Eisenlohr and Meier (1938), and they believed that the half-brucine salts were not present in *equal* amounts in the solid form (as thought by Marckwald). These authors suggested that as the *less* soluble salt crystallised out (during evaporation of the solution), some of the *more* soluble salt spontaneously changed into the *less* soluble salt to restore the equilibrium between the two; thus the final result was a mixture of the half-brucine salt containing a larger proportion of the *less soluble* diastereoisomer. If this be the case, then we are dealing with an example of asymmetric transformation (p. 394). Kenyon and Ross (1952) have also reinvestigated this reaction, and their work appears to show that the above reaction is a true asymmetric synthesis. According to these authors, when the half-brucine salt is heated, decarboxylation occurs with the intermediate formation of a *carbanion*. (I) and (II) both produce the *same* carbanion:

$$\text{I} \longrightarrow \begin{matrix} CH_3 \\ C_2H_5 \end{matrix} \Big\rangle \overset{-}{C}\cdot CO_2H[(-)\text{-brucine}] \longleftarrow \text{II}$$

Combination of this carbanion with a proton would produce diastereoisomers (III) and (IV) in different amounts, since, in general, diastereoisomers are formed at different rates.

Mckenzie (1905) reduced with aluminium amalgam pyruvic esters in which the alcohol was optically active, *e.g.*, (—)-amyl alcohol, (—)-menthol, etc. When the product, lactic acid ester, was hydrolysed, the resulting lactic acid was found to be slightly lævorotatory:

$$CH_3\cdot CO\cdot CO_2R + 2[H] \xrightarrow{Al/Hg} CH_3\cdot CHOH\cdot CO_2R \xrightarrow{H_2O} CH_3\cdot CHOH\cdot CO_2H$$

A special case of asymmetric synthesis is *absolute asymmetric synthesis.* This is the preparation of an optically active compound *without* the intermediate use of optically active reagents. The first conclusive evidence for an absolute asymmetric synthesis was obtained by Kuhn and Knopf (1930), who irradiated (±)-α-azidopropionic dimethylamide, $CH_3\cdot CH(N_3)\cdot CO\cdot N(CH_3)_2$, with *dextro* circularly polarised light and obtained a product that was slightly dextrorotatory. When the amide was irradiated with *lævo* circularly polarised light, the product was slightly lævorotatory.

Tartronic acid (hydroxymalonic acid), $CO_2H\cdot CHOH\cdot CO_2H$, may be prepared by heating bromomalonic acid with silver oxide suspended in water:

$$CHBr(CO_2H)_2 + \text{“ AgOH ”} \longrightarrow CHOH(CO_2H)_2 + AgBr$$

It is a crystalline solid which, heated to 160°, melts with the evolution of carbon dioxide and the formation of polyglycollide, $(C_2H_2O_2)_n$.

Malic acid (*hydroxysuccinic acid, hydroxybutanedioic acid*), $CO_2H\cdot CHOH\cdot CH_2\cdot CO_2H$, occurs in sour apples (Latin: *malum*, apple), fruits, berries, etc. It may be obtained from mountain-ash berries; the juice is expressed and boiled with calcium hydroxide solution. The precipitated calcium malate is collected by filtration and decomposed with the calculated quantity of dilute sulphuric acid. Malic acid is now being made synthetically by heating maleic acid with dilute sulphuric acid under pressure:

$$\begin{matrix} CH\cdot CO_2H \\ \| \\ CH\cdot CO_2H \end{matrix} + H_2O \xrightarrow{H_2SO_4} \begin{matrix} CHOH\cdot CO_2H \\ | \\ CH_2\cdot CO_2H \end{matrix} \qquad (100\%)$$

Malic acid may be conveniently prepared in the laboratory by heating bromosuccinic acid with silver oxide suspended in water:

$$\begin{matrix} CHBr\cdot CO_2H \\ | \\ CH_2\cdot CO_2H \end{matrix} + \text{“ AgOH ”} \longrightarrow \begin{matrix} CHOH\cdot CO_2H \\ | \\ CH_2\cdot CO_2H \end{matrix} + AgBr$$

Malic acid contains one asymmetric carbon atom, and can therefore exist in the D-, L- and DL-forms. Malic acid from natural sources is L(—);

synthetic malic acid is DL; D(+)-malic acid may be obtained by the careful reduction of D(+)-tartaric acid with concentrated hydriodic acid:

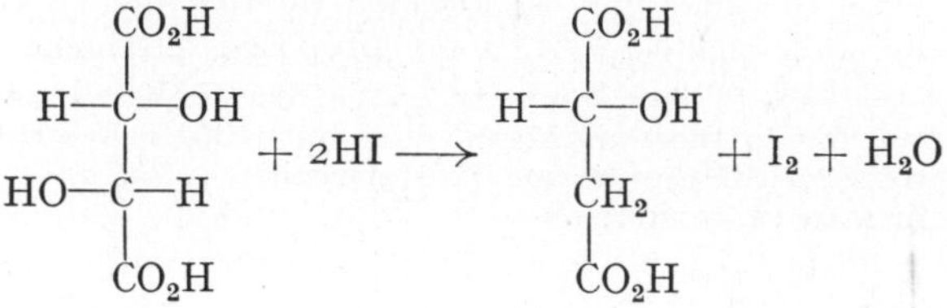

$$\begin{array}{c} CO_2H \\ | \\ H-C-OH \\ | \\ HO-C-H \\ | \\ CO_2H \end{array} + 2HI \longrightarrow \begin{array}{c} CO_2H \\ | \\ H-C-OH \\ | \\ CH_2 \\ | \\ CO_2H \end{array} + I_2 + H_2O$$

D(+)-Malic acid may also be obtained from the L(—)-isomer by means of the Walden inversion.

L(—)-Malic acid is a crystalline deliquescent solid, m.p. 100°, readily soluble in water and ethanol. It behaves both as an alcohol and acid. Inspection of the formula of malic acid shows it to be an α-hydroxyacid with respect to one carboxyl group, and a β-hydroxyacid with respect to the other. Such acids, when heated, undergo the reaction characteristic of the *β*-acid, *i.e.*, they eliminate a molecule of water to form an unsaturated acid (not the lactide). Thus, on heating, malic acid forms maleic anhydride and fumaric acid (*q.v.*):

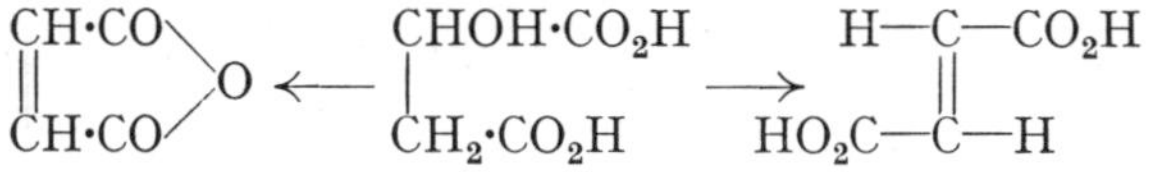

$$\begin{array}{l} CH{\cdot}CO \diagdown \\ \| \qquad\quad O \\ CH{\cdot}CO \diagup \end{array} \longleftarrow \begin{array}{l} CHOH{\cdot}CO_2H \\ | \\ CH_2{\cdot}CO_2H \end{array} \longrightarrow \begin{array}{c} H-C-CO_2H \\ \| \\ HO_2C-C-H \end{array}$$

Malic acid may be reduced to succinic acid by heating with hydriodic acid.

Malic acid is gradually replacing citric and tartaric acids in beverages, jellies, etc.

Tartaric acid (α : *α'dihydroxysuccinic acid*, 2 : 3-*dihydroxybutanedioic acid*), $CO_2H{\cdot}CHOH{\cdot}CHOH{\cdot}CO_2H$, contains two structurally identical carbon atoms, and can therefore exist in the D-, L-, DL- and *meso*-forms; all of these are known (Fig. 11).

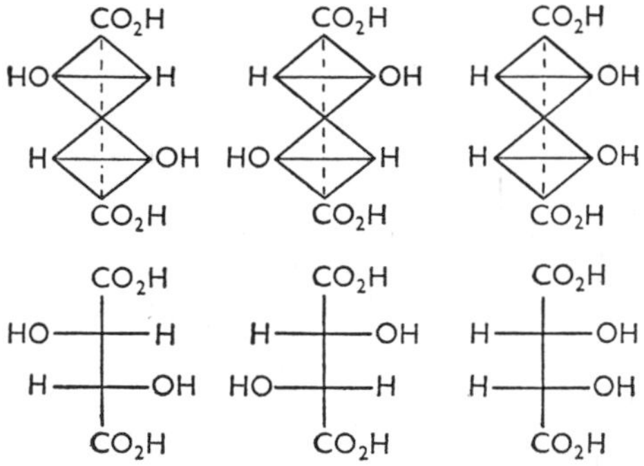

$$\begin{array}{ccc} \begin{array}{c} CO_2H \\ HO-\!\!\!\!-\!\!\!\!-H \\ H-\!\!\!\!-\!\!\!\!-OH \\ CO_2H \end{array} & \begin{array}{c} CO_2H \\ H-\!\!\!\!-\!\!\!\!-OH \\ HO-\!\!\!\!-\!\!\!\!-H \\ CO_2H \end{array} & \begin{array}{c} CO_2H \\ H-\!\!\!\!-\!\!\!\!-OH \\ H-\!\!\!\!-\!\!\!\!-OH \\ CO_2H \end{array} \\ \text{L(−)-tartaric acid} & \text{D(+)-tartaric acid} & \textit{meso}\text{-tartaric acid} \end{array}$$

FIG. 17.11.

The configurations of the tartaric acids are a troublesome problem. Fischer wrote the configuration of the natural dextrorotatory acid (*i.e.*, the (+)-acid) as shown above. It is possible to synthesise (—)-tartaric acid from D(+)-glyceraldehyde, and on this basis the (+)-acid would be L(+)-tartaric acid. This is in agreement with Rosanoff's scheme of building *up* from D(+)-glyceraldehyde. It is also possible, however, to degrade (+)-

tartaric acid into D(—)-glyceric acid, and hence (+)-tartaric acid will be D(+)-tartaric acid. Freudenberg assigned the D-configuration to the (+)-acid since this is the acid that is obtained by the direct oxidation of D-glucose. Cahn and Ingold (1951) have proposed a scheme to overcome difficulties in relating configurations to D(+)-glyceraldehyde, and according to them, natural dextrorotatory tartaric acid is (+)-αD: α'D-tartaric acid (this corresponds to D(+)-tartaric acid shown above).

When fumaric acid is treated with dilute alkaline permanganate, DL-tartaric acid is formed; maleic acid, under the same conditions, forms *meso*-tartaric acid (see also p. 403):

$$CO_2H\cdot CH{:}CH\cdot CO_2H + [O] \xrightarrow{KMnO_4} CO_2H\cdot CHOH\cdot CHOH\cdot CO_2H$$

Both DL- and *meso*-tartaric acid are formed when α : α'-dibromosuccinic acid is boiled with silver oxide suspended in water:

$$\begin{array}{l} CHBr\cdot CO_2H \\ | \\ CHBr\cdot CO_2H \end{array} + 2\text{ "AgOH" } \longrightarrow \begin{array}{l} CHOH\cdot CO_2H \\ | \\ CHOH\cdot CO_2H \end{array} + 2AgBr$$

DL- and *meso*-Tartaric acids are also formed by the hydrolysis of glyoxal cyanohydrin:

$$\begin{array}{l} CHO \\ | \\ CHO \end{array} + 2HCN \longrightarrow \begin{array}{l} CHOH\cdot CN \\ | \\ CHOH\cdot CN \end{array} \xrightarrow{H_2O} \begin{array}{l} CHOH\cdot CO_2H \\ | \\ CHOH\cdot CO_2H \end{array}$$

All the foregoing synthetic preparations clearly show the structure of tartaric acid.

***dextro*Tartaric acid, D(+)-tartaric acid,** occurs in the free state and as potassium hydrogen tartrate in the juice of grapes. During the fermentation of grapes, the acid potassium salt separates as a reddish-brown crystalline mass which is known as *argol*. When recrystallised, argol is converted into the purer substance (white), which is known as *cream of tartar*, from which D(+)-tartaric acid is obtained by dissolving it in water, and adding calcium hydroxide until the solution is nearly neutralised:

$$2KHC_4H_4O_6 + Ca(OH)_2 \longrightarrow K_2C_4H_4O_6 + CaC_4H_4O_6 + 2H_2O$$

The precipitated calcium tartrate is collected by filtration, and calcium chloride is added to the filtrate:

$$K_2C_4H_4O_6 + CaCl_2 \longrightarrow CaC_4H_4O_6 + 2KCl$$

The precipitate is collected by filtration, both lots of calcium tartrate are mixed and decomposed with the calculated quantity of dilute sulphuric acid:

$$CaC_4H_4O_6 + H_2SO_4 \longrightarrow H_2C_4H_4O_6 + CaSO_4$$

The precipitated calcium sulphate is removed by filtration and the filtrate evaporated to crystallisation; anhydrous crystals are obtained, m.p. 170°.

D(+)-Tartaric acid is soluble in water and ethanol but insoluble in ether. The calcium salt is insoluble in water but soluble in potassium hydroxide solution. When heated, tartaric acid is converted into pyruvic acid:

$$\begin{array}{l} CHOH\cdot CO_2H \\ | \\ CHOH\cdot CO_2H \end{array} \longrightarrow CH_3\cdot CO\cdot CO_2H + CO_2 + H_2O$$

Tartaric acid is reduced by hydriodic acid, first to malic acid and then to succinic acid.

Sodium potassium D(+)-tartrate, $NaKC_4H_4O_6 \cdot 4H_2O$, is known as *Rochelle salt*, and is used in the preparation of Fehling's solution. Fehling's solution, which contains a complex copper tartrate, is prepared by adding copper sulphate solution to an aqueous solution of Rochelle salt containing sodium hydroxide. The structure of the complex is uncertain; it may be (I).

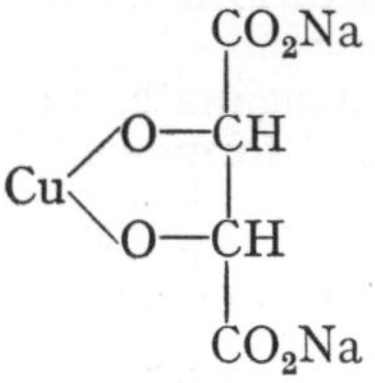

$$\text{Cu}\left\langle\begin{array}{l}\text{O—CH(CO}_2\text{Na)} \\ \text{O—CH(CO}_2\text{Na)}\end{array}\right. \quad \text{(I)}$$

$$\left(\begin{array}{l}\text{CHOH}\cdot\text{CO}_2\text{K} \\ | \\ \text{CHOH}\cdot\text{CO}_2\cdot\text{SbO}\end{array}\right)_2\cdot\text{H}_2\text{O} \quad \text{(II)}$$

$$\left[\begin{array}{l}\text{CO}_2\text{K} \\ | \\ \text{HC—O} \\ | \qquad\quad \rangle\text{Sb—OH} \\ \text{HC—O} \\ | \\ \text{CO}_2\text{H}\end{array}\right]_2\cdot\text{H}_2\text{O} \quad \text{(III)}$$

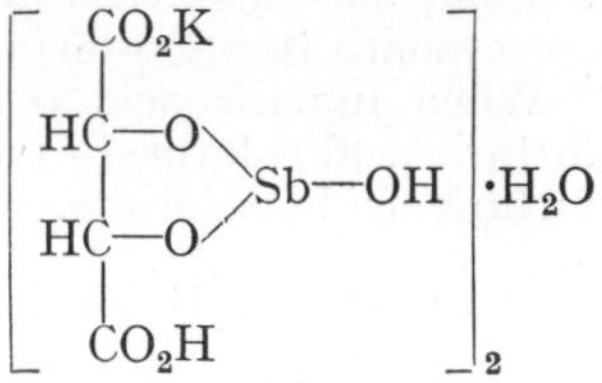

Potassium antimonyl D(+)-tartrate, known as *tartar emetic*, is usually given the formula (II). Its structure is uncertain; it may be (III).

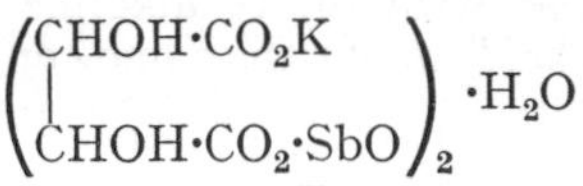

Tartar emetic may be prepared by boiling antimonous oxide with an aqueous solution of potassium hydrogen tartrate.

When heated with sodium hydroxide solution (or even with water), D(+)-tartaric acid is converted into DL-tartaric acid (29–33 per cent.) and *meso*-tartaric acid (13–17 per cent.).

D(+)-Tartaric acid is used in the preparation of effervescent drinks. The acid and tartar emetic are both used as mordants in dyeing and printing.

***lævo*Tartaric acid, L(—)-tartaric acid,** does not occur naturally. It may be obtained by the resolution of DL-tartaric acid. Physically and chemically, it is similar to D(+)-tartaric acid.

DL-Tartaric acid, racemic ta rtaric acid, crystallises as the hemihydrate, $(C_4H_6O_6)_2 \cdot H_2O$, m.p. 206°. In the solid state DL-tartaric acid exists as the *racemic compound*, but dissociates into the D- and L-forms in solution. DL-Tartaric acid is optically inactive by *external* compensation. It is obtained from the mother-liquors in the preparation of D(+)-tartaric acid, or by racemisation of the latter (together with *meso*-tartaric acid).

***meso*-Tartaric acid** (*i-tartaric acid*) crystallises as the monohydrate; the melting point of the anhydrous acid is 140°. *meso*-Tartaric acid is optically inactive by *internal* compensation, and may be obtained (together with DL-) by heating D(+)-tartaric acid with alkali. It may also be prepared by the oxidation of maleic acid with dilute alkaline permanganate. The prolonged oxidation of benzene with hydrogen peroxide in *tert.*-butanol containing a little osmium tetroxide produces *meso*-tartaric acid (and some allomucic and oxalic acids; Cook *et al.*, 1950).

Citric acid (β-*hydroxytricarballylic acid*, 2-*hydroxypropane*-1 : 2 : 3-*tricarboxylic acid*) occurs in many fruits, especially unripe fruits of the *citrus* group, *e.g.*, lemon juice contains about 6–10 per cent. citric acid. Citric acid is prepared from lemons by extracting the juice, boiling to coagulate the protein substances, and neutralising with calcium carbonate. The precipitated calcium citrate is collected by filtration and decomposed with the calculated quantity of dilute sulphuric acid. The precipitated calcium sulphate is removed by filtration and the filtrate evaporated to crystallisation; crystals of the monohydrate of citric acid are obtained.

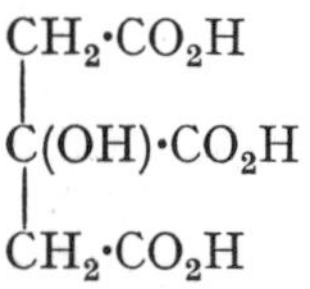

$$\begin{array}{l}\text{CH}_2\cdot\text{CO}_2\text{H} \\ | \\ \text{C(OH)}\cdot\text{CO}_2\text{H} \\ | \\ \text{CH}_2\cdot\text{CO}_2\text{H}\end{array}$$

Citric acid is now also manufactured by the fermentation of solutions of glucose, sucrose, or purified cane-molasses in the presence of certain inorganic salts, by various moulds or fungi, *e.g.*, *Citromyces pfefferianus*, *Aspergillus wentii*.

Citric acid may be synthesised from glycerol by the following reactions; this synthesis shows its structure:

$$CH_2OH\text{·}CHOH\text{·}CH_2OH \xrightarrow{HCl} CH_2Cl\text{·}CHOH\text{·}CH_2Cl \xrightarrow{[O]} CH_2Cl\text{·}CO\text{·}CH_2Cl \xrightarrow{HCN} CH_2Cl\text{·}C(OH)\text{·}CN\text{·}CH_2Cl \xrightarrow{KCN}$$

$$CH_2\text{·}CN\text{—}C(OH)\text{·}CN\text{—}CH_2\text{·}CN \xrightarrow{H_2O} CH_2\text{·}CO_2H\text{—}C(OH)\text{·}CO_2H\text{—}CH_2\text{·}CO_2H$$

Lawrence (1897) synthesised citric acid by means of the Reformatsky reaction (p. 346), starting with ethyl bromoacetate and oxalacetic ester:

$$CH_2Br\text{·}CO_2C_2H_5 + CO\text{·}CO_2C_2H_5\text{—}CH_2\text{·}CO_2C_2H_5 + Zn \longrightarrow$$

$$C_2H_5O_2C\text{·}CH_2\text{·}C(OZnBr)(CH_2\text{·}CO_2C_2H_5)\text{·}CO_2C_2H_5 \xrightarrow{acid} HO_2C\text{·}CH_2\text{·}C(OH)(CH_2\text{·}CO_2H)\text{·}CO_2H$$

The monohydrate of citric acid loses its water of crystallisation when heated at 130°, and melts at 153°. Citric acid is not optically active (it contains no asymmetric carbon atom). It behaves as an alcohol and a tribasic acid, *e.g.*, it forms the acetyl derivative and three series of salts. Calcium citrate is more soluble in cold water than in hot. Citric acid can therefore be readily distinguished from tartaric acid, since, if aqueous calcium chloride is added to a neutral solution of a citrate, no precipitate is formed, whereas a neutral tartrate precipitates calcium tartrate. If the cold citrate solution is warmed after the addition of calcium chloride, calcium citrate, $(C_6H_5O_7)_2Ca_3\text{·}4H_2O$, is precipitated. Furthermore, the calcium

$$\underset{(III)}{CH\text{·}CO_2H{=}C\text{·}CO_2H\text{—}CH_2\text{·}CO_2H} \xleftarrow{-H_2O} CH_2\text{·}CO_2H\text{—}C(OH)\text{·}CO_2H\text{—}CH_2\text{·}CO_2H \xrightarrow{-H\text{·}CO_2H} \underset{(I)}{CH_2\text{·}CO_2H\text{—}CO\text{—}CH_2\text{·}CO_2H}$$

(III) $\xrightarrow{-CO_2}$ (IV) $CH\text{·}CO_2H{=}C\text{·}CO_2H\text{—}CH_3$ and (V) $CH_2{=}C\text{·}CO_2H\text{—}CH_2\text{·}CO_2H$

(I) $\xrightarrow{-CO_2}$ (II) $CH_3\text{—}CO\text{—}CH_2\text{·}CO_2H$ $\xrightarrow{-CO_2}$ $CH_3\text{—}CO\text{—}CH_3$

(IV) $\xrightarrow{-H_2O}$ (VI) $CH.CO{=}C\text{·}CO(\text{—}CH_3)$, ring closed through O

(V) $\xrightarrow{-H_2O}$ (VII) $CH_2{=}C\text{·}CO\text{—}CH_2\text{·}CO$, ring closed through O

(I) is acetonedicarboxylic acid; (II) acetoacetic acid; (III) aconitic acid; (IV) citraconic and mesaconic acid (*cis-trans* isomers); (V) itaconic acid; (VI) citraconic (mesaconic) anhydride; (VII) itaconic anhydride.

citrate precipitate is insoluble in aqueous potassium hydroxide, whereas calcium tartrate is soluble.

Citric acid is used for making beverages and as a mordant in dyeing.

Citric acid is both an α- and β-hydroxy-acid; when heated to 150°, it eliminates a molecule of water to form *aconitic acid*. On pyrolysis, citric acid gives a number of products among which have been isolated *aconitic acid*, *citraconic* (*mesaconic*) and *itaconic anhydrides*, and acetone (I–VII).

When citric acid is heated with concentrated sulphuric acid, aconitic acid is obtained (41–44 per cent.). When treated with *fuming* sulphuric acid, citric acid forms acetonedicarboxylic acid (85–90 per cent.), a reaction which is characteristic of α-hydroxyacids.

Tricarballylic acid (*propane*-1 : 2 : 3-*tricarboxylic acid*), m.p. 166°, occurs in unripe beet-roots. It may be prepared by the reduction of aconitic acid, or from 1 : 2 : 3-tribromopropane as follows:

$$\begin{matrix} CH_2Br \\ | \\ CHBr \\ | \\ CH_2Br \end{matrix} \xrightarrow{KCN} \begin{matrix} CH_2 \cdot CN \\ | \\ CH \cdot CN \\ | \\ CH_2 \cdot CN \end{matrix} \xrightarrow[\text{(ii) HCl}]{\text{(i) aq. KOH}} \begin{matrix} CH_2 \cdot CO_2H \\ | \\ CH \cdot CO_2H \\ | \\ CH_2 \cdot CO_2H \end{matrix} \quad (70\%)$$

Tricarballylic acid may also be synthesised by the Michael condensation (p. 262) between diethyl fumarate and malonic ester, and heating the product, ethyl propane-1 : 1 : 2 : 3-tetracarboxylate, with concentrated hydrochloric acid:

$$C_2H_5O_2C \cdot CH{:}CH \cdot CO_2C_2H_5 + CH_2(CO_2C_2H_5)_2 \xrightarrow{C_2H_5ONa}$$

$$\begin{matrix} C_2H_5O_2C \cdot CH \cdot CH_2 \cdot CO_2C_2H_5 \\ | \\ CH(CO_2C_2H_5)_2 \end{matrix} \xrightarrow{HCl} \begin{matrix} CH_2 \cdot CO_2H \\ | \\ CH \cdot CO_2H \\ | \\ CH_2 \cdot CO_2H \end{matrix} \quad (88\text{–}90\%)$$

Tricarballylic esters have been used as plasticisers.

UNSATURATED DICARBOXYLIC ACIDS

The formula of the simplest unsaturated dicarboxylic acid is $CO_2H \cdot CH{:}CH \cdot CO_2H$. This formula actually represents two isomers: maleic acid and fumaric acid.

Maleic acid may be prepared:

(i) By heating malic acid at about 250°:

$$\begin{matrix} CHOH \cdot CO_2H \\ | \\ CH_2 \cdot CO_2H \end{matrix} \xrightarrow{-H_2O} \begin{matrix} CH \cdot CO_2H \\ \| \\ CH \cdot CO_2H \end{matrix} \xrightarrow{-H_2O} \begin{matrix} CH \cdot CO \\ \| \\ CH \cdot CO \end{matrix}\!\!>\!O \xrightarrow{+H_2O} \begin{matrix} CH \cdot CO_2H \\ \| \\ CH \cdot CO_2H \end{matrix}$$

(ii) By heating bromosuccinic acid with aqueous alkali; some fumaric acid is also obtained:

$$\begin{matrix} CHBr \cdot CO_2H \\ | \\ CH_2 \cdot CO_2H \end{matrix} + KOH \longrightarrow \begin{matrix} CH \cdot CO_2H \\ \| \\ CH \cdot CO_2H \end{matrix} + KBr + H_2O$$

(iii) Maleic anhydride is prepared industrially:

(*a*) By the oxidation of benzene with air in the presence of vanadium pentoxide as catalyst at 410–430°:

$$2\,C_6H_6 + 9O_2 \xrightarrow{V_2O_5} 2 \begin{matrix} CH \cdot CO \\ \| \\ CH \cdot CO \end{matrix}\!\!>\!O + 4CO_2 + 4H_2O$$

(*b*) As a by-product in the manufacture of phthalic anhydride from naphthalene (p. 664):

(*c*) By the oxidation of but-2-ene (from cracked petroleum) or crotonaldehyde with air in the presence of vanadium pentoxide as catalyst at 450°, *e.g.*,

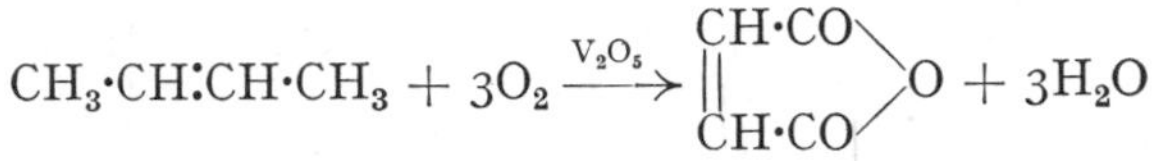

$$CH_3{\cdot}CH{:}CH{\cdot}CH_3 + 3O_2 \xrightarrow{V_2O_5} \begin{matrix} CH{\cdot}CO \\ \| \\ CH{\cdot}CO \end{matrix}\!\!>\!O + 3H_2O$$

(*d*) By the oxidation of furfural with sodium chlorate:

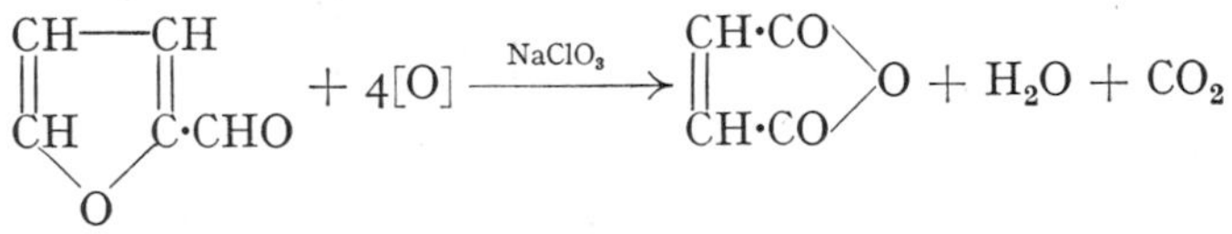

$$\begin{matrix} CH & \!\!-\!\!-\!\! & CH \\ \| & & \| \\ CH & & C{\cdot}CHO \\ & \diagdown O \diagup & \end{matrix} + 4[O] \xrightarrow{NaClO_3} \begin{matrix} CH{\cdot}CO \\ \| \\ CH{\cdot}CO \end{matrix}\!\!>\!O + H_2O + CO_2$$

The anhydride is converted into the acid by boiling with alkali, and then acidifying:

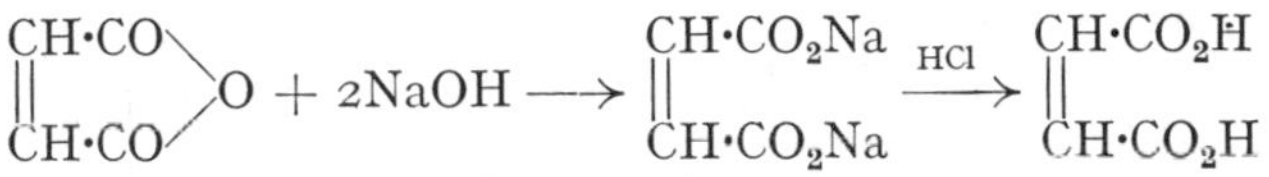

$$\begin{matrix} CH{\cdot}CO \\ \| \\ CH{\cdot}CO \end{matrix}\!\!>\!O + 2NaOH \longrightarrow \begin{matrix} CH{\cdot}CO_2Na \\ \| \\ CH{\cdot}CO_2Na \end{matrix} \xrightarrow{HCl} \begin{matrix} CH{\cdot}CO_2H \\ \| \\ CH{\cdot}CO_2H \end{matrix}$$

Maleic acid is a synthetic compound. It is a crystalline solid, m.p. 130°, soluble in water (79 g. per 100 ml. at 25°). When heated, some distils unchanged; the rest is converted into maleic anhydride. A much better yield of maleic anhydride is obtained by heating the acid with acetic anhydride. Maleic acid may be reduced catalytically or electrolytically to succinic acid. This reduction may also be effected by *cyclo*hexene and palladium (Braude *et al.*, 1954; see p. 460). It is oxidised by dilute alkaline permanganate to *meso*tartaric acid; this may be obtained in excellent yield by replacing the permanganate by potassium chlorate and osmium tetroxide. Prolonged heating of maleic acid at 150° converts it into fumaric acid. Maleic acid and its anhydride are used in the Diels–Alder synthesis (p. 459).

Maleic acid inhibits rancidity in milk powders, oils and fats. Maleic anhydride is used for making varnishes and lacquers.

Fumaric acid may be prepared:

(i) By heating maleic acid for some time at 150°.

(ii) By heating bromosuccinic acid with alkali; maleic acid is also formed.

(iii) By the Knoevenagel reaction (p. 263); malonic acid is condensed with glyoxylic acid in the presence of pyridine:

$$CO_2H{\cdot}CHO + CH_2(CO_2H)_2 \xrightarrow{\text{pyridine}} CO_2H{\cdot}CH{:}CH{\cdot}CO_2H + H_2O + CO_2$$

(iv) Fumaric acid is prepared industrially by boiling maleic acid with hydrochloric acid or sodium hydroxide. Another industrial preparation is the fermentation of glucose (and other carbohydrates) by, *e.g.*, *Rhizopus nigricans*.

Fumaric acid occurs in nature in many plants. It is a crystalline solid, m.p. 287°, slightly soluble in water (0·7 g. per 100 ml. at 25°). It does not form an anhydride of its own, but gives maleic anhydride when heated at 230°. It may be reduced to succinic acid, and is oxidised by alkaline permanganate to DL-tartaric acid; the latter is obtained in excellent yield if potassium chlorate and osmium tetroxide are used as the oxidising agent (*cf.* maleic acid). Fumaroyl chloride is formed when maleic anhydride is heated with phthaloyl chloride in the presence of zinc chloride.

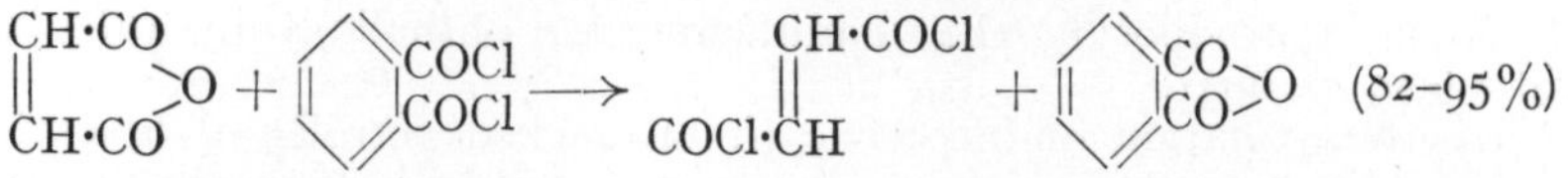

$$\begin{matrix} CH{\cdot}CO \\ \| \\ CH{\cdot}CO \end{matrix}\!\!>O + C_6H_4(COCl)_2 \longrightarrow \begin{matrix} CH{\cdot}COCl \\ \| \\ COCl{\cdot}CH \end{matrix} + C_6H_4\!\begin{matrix} CO \\ CO \end{matrix}\!\!>O \quad (82\text{–}95\%)$$

Many acid chlorides can be obtained in 95 per cent. yield by this method.

Maleic acid is a much stronger acid than fumaric acid (K_1 is the first dissociation constant, and K_2 the second):

	K_1	K_2	K_1/K_2
Maleic acid	$1{\cdot}2 \times 10^{-2}$	$6{\cdot}0 \times 10^{-7}$	20,000
Fumaric acid	$9{\cdot}55 \times 10^{-4}$	$4{\cdot}2 \times 10^{-5}$	22·6

At first sight, since the structures are identical, it might have been expected that the dissociation constants would be the same. The reason why they are so different is not certain. A possible explanation is that hydrogen bonding can occur in maleic but not in fumaric acid, thereby facilitating proton release in the former:

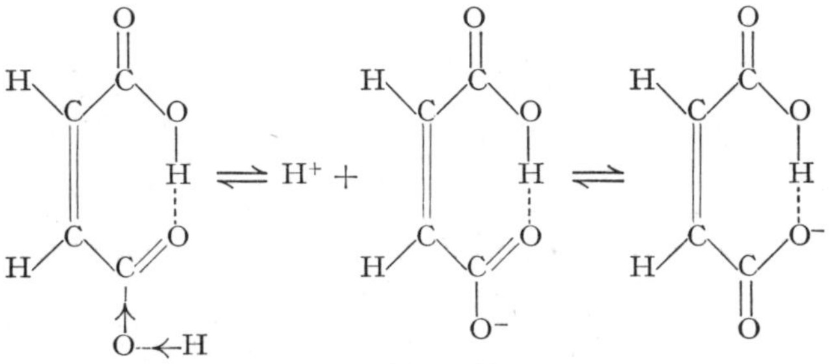

maleic acid

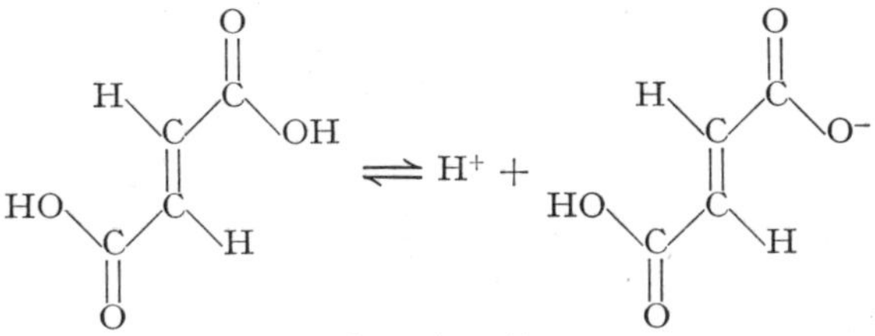

fumaric acid

Furthermore, since the maleic acid anion is stabilised by hydrogen bonding, and the corresponding fumaric anion is not, this offers an explanation why the second dissociation constant of maleic acid is less than that of fumaric acid.

GEOMETRICAL ISOMERISM

Maleic and fumaric acids both have the same molecular formula $C_4H_4O_4$, but differ in most of their physical and in many of their chemical properties, and neither is optically active. It was originally thought that they were structural isomers, and because of this, different names were assigned to each form (this applies to many other geometrical isomers—see text). It was subsequently shown, however, that maleic and fumaric acids were not structural isomers, *e.g.*, both (i) are catalytically reduced to succinic acid; (ii) add on hydrogen bromide to form bromosuccinic acid; (iii) add on water to form malic acid; (iv) are oxidised by alkaline permanganate to tartaric acid (the stereochemical relationships in reactions (ii), (iii) and (iv) have been ignored). Thus both acids have the same structure, *viz.*, $CO_2H{\cdot}CH{:}CH{\cdot}CO_2H$. Van't Hoff suggested that if we assume there is *no free rotation about a double bond,* two spatial arrangements are possible for the formula $CO_2H{\cdot}CH{:}CH{\cdot}CO_2H$, and these would account for the isomerism exhibited by maleic and fumaric acids. Using tetrahedral diagrams, van't Hoff represented a double bond by placing the tetrahedra edge to edge (Fig. 12). From a *mechanical* point of view, such an arrangement would be rigid,

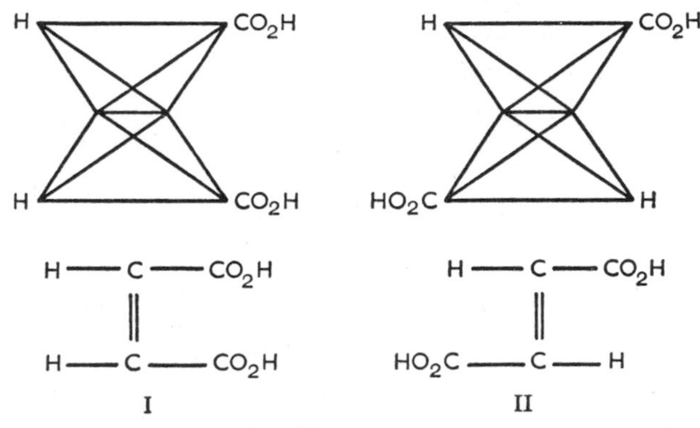

FIG. 17.12.

i.e., free rotation about the double bond is not to be expected. It is important to note that according to the above arrangement, *the two hydrogen atoms and the two carboxyl groups are all in one plane* (see also Fig. 13).

The problem now is to decide which formula represents maleic acid, and which fumaric acid. There is no general method for determining the configuration of geometrical isomers; the method used depends on the nature of the compound in question. The methods of cyclisation and dipole-moment measurements may be used to determine the configurations of maleic and fumaric acids.

Method of cyclisation. Wislicenus was the first to suggest the principle that *intramolecular* reactions are more likely to occur the closer together the reacting groups are in the molecule. This principle is generally true, but has led to incorrect results (as shown by other work) in certain cases, *e.g.*, the aromatic oximes (p. 638).

Of the two acids, only maleic acid forms the anhydride when heated. Fumaric acid does not form an anhydride of its own, but when strongly heated, gives maleic anhydride. If we accept the principle of cyclisation, then (I) is maleic acid, and (II) fumaric acid.

$$\begin{array}{l} H{-}C{-}COO\boxed{H} \\ \quad\; \| \\ H{-}C{-}CO\boxed{OH} \end{array} \longrightarrow \begin{array}{l} H{-}C{-}CO \\ \quad\; \| \\ H{-}C{-}CO \end{array}\!\!>\!O + H_2O$$

In fumaric acid, the two carboxyl groups are too far apart to react with each other.

Cyclisation reactions must be carried out carefully, since one isomer may be converted into the other in the cyclising process, and so lead to unreliable results. In the above reaction, somewhat vigorous conditions have been used; hence there is the possibility that interconversion has occurred. The correctness of the conclusion for the configurations of the two acids may be tested by hydrolysing maleic anhydride in the cold; only maleic acid is obtained. Under these mild conditions it is most unlikely that interconversion occurs, and so we may accept (I) as the configuration of maleic acid.

Method of dipole-moment measurements. (I) would be expected to have a larger dipole moment than (II), which, since it is symmetrical (it has a centre of symmetry), would be expected to have almost a zero dipole moment.

Measurements of the dipole moments of maleic and fumaric acids agree with the configurations assigned to each by the method of cyclisation.

The type of isomerism exhibited by maleic and fumaric acids is known as **geometrical isomerism.** For a compound to exhibit geometrical isomerism, the molecule must have a double bond about which there is no free rotation. Let us consider the compounds $Ca_2{:}Cb_2$, $Ca_2{:}Cbd$, $Cab{:}Cab$ and $Cab{:}Cad$:

```
a—C—a          a—C—a          a—C—b          a—C—b
  ||             ||             ||             ||
b—C—b          b—C—d          a—C—b          a—C—d
 (III)          (IV)            (V)            (VI)
```

Inspection of these formulæ shows that geometrical isomerism is possible in (V) and (VI), and impossible in (III) and (IV). Thus a double bond is not the only condition for geometrical isomerism; the groups attached to the two carbon atoms joined by the double bond must also be taken into consideration.

In the foregoing account of geometrical isomerism, the distribution of the carbon valencies was assumed to be tetrahedral (as postulated by van't Hoff). According to modern theory, in olefinic compounds the two unsaturated carbon atoms exhibit the *trigonal* mode of hybridisation, not the *tetrahedral*. Thus there are three coplanar valencies (σ-bonds), and the fourth (π-bond) at right angles to the trigonal hybrids. It is the overlap of the π-electrons which causes the resistance to rotation about the carbon–carbon double bond (Fig. 13; *cf.* Fig. 2.5, p. 25).

When addition occurs at the double bond, the trigonal arrangement in the olefin changes to the tetrahedral arrangement in the saturated compound. As we have seen (p. 23), the electron distribution round the axis of a single bond is symmetrical; consequently there is no force in the bond itself

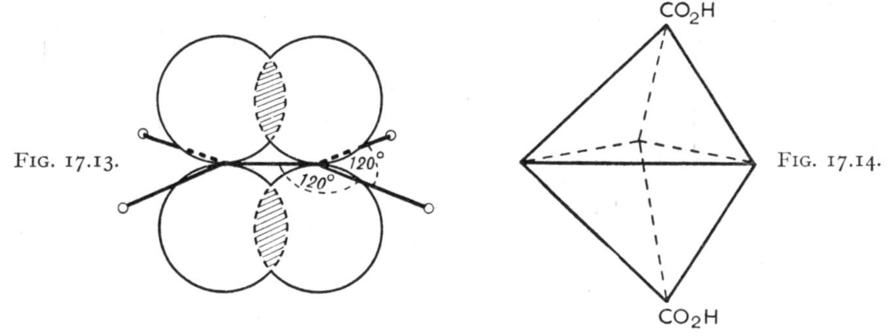

FIG. 17.13. FIG. 17.14.

restraining free rotation, and hence the saturated molecule takes up the position of least internal energy. This readily explains, *e.g.*, why maleic and fumaric acids both give the same succinic acid on reduction.

Geometrical isomerism is also possible in *cyclic* compounds, the ring structure being comparable to the double bond in olefinic compounds (in giving rise to a more or less rigid structure), *e.g.*, hexahydroterephthalic acids:

```
       CO2H     ¦      CO2H        CO2H           H
        | /CH2—¦—CH2\  |            | /CH2—CH2\  |
(VII)   C<      ¦      >C           C<          >C       (VIII)
        | \CH2—¦—CH2/  |            | \CH2—CH2/  |
        H       ¦       H           H           CO2H
```

Geometrical isomerism is also known as ***cis-trans* isomerism,** one isomer being the *cis* and the other *trans*. The *cis*-isomer is the one which (usually) has identical, or similar atoms or groups, on the *same* side. Thus maleic acid is *cis*-butenedioic acid, and fumaric acid is *trans*-butenedioic acid. Similarly, (VII) is *cis*-hexahydroterephthalic acid, and (VIII) *trans*-hexahydroterephthalic acid. It is interesting to note that both the hexahydroterephthalic acids are optically inactive; (VII) has a plane, and (VIII) a centre of symmetry.

Compounds with a triple bond cannot exhibit geometrical isomerism, *e.g.*, acetylenedicarboxylic acid, $CO_2H \cdot C \vdots C \cdot CO_2H$. According to van't Hoff's tetrahedral theory, a triple bond is represented as two tetrahedra placed face to face (Fig. 14). According to modern theory, in acetylenic compounds the two unsaturated carbon atoms exhibit the *digonal* mode of hybridisation. Examination of both the van't Hoff representation and the digonal structure shows that only one form of acetylene dicarboxylic acid is possible.

Properties of *cis-trans* isomers. Comparison of the properties of *cis*- and *trans*-isomers of known configurations shows certain regularities, *e.g.*, the melting point and stability of the *cis*- are *lower* than those of the *trans*-isomer; the density, refractive index, solubility, dipole moment, heat of combustion and the dissociation constant (if an acid) of the *cis*- are *greater* than those of the *trans*-isomer. It can be seen from these properties that the *cis*-isomer is usually the labile form. It is possible, by suitable means, to convert the labile *cis*-isomer into the stable *trans*-isomer; *e.g.*, maleic acid may be converted into fumaric acid by heating the solid, or a solution of the solid in water or benzene, to a temperature above its melting point (130°). The transformation may also be effected by treating it with a small amount of halogen in the presence of light. It is far more difficult to convert the *trans*-isomer into the *cis*-. Usually the best method is to irradiate the *trans*-isomer with ultra-violet light; the product is generally an equilibrium mixture of both isomers.

The mechanism of the conversion of *cis*- into *trans*-, and vice versa, is not fully understood.

The addition of various substances to the double bond of, *e.g.*, maleic and fumaric acids is difficult to interpret. Experiment has shown that maleic acid adds on bromine to form DL-dibromosuccinic acid, and fumaric acid adds on bromine to form *meso*-dibromosuccinic acid. These additions correspond to a *trans addition* of the two bromine atoms (full lines represent groups in front, and broken lines behind):

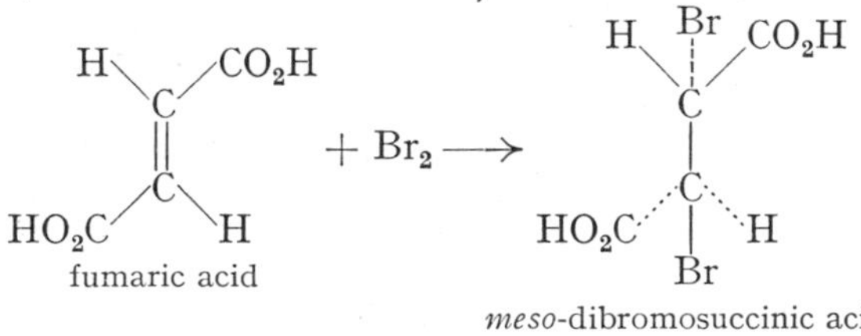

```
 H       CO2H                          H   Br  CO2H
   \    /                                \  :  /
     C                                      C
     ||          + Br2 ——>                  |
     C                                      C
   /    \                                 .·  | ·.
HO2C      H                           HO2C    |   H
                                             Br
 fumaric acid                      meso-dibromosuccinic acid
```

Similar results, *i.e.*, *trans*-addition, are also obtained when the addenda are chlorine, halogen acid or hypohalous acid. On the other hand, oxidation with dilute alkaline permanganate leads to *cis-addition*, maleic acid forming *meso*-tartaric acid, and fumaric acid DL-tartaric acid:

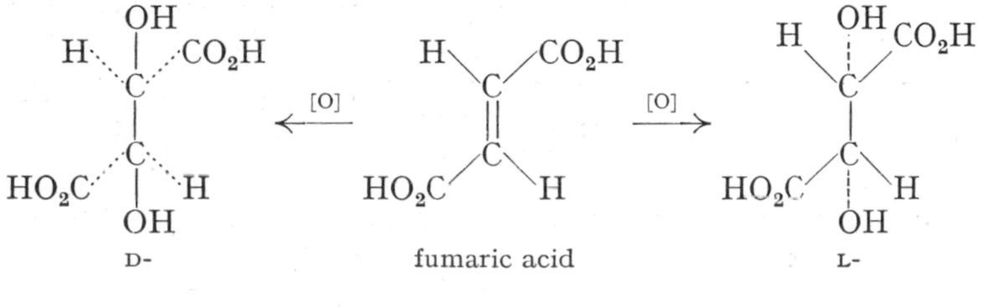

```
      OH                                                  H   OH  CO2H
 H·.  |  .·CO2H          H       CO2H                      \   :   /
     ·C·                   \    /                              C
      |        [O]           C             [O]                 |
      |      <——             ||           ——>                  |
     ·C·                     C                                 C
   .·  | ·.                /    \                            /  :  \
HO2C   |   H           HO2C      H                       HO2C   :   H
      OH                                                      OH
      D-              fumaric acid                             L-
```

The problem is further complicated by the fact that oxidation with Caro's acid causes the addition of the two hydroxyl groups to take place in the *trans*-position (see also p. 66).

The results of many experiments indicate that *trans*-addition to a double bond is usually, but not invariably, the case.

The mechanisms of the stereochemical additions to a double and a triple bond are still not certain. The addition of halogen is *trans*. If the two halogen atoms approach on the same side of the attacked molecule and add *simultaneously* to the two carbon atoms, *i.e.*, we have a four-centre side-approach reaction, the resulting addition must be *cis*. If the two halogen atoms add on *singly*, then *cis* or *trans* addition could result. Since *trans*-addition occurs in practice, the addition must occur by a *two-step* mechanism (*i.e.*, the halogen atoms must add on one at a time; *cf.* ethylene, p. 61). Roberts and Kimball (1937) suggested the addition to a double bond occurs via the formation of a *cyclic* planar compound, *e.g.*,

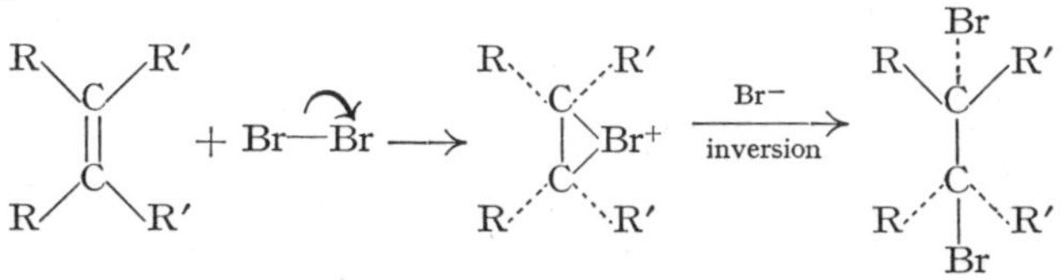

$$RR'C{=}CRR' + Br{-}Br \longrightarrow [\text{cyclic } Br^+ \text{ intermediate}] \xrightarrow[\text{inversion}]{Br^-} RR'CBr{-}CBrRR'$$

If the bromine ion attacks the planar compound from *behind*, then a Walden inversion occurs at this attacked carbon atom. Winstein and Lucas (1939) have demonstrated the existence of the above planar intermediate. It is possible that this intermediate is a resonance hybrid.

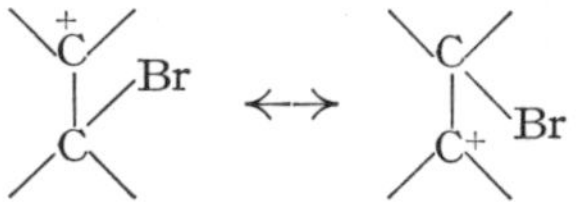

$$\overset{+}{C}{-}C{-}Br \longleftrightarrow Br{-}C{-}C^{+}$$

An alternative explanation for the addition of bromine across a double bond is as follows. At first the Br^+ ion is held loosely by the π-electrons to form a π-*complex* (Fig. 15*a*). The molecule is planar at this moment. Then tetrahedral hybridisation of C_1 occurs, C_2 still retaining its trigonal hybridisation (Fig. *b*).

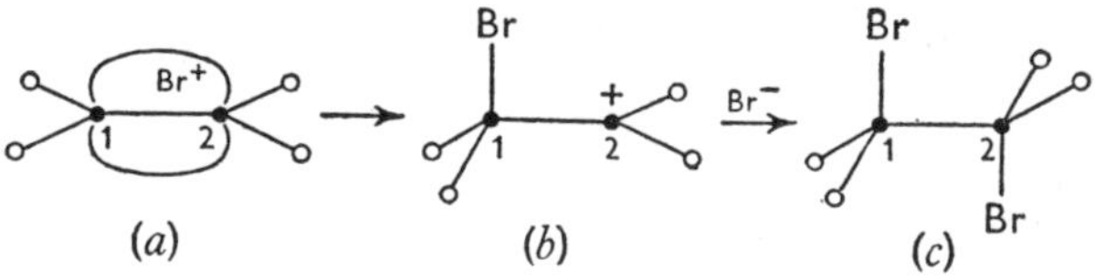

(*a*) (*b*) (*c*)

FIG. 17.15.

The bromine ion now attacks C_2, but does so on the side *remote* from the bromine atom on C_1, partly because of the repulsion of the bromine atom already on C_1, and partly because of the hindering effect of this bromine atom due to its actual bulk (spatial factor). When C_2 is attacked on the " under " side, it hybridises to the tetrahedral form, and does so with " inversion " (*i.e.*, in the opposite sense to C_1; Fig. *c*).

Geometrical isomerism accounts for the existence of many pairs of compounds, *e.g.*, the following acids: oleic (*cis*) and elaidic (*trans*); *iso*crotonic (*cis*) and crotonic (*trans*); angelic (*cis*) and tiglic (*trans*); etc.

Citraconic acid (*methylmaleic acid*) and **mesaconic acid** (*methylfumaric acid*) are geometrical isomers:

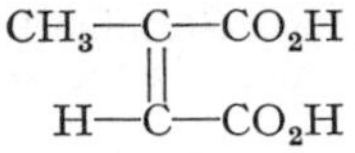

$$\begin{array}{c}CH_3-C-CO_2H\\ \|\\ H-C-CO_2H\end{array}\qquad\qquad\begin{array}{c}CH_3-C-CO_2H\\ \|\\ HO_2C-C-H\end{array}$$

citraconic acid 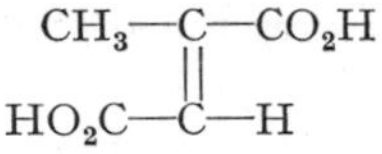　　　　mesaconic acid

Citraconic acid is a crystalline solid, m.p. 91°; it forms the anhydride. Citraconic acid may be prepared by heating itaconic anhydride and refluxing the product, citraconic anhydride, with water.

Mesaconic acid is a crystalline solid, m.p. 240°; it does not form an anhydride. It may be prepared by evaporating a mixture of citraconic anhydride and dilute nitric acid:

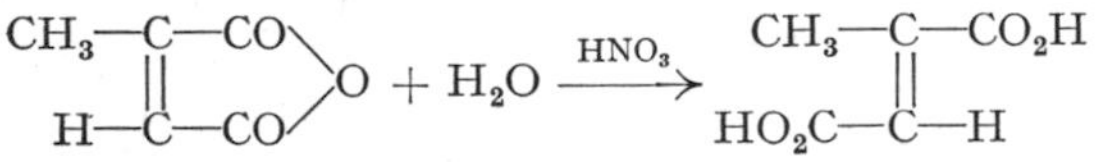

$$\begin{array}{c}CH_3-C-CO\diagdown\\ \|\quad\quad O\\ H-C-CO\diagup\end{array} + H_2O \xrightarrow{HNO_3} \begin{array}{c}CH_3-C-CO_2H\\ \|\\ HO_2C-C-H\end{array}\qquad(43\text{–}52\%)$$

Citraconic acid forms the anhydride more easily than maleic acid does, and mesaconic acid, when heated with acetic anhydride, readily gives citraconic anhydride.

Itaconic acid (*methylenesuccinic acid*), $CH_2{:}C(CO_2H){\cdot}CH_2{\cdot}CO_2H$, m.p. 162°, may be prepared by heating citric acid until it melts, and refluxing the product, itaconic anhydride (which distils over), with water.

Itaconic acid may also be prepared by the fermentation of glucose by *Aspergillus terreus*.

When itaconic anhydride is distilled rapidly, a large portion of it rearranges to citraconic anhydride:

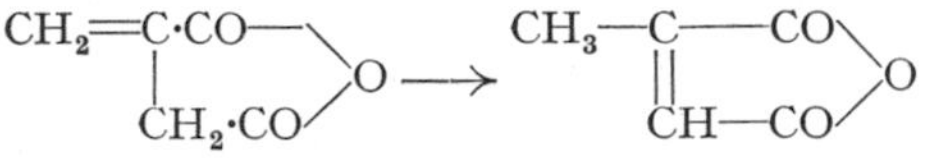

$$\begin{array}{c}CH_2{=}C{\cdot}CO-\diagdown\\ |\quad\quad\quad O\\ CH_2{\cdot}CO\diagup\end{array} \longrightarrow \begin{array}{c}CH_3-C-CO\diagdown\\ \|\quad\quad O\\ CH-CO\diagup\end{array}\qquad(68\text{–}72\%)$$

Esters of itaconic acid can be polymerised to form plastics.

Glutaconic acid, $CO_2H{\cdot}CH{:}CH{\cdot}CH_2{\cdot}CO_2H$ (isomeric with the above acids), may be prepared by heating a mixture of sodiomalonic ester and chloroform with sodium ethoxide:

$$2[CH(CO_2C_2H_5)_2]^-Na^+ + CHCl_3 \xrightarrow{C_2H_5ONa} (C_2H_5O_2C)_2CH{\cdot}CH{:}C(CO_2C_2H_5)_2$$

$$\xrightarrow[\text{(ii) HCl}]{\text{(i) KOH}} (HO_2C)_2CH{\cdot}CH{:}C(CO_2H)_2 \xrightarrow{\text{heat}} CO_2H{\cdot}CH{:}CH{\cdot}CH_2{\cdot}CO_2H$$

Glutaconic acid may also be prepared as follows (Lochte and Pickard, 1946):

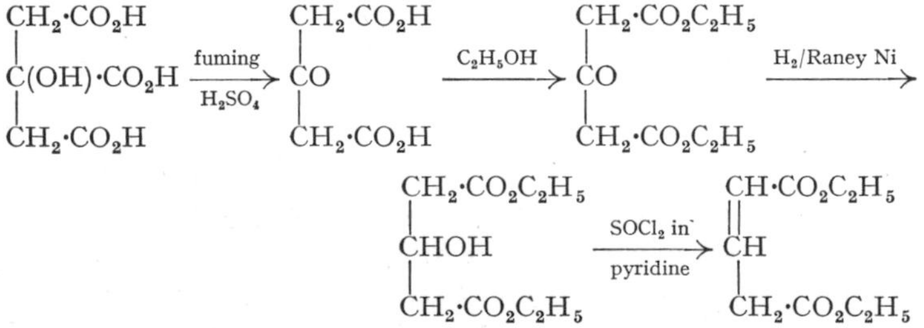

$$\begin{array}{l}CH_2{\cdot}CO_2H\\ |\\ C(OH){\cdot}CO_2H\\ |\\ CH_2{\cdot}CO_2H\end{array} \xrightarrow[H_2SO_4]{\text{fuming}} \begin{array}{l}CH_2{\cdot}CO_2H\\ |\\ CO\\ |\\ CH_2{\cdot}CO_2H\end{array} \xrightarrow{C_2H_5OH} \begin{array}{l}CH_2{\cdot}CO_2C_2H_5\\ |\\ CO\\ |\\ CH_2{\cdot}CO_2C_2H_5\end{array} \xrightarrow{H_2/\text{Raney Ni}}$$

$$\begin{array}{l}CH_2{\cdot}CO_2C_2H_5\\ |\\ CHOH\\ |\\ CH_2{\cdot}CO_2C_2H_5\end{array} \xrightarrow[\text{pyridine}]{SOCl_2\text{ in}} \begin{array}{l}CH{\cdot}CO_2C_2H_5\\ \|\\ CH\\ |\\ CH_2{\cdot}CO_2C_2H_5\end{array}\qquad(24\%)$$

Glutaconic acid is a crystalline solid, m.p. 138°. Although only one form has been prepared, in theory two geometrical isomers are possible:

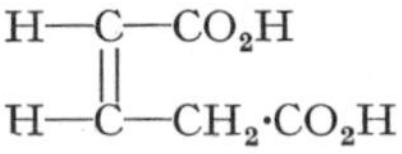

$$\begin{array}{c}H-C-CO_2H\\ \|\\ H-C-CH_2{\cdot}CO_2H\end{array}\qquad\qquad\begin{array}{c}H-C-CO_2H\\ \|\\ HO_2C{\cdot}CH_2-C-H\end{array}$$

cis-acid 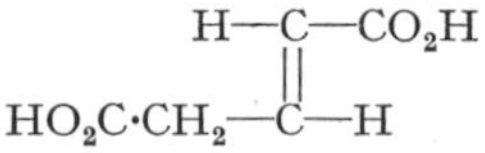　　　　*trans*-acid

Owing to the presence of two strongly negative (terminal) groups, the α-hydrogen atoms are readily eliminated as protons and can thereby give rise to a prototropic system:

$$-CO-CH{=}CH-CH_2-CO- \rightleftharpoons H^+ + -CO-CH{=}CH-\ddot{C}H-CO- \longleftrightarrow$$
$$-CO-\ddot{C}H-CH{=}CH-CO- \xrightleftharpoons{H^+} -CO-CH_2-CH{=}CH-CO-$$

This may be regarded as a three-carbon prototropic system. If, as is generally believed, this tautomeric system involves the enol form, it is, strictly speaking, a *pentad-enol* form (*cf.* p. 206). This prototropic change makes the *cis*- and *trans*-forms unstable; it has been shown that the known form is the *trans* isomer.

Glutaconic esters form sodio-derivatives with sodium ethoxide, and these react with alkyl halides:

$$C_2H_5O_2C{\cdot}CH{:}CH{\cdot}CH_2{\cdot}CO_2C_2H_5 \xrightarrow{C_2H_5ONa} [C_2H_5O_2C{\cdot}CH{:}CH{\cdot}CH{\cdot}CO_2C_2H_5]^-Na^+$$
$$\xrightarrow{CH_3I} C_2H_5O_2C{\cdot}CH{:}CH{\cdot}CH(CH_3){\cdot}CO_2C_2H_5$$

This is an example of vinylogy (p. 269).

Muconic acid, $CO_2H{\cdot}CH{:}CH{\cdot}CH{:}CH{\cdot}CO_2H$, m.p. 306°, may be prepared by heating α : α′-dibromoadipic acid with ethanolic potassium hydroxide:

$$CO_2H{\cdot}CHBr{\cdot}CH_2{\cdot}CH_2{\cdot}CHBr{\cdot}CO_2H \xrightarrow[\text{ethanol}]{KOH} CO_2H{\cdot}CH{:}CH{\cdot}CH{:}CH{\cdot}CO_2H$$

Muconic acid is formed by the oxidation of benzene in the animal body.

Aconitic acid (*propene*-1 : 2-3-*tricarboxylic acid*) occurs in the sugar-cane and beet-root, and in sorghum. It may be prepared by means of the Michael condensation between acetylenedicarboxylic ester and malonic ester:

$$C_2H_5O_2C{\cdot}C{\vdots}C{\cdot}CO_2C_2H_5 + CH_2(CO_2C_2H_5)_2 \xrightarrow{CH_3ONa}$$
$$\begin{matrix} C_2H_5O_2C{\cdot}C{:}CH{\cdot}CO_2C_2H_5 \\ | \\ CH(CO_2C_2H_5)_2 \end{matrix} \xrightarrow{HCl} \begin{matrix} CH{\cdot}CO_2H \\ \| \\ C{\cdot}CO_2H \\ | \\ CH_2{\cdot}CO_2H \\ \text{aconitic acid} \end{matrix}$$

Aconitic acid is prepared industrially from calcium aconitate, which is recovered from sugar-cane syrup residues. Another industrial method is to dehydrate citric acid with concentrated sulphuric acid at 120–150°.

Aconitic acid is used in pain-preventive and fever-reducing medicines. Its esters have been used as plasticisers, and in the manufacture of wetting agents. On heating, aconitic acid is readily decarboxylated to itaconic acid. Aconitic acid exists in two forms (*cis*- and *trans*-), *both* of which form anhydrides:

$$\begin{matrix} H-C-CO_2H \\ \| \\ HO_2C{\cdot}CH_2-C-CO_2H \\ \textit{cis}\text{-acid} \\ \text{m.p. } 125° \end{matrix} \qquad \begin{matrix} H-C-CO_2H \\ \| \\ HO_2C-C-CH_2{\cdot}CO_2H \\ \textit{trans}\text{-acid} \\ \text{m.p. } 194° \end{matrix}$$

The Stereochemistry of Carbon Compounds not Containing an Asymmetric Carbon Atom

As pointed out previously (p. 385), the presence of an asymmetric carbon atom is not essential for optical activity; the essential requirement is *the asymmetry of the molecule as a whole*. Allenes are compounds whose *structures* are asymmetric, and so should be resolvable. Several compounds of this type have been obtained

$$\begin{matrix} R & & R \\ | & & / \\ C{=}C{=}C & & \\ | & / & \\ R' & R' & \end{matrix} \qquad \vdots \qquad \begin{matrix} R & & R \\ \backslash & & | \\ C{=}C{=}C & & \\ \backslash & & | \\ R' & & R' \end{matrix}$$

in optically active forms, *e.g.*, where R = C_6H_5 (phenyl) and R′ = 1-$C_{10}H_7$ (1-naphthyl) [Mills and Maitland, 1936].

If both double bonds of allene are replaced by rings, *spirans* are obtained in which the rings are at right angles to each other. Hence by suitable substitution, it should be possible to obtain optically active *spiro*-compounds, *e.g.*, Backer (1928) resolved the following *spiro*heptane derivative.

HO_2C╲ ╱CH_2╲ ╱CH_2╲ ╱H
C C C
H╱ ╲CH_2╱ ╲CH_2╱ ╲CO_2H

Suitably *ortho*-substituted diphenyls are also compounds whose structures are asymmetric, the asymmetry arising from restricted rotation about the single bond joining the two benzene rings (p. 672).

The Optical Isomerism of Elements other than Carbon

Many quadricovalent elements whose valencies are distributed tetrahedrally have also been obtained in optically active forms, *e.g.*, silicon and tin.

Nitrogen can be tercovalent or quadricovalent unielectrovalent. In the latter compounds, if the charge on the nitrogen atom is ignored, the molecule then closely resembles carbon compounds. Thus, for example, the following compounds have been obtained in optically active forms.

CH_3╲ + ╱C_6H_5
N } I^-
$CH_2{=}CH{\cdot}CH_2$╱ ╲$CH_2{\cdot}C_6H_5$

allylbenzylmethylphenylammonium iodide
(Pope and Peachey, 1899)

H╲ ╱$CH_2{\cdot}CH_2$╲ + ╱$CH_2{\cdot}CH_2$╲ ╱H
C N C } Br^-
C_6H_5╱ ╲$CH_2{\cdot}CH_2$╱ ╲$CH_2{\cdot}CH_2$╱ ╲$CO_2C_2H_5$

4-carbethoxy-4′-phenylbispiperidinium-1 : 1′-spiran bromide (Mills and Warren, 1925)

CH_3╲ ╱C_6H_5
N
C_2H_5╱ ↘O

ethylmethylphenylamine oxide (Meisenheimer, 1908)

Racemisation of compounds of the type $\overset{+}{N}abde\}X^-$ is effected far more readily than with the carbon compounds, *Cabde*. The mechanism is believed to be due to the ready dissociation:

$$\overset{+}{N}abde\}X^- \rightleftharpoons Nabd + eX$$

The amine, N*abd* readily racemises (see below), and so the quaternary compound will racemise.

Tercovalent nitrogen offers a very interesting problem from the point of view of stereoisomerism. No tertiary amine, N*abd*, has yet been resolved. It was therefore suggested that such molecules were planar, but physico-chemical evidence, *e.g.*, dipole moment measurements, absorption spectra, etc., shows that the configuration of ammonia and amines is tetrahedral, the nitrogen atom being at one corner of the tetrahedron with a valency angle of about 109°. Meisenheimer

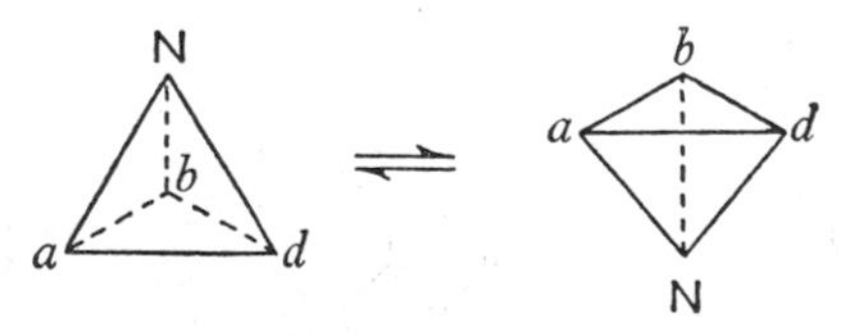

FIG. 17.16.

(1924) explained the failure to resolve tertiary amines as being due to the rapid oscillation of the nitrogen atom at right angles above and below the plane containing the three groups *a*, *b* and *d* (Fig. 16), *i.e.*, rapid optical inversion is occurring all the time. This explanation assumes that the nitrogen valency angles and bond lengths change. This inversion of amines, however, is better represented as an " umbrella " switch of bonds, *i.e.*, the bond lengths remain unaltered and only the nitrogen valency angles change. Theoretical considerations have shown that if the nitrogen atom were " anchored " by forming part of a ring, then the inversion (due to oscillation) would be inhibited. This has been confirmed by the resolution of Tröger's base.

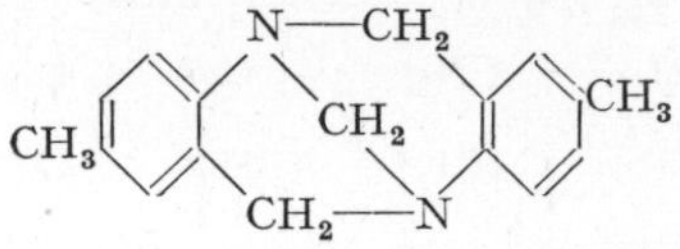

N—CH_2 ; CH_3 ; CH_2 ; CH_3 ; CH_2—N

Oximes are also compounds of tercovalent nitrogen. They exhibit geometrical isomerism, and some have also been obtained in optically active forms, *e.g.*, the oxime of *cyclo*hexanone-4-carboxylic acid (Mills and Bain, 1910).

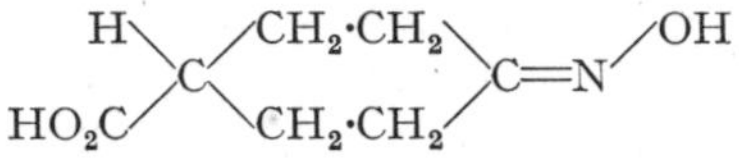

H, HO_2C > C < $CH_2·CH_2$, $CH_2·CH_2$ > C=N—OH

No tertiary phosphines have yet been resolved, but a number of quadricovalent phosphorus compounds have been obtained in optically active forms, *e.g.*,

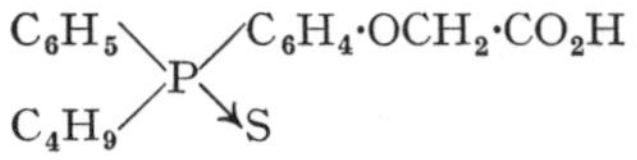

C_6H_5, C_4H_9 > P < $C_6H_4·OCH_2·CO_2H$, →S

(Davies and Mann, 1944)

CH_2, CH_2, $\overset{+}{P}$—C_6H_5, CH_2, C_6H_4OH } Br^-

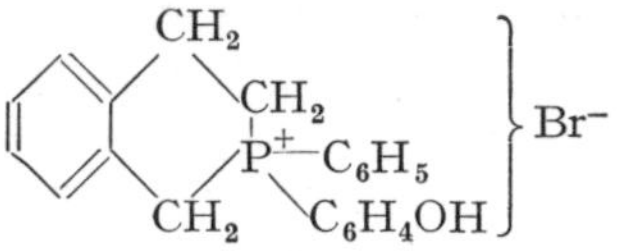

(Holliman and Mann, 1947)

Tercovalent and quadricovalent arsenic compounds have been resolved, *e.g.*,

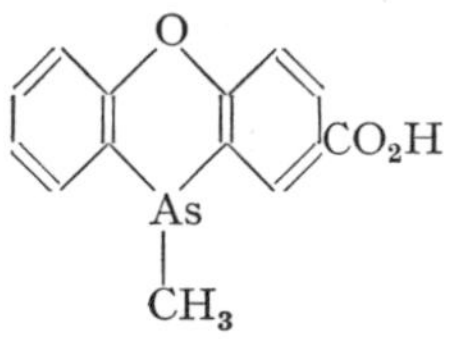

O, CO_2H, As, CH_3

(Lesslie and Turner, 1934)

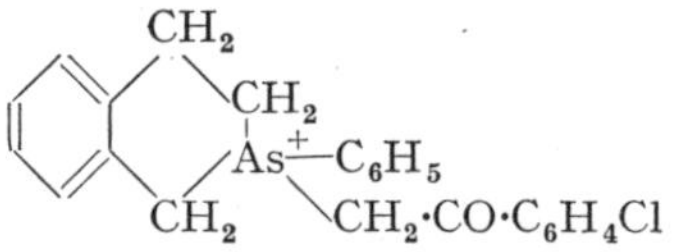

CH_2, CH_2, $\overset{+}{As}$—C_6H_5, CH_2, $CH_2·CO·C_6H_4Cl$

(Holliman and Mann, 1943)

Various sulphur compounds have also been resolved, *e.g.*,

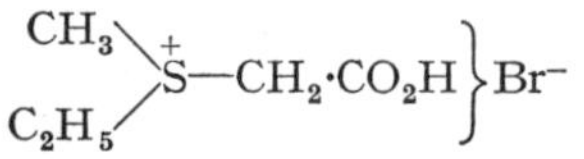

CH_3, C_2H_5 > $\overset{+}{S}$—$CH_2·CO_2H$ } Br^-

(Pope and Peachey, 1900)

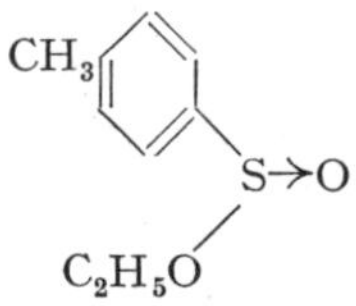

CH_3, S→O, C_2H_5O

(Phillips, 1925)

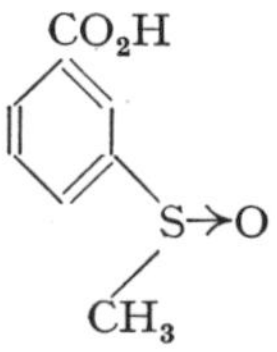

CO_2H, S→O, CH_3

(Phillips, 1926)

CH_2, CH_2, $\overset{+}{S}$—$CH_2·CO·C_6H_4Cl$, CH_2 } Br^-

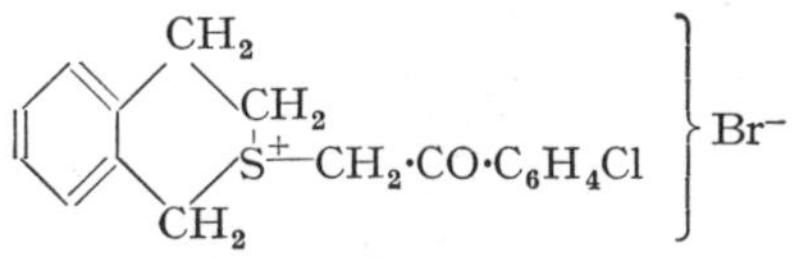

(Mann and Holliman, 1946)

In the sulphonium compounds, the sulphur atom is tercovalent unielectrovalent, and if it occupies one corner of a tetrahedron, the structure is asymmetric (*cf.* N*abd*). The structures of the sulphinic ester and sulphoxide are not certain. If the SO bond is dative (*i.e.*, the sulphur is tercovalent unielectrovalent) and the sulphur atom occupies one corner of a tetrahedron, then the optical isomerism is accounted for. If the SO bond is a double bond (*i.e.*, the sulphur is quadricovalent), then if the sulphur atom were at the *centre* of the tetrahedron, the molecules of the sulphinic ester and sulphoxide would be *flat*, and hence not

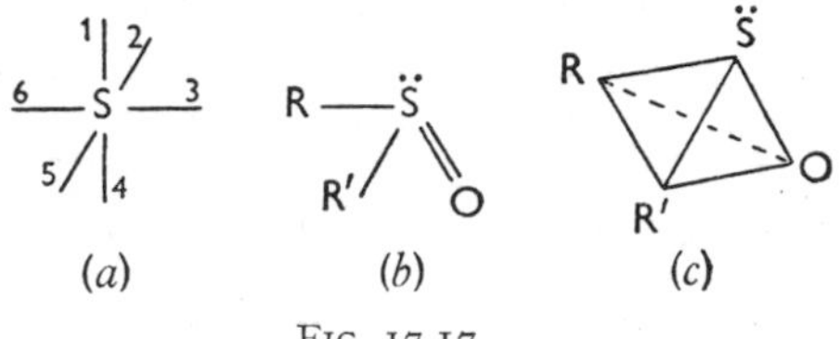

FIG. 17.17.

resolvable. It is possible, however, to assume the valency of sulphur is *six* (with the six valencies arranged *octahedrally* (Fig. 17*a*), and by leaving bonds 1 and 2 unused, a molecular structure is obtained which is *asymmetric*, the sulphur atom again now being at a *corner* of a tetrahedron (Figs. *b* and *c*).

QUESTIONS

1. Write out the structures and names of the isomeric hydroxyacids with the molecular formula $C_4H_8O_3$. How would you prepare each isomer, and how would you distinguish them from one another?
2. Name the products and state the conditions under which they are formed, when an α-, β-, γ- or δ-hydroxyacid is treated with:—EtOH, (*b*) AcCl, (*c*) PCl_5, (*d*) $KMnO_4$, (*e*) H_2SO_4, (*f*) HI, (*g*) heat.
3. Write an account of the preparation and properties of lactones, and include in your answer the preparation of large-ring lactones.
4. Describe the preparation and properties of:—(*a*) glycollic acid, (*b*) lactic acid, (*c*) hydracrylic acid, (*d*) malic acid, (*e*) D(+), L(−), DL- and *meso*-tartaric acids, (*f*) citric acid, (*g*) tricarballylic acid, (*h*) maleic acid, (*i*) fumaric acid, (*j*) aconitic acid.
Give an account of the *analytical* evidence for the structure of each acid mentioned.
5. Write an account of the theoretical basis of optical and geometrical isomerism. Discuss the case of:—(*a*) lactic acid, (*b*) tartaric acid, (*c*) the isomers with the formula $C_4H_4O_4$.
6. How many possible stereoisomers are there for each of the following:—(*a*) $CH_3{\cdot}CHCl{\cdot}CO_2H$, (*b*) $CH_2Br{\cdot}CH_2{\cdot}CO_2H$, (*c*) $Me_2C(OH){\cdot}CO_2H$, (*d*) Me·CHOH·CHOH·CO_2H, (*e*) Me·CHBr·CHCl·Me, (*f*) Et·CHOH·CHOH·Et, (*g*) $HO_2C{\cdot}CHBr{\cdot}CH_2{\cdot}CO_2Et$, (*h*) CH_2OH·CHOH·CHOH·CHO, (*i*) $CH_2{:}CH{\cdot}Me$, (*j*) Me·CH:CH·Me, (*k*) MeCHBr·CH:CH_2, (*l*) Me·CHOH·CH:CHMe, (*m*) $HO_2C{\cdot}CMe{:}C(CO_2H){\cdot}CHMe{\cdot}CO_2H$?
7. Write an account of :—(*a*) the resolution of racemic modifications, (*b*) racemisation, (*c*) the Walden inversion, (*d*) asymmetric synthesis, (*e*) asymmetric transformation.
8. Write an account of the properties of *cis-trans* isomers, paying special attention to:—(*a*) their addition reactions, (*b*) their interconversion, (*c*) the methods of determining their configurations.
9. Define and give examples of:—(*a*) the Dilution Principle, (*b*) isomerism, (*c*) structural isomerism, (*d*) chain isomerism, (*e*) position isomerism, (*f*) functional group isomerism, (*g*) metamerism, (*h*) tautomerism, (*i*) stereoisomerism, (*j*) optical isomerism, (*k*) geometrical isomerism, (*l*) diastereoisomerism, (*m*) restricted rotation, (*n*) plane of symmetry, (*o*) centre of symmetry, (*p*) flexible molecules.
10. Starting with AcOH, indicate by means of equations how you would prepare:—(*a*) tartronic acid, (*b*) malic acid, (*c*) tartaric acid, (*d*) maleic acid, (*e*) aconitic acid.
11. Write an account of the preparation and properties of glutaconic acid.

READING REFERENCES

Gilman, *Advanced Organic Chemistry*, Wiley (1942, 2nd ed.).
(i) Vol. I, Ch. 8 (*pp.* 707–714). Polyesters of hydroxyacids.
(ii) Vol. I, Ch. 4. Stereoisomerism.

Filachione and Fischer, The Purification of Lactic Acid, *Ind. Eng. Chem.*, 1946, **38**, 228.
Dascher *et al.*, The Industrial Application of Fumaric Acid. *ibid.*, 1941, **33**, 315.
Karow and Waksman, The Production of Citric Acid by Submerged Culture, *ibid.*, 1947, **39**, 821.
(This paper gives references to other fermentations.)

Mann and Pope, Dissymmetry and Asymmetry of Molecular Configuration, *Chem. and Ind.*, 1925, III, 833.
Stewart, *Stereochemistry*, Longmans, Green (1919).
Frankland, Pasteur Memorial Lecture, *J.C.S.*, 1897, **71**, 683.
Walker, Van't Hoff Memorial Lecture, *ibid.*, 1913, 1127.
Pope, Obituary Notice of Le Bel, *ibid.*, 1930, 2789.
Wheland, *Advanced Organic Chemistry*, Wiley (1949, 2nd ed.), Ch. 5–8.
Cahn and Ingold, Specification of Configuration about Quadrivalent Asymmetric Atoms, *J.C.S.*, **1951**, 612.
Bijvoet *et al.*, Determination of the Absolute Configuration of Optically Active Compounds by means of X-Rays, *Nature*, 1951, **168**, 271.
McCoubrey and Ubbelohde, The Configuration of Flexible Organic Molecules, *Quart. Reviews* (*Chem. Soc.*), 1951, **5**, 364.
Turner and Harris, Asymmetric Transformation, *ibid.*, 1947, **1**, 299.
Crombie, Geometrical Isomerism about Carbon–Carbon Double Bonds, *ibid.*, 1952, **6**, 101.
Kenyon and Ross, A New Mechanism for the Marckwald Asymmetric Synthesis, *J.C.S.*, **1952**, 2307.
Hudson, Emil Fischer's Stereo-Formulas, *Advances in Carbohydrate Chemistry*, Academic Press. Vol. 3 (1948), Ch. 1.
Organic Reactions, Wiley, Vol. VIII (1954), Ch. 7. β-Lactones.
Finar, *Organic Chemistry*, Longmans, Green, Vol. II (1956). Chh. 2–6.
McCasland and Proskow, The Conditions for Optical Inactivity, *J. Amer. Chem. Soc.*, 1956, **78**, 5646.
Klyne (Ed.), *Progress in Stereochemistry*, Butterworth (1954).

CHAPTER XVIII

CARBOHYDRATES

CARBOHYDRATES are substances with the general formula $C_x(H_2O)_y$, and were called carbohydrates (hydrates of carbon) because they contained hydrogen and oxygen in the same proportion as in water. Recently, a number of compounds have been discovered which are carbohydrates by chemical behaviour, but do not conform to the formula $C_x(H_2O)_y$, *e.g.*, rhamnose, $C_6H_{12}O_5$; rhamnohexose, $C_7H_{14}O_6$. It is also important to note that all compounds conforming to the formula $C_x(H_2O)_y$ are not necessarily carbohydrates, *e.g.*, formaldehyde, CH_2O; acetic acid, $C_2H_4O_2$; etc.

All carbohydrates are polyhydroxy aldehydes or ketones, or substances that yield these on hydrolysis.

Nomenclature. The names of the simpler carbohydrates end in *-ose*; carbohydrates with an aldehydic structure are known as *aldoses*, and those with ketonic, *ketoses*. The number of *carbon* atoms in the molecule is indicated by a Greek prefix, *e.g.*, a *tetrose* contains four carbon atoms, a *pentose* five, a *hexose* six, etc.

Carbohydrates are divided into two main classes, **sugars** and **polysaccharides** (*polysaccharoses*). Sugars are crystalline substances with a sweet taste and soluble in water. Polysaccharides are more complex than the sugars, their molecular weights being far greater. Most of them are non-crystalline substances which are not sweet, and are insoluble or less soluble in water, than the sugars.

Both classes of compounds have similar structures and both are produced by plants.

Sugars are subdivided into a number of groups as follows:

1. **Monosaccharides** (*monosaccharoses*). These are sugars which cannot be hydrolysed into smaller molecules. Their general formula is $C_nH_{2n}O_n$ (there are exceptions), where n is 2–10 (but see later). The most important monosaccharides are the pentoses and hexoses, and these are practically the only monosaccharides which occur naturally.

2. **Oligosaccharides.** These consist of:

   (i) **Disaccharides,** $C_{12}H_{22}O_{11}$, which yield *two* monosaccharide molecules on hydrolysis, *e.g.*, sucrose, maltose.

   (ii) **Trisaccharides,** $C_{18}H_{32}O_{16}$, which yield *three* monosaccharide molecules on hydrolysis, *e.g.*, raffinose.

   (iii) **Tetrasaccharides,** $C_{24}H_{42}O_{21}$, which yield *four* monosaccharide molecules on hydrolysis, *e.g.*, stachyose.

Polysaccharides (*polysaccharoses*) are carbohydrates which yield a large number of monosaccharide molecules on hydrolysis. The most widely spread polysaccharides have the general formula $(C_6H_{10}O_5)_n$, *e.g.*, starch, cellulose, etc.; a group of polysaccharides which are not so widely spread in nature is the *pentosans*, $(C_5H_8O_4)_n$.

Monosaccharides

The simplest monosaccharide is glycolaldehyde, $CH_2OH{\cdot}CHO$. This does not contain an asymmetric carbon atom and is therefore not optically active. Since all naturally occurring sugars are optically active, it is more satisfactory to exclude glycolaldehyde from the group of sugars, and to define sugars as optically active polyhydroxy-aldehydes or ketones.

Triose, $C_3H_6O_3$. *Glyceraldehyde,* $CH_2OH{\cdot}CHOH{\cdot}CHO$, is an *aldotriose.* It contains one asymmetric carbon atom, and can therefore exist in two optically active forms, D- and L-; both are known. Glyceraldehyde has now been chosen as the standard configuration in sugar chemistry (p. 383).

Dihydroxyacetone, $CH_2OH{\cdot}CO{\cdot}CH_2OH$, is not optically active, and hence, by the definition given above, is not a sugar. If the definition be rejected, *i.e.*, the proviso that a sugar is always optically active is rejected, then dihydroxyacetone will be a *ketotriose.*

Tetroses, $C_4H_8O_4$. The structure of an aldotetrose is $CH_2OH{\cdot}CHOH{\cdot}CHOH{\cdot}CHO$ (see p. 435).

There is only one structure possible for a *ketotetrose, viz.,* $CH_2OH{\cdot}CO{\cdot}CHOH{\cdot}CH_2OH$. This contains one asymmetric carbon atom, and corresponds to D- and L-*erythrulose,* which are synthetic compounds.

Pentoses, $C_5H_{10}O_5$. The *aldopentoses* are an important group of sugars (monosaccharides), and their structure has been elucidated as follows:

(i) Analysis and molecular-weight determinations show that the molecular formula of the aldopentoses is $C_5H_{10}O_5$.

(ii) When treated with acetic anhydride, aldopentoses form the tetra-acetate. This indicates the presence of four hydroxyl groups. Furthermore, since aldopentoses are not easily dehydrated, it can be assumed that no carbon atom is attached to two hydroxyl groups (*cf.* p. 157). As we shall see, this assumption is borne out by other reactions of the aldopentoses.

(iii) Aldopentoses form an oxime when treated with hydroxylamine, and therefore contain a carbonyl group.

(iv) When an aldopentose is oxidised with bromine-water, a tetrahydroxy-acid of formula $C_5H_{10}O_6$ is obtained. This indicates that the carbonyl group is present in an *aldehydic* group, since the acid obtained on oxidation contains the *same* number of carbon atoms as the original compound.

(v) When an aldopentose is oxidised with nitric acid, trihydroxyglutaric acid, $CO_2H{\cdot}(CHOH)_3{\cdot}CO_2H$, is obtained. This indicates that the five carbon atoms in the aldopentose are in a straight chain. This conclusion is supported by ascending the series by the *Kiliani reaction* (p. 425) and reducing the product, a polyhydroxyacid, with hydriodic acid; *n*-hexoic acid, $CH_3{\cdot}(CH_2)_4{\cdot}CO_2H$, is produced.

The foregoing reactions show that the structure of the aldopentoses is:

$$CHO{\cdot}CHOH{\cdot}CHOH{\cdot}CHOH{\cdot}CH_2OH$$

This contains three structurally different asymmetric carbon atoms, and can therefore exist in eight optically active forms. All are known, and correspond to the D- and L-forms of *arabinose, xylose, ribose* and *lyxose* (see p. 435).

L(+)-*Arabinose,* m.p. 158°, occurs naturally as pentosans (arabans) in various gums, *e.g.*, gum arabic. It is usually obtained by the hydrolysis of cherry-gum with dilute sulphuric acid.

D(—)-*Arabinose* occurs in certain glycosides.

D(+)-*Xylose* (wood-sugar), m.p. 145°, occurs as pentosans (xylans) in wood gums, bran and straw, from which it may be obtained by hydrolysis with dilute sulphuric acid.

D(—)-*Ribose,* m.p. 95°, occurs in plant nucleic acids, and in liver and pancreas nucleic acids.

All the other aldopentoses are synthetic compounds.

The chemical properties of the aldopentoses are similar to those of the aldohexoses (see glucose, below); pentoses do *not* undergo fermentation. All the aldopentoses are converted quantitatively into *furfural* when warmed with dilute acid:

$$C_5H_{10}O_5 \xrightarrow{HCl} \begin{array}{c} CH{=\!=}CH \\ | \quad\quad | \\ CH \quad C{\cdot}CHO \\ \diagdown \, O \, \diagup \end{array} + 3H_2O$$

Rhamnose is a hexose with the formula $CH_3{\cdot}(CHOH)_4{\cdot}CHO$; it is also known as *methylpentose* or 6-*deoxyhexose*. It occurs in several glycosides.

Ketopentoses with the structure $CH_2OH{\cdot}CO{\cdot}CHOH{\cdot}CHOH{\cdot}CH_2OH$ have been prepared. The molecule contains two structurally different asymmetric carbon atoms, and can therefore exist in four optically active forms. All are known, and correspond to D- and L-forms of *ribulose* and *xylulose*. All are synthetic compounds except L-xylulose which occurs in pentosuric urine.

Hexoses, $C_6H_{12}O_6$. The *aldohexoses* are another important group of monosaccharides, and their structure has been elucidated as follows (*cf.* aldopentoses):

(i) Analysis and molecular-weight determinations show that the molecular formula of the aldohexoses is $C_6H_{12}O_6$.

(ii) When treated with acetic anhydride, aldohexoses form the penta-acetate. This indicates the presence of five hydroxyl groups, and since aldohexoses are not easily dehydrated, it can be assumed that each hydroxyl group is attached to a different carbon atom.

(iii) Aldohexoses form an oxime when treated with hydroxylamine, and therefore contain a carbonyl group.

(iv) When an aldohexose is oxidised with bromine-water, a pentahydroxy-acid of formula $C_6H_{12}O_7$ is obtained. This indicates that the carbonyl group is present in an *aldehydic* group.

(v) When reduced with concentrated hydriodic acid and red phosphorus at 100°, aldohexoses give a mixture of 2-iodohexane and *n*-hexane. This indicates that the six carbon atoms in an aldohexose are in a straight chain. This conclusion is supported by ascending the series by the *Kiliani reaction* and reducing the product, a polyhydroxyacid, with hydriodic acid; *n*-heptoic acid, $CH_3{\cdot}(CH_2)_5{\cdot}CO_2H$, is produced.

The foregoing reactions show that the structure of the aldohexoses is:

$$CHO{\cdot}CHOH{\cdot}CHOH{\cdot}CHOH{\cdot}CHOH{\cdot}CH_2OH$$

This contains four structurally different asymmetric carbon atoms, and can therefore exist in sixteen optically active forms. All are known, and correspond to the D- and L-forms of *glucose, mannose, galactose, allose, altrose, gulose, idose* and *talose* (see p. 435). Only four of these occur naturally: D(+)-glucose, D(+)-mannose, D(+)-galactose, and D(+)-talose. D(−)-idose and D(+)-altrose have been isolated from the polysaccharide produced by the mould, *Penicillium varians*.

Although the foregoing evidence indicates an open-chain structure, there is further evidence which shows that the sugars actually exist as *six-membered rings*. In many cases, however, it is more convenient to use the open-chain structure, and although this is incorrect, nevertheless it gives a simpler picture of the properties of the sugars, since many reactions apparently involve first the opening of the ring (which is easily broken) and then re-action with the other reagent. The ring structure is hexagonal (I), but it is usually more convenient to use the planar formula (II), *e.g.*, α-D-glucose. (II) corresponds to the open-chain formula (III) (see also p. 431), and it should be noted that the usual way of drawing the conventional planar formula of an aldose is with the carbon chain vertical and the aldehyde group at the top. In the D-series the hydroxyl group is always to the right on the bottom asymmetric carbon atom. The L-series is then the enantiomorphs of the D-series.

```
     CH2OH                          H—C—OH ─┐             CHO
  H   |    H                          |      |              |
   |—O—|                            H—C—OH   |          H—C—OH
  / H   \                             |      O              |
  \ OH H/                          HO—C—H    |         HO—C—H
HO  |    OH                           |      |              |
   H  OH                            H—C—OH   |          H—C—OH
    (I)                               |      |              |
                                    H—C—────┘           H—C—OH
                                      |                     |
                                    CH2OH                 CH2OH
                                    (II)                  (III)
```

D(+)-**Glucose, dextrose** (*grape-sugar*), is found in ripe grapes, honey, and most sweet fruits; it is also a normal constituent of blood, and occurs in the urine of diabetics. Commercially, pure D(+)-glucose is manufactured by heating starch with dilute hydrochloric acid under pressure:

$$(C_6H_{10}O_5)_n + nH_2O \xrightarrow{HCl} nC_6H_{12}O_6$$

D(+)-Glucose is a white crystalline solid, m.p. 146°, readily soluble in water, but sparingly soluble in ethanol, and insoluble in ether. It has a sweet taste, but is not as sweet as cane-sugar. The relation between constitution and taste has not yet been worked out, but observations show that the groups $—CHOH{\cdot}CH_2OH$ and $—CO{\cdot}CHOH—$ confer a sweet taste on compounds containing either (or both) of them.

Naturally occurring glucose is dextrorotatory (hence name *dextrose*).

1. Glucose is a strong reducing agent, reducing both Fehling's solution and ammoniacal silver nitrate. It reduces more Fehling's solution than corresponds to one aldehyde group; this indicates that other groups in the chain (besides the aldehyde group) must be involved in the reduction.

2. When heated with sodium hydroxide, an aqueous solution of glucose turns brown (see also p. 429).

3. Glucose forms a cyanohydrin with hydrogen cyanide (see also the Kiliani reaction, p. 425):

$$CH_2OH{\cdot}(CHOH)_4{\cdot}CHO + HCN \longrightarrow CH_2OH{\cdot}(CHOH)_5{\cdot}CN$$

4. When glucose is treated with hydroxylamine, the oxime is formed:

$$CH_2OH{\cdot}(CHOH)_4{\cdot}CHO + NH_2{\cdot}OH \longrightarrow CH_2OH{\cdot}(CHOH)_4{\cdot}CH{=}N{\cdot}OH + H_2O$$

5. The reaction between glucose and phenylhydrazine is complicated. Stempel (1934) found that glucose reacts with glucose in dilute inorganic acids in an atmosphere of nitrogen to form *glucose phenylhydrazone*. Addition of acetic acid caused the formation of *glucosazone* (see p. 422). On the other hand, Bloink *et al.* (1951) have shown that if the containing vessel is filled with oxygen, then the osazone is obtained in the presence of inorganic acid. Diphenylhydrazine is a very good reagent for preparing sugar hydrazones.

6. When treated with a *mild* oxidising reagent, *e.g.*, bromine-water, glucose is oxidised to *gluconic acid*, m.p. 131°.

$$CH_2OH{\cdot}(CHOH)_4{\cdot}CHO + [O] \xrightarrow{Br_2/H_2O} CH_2OH{\cdot}(CHOH)_4{\cdot}CO_2H \quad (50\%)$$

The oxidation of only the aldehyde group in any sugar produces the corresponding *aldonic acid*, and is best carried out by electrolysing a solution of the aldose in the presence of calcium bromide and calcium carbonate (Isbell and Frush, 1931; Kiliani, 1933). Oxidation of a glucose solution with mercuric oxide in the presence of calcium carbonate gives a 70 per cent. yield of calcium gluconate (Candin, 1948). Gluconic acid is also formed by the fermentation of glucose by *Aspergillus niger* or *Penicillium chrysogenum*.

When treated with a *strong* oxidising agent, *e.g.*, nitric acid, glucose is oxidised to *saccharic acid* (some oxalic acid is also obtained):

$$CH_2OH\cdot(CHOH)_4\cdot CHO \xrightarrow[HNO_3]{[O]} CO_2H\cdot(CHOH)_4\cdot CO_2H \quad (40\text{–}46\%)$$

Oxidation of only the terminal $—CH_2OH$ group in an aldose produces the corresponding *-uronic* acid, *e.g.*, glucose forms *glucuronic acid*:

$$CH_2OH\cdot(CHOH)_4\cdot CHO \xrightarrow{[O]} CO_2H\cdot(CHOH)_4\cdot CHO$$

This oxidation is extremely difficult to carry out in the laboratory. One of the best methods of preparing glucuronic acid is to feed borneol (a terpene alcohol) to dogs; bornyl glucuronate is excreted in the urine. Glucuronic acid may be prepared in the laboratory by reducing the lactone of saccharic acid (*cf.* Kiliani reaction). Uronic acids may also be prepared by the oxidation of glycosides (p. 433) with nitrogen peroxide (Maurer *et al.*, 1947), or with oxygen in the presence of platinum as catalyst (Marsh, 1951). Heyns *et al.* (1953) have obtained the lactone of D-glucuronic acid by oxidising corn starch with fuming nitric acid (26% yield).

7. When reduced with sodium amalgam in aqueous solution, glucose is converted into the hexahydric alcohol, *sorbitol*:

$$CH_2OH\cdot(CHOH)_4\cdot CHO + 2[H] \longrightarrow CH_2OH\cdot(CHOH)_4\cdot CH_2OH \quad (50\%)$$

High-pressure catalytic reduction, or electrolytic reduction in acid solution of aldoses, is better than reduction with sodium amalgam, since aldoses tend to undergo rearrangement in alkaline solution (see p. 429). Sugars may also be reduced to the corresponding alcohols with sodium borohydride in aqueous solution (Abdel–Akher *et al.*, 1951).

Reduction of glucose with concentrated hydriodic acid and red phosphorus at 100° produces 2-iodohexane; prolonged heating finally gives *n*-hexane.

The electrolytic reduction of D-glucose in *alkaline* solution gives D-mannitol and the by-product *dodecitol*, m.p. 233–235°, formed by bimolecular reduction (Wolfrom *et al.*, 1951).

$$2CH_2OH\cdot(CHOH)_4\cdot CHO \xrightarrow{[H]} CH_2OH\cdot(CHOH)_{10}\cdot CH_2OH$$

8. Acetone condenses with glucose in the presence of hydrochloric acid to form 1 : 2-*iso*propylideneglucose and 1 : 2–5 : 6-di-*iso*propylideneglucose, *e.g.* (see also mutarotation, p. 429):

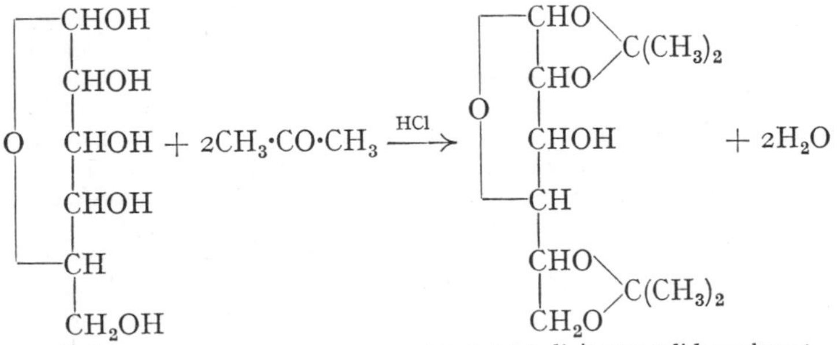

```
 ┌──CHOH                               ┌──CHO╲
 │   |                                 │   |    C(CH3)2
 │  CHOH                               │  CHO╱
 │   |                                 O   |
 O  CHOH + 2CH3·CO·CH3  ──HCl──>       │  CHOH              + 2H2O
 │   |                                 │   |
 │  CHOH                               └──CH
 │   |                                     |
 └──CH                                    CHO╲
     |                                     |    C(CH3)2
    CH2OH                                 CH2O╱
  δ-glucose                  1 : 2–5 : 6-di-isopropylideneglucose
```

The two hydroxyl groups involved in the condensation are usually on adjacent carbon atoms. These *iso*propylidene derivatives are stable to alkali, but are readily hydrolysed by acid.

9. When heated with concentrated hydrochloric acid, glucose (and any other aldohexose) is converted into lævulic acid:

$$C_6H_{12}O_6 \longrightarrow CH_3\cdot CO\cdot CH_2\cdot CH_2\cdot CO_2H + H\cdot CO_2H + H_2O$$

Glucose can also form hydroxymethylfurfural on treatment with hydrochloric acid:

$$C_6H_{12}O_6 \longrightarrow \begin{array}{c} CH{=}CH \\ HOCH_2\cdot C \quad C\cdot CHO \\ \diagdown O \diagup \end{array} + 3H_2O$$

This compound yields lævulic acid on acid treatment. Hence it it is possible that lævulic acid is produced from glucose via the intermediate formation of hydroxymethylfurfural.

10. Glucose is readily fermented by yeast to ethanol:

$$C_6H_{12}O_6 \longrightarrow 2C_2H_5OH + 2CO_2$$

11. Glucose forms *glucosates* with various metallic hydroxides, *e.g.*, with calcium hydroxide it forms calcium glucosate, $C_6H_{12}O_6\cdot CaO$; the structure of these glucosates is uncertain.

12. Glucose combines with monohydric alcohols, *e.g.*, methyl and ethyl alcohols, in the presence of hydrochloric acid, to form *glucosides* (pentoses behave in a similar manner).

D(+)-Mannose, m.p. 132°, may be obtained by carefully oxidising mannitol with nitric acid:

$$CH_2OH\cdot(CHOH)_4\cdot CH_2OH + [O] \xrightarrow{HNO_3} CH_2OH\cdot(CHOH)_4\cdot CHO + H_2O$$

Commercially, mannose is prepared by hydrolysing the polysaccharide *seminine* with boiling dilute sulphuric acid. Seminine (a *mannan*) occurs in many plants, particularly in the shell of the ivory nut, which is used as the starting material for D(+)-mannose.

Chemically, mannose behaves like glucose.

D(+)-Galactose (m.p. of monohydrate, 118°) is found in several polysaccharides (*galactans*), and is combined with glucose in the disaccharide *lactose*. Galactose may be prepared by hydrolysing lactose, and separating it from glucose by fractional crystallisation from water, in which glucose is more soluble than galactose.

Chemically, galactose behaves like glucose.

Ketohexoses. The only important ketohexose is **D(−)-fructose,** the structure of which has been elucidated as follows:

(i) Analysis and molecular-weight determinations show that the molecular formula of fructose is $C_6H_{12}O_6$.

(ii) When treated with acetic anhydride, fructose forms the penta-acetate. This indicates the presence of five hydroxyl groups, each being attached to a different carbon atom (*cf.* aldohexoses).

(iii) Fructose forms an oxime when treated with hydroxylamine, and therefore contains a carbonyl group.

(iv) When oxidised with nitric acid, fructose is converted into a mixture of trihydroxyglutaric, tartaric and glycollic acids. Since a mixture of acids each containing fewer carbon atoms than fructose is obtained, the carbonly group in fructose must be present in a *ketonic* group.

(v) Fructose may be reduced to a hexahydric alcohol, *sorbitol*, which, on reduction with hydriodic acid and red phosphorus at 100°, gives a mixture of 2-iodohexane and *n*-hexane. The formation of the latter two compounds indicates that the six carbon atoms in fructose are in a straight chain.

(vi) On ascending the series by the *Kiliani reaction*, and reducing the product with hydriodic acid, *n*-butylmethylacetic acid, $CH_3{\cdot}CH_2{\cdot}CH_2{\cdot}CH_2{\cdot}CH(CH_3){\cdot}CO_2H$, is obtained. This shows that the ketonic group in fructose is adjacent to one of the terminal carbon atoms (all the known ketohexoses have the ketonic group in this position).

The foregoing reactions show that the structure of fructose is:

$$CH_2OH{\cdot}CHOH{\cdot}CHOH{\cdot}CHOH{\cdot}CO{\cdot}CH_2OH$$

This contains three structurally different asymmetric carbon atoms, and can therefore exist in eight optically active forms. Of these the following six are known: D(—)- and L(+)-*fructose*, D(+)- and L(—)-*sorbose*, D(+)-*tagatose* and L(—)-*psicose*; only D(—)-fructose, L(—)-sorbose and D(+)-tagatose occur naturally (see also p. 436).

Naturally occurring fructose (*fruit-sugar*) is lævorotatory, and is therefore also known as *lævulose* (*cf.* dextrose). D(—)-Fructose is found in fruits and honey, and occurs combined with glucose in the disaccharide *cane-sugar*, from which it may be obtained by hydrolysis and fractional crystallisation. Fructose is prepared commercially by hydrolysis of *inulin*, a polysaccharide which occurs in dahlia tubers and Jerusalem artichokes:

$$(C_6H_{10}O_5)_n + nH_2O \xrightarrow{HCl} nC_6H_{12}O_6$$

Fructose is a white crystalline solid, m.p. 102° (with decomposition); it has a sweet taste, and is readily soluble in water but sparingly soluble in ethanol, and insoluble in ether.

1. Fructose is a strong reducing agent, reducing Fehling's solution and ammoniacal silver nitrate (*cf.* α-hydroxyketones, p. 223).

2. Fructose forms a cyanohydrin with hydrogen cyanide:

$$CH_2OH{\cdot}(CHOH)_3{\cdot}CO{\cdot}CH_2OH + HCN \longrightarrow CH_2OH{\cdot}(CHOH)_3{\cdot}C\begin{cases}CH_2OH\\OH\\CN\end{cases}$$

3. Fructose reacts with hydroxylamine to form the oxime:

$$CH_2OH{\cdot}(CHOH)_3{\cdot}CO{\cdot}CH_2OH + NH_2{\cdot}OH \longrightarrow$$
$$CH_2OH{\cdot}(CHOH)_3{\cdot}C({=}N{\cdot}OH){\cdot}CH_2OH + H_2O$$

4. When treated with phenylhydrazine, fructose forms the phenylhydrazone or osazone, according to the conditions (*cf.* glucose, above).

5. Nitric acid oxidises fructose to a mixture of trihydroxyglutaric, tartaric and glycollic acids. Fructose is *not* oxidised by bromine-water.

6. Fructose may be reduced to sorbitol (a hexahydric alcohol) by sodium amalgam and water, or catalytically, or electrolytically.

7. When heated with concentrated hydrochloric acid, fructose forms lævulic acid (in better yield than from any aldohexose; see glucose, above).

8. Fructose is fermented by yeast to ethanol:

$$C_6H_{12}O_6 \longrightarrow 2C_2H_5OH + 2CO_2$$

9. When treated with monohydric alcohols in the presence of hydrochloric acid, fructose forms *fructosides* (p. 433).

10. Fructose condenses with acetone to form an *iso*propylidene and a di-*iso*propylidene derivative (*cf.* glucose).

Reaction of glucose and fructose with phenylhydrazine. Fischer (1884, 1887) proposed the following series of reactions to account for the formation of an **osazone** when glucose or fructose is treated with excess of phenylhydrazine. According to this mechanism, a phenylhydrazone is first produced, and one of its hydroxyl groups, adjacent to the original aldehyde or ketonic group, is oxidised to a carbonyl group by a second molecule of phenylhydrazine which is reduced to aniline and ammonia; the carbonyl group now reacts with a third molecule of phenylhydrazine to form the osazone.

Glucose

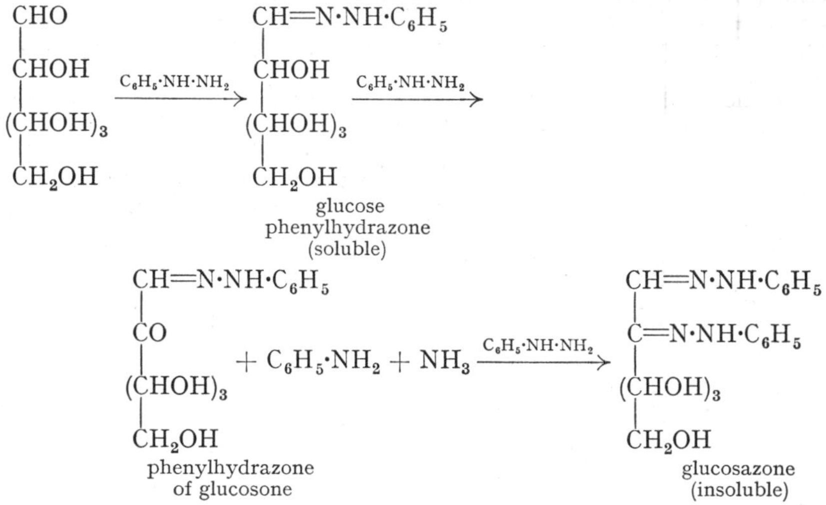

$$\begin{array}{l} CHO \\ | \\ CHOH \\ | \\ (CHOH)_3 \\ | \\ CH_2OH \end{array} \xrightarrow{C_6H_5{\cdot}NH{\cdot}NH_2} \begin{array}{l} CH{=}N{\cdot}NH{\cdot}C_6H_5 \\ | \\ CHOH \\ | \\ (CHOH)_3 \\ | \\ CH_2OH \end{array} \xrightarrow{C_6H_5{\cdot}NH{\cdot}NH_2}$$

glucose phenylhydrazone (soluble)

$$\begin{array}{l} CH{=}N{\cdot}NH{\cdot}C_6H_5 \\ | \\ CO \\ | \\ (CHOH)_3 \\ | \\ CH_2OH \end{array} + C_6H_5{\cdot}NH_2 + NH_3 \xrightarrow{C_6H_5{\cdot}NH{\cdot}NH_2} \begin{array}{l} CH{=}N{\cdot}NH{\cdot}C_6H_5 \\ | \\ C{=}N{\cdot}NH{\cdot}C_6H_5 \\ | \\ (CHOH)_3 \\ | \\ CH_2OH \end{array}$$

phenylhydrazone of glucosone — glucosazone (insoluble)

Fructose

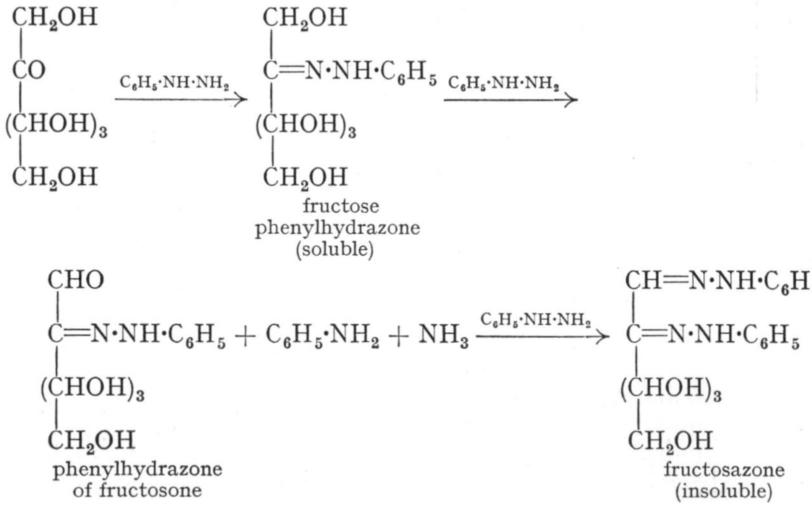

$$\begin{array}{l} CH_2OH \\ | \\ CO \\ | \\ (CHOH)_3 \\ | \\ CH_2OH \end{array} \xrightarrow{C_6H_5{\cdot}NH{\cdot}NH_2} \begin{array}{l} CH_2OH \\ | \\ C{=}N{\cdot}NH{\cdot}C_6H_5 \\ | \\ (CHOH)_3 \\ | \\ CH_2OH \end{array} \xrightarrow{C_6H_5{\cdot}NH{\cdot}NH_2}$$

fructose phenylhydrazone (soluble)

$$\begin{array}{l} CHO \\ | \\ C{=}N{\cdot}NH{\cdot}C_6H_5 \\ | \\ (CHOH)_3 \\ | \\ CH_2OH \end{array} + C_6H_5{\cdot}NH_2 + NH_3 \xrightarrow{C_6H_5{\cdot}NH{\cdot}NH_2} \begin{array}{l} CH{=}N{\cdot}NH{\cdot}C_6H_5 \\ | \\ C{=}N{\cdot}NH{\cdot}C_6H_5 \\ | \\ (CHOH)_3 \\ | \\ CH_2OH \end{array}$$

phenylhydrazone of fructosone — fructosazone (insoluble)

Although glucose and fructose are different sugars, both form the *same* osazone. This indicates that the two sugars differ only in the two carbon groups which take part in the formation of the osazone (see also below).

Osazones are yellow crystalline solids, and are used to characterise the sugars. All compounds containing the —CO·CHOH— group form osazones

(p. 223). A better means of identifying sugars is to convert the osazone into an *osotriazole* by heating with copper sulphate solution (Hudson, 1944). These triazoles are readily purified, and have sharp melting points.

$$\begin{array}{l} CH{=}N{\cdot}NH{\cdot}C_6H_5 \\ | \\ C{=}N{\cdot}NH{\cdot}C_6H_5 \\ \vdots \end{array} \xrightarrow{CuSO_4} \begin{array}{l} CH{=}N\diagdown \\ | \qquad\quad N{\cdot}C_6H_5 \\ C{=\!=}N\diagup \\ \vdots \end{array} + C_6H_5{\cdot}NH_2$$

Fischer's mechanism of osazone formation is difficult to accept because phenylhydrazine is a powerful reducing agent; this is the only reaction in which it behaves as an oxidising agent. Furthermore, Fischer's mechanism does not explain why only two carbon atoms should be involved; it might have been expected that other hydroxyl groups would be attacked as well as the second one.

Weygand (1940) suggested that osazone formation occurred via the *Amadori rearrangement*.

Glucose

$$\begin{array}{l} CHO \\ | \\ CHOH \\ \vdots \end{array} \xrightarrow{C_6H_5{\cdot}NH{\cdot}NH_2} \begin{array}{l} CH{=}N{\cdot}NH{\cdot}C_6H_5 \\ | \\ CHOH \\ \vdots \end{array} \rightleftharpoons \begin{array}{l} CH{\cdot}NH{\cdot}NH{\cdot}C_6H_5 \\ \| \\ C{-}OH \\ \vdots \end{array} \rightleftharpoons$$

$$\begin{array}{l} CH_2{\cdot}NH{\cdot}NH{\cdot}C_6H_5 \\ | \\ CO \\ \vdots \end{array} \xrightarrow{C_6H_5{\cdot}NH{\cdot}NH_2} \begin{array}{l} CH_2{\cdot}NH{\cdot}NH{\cdot}C_6H_5 \\ | \\ C{=}N{\cdot}NH{\cdot}C_6H_5 \\ \vdots \end{array} \rightleftharpoons$$

$$\begin{array}{l} CH{\cdot}NH{\cdot}NH{\cdot}C_6H_5 \\ \| \\ C{\cdot}NH{\cdot}NH{\cdot}C_6H_5 \\ \vdots \qquad (I) \end{array}$$

Fructose

$$\begin{array}{l} CH_2OH \\ | \\ CO \\ \vdots \end{array} \xrightarrow{C_6H_5{\cdot}NH{\cdot}NH_2} \begin{array}{l} CH_2OH \\ | \\ C{=}N{\cdot}NH{\cdot}C_6H_5 \\ \vdots \end{array} \rightleftharpoons \begin{array}{l} CHOH \\ \| \\ C{\cdot}NH{\cdot}NH{\cdot}C_6H_5 \\ \vdots \end{array} \rightleftharpoons$$

$$\begin{array}{l} CHO \\ | \\ CH{\cdot}NH{\cdot}NH{\cdot}C_6H_5 \\ \vdots \end{array} \xrightarrow{C_6H_5{\cdot}NH{\cdot}NH_2} \begin{array}{l} CH{=}N{\cdot}NH{\cdot}C_6H_5 \\ | \\ CH{\cdot}NH{\cdot}NH{\cdot}C_6H_5 \\ \vdots \end{array} \rightleftharpoons$$

$$\begin{array}{l} CH{\cdot}NH{\cdot}NH{\cdot}C_6H_5 \\ \| \\ C{\cdot}NH{\cdot}NH{\cdot}C_6H_5 \\ \vdots \qquad (I) \end{array}$$

Both glucose and fructose give (I), and this then forms the osazone as follows:

$$\begin{array}{l} CH{\cdot}NH{\cdot}NH{\cdot}C_6H_5 \\ \| \\ C{\cdot}NH{\cdot}NH{\cdot}C_6H_5 \\ \vdots \qquad (I) \end{array} \xrightarrow{-\,C_6H_5{\cdot}NH_2} \begin{array}{l} CH{=}N{\cdot}NH{\cdot}C_6H_5 \\ | \\ C{=}NH \\ \vdots \end{array} \quad or \quad \begin{array}{l} CH{=}NH \\ | \\ C{=}N{\cdot}NH{\cdot}C_6H_5 \\ \vdots \end{array}$$

$$\xrightarrow{C_6H_5{\cdot}NH{\cdot}NH_2} \begin{array}{l} CH{=}N{\cdot}NH{\cdot}C_6H_5 \\ | \\ C{=}N{\cdot}NH{\cdot}C_6H_5 \\ \vdots \end{array} + NH_3$$

Barry and Mitchell (1955) have given evidence to support the above mechanism in that it occurs via the Amadori rearrangement, but suggest that the two hydrogen atoms are removed by the hydrogen acceptor, the phenylhydrazinium cation:

$$\begin{array}{l} CH_2\cdot NH\cdot NH\cdot C_6H_5 \xrightarrow{-2H} CH{=}N\cdot NH\cdot C_6H_5 \\ | \qquad\qquad\qquad\qquad\qquad\quad | \\ CO \qquad\qquad\qquad\qquad\quad\; CO \end{array}$$

$$C_6H_5\cdot NH\cdot NH_3^+ + H \longrightarrow C_6H_5\cdot NH_2 + NH_3$$

These authors also propose the following mechanism to explain the Amadori rearrangement:

$$\text{R}'\text{-C}(=\text{N}\cdots\text{H}\text{-N(H)-C}_6\text{H}_5)\text{-C(H)(R)-O} \longrightarrow \text{H-C(R}')(\text{-NH-}) \text{N(C}_6\text{H}_5\text{)-H}\cdots\text{O=C(R)} \xrightarrow{-2H}$$

$$\text{R}'\text{-C}(=\text{N-N(C}_6\text{H}_5\text{)-H}\cdots\text{O=C-R}) \xrightarrow{C_6H_5\cdot NH\cdot NH_2} \begin{array}{l} R'\cdot C{=}N\cdot NH\cdot C_6H_5 \\ | \\ R\cdot C{=}N\cdot NH\cdot C_6H_5 \end{array}$$

Aldose: R = sugar residue; R′ = H.
Ketose: R′ = sugar residue; R = H.

It should be noted that Weygand's mechanism also does not explain why only the first two carbon atoms should be involved (*cf.* Fischer's mechanism). Fieser and Fieser (1944), however, have suggested that the osazone is stabilised by chelation:

$$\text{HC}{=}\text{N(-NH}\cdot\text{C}_6\text{H}_5)\cdots\text{H-N(C}_6\text{H}_5)\text{-N}{=}\text{C} \quad or \quad \text{HC}{=}\text{N-N(C}_6\text{H}_5)\text{-H}\cdots\text{N(-NH}\cdot\text{C}_6\text{H}_5){=}\text{C}$$

This is supported by work of Mester *et al.* (1955) who have obtained evidence to show that osazones are acyclic and that a chelate ring is present. These authors have also obtained evidence to show that the acyclic and ring forms are present in phenylhydrazones.

Osazones may be hydrolysed with hydrochloric acid, both phenylhydrazine radicals being eliminated; the dicarbonyl compound formed is known as an **osone,** *e.g.*, *glucosazone* forms *glucosone*:

$$\begin{array}{l} CH{=}N\cdot NH\cdot C_6H_5 \\ | \\ C{=}N\cdot NH\cdot C_6H_5 \\ | \\ (CHOH)_3 \\ | \\ CH_2OH \end{array} \xrightarrow{HCl} \begin{array}{l} CHO \\ | \\ CO \\ | \\ (CHOH)_3 \\ | \\ CH_2OH \end{array}$$

A more convenient method of obtaining the osone is to add benzaldehyde to a solution of the osazone; benzaldehyde phenylhydrazone is precipitated, leaving the osone in solution. The precipitate is removed by filtration and the filtrate evaporated; a white substance is obtained which is difficult to crystallise. Osones react with phenylhydrazine in the cold to form osazones.

Epimerisation. Aldoses which produce the same osazones must have identical configurations on all their asymmetric carbon atoms except the *alpha* (since only the aldehyde group and α-carbon atom are involved in osazone formation). Such sugars are known as **epimers**. Fischer (1890) changed an aldose into its epimer via the aldonic acid. The aldonic acid was heated with pyridine (or quinoline), whereupon it was converted into an equilibrium mixture of the original acid and its epimer. These were separated, and the epimeric acid lactone reduced to an aldose (see the Kiliani reaction below). The mechanism of epimerisation is not certain, but it is possibly similar to racemisation, *i.e.*, it takes place via the enol form; *e.g.*, epimerisation of glucose into mannose:

$$\begin{array}{c} CHO \\ | \\ H-C-OH \\ | \\ (CHOH)_3 \\ | \\ CH_2OH \\ \text{D(+) glucose} \end{array} \xrightarrow{Br_2/H_2O} \begin{array}{c} CO_2H \\ | \\ H-C-OH \\ | \\ (CHOH)_3 \\ | \\ CH_2OH \\ \text{gluconic acid} \end{array} \underset{}{\overset{\text{pyrdine}}{\rightleftharpoons}} \left[\begin{array}{c} C\begin{array}{l} /OH \\ \backslash OH \end{array} \\ \| \\ C-OH \\ | \\ (CHOH)_3 \\ | \\ CH_2OH \end{array}\right]$$

$$\rightleftharpoons \begin{array}{c} CO_2H \\ | \\ HO-C-H \\ | \\ (CHOH)_3 \\ | \\ CH_2OH \\ \text{mannonic acid} \end{array} \xrightarrow{\text{lactone reduced}} \begin{array}{c} CHO \\ | \\ HO-C-H \\ | \\ (CHOH)_3 \\ | \\ CH_2OH \\ \text{D(+)-mannose} \end{array}$$

The function of the pyridine (or quinoline) is to prevent the formation of the lactone of the aldonic acid.

This change of configuration of one of the asymmetric carbon atoms in a compound containing two or more asymmetric carbon atoms is known as *epimerisation*.

Method of ascending the sugar series. An aldose may be converted into its next higher aldose, *e.g.*, an aldopentose into an aldohexose, by means of the **Kiliani reaction** (1886). The aldopentose is dissolved in dilute hydrocyanic acid, and the cyanohydrin formed is hydrolysed with aqueous barium hydroxide. After acidification with the calculated quantity of dilute sulphuric acid and subsequent filtration, there is obtained an aqueous solution of a polyhydroxyacid with one more carbon atom than the aldopentose (yield: 70 per cent.). When this solution is evaporated to dryness, the γ-lactone is obtained (*cf.* p. 377) and this, on reduction with sodium amalgam in faintly acid solution, is converted into the aldohexose (yield: 30–40 per cent. on the acid):

$$
\begin{array}{ccccccccc}
 & & \mathrm{CN} & & \mathrm{CO_2H} & & \mathrm{CO}\text{—} & & \mathrm{CHO} \\
\mathrm{CHO} & & | & & | & & | & & | \\
| & & \mathrm{CHOH} & & \mathrm{CHOH} & & \mathrm{CHOH}\quad | & & \mathrm{CHOH} \\
\mathrm{CHOH} & \xrightarrow{\mathrm{HCN}} & \mathrm{CHOH} & \xrightarrow[\text{(ii) } \mathrm{H_2SO_4}]{\text{(i) } \mathrm{Ba(OH)_2}} & \mathrm{CHOH} & \longrightarrow & \mathrm{CHOH}\quad \mathrm{O} & \xrightarrow{\mathrm{Na/Hg}} & \mathrm{CHOH} \\
| & & | & & | & & | \qquad | & & | \\
\mathrm{CHOH} & & \mathrm{CHOH} & & \mathrm{CHOH} & & \mathrm{CH}\text{—} & & \mathrm{CHOH} \\
| & & | & & | & & | & & | \\
\mathrm{CHOH} & & \mathrm{CHOH} & & \mathrm{CHOH} & & \mathrm{CHOH} & & \mathrm{CHOH} \\
| & & | & & | & & | & & | \\
\mathrm{CH_2OH} & & \mathrm{CH_2OH} & & \mathrm{CH_2OH} & & \mathrm{CH_2OH} & & \mathrm{CH_2OH}
\end{array}
$$

Theoretically, two lactones are possible, since two cyanohydrins may be formed when hydrogen cyanide adds on to the aldopentose (a new asymmetric carbon is produced), *viz.*,

$$
\begin{array}{c}\mathrm{CHO} \\ \vdots\end{array} \xrightarrow{\mathrm{HCN}} \mathrm{H}\text{—}\begin{array}{c}\mathrm{CN} \\ | \\ \mathrm{C} \\ \vdots\end{array}\text{—}\mathrm{OH} + \mathrm{HO}\text{—}\begin{array}{c}\mathrm{CN} \\ | \\ \mathrm{C} \\ \vdots\end{array}\text{—}\mathrm{H}
$$

Thus two epimeric aldohexoses should be obtained. In practice, one cyanohydrin predominates because the asymmetry present in the molecule exerts a spatial directive influence on the addition of hydrogen cyanide (*cf.* asymmetric synthesis, p. 396). Hence the final product will be mainly one aldohexose, and very little of its epimer.

By means of the Kiliani reaction, it has been possible to prepare aldoses up to an aldodecose.

Hudson (1951) has modified the Kiliani reaction, using sodium cyanide instead of hydrocyanic acid. The proportions of the epimers were the reverse of those when hydrocyanic acid was used.

Sowden and Fischer (1947) have stepped up the aldose series by condensing the aldose with nitromethane in the presence of methanolic sodium methoxide, separating the 1-nitro-1-deoxy-compounds produced, converting each of these into its sodium salt and then hydrolysing with cold 60 per cent. sulphuric acid (*cf.* p. 288). The proportions of the epimers formed by this method are different from those produced by the Kiliani reaction.

$$
\begin{array}{c}\mathrm{CHO} \\ \vdots\end{array} + \mathrm{CH_3{\cdot}NO_2} \xrightarrow{\mathrm{CH_3ONa}} \begin{array}{c}\mathrm{CH_2{\cdot}NO_2} \\ | \\ \mathrm{CHOH} \\ \vdots\end{array} \longrightarrow \begin{array}{c}\mathrm{CH{=}NO_2Na} \\ | \\ \mathrm{CHOH} \\ \vdots\end{array} \xrightarrow{\mathrm{H_2SO_4}} \begin{array}{c}\mathrm{CHO} \\ | \\ \mathrm{CHOH} \\ \vdots\end{array}
$$

Sowden (1950) has stepped up an aldose into a *ketose* containing *two* additional carbon atoms using the above method except that 2-nitroethanol is used instead of nitromethane.

$$
\begin{array}{c}\mathrm{CHO} \\ \vdots\end{array} + \begin{array}{c}\mathrm{CH_2{\cdot}NO_2} \\ | \\ \mathrm{CH_2OH}\end{array} \xrightarrow{\mathrm{CH_3ONa}} \begin{array}{c}\mathrm{CH_2OH} \\ | \\ \mathrm{C{=}NO_2Na} \\ | \\ \mathrm{CHOH} \\ \vdots\end{array} \xrightarrow{\mathrm{H_2SO_4}} \begin{array}{c}\mathrm{CH_2OH} \\ | \\ \mathrm{CO} \\ | \\ \mathrm{CHOH} \\ \vdots\end{array}
$$

On the other hand, Wolfrom *et al.* (1946) have stepped up an aldose to a ketose with *one* more carbon atom by a modified Arndt–Eistert reaction (p. 310).

$$
\begin{array}{c}\mathrm{CHO} \\ \vdots\end{array} \xrightarrow{[\mathrm{O}]} \begin{array}{c}\mathrm{CO_2H} \\ \vdots\end{array} \xrightarrow{\mathrm{SOCl_2}} \begin{array}{c}\mathrm{COCl} \\ \vdots\end{array} \xrightarrow{\mathrm{CH_2N_2}'} \begin{array}{c}\mathrm{CHN_2} \\ | \\ \mathrm{CO} \\ \vdots\end{array} \xrightarrow[\mathrm{CH_3{\cdot}CO_2H}]{\text{aq.}} \begin{array}{c}\mathrm{CH_2OH} \\ | \\ \mathrm{CO} \\ \vdots\end{array}
$$

Method of descending the sugar series. There are three methods of converting a sugar into its next lower sugar, *e.g.*, a hexose into a pentose. All of these methods start with the aldohexose, and hence, in order to convert a ketohexose into a pentose, it is first necessary to transform it into an aldohexose (see later).

Wohl's method (1893). The aldohexose is converted into its oxime, which is then heated with acetic anhydride, whereupon the oxime is dehydrated to the cyano-compound with simultaneous acetylation of the hydroxyl groups. When this acetyl derivative is warmed with ammoniacal silver nitrate, the acetyl groups are removed by hydrolysis, and a molecule of hydrogen cyanide is eliminated with the formation of the aldopentose:

$$\begin{array}{l} CHO \\ | \\ CHOH \\ | \\ (CHOH)_3 \\ | \\ CH_2OH \end{array} \xrightarrow{NH_2\cdot OH} \begin{array}{l} CH{=}N\cdot OH \\ | \\ CHOH \\ | \\ (CHOH)_3 \\ | \\ CH_2OH \end{array} \xrightarrow{(CH_3\cdot CO)_2O} \begin{array}{l} CN \\ | \\ CH\cdot O\cdot CO\cdot CH_3 \\ | \\ (CH\cdot O\cdot CO\cdot CH_3)_3 \\ | \\ CH_2\cdot O\cdot CO\cdot CH_3 \end{array} \xrightarrow{\text{"AgOH"}} \begin{array}{l} CHO \\ | \\ (CHOH)_3 \\ | \\ CH_2OH \end{array} + AgCN \quad (55\%)$$

Zemplen (1917) modified Wohl's method by using a solution of sodium methoxide in chloroform instead of an aqueous solution of ammoniacal silver nitrate, to remove hydrogen cyanide and the acetyl groups, and thereby increased the yield of pentose to 60–70 per cent. Weygand *et al.* (1950) have treated the *oxime* with 1-fluoro-2 : 4-dinitrobenzene in aqueous sodium hydrogen carbonate; the products are the lower aldose (50–60% yield), hydrogen cyanide and 2 : 4-dinitrophenol.

Ruff's method (1898). The aldohexose is oxidised (by bromine-water) to the corresponding aldonic acid; when the calcium salt of this acid is treated with Fenton's reagent, it is converted into the aldopentose (*cf.* oxidation of α-hydroxyacids, p. 376):

$$\begin{array}{l} CHO \\ | \\ CHOH \\ | \\ (CHOH)_3 \\ | \\ CH_2OH \end{array} \xrightarrow{Br_2/H_2O} \begin{array}{l} CO_2H \\ | \\ CHOH \\ | \\ (CHOH)_3 \\ | \\ CH_2OH \end{array} \xrightarrow[H_2O_2/Fe^{2+}]{\text{Ca salt}} \begin{array}{l} CHO \\ | \\ (CHOH)_3 \\ | \\ CH_2OH \end{array} + CO_2 \quad (25\%)$$

Berezovski *et al.* (1949) have shown that calcium gluconate can be oxidised with hydrogen peroxide in the presence of ferric sulphate and barium acetate to give D-arabinose (44%).

Weerman's reaction (1913). This is the reaction whereby an α-hydroxy- or α-methoxy-amide is degraded by means of a cold solution of sodium hypochlorite (*cf.* Hofmann degradation, p. 192). The mechanism of the Weerman reaction is not certain, but according to Ault, Haworth and Hirst (1934), the reaction takes place as follows:

α-Hydroxyamides

$$\begin{array}{l} CO\cdot NH_2 \\ | \\ CHOH \\ | \\ R \end{array} \xrightarrow{NaOH/NaOCl} \left[\begin{array}{l} NCO \\ | \\ CHOH \\ | \\ R \end{array}\right] \xrightarrow{NaOH} \begin{array}{l} CHO \\ | \\ R \end{array} + NaNCO$$

α-Methoxyamides

$$\begin{array}{l}CO{\cdot}NH_2\\ |\\ CH{\cdot}O{\cdot}CH_3\\ |\\ R\end{array} \xrightarrow{NaOH/NaOCl} \left[\begin{array}{l}NCO\\ |\\ CH{\cdot}O{\cdot}CH_3\\ |\\ R\end{array}\right] \xrightarrow{NaOH} \begin{array}{l}CHO\\ |\\ R\end{array} + CO_2 + NH_3 + CH_3OH$$

Haworth, Peat and Whetstone (1938) carried out the descent of the sugars by the Weerman reaction, and obtained a 55 per cent. yield from the methylated amides.

Macdonald *et al.* (1953) have stepped down an aldose as follows:

$$\begin{array}{l}CHO\\ |\\ CHOH\\ |\\ R\end{array} \xrightarrow{C_2H_5SH} \underset{\text{mercaptal}}{\begin{array}{l}CH(SC_2H_5)_2\\ |\\ CHOH\\ |\\ R\end{array}} \xrightarrow{C_2H_5{\cdot}CO_3H} \underset{\text{disulphone}}{\begin{array}{l}CH(SO_2C_2H_5)_2\\ |\\ CHOH\\ |\\ R\end{array}} \xrightarrow{NH_4OH} \begin{array}{l}CHO\\ |\\ R\end{array} + CH_2(SO_2C_2H_5)_2$$

Hough *et al.* (1954) have found that this degradation is general, but that the structure of the disulphone may vary from one aldose to another.

$$\begin{array}{l}CH(SC_2H_5)_2\\ |\\ CHOH\\ |\\ R\end{array} \xrightarrow{[O]} \begin{array}{l}C(SO_2C_2H_5)_2\\ \|\\ CH\\ |\\ R\end{array} \xrightarrow{NH_4OH} \begin{array}{c}CH_2(SO_2C_2H_5)_2\\ +\\ CHO\\ |\\ R\end{array}$$

Perlin (1954) has shown that aldoses may be stepped down by direct oxidation with lead tetra-acetate or sodium bismuthate, *e.g.*, D-mannose gives D-arabinose (35%).

Conversion of an aldose into a ketose. The aldose is converted into its osazone, which is then hydrolysed with hydrochloric acid to the osone. On reduction with zinc and acetic acid, the osone is converted into the ketose (an aldehyde group is reduced more readily than a ketonic group):

$$\begin{array}{l}CH{=}N{\cdot}NH{\cdot}C_6H_5\\ |\\ C{=}N{\cdot}NH{\cdot}C_6H_5\\ \vdots\end{array} \xrightarrow{HCl} \begin{array}{l}CHO\\ |\\ CO\\ \vdots\end{array} \xrightarrow{[H]} \begin{array}{l}CH_2OH\\ |\\ CO\\ \vdots\end{array}$$

Conversion of a ketose into an aldose. The ketose is reduced (preferably by catalytic reduction, p. 429) to the corresponding polyhydric alcohol, which is then oxidised to a monocarboxylic acid (only one of the terminal CH_2OH groups being oxidised). On warming, the acid is converted into the γ-lactone which, on reduction with sodium amalgam in faintly acid solution, is converted into the aldose:

$$\begin{array}{l}CH_2OH\\ |\\ CO\\ |\\ CHOH\\ |\\ CHOH\\ |\\ CHOH\\ |\\ CH_2OH\end{array} \xrightarrow{H_2/Ni} \begin{array}{l}CH_2OH\\ |\\ CHOH\\ |\\ CHOH\\ |\\ CHOH\\ |\\ CHOH\\ |\\ CH_2OH\end{array} \xrightarrow[HNO_3]{[O]} \begin{array}{l}CO_2H\\ |\\ CHOH\\ |\\ CHOH\\ |\\ CHOH\\ |\\ CHOH\\ |\\ CH_2OH\end{array} \xrightarrow{heat} \begin{array}{l}CO{-}\!\!\!-\!\!\!-\!\!\!\urcorner\\ |\qquad\quad |\\ CHOH\quad |\\ |\qquad\quad O\\ CHOH\quad |\\ |\qquad\quad |\\ CH{-}\!\!\!-\!\!\!-\!\!\!\lrcorner\\ |\\ CHOH\\ |\\ CH_2OH\end{array} \xrightarrow{[H]} \begin{array}{l}CHO\\ |\\ CHOH\\ |\\ CHOH\\ |\\ CHOH\\ |\\ CHOH\\ |\\ CH_2OH\end{array}$$

Theoretically, two polyhydric alcohols may be formed on reduction of the ketose, due to the formation of a new asymmetric carbon atom:

$$\begin{array}{c} CH_2OH \\ | \\ CO \\ | \end{array} \xrightarrow{H_2/Ni} \begin{array}{c} CH_2OH \\ | \\ H{-}C{-}OH \\ | \end{array} + \begin{array}{c} CH_2OH \\ | \\ HO{-}C{-}H \\ | \end{array}$$

In practice, however, one predominates (*cf.* the Kiliani reaction). Furthermore, when these two alcohols are oxidised, oxidation may take place at *either* end of the chain, and hence the final product will be a mixture of *four* aldoses, but these will not be present to the same extent.

Lobry de Bruyn–van Ekenstein rearrangement (1890). When warmed with *concentrated* alkali, sugars first turn yellow, then brown and finally resinify (*cf.* aldehydes, p. 148). In the presence of *dilute* alkali or amines, sugars undergo rearrangement; *e.g.*, a dilute solution of glucose, in the presence of sodium hydroxide, is converted into an almost optically inactive solution from which has been isolated D(+)-glucose, D(+)-mannose, D(−)-fructose. The same mixture is obtained if the starting material is D(−)-fructose or D(+)-mannose. It has been suggested that the re-arrangement occurs through 1:2-enolisation. Topper *et al.* (1951), using deuterium oxide, support this enolisation mechanism, but conclude that mannose and fructose cannot arise from the same enediol, and suggest there are *two* geometrical isomeric enediol intermediates, both being capable of changing into fructose.

$$\underset{\text{D(+)-glucose}}{\begin{array}{c} CHO \\ | \\ H{-}C{-}OH \\ | \end{array}} \rightleftharpoons \underset{\textit{trans}\text{-diol}}{\left[\begin{array}{c} HO{-}C{-}H \\ \| \\ C{-}OH \\ | \end{array}\right]} \rightleftharpoons \underset{\text{D(−)-fructose}}{\begin{array}{c} CH_2OH \\ | \\ C{=}O \\ | \end{array}} \rightleftharpoons \underset{\textit{cis}\text{-diol}}{\left[\begin{array}{c} HO{-}C{-}H \\ \| \\ HO{-}C \\ | \end{array}\right]} \rightleftharpoons \underset{\text{D(+)-mannose}}{\begin{array}{c} CHO \\ | \\ HO{-}C{-}H \\ | \end{array}}$$

Since the Lobry de Bruyn–van Ekenstein rearrangement takes place in alkaline media, it is best to carry out reactions with the sugars in neutral or acid media.

Lobry de Bruyn's "glutose," obtained by heating fructose with lead hydroxide, has been shown by Schneider *et al.* (1952) to be D-psicose (p. 436). D-Psicose has also been isolated from the products formed by warming D-glucose with aqueous ammonia at 37° (Hough *et al.*, 1953).

Mutarotation. When a monosaccharide is dissolved in water, the optical rotatory power of the solution gradually changes until it reaches a constant value. *E.g.*, a freshly prepared solution of glucose has a specific rotation of +110°; when this solution is allowed to stand, the specific rotation falls to +52·5°, and remains constant at this value. The final stage can be reached more rapidly either by heating the solution or by adding some catalyst which may be an acid or a base. This change in value of the specific rotation is known as **mutarotation.** All *reducing* sugars (except some ketoses) undergo mutarotation. To account for mutarotation, Tollens (1883) suggested an oxide ring structure for D(+)-glucose, whereby *two* forms would be produced, since, in the formation of the ring, another asymmetric carbon atom (which can exist in *two* configurations) is produced (*cf.* the Kiliani reaction). Tollens assumed that a five-membered ring (the γ-form) was produced (I) and (II). The difficulty of this suggestion was that there was no experimental evidence for the existence of these two forms. Tanret (1895), however, isolated two isomeric forms of D(+)-glucose, thus apparently verifying Tollens' supposition (see later). The two forms are called α- and β-D(+)-γ-glucose; (I) is the α-form, and (II) the β-.

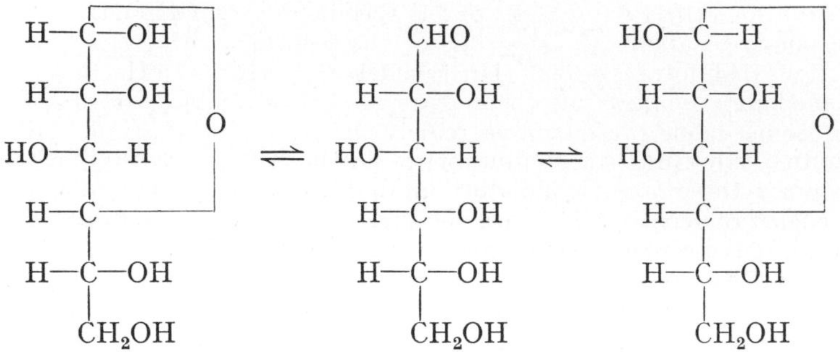

```
      ┌─────────┐                                   ┌─────────┐
  H—C—OH       │            CHO                HO—C—H        │
     |         │             |                    |          │
  H—C—OH       │         H—C—OH                H—C—OH        │
     |         O             |                    |          O
 HO—C—H        │    ⇌   HO—C—H         ⇌     HO—C—H         │
     |         │             |                    |          │
  H—C──────────┘         H—C—OH                H—C───────────┘
     |                       |                    |
  H—C—OH                 H—C—OH                H—C—OH
     |                       |                    |
    CH2OH                   CH2OH                CH2OH
    (I)                                          (II)
```

Ring formation of a sugar is really hemiacetal formation, one alcohol group of the sugar forming a hemiacetal with the aldehyde group of the *same* molecule, thus producing a ring structure which is known as the *lactol* form of the sugar.

Later work by Haworth, Hirst and their co-workers (1926 onwards) has shown that glucose (and other sugars) exists, not as a five-membered ring, but as a six-membered ring, the two forms being α- and β- D(+)-δ-glucose:

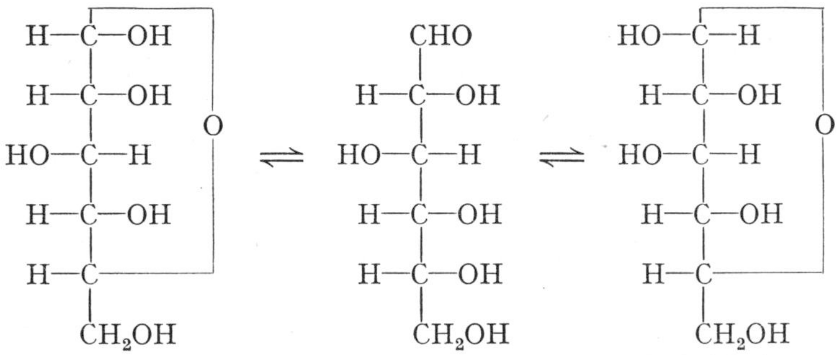

```
      ┌─────────┐                                   ┌─────────┐
  H—C—OH       │            CHO                HO—C—H        │
     |         │             |                    |          │
  H—C—OH       │         H—C—OH                H—C—OH        │
     |         O             |                    |          O
 HO—C—H        │    ⇌   HO—C—H         ⇌     HO—C—H         │
     |         │             |                    |          │
  H—C—OH       │         H—C—OH                H—C—OH        │
     |         │             |                    |          │
  H—C──────────┘         H—C—OH                H—C───────────┘
     |                       |                    |
    CH2OH                   CH2OH                CH2OH
 α-D(+)-δ-glucose                            β-D(+)-δ-glucose
```

Mechanism of mutarotation. According to Lowry (1925), mutarotation is not possible without the presence of an amphiprotic solvent, *i.e.*, a solvent which can function both as an acid and a base, *e.g.*, water. It appears that when mutarotation takes place, the ring must open and then reclose in the inverted position or in the original position. Lowry suggested that in water the *aldehydrol* was formed as an intermediate product by a concerted mechanism (p. 208):

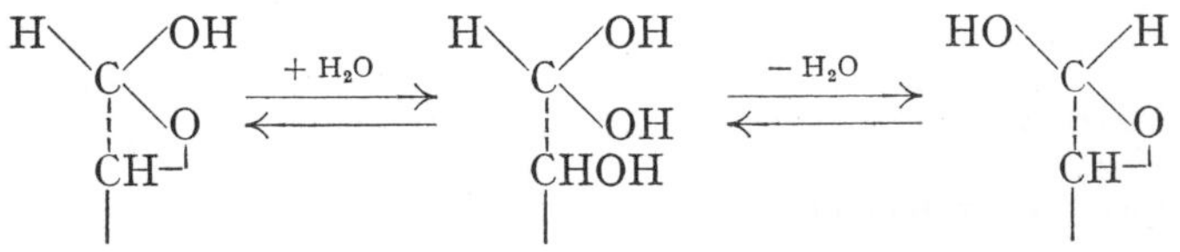

```
 H\   /OH               H\   /OH               HO\   /H
    C        + H2O          C        - H2O          C
    ¦ \O    ⇌               ¦ \OH   ⇌              ¦ \O
   CH—┘                   CHOH                    CH—┘
    |                       |                       |
```

Lowry and Faulkner (1925) showed that mutarotation is arrested in pyridine solution (basic solvent) and in cresol solution (acidic solvent), but that it takes place in a mixture of pyridine and cresol.

The ordinary form of D(+)-glucose is the α-isomer, m.p. 146°, specific rotation +110°, and may be prepared by crystallisation of glucose from cold ethanol. The β-isomer, m.p. 148–150°, specific rotation +19·7°, may be obtained by crystallising glucose from hot pyridine. Both forms show mutarotation, the final value of the specific rotation being 52·56°. This corresponds to about 38 per cent. of the α-form and 62 per cent. of the β-. It is therefore assumed that whenever a sugar is formed in solution, it immediately changes into a mixture of the two isomeric forms, the open chain isomer being present in extremely small amount, if at all. The cyclic structure of the sugars accounts for the following facts: (i) the existence of two isomers, *e.g.*, α- and β-glucose; (ii) mutarotation; (iii) glucose and other aldoses do not give certain characteristic reactions of aldehydes, *e.g.*, Schiff's reaction, do not form a bisulphite or an aldehyde-ammonia compound. Recently, however, it has been shown that by preparing Schiff's reagent in a special way, it becomes very sensitive, simple aldoses restoring the pink colour to this solution; the monosaccharide aldoses react strongly, but the disaccharide aldoses react weakly (Tobie, 1942). This reaction with a sensitive Schiff's reagent appears to indicate that some, although a very small amount, of the open-chain form of a sugar is present in solution in equilibrium with the two ring forms.

Haworth (1926) proposed a six-membered ring formula (hexagonal formula) based on the *pyran* ring which is almost planar. The **pyranose** structure is applicable to nearly all the sugars, and is supported by X-ray

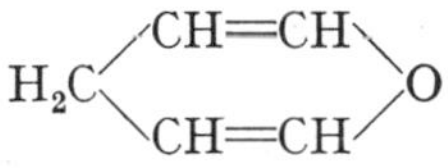

pyran

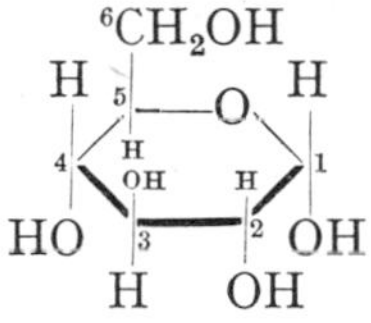

(*a*)

crystal analysis (of the sugars). Thus α-D(+)-δ-glucose is called α-D(+)-*glucopyranose*, and its perspective (*i.e.*, hexagonal) formula is (*a*).

Reeves (1950) has shown that the conformation of α-D(+)-glucopyranose is (*b*) and that of the β-form is (*c*). Both have the chair form, but in the

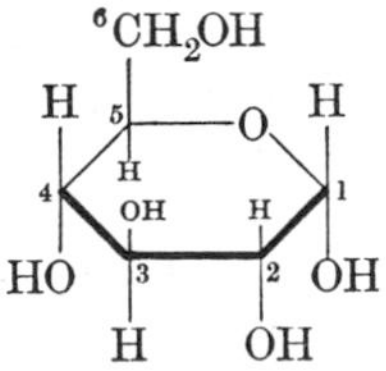

α-form β-form

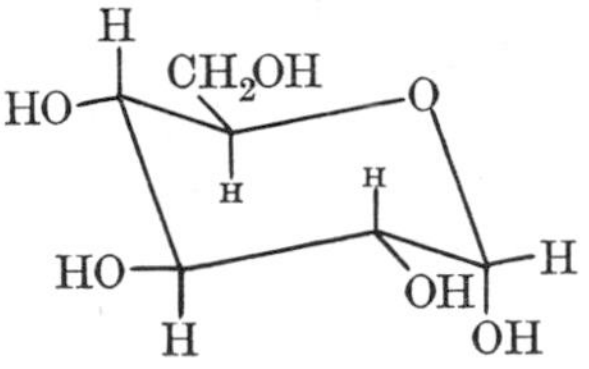

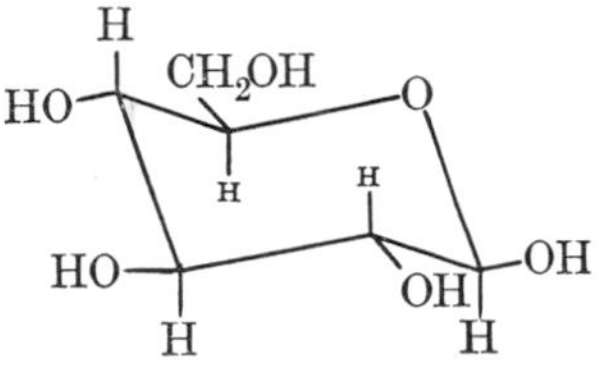

(*a*) (*b*) (*c*)

former the glycosidic hydroxyl is axial and in the latter equatorial (see also p. 466).

Furthermore, it has been shown (Irvine, Haworth *et al.*) that glucose, fructose, etc., can also exist as five-membered rings, which may be regarded as derivatives of *furan*. So far, the γ- or **furanose** sugars (corresponding to Tollens' suggestion) have not been isolated in the free state, but some of their derivatives have been prepared, *e.g.*, methyl α-D(+)-γ-glucoside (see below). Thus α-D(+)-γ-glucose or α-D(+)-glucofuranose would (if it existed) have perspective (*i.e.*, pentagonal) formula (III); methyl α-D(+)-γ-glucoside or methyl α-D(+)-glucofuranoside (a known compound) has formula (IV):

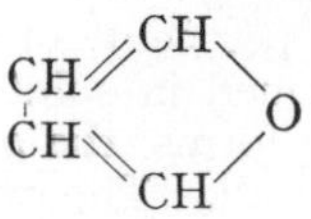

furan 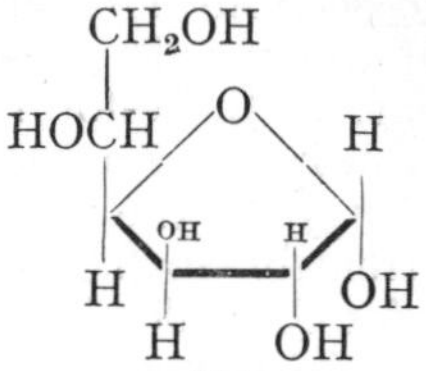 — (III) 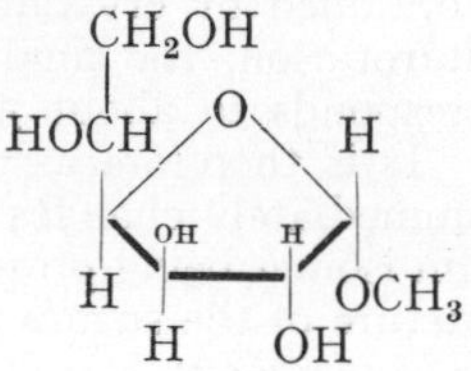 — (IV)

Pentoses also normally exist in the pyranose form, and derivatives of the furanose form have been prepared.

Conversion of the plane-diagrams into the perspective formulæ may be done as follows. (V) is α-D-glucopyranose, and if the H on C_5 is interchanged with the group CH_2OH, then a Walden inversion has been effected;

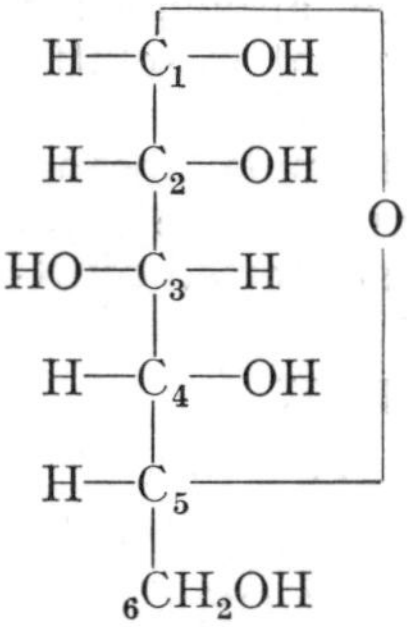

(V) 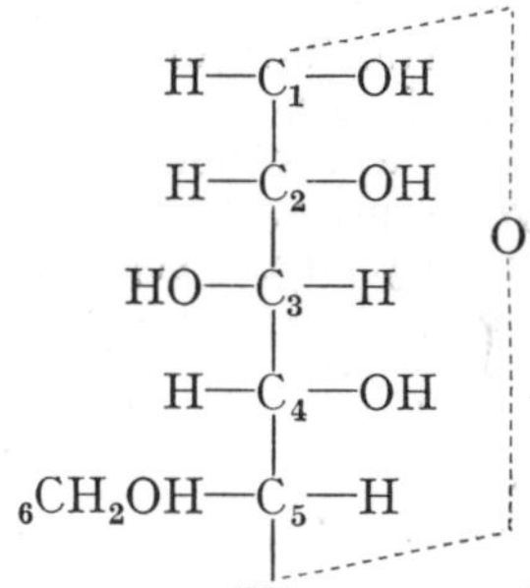 — (VI) 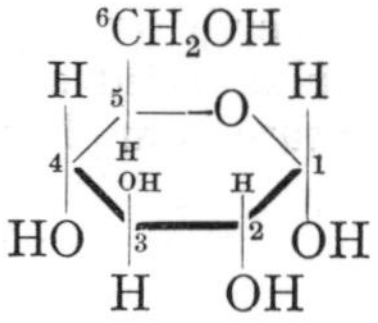 — (VII)

and if the H is now interchanged with the point of attachment of the oxygen ring, another Walden inversion is effected, and so the original configuration of (V) is retained; thus we now have (VI) (with no change in configuration). Since all horizontal bonds indicate groups lying above the plane of the paper, and vertical bonds groups lying behind this plane (see p. 347), then by twisting (VI) so that the oxide ring is perpendicular to the plane of the paper, and placing the oxygen atom as shown, (VII) is obtained. Thus, to change from (VI) to (VII), first draw the hexagon (as shown in (VII)), and then place all the groups on the left-hand side in (VI) above the plane of the ring in (VII), and all those on the right-hand side in (VI) below the plane of the ring in (VII).

In a similar way, perspective formulæ may be obtained for the furanose sugars, *e.g.*, methyl β-D(+)-fructofuranoside.

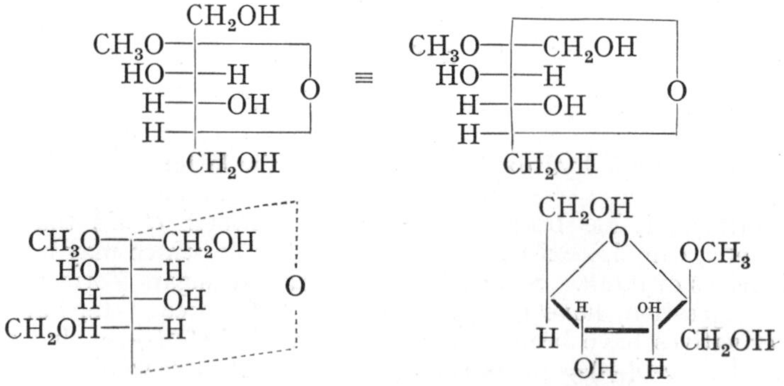

There is a certain amount of evidence to show that oximes, phenylhydrazones and osazones exist in both the open-chain and cyclic forms; *e.g.*, the oxime of glucose may have either of the following structures (p. 384):

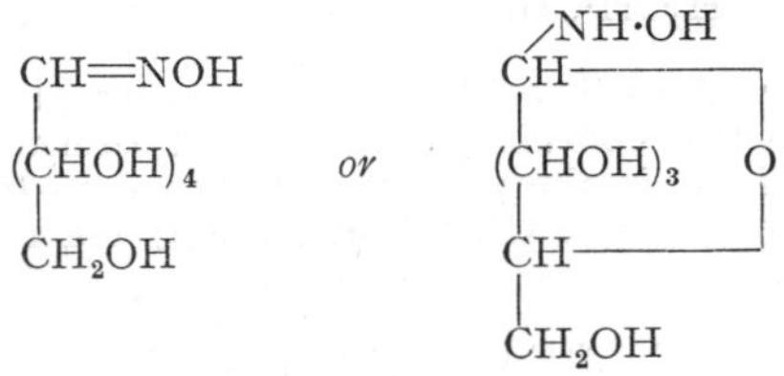

```
CH=NOH                      /NH·OH
|                         CH——————————┐
(CHOH)₄         or        |           |
|                         (CHOH)₃     O
CH₂OH                     |           |
                          CH——————————┘
                          |
                          CH₂OH
```

Just as simple hemiacetals react with another molecule of an alcohol to form acetals (p. 149), so can the hemiacetal form (lactol) of a sugar react with a molecule of an alcohol to form the acetal derivative, which is known under the generic name of **glycoside**; those of glucose are known as *glucosides*; of fructose, *fructosides*, etc. *E.g.*, ethyl α-D(+)-glucopyranoside, prepared by refluxing glucose in excess ethanol in the presence of a small amount of hydrochloric acid, is:

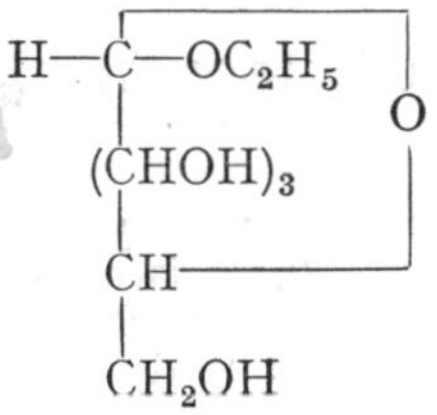

```
     ┌────────────────┐
H—C—OC₂H₅            |
   |                  O
   (CHOH)₃            |
   |                  |
   CH—————————————————┘
   |
   CH₂OH
```

These glycosides are stable compounds, and do not undergo many of the reactions of the sugars, *e.g.*, they show no reducing properties, they do not mutarotate, etc. The non-sugar part of a glycoside is known as the *aglycon*, and in most of the glycosides which occur naturally the aglycon is a phenolic compound; *e.g.*, the aglycon in *salicin* is *salicyl alcohol*; in *indican*, *indoxyl*.

Synthesis of the monosaccharides. Plant cells convert carbon dioxide (of the atmosphere) into carbohydrates. Experimental work has shown that the oxygen evolved in this synthesis is provided by water, and so the overall equation may be written:

$$6CO_2 + 6H_2O \longrightarrow C_6H_{12}O_6 + 6O_2$$

This takes place in the presence of chlorophyll and sunlight, and the process is known as *photosynthesis*. Calvin *et al.* (1954) have shown that photosynthesis occurs via a complex series of reactions, and that two monosaccharides, ribulose and sedoheptulose, play an essential part in the photosynthesis of carbohydrates.

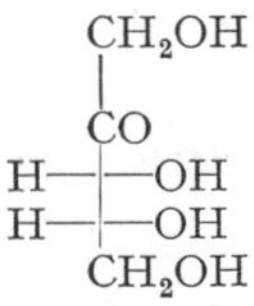

```
                          CH₂OH
     CH₂OH                |
     |                    CO
     CO               HO——|——H
  H——|——OH             H——|——OH
  H——|——OH             H——|——OH
     CH₂OH             H——|——OH
                          CH₂OH
    ribulose           sedoheptulose
```

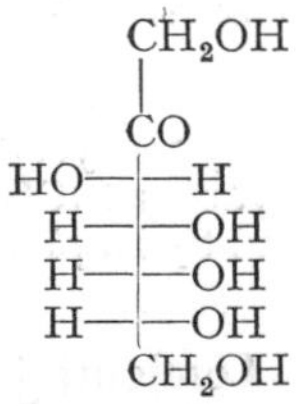

In the laboratory, the sugars have been synthesised in various ways:

(i) By the aldol condensation (p. 146) of formaldehyde in the presence of calcium hydroxide; the product is a mixture of compounds among which is a number of hexoses. This hexose mixture, known as *formose*, has been shown to contain DL-fructose (Butlerow, 1861; Loew, 1886).

(ii) By the aldol condensation of glycolaldehyde in the presence of sodium hydroxide; the product is formose (E. Fischer, 1887):

$$3CH_2OH{\cdot}CHO \xrightarrow{NaOH} C_6H_{12}O_6$$

(iii) When oxidised with nitric acid or bromine-water, glycerol yields a product known as *glycerose*, which contains, among other things, glyceraldehyde and dihydroxyacetone. These, in the presence of barium hydroxide, are converted into a mixture of α- and β-*acrose* (E. Fischer, 1887); α-acrose is DL-fructose and β-acrose is DL-sorbose:

$$CH_2OH{\cdot}CHOH{\cdot}CHO + CH_2OH{\cdot}CO{\cdot}CH_2OH \longrightarrow CH_2OH{\cdot}CO{\cdot}(CHOH)_3{\cdot}CH_2OH$$

Starting with α-acrose, Fischer isolated DL-fructosazone (DL-glucosazone), and making use of reduction, oxidation and epimerisation, he converted DL-fructosazone into D(−)-fructose, D(+)-glucose, D(+)-mannose and other aldohexoses.

(iv) When hydrolysed with barium hydroxide solution, dibromoacraldehyde forms a mixture of α- and β-acrose (E. Fischer, 1887):

$$CH_2Br{\cdot}CHBr{\cdot}CHO \xrightarrow{Ba(OH)_2} CH_2OH{\cdot}CHOH{\cdot}CHO \xrightarrow{dimerises} CH_2OH{\cdot}CO{\cdot}(CHOH)_3{\cdot}CH_2OH$$

(v) When allowed to stand in a barium hydroxide solution containing a small amount of iodine, D(+)-glyceraldehyde is converted into a mixture of D(−)-fructose and D(+)-sorbose (H. Fischer and Baer, 1936). These authors believed that part of the glyceraldehyde rearranged to dihydroxyacetone (p. 243), which then condensed with unchanged glyceraldehyde to form the ketohexoses. They supported their belief by showing that the same products were obtained in a much shorter time when D(+)-glyceraldehyde and dihydroxyacetone were used as the starting materials.

(vi) By means of the Kiliani reaction, sugars up to a decose have been prepared.

Two ketoheptoses have been isolated from natural sources, *viz.*, *mannoheptulose* from the *Avocado pear*, and *altroheptulose* (*sedoheptulose*) from the leaves of *Sedum spectabile*.

(vii) A number of aldoses have been prepared by the oxidation of polyhydric alcohols, *e.g.*, mannitol, on oxidation with nitric acid, yields mannose.

Only three natural sugars are known which are not straight-chain compounds:

apiose $(CH_2OH)(CH_2OH)\rangle COH{\cdot}CHOH{\cdot}CHO$

hamamelose $CH_2OH{\cdot}(CHOH)_2{\cdot}C(OH)(CH_2OH)(CHO)$

The third sugar, (−)-cordycepose (isolated from a glycoside in 1951), has been shown to be 3-deoxyapiose, $(CH_2OH)_2{\cdot}CH{\cdot}CHOH{\cdot}CHO$. This and D(+)-apiose have been synthesised by Raphael *et al.* (1955).

Configuration of the Monosaccharides

Aldotrioses. Glyceraldehyde is the only aldotriose, and has been chosen as arbitrary standard (p. 383).

CHO H—|—OH CH_2OH	CHO HO—|—H CH_2OH
D(+)-glyceraldehyde	L(−)-glyceraldehyde

Aldotetroses, $CH_2OH{\cdot}CHOH{\cdot}CHOH{\cdot}CHO$. This structure contains two asymmetric carbon atoms, and so there are four optical isomers (two pairs of enantiomorphs). All are known, and correspond to D- and L-threose and D- and L-erythrose. D(+)-Glyceraldehyde may be stepped up by the Kiliani reaction to give D(—)-threose and D(—)-erythrose. The question now is: which is which?

CHO
H—|—OH
CH_2OH

CHO	CHO
H—|—OH	HO—|—H
H—|—OH	H—|—OH
CH_2OH	CH_2OH
D(—)-erythrose	D(—)-threose
(I)	(II)

On oxidation, D-erythrose forms *meso*tartaric acid. Therefore D-erythrose must be (I), and consequently (II) must be D-threose.

The tetroses are synthetic compounds.

Aldopentoses, $CH_2OH{\cdot}CHOH{\cdot}CHOH{\cdot}CHOH{\cdot}CHO$. This structure contains three asymmetric carbon atoms, and so there are eight optical isomers (four pairs of enantiomorphs). All are known. D-Erythrose, when stepped up by the Kiliani reaction, gives D(—)-ribose and D(—)-arabinose. Similarly, D-threose gives D(+)-xylose and D(—)-lyxose.

D-erythrose		D-threose	
CHO	CHO	CHO	CHO
H—|—OH	HO—|—H	H—|—HO	HO—|—H
H—|—OH	H—|—OH	HO—|—H	HO—|—H
H—|—OH	H—|—OH	H—|—OH	H—|—OH
CH_2OH	CH_2OH	CH_2OH	CH_2OH
D(—)-ribose	D(—)-arabinose	D(+)-xylose	D(—)-lyxose
(III)	(IV)	(V)	(VI)

(III) and (IV) must be ribose and arabinose, but which is which? On oxidation with nitric acid, arabinose gives an optically active dicarboxylic acid (a trihydroxyglutaric acid), whereas ribose gives an optically inactive dicarboxylic acid. When the terminal groups (*i.e.*, CHO and CH_2OH) of (III) are oxidised to carboxyl groups, the molecule produced possesses a plane of symmetry, and so this acid is inactive. The dicarboxylic acid produced from (IV), however, has no plane (or any other element) of symmetry, and so is optically active. Thus (III) is D-ribose and (IV) is D-arabinose.

(V) and (VI) must be xylose and lyxose, but which is which? The former, on oxidation, gives an optically inactive dicarboxylic acid, whereas the latter gives an optically active dicarboxylic acid. Therefore (V) is D-xylose and (VI) is D-lyxose.

Aldohexoses, $CH_2OH{\cdot}CHOH{\cdot}CHOH{\cdot}CHOH{\cdot}CHOH{\cdot}CHO$. This structure contains four asymmetric carbon atoms, and so there are sixteen optical isomers (eight pairs of enantiomorphs). All are known, and may be prepared by stepping up the aldopentoses: D-ribose gives D(+)-allose and D(+)-altrose; D-arabinose gives D(+)-glucose and D(+)-mannose; D-xylose gives D(—)-gulose and D(—)-idose, and D-lyxose gives D(+)-galactose and D(+)-talose.

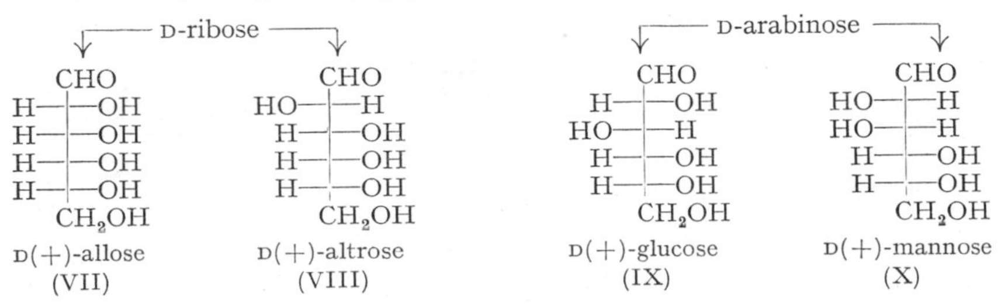

D(+)-allose (VII) D(+)-altrose (VIII) D(+)-glucose (IX) D(+)-mannose (X)

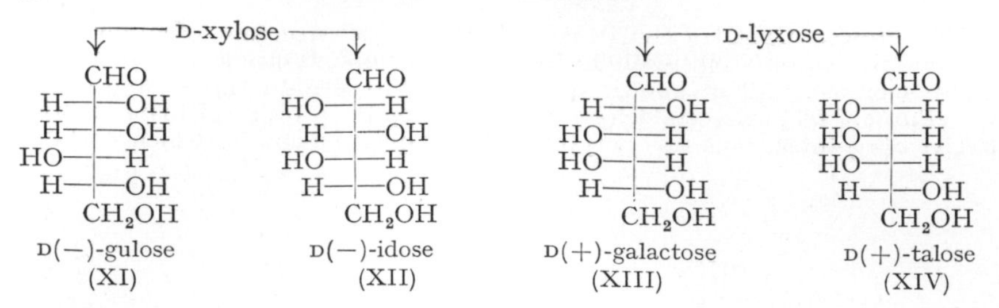

D(−)-gulose (XI) D(−)-idose (XII) D(+)-galactose (XIII) D(+)-talose (XIV)

(VII) and (VIII) must be allose and altrose, but which is which? On oxidation with nitric acid, the former gives an optically inactive (allomucic) and the latter an optically active (talomucic) dicarboxylic acid. Therefore (VII) is allose and (VIII) is altrose.

(XIII) and (XIV) must be galactose and talose, but which is which? On oxidation with nitric acid, the former gives an optically inactive (mucic) and the latter an optically active (talomucic) dicarboxylic acid. Therefore (XIII) is galactose and (XIV) is talose.

The elucidation of the configurations of the remaining four aldohexoses is not quite so simple, since, on oxidation with nitric acid, glucose and mannose *both* give optically active dicarboxylic acids, as also do gulose and idose; in all four configurations (IX, X, XI, XII), replacement of the two terminal groups (CHO and CH_2OH) by carboxyl groups leads to dicarboxylic acid whose structures have no plane (or any other element) of symmetry. It has been found, however, that the dicarboxylic acid from glucose (saccharic acid) is the same as that produced from gulose. Actually the two saccharic acids obtained are enantiomorphs, D-glucose giving D-saccharic acid and D-gulose L-saccharic acid. Since saccharic acid, $CO_2H{\cdot}(CHOH)_4{\cdot}CO_2H$, is produced by the oxidation of the terminal groups with the rest of the molecule unaffected, it therefore follows that the "rest of the molecule" must be the same for both glucose and gulose. Inspection of formulæ (IX, X, XI and XII) shows that only (IX) and (XI) have the "rest of the molecule" the same; by interchanging the CHO and CH_2OH groups of (IX), (XI) is obtained. Therefore (IX) must be glucose (since we know that glucose is obtained from arabinose), and (XI) must be gulose. Consequently (X) is mannose and (XII) is idose.

Ketohexoses. Fructose is a ketohexose, and natural fructose is lævorotatory. Since D-glucose gives the *same* osazone as natural fructose, the latter must be D(−)-fructose. Furthermore, since osazone formation involves only the first two carbon atoms in a sugar, it therefore follows that the configuration of the rest of the molecule in glucose and fructose must be the same. Hence the configuration of D(−)-fructose is (XV).

D(−)-fructose (XV)		osazone		D(+)-glucose
CH_2OH		$CH{=}N{\cdot}NH{\cdot}C_6H_5$		CHO
CO	$\xrightarrow{C_6H_5{\cdot}NH{\cdot}NH_2}$	$C{=}N{\cdot}NH{\cdot}C_6H_5$	$\xleftarrow{C_6H_5{\cdot}NH{\cdot}NH_2}$	H— —OH
HO— —H		HO— —H		HO— —H
H— —OH		H— —OH		H— —OH
H— —OH		H— —OH		H— —OH
CH_2OH		CH_2OH		CH_2OH

The configurations of the other ketohexoses are:

D(+)-sorbose	D(+)-tagatose	L(−)-psicose
CH_2OH	CH_2OH	CH_2OH
CO	CO	CO
H— —OH	HO— —H	HO— —H
HO— —H	HO— —H	HO— —H
H— —OH	H— —OH	HO— —H
CH_2OH	CH_2OH	CH_2OH

Determination of the Size of Sugar-rings

E. Fischer (1893) refluxed glucose with excess methanol in the presence of a small amount of hydrochloric acid and obtained a white crystalline solid containing *one* methyl group. This compound was no longer reducing, and also did not form an osazone. Thus Fischer had prepared methyl glucoside. Ekenstein (1894) isolated a second isomer from the same reaction, and Fischer explained the existence of these two isomers by suggesting a *ring* structure for them, and followed Tollens in believing that they were five-membered rings.

$$
\begin{array}{l} CHOH \\ (CHOH)_2 \quad O \\ CH \\ CHOH \\ CH_2OH \\ \text{D-glucose} \end{array}
\xrightarrow[HCl]{CH_3OH}
\begin{array}{l} H{-}C{-}OCH_3 \\ (CHOH)_2 \quad O \\ CH \\ CHOH \\ CH_2OH \\ \text{methyl } \alpha\text{-D-glucofuranoside} \end{array}
+
\begin{array}{l} CH_3O{-}C{-}H \\ (CHOH)_2 \quad O \\ CH \\ CHOH \\ CH_2OH \\ \text{methyl } \beta\text{-D-glucofuranoside} \end{array}
$$

There was no experimental evidence for the existence of a five-membered ring, and it was shown to be incorrect by Haworth, Hirst and their co-workers (1926 onwards). They proved that the above glucosides were *six-membered* rings, *i.e.*, glucopyranosides. Their method was to fully methylate the glucoside (I), hydrolyse the product, methyl tetramethyl-α-D-glucoside (II) to tetramethyl-α-D-glucose (III), oxidise this with bromine-water at 90° to the lactone (IV), and then to oxidise this with nitric acid. The product obtained was shown to be xylotrimethoxyglutaric acid (V; this can be obtained directly by the oxidation of methylated xylose). The most reasonable interpretation of these results is in accordance with the assumption that methyl glucoside is a six- and *not* a five-membered ring. Thus:

$$
\begin{array}{l} CHOCH_3 \\ CHOH \\ CHOH \quad O \\ CHOH \\ CH \\ CH_2OH \\ \text{(I)} \end{array}
\xrightarrow[NaOH]{(CH_3)_2SO_4}
\begin{array}{l} CHOCH_3 \\ CHOCH_3 \\ CHOCH_3 \quad O \\ CHOCH_3 \\ CH \\ CH_2OCH_3 \\ \text{(II)} \end{array}
\xrightarrow{HCl}
\begin{array}{l} CHOH \\ CHOCH_3 \\ CHOCH_3 \quad O \\ CHOCH_3 \\ CH \\ CH_2OCH_3 \\ \text{(III)} \end{array}
$$

$$
\xrightarrow{Br_2/H_2O}
\begin{array}{l} CO \\ CHOCH_3 \\ CHOCH_3 \quad O \\ CHOCH_3 \\ CH \\ CH_2OCH_3 \\ \text{(IV)} \end{array}
\xrightarrow{HNO_3}
\begin{array}{l} CO_2H \\ CHOCH_3 \\ CHOCH_3 \\ CHOCH_3 \\ CO_2H \\ \text{(V)} \end{array}
$$

Fischer (1914) also prepared methyl glucoside by dissolving glucose in methanol and letting it stand at *room temperature* in the presence of hydrochloric acid. He now obtained compounds which Haworth *et al.*, using the above method, showed to be *five*-membered rings, *i.e.*, methyl D-glucofuranosides.

Hudson (1937, 1939) has also determined the size of sugar-rings, but his method was to oxidise methyl glycosides with periodic acid. As we have seen (p. 67), periodic acid splits 1 : 2-glycols, and *one molecule of acid* is used for *each pair of adjacent alcoholic groups, e.g.*,

$$\text{R·CHOH·CHOH·R}' \xrightarrow{1\text{HIO}_4} \text{R·CHO} + \text{R}'\text{·CHO}$$

$$\text{R·CHOH·CHOH·CHOH·R}' \xrightarrow{2\text{HIO}_4} \text{R·CHO} + \text{H·CO}_2\text{H} + \text{R}'\text{·CHO}$$

Compounds containing an aldehyde or ketonic group adjacent to an alcoholic group are also attacked by periodic acid in a similar manner to glycols:

$$\text{R·CHOH·CHO} \xrightarrow{1\text{HIO}_4} \text{R·CHO} + \text{H·CO}_2\text{H}$$

$$\text{R·CO·CHOH·R}' \xrightarrow{1\text{HIO}_4} \text{R·CO}_2\text{H} + \text{R}'\text{·CHO}$$

Thus an aldopentose, if it had an *open-chain* structure, would require *four* molecules of periodic acid, and the products would be four molecules of formic acid and one molecule of formaldehyde (from the terminal CH_2OH group).

$$\text{CHO·CHOH·CHOH·CHOH·CH}_2\text{OH} \xrightarrow{4\text{HIO}_4} 4\text{H·CO}_2\text{H} + \text{CH}_2\text{O}$$

Thus estimating the periodic acid used and the formic acid and/or formaldehyde produced will indicate the number, in pairs, of *free* oxidisable groups (CHOH, CHO or CO).

Oxidation of methyl glucoside (produced under reflux conditions; see above) uses *two* molecules of periodic acid and produces *one* molecule of formic acid. Only one structure fits these facts, namely, a *six-membered* ring.

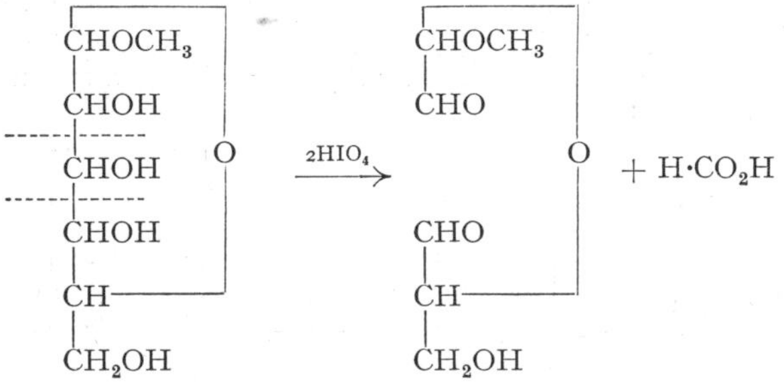

$$\begin{array}{l|c} \text{CHOCH}_3 & \\ \text{CHOH} & \\ \text{CHOH} & \text{O} \\ \text{CHOH} & \\ \text{CH}\text{—} & \\ \text{CH}_2\text{OH} & \end{array} \xrightarrow{2\text{HIO}_4} \begin{array}{l|c} \text{CHOCH}_3 & \\ \text{CHO} & \\ & \text{O} \\ \text{CHO} & \\ \text{CH}\text{—} & \\ \text{CH}_2\text{OH} & \end{array} + \text{H·CO}_2\text{H}$$

The other product of the oxidation has also been isolated and characterised by Hudson. It should be noted that the successful application of this method depends on the fact that the oxide ring in glycosides is stable during the oxidation.

Since methylation of sugars under different conditions produces different sized rings, the question is: what is the size of the ring in the original sugar? Various sources of evidence, *e.g.*, X-ray analysis, show that the normal sugars are *pyranoses*.

One other point will be mentioned here, and that is the configuration of the *first* carbon atom. When the open-chain structure is closed to form the ring, two configurations of the new asymmetric carbon atom are possible, the one with the hydrogen to the left (the α-form), and the one with the hydrogen to the right (the β-). This is an *arbitrary* arrangement, but in recent years it has been shown quite conclusively that the α- and β-forms actually have the configurations originally arbitrarily assigned to them, *e.g.*, X-ray analysis of α-D-glucose has shown that the 1 : 2-hydroxyl groups are in the *cis*-position (McDonald *et al.*, 1950).

Disaccharides

All the disaccharides are crystalline solids, soluble in water, and fall into two classes, the *reducing* sugars and the *non-reducing* sugars.

Just as methanol forms methylglycosides with the monosaccharides, so can other hydroxy-compounds form similar unions with the monosaccharides. Since the latter are themselves hydroxy-compounds, it is possible that they can link up with themselves to form acetals, *i.e.*, glycosides in which the aglycon is another sugar molecule. Actually, three such compounds occur in nature: *sucrose, maltose* and *lactose.*

Sucrose, cane-sugar, $C_{12}H_{22}O_{11}$, is one of the most important compounds commercially, and is obtained from the sugar-cane and sugar-beet. Sugar-cane is cut into small pieces, crushed, and the juice pressed out. The juice is warmed and run into settling tanks; it is then decanted from the sediment and made alkaline with calcium hydroxide, whereupon some impurities are precipitated. The liquid is now steamed to coagulate protein matter, allowed to settle, and the clear juice concentrated to a syrup by evaporation under reduced pressure. The syrup is allowed to cool; some crystallises (about 65 per cent.), and the rest remains as a thick solution. The crystalline material is collected by centrifuging, and the thick liquid, which is known as *molasses,* will not crystallise.

The sugar so obtained is brown, and has an unpleasant odour. It is dissolved in water, the solution decolorised with animal charcoal or with norit (coconut charcoal), filtered, concentrated under reduced pressure, and allowed to crystallise.

If it is desired to recover the sugar from molasses, the latter may be mixed with a fresh lot of syrup or treated chemically. Chemical treatment consists in diluting the molasses with water and adding calcium hydroxide with vigorous agitation, whereupon calcium saccharate, $C_{12}H_{22}O_{11}\cdot 3CaO$, is precipitated. This is collected by filtration, suspended in water, and decomposed by passing in carbon dioxide. The precipitated calcium carbonate is removed by filtration and the filtrate is evaporated, etc. (see above).

The sugar-beet is sliced, extracted with hot water, the solution agitated with calcium hydroxide and carbon dioxide blown in. The calcium carbonate, which is precipitated, carries down with it nearly all the impurities. The liquid is filtered and the filtrate evaporated, etc.

Sucrose is a white crystalline solid, m.p. 180°, soluble in water. When heated above its melting point, it forms a brown substance known as caramel. Concentrated sulphuric acid chars sucrose, the product being almost pure carbon. Sucrose is dextrorotatory, its specific rotation being +66·5°. On hydrolysis with dilute acids, sucrose yields an equimolecular mixture of D(+)-glucose and D(—)-fructose:

$$C_{12}H_{22}O_{11} + H_2O \xrightarrow{HCl} \underset{\text{glucose}}{C_6H_{12}O_6} + \underset{\text{fructose}}{C_6H_{12}O_6}$$

Since D(—)-fructose has a greater specific rotation than D(+)-glucose, the resulting mixture is lævorotatory. Because of this, the hydrolysis of cane-sugar is known as *the inversion of cane-sugar* (this is not to be confused with the *Walden inversion*), and the mixture is known as *invert sugar.* The inversion (*i.e.*, hydrolysis) of cane-sugar may also be effected by the enzyme *invertase* which is found in yeast.

Controlled oxidation of sucrose in alkaline solution with air gives D-arabonic acid. Oxidation of sucrose with nitric acid under different conditions gives either oxalic acid (80 per cent.), tartaric acid (40 per cent.), or saccharic acid (30 per cent.). Hydrogenation of sucrose under controlled conditions gives a mixture of mannitol and sorbitol (these may be separated by fractional crystallisation).

Sucrose is *not* a reducing sugar, *e.g.*, it will not reduce Fehling's solution; it does not form an oxime or an osazone, and does not undergo mutarotation.

This indicates that neither the aldehyde group of glucose nor the ketonic group of fructose is free in sucrose. Thus a tentative structure of sucrose is one in which the two molecules, glucose and fructose, are linked by the aldehyde group of the former and ketonic group of the latter. This has been amply confirmed by further work, and the structure of sucrose has been shown to be:

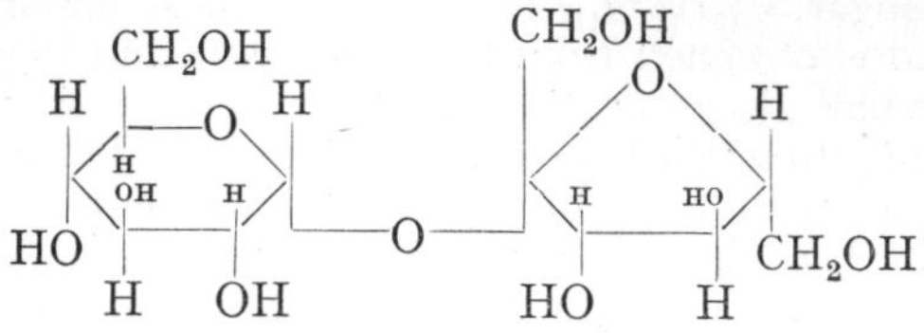

It should be noted that the fructose molecule in sucrose exists as the γ-form, and that when sucrose is hydrolysed, it is the δ-form of fructose which is isolated.

Maltose (*malt-sugar*), $C_{12}H_{22}O_{11}$, is produced by the action of malt (which contains the enzyme *diastase*) on starch:

$$(C_6H_{10}O_5)_n + \frac{n}{2} H_2O \xrightarrow{\text{diastase}} \frac{n}{2} C_{12}H_{22}O_{11}$$

Maltose is a white crystalline solid, m.p. 160–165°, soluble in water, and is dextrorotatory. When it is hydrolysed with dilute acids or by the enzyme *maltase*, maltose yields two molecules of D(+)-glucose. Maltose is a reducing sugar, *e.g.*, it reduces Fehling's solution; it forms an oxime and an osazone, and undergoes mutarotation. This indicates that at least one aldehyde group (of the two glucose molecules) is free in maltose. Further work has shown that the structure of maltose is:

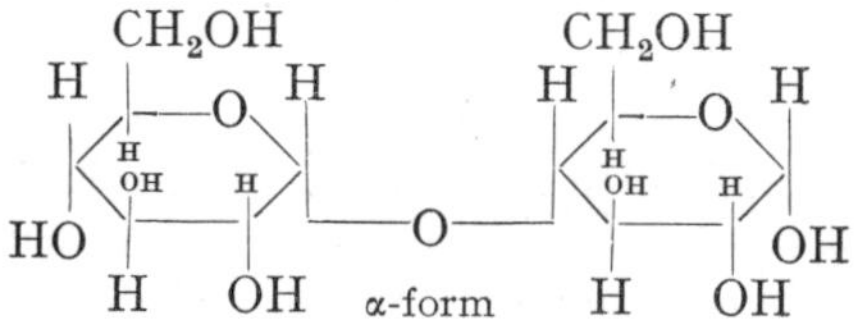

α-form

The hemiacetal link of one glucose molecule (the reducing half) is unchanged, but that of the other (the non-reducing half) has been converted into the acetal link.

Cellobiose, $C_{12}H_{22}O_{11}$, may be obtained from cellulose by acetylating good filter paper (which is almost pure cellulose) with acetic anhydride in the presence of concentrated sulphuric acid. The octa-acetate of cellobiose so obtained is saponified with potassium hydroxide or with sodium ethoxide, whereupon cellobiose is produced.

Cellobiose is a white crystalline solid, m.p. 225°, soluble in water, and dextrorotatory. When hydrolysed with dilute acids or by the enzyme *emulsin*, it yields two molecules of D(+)-glucose. It is a reducing sugar, forms an oxime and osazone, and undergoes mutarotation. Its structure has been shown to be:

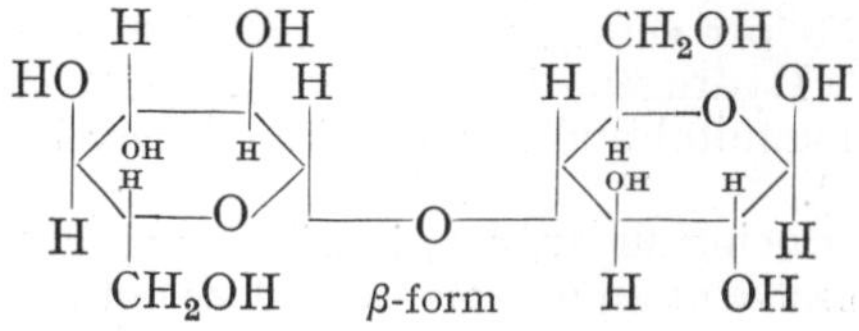

β-form

Lactose (*milk-sugar*), $C_{12}H_{22}O_{11}$, occurs in the milk of all animals, and is prepared commercially from whey by evaporation to crystallisation; whey is obtained as a by-product in the manufacture of cheese.

Lactose is a white crystalline solid, m.p. 203° (with decomposition), soluble in water, and is dextrorotatory. It is hydrolysed by dilute acids or by the enzyme *lactase*, to an equimolecular mixture of D(+)-glucose and D(+)-galactose. Lactose is a reducing sugar, forms an oxime and osazone, and undergoes mutarotation. Its structure has been shown to be:

α-form

Sucrose, maltose and lactose are three disaccharides which occur naturally. Cellobiose may be prepared from cellulose. Two other disaccharides which have been prepared are **melibiose** (from the trisaccharide *raffinose*), and **gentiobiose** (from the trisaccharide *gentianose*). These differ from the other disaccharides in that the two monosaccharide molecules are linked by the *sixth* carbon atom (the aldehyde carbon atom being number one) of the reducing monosaccharide:

melibiose (β-form)

gentiobiose (β-form)

Polysaccharides

The polysaccharides are high polymers of the monomeric sugars and are analogous to the synthetic long-chain polymers.

Inulin occurs in many plants, *e.g.*, in the roots of the dandelion, in the tubers of the dahlia and in certain lichens. It is a white powder, insoluble in cold water, and in hot water forms a colloidal solution which does not form a gel on cooling. Inulin solutions do not give any colour with iodine. Inulin is hydrolysed by dilute acids to D(−)-fructose, and therefore the structure of inulin is based on the fructose unit. The empirical formula of inulin is usually given as $(C_6H_{10}O_5)_n$, but more accurately, it is $(C_6H_{10}O_5)_n{\cdot}H_2O$, since in the formation of inulin n-1 molecules of water are eliminated from n-molecules of fructose. Molecular-weight determinations (by chemical methods) appear to indicate the value of 5000 (about 30 units).

Starch, $(C_6H_{10}O_5)_n$, occurs in all green plants; the commercial sources of starch are maize, wheat, barley, rice, potatoes, and sorghum. The plant cells are broken down by grinding and washing with water; the extract is passed over five sieves, the starch granules passing through and the other materials being retained. The starch granules are collected and dried with hot air, the product now containing about 20 per cent. water.

Starch consists of two fractions, one being known as α-**amylose** (the "A" fraction), and the other as β-**amylose** or **amylopectin** (the "B" fraction); the former comprises 10–20 per cent. of starch, and the latter 80–90 per cent. α-Amylose is soluble in water, and the solution gives a blue colour with iodine. An aqueous solution of α-amylose slowly forms a precipitate, since α-amylose has a strong tendency to "revert" to the insoluble state in solution. Amylopectin is insoluble in water, is stable in contact with water, and gives a violet colour with iodine. α-Amylose and amylopectin are both hydrolysed to maltose by the enzyme diastase, and to D(+)-glucose by dilute acids (amylopectin gives about 50% of maltose).

The determination of the molecular weight of α-amylose by means of osmotic pressure measurements gives a value of 10,000–50,000; the molecular weight of amylopectin (by osmotic pressure measurements) is 50,000–100,000 (see also cellulose, below). The structures of α-amylose and amylopectin are not known with certainty, but the work done so far appears to indicate that α-amylose consists of linear chains, and that amylopectin contains branched chains. Furthermore, the glucose units exist in the α-form in starch.

The **dextrins,** $(C_6H_{10}O_5)_n$, are produced by the partial hydrolysis of starch by boiling with water under pressure at about 250°. They are white powders, and are used for making adhesives and confectionery, for sizing paper, etc.

Glycogen, $(C_6H_{10}O_5)_n$, is found in nearly all animal cells, occurring mainly in the liver; it is the reserve carbohydrate of animals, and so is often known as "*animal starch*". It has also been isolated from plant sources (Hassid and McCready, 1941).

Glycogen is a white powder, soluble in water, the solution giving a purplish-red colour with iodine. On hydrolysis with dilute acid, glycogen gives D(+)-glucose. The molecular weight of glycogen has been given as 500,000–800,000, and it appears that glycogen contains highly branched chains.

Pectins are found in plant and fruit juices. Their characteristic property is the ability of their solutions to gelate, *i.e.*, form jellies. They have a high molecular weight, and appear to be polygalacturonic acids with the carboxyl groups partially esterified with methanol.

Cellulose, $(C_6H_{10}O_5)_n$, is the main constituent of the cell-wall of plants; it is the most widely distributed organic compound. Recently it has been found to occur in certain animal tissues.

The main source of cellulose is cotton and wood. Cotton is almost pure cellulose, but wood also contains *lignin,* which is not a polysaccharide. Lignin is separated from cellulose by digesting wood chips at 130–150° with an aqueous solution containing calcium and magnesium hydrogen sulphites; the lignin is soluble. This method of preparing cellulose is known as the *sulphite process.* Another method, the "*sulphate process*", consists in digesting wood with a solution of sodium hydroxide, sodium sulphide and sulphur; again only the lignin is soluble.

The **hemicelluloses** comprise a group of polysaccharides which also occur as the constituent of the cell-wall of plants. Many hemicelluloses give glucose, mannose and galactose on hydrolysis.

Cellulose is a white solid, insoluble in water but soluble in ammoniacal copper hydroxide solution (*Schweitzer's reagent*). Careful hydrolysis of cellulose gives cellobiose; it is also possible to isolate *cellotriose* (trisaccharide) and *cellotetrose* (tetrasaccharide). All of these saccharides, on further hydrolysis, yield only D(+)-glucose which exists in the β-form in cellulose (*cf.* starch).

Molecular-weight determinations of cellulose give different values according to the method used, *e.g.*, chemical methods give a value of 20,000–40,000; viscosity method, 150,000–200,000; and by means of the ultracentrifuge, 300,000–500,000. Of all the methods for measuring the molecular weight of large molecules (including the method of osmotic pressure), probably that by the ultracentrifuge is the most reliable In any case, the value of n in $(C_6H_{10}O_5)_n$ is uncertain for all the polysaccharides.

Artificial silk. The term **rayon** is used collectively to cover all synthetic or manufactured fibres from cellulose, but it is usually most often applied to viscose yarns. There are four processes for obtaining synthetic fibres from cellulose; cellulose nitrate, cellulose acetate, cuprammonium and viscose processes. The cellulose for these purposes is best obtained from wood-pulp and cotton-linters; other sources give rise to inferior yarns.

Cellulose nitrates (*nitrocellulose*). When treated with a mixture of concentrated nitric and sulphuric acids, cellulose is converted into its highest nitrate ester, the trinitrate (each glucose unit in cellulose has three free hydroxyl groups). Cellulose trinitrate is known as *gun-cotton*; it is insoluble in a mixture of ethanol and ether, is explosive, and is used in the manufacture of smokeless powders.

By using a diluted mixture of nitric and sulphuric acid, the lower nitrates of cellulose, the mono- and di-nitrates, are obtained. These lower nitrates, in the *solid* state, are known as **pyroxylin.** Pyroxylin is soluble in a mixture of ethanol and ether, the solution being known as **collodion.** When heated with ethanol and camphor or camphor substitutes, pyroxylin is converted into **celluloid.**

The oldest method—the *Chardonnet process*—of preparing artificial silk involves the use of cellulose nitrate (pyroxylin) in one of its stages. The pyroxylin is dissolved in a mixture of ethanol and ether to give collodion, which is then forced through glass capillary tubes into the air, whereupon the solvent evaporates, leaving filaments of cellulose nitrate. These filaments are digested with sodium hydroxide or sodium hydrogen sulphate solutions to " denitrate " the cellulose nitrate to cellulose. This process of preparing artificial silk is expensive due to the high cost of the chemicals.

Cellulose acetate (*celanese silk*). When acetylated with acetic anhydride in the presence of sulphuric acid, cellulose is converted into cellulose triacetate. When the reaction is complete, water is added to decompose the triacetate into the diacetate (approximately). The diacetate is washed, dried, and dissolved in a mixture of organic solvents (of which acetone is generally the main constituent). The solution is then forced through a spinneret into a warm chamber, whereupon the solvent evaporates leaving behind fine threads of cellulose acetate.

Cellulose acetate silk burns with difficulty, but is expensive. Cellulose acetate is also used for making non-inflammable photographic and motion-picture films, non-shatterable glass, lacquers and varnishes.

Esters other than the acetate are also used for the above purposes, *e.g.*, cellulose formate, propionate and butyrate.

Cuprammonium process (*cupra silk*). In the cuprammonium process, cellulose is dissolved in ammoniacal copper hydroxide solution, which is then forced through a spinneret into a sulphuric acid bath, whereupon cellulose is precipitated as fine threads. Cupra silk has the very big advantage of being cheap.

Viscose rayon. In the viscose process, cellulose is digested with sodium hydroxide solution, and then carbon disulphide is passed into the solution. A mixture of sodium cellulose xanthates, soluble in sodium hydroxide, is formed (*cf.* p. 324): R = cellulose:

$$R{-}OH + CS_2 + NaOH \longrightarrow S{=}C\begin{matrix}\diagup OR \\ \diagdown SNa\end{matrix} + H_2O$$

This alkaline solution has a high viscosity, and hence the silk obtained by this process was named *viscose* rayon. The viscose solution is forced through a spinneret into a sulphuric acid bath, whereupon cellulose is precipitated as fine threads. Of all artificial silks, viscose rayon is produced in the largest quantity.

Cellophane is made by extruding a viscose solution through a long narrow slit into an acid bath, whereupon cellulose is precipitated as very thin sheets. These sheets are made moisture-proof by coating with a transparent nitrocellulose lacquer.

Some cellulose ethers, particularly the ethyl ether, are used in the manufacture of plastics.

When agitated with about 20 per cent. aqueous sodium hydroxide, cellulose swells; apparently cellulose combines with the sodium hydroxide to form a sodio-cellulose. This is unstable, and is readily decomposed into cellulose by the addition of water, but the cellulose has a number of its physical properties changed, *e.g.*, it absorbs dyes more readily than untreated cellulose. This " reactive " form of cellulose is known as *mercerised cellulose*.

Cellulose may be oxidised by nitrogen dioxide to give a product which retains its original form and much of the original tensile strength. It appears that about half of the CH_2OH groups (alternately) are oxidised to carboxyl, thereby giving a compound readily soluble in sodium hydroxide. This oxidised cellulose is useful in medicine, *e.g.*, it possesses hæmostatic properties, and is useful as sterile gauze.

QUESTIONS

1. What are the carbohydrates and how are they classified?
2. Outline the evidence for the structural formulæ of:—(*a*) the aldopentoses, (*b*) the ketohexoses, (*d*) sucrose, (*e*) maltose, (*f*) lactose.
3. Name the compounds and state the conditions under which they are formed when glucose, fructose, sucrose and maltose, respectively, are treated with:—(*a*) Tollens' reagent, (*b*) Fehling's solution, (*c*) NaOH, (*d*) HCN, (*e*) $NH_2{\cdot}OH$, (*f*) $C_6H_5{\cdot}NH{\cdot}NH_2$, (*g*) oxidising agents, (*h*) reducing agents, (*i*) HCl, (*j*) $Ca(OH)_2$, (*k*) EtOH, (*f*) Me_2CO, (*m*) Ac_2O, (*n*) MeI, (*o*) Me_2SO_4, (*p*) micro-organisms, (*q*) enzymes.
4. How are the following compounds prepared commercially:—(*a*) D(+)-glucose, (*b*) D(+)-mannose, (*c*) D(+)-galactose, (*d*) D(−)-fructose, (*e*) D(−)-arabinose, (*f*) sucrose, (*g*) maltose, (*h*) lactose, (*i*) inulin, (*j*) starch, (*k*) cellulose?
5. Write an account of:—(*a*) the methods of descending and ascending the sugar series, (*b*) the conversion of an aldose into a ketose and vice-versa, (*c*) the synthesis of the sugars.
6. Show, by means of equations, how you would convert D(+)-glucose into:—(*a*) D(+)-mannose, (*b*) D(−)-arabinose, (*c*) mannitol, (*d*) methylglucoside, (*e*) ethylfructoside.
7. Write an account of:—(*a*) mutarotation, (*b*) the pyranose structure of the sugars, (*c*) the furanose structure of the sugars, (*d*) the configuration of the sugars.
8. Define and give examples of:—(*a*) the Amadori rearrangement, (*b*) epimerisation, (*c*) the Kiliani reaction, (*d*) Wohl's method, (*e*) Zemplen's method, (*f*) Ruff's method, (*g*) Weerman's reaction, (*h*) the Lobry de Bruyn–van Ekenstein rearrangement, (*i*) glycoside, (*j*) the inversion of cane-sugar, (*k*) an enzyme.
9. Discuss the methods of determining the molecular weight of macromolecules.
10. Write an account of the chemistry involved in the utilisation of cellulose in industry.

READING REFERENCES

Weygand, The Theory of Osazone Formation, *Ber.*, 1940, **73B**, 1284.
Barry and Mitchell, Mechanism of Osazone Formation, *Nature*, 1955, **175**, 220.
Oertly and Meyers, Constitution and Taste, *J. Amer. Chem. Soc.*, 1919, **41**, 855.
Tobie, A Supersensitive Schiff's Reagent, *Ind. Eng. Chem.* (*Anal. Ed.*), 1942, **14**, 405.
Mullin, Synthetic Fibres, *Ind. Eng. Chem.* 1930, **22**, 461
Ott, Cellulose Derivatives for Plastics, *ibid.*, 1940, **32**, 1641.
Hussey and Scherer, Rayon—Today and Tomorrow, *J. Chem. Educ.*, 1930, **7**, 2543.
Marsh and Wood, *Introduction to the Chemistry of Cellulose*, Chapman and Hall (1945).
Nord, The Fermentation of Glucose, *Chem. Reviews*, 1940, **23**, 423.
Gilman, *Advanced Organic Chemistry*, Wiley. (1942, 2nd ed.) Vol. II, Ch. 20 and 21, Carbohydrates; Ch. 22, Cellulose.
Percival, *Structural Carbohydrate Chemistry*, Muller (1950).
Honeyman, *Chemistry of the Carbohydrates*, Oxford Univ. Press (1948).
Shearon *et al.*, Cane Sugar Refining, *Ind. Eng. Chem.*, 1951, **43**, 552 (also pp. 603–638).
Gilman, *Advanced Organic Chemistry*, Wiley (1953). Vol. IV, Ch. 9. Starch.
Finar, *Organic Chemistry*. Longmans, Green. Vol. II (1956), Ch. VII. Carbohydrates.
Stacey, Industrial and Medical Uses of Carbohydrates, *Chem. and Ind.*, **1956**, 1398.
Arcus and Greenwood, The Hofmann Reaction with α- and β-Hydroxyamides, *J.C.S.*, **1953**, 1937.

CHAPTER XIX

ALICYCLIC COMPOUNDS

THERE is a large number of compounds which contain closed rings comprised of carbon atoms only. These compounds are known collectively as **carbocyclic** or **homocyclic** compounds. In this group falls a class of compounds which resemble the aliphatic compounds in many ways, and hence they are often called **alicyclic** compounds (*ali*phatic *cyclic* compounds). The saturated alicyclic hydrocarbons have the general formula C_nH_{2n} (the same as that of the olefins); they do not contain a double bond but possess a ring structure.

Nomenclature. Since the saturated alicyclic hydrocarbons contain a number of methylene groups joined together to form a ring, they are known as the **polymethylenes,** the number of carbon atoms in the ring being indicated by a Greek or Latin prefix, *e.g.*,

CH_2, CH_2, CH_2 *or* [triangle]
trimethylene

CH_2, $CH_2—CH_2$, CH_2, $CH_2—CH_2$ *or* [hexagon]
hexamethylene

According to the I.U.C. system, the saturated monocyclic hydrocarbons take the names of the corresponding open-chain saturated hydrocarbons, preceded by the prefix *cyclo*-, and they are known collectively as the *cyclo*-paraffins or *cyclo*alkanes, and if the alicyclic hydrocarbon is unsaturated, the rules applied to the olefins are used (p. 58), *e.g.*,

$CH_2—CH_2$ / $CH_2—CH_2$
*cyclo*butane

$CH_2—CH_2$, CH, $CH_2—CH$
*cyclo*pentene

CH_2, CH=CH, CH_2, CH=CH
*cyclo*hexa-1 : 4-diene

In addition to the simple monocyclic compounds, there are more complicated compounds with bridges linked across the ring, *e.g.*,

H_2C, CH, CH_2, CH_2, H_2C, CH_2, CH
bicyclo-[2.2.1]-heptane

CH—CH_2, CH_2, CH_2, CH—CH_2
bicyclo-[3.1.0]-hexane

Unfortunately, the I.U.C. system of nomenclature does not mention bridged systems, and so there is no uniformity in naming these compounds. One method in use considers the compound to be composed of two rings, and prefixes the name by *bicyclo* followed by the name of the hydrocarbon which is that of the *total number of carbon atoms in the ring systems*. The name, as obtained above, is preceded by numbers placed in square brackets; these denote respectively the number of carbon atoms in the *right* bridge, *left* bridge and *middle* bridge (see the above examples). When there are substituents in the bridges, numbering is started at the carbon atom at one end of the *middle* bridge, carried on around the *longer* way to the other end of the middle bridge, then further around to the beginning and finally along the middle bridge itself, *e.g.*,

CH_3
7 CH_2—1 C—2 $CH{\cdot}C_2H_5$
8 $CH{\cdot}CH_3$, 3 CH_2
6 CHCl—5 CH—4 CH_2

6-chloro-2-ethyl-1 : 8-dimethyl-*bicyclo*-[3.2.1]-octane

*CYCLO*ALKANES AND *CYCLO*ALKENES

Five- and six-membered *cyclo*paraffins occur in petroleum (the *naphthenes*; see p. 51); three-, four- and five-membered rings occur in terpenes, the most important class of alicyclic compounds. Many cyclic acids also occur in petroleum; these are known as the *naphthenic acids* and are mainly *cyclo*pentane derivatives. Some *cyclo*pentene derivatives of the fatty acids occur naturally, and are important in medicine.

General methods of preparation of alicyclic compounds. It is interesting to note that up to about 1880, organic chemists thought that there were only two classes of compounds, aliphatic and aromatic; *e.g.*, V. Meyer (1876) believed that rings smaller than six carbon atoms were never likely to be obtained. Since 1882, however, many methods have been introduced to prepare various sized rings. The following methods are typical.

1. When $\alpha\omega$-dihalogen derivatives of the paraffins are treated with sodium or zinc, the corresponding *cyclo*paraffin is formed (Freund, 1882), *e.g.*, 1 : 3-dibromopropane forms *cyclo*propane:

$$CH_2\begin{cases}CH_2Br\\CH_2Br\end{cases} + Zn \longrightarrow CH_2\begin{cases}CH_2\\ |\\CH_2\end{cases} + ZnBr_2$$

This method is really an extension of the Wurtz reaction and may be regarded as an *internal* Wurtz reaction.

$\alpha\omega$-Dihalogen derivatives of the paraffins in which the two halogen atoms are further apart than the 1 : 6 positions, do not form ring compounds but undergo the Wurtz reaction (at each end) to form long-chain paraffins; *e.g.*, decamethylene bromide, $Br{\cdot}(CH_2)_{10}{\cdot}Br$, in ether, reacts with sodium to form *normal* paraffins C_{20}, C_{30}, C_{40}, C_{50}, C_{60}, C_{70}, and higher members (Carothers, 1930).

2. When the calcium or barium salt of a dicarboxylic acid is distilled, a cyclic ketone is formed (Wislicenus, 1893), *e.g.*, barium adipate gives *cyclo*pentanone:

$$\begin{matrix}CH_2{\cdot}CH_2{\cdot}COO\\ |\\ CH_2{\cdot}CH_2{\cdot}COO\end{matrix}\Big\rangle Ba \longrightarrow \begin{matrix}CH_2{\cdot}CH_2\\ |\\ CH_2{\cdot}CH_2\end{matrix}\Big\rangle CO + BaCO_3$$

Three-membered rings cannot be prepared by this method.

Cyclic ketones may readily be converted into the corresponding *cyclo*paraffins by means of the Clemmensen reduction, *e.g.*,

$$CH_2\Big\langle\begin{matrix}CH_2{\cdot}CH_2\\CH_2{\cdot}CH_2\end{matrix}\Big\rangle CO + 4[H] \xrightarrow[HCl]{Zn/Hg} CH_2\Big\langle\begin{matrix}CH_2{-}CH_2\\CH_2{-}CH_2\end{matrix}\Big\rangle CH_2 + H_2O \quad (g.)$$

Alternatively, the conversion may be effected by either of the following two methods:

$$\text{(i)}\quad \begin{matrix}CH_2{-}CH_2\\ |\\ CH_2{-}CH_2\end{matrix}\Big\rangle CO \xrightarrow{Na/C_2H_5OH} \begin{matrix}CH_2{-}CH_2\\ |\\ CH_2{-}CH_2\end{matrix}\Big\rangle CHOH \xrightarrow{\text{HI at } 0^\circ}$$

$$\begin{matrix}CH_2{-}CH_2\\ |\\ CH_2{-}CH_2\end{matrix}\Big\rangle CHI \xrightarrow[Zn/HCl]{[H]} \begin{matrix}CH_2{-}CH_2\\ |\\ CH_2{-}CH_2\end{matrix}\Big\rangle CH_2$$

(ii)

$$CH_2\langle{}^{CH_2-CH_2}_{CH_2-CH_2}\rangle CO \xrightarrow{Na/C_2H_5OH} CH_2\langle{}^{CH_2-CH_2}_{CH_2-CH_2}\rangle CHOH$$

$$\xrightarrow[(KHSO_4;\ heat)]{-H_2O} CH_2\langle{}^{CH_2-CH_2}_{CH_2-CH}\rangle\!\!\!\!=CH \xrightarrow{H_2/Ni} CH_2\langle{}^{CH_2-CH_2}_{CH_2-CH_2}\rangle CH_2$$

3. Six-membered alicyclic compounds may very conveniently be prepared by the reduction of benzene and its derivatives. Catalytic reduction under pressure using nickel is the most satisfactory, *e.g.*, phenol is almost quantitatively converted into *cyclo*hexanol:

$$C_6H_5OH + 3H_2 \xrightarrow[200^\circ]{Ni} C_6H_{11}OH$$

Reduction may also be carried out at room temperature and at atmospheric pressure by using Adams' platinum catalyst (see p. 60).

4. Various alicyclic compounds may be prepared by the condensation between certain dihalogen derivatives of the paraffins and sodiomalonic ester or sodioacetoacetic ester (Perkin junior, 1883), *e.g.*,

(i) Ethylene bromide condenses with *one* molecule of malonic ester in the presence of *two* molecules of sodium ethoxide to form *cyclo*propane-1 : 1-dicarboxylic ester. This reaction may be formulated (see p. 218):

$$CH_2(CO_2C_2H_5)_2 + 2NaOC_2H_5 \longrightarrow CNa_2(CO_2C_2H_5)_2 + 2C_2H_5OH$$

$$\begin{array}{l}CH_2Br\\|\\CH_2Br\end{array} + CNa_2(CO_2C_2H_5)_2 \longrightarrow \begin{array}{l}CH_2\\|\\CH_2\end{array}\!\!\rangle C(CO_2C_2H_5)_2 + 2NaBr$$

This ester may be converted into *cyclo*propanecarboxylic acid by the usual procedure used in malonic ester syntheses:

$$\begin{array}{l}CH_2\\|\\CH_2\end{array}\!\!\rangle C(CO_2C_2H_5)_2 \xrightarrow[(ii)\ HCl]{(i)\ KOH} \begin{array}{l}CH_2\\|\\CH_2\end{array}\!\!\rangle C(CO_2H)_2 \xrightarrow{heat} \begin{array}{l}CH_2\\|\\CH_2\end{array}\!\!\rangle CH{\cdot}CO_2H + CO_2$$

(ii) Ethylene bromide condenses with *two* molecules of sodiomalonic ester to form butane-1 : 1 : 4 : 4-tetracarboxylic ester:

$$\begin{array}{l}CH_2Br\\|\\CH_2Br\end{array} + 2CHNa(CO_2C_2H_5)_2 \longrightarrow \begin{array}{l}CH_2{\cdot}CH(CO_2C_2H_5)_2\\|\\CH_2{\cdot}CH(CO_2C_2H_5)_2\end{array} + 2NaBr$$

On treatment with excess sodium ethoxide, this tetracarboxylic ester forms the disodio-derivative, which, when treated with iodine, is converted into a *cyclo*butane derivative. If methylene iodide is used instead of iodine, the *cyclo*pentane derivative is obtained:

$$\begin{array}{l}CH_2{\cdot}CH(CO_2C_2H_5)_2\\|\\CH_2{\cdot}CH(CO_2C_2H_5)_2\end{array} \xrightarrow{2NaOC_2H_5} \begin{array}{l}CH_2{\cdot}CNa(CO_2C_2H_5)_2\\|\\CH_2{\cdot}CNa(CO_2C_2H_5)_2\end{array} \xrightarrow{I_2}$$

$$\begin{array}{l}CH_2{\cdot}C(CO_2C_2H_5)_2\\|\quad\ \ |\\CH_2{\cdot}C(CO_2C_2H_5)_2\end{array} \xrightarrow[(ii)\ HCl]{(i)\ KOH} \begin{array}{l}CH_2{\cdot}C(CO_2H)_2\\|\quad\ \ |\\CH_2{\cdot}C(CO_2H)_2\end{array} \xrightarrow{heat} \begin{array}{l}CH_2{\cdot}CH{\cdot}CO_2H\\|\quad\ \ |\\CH_2{\cdot}CH{\cdot}CO_2H\end{array} + 2CO_2$$

Thus, by using the appropriate dihalogen derivatives of the paraffins under suitable conditions, it is possible to prepare rings containing 3–7 carbon atoms (the yield being highest for the 5- and lowest for the 7-membered ring; see later).

Acetoacetic ester may also be used to prepare ring compounds (see p. 213), *e.g.*,

$$CH_2\begin{cases}CH_2{-}CH_2Br\\CH_2{-}CH_2Br\end{cases} + CH_2\begin{cases}CO{\cdot}CH_3\\CO_2C_2H_5\end{cases} \xrightarrow[\text{(2 steps)}]{2NaOC_2H_5} CH_2\begin{cases}CH_2{-}CH_2\\CH_2{-}CH_2\end{cases}C\begin{cases}CO{\cdot}CH_3\\CO_2C_2H_5\end{cases}$$

1-acetyl-*cyclo*hexane-1-carboxylic ester

Hydrolysis and decarboxylation of this compound produce *cyclo*hexyl methyl ketone.

By using acetoacetic ester, it is possible to prepare rings containing 3, 5, 6 and 7 carbon atoms, but not 4; all attempts to prepare a 4-membered ring result in the formation of a dihydropyran derivative (p. 737):

$$(CH_2)_3\begin{cases}Br\\Br\end{cases} + NaCH\begin{cases}CO_2C_2H_5\\CO{\cdot}CH_3\end{cases} \longrightarrow BrH_2C{-}CH_2{-}CH_2{-}C(CO_2C_2H_5){=}C(OH){\cdot}CH_3 \xrightarrow{-HBr}$$

$$\text{dihydropyran: } H_2C{-}CH_2{-}C{\cdot}CO_2C_2H_5{=}C{\cdot}CH_3{-}O{-}CH_2 \text{ (ring)}$$

5. Certain cyclic ketones can be obtained by the **Dieckmann reaction** (1901). This reaction is an *intramolecular* acetoacetic ester condensation (Claisen condensation); the reaction is carried out by treating the esters of adipic, pimelic or suberic acids with sodium, whereupon 5-, 6- or 7-membered rings, respectively, are obtained; *e.g.*, adipic ester forms *cyclo*pentanone:

$$\begin{matrix}CH_2{-}CH_2{-}CO\boxed{OC_2H_5}\\|\\CH_2{-}C\boxed{H}_2{-}COOC_2H_5\end{matrix} \xrightarrow{Na} \begin{matrix}CH_2{-}CH_2\\|\\CH_2{-}C(CO_2C_2H_5)\end{matrix}{\Large\rangle}CONa \xrightarrow{H_2O}$$

$$\begin{matrix}CH_2{-}CH_2\\|\\CH_2{-}CH{\cdot}CO_2C_2H_5\end{matrix}{\Large\rangle}CO \xrightarrow[\text{hydrolysis}]{\text{acid}} \begin{matrix}CH_2{-}CH_2\\|\\CH_2{-}CH{\cdot}CO_2H\end{matrix}{\Large\rangle}CO \xrightarrow{\text{heat}} \begin{matrix}CH_2{-}CH_2\\|\\CH_2{-}CH_2\end{matrix}{\Large\rangle}CO + CO_2 \quad (74\text{–}86\%)$$

Esters lower than adipic ester may form products by *intermolecular* condensation and cyclisation, *e.g.*, in the presence of sodium or sodium ethoxide, ethyl succinate forms *succinosuccinic ester* (*cyclo*hexane-2 : 5-dione-1 : 4-dicarboxylic ester):

$$\begin{matrix}CO_2C_2H_5 & \\ HC\boxed{H\ \ C_2H_5O}OC & \\ CH_2 & CH_2\\ CO\boxed{OC_2H_5\ \ H}CH & \\ & CO_2C_2H_5\end{matrix} \xrightarrow{Na} \begin{matrix} & CO_2C_2H_5 & \\ & CH & \\ H_2C & & CO\\ OC & & CH_2\\ & CH & \\ & CO_2C_2H_5 & \end{matrix} + 2C_2H_5OH \quad (80\%)$$

On the other hand, five-membered ring compounds may be prepared by the intermolecular condensation between oxalic and glutaric esters:

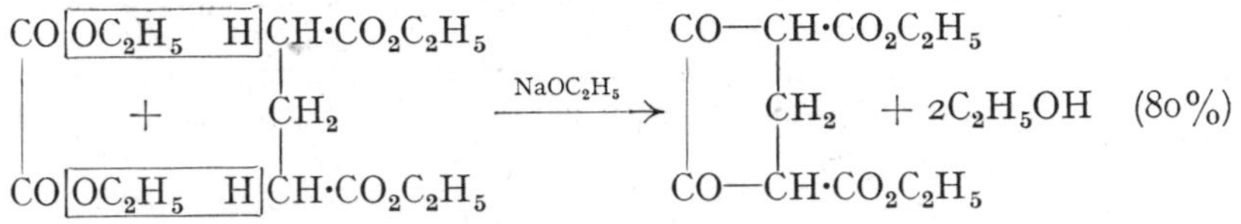

$$\begin{array}{l} CO\boxed{OC_2H_5 \;\; H}CH{\cdot}CO_2C_2H_5 \\ \quad + \qquad\quad CH_2 \\ CO\boxed{OC_2H_5 \;\; H}CH{\cdot}CO_2C_2H_5 \end{array} \xrightarrow{NaOC_2H_5} \begin{array}{l} CO{-}CH{\cdot}CO_2C_2H_5 \\ \quad\;\; CH_2 \\ CO{-}CH{\cdot}CO_2C_2H_5 \end{array} + 2C_2H_5OH \quad (80\%)$$

6. Cyclic ketones may be obtained by a modified Thorpe's reaction (1909). Thorpe's reaction is the condensation of cyano-compounds in the presence of sodium ethoxide to form the dimers; the cyano-compound must have at least one active hydrogen atom (*cf.* p. 279), *e.g.*,

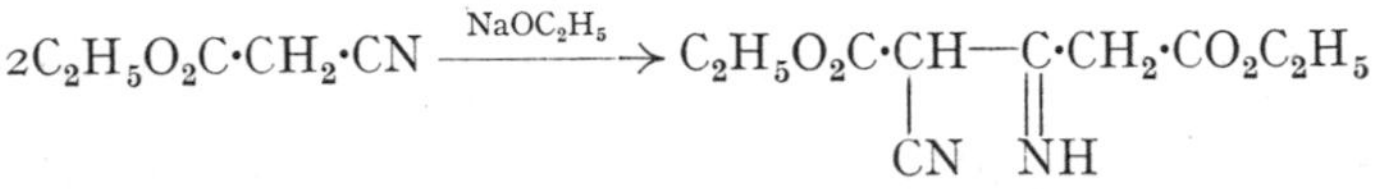

$$2C_2H_5O_2C{\cdot}CH_2{\cdot}CN \xrightarrow{NaOC_2H_5} C_2H_5O_2C{\cdot}\underset{CN}{CH}{-}\underset{NH}{\overset{\|}{C}}{\cdot}CH_2{\cdot}CO_2C_2H_5$$

By using the dicyano-derivative of an ester, it is possible to obtain a cyclic ketonic acid; *e.g.*, $\alpha:\delta$-dicyanovaleric ester undergoes cyclisation in the presence of sodium ethoxide:

$$\begin{array}{l} CH_2{-}CH_2{\cdot}CN \\ \qquad\quad CN \\ CH_2{-}CH{\cdot}CO_2C_2H_5 \end{array} \xrightarrow{NaOC_2H_5} \begin{array}{l} CH_2{-}CH{\cdot}CN \\ \qquad\quad >C{=}NH \\ CH_2{-}CH{\cdot}CO_2C_2H_5 \end{array} \xrightarrow[\text{hydrolysis}]{\text{acid}}$$

$$\begin{array}{l} CH_2{-}CH{\cdot}CO_2H \\ \qquad\quad >CO \\ CH_2{-}CH{\cdot}CO_2H \end{array} \xrightarrow{\text{heat}} \begin{array}{l} CH_2{-}CH_2 \\ \qquad\quad >CO \\ CH_2{-}CH_2 \end{array}$$

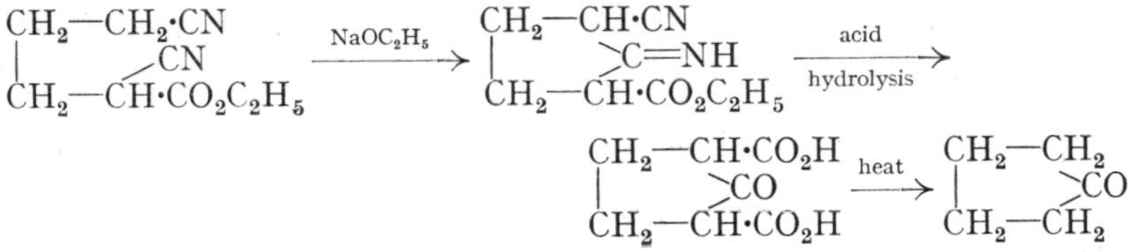

Dicyano-compounds have also been used to prepare large ring compounds (p. 469).

7. (i) Hydroxy-cyclic compounds may be prepared by reducing certain diketones with magnesium amalgam; the reaction is a pinacol reduction (*cf.* p. 151). *E.g.*, heptane-2 : 6-dione forms 1 : 2-dimethyl*cyclo*pentane-1 : 2-diol:

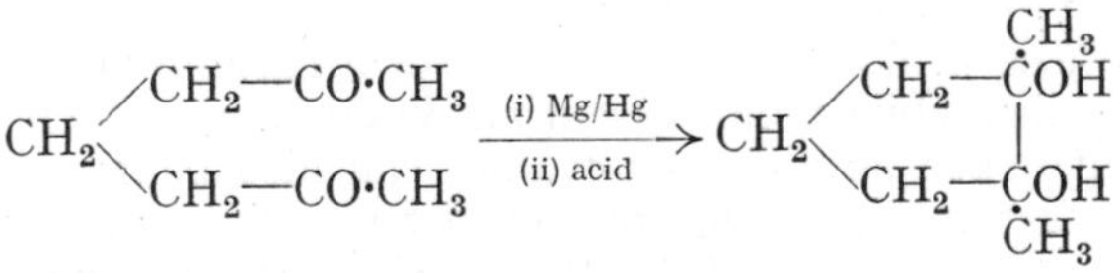

$$CH_2\begin{array}{l} \diagup CH_2{-}CO{\cdot}CH_3 \\ \diagdown CH_2{-}CO{\cdot}CH_3 \end{array} \xrightarrow[\text{(ii) acid}]{\text{(i) Mg/Hg}} CH_2\begin{array}{l} \diagup CH_2{-}C(CH_3)OH \\ \diagdown CH_2{-}C(CH_3)OH \end{array}$$

(ii) Hydroxycyclic compounds may also be prepared by an *intramolecular* Grignard reaction on certain bromo-ketones; *e.g.*, when treated with magnesium in ethereal solution, 6-bromohexan-2-one forms the corresponding Grignard reagent which, due to the proximity of the carbonyl group, undergoes intramolecular reaction to form a cyclic compound:

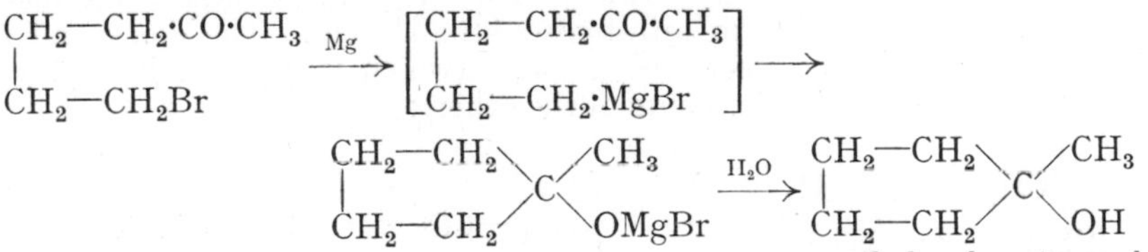

$$\begin{array}{l} CH_2{-}CH_2{\cdot}CO{\cdot}CH_3 \\ CH_2{-}CH_2Br \end{array} \xrightarrow{Mg} \left[\begin{array}{l} CH_2{-}CH_2{\cdot}CO{\cdot}CH_3 \\ CH_2{-}CH_2{\cdot}MgBr \end{array}\right] \longrightarrow$$

$$\begin{array}{l} CH_2{-}CH_2\diagdown \\ CH_2{-}CH_2\diagup \end{array} C \begin{array}{l} \diagup CH_3 \\ \diagdown OMgBr \end{array} \xrightarrow{H_2O} \begin{array}{l} CH_2{-}CH_2\diagdown \\ CH_2{-}CH_2\diagup \end{array} C \begin{array}{l} \diagup CH_3 \\ \diagdown OH \end{array}$$

1-methyl-*cyclo*pentan-1-ol

Methods (i) and (ii) work very well for the preparation of *five-* and *six-*membered rings. The reason for this will be discussed later (p. 463), where it will also be seen why the Dieckmann reaction is limited to the formation of 5-, 6- and 7-membered rings.

8. **Diels–Alder Reaction** or **Diene–Synthesis** (1928). A simple example of the Diels–Alder reaction is the addition to a conjugated diene of an ethylenic compound in which the double bond is adjacent to a carbonyl group; *e.g.*, butadiene combines with acraldehyde at 100° to form tetrahydrobenzaldehyde:

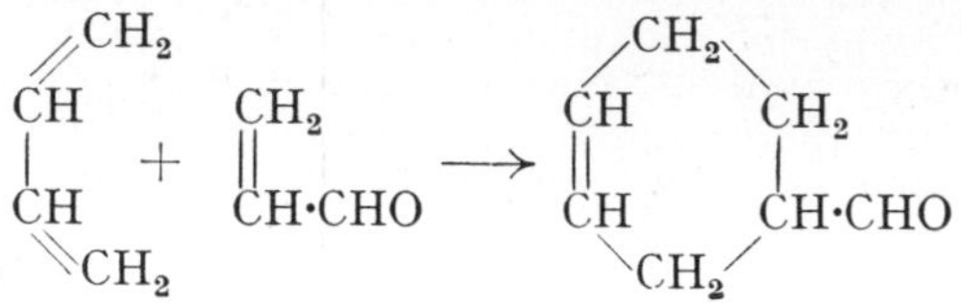

$$\begin{array}{l} CH_2 \\ \| \\ CH \\ | \\ CH \\ \| \\ CH_2 \end{array} + \begin{array}{l} CH_2 \\ \| \\ CH{\cdot}CHO \end{array} \longrightarrow \begin{array}{ccc} & CH_2 & \\ CH & & CH_2 \\ \| & & | \\ CH & & CH{\cdot}CHO \\ & CH_2 & \end{array}$$

In general, the diene synthesis is the following type of condensation:

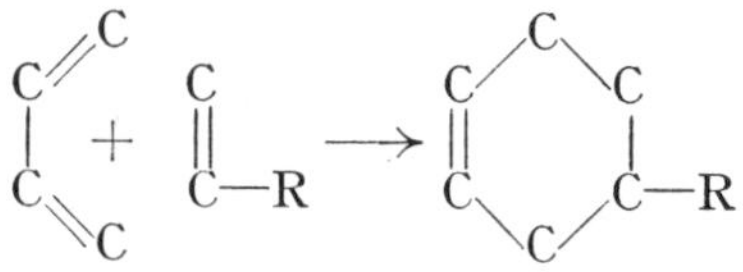

$$\begin{array}{l} C{=}C \\ | \\ C{=}C \end{array} + \begin{array}{l} C \\ \| \\ C{-}R \end{array} \longrightarrow \begin{array}{ccc} & C & \\ C & & C \\ \| & & | \\ C & & C{-}R \\ & C & \end{array}$$

and

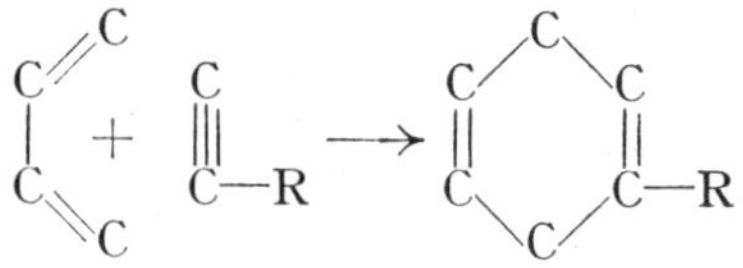

$$\begin{array}{l} C{=}C \\ | \\ C{=}C \\ \text{A} \end{array} + \begin{array}{l} C \\ \| \! | \\ C{-}R \\ \text{B} \end{array} \longrightarrow \begin{array}{ccc} & C & \\ C & & C \\ \| & & \| \\ C & & C{-}R \\ & C & \end{array}$$

Compound A is usually referred to as the **diene** (whether it be a conjugated diene, polyene, enyne or diyne), and compound B is usually referred to as the **dienophile.** R is usually a group which contains a carbonyl group attached to one of the ethylenic or acetylenic carbon atoms, *i.e.*, the dienophile is usually an αβ-unsaturated carbonyl compound, *e.g.* αβ-unsaturated acids, acid anhydrides, esters, aldehydes or ketones; the dienophile may also be a quinone (see p. 698). The presence of a carbonyl group (a negative group) in the dienophile is not essential: compounds which contain other negative groups such as nitro- or cyano-, can also behave as dienophiles. In certain cases, the dienophile may even be an unsaturated hydrocarbon (see p. 477). Nevertheless, the diene synthesis takes place most readily when the dienophile contains a carbonyl group, and the most useful dienophile is *maleic anhydride*.

The compound formed by the condensation of A with B is known as the **adduct.** The adduct is always a six-membered ring, the addition taking place in the 1 : 4-positions (see also below). The mechanism of the diene synthesis is uncertain; it may possibly be as follows. Butadiene and maleic anhydride condense to form tetrahydrophthalic acid. The diene and the dienophile undergo the electromeric effect (which is brought into play in each molecule at the requirements of the other):

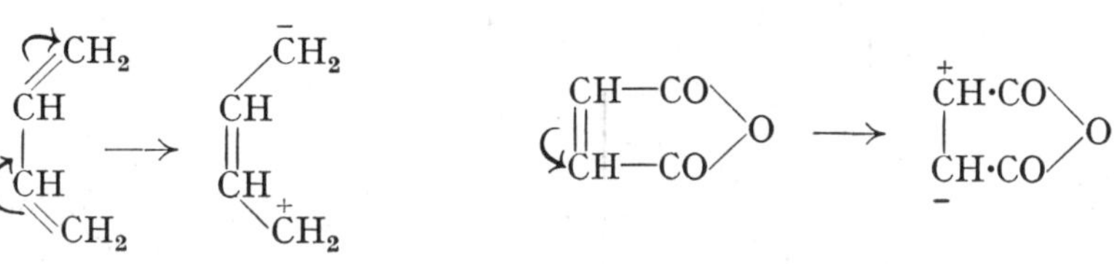

$$\begin{array}{l} CH_2 \\ \| \\ CH \\ | \\ CH \\ \| \\ CH_2 \end{array} \longrightarrow \begin{array}{l} \overset{-}{C}H_2 \\ | \\ CH \\ \| \\ CH \\ | \\ \overset{+}{C}H_2 \end{array} \qquad \begin{array}{l} CH{-}CO \\ \| \qquad\quad \rangle O \\ CH{-}CO \end{array} \longrightarrow \begin{array}{l} \overset{+}{C}H{\cdot}CO \\ | \qquad\quad \rangle O \\ \underset{-}{C}H{\cdot}CO \end{array}$$

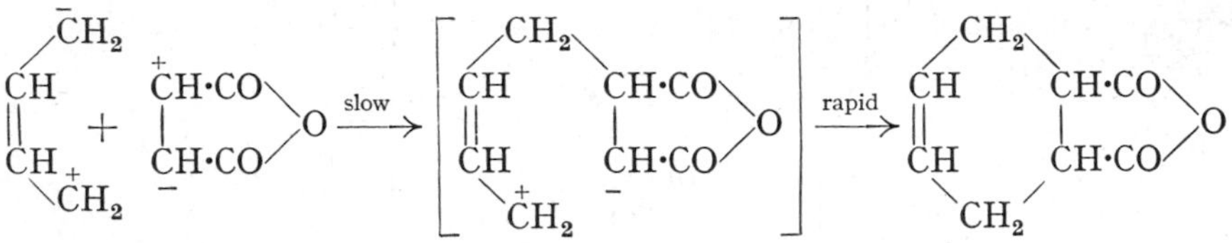

$$\begin{matrix} \overset{-}{C}H_2 \\ CH \\ \| \\ CH_+ \\ CH_2 \end{matrix} + \begin{matrix} \overset{+}{C}H\cdot CO \\ | \\ \underset{-}{C}H\cdot CO \end{matrix}\!\!>O \xrightarrow{\text{slow}} \left[\begin{matrix} CH_2 \\ CH \quad CH\cdot CO \\ \| \quad\quad | \\ CH \quad CH\cdot CO \\ \overset{+}{C}H_2 \quad - \end{matrix} \!\!>O \right] \xrightarrow{\text{rapid}} \begin{matrix} CH_2 \\ CH \quad CH\cdot CO \\ \| \quad\quad | \\ CH \quad CH\cdot CO \\ CH_2 \end{matrix}\!\!>O$$

By a similar mechanism one can explain the formation from isoprene and acraldehyde of methyltetrahydrobenzaldehyde in which the methyl group is in the 4-position:

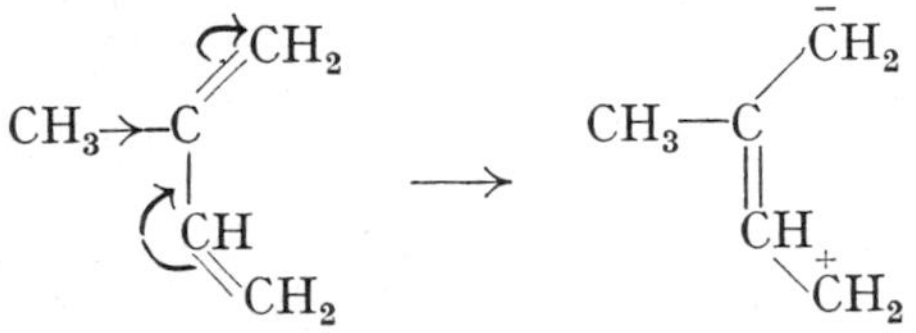

$$CH_3 \rightarrow C(=CH_2)-CH=CH_2 \longrightarrow CH_3-C(\overset{-}{C}H_2)=CH-\overset{+}{C}H_2$$

Owing to the electron repelling effect of a methyl group, isoprene undergoes the electromeric effect as shown above, and not in the opposite direction as shown below:

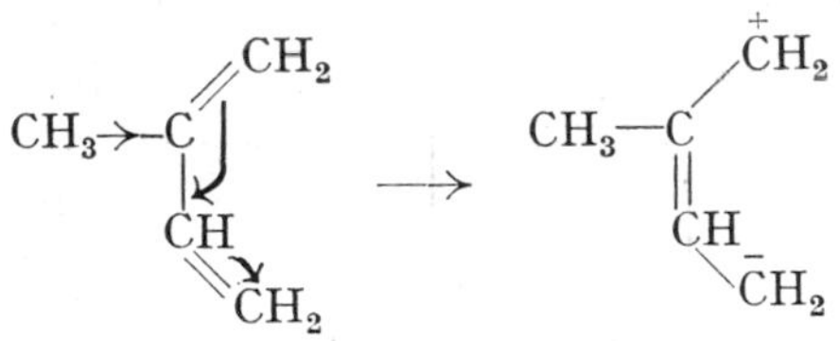

$$CH_3 \rightarrow C(=CH_2)-CH=CH_2 \longrightarrow CH_3-C(\overset{+}{C}H_2)=CH-\overset{-}{C}H_2$$

Owing to the inductive effect of the carbonyl group, acraldehyde undergoes the electromeric effect as follows:

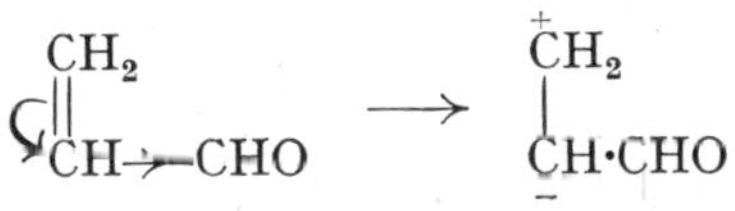

$$CH_2=CH \rightarrow CHO \longrightarrow \overset{+}{C}H_2-\underset{-}{C}H\cdot CHO$$

Condensation then takes place between the two activated molecules:

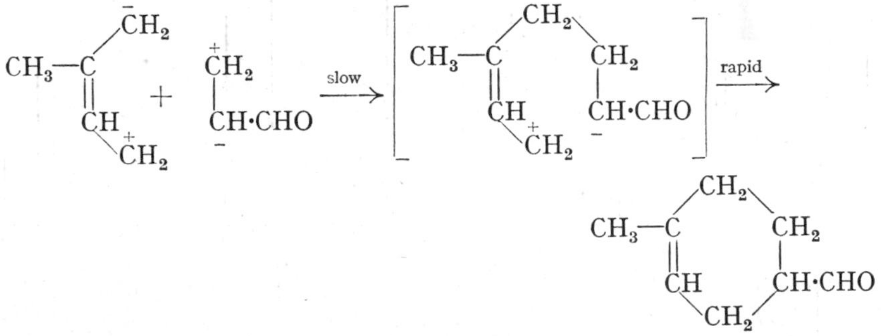

$$CH_3-C(\overset{-}{C}H_2)=CH-\overset{+}{C}H_2 + \overset{+}{C}H_2-\underset{-}{C}H\cdot CHO \xrightarrow{\text{slow}} \left[CH_3-C(CH_2-CH_2-\underset{-}{C}H\cdot CHO)=CH-\overset{+}{C}H_2 \right] \xrightarrow{\text{rapid}}$$

$$\begin{matrix} CH_2 \\ CH_3-C \quad\quad CH_2 \\ \| \quad\quad\quad | \\ CH \quad\quad CH\cdot CHO \\ CH_2 \end{matrix}$$

In addition to acyclic dienes, cyclic and semi-cyclic compounds containing two double bonds in conjugation may also act as dienes, *e.g.*,

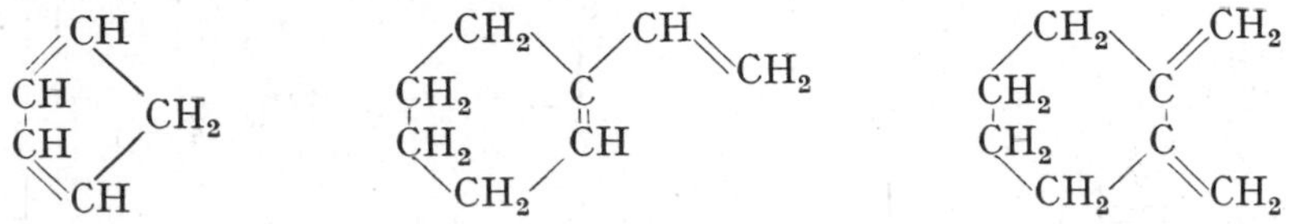

$$\begin{matrix} CH \\ CH \quad\; \\ \quad\quad CH_2 \\ CH \quad\; \\ CH \end{matrix} \qquad \begin{matrix} CH_2 \quad CH{=}CH_2 \\ CH_2 \quad C \\ CH_2 \quad CH \\ CH_2 \end{matrix} \qquad \begin{matrix} CH_2 \quad\; CH_2 \\ CH_2 \quad C \\ CH_2 \quad C \\ CH_2 \quad\; CH_2 \end{matrix}$$

With cyclic dienes it is possible to prepare *bridge-compounds*, *e.g.*, *endo-methylene*-tetrahydrophthalic anhydride (see also below):

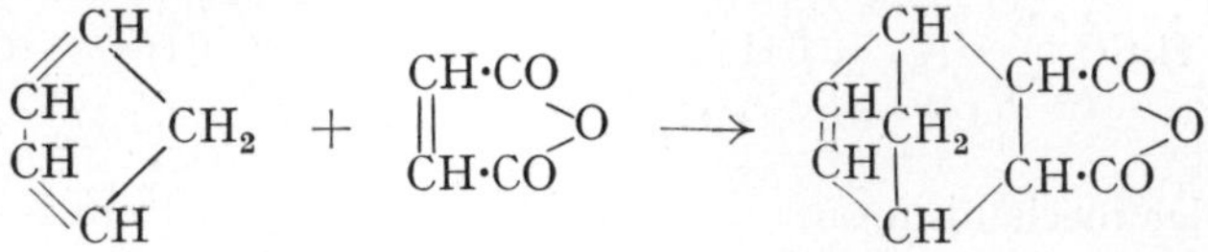

Aromatic compounds with a side-chain containing an ethylene double bond in conjugation with the ring system (*phenyl-vinyl* conjugation) can also act as dienes, *e.g.*, styrene. It also appears that only purely aromatic hydrocarbons containing at least three *linear* benzene rings can behave as dienes, *e.g.*, diphenyl does not whereas anthracene does (the dotted lines indicate the points of ring closure; see also quinol, p. 608).

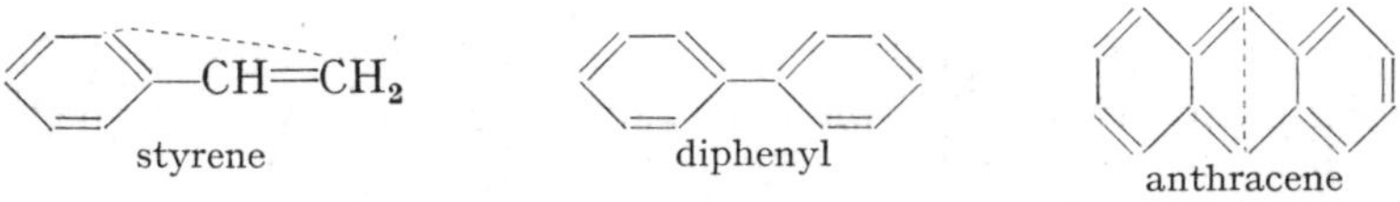

styrene diphenyl anthracene

Some heterocyclic compounds also behave as dienes in the Diels–Alder reaction to form bridged compounds which contain a hetero-atom, *e.g.*, furan condenses with maleic anhydride to form *dihydronorcantharidin*:

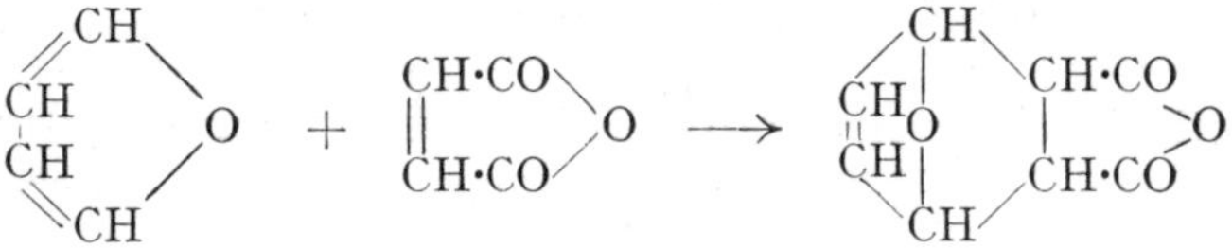

No catalyst is required for the Diels–Alder reaction, and the addition always appears to be *cis*, *i.e.*, the dienophile retains its original configuration, *e.g.*, butadiene with maleic acid gives *cis*-1 : 2 : 5 : 6-tetrahydrophthalic acid whereas with fumaric acid the corresponding *trans* compound is obtained.

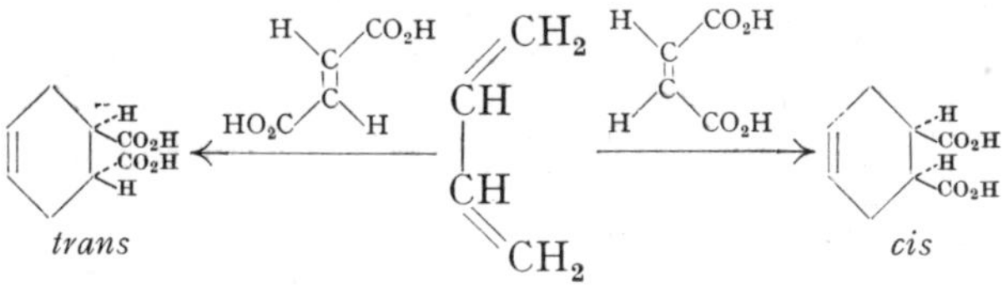

trans *cis*

It has also been found that the addition of *cis*-acids (and anhydrides) is faster than that of the corresponding *trans*-acids.

When the diene is cyclic, two adducts are possible, *endo*- and *exo*-, the dienophile still retaining its original configuration in both, *e.g.*, *cyclo*pentadiene and maleic anhydride:

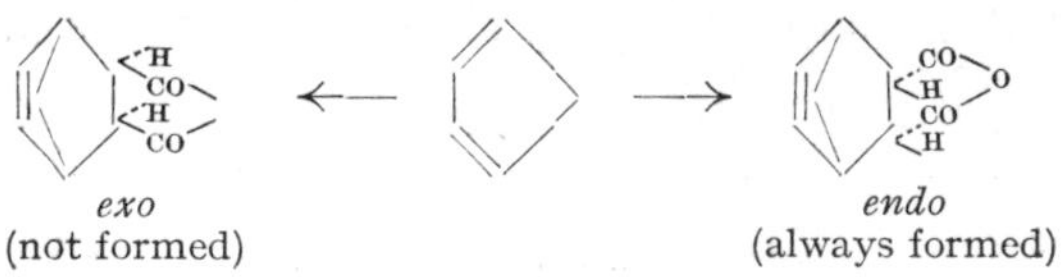

exo (not formed) *endo* (always formed)

In practice only the *endo* form is obtained.

It has now been found that acraldehyde may function as a diene, the product being a dihydropyran (Smith *et al.*, 1951); *e.g.*,

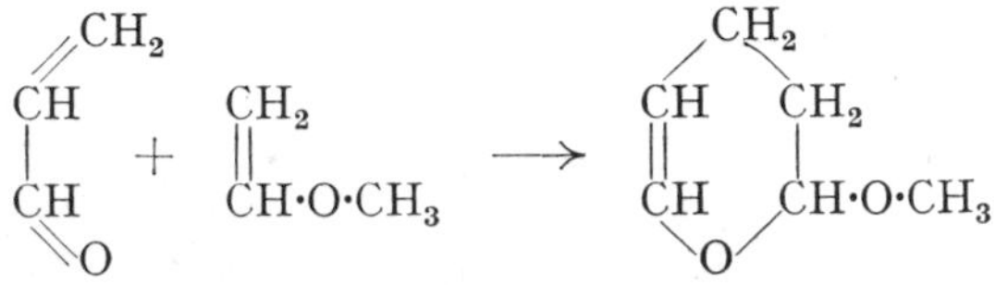

$$\begin{matrix} & CH_2 \\ & /\!/ \\ CH & \\ | & \\ CH & \\ & \backslash\!\backslash O \end{matrix} + \begin{matrix} CH_2 \\ \| \\ CH{\cdot}O{\cdot}CH_3 \end{matrix} \longrightarrow \begin{matrix} & CH_2 & \\ CH & & CH_2 \\ \| & & | \\ CH & & CH{\cdot}O{\cdot}CH_3 \\ & O & \end{matrix}$$

Recently, it has been found that maleic anhydride will also add on to *mono-olefinic* and *non-conjugated polyolefinic* acids or esters at 200–250°, *e.g.*,

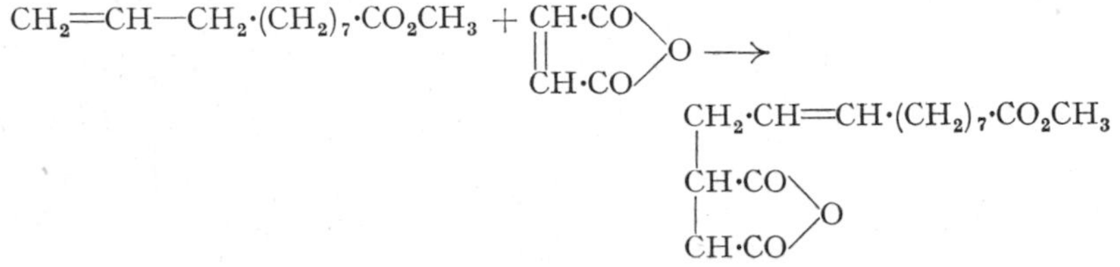

$$CH_2{=}CH{-}CH_2{\cdot}(CH_2)_7{\cdot}CO_2CH_3 + \begin{matrix} CH{\cdot}CO \\ \| \\ CH{\cdot}CO \end{matrix}\!\!>O \longrightarrow \begin{matrix} CH_2{\cdot}CH{=}CH{\cdot}(CH_2)_7{\cdot}CO_2CH_3 \\ | \\ CH{\cdot}CO \\ | \\ CH{\cdot}CO \end{matrix}\!\!>O$$

General properties of the *cyclo*paraffins. *cyclo*Paraffins usually boil at higher temperatures than the corresponding paraffins. In many chemical respects they are similar to the paraffins, but in others they are different in that the lower members form addition products with ring *fission*. Hydrogen bromide attacks *cyclo*propane to form *n*-propyl bromide, but has no effect on other *cyclo*paraffins. Hydrogen iodide attacks both *cyclo*propane and *cyclo*butane to form *n*-propyl iodide and *n*-butyl iodide, respectively; *cyclo*butane is attacked only when heated, no action taking place at room temperature. The higher *cyclo*paraffins are not affected by hydrogen iodide in the cold or on moderate heating. Bromine attacks *cyclo*propane to form 1 : 3-dibromopropane; the higher members form *cyclo-substituted* products with bromine. When heated with hydrogen in the presence of nickel at 80°, *cyclo*propane is converted into propane; *cyclo*butane yields *n*-butane at 120°, and *cyclo*pentane yields *n*-pentane at 300°. The higher *cyclo*paraffins are not attacked by hydrogen in the presence of nickel. All the foregoing reactions indicate that the stability of the ring increases as the ring becomes larger.

Generally, derivatives of the *cyclo*paraffins very closely resemble the paraffins in those properties which do not involve ring fission, *e.g.*, cyclic acids may be converted into esters, acid chlorides, acid amides, etc.; cyclic ketones may be reduced to cyclic alcohols, etc. Owing to the presence of the ring, however, various derivatives of the *cyclo*paraffins are capable of exhibiting geometrical isomerism (see, *e.g.*, *cyclo*propane).

Opening of rings. Three- and four-membered rings may readily be opened by means of hydrogen iodide or by catalytic reduction. The rings of higher members may be opened by oxidation of the cyclic alcohol, or ketone, or *cyclo*olefin, and in some cases, by the oxidation of the *cyclo*alkane itself.

Changing the size of rings. On treatment with particular reagents, certain derivatives of the *cyclo*paraffins undergo rearrangement, the ring becoming either smaller or larger (see, *e.g.*, *cyclo*butylamine and *cyclo*pentanone, below).

Acetoxylation of the double bond in *cyclo*olefins. Lead tetra-acetate attacks double bonds in *cyclo*-olefins to form 1 : 2-diacetates, the addition products usually being a mixture of the *cis* and *trans* compounds, *e.g.*, *cyclo*hexene forms a mixture of *cis*- and *trans*-*cyclo*hexanediol

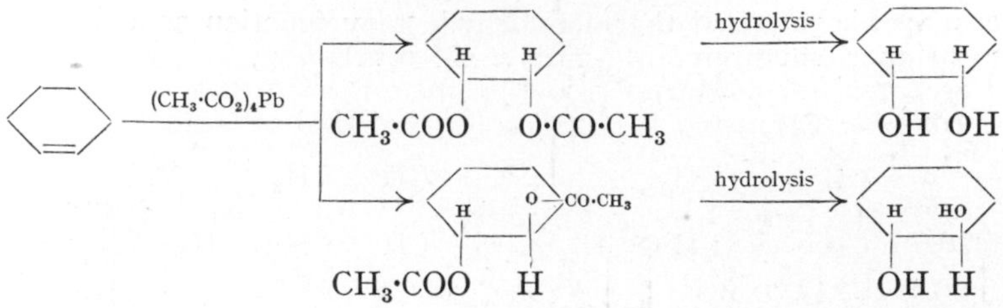

$$\text{cyclohexene} \xrightarrow{(CH_3\cdot CO_2)_4Pb} \begin{cases} cis\text{-}CH_3\cdot COO\text{—}C_6H_{10}\text{—}O\cdot CO\cdot CH_3 \xrightarrow{\text{hydrolysis}} cis\text{-}HO\text{—}C_6H_{10}\text{—}OH \\ trans\text{-}CH_3\cdot COO\text{—}C_6H_{10}\text{—}O\cdot CO\cdot CH_3 \xrightarrow{\text{hydrolysis}} trans\text{-}HO\text{—}C_6H_{10}\text{—}OH \end{cases}$$

***cyclo*Propane,** b.p. $-34°$, may be prepared by the action of zinc on trimethylene bromide (p. 446). A recent method of preparation is to chlorinate propane, separate the 1 : 3 -dichloro-isomer, and close the ring by means of zinc dust and sodium iodide.

*cyclo*Propane is one of the best anæsthetics known. When heated to a high temperature, preferably in the presence of a catalyst, *e.g.*, platinum, *cyclo*propane is converted into propylene.

*cyclo*Propane derivatives may be prepared by the action of diazomethane on ethylenic compounds; the pyrazoline compounds formed eliminate nitrogen when heated with copper powder to form *cyclo*propane derivatives, *e.g.*,

$$\underset{\text{ethyl maleate}}{\overset{CH\cdot CO_2C_2H_5}{\underset{CH\cdot CO_2C_2H_5}{\|}}} + CH_2N_2 \longrightarrow \begin{array}{l} CH_2\text{—}CH\cdot CO_2C_2H_5 \\ |\qquad\quad | \\ NH\quad C\cdot CO_2C_2H_5 \\ \quad\diagdown N \diagup\!\!\diagup \end{array} \xrightarrow{Cu} CH_2\!\!<\!\!\begin{array}{l} CH\cdot CO_2C_2H_5 \\ | \\ CH\cdot CO_2C_2H_5 \end{array} + N_2$$

Many *cyclo*propanecarboxylic acids are known; some exhibit geometrical and optical isomerism, *e.g.*, *cyclo*propane-1 : 2-dicarboxylic acid exists in the *cis*-form (optically inactive; it has a plane of symmetry) and the *trans*-form which is optically active (it has neither a plane nor a centre of symmetry):

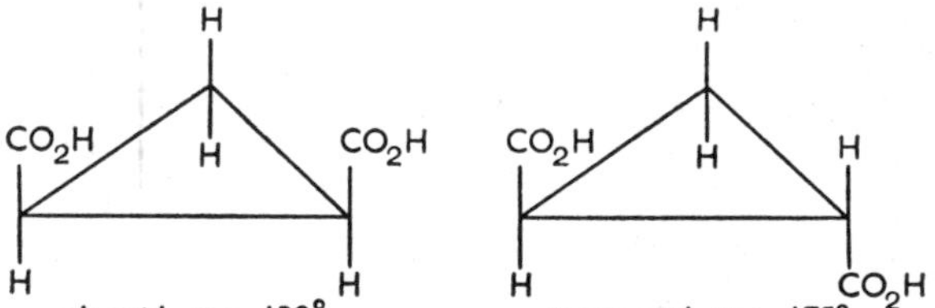

cis acid, m.p. 139° — ring carbons bearing CO_2H (up) and H (down) on each of C-1 and C-2; CH_2 at the apex.

trans acid, m.p. 175° — C-1: CO_2H (up), H (down); C-2: H (up), CO_2H (down); CH_2 at the apex.

***cyclo*Propylamine,** b.p. 50°, on treatment with nitrous acid forms allyl alcohol instead of the expected *cyclo*propanol (see *cyclo*butylamine, below):

$$\begin{array}{l} CH_2 \\ | \\ CH_2 \end{array}\!\!>\!CH\cdot NH_2 + HNO_2 \longrightarrow CH_2\!=\!CH\cdot CH_2OH + N_2 + H_2O$$

*cyclo*Propanol has not yet been prepared in a pure form; it readily re-arranges to propionaldehyde. It has been prepared in a crude form by several methods (Roberts *et al.*, 1951), *e.g.*,

$$\begin{array}{l} CH_2 \\ | \\ CH_2 \end{array}\!\!>\!CHCl \xrightarrow{Mg} \begin{array}{l} CH_2 \\ | \\ CH_2 \end{array}\!\!>\!CHMgCl \xrightarrow[(ii)\ H_2O]{(i)\ O_2} \begin{array}{l} CH_2 \\ | \\ CH_2 \end{array}\!\!>\!CHOH$$

***cyclo*Butane,** b.p. $-15°$. *cyclo*Butane derivatives may be prepared by means of the malonic ester synthesis, and by polymerising certain ketens (p. 272). Curiously enough, it appears that *cyclo*butane cannot be prepared by ring closure of 1 : 4-dihalogen derivatives of *n*-butane (this is contrary to expectation by Baeyer's Strain Theory, p. 463). Many derivatives of *cyclo*butane were known long before the parent hydrocarbon was obtained. This was first prepared by Willstätter (1907) by the following laborious process, using the *Hofmann exhaustive methylation reaction* (p. 732):

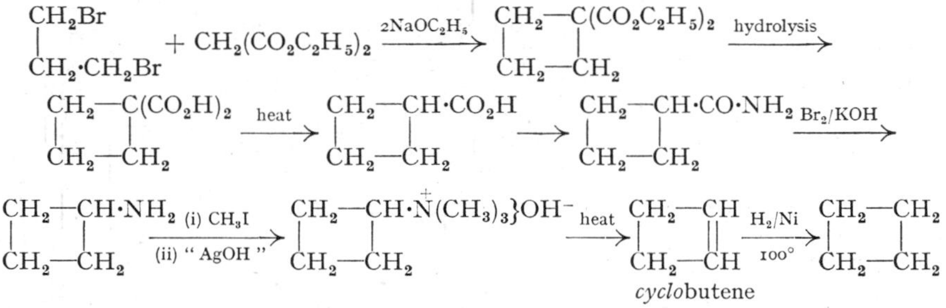

$$\begin{array}{l} CH_2Br \\ | \\ CH_2{\cdot}CH_2Br \end{array} + CH_2(CO_2C_2H_5)_2 \xrightarrow{2NaOC_2H_5} \begin{array}{l} CH_2-C(CO_2C_2H_5)_2 \\ |\qquad\quad | \\ CH_2-CH_2 \end{array} \xrightarrow{\text{hydrolysis}}$$

$$\begin{array}{l} CH_2-C(CO_2H)_2 \\ |\qquad\quad | \\ CH_2-CH_2 \end{array} \xrightarrow{\text{heat}} \begin{array}{l} CH_2-CH{\cdot}CO_2H \\ |\qquad\quad | \\ CH_2-CH_2 \end{array} \longrightarrow \begin{array}{l} CH_2-CH{\cdot}CO{\cdot}NH_2 \\ |\qquad\quad | \\ CH_2-CH_2 \end{array} \xrightarrow{Br_2/KOH}$$

$$\begin{array}{l} CH_2-CH{\cdot}NH_2 \\ |\qquad\quad | \\ CH_2-CH_2 \end{array} \xrightarrow[\text{(ii) “AgOH”}]{\text{(i) } CH_3I} \begin{array}{l} CH_2-CH{\cdot}\overset{+}{N}(CH_3)_3\}OH^- \\ |\qquad\quad | \\ CH_2-CH_2 \end{array} \xrightarrow{\text{heat}} \begin{array}{l} CH_2-CH \\ |\qquad\quad \| \\ CH_2-CH \end{array} \xrightarrow[100^\circ]{H_2/Ni} \begin{array}{l} CH_2-CH_2 \\ |\qquad\quad | \\ CH_2-CH_2 \end{array}$$

*cyclo*butene

***cyclo*Propene** has been prepared in a similar manner from *cyclo*propylamine.

Pines *et al.* (1953) have prepared *cyclo*butane from *cyclo*butanecarboxylic acid as follows:

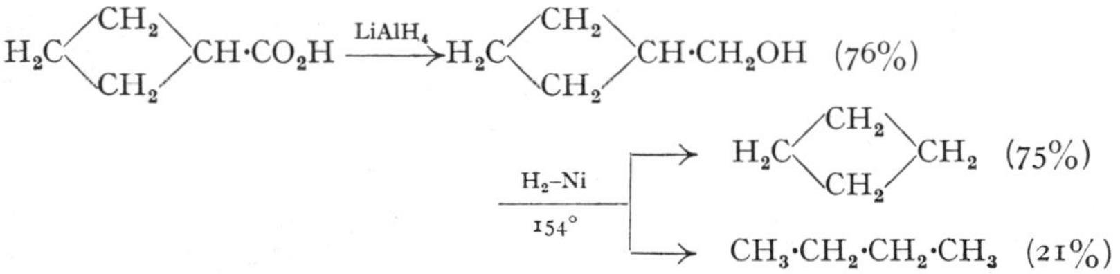

$$H_2C\langle{}^{CH_2}_{CH_2}\rangle CH{\cdot}CO_2H \xrightarrow{LiAlH_4} H_2C\langle{}^{CH_2}_{CH_2}\rangle CH{\cdot}CH_2OH \quad (76\%)$$

$$\xrightarrow[154^\circ]{H_2\text{–}Ni} \begin{cases} H_2C\langle{}^{CH_2}_{CH_2}\rangle CH_2 \quad (75\%) \\ CH_3{\cdot}CH_2{\cdot}CH_2{\cdot}CH_3 \quad (21\%) \end{cases}$$

***cyclo*Butene,** b.p. 2°, shows the ordinary olefinic reactions. Willstätter was unable to convert *cyclo*butene into *cyclo*butadiene, $\begin{array}{l} CH-CH \\ \|\qquad \| \\ CH-CH \end{array}$. The existence of this compound is doubtful; if it does exist, it is very unstable. On the other hand, the following *aromatic* derivatives of *cyclo*butadiene are known: diphenylene (I; Lothrop, 1941), di-2 : 3-naphthylene (II; Curtis *et al.*, 1954), and di-1 : 2-naphthylene (III; Cava *et al.*, 1955).

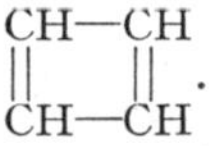

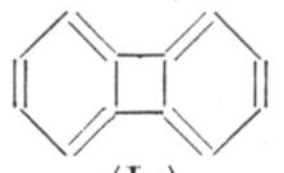

(I*a*) 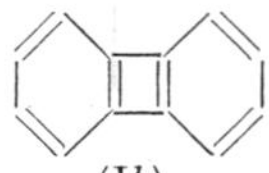 (I*b*) 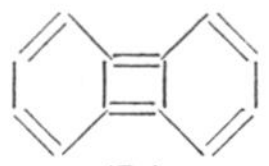 (I*c*)

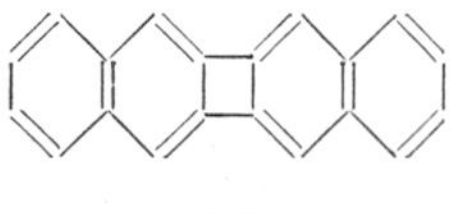

(II) 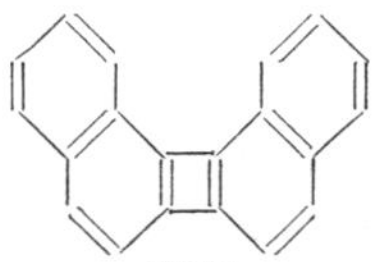 (III) 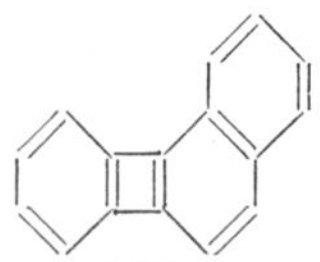 (IV) 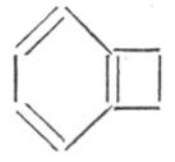 (V)

(I) and (II) are pale yellow in colour and stable thermally, but (III) is red and resinifies on heating. It might be noted that three resonating structures are possible for diphenylene, but only two can be regarded as *cyclo*butadiene derivatives, *viz.*, (I*b*) and (I*c*); (I*a*) is a *cyclo*butane derivative. Cava *et al.* (1956) have prepared (IV) and (V) (the latter is a *cyclo*butene derivative).

***cyclo*Butylamine,** b.p. 82°, when treated with nitrous acid, gives a mixture of *cyclo*butanol and *cyclo*propylcarbinol, the latter being produced by ring contraction:

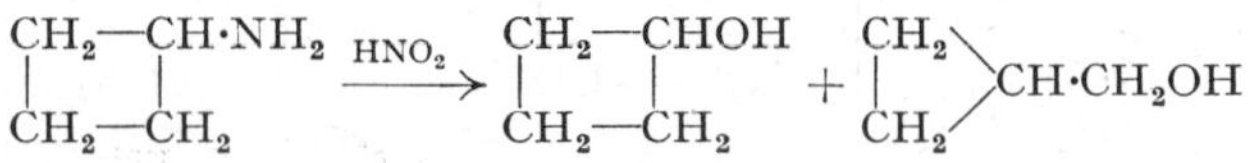

$$\begin{array}{l} CH_2-CH{\cdot}NH_2 \\ |\qquad\quad | \\ CH_2-CH_2 \end{array} \xrightarrow{HNO_2} \begin{array}{l} CH_2-CHOH \\ |\qquad\quad | \\ CH_2-CH_2 \end{array} + \begin{array}{l} CH_2 \\ | \\ CH_2 \end{array}\rangle CH{\cdot}CH_2OH$$

This rearrangement of cyclic amines is known as the **Demjanov rearrangement** (1903).

If *cyclo*butylmethylamine is treated with nitrous acid, ring expansion by the Demjanov rearrangement takes place; four products are obtained: *cyclo*butylcarbinol, methylene*cyclo*butane, *cyclo*pentanol and *cyclo*pentene:

$$\begin{array}{l} CH_2—CH{\cdot}CH_2{\cdot}NH_2 \\ |\qquad\quad | \\ CH_2—CH_2 \end{array} \xrightarrow{HNO_2} \begin{array}{l} CH_2—CH{\cdot}CH_2OH \\ |\qquad\quad | \\ CH_2—CH_2 \end{array} + \begin{array}{l} CH_2—C{:}CH_2 \\ |\qquad\ \ | \\ CH_2—CH_2 \end{array}$$

$$+ \begin{array}{l} CH_2—CH_2\diagdown \\ |\qquad\qquad\quad CHOH \\ CH_2—CH_2\diagup \end{array} + \begin{array}{l} CH_2—CH_2\diagdown \\ |\qquad\qquad\quad CH \\ CH_2—CH\diagup\!\!\diagup \end{array}$$

*cyclo*Propylmethylamine and some larger ring amines behave in a similar manner, and so by means of the Demjanov rearrangement it is possible to prepare seven- and eight-membered rings.

The mechanism of the Demjanov rearrangement probably involves a carbonium ion which then undergoes rearrangement (by the Whitmore mechanism, p. 160).

$$\begin{array}{l} CH_2—CH{\cdot}CH_2{\cdot}NH_2 \\ |\qquad\quad | \\ CH_2—CH_2 \end{array} \xrightarrow{HNO_2} \begin{array}{l} CH_2—CH{\cdot}CH_2—\overset{+}{N}{\equiv}N \\ |\qquad\quad | \\ CH_2—CH_2 \end{array}$$

$$\downarrow -N_2$$

$$\begin{array}{l} CH_2—CH{\cdot}CH_2OH \\ |\qquad\quad | \\ CH_2—CH_2 \end{array} \xleftarrow{OH^-} \begin{array}{l} CH_2—CH{\cdot}\overset{+}{C}H_2 \\ |\qquad\quad | \\ CH_2—CH_2 \end{array} \xrightarrow{-H^+} \begin{array}{l} CH_2—C{=}CH_2 \\ |\qquad\ \ | \\ CH_2—CH_2 \end{array}$$

$$\downarrow$$

$$\begin{array}{l} CH_2—CHOH \\ |\qquad\qquad\ \ CH_2 \\ CH_2—CH_2 \end{array} \xleftarrow{OH^-} \begin{array}{l} CH_2—\overset{+}{C}H\diagdown \\ |\qquad\qquad\quad CH_2 \\ CH_2—CH_2\diagup \end{array} \xrightarrow{-H^+} \begin{array}{l} CH_2—CH\diagdown\!\!\diagdown \\ |\qquad\qquad\quad CH \\ CH_2—CH_2\diagup \end{array}$$

This mechanism can also be used to explain the formation (as the main product) of *cyclo*pentyl bromide by the action of hydrobromic acid on *cyclo*butylmethanol.

$$\begin{array}{l} CH_2—CH{\cdot}CH_2OH \\ |\qquad\quad | \\ CH_2—CH_2 \end{array} \xrightarrow{HBr} \begin{array}{l} CH_2—CH{\cdot}CH_2\overset{+}{O}H_2 \\ |\qquad\quad | \\ CH_2—CH_2 \end{array} \xrightarrow{-H_2O}$$

$$\begin{array}{l} CH_2—CH{\cdot}\overset{+}{C}H_2 \\ |\qquad\quad | \\ CH_2—CH_2 \end{array} \longrightarrow \begin{array}{l} CH_2—\overset{+}{C}H\diagdown \\ |\qquad\qquad\quad CH_2 \\ CH_2—CH_2\diagup \end{array} \xrightarrow{Br^-} \begin{array}{l} CH_2—CHBr \\ |\qquad\qquad\ \ CH_2 \\ CH_2—CH_2 \end{array}$$

***cyclo*Pentane,** b.p. 50°, may be prepared by cyclising 1 : 5-dibromopentane with zinc or, better, by reducing *cyclo*pentanone by the Clemmensen method.

Methyl*cyclo*pentane, $\begin{array}{l} CH_2—CH_2\diagdown \\ |\qquad\qquad\quad CH{\cdot}CH_3 \\ CH_2—CH_2\diagup \end{array}$, b.p. 72°, is an interesting compound in that when heated above 450° in the presence of chromic oxide, it rearranges to *cyclo*hexane.

*cyclo*Pentanone, b.p. 130°, when treated with diazomethane, undergoes ring expansion to form *cyclo*hexanone:

$$\begin{array}{l} CH_2—CH_2\diagdown \\ |\qquad\qquad\quad CO \\ CH_2—CH_2\diagup \end{array} + CH_2N_2 \longrightarrow CH_2\begin{array}{l} \diagup CH_2—CH_2\diagdown \\ \qquad\qquad\qquad\quad CO \\ \diagdown CH_2—CH_2\diagup \end{array} + N_2$$

This reaction has been used to prepare seven- to ten-membered cyclic ketones (Kohler *et al.*, 1939). The mechanism is possibly:

$$(CH_2)_n C{=}O + \overset{-}{:}CH_2{-}\overset{+}{N}{\equiv}N \longrightarrow (CH_2)_n C\begin{array}{l} \diagup CH_2{-}\overset{+}{N}{\equiv}N \\ \diagdown \overset{-}{O} \end{array} \xrightarrow{-N_2}$$

$$(CH_2)_n C\begin{array}{l} \diagup \overset{+}{C}H_2 \\ \diagdown \overset{-}{O} \end{array} \longrightarrow (CH_2)_n\begin{array}{l} \diagup CH_2 \\ \quad | \\ \diagdown \overset{+}{C}{-}\overset{-}{O} \end{array} \longleftrightarrow (CH_2)_n\begin{array}{l} \diagup CH_2 \\ \quad | \\ \diagdown C{=}O \end{array}$$

*cyclo*Pentanone (and other cyclic ketones) undergoes the Knoevenagel reaction (p. 263) *with formation of the double bond in the ring, e.g.,*

$$\begin{array}{l} CH_2{-}CH_2 \diagdown \\ | \qquad\qquad\quad CO \\ CH_2{-}CH_2 \diagup \end{array} + CH_2\begin{array}{l} \diagup CN \\ \diagdown CO_2C_2H_5 \end{array} \longrightarrow \begin{array}{l} CH_2{-}CH_2 \diagdown \\ | \qquad\qquad\quad C{-}CH\begin{array}{l} \diagup CN \\ \diagdown CO_2C_2H_5 \end{array} \\ CH_2{-}CH \diagup\!\!\diagup \end{array}$$

***cyclo*Pentene,** b.p. 45°, may be prepared by dehydrating *cyclo*pentanol or by heating *cyclo*pentyl bromide with ethanolic potassium hydroxide.

Some *cyclo*pentene derivatives of the fatty acids are very important, since they are useful in the treatment of leprosy and tuberculosis. Two acids, which occur in chaulmoogra oil, have been used from early times in the treatment of leprosy; both acids are optically active, the naturally occurring form being the (+):

$$\begin{array}{l} CH{=}CH \diagdown \\ | \qquad\qquad\quad CH{\cdot}(CH_2)_{10}{\cdot}CO_2H \\ CH_2{-}CH_2 \diagup \end{array} \qquad \begin{array}{l} CH{=}CH \diagdown \\ | \qquad\qquad\quad CH{\cdot}(CH_2)_{12}{\cdot}CO_2H \\ CH_2{-}CH_2 \diagup \end{array}$$

hydnocarpic acid, m.p. 60°   *chaulmoogric acid*, m.p. 68°

***cyclo*Pentadiene,** b.p. 41°, is found in the crude benzene that is obtained from coal tar. It readily polymerises at room temperature into the dimer, di*cyclo*pentadiene; at high temperature it forms high polymers. The hydrogen atoms of the methylene group are very reactive, *e.g.*, *cyclo*pentadiene reacts with Grignard reagents to form a hydrocarbon and *cyclo*pentadienylmagnesium halide:

$$\begin{array}{l} CH{=}CH \diagdown \\ | \qquad\qquad\quad CH_2 \\ CH{=}CH \diagup \end{array} + RMgX \longrightarrow \begin{array}{l} CH{=}CH \diagdown \\ | \qquad\qquad\quad CH{\cdot}MgX \\ CH{=}CH \diagup \end{array} + RH$$

Owing to the presence of the reactive methylene group, *cyclo*pentadiene also condenses with aldehydes or ketones in the presence of sodium ethoxide to form *fulvenes*:

$$\begin{array}{l} CH{=}CH \diagdown \\ | \qquad\qquad\quad CH_2 \\ CH{=}CH \diagup \end{array} + O{=}C\begin{array}{l} \diagup R \\ \diagdown R' \end{array} \xrightarrow{NaOC_2H_5} \begin{array}{l} CH{=}CH \diagdown \\ | \qquad\qquad\quad C{=}C\begin{array}{l} \diagup R \\ \diagdown R' \end{array} \\ CH{=}CH \diagup \end{array} + H_2O$$

Fulvenes are derivatives of the unstable compound fulvene ($R = R' = H$). The fulvenes are coloured substances, the colour deepening with increase in size of the alkyl groups, R and R′.

The reactivity of the methylene group may be due to the fact that when *cyclo*pentadiene loses a proton from the methylene group, the *cyclo*pentadiene carbanion produced can behave as a resonance hybrid. The ion contains less

$$C_5H_4H_2 \xrightarrow{-H^+} [\text{ring with } \overset{\cdot\cdot}{\underset{H}{C}}{}^{-}] \longleftrightarrow [\text{ring with } :^{-} \text{ on adjacent C}, \underset{H}{C}] \longleftrightarrow [\text{ring with } ^{-}: \text{ on other adjacent C}, \underset{H}{C}]$$

energy than *cyclo*pentadiene itself (the former has acquired stabilisation due to resonance), and it is this possibility of becoming more stable that acts as the " driving force " to achieve this more stable state. It should also be noted that in the *cyclo*pentadienyl carbanion there is a sextet of electrons; this gives rise to aromatic properties (p. 485).

***cyclo*Pentadiene complexes.** Pauson *et al.* (1951) treated *cyclo*pentadienylmagnesium bromide with ferric chloride, their object being the preparation of di*cyclo*pentadienyl (*cf.* p. 342).

$$6C_5H_5MgBr + 2FeCl_3 \longrightarrow 3C_5H_5 - C_5H_5 + 2Fe + 3MgBr_2 + 3MgCl_2$$

The reaction, however, did not proceed in this manner; instead, these authors isolated di*cyclo*pentadienyliron, which is formed by the reduction of the ferric chloride to ferrous chloride, and the latter then reacting with the Grignard reagent:

$$2C_5H_5MgBr + FeCl_2 \longrightarrow (C_5H_5)_2Fe + MgBr_2 + MgCl_2$$

This iron complex was named **ferrocene** by Woodward *et al.* (1952).

Many di*cyclo*pentadienyls have now been prepared, the methods of preparation being by the use of the Grignard reaction (as shown above), by direct reaction between *cyclo*pentadiene vapour and a heated metal or metal carbonyl, or by reaction between the sodium salt of *cyclo*pentadiene and a metal halide (in tetrahydrofuran or liquid ammonia solution); *e.g.*, $(C_5H_5)_2Cr$, $(C_5H_5)_2Mn$, $(C_5H_5)_2Co$, etc. A convenient preparation of ferrocene itself is the mercuration of *cyclo*pentadiene followed by treatment of the product with iron (Isslieb *et al.*, 1956).

Originally, structure (I) was assigned to ferrocene, but the high stability of

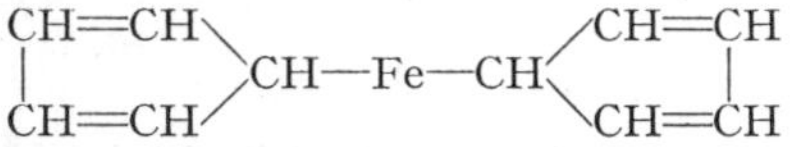

CH=CH⟩CH—Fe—CH⟨CH=CH
CH=CH   CH=CH

(I)

Fe   Fe

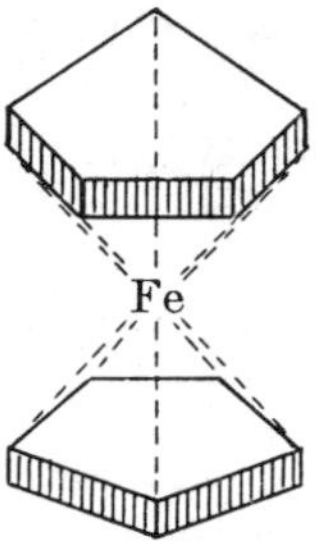

(II) 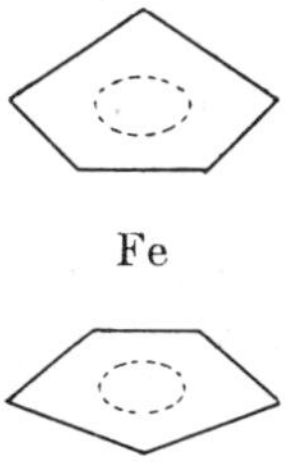   (III)

the molecule showed that this was unlikely. Ferrocene has a zero dipole moment, and the molecule is therefore symmetrical. Furthermore, the infra-red spectrum showed that all of the C—H bonds are equivalent, and so, on this evidence, structure (II) was proposed and has been confirmed by X-ray analysis, *i.e.*, that the two five-membered rings lie in parallel planes with the iron atom placed symmetrically between the two. This is a " sandwich " structure, and it is believed that the sextet of π-electrons of the *cyclo*pentadienyl carbanion (represented by the circle in III) are shared with the metal atom.

Ferrocene is an orange solid, and its reactions are aromatic, *e.g.*, it undergoes the Friedel–Crafts reaction.

***cyclo*Hexane,** b.p. 81°, occurs in petroleum. When reduced with hydrogen iodide at 250°, benzene is converted into a mixture of *cyclo*hexane and methyl*cyclo*pentane. Pure *cyclo*hexane may be conveniently prepared by the reduction of *cyclo*hexanone, and is prepared industrially by the hydrogenation of benzene in the presence of nickel at 200°. Another industrial method is the hydrogenation of phenol, dehydrating the product *cyclo*hexanol to *cyclo*hexene, which is then catalytically hydrogenated to *cyclo*hexane; the process is carried out without isolating the intermediate compounds:

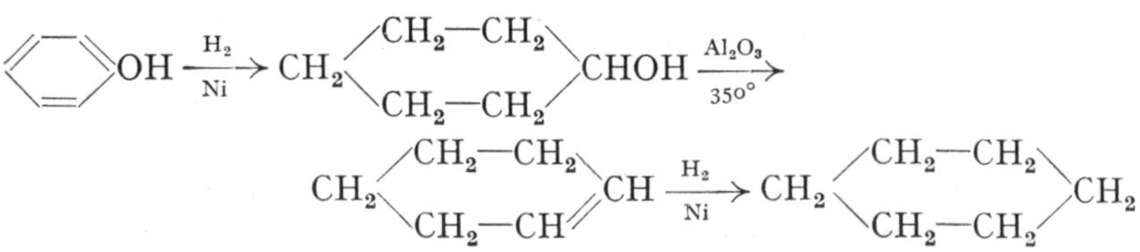

$$C_6H_5OH \xrightarrow[Ni]{H_2} CH_2\langle{}^{CH_2-CH_2}_{CH_2-CH_2}\rangle CHOH \xrightarrow[350^\circ]{Al_2O_3}$$

$$CH_2\langle{}^{CH_2-CH_2}_{CH_2-CH}\rangle CH \xrightarrow[Ni]{H_2} CH_2\langle{}^{CH_2-CH_2}_{CH_2-CH_2}\rangle CH_2$$

Many benzene derivatives may be reduced to the corresponding *cyclo*hexane compounds, and because of this, *cyclo*hexane and its derivatives are known as the **hydroaromatic compounds.** The cyclic terpenes are hydroaromatic compounds, *e.g.*,

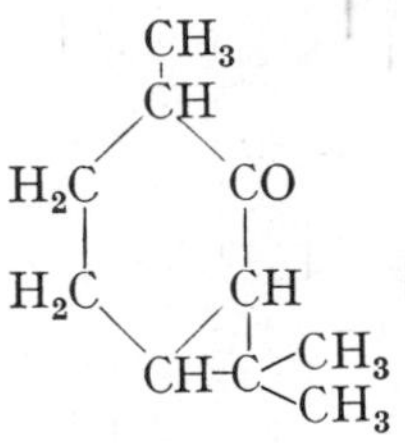

CH_3 / CH / H_2C CO / H_2C CH / $CH{-}C(CH_3)_2$

carone

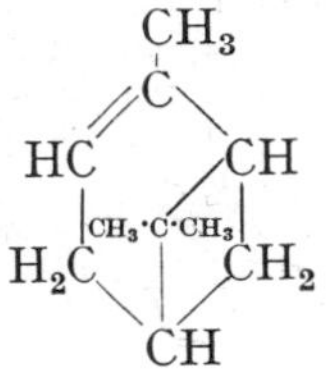

CH_3 / C / HC CH / $CH_3{\cdot}C{\cdot}CH_3$ / H_2C CH_2 / CH

α-pinene

CH_3 / C / H_2C CO / $CH_3{\cdot}C{\cdot}CH_3$ / H_2C CH_2 / CH

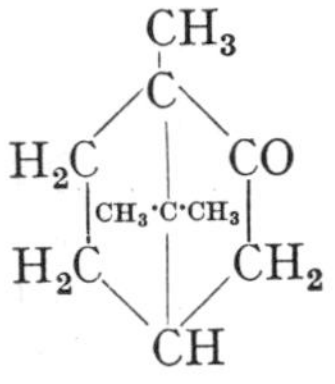

camphor

Hot concentrated nitric acid oxidises *cyclo*hexane to adipic acid, and fuming sulphuric acid converts it into benzenesulphonic acid:

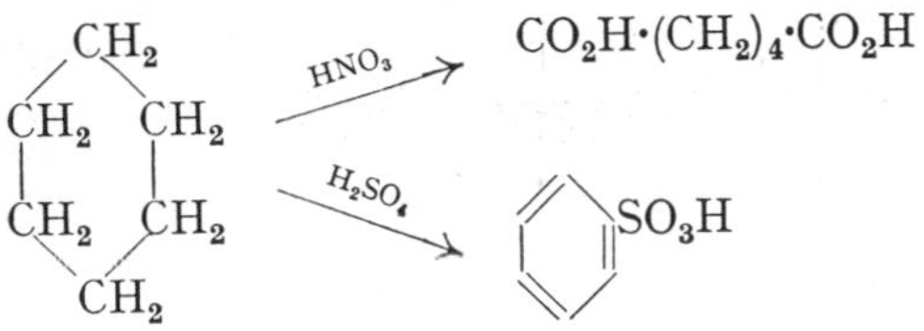

$$C_6H_{12} \xrightarrow{HNO_3} CO_2H{\cdot}(CH_2)_4{\cdot}CO_2H$$

$$C_6H_{12} \xrightarrow{H_2SO_4} C_6H_5{\cdot}SO_3H$$

For a consideration of the spatial arrangement of the carbon atoms in *cyclo*hexane, see p. 465.

***cyclo*Hexanol,** m.p. 24°, is prepared industrially by the catalytic hydrogenation of phenol. It undergoes the general reactions of an aliphatic secondary alcohol. It is converted by gentle oxidation (dilute nitric acid) into *cyclo*hexanone; vigorous oxidation (concentrated nitric acid) produces adipic acid.

***cyclo*Hexanone,** b. p. 157°, may be prepared by the oxidation of *cyclo*hexanol. α-Halogeno-*cyclo*hexanones undergo the *Favorsky reaction* when treated with alkali, *i.e.*, the six-membered ring changes to a five-membered ring carboxylic acid, *e.g.*,

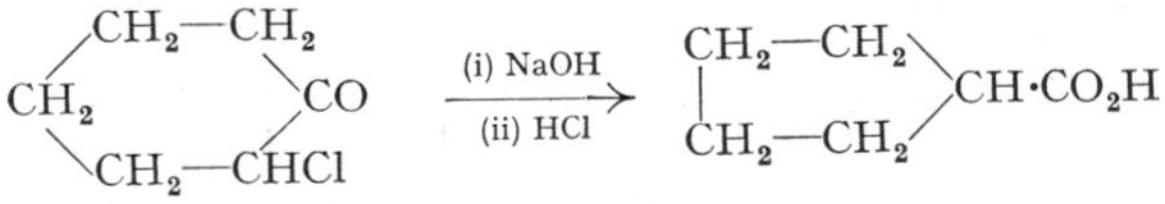

$$CH_2{<}\begin{matrix}CH_2{-}CH_2\\CH_2{-}CHCl\end{matrix}{>}CO \xrightarrow[\text{(ii) HCl}]{\text{(i) NaOH}} \begin{matrix}CH_2{-}CH_2\\CH_2{-}CH_2\end{matrix}{>}CH{\cdot}CO_2H$$

Loftfield (1951), using the isotope ^{14}C as tracer, was led to suggest the following mechanism:

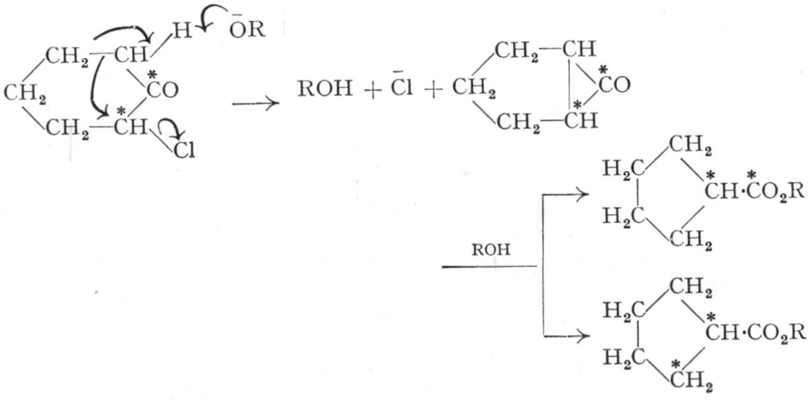

$$CH_2{<}\begin{matrix}CH_2{-}CH\\CH_2{-}CH{-}Cl\end{matrix}{>}\overset{*}{C}O \;(+\; H{-}\bar{O}R) \longrightarrow ROH + \bar{C}l + CH_2{<}\begin{matrix}CH_2{-}CH\\CH_2{-}CH\end{matrix}{>}\overset{*}{C}O$$

$$\xrightarrow{ROH} \begin{cases} H_2C{-}CH_2{-}\overset{*}{C}H{\cdot}\overset{*}{C}O_2R \ (\text{ring with } H_2C, CH_2) \\ H_2C{-}CH_2{-}\overset{*}{C}H{\cdot}CO_2R \ (\text{ring with } \overset{*}{C}H_2) \end{cases}$$

The rings of cyclic ketones may be opened by oxidation with Caro's acid to give lactones. This reaction has been used to prepare large ring lactones (p. 379).

***cyclo*Hexane-1 : 4-diol,** *quinitol*, may be prepared by the catalytic reduction of quinol (p. 607):

$$HO\langle\bigcirc\rangle OH \xrightarrow{H_2/Ni} CHOH\begin{matrix}\diagup CH_2-CH_2 \diagdown \\ \diagdown CH_2-CH_2 \diagup\end{matrix}CHOH$$

Quinitol exists in both the *cis*- and *trans*-forms:

cis-quinitol, m.p. 102°   *trans*-quinitol, m.p. 139°

Both forms are optically inactive; the *cis* has a plane of symmetry, and the *trans* a centre of symmetry.

***cyclo*Hexanepentol** (*pentahydroxy*cyclo*hexane*), $CHOH\begin{matrix}\diagup CHOH-CHOH \diagdown \\ \diagdown CHOH-CHOH \diagup\end{matrix}CH_2$, exists in a number of stereoisomeric forms. A (+)-form, m.p. 234°, occurs in acorns: this form is known as **(+)-quercitol.**

***cyclo*Hexanehexol, inositol,** *hexahydroxy*cyclo*hexane*, can exist in eight geometrical isomeric forms, of which only one is optically active (see formula). The (+)- and (−)-forms of this isomer (m.p. 248°) occur in plants as the hexaphosphoric ester, which is known as *phytin*. Some of the optically inactive forms also occur as their hexaphosphoric esters. One of the optically inactive forms is present in the vitamin B complex; it appears to have growth-promoting properties in chicks, and is an anti-alopecia factor (anti-baldness) in mice.

Hexachloro*cyclo*hexane, $C_6H_6Cl_6$, exists in a number of geometrical isomeric forms, one of which is a powerful insecticide (see p. 518).

***cyclo*Hexene** (*tetrahydrobenzene*), b.p. 83°, may conveniently be prepared by dehydrating *cyclo*hexanol with sulphuric acid. It has the usual properties of an olefin.

A number of *cyclo*hexene derivatives may be prepared by means of the Diels–Alder reaction.

Braude, Linstead *et al.* (1952–) have shown that hydrogen transfer takes place in the presence of palladium as catalyst (and below 100°) between *cyclo*hexene and a wide variety of acceptors containing a multiple bond, *e.g.*, ethylenic and acetylenic compounds, nitro-, azo- and azoxy-compounds. It is also possible to reduce only one nitro-group in compounds containing two or more, *e.g.*, *p*-dinitrobenzene to *p*-nitroaniline:

$$NO_2\langle\bigcirc\rangle NO_2 \xrightarrow{[H]} NH_2\langle\bigcirc\rangle NO_2$$

*cyclo*Hexene itself, under the above conditions, undergoes disproportionation to give benzene and *cyclo*hexane.

$$3\ \text{cyclohexene} \xrightarrow{Pd} 2\ \text{cyclohexane} + \text{benzene}$$

Thus an excess of *cyclo*hexene is required in reductions to off-set this competing disproportionation, and it has been shown that there is a direct hydrogen transfer between *cyclo*hexene and the hydrogen acceptor.

***cyclo*Hexadienes** (*dihydrobenzenes*). There are two isomeric *cyclo*hexadienes, the 1 : 3- (b.p. 81°) and the 1 : 4- (b.p. 86°). They readily polymerise and undergo the usual reactions of a diolefin. Since *cyclo*hexa-1 : 3-diene contains a conjugated system of double bonds, it can undergo both the 1 : 2- and 1 : 4-addition reactions (see p. 79).

***cyclo*Hexatriene** is **benzene,** and differs enormously in its chemical properties from the *cyclo*alkenes and *cyclo*alkadienes. Benzene has "*aromatic properties*" (see benzene, p. 479).

$$(CH_3)_2C\begin{matrix}CH_2-CO\\ CH_2-CO\end{matrix}CH_2$$

5 : 5-Dimethyl*cyclo*hexane-1 : 3-dione, dimedone, is a solid, m.p. 148°. It is a very sensitive reagent for formaldehyde, which may be estimated gravimetrically with this reagent:

$$2(CH_3)_2C\begin{matrix}CH_2-CO\\ CH_2-CO\end{matrix}CH_2 + H{\cdot}CHO \longrightarrow$$

$$(CH_3)_2C\begin{matrix}CH_2-CO\\ CH_2-CO\end{matrix}CH-CH_2-CH\begin{matrix}CO-CH_2\\ CO-CH_2\end{matrix}C(CH_3)_2 + H_2O$$

***cyclo*Heptane,** b.p. 118°, occurs in petroleum; it may be prepared by the reduction of *cyclo*heptanone.

Tropolone (*cyclo*heptatrienolone) is a cyclic α-hydroxyketone; it has a seven-membered ring containing three double bonds. Dewar (1945), who proposed its structure, also predicted that it would have *aromatic* properties, and this has now been confirmed. The tropolone system occurs in certain natural products. It may be prepared from tropilidene (*cyclo*heptatriene) as follows:

$$\text{tropilidene} \xrightarrow[\text{NaOH}]{\text{KMnO}_4} \text{diketone (HC=CH–CO–CO–CH=CH ring with CH}_2\text{)} \xrightarrow{\text{enolises}} \text{tropolone (O, OH)}$$

Tropolone is very weakly acidic; it is also basic, *e.g.*, it forms a hydrochloride. It is attacked by electrophilic reagents to give *substitution* products, *e.g.*, it is readily brominated and nitrated. On heating with alkali, it is isomerised to benzoic acid. Ultraviolet absorption studies have shown that tropolone is planar (see also p. 485).

***cyclo*Octane,** m.p. 11·8°, may be obtained by the catalytic reduction of *cyclo*-octene, *cyclo*-octadiene or *cyclo*-octatetraene (Willstätter, 1911).

(1 : 3 : 5 : 7)-***cyclo*Octatetraene** was first obtained by Willstätter (1911, 1913), who prepared it from the alkaloid *pseudo*-pelletierine (ψ-pelletierine) by means of the Hofmann exhaustive methylation method (p. 732):

$$\begin{matrix}CH_2-CH-CH_2\\ CH_2\quad N{\cdot}CH_3\quad CO\\ CH_2-CH-CH_2\end{matrix} \longrightarrow \begin{matrix}CH=CH-CH\\ CH\qquad CH\\ CH-CH=CH\end{matrix}$$

ψ-pelletierine → *cyclo*-octatetraene

In 1939, Willstätter's results were questioned by a number of workers who believed that Willstätter had prepared, not *cyclo*-octatetraene, but *styrene*, $C_6H_5{\cdot}CH{:}CH_2$, which has somewhat similar properties to those recorded for *cyclo*-octatetraene. Cope and Overberger (1947), however, prepared *cyclo*-octatetraene from synthetic ψ-pelletierine, and found it to have the physical properties reported originally; these authors (1948) also duplicated Willstatter's work from natural *ψ*-pelletierine.

Reppe (1940) prepared *cyclo*-octatetraene in large quantities by the polymerisation of acetylene under pressure in the presence of a nickel compound, *e.g.*, nickel cyanide, as catalyst, in tetrahydrofuran solution:

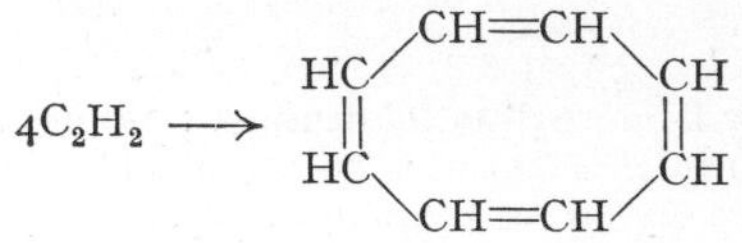

$$4C_2H_2 \longrightarrow \text{HC(=CH)–CH=CH–CH=CH–CH=CH–(cyclo-octatetraene)}$$

cyclo-Octatetraene is a yellow liquid, b.p. 142–143°. It behaves as a typical unsaturated compound, *e.g.*, it adds on bromine, halogen acids, etc. It can be reduced catalytically to *cyclo*-octane, and this, on oxidation with concentrated nitric acid, yields suberic acid. A better yield of suberic acid is obtained by reducing *cyclo*-octatetraene to *cyclo*-octene and oxidising this with nitric acid. *cyclo*-Octatetraene is therefore a potential commercial source of suberic acid:

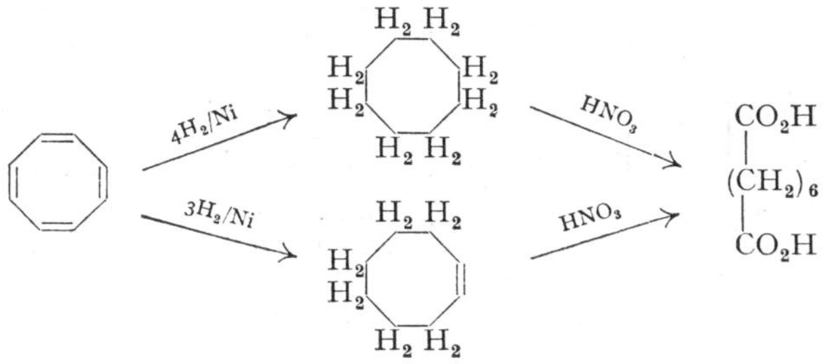

$$\text{cyclo-octatetraene} \xrightarrow{4H_2/Ni} \text{cyclo-octane} \xrightarrow{HNO_3} CO_2H\cdot(CH_2)_6\cdot CO_2H$$

$$\text{cyclo-octatetraene} \xrightarrow{3H_2/Ni} \text{cyclo-octene} \xrightarrow{HNO_3} CO_2H\cdot(CH_2)_6\cdot CO_2H$$

The *olefinic* properties of *cyclo*-octatetraene are somewhat surprising at first sight. Since the molecule contains a *closed* conjugated system, one might have expected delocalisation of bonds, thereby giving rise to aromatic character (*cf.* p. 485). If, however, delocalisation occurred, the molecule would be planar and therefore in a state of strain (the angle of a regular octagon is 135°, and that of carbon trigonally hybridised is 120°). X-Ray analysis has indicated that the *cyclo*-octatetraene molecule contains *alternate single and double bonds* and that the ring is non-planar (Kaufman *et al.*, 1948). The presence of this conjugated system has been supported by infra-red and Raman absorption spectra studies. These results account for *aliphatic* properties. Treibs (1950) has shown from models of *cyclo*-octatetraene that one form—a basket shape (" tub ")—has no internal stresses. This conformation is supported by electron-diffraction studies (Karle, 1952).

***cyclo*Alkynes.** Ring compounds containing one triple bond have now been prepared, but the smallest obtained so far is *cyclo*-octyne. Eglinton *et al.* (1956) have prepared cyclic conjugated di-ynes containing fourteen or more carbon atoms, and from a study of molecular models these authors believe that the smallest reasonably stable ring containing two acetylenic bonds is twelve-membered. The preparation of these compounds offers a new means of synthesising macrocyclic compounds (p. 469). The following example illustrates the method used. Tetradeca-1 : 13-di-yne, on treatment with excess of cupric acetate in methanolic pyridine, in high dilution (see p. 379), forms *cyclo*tetradeca-1 : 3-di-yne and also some of the cyclic dimer *cyclo*-octacosa-1 : 3 : 15 : 17-tetra-yne.

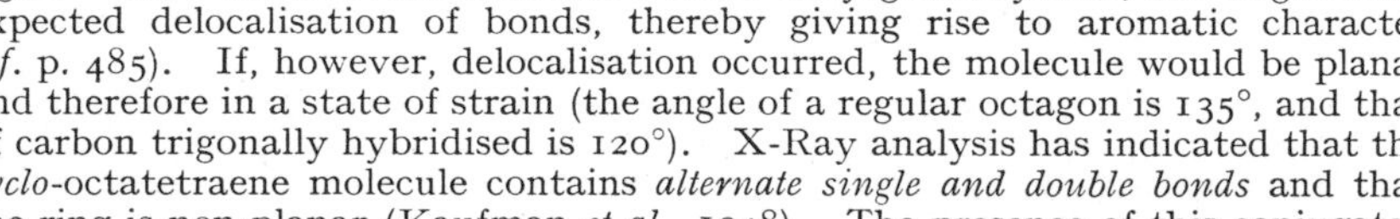

$$CH{\equiv}C\cdot(CH_2)_{10}\cdot C{\equiv}CH \longrightarrow \left[\begin{array}{c} C{\equiv}C{-}C{\equiv}C \\ (CH_2)_{10} \end{array}\right] + \left[\begin{array}{ccc} & C{\equiv}C{-}C{\equiv}C & \\ (CH_2)_{10} & & (CH_2)_{10} \\ & C{\equiv}C{-}C{\equiv}C & \end{array}\right]$$

These, on catalytic hydrogenation (platinum), gave respectively *cyclo*tetradecane ($C_{14}H_{28}$) and *cyclo*octacosane ($C_{28}H_{56}$).

Baeyer's Strain Theory. Baeyer (1885) was the first to point out that the angle subtended by the corners and centre of a regular tetrahedron—190° 28′—lies between the values of the angles in a regular pentagon (108°) and a regular hexagon (120°). On this observation was based the **Baeyer Strain Theory.** According to the Strain Theory, the valency angle can be altered from this normal value (109° 28′), but when altered, a strain is set up in the molecule, and the greater the deviation from the normal angle, the greater is the strain. Thus, according to Baeyer, five- and six-membered rings form most readily, and are the most stable because they involve the least strain (or distortion) from the normal valency angle.

The following arguments are based on the assumption that the rings are planar. In *cyclo*propane the three carbon atoms each occupy a corner of an equilateral triangle. Since the angles of an equilateral triangle are 60°, the distortion in *cyclo*propane will be $\frac{1}{2}(109° \ 28' - 60°) = +24° \ 44'$ (Fig. 1). When the carbon valencies are forced *together*, the strain is said to be *positive*; when forced *apart, negative.* Thus the *cyclo*propane molecule will be under a very large strain, and hence should be difficult to prepare, and should not be very stable.

In *cyclo*butane the distortion is $\frac{1}{2}(109° \ 28' - 90°) = +9° \ 44'$, a value which is considerably less than that for *cyclo*propane. Experimental work shows that *cyclo*butane derivatives are more easily formed and are more stable than *cyclo*propane compounds; this supports the Strain Theory.

In *cyclo*pentane the distortion is $\frac{1}{2}(109° \ 28' - 108°) = +0° \ 44'$; in *cyclo*hexane, $\frac{1}{2}(109° \ 28' - 120°) = -5° \ 16'$; in *cyclo*heptane, $\frac{1}{2}(109° \ 28' - 128° \ 34') = -9° \ 33'$; etc.

Thus five- and six-membered rings involve the least distortion and hence the ease of formation and stability should be a maximum in these compounds. The Strain Theory agrees reasonably well with the properties of ring compounds containing *six or less* carbon atoms; *e.g.*, we can now see why only the 1 : 4- and 1 : 5-dicarboxylic acids form cyclic anhydrides, and the 1 : 6- and 1 : 7- cyclic ketones (p. 363); why only γ- and δ-hydroxyacids readily form lactones (p. 377); etc. Measurements of the dipole moments of simple compounds of oxygen, nitrogen and sulphur show that the valency angles of these elements lie between 100° and 110°. Hence the presence of these elements in ring compounds will not greatly affect the stability of five- and six-membered rings in which they are present (see also the heterocyclic compounds, Ch. XXX).

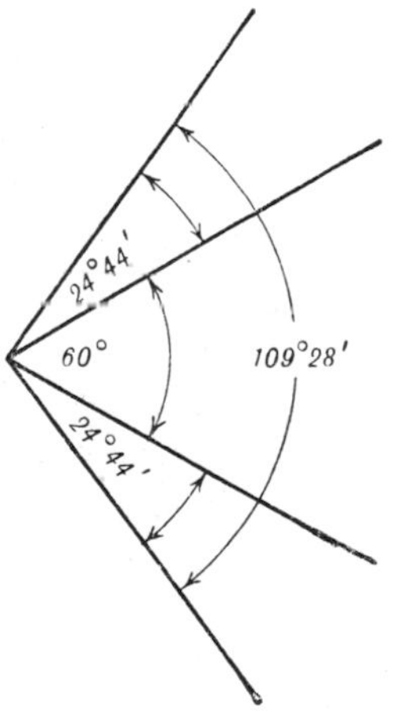

FIG. 19.1.

The Strain Theory has been used to account for the great reactivity of the double bond. The double bond was considered to be a *two-membered ring*; the distortion is therefore $\frac{1}{2}(109° \ 28' - 0°) = +54° \ 44'$. This involves the greatest distortion (strain) and consequently the least stability, *i.e.*, the greatest tendency to open or react. This reasoning for the double bond may have been helpful, but further consideration shows it to be inadequate, *e.g.*, the double bond is formed so easily that it would appear to be under very small strain, if any (see also later).

Modifications of Baeyer's Strain Theory. The formation and stability of ring compounds have been studied in great detail, particularly by Thorpe and Ingold and their co-workers (1915, onwards). Thorpe and Ingold suggested that the carbon valency angle of 109° 28′ is probably only obtained when the carbon atom has four identical groups attached to it, *e.g.*, in *neo*pentane, $\alpha = \beta = 109° \ 28'$. In compound I, since the methylene group has a greater volume than a hydrogen atom, it requires more space. Consequently, angle β will be greater than α, *i.e.*, the pushing apart of the valencies C—CH_2 causes the valencies C—H to approach. Thus, angle β is greater and α less than 109° 28′. On the other hand, in compound II, since a methyl group has a greater volume than a methylene group, angle α is greater and β less than normal, *i.e.*, the two methylene groups are brought closer together in (II) than in (I). Therefore the distortion (strain)

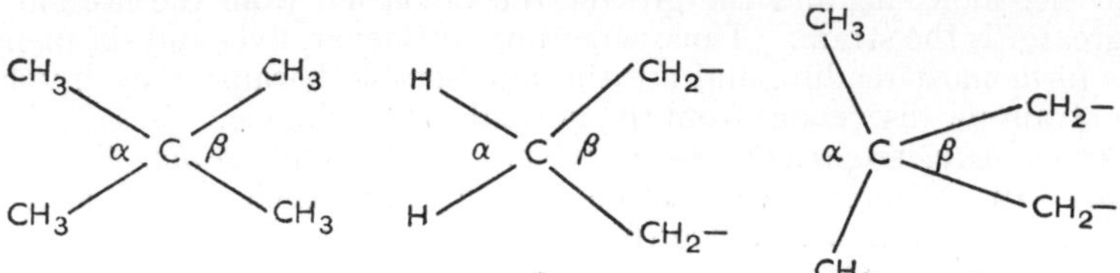

*neo*pentane I II

necessary to bring about three- or four-membered ring formation in (II) will be less than in (I), and the compound obtained should be more stable. This is observed in practice, *e.g.*, (i) β : β-dimethylglutaric acid forms an anhydride far more easily than does glutaric acid. (ii) Adipic acid is converted into *cyclo*pentanone when heated with acetic anhydride and then distilled at 300° (p. 362); α : α′-dimethyladipic acid forms the corresponding dimethyl*cyclo*pentanone derivative very easily when warmed with acetic anhydride.

Since the deflection from the normal valency angle can only be very small (see below), this factor can play very little, if any, part in this problem. A more likely solution is as follows. The carbon chain in unsubstituted dicarboxylic acids is believed to be zig-zag (Fig. 2). On the other hand, in β : β-dimethylglutaric acid,

(*a*) (*b*)

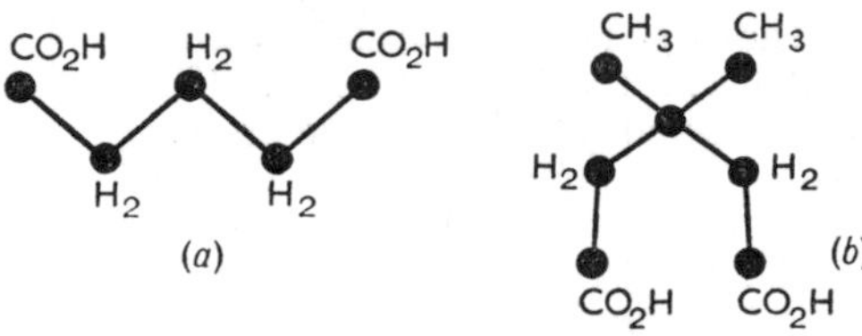

FIG. 19.2.

it is possible that the presence of the two methyl groups gives rise to a different spatial arrangement. The methyl group, due to its large volume (relative to hydrogen), forces the carboxyl to take up the position shown in Fig. 2 (*b*). Thus, owing to spatial effects, the zig-zag nature of the chain is forced to become coiled. This brings the reacting groups closer together, thereby facilitating anhydride formation.

Baeyer's Strain Theory is based on a mechanical concept of valency, and served its purpose in stimulating research in the field of cyclic compounds. Now we have the electronic theory of valency, and the reactivity of double bonds has been explained by the π-electrons. Furthermore, as pointed out on p. 24, when four identical groups are attached to a carbon atom, the four carbon valencies are equivalent, and the valency angle is 109° 28′. When the groups are different, the four valencies are no longer equivalent but now point towards the four corners of an *irregular* tetrahedron. Since there are no double bonds in *cyclo*propane, the carbon atoms cannot be in a state of trigonal hybridisation. If the configuration of *cyclo*propane were an equilateral triangle, then the ring valency angle of each carbon atom would be 60°. This value is impossible, since the carbon valency angle can never be less than 90° (when they are pure *p*-orbitals). Furthermore, mixture of *p* with *s*-orbitals *opens* the valency angle. According to Coulson *et al.* (1949), calculation has shown that the smallest carbon valency angle that one can reasonably expect to have is 104°. Coulson has therefore suggested that in *cyclo*propane, the carbon hybridised orbitals are not pointing towards one another in the same straight line, and consequently there is a loss of overlap (Fig. 3*a*). It is this loss of overlap that gives rise to instability, the *cyclo*propane molecule being in a state of "strain" due to "bent" bonds. Applying this argument to *cyclo*butane (Fig. 3*b*), we see that this molecule also has "bent" bonds, but loss of overlap is less in this case than for *cyclo*propane, and so the former will be more stable than the latter.

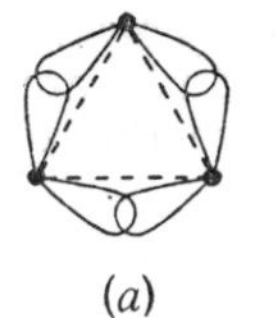

(*a*)

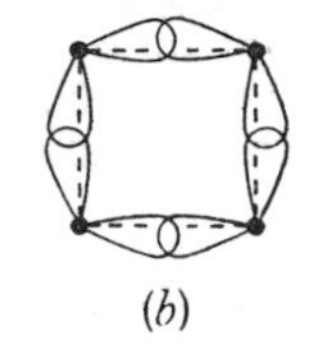

(*b*)

FIG. 19.3.

Theory of Strainless Rings. According to Baeyer's Strain Theory (which postulates planar rings), a parallel will exist between the ease of formation of a ring and the stability of that ring. This implied that very large rings were difficult, if at all possible, to prepare, due to the great strain involved

TABLE VIII

Number of carbon atoms in the ring	Heat of combustion in kg. cal./CH_2
2	170
3	166·5
4	163·8
5	158·7
6	157·2
7	158·2
8, ---	158–159
n-paraffins	157·5

in the ring. Chemical stability may be measured in various ways, *e.g.*, by the heat of formation, heat of combustion, dipole moment, absorption spectra, etc. One of the most convenient to work with in respect to hydrocarbons is the heat of combustion. If the strain in a ring changes with the size of the ring, then this should be observed by changes in the heat of combustion.

According to the results shown in Table VIII, stability increases up to the five- and six-membered rings and then remains effectively constant. This can be explained by rejecting the postulate that all rings are planar, and by assuming that rings with six or more carbon atoms are *puckered*, the *normal* valency angle being retained and thereby producing *strainless* rings. Such a suggestion was first made by Sachse (1890), and according to him, *cyclo*hexane exists in two forms, both of which are strainless (Fig. 4).

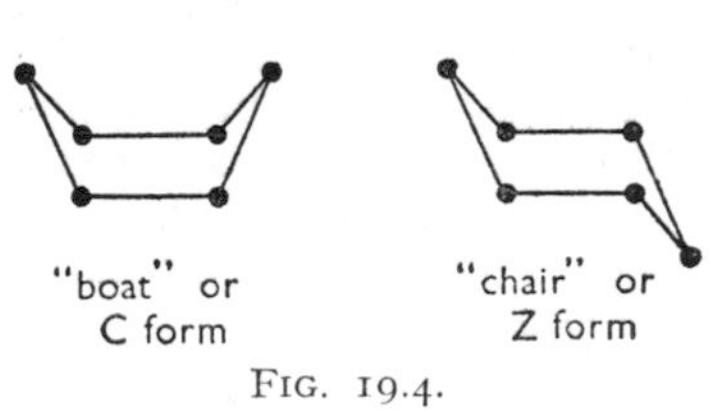

FIG. 19.4.

The two forms of *cyclo*hexane are also known as the chair and boat **conformations,** the term conformation being used to denote different spatial arrangements of the atoms of a given molecular structure, the arrangements being produced by twisting or rotation of bonds. The terms *rotational isomer* and *constellation* have also been used in the same sense as conformation.

Although the two conformations are free from *angle strain,* forces due to **steric repulsion**, *i.e.*, forces between non-bonded atoms (in close proximity), are present, and these are different in the two conformations. Turner (1952) has introduced a simple method of calculating this energy difference.

In the chair form (Fig. 5*a*) all the C—H bonds on adjacent carbon atoms are in the skew position (projection of the hydrogen atoms on two adjacent carbon atoms on a plane perpendicular to the bonding line shows the hydrogen atoms are in the skew form; *cf.* ethylene chloride, p. 387). In the boat form (Fig. 5*c*), however, four of the C—H bonds are skew (1 : 2, 3 : 4, 4 : 5, and 6 : 1), and two are eclipsed (2 : 3 and 5 : 6). According to Pitzer (1940), a skew interaction of hydrogens in *n*-butane has a value of 0·8 kg.

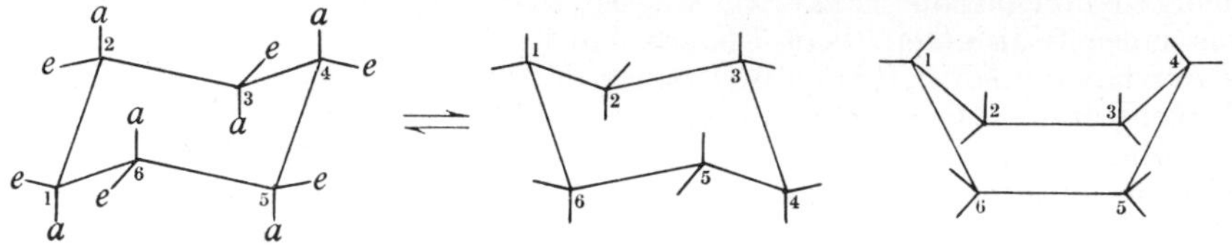

(*a*) (*b*) (*c*)

FIG. 19.5.

cal. and an eclipsed 3·6 kg. cal. (the conformations of *n*-butane are similar to those of ethylene chloride; replace Cl by CH_3). Thus the **steric strain** in the chair form is 6 × 0·8 = 4·8 kg. cal., and in the boat form 4 × 0·8 + 2 × 3·6 = 10·4 kg. cal. Hence the difference is 5·6 kg. cal. This is a minimum difference, since the steric repulsion between the hydrogens pointing towards each other at 1 and 4 (Fig. 5*c*) has been ignored (the actual value of this repulsion is uncertain). Thus the chair form will be more stable than the boat, but the energy difference of 5·6 kg. cal. between the two is too small for stability, and so neither retains its identity, each being readily converted into the other. Hassel (1943), however, has shown by electron diffraction studies that at room temperature most of the molecules exist mainly in the chair form, *i.e.*, the chair conformation is the preferred one.

Since the boat conformation occurs in relatively few cases, we shall confine our attention to the chair form. Consideration of the C—H bonds in this form shows that there are two sets of six. In one set the six C—H bonds are parallel to the axis of the ring (Fig. 5*a*); these are the **axial** (*a*) **bonds** (or ε- or *polar* bonds). In the other set the six C—H bonds make an angle of 109° 28′ with the axis (or ±19° 28′ with the horizontal plane of the ring; Fig. 5*a*); these are the **equatorial** (*e*) **bonds** (or κ-bonds). Each carbon atom has one axial and one equatorial bond, and because of the flexibility of the chair conformation, one form (Fig. 5*a*) can readily change into the other (Fig. 5*b*), and when this occurs all hydrogens originally axial now become equatorial, and *vice-versa*. The two forms are identical.

Calculations have shown that in the chair conformation the distances between pairs of hydrogen atoms are (Angyal and Mills, 1952):

1*e* : 2*e*, 2·49A; 1*e* : 2*a*, 2·49A;
1*a* : 2*a*, 3·06A; 1*a* : 3*a*, 2·51A.

The nearest four hydrogens to the equatorial hydrogen at 1 are those on 2 (*a* and *e*) and 6 (*a* and *e*), whereas for the axial hydrogen at 1 these four hydrogens are the axial hydrogens on 3 and 5 and the equatorial on 2 and 6 (see Fig. 5*a*). Thus a 1 : 2-interaction for two adjacent equatorial hydrogens or for an equatorial and an adjacent axial hydrogen is about the same as for a 1 : 3-interaction for two *meta* axial hydrogens.

Now let us consider the problem when one hydrogen atom in *cyclo*hexane is replaced by some substituent which, of necessity, must be larger than a hydrogen atom. A study of accurate scale models has shown that in monosubstituted *cyclo*hexanes, an axial substituent at 1 is closer to the two axial hydrogens at 3 and 5 than an equatorial substituent at 1 is to the four hydrogens at 2 and 6. Thus 1 : 3-interactions will be greater than 1 : 2-

interactions, and so, in general, a monosubstituted *cyclo*hexane will assume the conformation in which the substituent occupies an equatorial position. This has been confirmed experimentally, *e.g.*, Hassel (1950) has shown from electron-diffraction studies that the chlorine in chloro*cyclo*hexane is equatorial (predominantly).

From what has been said above, we can now say that **conformational analysis** is the study of the existence of one or more preferred conformations in a given molecular structure, and the relating of the physical and chemical properties to this preferred conformation.

Let us now consider the application of conformational analysis to 1 : 2-disubstituted *cyclo*hexanes in which the two substituents are identical. According to the classical ideas of stereochemistry, there are two forms possible, *cis* and *trans*. The conformation of the *cis* configuration *must* have one axial and one equatorial substituent (Fig. 6). The two conforma-

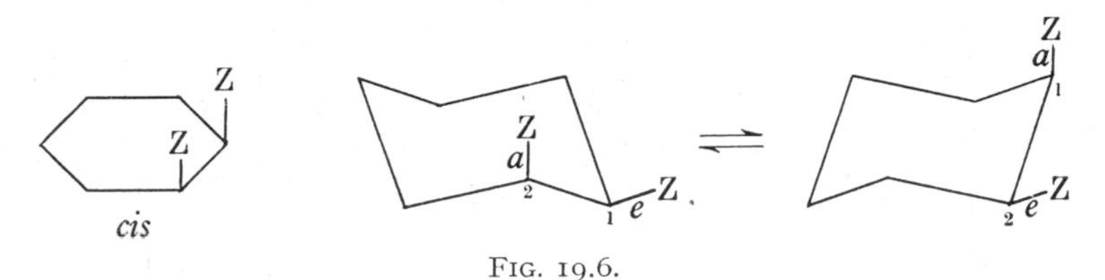

FIG. 19.6.

tions are mirror images and are *not* superimposable. Hence, if each were sufficiently stable, they would form a pair of enantiomorphs. Such compounds have never yet been resolved (their interconversion is very easy).

The *trans* configuration can exist in two different conformations, 1*a* : 2*a* and 1*e* : 2*e* (Fig. 7), but from what has been said above, the *trans*-1*e* : 2*e* form will be more stable than the *trans*-1*a* : 2*a*, and this *trans* form will be more stable than the *cis*.

The above arguments can be applied to the 1 : 3- and 1 : 4-disubstituted *cyclo*hexanes, and to the polysubstituted derivatives, and it will be found that the chair conformation with the maximum number of equatorial substituents will be the preferred form. This generalisation, however, is only true when other forces due to, *e.g.*, dipole interactions, hydrogen bonding, are absent. When these " disturbing " factors are present, they may be large enough to outweigh the 1 : 3-interactions, *e.g.*, infrared spectra studies have shown that the bromine in 2-bromo*cyclo*hexanone is predominantly *axial* (Fig. 7). The C—Br and C=O bonds are both strongly polar, and when the bromine is equatorial the dipolar repulsion is a maxi-

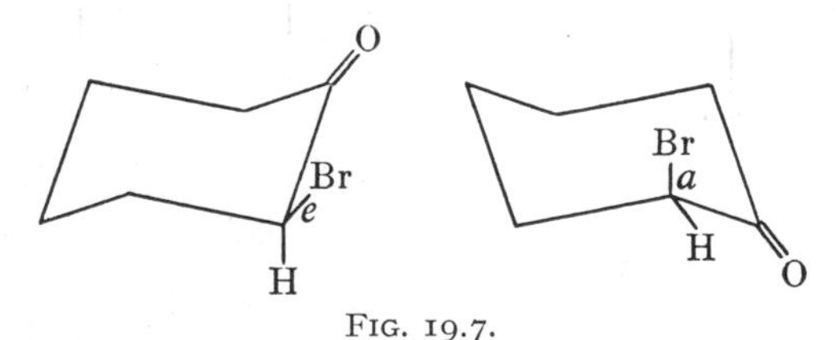

FIG. 19.7.

mum, and a minimum when the bromine is axial. Since the axial form predominates, the equatorial dipolar repulsion must be much larger than the 1 : 3-interactions.

It is also instructive to consider one example of a 1 : 2-disubstituted *cyclo*hexane in which the two substituents are different, *e.g.*, *cis*-2-methyl*cyclo*hexanol. Since 1 : 3-interactions will be most powerful when the larger group is axial, the preferred form will therefore be the one in which the larger group is equatorial. Thus, since the methyl group is greater than hydroxyl, the preferred form of *cis*-2-methyl*cyclo*hexanol is 1*a*-OH : 2*e*-CH_3.

As an example of the effect of conformation on the rate of reactions let us consider hydroxy-derivatives. If the hydroxyl group is axial, then because of its proximity to the other two axial hydrogens (*i.e.*, because of the steric hindrance from 3 and 5), it would be expected that this hydroxyl would be esterified with greater difficulty than the corresponding equatorial compound. This has been shown to be so in many cases, *e.g.*, steroid alcohols.

Fused systems. Since the boat and chair forms of *cyclo*hexane are readily interconvertible, neither form can be isolated. Mohr (1918), however, elaborated Sachse's theory and predicted that the fusion of two *cyclo*hexane rings, *e.g.*, in decalin, should produce *cis* and *trans* forms which should be stable enough to retain their identities. Both forms have now been prepared. Several conventions have been introduced to represent these isomers. One uses *full* lines to represent groups *above* the plane of the molecule, and *broken* lines to represent those *below*. Another convention uses a black dot to represent a hydrogen atom above the plane, and the ordinary lines of the formula to indicate a hydrogen atom below the plane. Thus the decalins may be drawn:

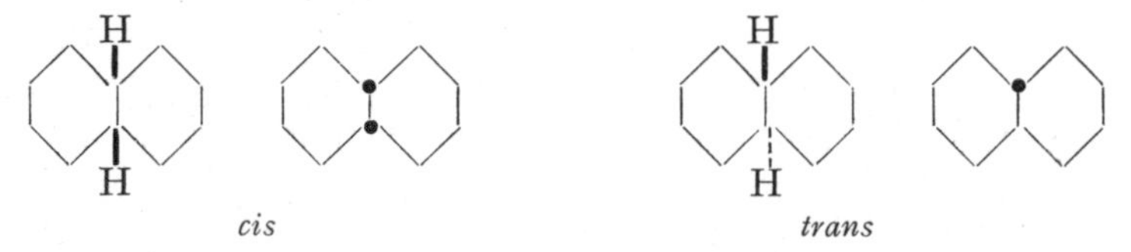

Fig. 8 shows the original diagrammatical method of representing *cis*-decalin by the fusion of two boat forms, and *trans*-decalin by the fusion of two chair

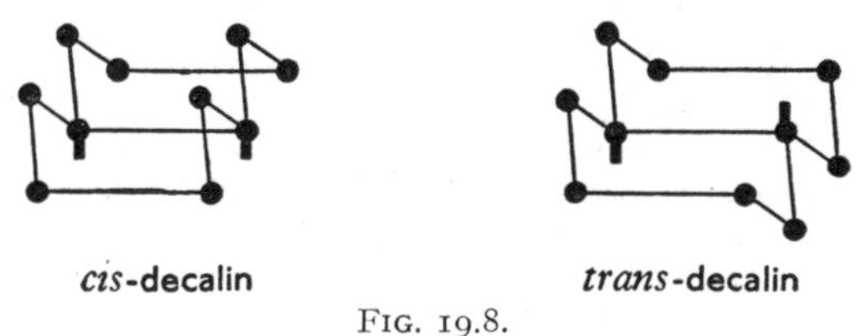

FIG. 19.8.

forms. The configurations of decalin, however, are now known to be more complicated than this, the complication arising from the fact that a number of

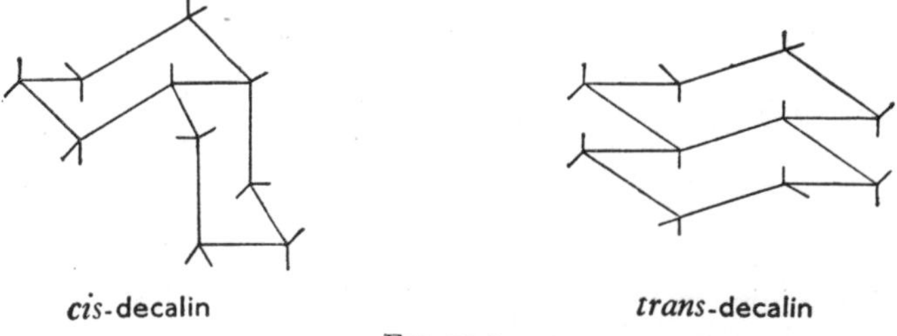

FIG. 19.9.

strainless modifications are possible which differ in the type of " locking ", *i.e.*, whether axial or equatorial bonds are used to fuse the rings. According to Hassel *et al.* (1946), *cis*- and *trans*-decalin are as shown in Fig. 9. In both cases the *cyclo*hexane rings are *all chair forms*; the *cis* form is produced by joining one axial and one equatorial bond of each ring, whereas the *trans* form is produced by joining the two rings by equatorial bonds only. Calculation has shown that the *cis* isomer has 2·4 kg. cal. energy content more than the *trans*. It is also of interest to note that if the decalins are regarded as 1 : 2-disubstituted *cyclo*hexanes, then the *trans* form (1*e* : 2*e*) would be expected to be more stable than the *cis* (1*e* : 2*a*).

From the foregoing account it can be seen that the Sachse–Mohr theory does not deny the existence of large rings. On the contrary, it implies that if it is possible to prepare large rings, these rings would be stable. This has been amply confirmed in recent years. Electron diffraction studies of *cyclo*hexane show it to be a puckered ring, the carbon atoms having the normal valency angle (109° 28′). Also, Ruzicka, from 1926 onwards, has prepared large rings which are stable (strainless).

Preparation of large ring compounds. Up to 1926, the largest ring compound known contained eight carbon atoms. Ruzicka and his co-workers (1926, onwards) prepared large rings containing up to thirty-four carbon atoms. Their first method was to distil the calcium salts of dibasic acids, this method being limited to the preparation of *cyclo*pentanone, *cyclo*hexanone and *cyclo*heptanone; the yields were poor. Ruzicka and his co-workers increased the yields, and also were able to obtain larger rings, by

$$(CH_2)_8\begin{matrix} / CH_2 \backslash \\ \backslash CH_2 / \end{matrix}CO \quad (I) \qquad (CH_2)_{10}\begin{matrix} / CO \backslash \\ \backslash CO / \end{matrix}(CH_2)_{10} \quad (II)$$

distilling *in vacuo* at about 300° the thorium, cerium or yttrium salt mixed with copper powder (which aids heat conduction). Usually a number of products was obtained by the distillation of a particular acid, *viz.*, a cyclic hydrocarbon, a cyclic monoketone and a cyclic diketone; *e.g.*, the yttrium salt of the dibasic acid $(CH_2)_{10}(CO_2H)_2$ gave a cyclic hydrocarbon, the cyclic monoketone I, and the cyclic diketone II.

The mechanism of these cyclisations is obscure. Ruzicka suggested that ring closure depends on: (*a*) the distance between the two carboxyl groups, and (*b*) the stability of the ring formed. He obtained the highest yield for five- and six-membered rings.

Reduction of the cyclic ketones and diketones by Clemmensen's method converted them into cyclic hydrocarbons. Conversion into the cyclic hydrocarbon was also carried out by reducing the cyclic ketone to the cyclic alcohol (with sodium and ethanol), dehydrating this (with potassium hydrogen sulphate), and then catalytically reducing the *cyclo*-olefin thus produced. By these methods, Ruzicka prepared cyclic compounds containing up to thirty-four carbon atoms in the ring. The structure of the ring compound (the cyclic ketone) was established by oxidation to the αω-dicarboxylic acid.

Ziegler and his co-workers (1933) used an entirely different method for preparing large ring compounds. They made use of the *high-dilution principle* (p. 379), obtaining large rings by the intramolecular condensation of αω-*normal* aliphatic dicyanides in the presence of alkali derivatives of secondary amines. In order to apply the high-dilution principle, it is necessary to have all the reactants in solution. Thus lithium derivatives (of secondary amines) are the most satisfactory, since they are soluble in ether (they are covalent compounds). The mechanism of the reaction is not certain; it may be as follows:

$$(CH_2)_n\begin{cases}CH_2{\cdot}CN\\CH_2{\cdot}CN\end{cases}\xrightarrow{LiN(C_6H_5)(C_2H_5)}(CH_2)_n\begin{cases}\overset{\displaystyle Li}{\overset{|}{C}}H{\cdot}CN\\CH_2{\cdot}CN\end{cases}+C_6H_5{\cdot}NH{\cdot}C_2H_5\longrightarrow$$

$$(CH_2)_n\begin{cases}CH{\cdot}CN\\CH_2\end{cases}\!\!\!>C{=}NLi\xrightarrow[\text{hydrolysis}]{\text{acid}}(CH_2)_n\begin{cases}CH{\cdot}CN\\CH_2\end{cases}\!\!\!>C{=}NH\longrightarrow$$

$$(CH_2)_n\begin{cases}CH{\cdot}CO_2H\\CH_2\end{cases}\!\!\!>CO\xrightarrow{\text{heat}}(CH_2)_n\begin{cases}CH_2\\CH_2\end{cases}\!\!\!>CO$$

The high dilution was effected by very slowly adding a dilute solution of the dicyanide in ether to a solution of the lithium compound in ether. This method may be regarded as an extension of the Thorpe reaction (p. 449).

In addition to cyclic monoketones, cyclic diketones are obtained, and are believed to be formed as follows:

$$\begin{matrix}CN{\cdot}CH_2{\cdot}(CH_2)_n{\cdot}CN\\+\\CN{\cdot}(CH_2)_n{\cdot}CH_2{\cdot}CN\end{matrix}\xrightarrow{LiN(C_6H_5)(C_2H_5)}\begin{matrix}CN{\cdot}CH{\cdot}(CH_2)_n{\cdot}C{=}NLi\\|\qquad\qquad\qquad|\\LiN{=}C{\cdot}(CH_2)_n{-}CH{\cdot}CN\end{matrix}\xrightarrow[\text{hydrolysis}]{\text{acid}}$$

$$\begin{matrix}CO_2H{\cdot}CH{\cdot}(CH_2)_n{\cdot}CO\\|\qquad\qquad\qquad|\\CO{\cdot}(CH_2)_n{\cdot}CH{\cdot}CO_2H\end{matrix}\xrightarrow{\text{heat}}\begin{matrix}CH_2{\cdot}(CH_2)_n{\cdot}CO\\|\qquad\qquad\qquad|\\CO{-}(CH_2)_n{\cdot}CH_2\end{matrix}$$

This method of preparing large ring compounds is superior to Ruzicka's, since the yields are better (up to 85 per cent.).

Hunsdiecker (1942) has prepared large rings by condensing an ω-bromo-acyl chloride with sodioacetoacetic ester, subjecting the product to " acid hydrolysis " with methanolic sodium methoxide, then replacing the bromine atom by iodine, and finally cyclising the product by boiling in butanone in the presence of potassium carbonate. The cyclic keto-ester is then treated with sulphuric acid, whereupon the β-keto-acid produced spontaneously decarboxylates:

$$Br{\cdot}(CH_2)_n{\cdot}COCl+[CH_3{\cdot}CO{\cdot}CH{\cdot}CO_2C_2H_5]^-Na^+\longrightarrow$$

$$Br{\cdot}(CH_2)_n{\cdot}CO{\cdot}\overset{\displaystyle CO{\cdot}CH_3}{\overset{|}{C}}H{\cdot}CO_2C_2H_5+NaCl\xrightarrow[CH_3OH]{CH_3ONa}Br{\cdot}(CH_2)_n{\cdot}CO{\cdot}CH_2{\cdot}CO_2CH_3$$

$$\xrightarrow[\text{acetone}]{NaI}I{\cdot}(CH_2)_n{\cdot}CO{\cdot}CH_2{\cdot}CO_2CH_3$$

$$\xrightarrow[\text{butanone}]{K_2CO_3}(CH_2)_n\begin{cases}CO\\|\\CH{\cdot}CO_2CH_3\end{cases}\xrightarrow{H_2SO_4}(CH_2)_n\begin{cases}CO\\|\\CH_2\end{cases}$$

Prelog (1947) and Stoll (1947) have prepared large ring compounds from dicarboxylic esters containing nine or more carbon atoms. The ester is made to undergo the acyloin synthesis (p. 180) by heating in xylene solution with sodium, and finally acidifying.

$$(CH_2)_n\begin{cases}CO_2R\\CO_2R\end{cases}\longrightarrow(CH_2)_n\begin{cases}CO\\|\\CHOH\end{cases}$$

The yields by this method exceed those by any other given above, and an added advantage is that the reaction does not have to be carried out at high dilution.

Recently large rings have been prepared by treating the ethereal solution of acid chlorides of the dibasic acids with triethylamine; an aldoketen is formed first, and this then cyclises (Blomquist and Spencer, 1947, 1948):

$$\begin{array}{c} COCl \\ | \\ (CH_2)_n \\ | \\ COCl \end{array} \longrightarrow \begin{array}{c} CH{=}CO \\ | \\ (CH_2)_{n-2} \\ | \\ CH{=}CO \end{array} \longrightarrow (CH_2)_n{=}CO + (CH_2)_n\!\!\begin{array}{c} CO \\ \\ CO \end{array}\!\!(CH_2)_n$$

Large rings have also been prepared via *cyclo*-ynes and -di-ynes (p. 462).

The **paracyclophanes** form another type of large ring system in that they contain two benzene rings joined in the *para*-positions. Cram *et al.* (1954) have prepared them as follows (using the Friedel–Crafts reaction (p. 502), the Willgerodt reaction (p. 634), and the acyloin synthesis), *e.g.*,

$$(CH_2)_4(C_6H_5)_2 \xrightarrow[AlCl_3]{(CH_3\cdot CO)_2O} (CH_2)_4(C_6H_4\cdot CO\cdot CH_3)_2 \xrightarrow[\text{(ii) } CH_3OH\,-\,HCl]{\text{(i) S + morpholine}}$$

$$(CH_2)_4(C_6H_4\cdot CH_2\cdot CO_2CH_3)_2 \xrightarrow[Pt]{H_2} (CH_2)_4(C_6H_{10}\cdot CH_2\cdot CO_2CH_3)_2$$

$$\xrightarrow[\text{(ii) } CH_3\cdot CO_2H]{\text{(i) Na}} (CH_2)_4\begin{array}{c} C_6H_{10}\cdot CH_2\cdot CHOH \\ | \\ C_6H_{10}\cdot CH_2\cdot CO \end{array} \xrightarrow[HCl]{Zn/Hg} (CH_2)_4\begin{array}{c} C_6H_{10} \\ \\ C_6H_{10} \end{array}(CH_2)_4$$

$$\xrightarrow[-\ 12H]{Pd} (CH_2)_4\begin{array}{c} C_6H_4 \\ \\ C_6H_4 \end{array}(CH_2)_4$$

Cram *et al.* (1951) have also prepared paracyclophanes by the action of sodium on the following compound ($n \geqq 2$):

$$BrCH_2-C_6H_4-(CH_2)_n-C_6H_4-CH_2Br$$

These large ring compounds are very stable, *e.g.*, they are not affected by hydrogen chloride at 200° or by hydrogen iodide at 250°. They cannot therefore be planar (the negative strain would be very large); X-ray analysis has shown that the rings are puckered—the carbon retaining its normal tetrahedral valency angle—and that they consist of two parallel portions (this applies to rings containing more than twenty carbon atoms).

Although these large rings are free from angle strain, they are, however, subject to steric strain produced by steric repulsion (*cf.* *cyclo*hexane, p. 466). Since all puckered rings are subject to this strain, it was thought that the physical and chemical properties of large rings would be similar to those of *cyclo*hexane. It has now been shown, however, that the properties of large rings depend on the size of the ring. The reason for this is not certain, but one suggestion is that shielding of a reactive centre will vary with the size of the ring, *e.g.*, a cyclic ketone could be (III) (" O-outside ") or (IV) (" O-inside "). Now medium-sized ketones combine with nitromalonaldehyde,

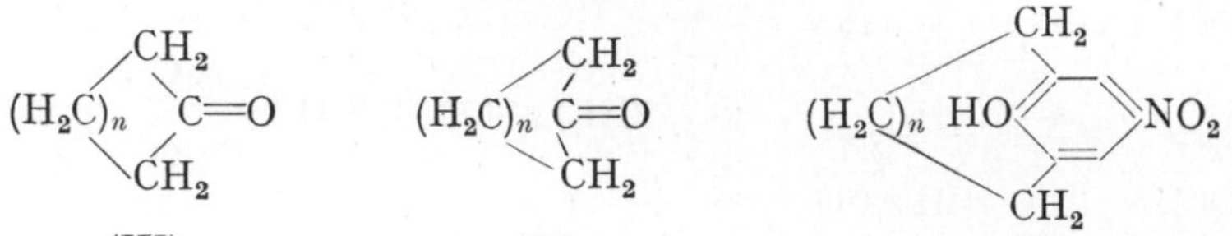

$$(H_2C)_n{<}^{CH_2}_{CH_2}{>}C{=}O \quad \text{(III)} \qquad (H_2C)_n{<}^{CH_2}_{CH_2}{>}C{=}O \quad \text{(IV)} \qquad (H_2C)_n{<}^{CH_2}_{CH_2}{>}C_6H_2(OH)NO_2 \quad \text{(V)}$$

$NO_2{\cdot}CH(CHO)_2$, to form *p*-nitrophenols, (V) (Prelog *et al.*, 1948). It therefore follows that the carbonyl group is shielded as in (IV).

Two large carbon-ring compounds occurring in nature are *civetone* and *muscone*.

Civetone, $C_{17}H_{30}$, m.p. 31°, occurs in the civet and is the cause of the civet odour. Its constitution was elucidated by Ruzicka (1926, 1927). It was shown to be a ketone (carbonyl group present and compound non-reducing), and to contain a double bond (adds on bromine). When catalytically reduced, civetone absorbs one molecule of hydrogen (therefore one double bond present) to form *dihydrocivetone* (m.p. 63°). Oxidation of this compound with chromic acid gives a dicarboxylic acid, $C_{17}H_{32}O_4$, which was shown to be pentadecane-1 : 15-dicarboxylic acid; this acid was also synthesised. Since this acid contains the same number of carbon atoms as the original ketone, Ruzicka inferred that the ketone was a seventeen-membered ring compound; this was supported by evidence obtained from the study of the molecular refraction of the ketone. Thus the structure of dihydrocivetone is $\begin{matrix} CH_2{\cdot}(CH_2)_7 \\ | \\ CH_2{\cdot}(CH_2)_7 \end{matrix}\!\!>CO$.

Reduction of civetone by Clemmensen's method produces *civetane* (which contains a double bond), and this, on ozonolysis, gives the same dicarboxylic acid as before (from dihydrocivetone). This again indicates a seventeen-membered ring containing one double bond. To find the position of the double bond in civetone, Ruzicka oxidised civetone with sodium hypobromite, and obtained a mixture of succinic, pimelic, suberic and azelaic acids. Since the structure of azelaic acid is $CO_2H{\cdot}(CH_2)_7{\cdot}CO_2H$, the double bond in civetone must be at least on C_9 (the carbon atom of the CO group being C_1), since to obtain azelaic acid there must be seven methylene groups between the carbonyl group and the double bond. The formula which fits this is $\begin{matrix} CH{\cdot}(CH_2)_7 \\ \| \\ CH{\cdot}(CH_2)_7 \end{matrix}\!\!>CO$. This structure was confirmed by controlled oxidation of civetone with potassium permanganate; a ketodibasic acid was obtained, and its structure was determined by synthesis by heating the methyl acid ester of azelaic acid with iron powder:

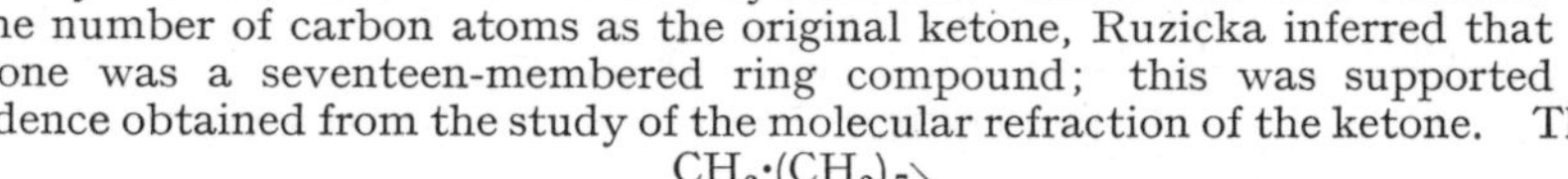

$$\begin{matrix} CH{\cdot}(CH_2)_7 \\ \| \\ CH{\cdot}(CH_2)_7 \end{matrix}\!\!>CO \xrightarrow{[O]} \begin{matrix} HO_2C{\cdot}(CH_2)_7 \\ \\ HO_2C{\cdot}(CH_2)_7 \end{matrix}\!\!>CO \xleftarrow[\text{(ii) hydrolysis}]{\text{(i) Fe}} 2\begin{matrix} CH_3O_2C \\ \\ HO_2C \end{matrix}\!\!>(CH_2)_7$$

The structure of civetone has been confirmed by a number of syntheses.

Muscone (*muskone*), $C_{16}H_{30}O$, occurs in natural musk (from the musk deer). It is a thick colourless oil and is optically active. Its structure was elucidated by Ruzicka. Its molecular formula is $C_{16}H_{30}O$, and it was shown to be a ketone. Since it was also shown to be saturated, it must therefore be cyclic, since if it were an open-chain compound, its formula would be $C_{16}H_{32}O$; if it had contained more than one ring, the number of hydrogen atoms would have been less than thirty. Since muscone is optically active, it must contain at least one asymmetric carbon atom: further work has shown it contains only one (see below).

The investigation of the odours of cyclic compounds was then used to elucidate the structure of muscone. Ruzicka was led to adopt this procedure because he had found that civetone and dihydrocivetone had about the same odour, *i.e.*, he assumed that similar structures gave rise to similar odours (this might be termed a *physiologico-chemical* method). Ruzicka found that the odour of muscone was identical with that of synthetic *cyclo*pentadecanone and its methyl derivatives (see also below). He believed that muscone was therefore a methyl derivative of the fifteen-membered cyclic ketone. This was proved by preparing *cyclo*-pentadecanone (by distillation of the thorium salt of tetradecane-1 : 14-dicarboxylic acid), treating it with methylmagnesium iodide, and dehydrating the tertiary alcohol so produced to the olefin which was then catalytically reduced to methyl*cyclo*pentadecane:

$$\begin{array}{l} CH_2\text{---}CO \\ | \qquad\quad | \\ (CH_2)_{12}\text{---}CH_2 \end{array} \xrightarrow[\text{(ii) } H_2O]{\text{(i) } CH_3MgI} \begin{array}{l} \qquad\quad CH_3 \\ CH_2\text{---}\dot{C}OH \\ | \qquad\quad | \\ (CH_2)_{12}\text{---}CH_2 \end{array} \xrightarrow{-H_2O}$$

$$\begin{array}{l} \qquad\quad CH_3 \\ CH_2\text{---}\dot{C} \\ | \qquad\quad \| \\ (CH_2)_{12}\text{---}CH \end{array} \xrightarrow{H_2/Ni} \begin{array}{l} \qquad\quad CH_3 \\ CH_2\text{---}\dot{C}H \\ | \qquad\quad | \\ (CH_2)_{12}\text{---}CH_2 \end{array}$$

Methyl*cyclo*pentadecane is also obtained when muscone is reduced by the Clemmensen method.

The problem now was to determine the position of the methyl group with respect to the carbonyl group. When oxidised with chromic acid, muscone yields two acids with the formula $C_{14}H_{28}(CO_2H)_2$ and a mixture of lower dicarboxylic acids. The properties of the acids with the formula $C_{14}H_{28}(CO_2H)_2$ agreed with the properties of synthetic α- and β-methyltridecane-1 : 11-dicarboxylic acids, both of which may be expected from the oxidation of a fifteen-membered ring ketone with a methyl group in the β-position with respect to the carbonyl group:

$$\begin{array}{l} (CH_2)_{12}\text{---}\overset{\beta}{\vdots}\text{---}CO \\ | \qquad\qquad\quad |\alpha \\ CH_3{\cdot}CH\text{------}CH_2 \end{array} \xrightarrow{CrO_3} \begin{cases} CO_2H{\cdot}CH(CH_3){\cdot}(CH_2)_{12}{\cdot}CO_2H & \alpha\text{-acid} \\ CO_2H{\cdot}CH_2{\cdot}CH(CH_3){\cdot}(CH_2)_{11}{\cdot}CO_2II & \beta\text{-acid} \end{cases}$$

This evidence, however, is not conclusive for the structure of muscone. Muscone was finally shown to contain the methyl group in the β-position by synthesis.

Civetone and muscone are both used in perfumery. Investigation of the relationship between ring size and odours of cyclic ketones is as follows: C_5, bitter almonds; C_6, mint; C_7–C_9, transition to camphor; C_{10}–C_{13}, transition to cedar: C_{14}–C_{16}, transition to musk with maximum musk odour at C_{15}; C_{17}, civetone; C_{18}, very weak civetone; from C_{19} onwards, the odour decreases very rapidly.

*cyclo*Pentadecanone is used in perfumery under the name of *exaltone*.

QUESTIONS

1. Discuss the general methods for preparing alicyclic compounds.

2. Starting with any *readily accessible open-chain* compounds you like, suggest a synthesis for each of the following:—(*a*) *cyclo*pentane, (*b*) *cyclo*heptanone, (*c*) *cyclo*-hexane-1 : 3-dione, (*d*) *cyclo*pentane-1 : 2-dione, (*e*) *cyclo*hexene, (*f*) 1 : 5-diMe-*cyclo*-penta-1 : 4-diene, (*g*) hexahydrobenzoic acid, (*h*) endoethylene-hexahydrobenzoic acid, (*i*) endomethylene-hexahydrophthalic acid, (*j*) *cyclo*pentylacetic acid.

3. Describe *two* methods of preparation of each of the *cyclo*alkanes containing 3—6 carbon atoms.

Name the compounds and state the conditions under which they are formed when each of the above hydrocarbons is treated with:—(*a*) Br_2, (*b*) HBr, (*c*) HI, (*d*) HCl, (*e*) heat, (*f*) H_2, (*g*) HNO_3, (*h*) H_2SO_4.

4. Write an account of:—(*a*) the Baeyer Strain Theory, (*b*) the Theory of Strainless Rings, (*c*) the preparation of large-ring compounds.

5. What is meant by the term *chemical stability*? Discuss the various methods which may be used to measure chemical stability.

6. Discuss the structure of civetone and muscone.

7. Define and give examples of:—(*a*) the Freund reaction, (*b*) the Wislicenus reaction, (*c*) the Perkin junior reaction, (*d*) the Dieckmann reaction, (*e*) the Thorpe reaction,

(*f*) the Diels–Alder reaction, (*g*) the Clemmensen reduction, (*h*) the Knoevenagel reaction, (*i*) the Demjanov rearrangement.

8. Discuss the preparation and properties of (*a*) tropolone, (*b*) ferrocene, (*c*) *cyclo*hexene, (*d*) the paracyclophanes.

9. Write an essay on conformational analysis.

READING REFERENCES

Perkin, The Early History of the Synthesis of Closed Carbon Chains, *J.C.S.*, **1929**, 1347.

Gilman, *Advanced Organic Chemistry*, Wiley (1942, 2nd ed.). Vol. I, Ch. 2. Alicyclic Compounds and the Theory of Strain.

Norton, The Diels–Alder Diene Synthesis, *Chem. Reviews*, 1942, **31**, 319.

Organic Reactions, Wiley, Vol. IV (1948), Ch. 1 and 2. Vol. V (1949), Ch. 3. The Diels–Alder Reaction.

*cyclo*Polyolefins (Reppe), *B.I.O.S.*, No. 137; Item No. 22, London, H.M.S.O.

Ruzicka, Many Membered Carbon Rings, *Chem. and Ind.*, 1935, **54**, 2.

Craig, The Chemistry of Eight-Membered Carbocycles, *Chem. Reviews*, 1951, **49**, 103.

Cook and Loudon, The Tropolones, *Quart. Reviews* (*Chem. Soc.*), 1951, **5**, 99.

Brooks, *The Chemistry of Nonbenzenoid Hydrocarbons*, Reinhold (1950, 2nd ed.).

Prelog, Newer Developments of the Chemistry of Many-membered Ring Compounds, *J.C.S.*, **1950**, 420.

Cook (Ed.), *Progress in Organic Chemistry*, Butterworth, Vol. III (1955), Ch. 2. Non-Benzenoid Aromatic Compounds. Ch. 3. The Fulvenes.

Cram *et al.*, The Preparation of Paracyclophanes, *J. Amer. Chem. Soc.*, 1954, **76**, 4406.

Pauson, Ferrocene and Related Compounds, *Quart. Reviews* (*Chem. Soc.*), 1955, **9**, 391.

Braude, Linstead *et al.*, Hydrogen Transfer, *J.C.S.*, **1954**, 3578, 3586, 3595.

Klyne (Ed.), *Progress in Stereochemistry*, Butterworth. Vol. I (1954), Ch. 2. The Conformation of Six-membered Ring Systems.

Newman (Ed.), *Steric Effects in Organic Chemistry*, Wiley (1956), Ch. 1. Conformational Analysis.

Barton and Cookson, The Principles of Conformational Analysis, *Quart. Reviews* (*Chem. Soc.*), 1956, **10**, 44.

CHAPTER XX

AROMATIC COMPOUNDS

SIMPLE AROMATIC HYDROCARBONS

EARLY in the development of Organic Chemistry, organic compounds were arbitrarily classified as either aliphatic or aromatic. The aliphatic compounds were so named because the first members of this class to be studied were the fatty acids (see p. 33). The term *aliphatic* is now reserved for any compound that has an *open-chain* structure.

In addition to the aliphatic compounds, there was a large number of compounds which were obtained from natural sources, *e.g.*, resins, balsams, "aromatic" oils, etc., which comprised a group of compounds whose structures were unknown but had one thing in common: a pleasant odour. Thus these compounds were arbitrarily classified as *aromatic* (Greek: *aroma*, fragrant smell). Careful examination of these compounds showed that they contained a higher percentage carbon content than the corresponding aliphatic hydrocarbons, and that most of the simple aromatic compounds contained at least *six* carbon atoms. Furthermore, it was shown that when aromatic compounds were subjected to various methods of treatment, they often produced benzene or a derivative of benzene. If attempts were made to convert aromatic compounds into compounds with fewer carbon atoms than six (as in benzene), the whole molecule generally disrupted. It became increasingly evident that aromatic compounds were related to benzene, and this led to reserving the term aromatic for benzene and its derivatives. Thus aromatic compounds are *benzenoid* compounds; these are cyclic, but their properties are totally different from those of the alicyclic compounds.

Benzene (*phene*), C_6H_6, was first isolated by Faraday (1825) from cylinders of compressed illuminating gas obtained from natural sources. In 1845, benzene was found in coal-tar by Hofmann, and this is still the main source of benzene and its derivatives.

When coal is destructively distilled, four fractions are obtained: coal-gas, coal-tar, ammoniacal liquors and coke.

Coal-tar. The composition of coal-tar depends on the method of carbonisation, *viz.*, the type of retort used, the temperature and the time taken for carbonisation. Water is removed from tar by slow heating and the tar is then fractionated. The number of fractions taken varies; a typical sample is shown in Table IX.

TABLE IX

Number of fraction	Temperature range	Name of fraction	Specific gravity	Percentage by volume
1	Up to 170°	Crude light oil	0·970	2·25
2	170–230°	Middle oil or Carbolic oil	1·005	7·5
3	230–270°	Heavy oil or Creosote oil	1·033	16·5
4	270–360°	Green oil or Anthracene oil	1·088	12
5		Pitch (left in retort)		about 56

The crude light-oil fraction is washed successively with concentrated sulphuric acid, water, sodium hydroxide and water. The sulphuric acid removes basic substances such as pyridine, and also removes some of the thiophen; the sodium hydroxide removes phenols. The washed light oil is now distilled. Various fractions may be taken, *e.g.*, the fraction collected up to 110° is known as "90 per cent. *benzol*" (70 per cent. benzene, 24 per cent. toluene and some xylene). Pure xylene is obtained from the fraction between 110–140°. The distillate between 140–170° is known as "*solvent naphtha*" or *benzine* (consists mainly of xylenes, cumenes, etc.); it is used as a solvent for resins, rubber, paints, etc. The fraction "90 per cent. benzol" gives pure benzene, toluene and xylene on careful fractionation; about 9·5 per cent. benzene and 8·7 per cent. toluene are obtained from the crude light-oil fraction. Enslin *et al.* (1956) have separated mixtures of benzene homologues by means of reversed-phase partition chromatography.

Benzene was first synthesised by Berthelot (1870) by passing acetylene through a red-hot tube:

$$3C_2H_2 \longrightarrow C_6H_6$$

The polymerisation is more involved than this, since many other cyclic products are also obtained, *e.g.*, styrene and naphthalene (Goubeau *et al.*, 1953). Reppe *et al.* (1948) have shown that acetylene is converted into benzene (80 per cent. yield) in the presence of dicarbonyldi(triphenylphosphino)-nickel $[(CO)_2Ni(PPh_3)_2]$.

Benzene may be prepared in the laboratory by many methods, most of which depend on the decarboxylation of aromatic acids, *e.g.*, by heating benzoic acid with soda-lime:

$$C_6H_5\text{·}CO_2Na + NaOH/CaO \longrightarrow C_6H_6 + Na_2CO_3$$

or by heating phthalic acid with calcium oxide:

$$C_6H_4(CO_2H)_2 + 2CaO \longrightarrow C_6H_6 + 2CaCO_3$$

Preparation of benzene and its homologues from petroleum. Aromatic compounds can be extracted from petroleum in which they occur naturally. They are also prepared from the non-aromatic constituents of petroleum by two methods:

(i) **Hydroforming** or **catalytic reforming.** This method is based on dehydrogenation, cyclisation and isomerisation reactions, and the aromatic compounds obtained contain the same number of carbon atoms as the aliphatic starting materials. Very good catalysts which effect dehydrogenation and cyclisation are the oxides of chromium, vanadium and molybdenum carried on an alumina support. Hydroforming is carried out under a pressure of 150–300 lb./sq. in. at 480–550° in the presence of the catalyst. Cyclisation may be brought about on any paraffin or olefin having at least six carbon atoms in a straight chain. The mechanism of the reaction is not known with certainty, but it appears probable that the paraffin is first dehydrogenated to the olefin, which then cyclises to the aromatic hydrocarbon. The following are the most important examples of hydroforming:

$$\underset{n\text{-hexane}}{CH_3\text{·}(CH_2)_4\text{·}CH_3} \longrightarrow \underset{\text{benzene}}{C_6H_6} + 4H_2$$

$$\underset{n\text{-heptane}}{CH_3\text{·}(CH_2)_5\text{·}CH_3} \longrightarrow \underset{\text{toluene}}{C_6H_5\text{·}CH_3} + 4H_2$$

$$\underset{n\text{-octane}}{CH_3\text{·}(CH_2)_6\text{·}CH_3} \longrightarrow \underset{\text{xylene (three isomers)}}{C_6H_4(CH_3)_2} + \underset{\text{ethylbenzene}}{C_6H_5\text{·}C_2H_5}$$

It is interesting to note that catalytic reforming was originally intended to raise the octane number of petrol (see p. 52).

(ii) **High-temperature cracking in the presence of a catalyst.** This method was also originally used to raise the octane number of petrol. The charging stock may be cracked at about 650–680° in tubes packed with metallic dehydrogenation catalysts (which are the same as those used in hydroforming). By this means the following aromatic hydrocarbons have been isolated from the cracked paraffins: benzene, toluene, xylenes, naphthalene, anthracene and many other polynuclear hydrocarbons. There appears to be a large amount of evidence to show that the mechanism of the formation of the aromatic compounds is via the Diels–Alder reaction, *i.e.*, low-molecular-weight olefins and diolefins are produced in the cracking process, and these condense to form aromatic hydrocarbons as follows, *e.g.*,

$$ + \begin{matrix} CH_2 \\ \| \\ CH_2 \end{matrix} \longrightarrow \quad \longrightarrow \quad + 2H_2$$

If this is the mechanism of the reaction, then it is an example of the Diels–Alder reaction in which the dienophile does not contain a negative group (see p. 450). It should be noted, however, that the conditions used are not the same as those in the usual Diels–Alder reaction: this is carried out up to about 100°; cracking is carried out at a far higher temperature.

Properties of benzene. Benzene is a colourless liquid, m.p. 5·5°, b.p. 80°, with a peculiar smell. It is inflammable, burning with a smoky flame, a property which is characteristic of most aromatic but not of most aliphatic compounds, and is due to the high carbon content of the former. Benzene is insoluble in water, but is miscible with ethanol and ether in all proportions. It is a very good solvent for fats, resins, sulphur, iodine, etc., and is used in dry cleaning. It is also used as a motor fuel (" benzol ") and for the manufacture of nitrobenzene, dyes, drugs, etc.

Benzene is a very stable compound; it is very slowly attacked by a solution of chromic acid or acid permanganate (both powerful oxidising agents) to form carbon dioxide and water. It can be reduced catalytically to *cyclo*hexane, but the partially hydrogenated products, dihydro- and tetrahydrobenzene, have not been isolated in this reaction. Lithium in anhydrous ethylamine, however, reduces benzene to *cyclo*hexene and *cyclo*hexane (Benkeser *et al.*, 1955). It might also be noted here that nickel is an extremely good catalyst for the catalytic reduction of the benzene nucleus, whereas copper chromite is useful when it is desired to retain this nucleus, *i.e.*, to reduce a side-chain only. The heats of hydrogenation of benzene in stages have been calculated and the values found are

$$C_6H_6 \xrightarrow[-5\cdot6]{} C_6H_8 \xrightarrow[+26\cdot7]{} C_6H_{10} \xrightarrow[+28\cdot6]{} C_6H_{12} \quad \text{kg.cal./mole.}$$

These values indicate that the reduction of the first double bond is different from that of the second and third.

When heated with hydrogen iodide at 250°, benzene is converted into a mixture of *cyclo*hexane and methyl*cyclo*pentane. The action of chlorine and bromine on benzene depends on the conditions. In bright sunlight, halogen forms *addition* products with benzene, *e.g.*, chlorine adds on to form benzenehexachloride, $C_6H_6Cl_6$. In the absence of direct sunlight, benzene undergoes *substitution* with halogen; the reaction is slow, but in the presence of a halogen carrier, *e.g.*, iron or iodine, substitution is rapid. Thus, with chlorine, benzene forms chlorobenzene, C_6H_5Cl, dichlorobenzenes, $C_6H_4Cl_2$, etc. When benzene is heated with concentrated nitric acid or concentrated sulphuric acid, substitution products of benzene are obtained:

$$C_6H_6 + HNO_3 \longrightarrow C_6H_5{\cdot}NO_2 + H_2O$$
nitrobenzene

$$C_6H_6 + H_2SO_4 \longrightarrow C_6H_5{\cdot}SO_3H + H_2O$$
benzenesulphonic acid

Isomerism of benzene derivatives. Since all the six hydrogen atoms in benzene are equivalent (p. 484) only one monobromobenzene, mononitrobenzene, etc., is possible. In many compounds the univalent radical C_6H_5- is known as **phenyl,** and is represented by the abbreviation Ph or ϕ, *e.g.*, chlorobenzene may be written PhCl or ϕCl. When dealing with *any* univalent aromatic radical, the symbol Ar is used.

When two hydrogen atoms in benzene are replaced by two univalent radicals (which may be the same or different), three isomers are possible (position isomerism):

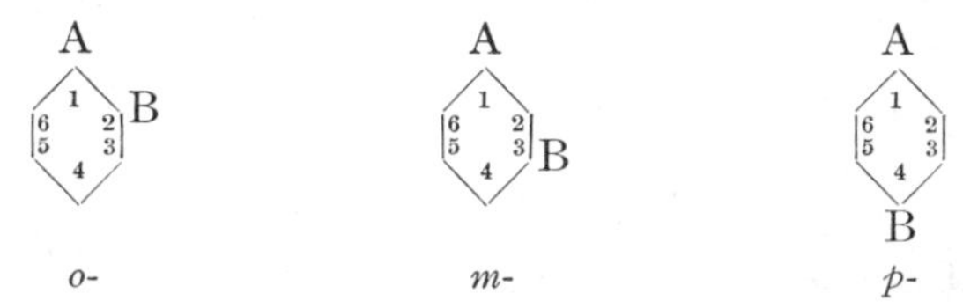

o- *m*- *p*-

Since the six hydrogen atoms in benzene are equivalent, the positions 1 : 2- and 1 : 6- are equivalent. The 1 : 2-(1 : 6-)disubstituted benzene derivative is known as the *ortho*- (*o*-) compound. The 1 : 3- and 1 : 5-positions are equivalent and a 1 : 3-(1 : 5)-disubstituted derivative is known as the *meta*-(*m*)-compound. The 1 : 4-disubstituted derivative is known as the *para*-(*p*)-compound. The bivalent radical $C_6H_4<$ is known as the **phenylene** radical, *e.g.*, *m*-phenylenediamine.

In the case of trisubstitution derivatives of benzene, the number of isomers depends on the nature of the substituent groups.

(i) If the three substituent groups are identical, then three isomers are possible:

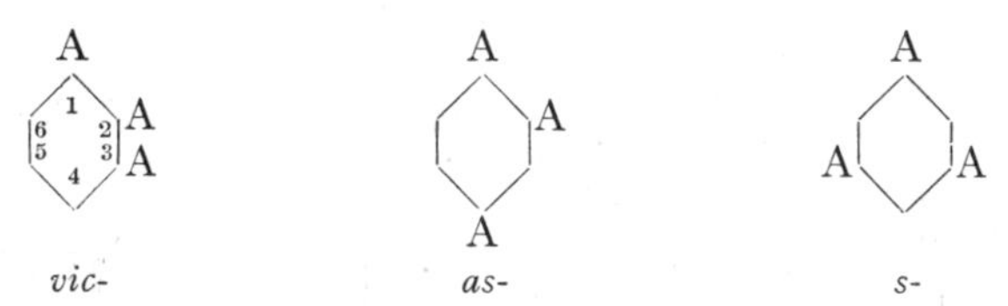

vic- *as*- *s*-

The 1 : 2 : 3-isomer is known as the *vicinal*- (*vic*-) compound; the 1 : 2 : 4- as the *unsymmetrical* or *asymmetrical* (*unsym*- or *as*-) compound; and the 1 : 3 : 5- as the *symmetrical* (*sym*- or *s*-) compound.

(ii) If two substituent groups are identical and the third different, then six isomers are possible.

(iii) If all three substituent groups are different, then ten isomers are possible.

There are no characteristic names for the individual isomers in groups (ii) and (iii), and so the positions of side-chains and substituent groups are indicated by numbers (this may also be applied to (i) and to disubstituted derivatives). Numbering is usually carried out to give the *lowest* sum (*cf.* p. 41. Prior to April, 1950, *British Chemical Abstracts* gave the number 1 to one of the following groups: CH_3, SO_3H, CO_2H, CN, CHO, OH, or NH_2. When two or more of these groups are present, the number 1 was always assigned to the group *earlier* in the list. The *Chemical Society* has now adopted the alphabetical order for prefixes (see p. 41), but when two or more *functional groups* are present, number 1 is to be given to the *principal* function. The usual order for choosing the principal function is given on p. 221. For convenience of fixing the orientation (position of groups), the ring should be oriented with position 1 at the top and with the numbers proceeding in a *clockwise* direction. If a letter (*o*, *m*, *p*) is used, the principal function is still given position 1. The general rule is: **if the functional group is named as a suffix, this group is given number 1.** In many cases, however, it may be better to name aromatic compounds by using the *trivial* names of the *simple* (or *parent*) hydrocarbon. When this scheme is used, *the root name decides where numbering starts.* The following examples show the application of the above rules:

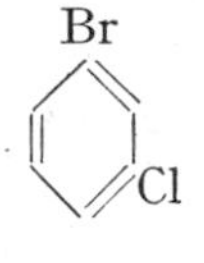

Br, Cl
1-bromo-3-chlorobenzene; *m*-bromochlorobenzene

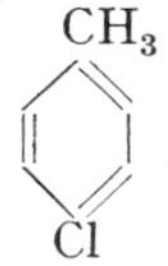

CH_3, Cl
p-chlorotoluene

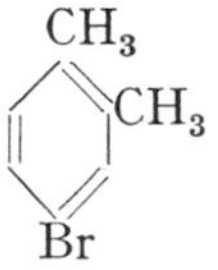

CH_3, CH_3, Br
4-bromo-1 : 2-dimethylbenzene (rule of lowest numbers); 4-bromo-*o*-xylene

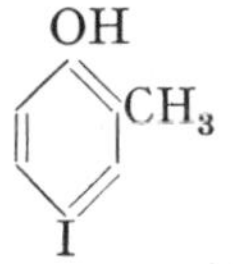

OH, CH_3, I
4-iodo-2-methylphenol; *p*-iodo-*o*-cresol (in both names, the suffix is -ol; therefore this group is given number 1)

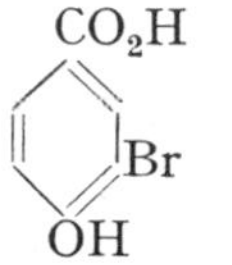

CO_2H, Br, OH
3-bromo-4-hydroxybenzoic acid; 3-bromo-*p*-hydroxybenzoic acid

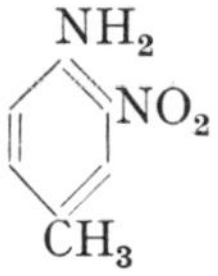

NH_2, NO_2, CH_3
2-nitro-*p*-toluidine (the amino-group is in the suffix; therefore this group is given position 1); 4-amino-3-nitrotoluene (toluene is the parent, and so numbering starts at the *methyl* group).

Structure of benzene. Analysis and molecular-weight determinations show that the molecular formula of benzene is C_6H_6. The corresponding paraffin is hexane, C_6H_{14}, and since the number of hydrogen atoms in benzene is much less, it is to be expected that benzene would exhibit marked " unsaturated reactions ". This is found to be so in practice, *e.g.*,

(i) Benzene adds on halogen, the maximum number of halogen atoms being six.

(ii) Benzene may be catalytically hydrogenated to *cyclo*hexane, the maximum number of hydrogen atoms added is six.

(iii) Benzene forms a *triozonide*, $C_6H_6(O_3)_3$.

All these reactions indicate that benzene contains *three* double bonds. Further examination, however, shows that these double bonds behave in a most remarkable manner in comparison with double bonds in aliphatic compounds, *e.g.*,

(iv) Alkaline permanganate has no action on benzene in the cold, but on prolonged boiling, benzene is broken down into carbon dioxide and water.

(v) In the absence of sunlight (and preferably in the presence of a halogen carrier), benzene undergoes substitution when treated with halogen (*cf.* however, *iso*butene, p. 76).

(vi) Halogen acids do *not* add on to benzene.

Reactions (i)–(vi) lead to the conclusion that benzene contains three double bonds, but that these double bonds are different from aliphatic double bonds. This difference gives rise to " aromatic properties " (unusual degree of saturation, stability, etc.; see also later). The problem was now to decide what is the structure of benzene, and this is one of the most interesting problems in organic chemistry; the final word still remains to be written.

Kekulé (1865) was the first to suggest a ring structure for benzene. He proposed formula I, and believed (*but did not prove*) that this formula satisfied the following points:

(i) That benzene contains three double bonds.

(ii) That all the six hydrogen atoms in benzene are equivalent; consequently there is only one possible mono-substituted derivative, and there are three possible disubstitution products of benzene.

Kekulé's theory stimulated a large amount of research into the structure of aromatic compounds, a notable result being achieved by Ladenburg in 1874, when he *proved experimentally* that all the six hydrogen atoms in benzene were equivalent.

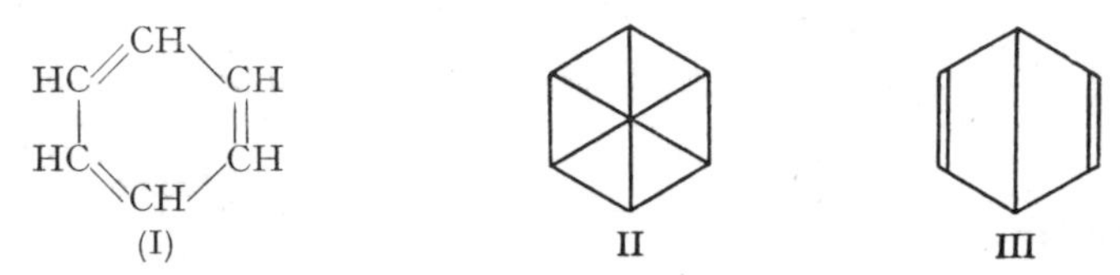

Kekulé's formula, however, did not explain the peculiar behaviour of the three double bonds in benzene. Claus (1867) therefore introduced his diagonal formula, (II), to overcome this difficulty. This formula also appeared to suggest a reason for the simultaneous formation of *o*- and *p*-compounds (see later). In 1882, Claus modified his formula, now postulating that the *para*-bonds were not like ordinary bonds, but could be easily ruptured.

Dewar (1867) suggested a number of formulæ for benzene, one being (III). This is not perfectly symmetrical and therefore was unacceptable (but see later). Ladenburg (1869) attacked Kekulé's formula on the grounds that it should give *four* disubstituted derivatives:

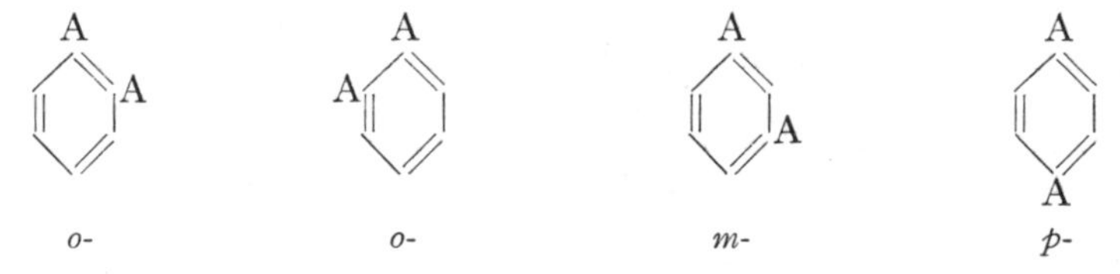

Thus there should be *two ortho*-derivatives, 1 : 2- and 1 : 6-; these have never been observed in practice. Ladenburg therefore proposed his prism formula, (IV). The six carbon atoms are at the corners of a regular prism, the edges of which denote linkages. This formula does not contain any double bonds, and therefore does not account for the addition products of benzene.

V. Meyer (1870) opposed Ladenburg; he pointed out that the 1 : 2- and 1 : 6-derivatives differed only in the position of double bonds and believed that this difference would be too slight to be noticeable. V. Meyer thus supported Kekulé's formula.

Kekulé (1872) felt that too much importance was being attached to the possible difference between the 1 : 2- and 1 : 6-positions, and pointed out that the difficulty arose from the inadequate representation of molecules by structural formulæ. According to Kekulé, the carbon atoms in benzene were continually in a state of vibration, and due to this vibration, each C—C pair had a single bond half of the time and a double bond the other half. This amounts to an oscillation between the two forms (V) and (VI), each molecule spending half its time in (V) and the other half in (VI). Thus neither (V) nor (VI) represents the benzene molecule satisfactorily; benzene is a " combination " of the two, and so all bonds will be identical (neither single nor double), and hence there is no real difference between 1 : 2- and 1 : 6-disubstituted benzenes.

(IV) 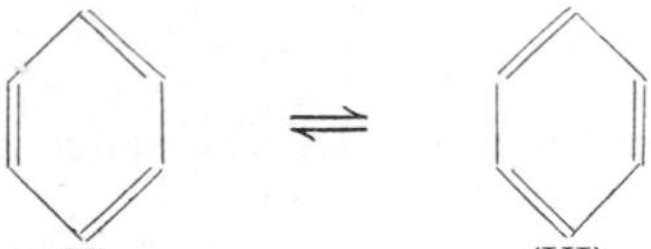 (V) ⇌ (VI)

In 1932, Levine and Cole subjected *o*-xylene to ozonolysis and obtained glyoxal, methylglyoxal and dimethylglyoxal. These authors supported Kekulé's oscillation (tautomeric) hypothesis, arguing that the three carbonyl compounds could not be obtained unless *two* forms of *o*-xylene were present (see, however, p. 484):

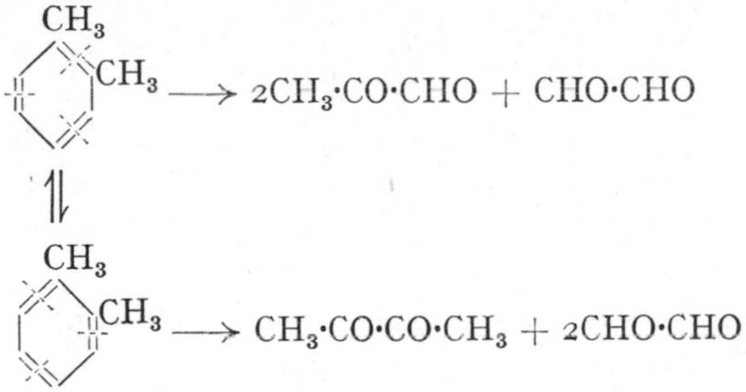

CH_3, CH_3 ⟶ $2CH_3·CO·CHO + CHO·CHO$

⇅

CH_3, CH_3 ⟶ $CH_3·CO·CO·CH_3 + 2CHO·CHO$

Baeyer (from about 1884–1892) carried out a detailed investigation of benzene and some of its derivatives in order to decide between the formulæ of Kekulé and Ladenburg. One of the first things Baeyer proved was that hexamethylene (*cyclo*hexane) and hexahydrobenzene were identical, thus establishing the ring structure of benzene (which Kekulé had assumed). Baeyer observed that as soon as one double bond was removed from benzene, the " saturation " properties were lost, and that dihydrobenzene (*cyclo*-hexadiene) behaved as would be expected of a diolefin. Baeyer showed that no *para* linkage was apparently present and hence rejected Claus' diagonal formula; he also rejected Dewar's formula for similar reasons. Baeyer also showed, by investigation of various benzene derivatives, that Ladenburg's prism formula was untenable. Baeyer concluded that benzene contained six carbon atoms in a ring, but did not accept Kekulé's formula. He adopted a suggestion of Armstrong (1887) and proposed what is known as the Armstrong–Baeyer centric formula (VII). According to this, the

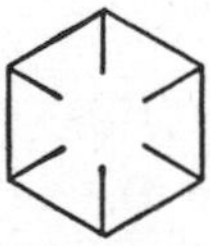

(VII)  (VIII)

fourth valency of each carbon atom is represented as directed towards the centre of the ring but not actually linked to its opposite neighbour as in the Claus formula. This centric bond is not real but potential; by mutual action the power of each is rendered latent and there is a condition of equilibrium. Such a centric formula is unknown in aliphatic chemistry, and thus this formula could account for "aromatic properties". When benzene is converted into dihydrobenzene,* the condition of equilibrium is destroyed, resulting in the production of normal double bonds:

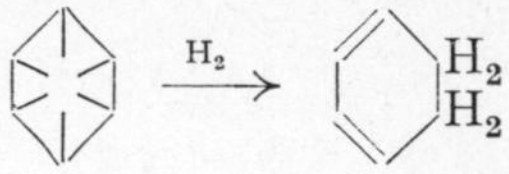

$$\xrightarrow{H_2} \quad H_2 \quad H_2$$

Thus this accounts for the difference in behaviour between benzene and its reduction products.

The centric formula, however, is unsatisfactory for several reasons, *e.g.*, it did not explain the stability of the ring or the behaviour of the polynuclear hydrocarbons. The outcome of Baeyer's work was that "aromatic properties" depend on the peculiar symmetrical arrangement of the fourth valency of each carbon atom in the ring.

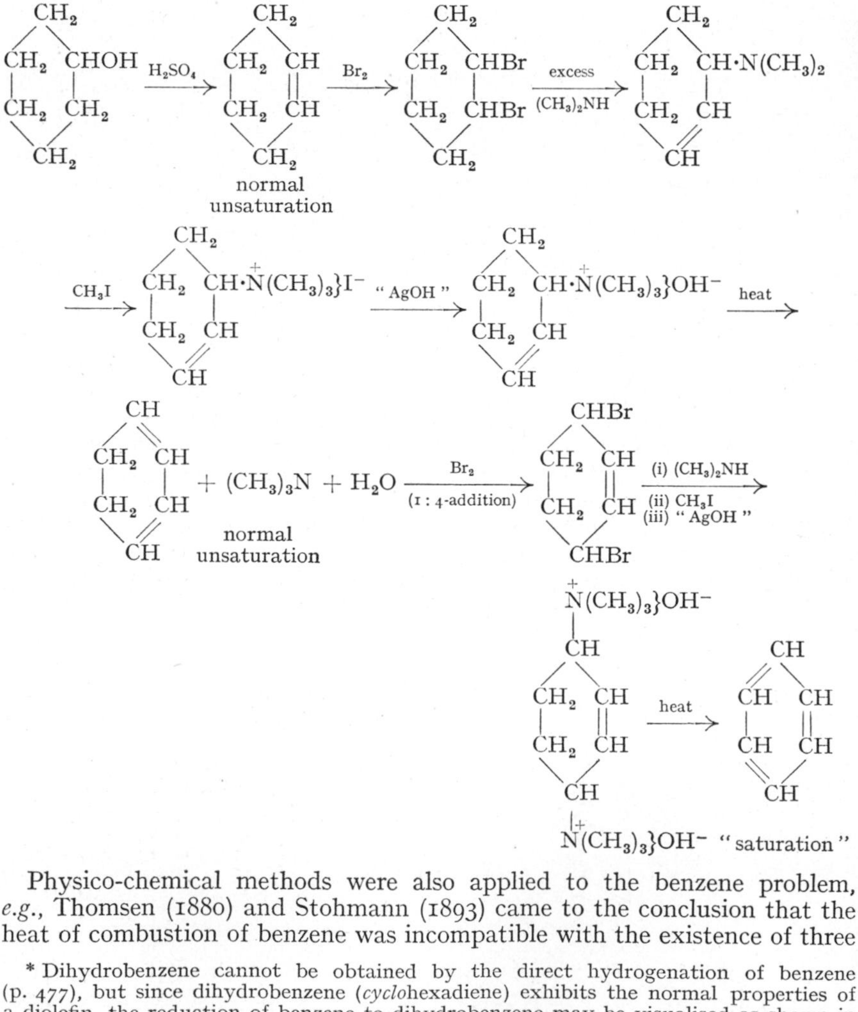

CH_2, CH_2, CHOH, CH_2, CH_2, CH_2 $\xrightarrow{H_2SO_4}$ CH_2, CH_2, CH, CH_2, CH, CH_2 (normal unsaturation) $\xrightarrow{Br_2}$ CH_2, CH_2, CHBr, CH_2, CHBr, CH_2 $\xrightarrow[(CH_3)_2NH]{excess}$ CH_2, CH_2, $CH{\cdot}N(CH_3)_2$, CH_2, CH, CH

$\xrightarrow{CH_3I}$ CH_2, CH_2, $CH{\cdot}\overset{+}{N}(CH_3)_3\}I^-$, CH_2, CH, CH $\xrightarrow{\text{"AgOH"}}$ CH_2, CH_2, $CH{\cdot}\overset{+}{N}(CH_3)_3\}OH^-$, CH_2, CH, CH $\xrightarrow{heat}$

CH, CH_2, CH, CH_2, CH, CH + $(CH_3)_3N$ + H_2O (normal unsaturation) $\xrightarrow[(1:4\text{-addition})]{Br_2}$ CHBr, CH_2, CH, CH_2, CH, CHBr $\xrightarrow[\text{(ii) } CH_3I \text{ (iii) "AgOH"}]{\text{(i) } (CH_3)_2NH}$

$\overset{+}{N}(CH_3)_3\}OH^-$, CH, CH_2, CH, CH_2, CH, CH, $\overset{+}{N}(CH_3)_3\}OH^-$ $\xrightarrow{heat}$ CH, CH, CH, CH, CH, CH "saturation"

Physico-chemical methods were also applied to the benzene problem, *e.g.*, Thomsen (1880) and Stohmann (1893) came to the conclusion that the heat of combustion of benzene was incompatible with the existence of three

* Dihydrobenzene cannot be obtained by the direct hydrogenation of benzene (p. 477), but since dihydrobenzene (*cyclo*hexadiene) exhibits the normal properties of a diolefin, the reduction of benzene to dihydrobenzene may be visualised as shown in the equation.

double bonds. On the other hand, Bruhl (1880) believed that the value of the refractive index of benzene proved their existence. These methods are particularly interesting in that they are some of the first examples of the application of physico-chemical methods to the elucidation of the structure of organic compounds.

In 1899, Thiele applied his theory of partial valency (p. 79) to the benzene problem, and suggested formula (VIII). This formula dispenses with Kekulé's oscillation hypothesis, and in this formula there is no real difference between " single " and " double " bonds, and so accounts for there being no difference between the 1 : 2- and 1 : 6-positions. At the same time it also accounts for the " saturation " of benzene.

The introduction of one double bond into *cyclo*hexane leads to normal unsaturated properties. Introduction of a second double bond enhances the addition reactivity, but the introduction of a third double bond causes " saturation ". Willstätter introduced successively one, two and three double bonds into *cyclo*hexanol as shown on p. 482 (using the method of exhaustive methylation; see p. 732).

The conclusion that may be drawn from this experiment is that the ring is intact, contains three double bonds, and that the introduction of the third double bond causes a complete change in properties of the resulting compound.

If Thiele's formula is correct, *i.e.*, " aromatic character " is due to the symmetrical conjugation of the benzene ring, then *cyclo*octatetraene should also exhibit " aromatic character ". Willstätter prepared this compound with a view to testing Thiele's formula for benzene, and found that it had typical unsaturated properties (see p. 461), whereas, owing to its symmetrical conjugation (structure IX), it would have been expected to resemble benzene (see also p. 485). This led to a revival of Kekulé's oscillation formulæ and some of the modifications mentioned (other than Thiele's formula). The difficulty with the Kekulé formula is that it represents benzene with three double bonds, and the oscillation does not account for the difference in behaviour between these and olefinic bonds.

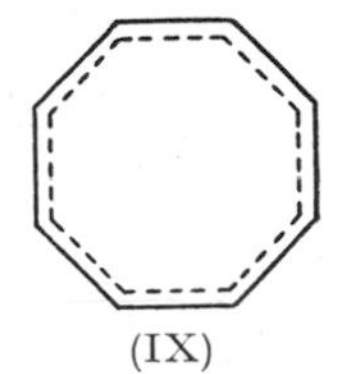
(IX)

Present-day position regarding the formula of benzene. The approach at the present time is still an attempt to account for the fourth valency of each carbon atom in the benzene ring. Related to this is the question of defining " aromatic character ", about which there is still no agreement. The general feeling is that " aromatic character " is the lack of reactivity of the double bonds in benzene, the stability of the ring system and the different behaviour of such groups as amino, hydroxyl, etc. (when they are attached to the benzene ring).

Many theories have been put forward to account for the lack of reactivity of the benzene ring. One of the early modern theories is the *aromatic sextet theory*, which was originally suggested by Bamberger (1891) and modified according to electronic theory by Robinson (1925), Ingold (1928) and Hückel (1931). The essence of the aromatic sextet theory is that there are six electrons more than necessary to link together the six carbon atoms. These six electrons, one electron being contributed by each carbon atom, form a " closed group ", and it is this closed group which gives rise to " aromatic properties ". This closed group is not possible in aliphatic compounds but is possible in heterocyclics, and so these also exhibit aromatic properties:

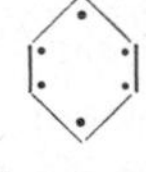
benzene

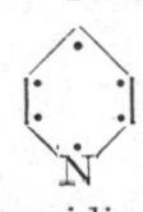

pyridine

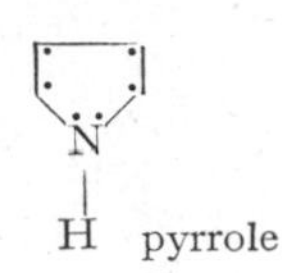

pyrrole

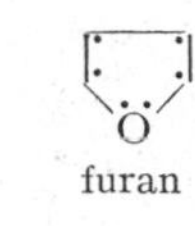

furan

It should be noted that the hetero-atom in five-membered rings contributes *two* electrons to the aromatic sextet.

A very highly favoured theory for the aromatic properties of benzene uses the idea of resonance. According to this, benzene is believed to be a resonance hybrid of the resonating structures (X–XIV):

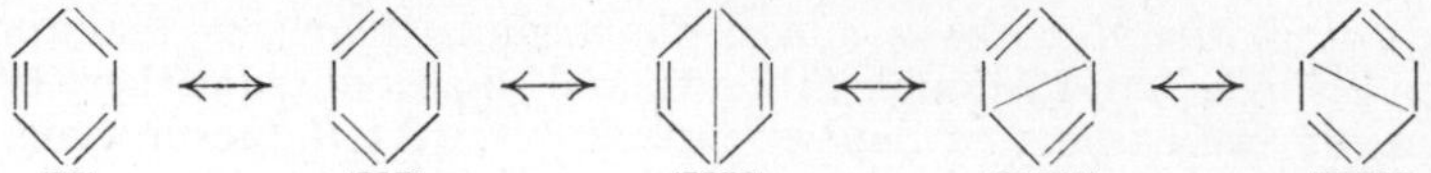

(X) ⟷ (XI) ⟷ (XII) ⟷ (XIII) ⟷ (XIV)

(X) and (XI) are Kekulé structures, which are far more stable that (XII), (XIII) and (XIV), which are Dewar structures. The instability of the latter is due to the formation of weak formal bonds (*cf.* butadiene, p. 81; it is interesting to note that a combination of the three Dewar structures gives, in effect, the Claus diagonal formula). Thus the Kekulé structures contribute far more to resonance (about 80 per cent.) than do the Dewar structures (about 20 per cent.). Furthermore, since the two Kekulé structures are equivalent, the stability of the resulting resonance hybrid is very high; the resonance energy of benzene has been shown to be about 39 kg. cal./mole. Resonance therefore makes benzene relatively stable in comparison with aliphatic unsaturated compounds; hence its " aromatic properties ".

Thermochemical calculations show that the heat change associated with the dehydrogenation of *cyclo*hexane to benzene, *i.e.*, the introduction of three double bonds, is about 85–95 kg. cal./mole. The experimental value is 48 kg. cal./mole. The difference, 37 kg. cal./mole, is attributed to resonance energy (this value agrees with that obtained by other methods). Thus benzene contains less energy than is expected and consequently is more stable than is expected.

Resonance gives each C—C bond in benzene some double bond character, and this has been shown to be so by measurements of the distance between two adjacent carbon atoms in various compounds. The C—C bond length (in ethane, propane, etc.) is 1·54A; the C=C bond (in ethylene) is 1·33A; and the C≡C bond (in acetylene) is 1·20A. The C—C bond length in benzene has been shown to be 1·39A, a value which lies between that of a single and that of a double bond. Furthermore, it has also been found that all the C—C bonds in benzene are the same, thus indicating the symmetrical nature of the benzene ring.

According to Haayman and Wibaut (1939), ozonolysis of *o*-xylene agrees with a resonating structure for the benzene ring. These authors found the composition of the mixture to be roughly 0·88 molecule dimethylglyoxal, 2 molecules methylglyoxal, and 3·2 molecules glyoxal. The calculated ratio should be 1 : 2 : 3 if the two Kekulé structures contribute equally; the experimental results agree fairly well with the theoretical value. The ozonolysis of *o*-xylene is an interesting example of the same experimental results being explained differently; one explanation is that *o*-xylene is a resonance hybrid (Haayman and Wibaut), and the other, a tautomeric mixture (Levine and Cole; p. 481).

In compounds of the type $Ca_2{=}Ca_2$, all the atoms are in the same plane (see p. 405). Since all the C—C bonds in benzene have double bond character due to resonance, it would therefore appear that the benzene ring should be planar, and that substituted groups should also be in the same plane (as the benzene ring). Evidence that the benzene ring is planar has been obtained from studies of X-ray analysis, dipole moments, Raman spectra, infrared spectra and electron diffraction photographs of benzene vapour.

Now let us consider the benzene molecule from the point of view of M.O. theory. Spectroscopic studies and X-ray analysis have shown that benzene is a regular flat hexagon (angle 120°), with all six hydrogen atoms lying in the same plane (of the ring) and each C—C—H valency angle also being 120°. *Thus each carbon atom is in a state of trigonal hybridisation.* Hence, in benzene, there are six σ C—H bonds, six σ C—C bonds and six $2p_z$ electrons (one on each carbon atom) which are all parallel and perpendicular to the plane of the ring (Fig. 1*a*).

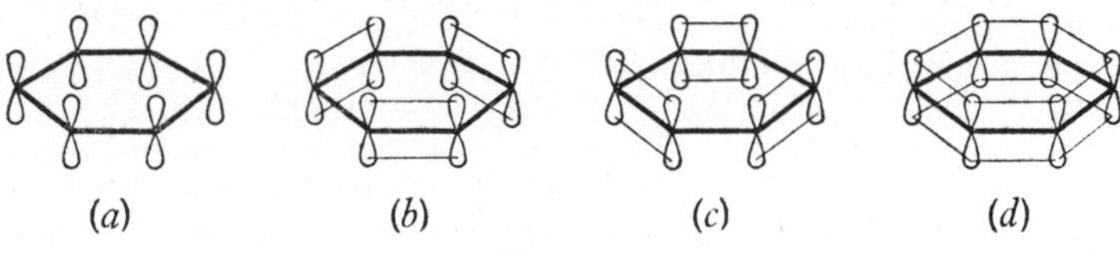

FIG. 20.1.

These electrons can be paired in two ways, both being equally good (*b* and *c*). Each $2p_z$ electron, however, overlaps its neighbours equally, and therefore all six can be treated as forming *an M.O. embracing all six carbon atoms,* and so are completely delocalised (Fig. *d*; *cf.* p. 81). Since six $2p_z$ electrons are involved, six M.O.s are possible, three bonding and three antibonding (p. 27). These are as shown ((I), (II), (III) are bonding, and (IV), (V), (VI) are anti-bonding); all have a node in the plane of the ring; but (II) and (III) have one node, (IV) and

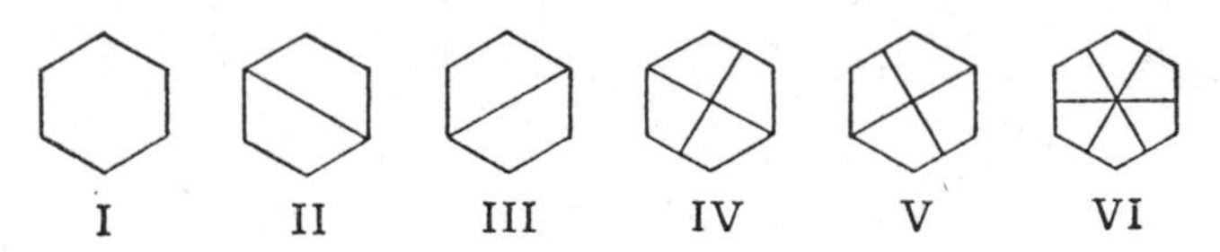

(V) two, and (VI) three nodes perpendicular to the plane of the ring. Now, as we have seen (p. 9), no more than two electrons can occupy any particular M.O. Furthermore, in the ground state, the six $2p_z$ electrons of benzene will occupy, in pairs, the M.O.s of lowest energy. These three are (I), (II) and (III) (these are the M.O.s in which the number of nodes are fewer than in (IV), (V) and (VI); see p. 27). When benzene is in an excited state (p. 22), one or more of the π-electrons will occupy the higher energy level M.O.s.

In the ground state, the total energy of the three pairs of *delocalised* π-electrons (Fig. *d*) is less than that of three pairs of *localised* π-electrons (Fig. *b* or *c*), and hence the benzene molecule is stabilised by delocalisation (resonance).

It appears probable that the unique character of aromatic compounds is the presence of six *carbons atoms* (*in the trigonal state*) *in a ring that is planar.* Only this number can give rise to a *completely* strainless planar structure. If the π-electrons in *cyclo*-octatetraene were delocalised, the molecule would be planar, and therefore under strain (p. 462). It is possibly this strain that prevents the molecule becoming planar, and consequently prevents the appearance of aromatic properties. On the other hand, ultra-violet absorption spectrum studies have shown that the tropolone ring is *planar* (p. 461). Presumably it is under some strain, but not enough to prevent delocalisation, and so will exhibit aromatic properties.

From the foregoing it can be seen that one could define aromatic compounds as those *cyclic* compounds in which *all the ring atoms are embraced by one M.O.* Such compounds will therefore have a large delocalisation energy (resonance energy). The ring may be *homocyclic* (*i.e.*, contain only carbon atoms) or *heterocyclic* (*i.e.*, contain one or more atoms other than carbon). Furthermore, the rings may be odd or even, *provided a " closed circuit " of six π-electrons is present.* In odd-membered rings, one atom must supply *two p*-electrons (see heterocyclic compounds).

In writing the benzene formula, it is usual to use the Kekulé formula. Moreover, owing to the arguments about the double bonds, chemists early adopted the plane hexagon, ⬡, which is still often used. This is referred to as the *benzene ring* or *benzene nucleus*, and any carbon radical joined to the nucleus is known as the *side-chain*.

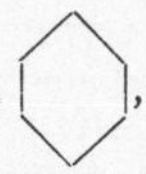

Orientation. The problem of assigning positions of substituents in disubstituted and higher substituted derivatives of benzene is known as *orientation*.

(i) **Körner's absolute method** (1874). This method is based on the principle that the introduction of a third substituent into the *p*-isomer gives *one* trisubstituted product, the *o*-isomer *two*, and the *m*-isomer *three* trisubstituted products. Körner applied this principle to establish the orientation of the isomeric dibromobenzenes. He nitrated each isomer and examined the number of nitrated products. One isomer gave *one* dibromo-nitrobenzene; this isomer is therefore the *p*-compound. Another gave *two* dibromo-nitrobenzenes; this is therefore the *o*-compound; and the third gave *three* and is therefore the *m*-compound:

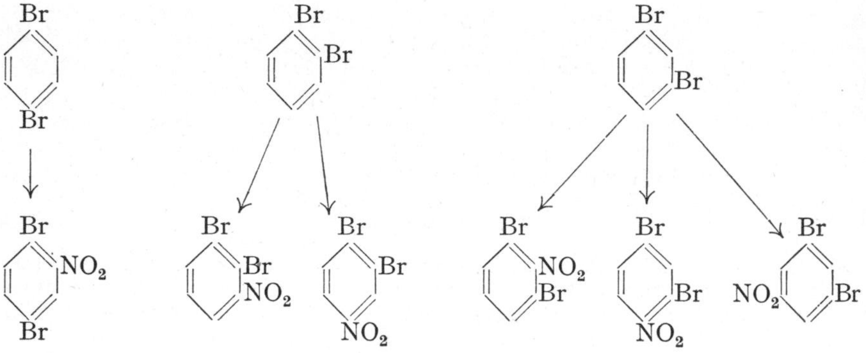

Br Br Br
Br Br Br
Br Br Br Br Br Br
NO_2 Br NO_2 Br NO_2 Br Br NO_2 Br
Br NO_2 Br NO_2

Körner also introduced a third bromine atom instead of a nitro-group (the number of isomers produced is independent of the nature of the third substituent).

In practice, this method is often difficult, if not impossible, since all the trisubstituted products cannot always be isolated due to the formation of some in very small amount.

The reverse procedure to Körner's method is often useful, *i.e.*, one group of the isomeric trisubstituted derivatives is removed, *e.g.*, Griess (1874) distilled the six diaminobenzoic acids (all known) with soda-lime. He obtained three phenylenediamines; three acids gave the same diamine, which is therefore the *m*-isomer; two acids gave the same diamine, which is therefore the *o*-isomer; and one acid gave one diamine, which is therefore the *p*-isomer.

(ii) **The relative method.** In this method the compound in question is converted into or synthesised from a substance of *previously determined orientation*; *e.g.*, reduction of one or both nitro-groups in *m*-dinitrobenzene gives rise to *m*-nitroaniline and *m*-phenylenediamine respectively:

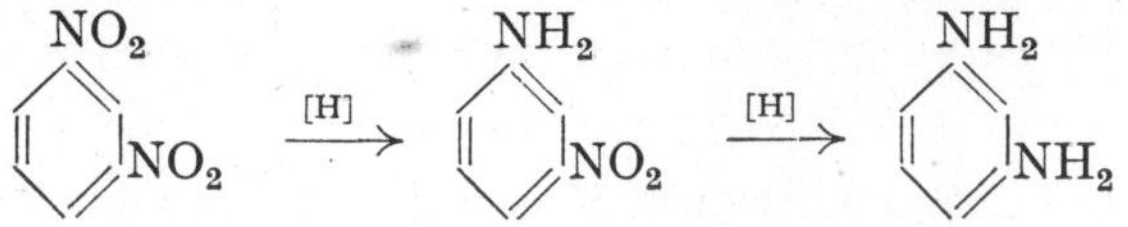

NO_2 NH_2 NH_2
NO_2 $\xrightarrow{[H]}$ NO_2 $\xrightarrow{[H]}$ NH_2
m-isomer *m*-isomer *m*-isomer

Another example is the *replacement* of one group by another, *e.g.*, *m*-benzenedisulphonic acid on fusion with sodium hydroxide gives *m*-dihydroxybenzene:

$$C_6H_4(SO_3H)_2 \xrightarrow{NaOH} C_6H_4(OH)_2$$

A classical example of the relative method of orientation is the case of the three benzenedicarboxylic acids. This starts with mesitylene. Mesitylene may be prepared by distilling acetone with sulphuric acid, and Baeyer *assumed* it to be *s*-trimethylbenzene, arguing that the reaction can be

$$3CH_3\cdot CO\cdot CH_3 \xrightarrow{H_2SO_4} C_6H_3(CH_3)_3 + 3H_2O$$

formulated only if the symmetrical structure of mesitylene is assumed. This assumption was later proved correct by Ladenburg (1874). Mesitylene may be converted into dimethylbenzene, which, in turn, may be converted into a benzenedicarboxylic acid:

$$\underset{\text{mesitylene}}{C_6H_3(CH_3)_3} \xrightarrow[HNO_3]{\text{dilute}} \underset{\text{mesitylenic acid}}{C_6H_3(CH_3)_2CO_2H} \xrightarrow[\text{lime}]{\text{soda-}} C_6H_4(CH_3)_2 \xrightarrow{KMnO_4} \underset{\textit{iso}\text{phthalic acid}}{C_6H_4(CO_2H)_2}$$

The dimethylbenzene must be the *m*-isomer whichever methyl group in mesitylene is oxidised. Hence the benzenedicarboxylic acid must be the *m*-isomer, which is known as *iso*phthalic acid. Of the three isomeric benzenedicarboxylic acids only one, phthalic acid, forms the anhydride; the other two, *iso*phthalic acid and the one known as terephthalic acid, do not form anhydrides at all. Thus phthalic acid is the *o*-isomer (by analogy with succinic acid; *cf.* p. 357); and terephthalic acid is consequently the *p*-isomer:

$$C_6H_4(CO_2H)_2 \longrightarrow C_6H_4{<}^{CO}_{CO}{>}O + H_2O$$

Another example of the relative method is the nitration of *o*- and *p*-nitrotoluenes; both give the *same* dinitrotoluene derivative, which, therefore, must be the *m*-dinitro-compound:

$$o\text{-}CH_3C_6H_4NO_2 \xrightarrow{HNO_3} CH_3C_6H_3(NO_2)_2 \xleftarrow{HNO_3} p\text{-}CH_3C_6H_4NO_2$$

The relative method of orientation is based on the assumption that atoms or groups remain in the same positions or exchange positions with the incoming groups. It is also based on the assumption as to the structure of the *starting* material. Sometimes one or both of these assumptions are right, and sometimes they are wrong. Baeyer's assumption for the mesitylene formula was correct. On the other, hand, *o*-, *m*- and *p*-bromobenzene-sulphonic acids all give *m*-dihydroxybenzene (resorcinol) when fused with sodium hydroxide. These fusions are carried out at about 300°, and since the conditions are vigorous, the interpretation of the results always contains an element of doubt. Thus Körner's absolute method is more satisfactory theoretically, but unfortunately it is often difficult to carry out in practice (see below).

(iii) **Method of dipole measurements.** In those cases where the two substituents are either atoms or simple groups, the determination of the dipole moment of the compound may often be used to ascertain the orientation, *e.g.*, the dichlorobenzenes. The observed dipole moment of the C—Cl bond (in chlorobenzene) is 1·55D. By using this value, it is possible to calculate the dipole moments of the *o*-, *m*- and *p*-dichlorobenzenes, and by comparing these calculated values with those observed, the orientation of the isomers may be decided:

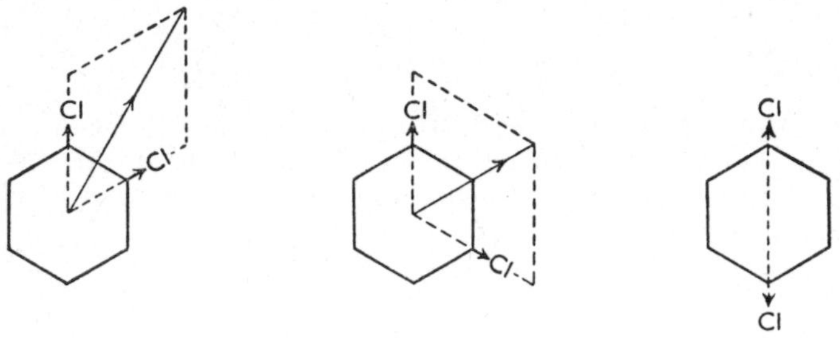

	o-	*m*-	*p*-
calc.	2·67 D	1·55 D	O
obs.	2·3 D	1·48 D	O

Substitution in the benzene ring. When one group is introduced into the benzene ring, only one compound is produced. When, however, a second group is introduced, three isomers are possible:

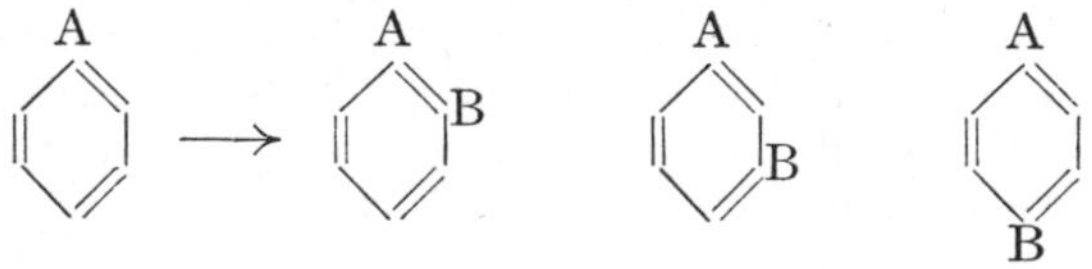

Holleman (1895, onwards) studied aromatic substitution in great detail, and found that *when the second group enters the benzene nucleus, the main product is either a mixture of the* o- *and* p-*isomers or the* m-*isomer.* Pure *o*-*p*- or *m*-substitution is rare, all three isomers being obtained simultaneously; but since the velocities of their formation are very different, the slowest one results in the formation of very little of that derivative (hence the difficulty of Körner's absolute method of orientation). Holleman (1910) found that the rate of *o*-*p*-substitution is very much greater than *m*-; *e.g.*, if phenol is treated with bromine-water, *s*-tribromophenol is obtained extremely rapidly (and quantitatively); thus the *o*- and *p*-positions are very active. On the other hand, when nitrobenzene is brominated, *m*-bromonitrobenzene (60–70 per cent. yield) is obtained. This reaction, however, is slow; thus the *m*-position is not very active.

Experiments of this kind have led to the conclusion that usually *o*-*p*-

substitution is associated with *activation* of the benzene nucleus, *i.e.*, reaction is faster than in benzene itself, whereas *m*-substitution is associated with *deactivation* of the nucleus, *i.e.*, reaction is slower than in benzene.

Rules of orientation. Experience shows that the nature of group A already present in the nucleus determines the position taken by the incoming group.

Class I directs the incoming group to the *o*- and *p*-positions. In this class, A may be any one of the following:—R, OH, OR, NH_2, NH·R, NR_2, $NH·CO·CH_3$, Cl, Br, I, F, CH_2Cl, SH, Ph, etc.

Class II directs the incoming group to the *m*-position. In this class, A may be any one of the following:—NO_2, CHO, CO_2H, CO_2R, SO_3H, SO_2Cl, $CO·CH_3$, CN, CCl_3, etc.

It is important to remember that each of the above groups directs *mainly* to the *o-p-* or *m*-positions; the direction is not *exclusively* one or the other.

Many *empirical* rules have been formulated to predict the course of substitution in the benzene ring.

Körner (1874), *Hübner* (1875) and *Noelting* (1876) suggested that basic or weakly acidic groups produce *o-p*-substitution, whereas strongly acidic groups produce *m*-substitution; *e.g.*, the basic amino-group, NH_2, and the weakly acidic phenolic group, OH, are *o-p*-orienting; the strongly acidic carboxyl and sulphonic acid groups, CO_2H and SO_3H, are *m*-orienting.

Crum-Brown and Gibson Rule (1892). According to this rule, if compound HA can be directly oxidised to HAO, then A is *m*-orienting. If HA cannot be directly oxidised to HAO, then A is *o-p*-orienting. *E.g.*, if A is the nitro-group, then HA is HNO_2; now HNO_2 can be directly oxidised to HNO_3; therefore the nitro-group is *m*-orienting. If A is OH, then HA is H_2O. H_2O cannot be directly oxidised to H_2O_2, and therefore OH is *o-p*-orienting. Actually, however, at high temperature, the following equilibrium exists:

$$2H_2O + O_2 \rightleftharpoons 2H_2O_2$$

Also, when water is exposed to ultra-violet light in the presence of air (oxygen), hydrogen peroxide is produced.

When A is CH_3, HA is CH_4, and HAO is CH_3OH. Since methane can be directly oxidised to methanol, CH_3 should therefore be *m*-orienting; actually it is *o-p*. Thus there are exceptions to the Crum-Brown and Gibson rule, and these arise from the difficulty of deciding the meaning of *direct* oxidation.

Vorländer's rule (1902). According to this rule, if A has unsaturated valencies it is *m*-orienting, *e.g.*, NO_2, SO_3H, CN, etc. If A is saturated it is *o-p*-orienting, *e.g.*, CH_3, OH, Cl, etc. This rule has exceptions, *e.g.*, in cinnamic acid, $C_6H_5·CH = CH·CO_2H$, A is $CH = CH·CO_2H$. This should produce *m*-substitution, but in practice it is *o-p*-orienting.

Hammick–Illingworth Rule (1930). (i) If in the benzene derivative $C_6H_5·XY$, Y is in a higher group in the periodic table than X, or if, being in the same group, Y is of lower atomic weight than X (*i.e.*, *higher* in the same group), then a second atom or group entering the nucleus goes to the *m*-position.

(ii) In all other cases, including that in which XY is a single atom, *o-p*-substitution takes place.

(iii) The effect of ionic charges on XY is given by the statement that a positive charge directs *m*- and a negative charge *o-p*-.

It is important to note that when the atoms joining the groups X and Y are the same, *e.g.*, —N=N—, —C=C—, the group XY is *o-p*-orienting (this follows from statement ii). For mixed groupings, *e.g.*, $CHCl_2$, CH_2Cl, etc., the strict rule may be applied and thereby the correct orientation will be obtained. Thus in $CHCl_2$ the part CH is *o-p*-orienting and the part CCl, *m*-; in practice, both orientations are obtained.

Of all the empirical rules of orientation, the Hammick–Illingworth rule is the most satisfactory. There are apparently only two exceptions, the nitroso- and iodoxy-groups (see p. 497).

Another kind of approach to the problem of orientation was presented by

Flurscheim (1902), who proposed the *theory of alternating affinities*. Subsequently, Vorländer (1919), Lapworth (1920) and Fry (1921) all put forward a somewhat similar theory—*the theory of alternating polarities* (which is essentially similar to Flurscheim's theory). According to these theories, if group A is a *positive* group, then *m*-substitution takes place; if A is a *negative* group, then *o-p-*. The charged group is supposed to produce positive and negative charges alternately in the nucleus as shown, and substitution occurs in the positions negatively charged:

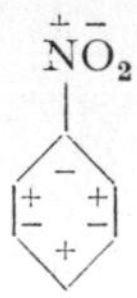

$\overset{+\,-}{NO_2}$ $\overset{-\,+}{NH_2}$

positive group 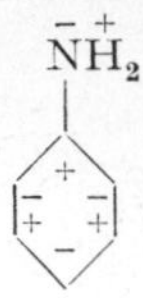 negative group

It follows from this theory of alternating polarities that changing the sign of the charge on group A will bring about a change in orientation. Thus one group under different conditions can change its orienting influence, *e.g.*, (*a*) the carboxyl group is normally *m*-orienting. If, however, substitution is carried out on the sodium salt, *i.e.*, with the carboxylate *ion*, $—CO_2^-$, present, then *o-p*-substitution results. (*b*) The amino-group is normally *o-p*-orienting, but in strongly acid solution, *i.e.*, when the $—\overset{+}{N}H_3$ ion is present, a large amount of *m*-substitution takes place.

The present-day position with regard to the directive power of groups is essentially in agreement with the theory of alternate polarities, but gives a more precise explanation for the production of the charges in group A and in the various positions in the ring (see later). Furthermore, quantitative experiments have shown that the actual amounts of each isomer produced depend on the temperature, nature of the solvent and the presence or absence of catalysts (see text).

Introduction of a third group into the benzene ring. The position taken up by a third group entering the ring depends on the nature of the two groups already present. Experiments by Holleman have shown that:—

(i) When both groups belong to class I, the directive power of each group is in the following order:

$$OH > NH_2 > NR_2 > NH{\cdot}CO{\cdot}CH_3 > Cl > Br > I > CH_3$$

If the *p*-position is unoccupied, then generally this position is entered preferably to the *o*-, *i.e.*, more of the *p*-isomer is formed than the *o*-, *e.g.*,

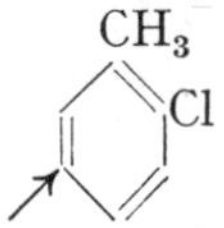

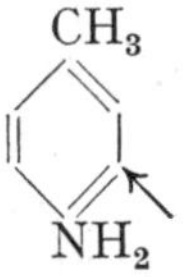

CH_3 Cl CH_3 NH_2

(ii) When both groups belong to class II, then it is difficult to introduce a third group, and the directive power of each group is:

$$CO_2H > SO_3H > NO_2$$

Thus (number of arrow-heads represent qualitatively the amount of substitution):

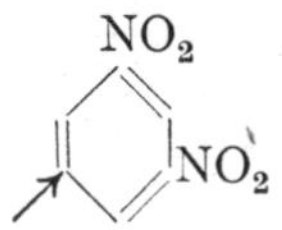

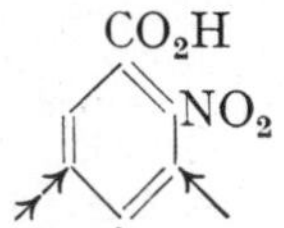

NO_2 NO_2 CO_2H NO_2

two isomers

(iii) When the two groups direct differently, *i.e.*, belong to classes I and II, then class I takes precedence. Furthermore, if the orientations reinforce each other, the third group enters almost entirely one position, *e.g.*,

CH_3 ... NO_2 Cl ... NO_2

two isomers

Separation of isomers. This usually means the separation of the *o*- and *p*-isomers. There are three common methods:

(i) Steam distillation may be used, since the *o*-isomer is often steam-volatile whereas the *p*- is not. This method of separation is particularly applicable to *o*-hydroxy-compounds.

(ii) The boiling points of *o*- and *p*-isomers are often very close together and so it is difficult to separate them by fractional distillation. Their melting points, however, are usually very different, that of the *p*-isomer being much higher than that of the *o*-. Thus these isomers may be separated by filtration; it may be necessary to cool the mixture in order to get the *p*-isomer in the solid form.

(iii) Chemical methods of separation may be used in certain cases (see, *e.g.*, p. 584).

MECHANISM OF AROMATIC SUBSTITUTION

There are three possible mechanisms for aromatic substitution: electrophilic, nucleophilic and free-radical. Of these the common substitution reactions are those which involve electrophilic reagents.

Electrophilic substitution. All the evidence obtained from kinetic studies of electrophilic substitutions has shown that these reactions occur by an S_E2 mechanism involving the intermediate formation of a transition state. Let us first consider the case of benzene itself. A theoretically possible transition state is one in which the attacked carbon atom changes its state of hybridisation from trigonal to tetrahedral (Wheland, 1942). Thus this carbon atom is removed from conjugation with the rest of the system, but the latter, although no longer benzenoid, still has a conjugated system which exhibits resonance. This resulting positive ion is known as the *pentadienyl* (*pentadienate*) *cation* (*cf.* p. 457).

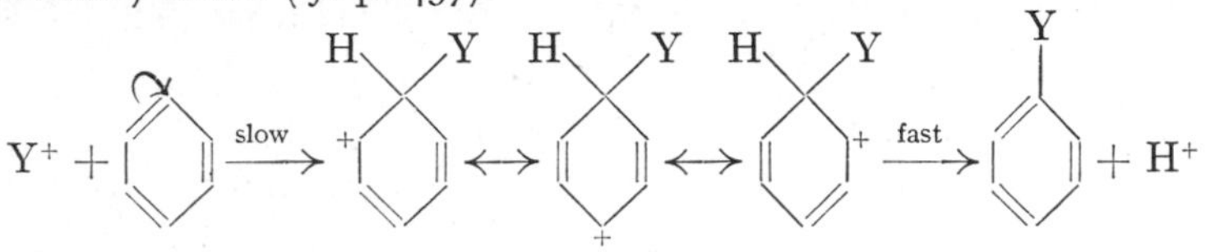

Y^+ + C_6H_6 $\xrightarrow{\text{slow}}$ [H, Y ... +] $\longleftrightarrow$ [H, Y ... +] $\longleftrightarrow$ [H, Y ... +] $\xrightarrow{\text{fast}}$ C_6H_5Y + H^+

The three resonating structures contributing to the transition state are often combined, and the transition state is then represented as follows:

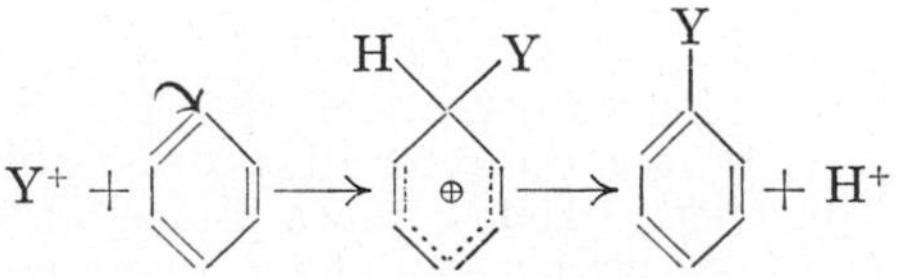

Y^+ + C_6H_6 $\longrightarrow$ [H, Y ... ⊕] $\longrightarrow$ C_6H_5Y + H^+

The resonance energy of this cation will not be as great as that of benzene, but by the expulsion of a proton the molecule can revert to the benzenoid state.

Consideration of the mechanism of aromatic substitution from the M.O. point of view gives much the same picture as described above. A transition state is formed as before, but now two of the original six π-electrons forming the "closed circuit" are partially localised to form a σ-bond with the attacking electrophilic reagent. Formation of this bond in the transition state involves change from trigonal to tetrahedral hybridisation at the carbon atom where reaction actually occurs. The remaining four π-electrons occupy M.O.'s embracing the other five carbon atoms, *i.e.*, a delocalised pentadienyl cation exists in the transition state. Because of the partial localisation to form a σ-bond, this transition state is also called a σ-complex.

Effect of substituents in electrophilic substitution. It has been previously pointed out (p. 488) that the rules of orientation are empirical. It is possible, however, to obtain a definite physical basis for orientation from the electronic theories of organic chemistry. As a result of a very large amount of work, it has been found that at least three factors must be considered, the most widely studied of which is the polar effect of the substituent group on the nucleus. The other two factors are discussed later (see *ortho-para* ratio, p. 498).

Polar effects. In *o-p*-substitutions group A causes these positions to become points of high electron density; hence substitution will take place in the *o-p*-positions with electrophilic reagents. Furthermore, owing to the *increased electron density* in the *o-p*-positions, group A is associated with *activation* of the benzene ring, *i.e.*, further substitution is facilitated by the presence of an *o-p*-orienting group.

In *m*-substitution, group A causes a withdrawal of electrons from the *o*- and *p*-positions, leaving the *m*-position practically unaffected. Thus the *m*-position becomes a point of *relatively* high electron density, and so substitution takes place in the *m*-position with electrophilic reagents. Since the *m*-position is *almost unaffected*, and the *o*- and *p*-positions *decrease in electron density*, group A is associated with *deactivation* of the benzene ring, *i.e.*, further substitution is made more difficult by the presence of a *m*-orienting group.

The problem that now confronts us is: How are changes in electron densities brought about by group A? The following detailed account shows that these are caused by the inductive, electromeric and resonance (mesomeric) effects.

When the group present in the ring is OH, OR, NH_2, etc., the product of further substitution is mainly *o-p*. A property common to all these groups is that the atom adjacent to the nucleus—the "key atom"—has at least one lone pair of electrons. The resonance effect gives rise to *increased* electron densities in the *o-p*-positions, *e.g.*,

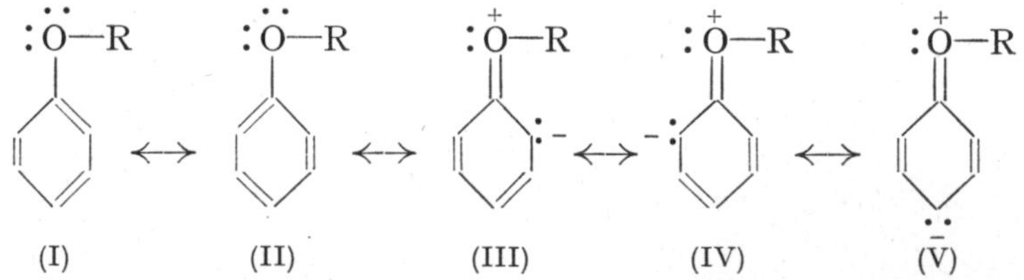

(I) ⟷ (II) ⟷ (III) ⟷ (IV) ⟷ (V)

(I) and (II) are the normal structures; (III) and (IV) are *o*-quinonoid, and (V) is *p*-quinonoid. (I–V) are the resonating structures, $C_6H_5{\cdot}O{\cdot}R$ being a resonance hybrid of them. Hence the actual state of $C_6H_5{\cdot}O{\cdot}R$ is a molecule having small negative charges at the two *o*-positions and at the *p*-position. Thus substitution with electrophilic reagents takes place in these positions, and is facilitated owing to the excess electron densities, since it is reasonable to suppose that an electrophilic reagent will attack at the point where the electron density is highest. Ingold speaks of these electronic displacements as the *Mesomeric Effect* (M). When the electronic displacement is *away* from the group and *towards* the ring, the effect is said to be +M; if in the opposite direction, then −M.

In addition to the *permanent* resonance effect (mesomeric effect), there will also be present the *Electromeric Effect* (E), which is brought into play by the attacking reagent. Thus:

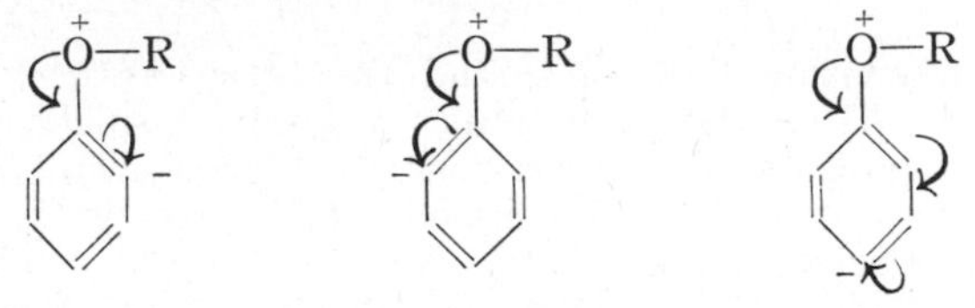

It can be seen that the electromeric effect assists the resonance effect and so at the demand of the attacking reagent (electrophilic) the *o*- and *p*-positions become strongly activated. Since the Electromeric Effect (E) is used in the same sense as the Mesomeric Effect (M) it can be seen that *o*-*p*-substitution will take place when the effects are +M and +E. The sum of these two effects is known as the *Tautomeric Effect* (T).

In addition to the M and E effects. Ingold has proposed the *Inductomeric Effect*, and has summarised the possible polar influences of groups as follows (see also p. 15):

Electronic Mechanism	Electrical Classification	
	Polarisation (permanent)	Polarisability (time-variable)
General Inductive (→—) (I)	Inductive (+ or −I)	Inductomeric
Tautomeric (↷) (T)	Mesomeric (+ or −M)	Electromeric (+ or −E)

When the group present in the ring is NO_2, CO_2H, COR, SO_3H, etc., the product of further substitution is mainly *m*-. All these groups, by virtue of having at least one strongly electron-attracting atom and a double or triple bond conjugated to the benzene ring, cause an electron displacement *away* from the nucleus and towards the group (*i.e.*, a −M effect), *e.g.*, $C_6H_5 \cdot CO \cdot R$, $C_6H_5 \cdot NO_2$ and $C_6H_5 \cdot SO_3H$.

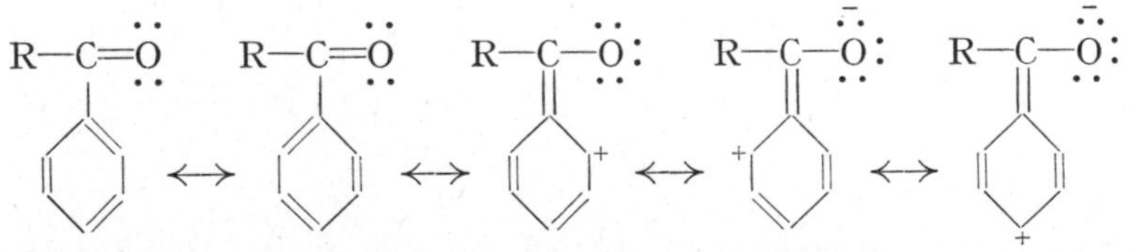

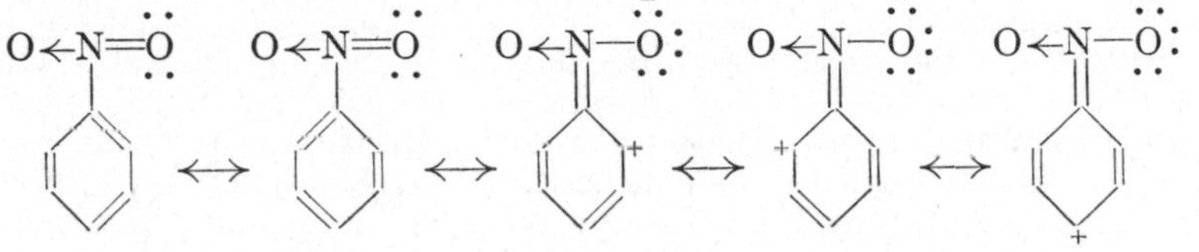

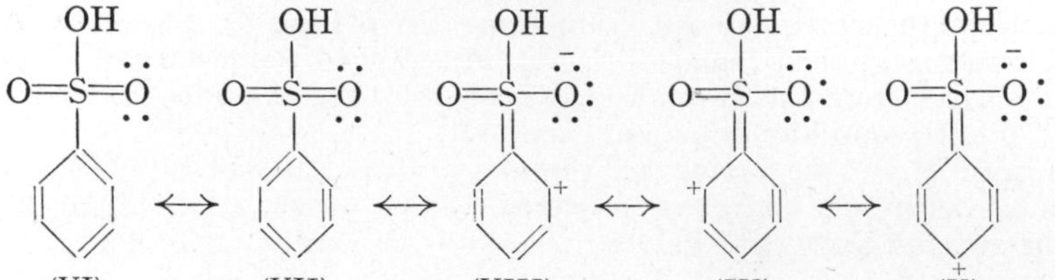

(VI) ⟷ (VII) ⟷ (VIII) ⟷ (IX) ⟷ (X)

(VI–X) are resonating structures, and the actual states of C_6H_5·CO·R, C_6H_5·NO_2 and C_6H_5·SO_3H are molecules which have small positive charges in the *o*- and *p*-positions, *i.e.*, the *m*-positions have a *relatively* high electron density with respect to the *o*-*p*-positions. The above groups are therefore *m*-orienting to electrophilic reagents.

The relative high electron density of the *m*-positions with respect to the *o*-*p*-positions is due to the *withdrawal* of electrons from the *o*-*p*-positions (*i.e.*, —M effect), and not due to a gain of electrons in the *m*-positions. Hence *m*-substitution is due to deactivation of the whole nucleus, particularly in the *o*-*p*-positions.

The electromeric effect will assist the resonance effect in deactivating the ring, and so for *m*-substitution we have —M —E, *i.e.*, —T. Furthermore, since all *m*-orienting groups contain at least one strongly electron-attracting atom, the inductive effect of this atom will also help to withdraw electrons from the *o*-*p*-positions. In this case the M, E and I effects all assist one another, the net result being —T —I.

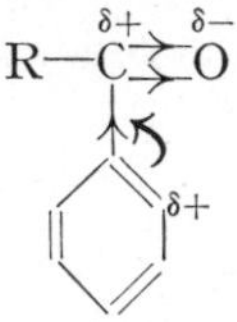

The electron-attracting power (I effect) of an atom alone cannot decide whether the substituent atom or group will be *o*-*p*- or *m*-orienting; *e.g.*, Cl, OH, NH_2, etc. have a strong —I effect and therefore tend to withdraw electrons from the ring, *i.e.*, the —I effect tends to promote *m*-substitution, and not *o*-*p*- as is the case in practice. The "key-atom" in all of these groups, however, has at least one lone pair of electrons, and consequently both the resonance and electromeric effects are possible. Since these effects together are stronger than the I effect, the above atoms or groups become *o*-*p*-orienting, *e.g.*,

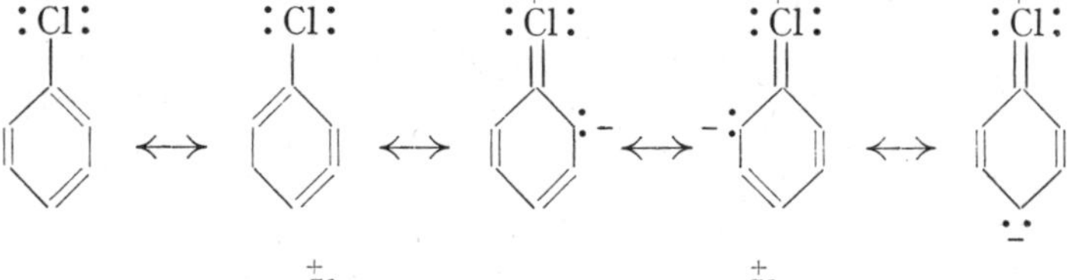

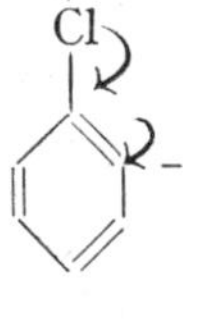

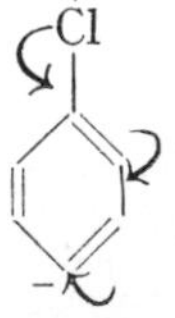

Thus for C_6H_5Cl, we have +T —I, and since T is greater than I, the result is *o*-*p*-substitution.

Although chlorine is *o*-*p*-orienting, it is more difficult to nitrate chlorobenzene than benzene, *i.e.*, chlorine *deactivates* the ring (*cf.* above). According to Ingold (1933), the —I effect of chlorine deactivates the ring, and the +M effect is too small to be significant. When, however, the +E effect is brought into play by the attacking reagent, the *o*- and *p*-positions are raised in electron density above the *m*-, but the increase is not as great as that which occurs in benzene itself. Consequently, although chlorine is *o-p*-orienting, it deactivates the ring.

As we have seen in the foregoing, the amino-group in aniline is *o-p*-orienting; *e.g.*, bromination of aniline produces 2:4:6-tribromoaniline; nitration with nitric acid produces a mixture of *o*- and *p*-nitroanilines. On the other hand, if the nitration is carried out in the presence of concentrated sulphuric acid, a large amount of *m*-nitroaniline is obtained. This is believed to be due to the formation of the $-\overset{+}{N}H_3$ group, the positive charge of which exerts a strong $-I$ effect, thereby withdrawing electrons from the ring; also, there is now no lone pair (on the nitrogen atom) available for the $+M$ and $+E$ effects. Thus the *o*- and *p*-positions become points of low electron densities and so *m*-substitution takes place. This effect of the positive charge is well brought out by the nitration of the following compounds (Ingold, 1926, 1927):

Side-chain . .	$\cdot\overset{+}{N}Me_3$	$\cdot CH_2\cdot\overset{+}{N}Me_3$	$\cdot(CH_2)_2\cdot\overset{+}{N}Me_3$	$\cdot(CH_2)_3\cdot\overset{+}{N}Me_3$
m- (per cent.) . .	100	88	19	5

The amount of *m*-substitution decreases with increasing length of the carbon chain (the inductive effect decreases rapidly from the source). Other positive centres also behave in a similar manner, and it should be noted that positively charged substituents are the strongest types of *m*-orienting groups. Furthermore, the *m*-orienting power for key atoms in the same periodic group decreases as the atomic weight increases, *i.e.*, $\overset{+}{N}>\overset{+}{P}>\overset{+}{As}>\overset{+}{Sb}$. Although each of these atoms has a unit positive charge, the nucleus becomes progressively larger (from left to right) and consequently nuclear screening increases.

Since *m*-substitution is 100 per cent. when the side-chain is $\overset{+}{N}Me_3$, this would suggest that there is a very large difference in electron densities at the *m*- and *p*-positions. Roberts *et al.* (1951), however, have shown that the charge densities in these two positions do not differ very much. Thus some other factor operates. Since the transition state is formed as an intermediate, the relative stabilities of the *o*-, *m*- and *p*-transition states will be a factor in deciding the position taken up by the entering group (but see below). Roberts *et al.* have shown that the *m*-transition state is more stable than the *p*-, the energy difference being 10 kg. cal., a value large enough to account for the complete *m*-substitution actually observed.

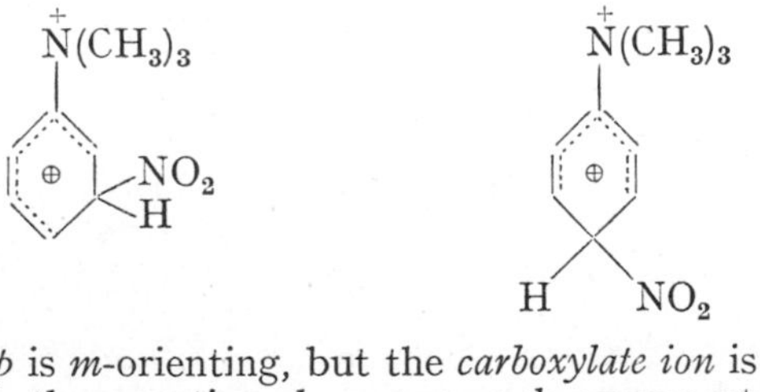

$\overset{+}{N}(CH_3)_3$ ⊕ NO$_2$ H $\overset{+}{N}(CH_3)_3$ ⊕ H NO$_2$

The *carboxyl group* is *m*-orienting, but the *carboxylate ion* is *o-p*-orienting. This is attributed to the negative charge on each oxygen atom giving the carboxylate ion

δ+ δ+ C=O OH   δ− δ− C O$^{-\frac{1}{2}}$ O$^{-\frac{1}{2}}$

electron-repelling properties (+I) in contrast to the carboxyl group which is electron-attracting (−I).

Similarly, on the −I effect of a carboxyl group, it would be expected that *m*-substitution would result in cinnamic acid. In practice, however, the

δ+ δ+ —CH=CH—C(=O)OH

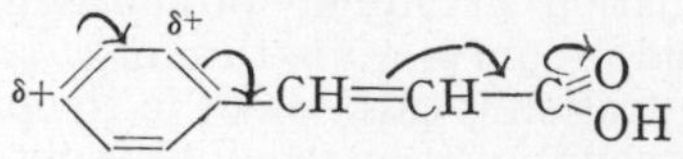

main product is a mixture of the *o*- and *p*-compounds. This has been attributed to the *o*- and *p*-transition states being more stable than the *m*-, and so reaction occurs through the former rather than the latter (Roberts *et al.*, 1951).

It has already been stated that the generally accepted theory of electrophilic aromatic substitution is that it probably proceeds through the transition state (σ-complex), and that the formation of this intermediate is the rate-determining step. Melander (1950) has shown that in nitration and bromination there is no hydrogen isotope effect; he showed that tritium and protium are displaced at essentially identical rates. This indicates that the breaking of the C—H bond has made little or no progress in the rate-determining transition states of these reactions. Recent kinetic studies, together with isotope effect measurements, have also established a two-step mechanism, *i.e.*, via a transition state, for certain coupling reactions, etc. (Zollinger, 1955; Schubert *et al.*, 1956). Hammond (1955), however, does not think that the evidence obtained from the kinetic isotope effects is conclusive in showing that the formation of the transition state is rate-determining.

The polar effect of an alkyl group in the alkylbenzenes is particularly interesting. Since alkyl groups are electron-repelling (+I), the *o*-*p*-positions become points of high electron density, and consequently alkyl groups are

R→ δ− R→ δ−

o-*p*-orienting. Since the order of the inductive effect of alkyl groups is (p. 97):

methyl<ethyl<propyl<*iso*propyl<*t*.-butyl

the dipole moment of the alkylbenzenes should be greatest for *t*.-butylbenzene and least for toluene. This has been found to be so in practice. It can also be expected that *p*-methylbenzyl bromide would ionise more readily than benzyl bromide, and this also has been shown to be so experimentally.

—CH_2—Br CH_3→ —CH_2—Br

Furthermore, on the basis of increasing electron-release from methyl to *t*.-butyl, it would be expected that the ease of ionisation of the bromine atom would reach a maximum in *p*-*t*.-butylbenzyl bromide. In practice, however, the results are exactly reversed, the electron-releasing effect being greatest in *p*-methylbenzyl bromide. Thus some effect other than the inductive effect must be operating. This effect, as we have seen, has been explained by hyperconjugation (p. 253). Hyperconjugation decreases as the number of hydrogen atoms linked to the α-carbon atom decreases, *i.e.*, hyperconjugation is a maximum with the methyl group and a minimum (zero) with the *t*.-butyl group. Thus there are two effects operating to activate the *o*- and *p*-positions, the inductive being greatest in the *t*.-butyl group and the hyperconjugative being greatest in the methyl group. In toluene, the hyperconjugative (no-bond resonance) and +I effect will produce *o-p*-substitution (the latter effect has been described above):

$$\mathrm{H_2\overset{H}{\ddot{C}}-C_6H_5 \longleftrightarrow H_2C{=}\overset{\overset{+}{H}}{}\;C_6H_5^{\ddot{-}} \longleftrightarrow H_2C{=}\overset{\overset{+}{H}}{}\;C_6H_5\!:^-}$$

In *t.*-butylbenzene only the inductive effect operates to give *o-* and *p*-substitution. When *p-t.*-butyltoluene is nitrated, the main product is the one with the nitro-group *ortho* to the methyl. Thus the hyperconjugative effect of the methyl group is greater than the inductive effect of the *t.*-butyl group. (This discussion has omitted the effects of steric hindrance at the *o*-position; see *ortho-para* ratio, p. 498, for an account of this problem.) Thus, on the *hyperconjugative* effect, one would expect the dipole moment of methylbenzene to be greater than that of *t.*-butylbenzene (which would be zero). As we have seen above, the values are actually reversed. The reason for this is not certain. According to Baker (1939), the inductive effect increases from toluene to *t.*-butylbenzene, but the dipole moment of the former is due mainly to hyperconjugation and that of the latter mainly to induction.

Hyperconjugation may also be used to explain, for example, the *m*-orienting power of the CCl_3 group:

$$\mathrm{Cl_2\overset{Cl}{\ddot{C}}-C_6H_5 \longleftrightarrow Cl_2C{=}\overset{\bar{Cl}}{}\;C_6H_5^{+} \longleftrightarrow Cl_2C{=}\overset{\bar{Cl}}{}\;C_6H_5^{+}}$$

The general effect of a substituent on the introduction of a second group may be summarised as follows:

(i) +I substituent: increases *o*-reactivity more than *p*-.
(ii) −I ,, : decreases *o*- ,, ,, ,, *p*-.
(iii) −M ,, : decreases *p*- ,, ,, ,, *o*-.
(iv) +T ,, : increases *p*- ,, ,, ,, *o*-.
(v) Steric factor : decreases *o* reactivity.

From the M.O. point of view, the methyl group of toluene can behave as a "compound atom" with a π-orbital, and this conjugates with the benzene ring (Fig. 2; *cf.* p. 255). This produces an increase in charge densities at the *o-* and *p*-positions.

The *m*-orienting effect of the CCl_3 group may be explained by assuming that one chlorine atom ionises. This leaves the carbon atom with a positive charge. The "closed circuit" of the benzene ring can now extend itself to cover this carbon atom, thereby stabilising the molecule (Fig. 3). This extended conjuga-

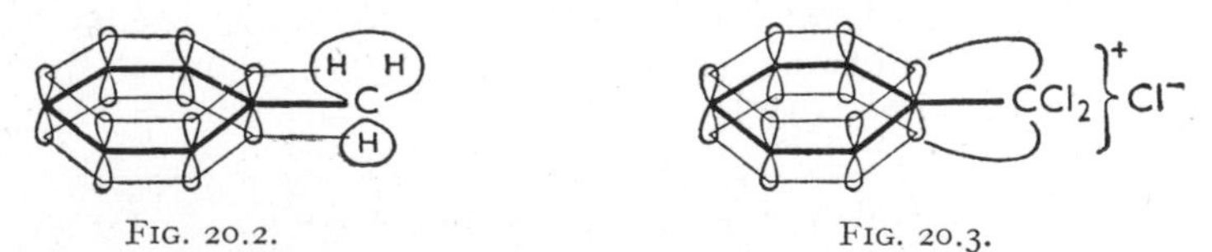

FIG. 20.2. FIG. 20.3.

tion can probably be extended further by contributions of the p_z lone pairs on each of the two chlorine atoms remaining attached to the carbon atom. The final result is a decrease in charge densities at the *o-* and *p*-positions.

It has been pointed out (p. 489) that the nitroso- and iodoxy-groups are apparently exceptions to the Hammick–Illingworth rule. Thus, if the nitroso-group had the same effect as a nitro-group, then it should give rise to *m*-substitution with electrophilic reagents. Unfortunately, electrophilic reagents, when used in the usual way, destroy the nitroso-group. Ingold (1925) and Le Fèvre (1931), however, nitrated and brominated nitrosobenzene under special conditions and obtained the *p*-derivatives. If we assume that no unusual factors (*e.g.*, dimerisation; see p. 290) were operating under these special conditions, the results may be explained by the operation of a + E effect (I) in nitrosobenzene. On the other hand, it appears that − E effect (II) can operate in the presence of a nucleophilic reagent, *e.g.*, in *o*- and *p*-bromonitrosobenzene the bromine is readily removed by hydrolysis. This indicates that the nitroso-group is acting in the same way as a nitro-group, *i.e.*, it is *m*-orienting to electrophilic reagents and *o*-*p*- to nucleophilic reagents. Thus nitrosobenzene can undergo two electromeric directions, and the direction will be determined by the nature of the attacking reagent.

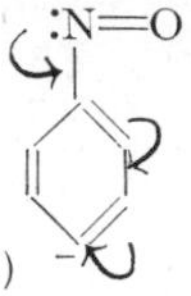

:N=O :N=O

(I) 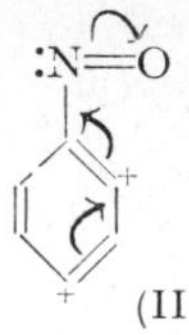 (II)

According to the Hammick–Illingworth rule, the iodoxy-group, IO_2, would be expected to be *o*-*p*-orienting. It has been shown, however, that this group is *m*-orienting, *e.g.*, nitration of iodoxybenzene produces almost 100 per cent. of the *m*-derivative (Masson *et al.*, 1935). Thus the iodoxy-group is *m*-orienting in *acid* solution, and this may be due to the formation of a positive charge on the iodine atom, *i.e.*, to the formation of $C_6H_5—\overset{+}{I}O_2$.

***Ortho-para* ratio.** Since there are two *o*-positions and only one *p*-position, it might be expected that there would be twice as much *o*- as *p*-substitution if the group present affected the electron density of each position to the same extent, *i.e.*, the *o*/*p* ratio should be 2/1. This is rarely observed in practice; for some substituents *o*-substitution is favoured, and for others *p*-substitution.

Theoretical considerations of Hughes and Ingold (1937) have shown that in the formation of the transition state (pentadienyl cation or σ-complex; p. 491), the entering group should approach the ring in a *lateral* direction with respect to the plane of the ring, *i.e.*, approach (and ejection) of groups can only occur in a direction at right angles to the ring. Hence it is reasonable to infer that, in addition to its polar effects, the actual size of the *o*-substituent and the entering group, *i.e.*, steric (spatial) effects, will also operate in determining the amount of *o*- and *p*-substitution. This purely spatial effect will affect only the *o*-positions. Polar effects, as we have seen, are transmitted mainly to the *o*- and *p*-positions, with very little change in the *m*-positions. Thus the *m*/*p* ratio will indicate only the polar influences at these two positions, whereas the *o*/*m* and *o*/*p* ratios will indicate effects due to both polar and spatial influences. The following results have been obtained for mononitration (1, Jones *et al.*, 1947; 2 and 3, Brown *et al.*, 1954; 4, Nelson *et al.*, 1951):

No.	Compound	*o*	*m*	*p*	*o*/*p*	*o*/*m*	*p*/*m*
1	Ph·Me	58·5	4·4	37·2	1·57	13·3	8·5
2	Ph·Et	45	6·5	48·5	0·93	6·9	7·5
3	$Ph·CHMe_2$	30	7·7	62·3	0·48	3·9	8·1
4	$Ph·CMe_3$	15·8	11·5	72·7	0·22	1·4	6·3

It can be seen that as the size of the alkyl group increases, the proportion of the *o*-product decreases. The question then is: Is this purely a spatial effect, or are there in addition some other factors operating? One possible influence is that due to hyperconjugation, since this decreases from methyl to *t*.-butyl (p. 496). The ratio *p/m*, however, does not vary much in this series, and so it may be concluded that the *polar* effects of the four alkyl groups are nearly the same (Nelson, 1951). This conclusion is supported by other work, and thus the decreased *o*-substitution can be attributed to the steric requirements of the alkyl substituents.

In addition to the steric effect of the substituent group, there is also the steric effect of the *entering* group. Thus it has been shown that in the alkylation of toluene, as the size of the entering group increases, so the *o/p* ratio decreases.

de la Mare *et al.* (1956) found that the ratio of isomers produced in the acid-catalysed bromination of toluene by hypobromous acid is: *o*-, 70·3%; *m*-, 2·3%; *p*-, 27·4%. The reagent was a positively charged brominating species, either the brominium cation Br^+ or the hypobromous acidium ion $BrOH_2^+$. The reaction is thus electrophilic, and there is a great similarity in partial rate factors between this bromination (I) and nitration (II). The results, however, show more resistance to the *o*-entry of the nitro-group than to the bromo-group. de la Mare has explained this by suggesting that in the transition state the initially *linear* nitronium ion now becomes distorted (*triangular*), and therefore the effective radius of the nitro-group in the direction of the flanking *o*-methyl group is likely to be greater than that of the spherical bromine substituent.

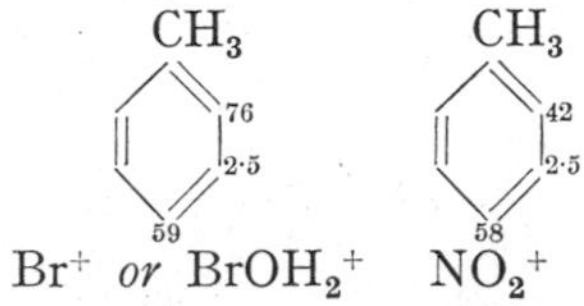

CH_3 (76, 2·5, 59) Br^+ *or* $BrOH_2^+$ (I)

CH_3 (42, 2·5, 58) NO_2^+ (II)

The existence of the steric factor is also supported by spectroscopic work. When, owing to steric hindrance, the two substituent groups are forced out of the same plane, one spectral effect is a decrease in absorption intensity. The absorption intensity of the *p*-halogenonitrobenzenes is in the order I>Br>Cl>F, and the order of the *o*-compounds is the reverse. This difference is attributed to the steric inhibition of uniplanarity of the phenyl and nitro-groups by the *o*-halogen substituent. At the same time, the energy of activation (in the transition state) is also affected (Brown *et al.*, 1955).

Not only must the polar and steric factors be considered, but also one arising from the electrostatic forces set up between the substituent and the entering group, *e.g.*, Sandin *et al.* (1947) nitrated aryl halides and obtained the following results:

Compound	*o*	*p*	*o/p*
C_6H_5F	12·6	87·4	0·14
C_6H_5Cl	30·1	73·1	0·41
C_6H_5Br	37·2	62·5	0·59

All the halogens are *o*-*p*-orienting, and since the halogen *increases* in size from fluorine to bromine, then, on the basis of the steric effect also operating, the ratio *o/p* would be expected to fall. This ratio, however, actually rises, and so some other factor must be operating. One explanation that has been offered is that there is interaction between the C—X bond moment and the entering group Y, and that these forces will be different for the *o*- and *p*-positions in the transition state (the C—X dipole *decreases* from F to Br).

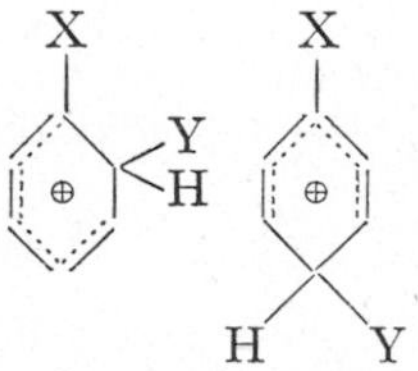

X, Y, H, ⊕ — X, ⊕, H, Y

Nucleophilic substitution. Nucleophilic substitution in benzene itself is not known to occur, but it does occur in various substituted benzenes, and here again the general opinion is that the reaction proceeds via a transition state. For benzene itself, *if* the reaction were possible, the substitution could be written:

$$Y^- + C_6H_6 \xrightarrow{\text{slow}} [C_6H_6Y]^- \leftrightarrow [C_6H_6Y]^- \leftrightarrow [C_6H_6Y]^- \xrightarrow{\text{fast}} C_6H_5Y + H^-$$

Thus the transition state (σ-complex) in this case is the *pentadienyl anion*, and may be written as (III). When a *m*-orienting group is present in the benzene nucleus, there will be a deficiency of electrons in the *o*- and *p*-positions, and so it is these positions which are attacked by nucleophilic reagents. Furthermore, it appears that substitution of hydrogen by a nucleophilic reagent occurs only when nitro groups are present, *e.g.*, when heated with sodium hydroxide, nitrobenzene is converted into *o*-nitrophenol.

$$C_6H_5NO_2 + OH^- \longrightarrow C_6H_4(OH)NO_2 + H^-$$

(III)

The term nucleophilic aromatic substitution is also used for *replacement reactions* in which substituents such as Cl, Br, NO_2, etc., are expelled together with their bonding electrons and replaced by the attacking nucleophilic reagent such as OH^-, OCH_3^-, etc. This type of nucleophilic aromatic substitution can occur either by the S_N2 mechanism, *e.g.*, the conversion of chlorobenzene into phenol:

$$C_6H_5Cl + NaOH \xrightarrow{300^\circ} C_6H_5OH + NaCl$$

or by an S_N1 mechanism, *e.g.*, the uncatalysed decomposition in water of benzenediazonium salts to phenol:

$$C_6H_5{\cdot}N_2^+ \xrightarrow{\text{slow}} N_2 + C_6H_5^+ \xrightarrow[\text{fast}]{H_2O} C_6H_5OH$$

It should also be noted that nucleophilic aromatic substitution can occur with rearrangement, the entering group taking up a position different from that of the expelled group (*cf.* the relative method of orientation, p. 486; see also cine-substitution, p. 521).

Finally, there is also the type of nucleophilic aromatic substitution often referred to as *activated nucleophilic aromatic substitution.* In this type of substitution, the replacement of a group is facilitated by the presence of an *o*- or *p*- strongly negative group (see, *e.g.*, chloronitrobenzenes, p. 522).

Free-radical substitution. In homolytic substitution, since the attacking agent is uncharged, it might be expected that the (polar) orienting influence of the substituent would be without effect, *i.e.*, the ratios of *o* : *m* : *p* would be 2 : 2 : 1. In practice, however, substitution is mainly *o*- and *p*-, irrespective of the nature of the group already present in the ring. Three transition states are possible (*pentadienyl radicals*) for free-radical attack. Let us first consider the *o*-pentadienyl radical; this will be a resonance hybrid of three resonating structures:

$$C_6H_5X \xrightarrow{Y\cdot} [C_6H_5XY]\cdot \leftrightarrow [C_6H_5XY]\cdot \leftrightarrow [C_6H_5XY]\cdot$$

Thus the *o*-, *m*- and *p*-transition states may be written as follows:

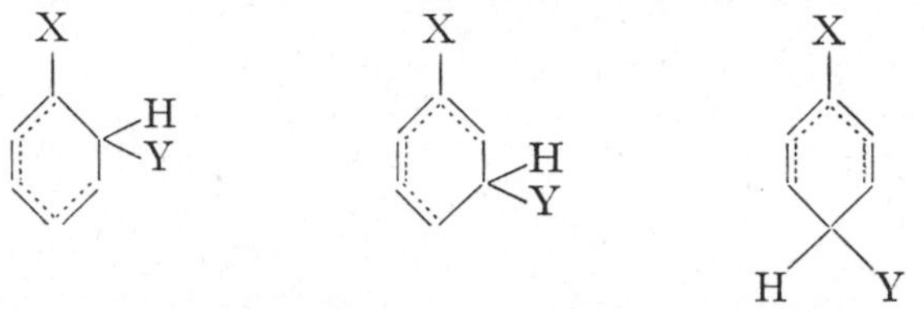

Since *o*- and *p*-substitution predominate, the energies of these transition states must be lower than that of the *m*-. The reason for this is uncertain.

One method of studying organic reactions has been to calculate the *charge densities* (π-electron densities) of the various positions in the molecule. The assumption has then been made that these quantities are related to the chemical reactivites to charged reagents.

In conjugated systems, only the π-electrons are considered, since the σ-electrons are localised and consequently very little affected by external influences. The π-electrons cover the whole benzene nucleus, and since they are easily polarised, *i.e.*, readily affected by external electrical influences, any change at one point in the molecule will be propagated to another. Hence the presence of a substituent group in the benzene nucleus will affect the π-electron distribution throughout the whole molecule, *i.e.*, the charge densities, and consequently the chemical reactivities of distant positions will be affected by the substituent group. These changes will, as one might expect, depend largely on the nature of the substituent group.

Substitution reactions of benzene involve three types of reagents, electrophilic, nucleophilic and free-radical. Since electrophilic reagents are electron-seeking reagents, they will attack the carbon atom which has the *highest* charge density. Since nucleophilic reagents supply a pair of electrons, these reagents will attack the carbon atom which has the *lowest* charge density. (Reactions involving free radicals are more difficult to deal with, and will not be discussed here.)

It can be seen from the foregoing discussion that if we know the charge densities of all the atoms in the molecule, we are in a position to say where attack will occur with electrophilic or nucleophilic reagents. π-Electron densities have been calculated for many molecules (particularly by Coulson and his co-workers). Let us first consider benzene itself. This is a symmetrical molecule, and so all the charge densities are equal, the value being unity (as shown by calculation). Thus all the carbon atoms in benzene are attacked equally well by electrophilic reagents.

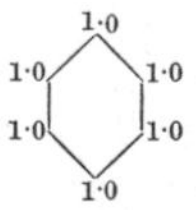

Now let us consider aniline. The nitrogen atom has a lone pair of electrons which can conjugate with the π-electrons of the benzene ring (Fig. 4*a*). This

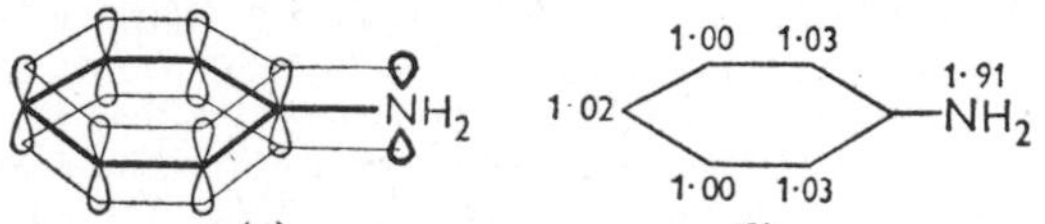

(*a*) (*b*)

FIG. 20.4.

results in the nitrogen losing " full control " of this lone pair, but owing to the strong electron-attracting power of nitrogen, the loss of control is fairly small. The new π-electron densities are shown in (*b*). Since the nitrogen " started off " with full control of its lone pair, its π-electron density was originally 2. In the conjugated molecule, the value is 1·91. Thus the nitrogen atom acquires a small positive charge (*cf.* resonance theory), and the net result is increased charge densities on *o*- and *p*-carbon atoms, the *m*-carbon atoms remaining unaffected. Thus electrophilic attack on aniline will occur at the *o*- and *p*-positions, and according to the above figures, preferentially at the *o*-position. Similarly, a lone pair of electrons of the chlorine atom in chlorobenzene will conjugate with the benzene ring, the chlorine thereby acquiring a small positive charge and the *o*- and *p*-positions increasing their charges above unity, whereas the charge density of the *m*-position remains sensibly the same (unity).

Now let us consider nitrobenzene. The nitro-group itself is conjugated, with the nitrogen atom positively charged (Fig. 5*a*). When the nitro-group conjugates with the ring (Fig. *b*), the nitrogen atom *attracts* towards itself the ring

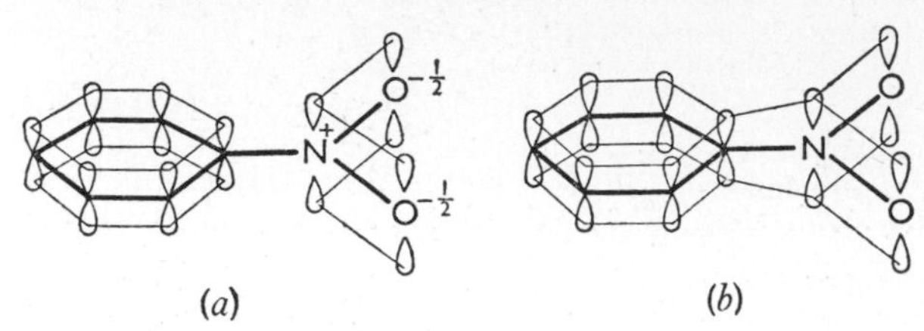

FIG. 20.5.

π-electron cloud, and thereby *decreases* the charge densities on the carbon atoms in the ring, more so at the *o*- and *p*-positions than at the *m*-position (as shown by calculation). Thus *electrophilic* attack will occur at the *m*-position, and *nucleophilic* attack at the *o*- and *p*-positions.

Calculation of the charge distribution in conjugated compounds is usually a laborious process. Coulson *et al.* (1940) have shown that the calculation is simple for *alternant hydrocarbons* (A.H.). In these it is possible to divide the atoms of the resonating part of the molecule into two groups (sometimes called *starred* and *unstarred*) such that no atom of one group is adjacent to another atom of the *same* group, but is always adjacent to one or more atoms of the *other* group. Thus benzene, naphthalene and anthracene are A.H.'s, but fulvene is not.

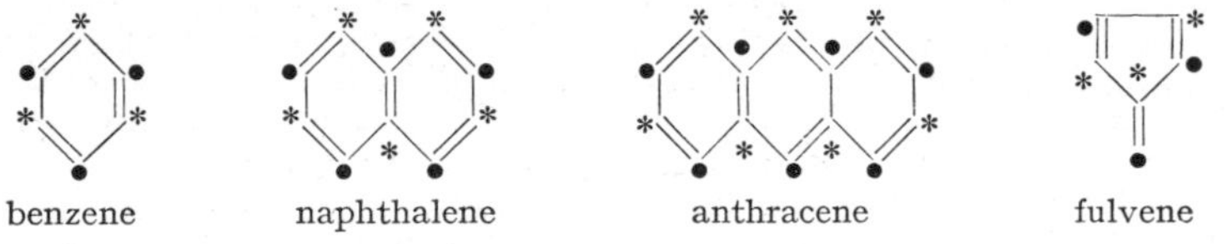

Furthermore, no odd-membered ring can be alternant, and with A.H.'s Coulson has shown that all the carbon atoms have a charge density of unity (which is not generally true for non-A.H.'s).

Another method of studying organic reactions has been to assume that the reactivity of a double bond is related to its double-bond character (or bond order; see p. 82). This assumption agrees quite well with the experimental results. The greater the double-bond character, the greater will be the reactivity at this point in the molecule. In benzene all the bonds have the same double-bond character, and so no particular carbon atom will be attacked preferentially. In the case of more complex aromatic hydrocarbons, *e.g.*, naphthalene, the double-bond character differs in various parts of the molecule, and so attack at some carbon atoms is easier than at others. Badger (1948–50) has found that osmium tetroxide is the most satisfactory reagent for the determination of the relative reactivity of aromatic double bonds. This reagent does not attack benzene, but attacks polycyclic compounds containing pronounced double-bond character (see, *e.g.*, naphthalene, p. 685).

General Methods of Preparation of the Benzene Homologues

Friedel–Crafts reaction (1877). This reaction involves the introduction of an alkyl or acyl group into the benzene ring in the presence of a catalyst. Recently, the Friedel–Crafts reaction has been applied to certain aliphatic and alicyclic compounds.

The aromatic compounds may be hydrocarbons, aryl chlorides and bromides, mono- and polyhydric phenols or their ethers, amines, aldehydes, acids, quinones, and certain derivatives of heterocyclic compounds. The alkylating agents may be alkyl halides, aliphatic alcohols, olefins, ethers and alkyl esters of organic and inorganic acids. From the point of view of convenience, the alkylating agent is usually confined to alkyl halides, alcohols and olefins. The acylating agents may be acid chlorides or anhydrides, acids, or esters.

Many catalysts may be used, *e.g.*, the chlorides of aluminium, iron (ferric), zinc, tin (stannic); boron trifluoride, hydrogen fluoride, sulphuric acid, phosphoric acid, and a mixture of silica and alumina. Acylations may also be effected in the presence of perchloric acid as catalyst (Burton *et al.*, 1950). Recently it has been found that benzene will react with an alkyl halide or acyl chloride in the *absence* of a catalyst, but in this case the reaction must be carried out under pressure (Sachanen and Cæsar, 1946).

Of all the catalysts mentioned, aluminium chloride (the one originally used by Friedel and Crafts) is the best, and gives satisfactory yields when the alkylating agent is an alkyl halide, alcohol or an olefin. The amount of catalyst required depends on the nature of the alkylating agent used, *e.g.*, with alkyl halides or olefins, about 0·2–0·4 molecule of aluminium chloride (using the formula $AlCl_3$) is necessary. With alcohols (ethers, etc.), however, a larger amount of catalyst (one or more molecules) is necessary:

$$C_6H_6 + CH_3Cl \xrightarrow[\text{(0·2 mol.)}]{AlCl_3} C_6H_5 \cdot CH_3 + HCl$$

$$C_6H_6 + C_2H_4 \xrightarrow[\text{(0·2 mol.)}]{AlCl_3} C_6H_5 \cdot C_2H_5$$

$$C_6H_6 + C_2H_5OH \xrightarrow[\text{(1 mol.)}]{AlCl_3} C_6H_5 \cdot C_2H_5 + H_2O$$

The orientation of the products in the alkylation of an alkylbenzene with aluminium chloride as catalyst depends on the temperature of the reaction. Thus Norris *et al.* (1939) obtained the following yields (per cent.):

$$C_6H_5CH_3 \xrightarrow[AlCl_3]{CH_3Cl} \text{o-}C_6H_4(CH_3)_2 + \text{m-}C_6H_4(CH_3)_2 + \text{p-}C_6H_4(CH_3)_2$$

Temperature	ortho	meta	para
0°	53·5	27·3	19·2
55°	12·2	87·1	0·7
106°	1·8	98·2	0·0

The reason for this is not certain. On the other hand, with boron trifluoride, which is very useful with alcohols and olefins (as is hydrogen fluoride), the main product of disubstitution is the *p*-derivative; sulphuric acid also produces mainly the *p*-derivative.

$$C_6H_5CH_3 + ROH \xrightarrow[\text{(0·6 mol.)}]{BF_3} \text{p-}CH_3C_6H_4R + H_2O$$

Boron trifluoride does not catalyse alkylations with alkyl chlorides or bromides, but the reaction can be carried out in the presence of water or alcohol (Hennion *et al.*, 1943). On the other hand, alkylation with alkyl fluorides is readily carried out with boron trifluoride as catalyst (Burwell *et al.*, 1942; Oláh *et al.*, 1957).

The Friedel–Crafts reaction is often the most useful method of introducing an alkyl group into the benzene ring. The ease of alkylation with an alkyl halide depends on the nature of the alkyl radical and the halogen atom. The ease of alkylation for a given halogen atom is tertiary halide > secondary > primary; and for a given alkyl radical, alkyl fluoride > chloride > bromide > iodide (this is the reverse order of the usual reactivity of alkyl halides).

The Friedel–Crafts reaction is usually carried out in the presence of a solvent, but if one of the reactants is a liquid hydrocarbon, *e.g.*, benzene, this may be used as solvent as well. The solvents generally used are nitrobenzene, light petrol, or carbon disulphide, and the solvent sometimes affects the orientation (see p. 686). At the end of the reaction the complex (see later) is usually decomposed by ice-cold concentrated hydrochloric acid.

The Friedel–Crafts reaction has certain drawbacks:

(i) The structure of the alkyl group plays a part in the alkylation, *e.g.*, it is easy to introduce a methyl, ethyl or *iso*propyl group, but usually difficult to introduce a *n*-propyl or *n*-butyl group, since these tend to rearrange to the *iso*-radicals. *iso*Butyl halides very readily give a *tert.*-butyl substitution product. If the reaction is carried out in the cold with benzene and *n*-propyl chloride, the *n*-propyl radical is introduced:

$$C_6H_6 + CH_3\cdot CH_2\cdot CH_2Cl \xrightarrow[\text{cold}]{AlCl_3} C_6H_5\cdot CH_2\cdot CH_2\cdot CH_3 + HCl$$

If, however, the reaction is carried out at higher temperatures, the *iso*propyl radical is mainly introduced:

$$C_6H_6 + CH_3\cdot CH_2\cdot CH_2Cl \xrightarrow[\text{heat}]{AlCl_3} C_6H_5\cdot CH(CH_3)_2 + HCl$$

The catalyst itself also affects isomerisation, *e.g.*, *n*-alcohols usually alkylate at low temperatures without rearrangement taking place when aluminium chloride is used, but rearrangement occurs when boron trifluoride or sulphuric acid is used, a primary alcohol giving rise to a secondary alkyl radical, and a secondary alcohol to a tertiary alkyl radical.

A very good means of introducing the *n*-propyl radical is to use *cyclo*propane as the alkylating agent:

$$C_6H_6 + CH_2\begin{matrix}\diagup CH_2 \\ | \\ \diagdown CH_2\end{matrix} \xrightarrow{AlCl_3} C_6H_5\cdot CH_2\, CH_2\cdot CH_3 \quad (65\%)$$

Acid chlorides may be used to introduce long straight-chain groups (see below).

(ii) It is not always possible to stop the reaction at the required stage, *i.e.*, there is always a tendency to over-alkylate, *e.g.*,

$$C_6H_6 + CH_3Cl \xrightarrow{AlCl_3} C_6H_5\cdot CH_3 \xrightarrow{CH_3Cl} C_6H_4(CH_3)_2$$

Over-alkylation, due to the presence of the first alkyl group in the ring increasing the ease of further alkylation, may be partly prevented by using a large excess of the hydrocarbon.

(iii) The Friedel–Crafts reaction is reversible, *i.e.*, an alkyl group may be removed, especially at high temperatures. This renders the structure of the

$$2\,C_6H_5\cdot CH_3 \xrightarrow{AlCl_3} C_6H_4(CH_3)_2 + C_6H_6$$

product uncertain in a number of cases.

(iv) The presence of a negative group (*m*-orienting group) in the ring hinders or inhibits the Friedel–Crafts reaction, *e.g.*, nitrobenzene, $C_6H_5\cdot NO_2$, and acetophenone, $C_6H_5\cdot CO\cdot CH_3$, do not undergo the Friedel–Crafts reaction. On the other hand, if a strongly activating group (*o-p*-orienting group) is present in either of the above two compounds, reaction can take place, *e.g.*, *o*-nitroanisole reacts with *iso*propanol in the presence of hydrogen fluoride to form 2-nitro-4-*iso*-propylanisole:

$$C_6H_4(OCH_3)(NO_2) + CH_3\cdot CHOH\cdot CH_3 \xrightarrow{HF} C_6H_3(OCH_3)(NO_2)(CH(CH_3)_2) + H_2O \ (84\%)$$

This hindering effect can be used to advantage for preparing a monoalkylated benzene (free from dialkylated-product):

$$C_6H_6 + CH_3\cdot COCl \xrightarrow[\text{(1 mole)}]{AlCl_3} C_6H_5\cdot CO\cdot CH_3 \xrightarrow{[H]} C_6H_5\cdot CH_2\cdot CH_3$$

The acetophenone (which is not further attacked) may be readily reduced to ethylbenzene by the Clemmensen method.

(v) For phenols and acids it is better to use boron trifluoride than aluminium chloride, since the latter forms aluminium salts, thereby necessitating the use of a large excess of aluminium chloride:

$$ArOH + AlCl_3 \longrightarrow ArOAlCl_2 + HCl$$
$$Ar\cdot CO_2H + AlCl_3 \longrightarrow Ar\cdot CO_2AlCl_2 + HCl$$

MECHANISM OF THE FRIEDEL–CRAFTS REACTION

Alkyl halides. Until recently it was generally believed that all Friedel–Crafts reactions proceeded by a free carbonium ion mechanism involving the intermediate formation of a complex (and a pentadienyl cation):

$$RCl + AlCl_3 \rightleftharpoons [R{-}Cl{-}AlCl_3] \rightleftharpoons R^+ + AlCl_4^-$$
$$ArH + R^+ \rightleftharpoons \left[Ar{<}^{H}_{R}\right]^+ \longrightarrow Ar\cdot R + H^+$$
$$H^+ + AlCl_4^- \longrightarrow HCl + AlCl_3$$

Brown *et al.* (1953), however, have shown that this mechanism is not general, and have presented strong evidence that for at least primary halides the reaction proceeds by a bimolecular nucleophilic substitution mechanism (S_N2) which involves the complex.

$$RCl + AlCl_3 \rightleftharpoons R{-}Cl{-}AlCl_3$$
$$ArH + R{-}Cl{-}AlCl_3 \rightleftharpoons \overset{\delta+}{Ar}{<}^{H}_{R\cdots Cl\cdots \overset{\delta-}{AlCl_3}}$$
$$\rightleftharpoons \left[Ar{<}^{H}_{R}\right]^+ AlCl_4^- \rightleftharpoons Ar\cdot R + HCl + AlCl_3$$

Further work by Brown *et al.* (1956) on the alkylation of benzene and toluene with alkyl bromides in the presence of aluminium bromide supports the above mechanism. These authors also suggest that the transition state is best described in terms of a nucleophilic attack by the aromatic compound on a strongly polarised $RBr{-}AlBr_3$ addition compound, and that as branching in the alkyl bromide increases, the C—Br bond in the transition state becomes more and more ionic and finally, at some point in the series, the reaction proceeds through a free carbonium ion mechanism. It was also shown that the isomer distribution in *methylation* is not independent of the halogen atom in the methyl halide. This therefore precludes the free carbonium ion mechanism in methylation and suggests the bimolecular mechanism. It is also believed that the solvent S (which can also be a hydrocarbon) co-ordinates with the aluminium bromide

$$Al_2Br_6 + 2S \rightleftharpoons 2S—AlBr_3$$

$$RBr + S—AlBr_3 \rightleftharpoons R—Br—AlBr_3 + S$$

$$ArH + R—Br—AlBr_3 \rightleftharpoons \left[Ar{<}^{H}_{R}\right]^+ AlBr_4^-$$

$$\xrightarrow{S} Ar{\cdot}R + HBr + S—AlBr_3$$

It has previously been pointed out (p. 100) that *n*-propyl halides tend to rearrange, resulting in the introduction of an *iso*propyl radical. The mechanism of this reaction is uncertain. It has been observed that *n*-propyl halides isomerise in the presence of aluminium chloride:

$$CH_3{\cdot}CH_2{\cdot}CH_2Cl \xrightarrow{AlCl_3} CH_3{\cdot}CHCl{\cdot}CH_3$$

According to Mckenna and Sowa (1937), this rearrangement might take place first and then the *iso*propyl halide alkylates.

Alcohols. Here again the generally accepted mechanism is believed to be ionic, *e.g.*,

$$ROH + BF_3 \rightleftharpoons \left[\begin{array}{c} H \\ | \\ R—O—BF_3 \end{array}\right] \rightleftharpoons R^+ + HOBF_3^-$$

$$ArH + R^+ \rightleftharpoons \left[Ar{<}^{H}_{R}\right]^+ \longrightarrow Ar{\cdot}R + H^+$$

$$H^+ + HOBF_3^- \longrightarrow [H_2O{\cdot}BF_3] \longrightarrow H_2O + BF_3$$

However, in view of the work done with alkyl halides, it is possible that alkylation with alcohols may also proceed by an S_N2 mechanism.

Olefins. It appears that a trace of water is necessary to catalyse this reaction, and based on this it has been suggested that the actual alkylating agent is the alkyl chloride which is produced as follows:

$$AlCl_3 + 3H_2O \longrightarrow Al(OH)_3 + 3HCl$$

$$C_2H_4 + HCl \xrightarrow{AlCl_3} C_2H_5Cl$$

Acyl chlorides. The generally accepted mechanism of acylation, until recently, was an ionic one involving the intermediate formation of an acyl cation:

$$R{\cdot}COCl + AlCl_3 \rightleftharpoons [R{\cdot}CO—Cl—AlCl_3] \rightleftharpoons R{\cdot}CO^+ + AlCl_4^-$$

$$ArH + R{\cdot}CO^+ \rightleftharpoons \left[Ar{<}^{H}_{CO{\cdot}R}\right]^+ \longrightarrow Ar{\cdot}CO{\cdot}R + H^+$$

According to Brown *et al.* (1954), this ionic mechanism cannot operate in the case of toluene, which acylates in the *p*-position. These authors suggest a substitution mechanism involving a " larger " attacking reagent to account for the steric requirements. This reagent may be the complex $R{\cdot}COX{\cdot}AlX_3$ itself or a solvated complex. Thus the following S_N2 mechanism has been proposed:

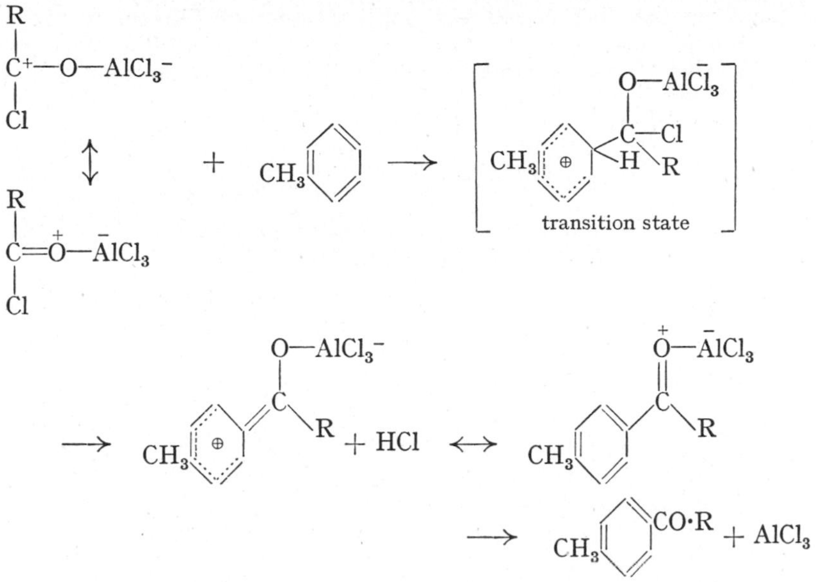

$$R{-}C^{+}(Cl){-}O{-}AlCl_3^{-} \longleftrightarrow R{-}C(Cl){=}\overset{+}{O}{-}\overset{-}{A}lCl_3$$

$$+ \; CH_3C_6H_5 \longrightarrow \left[CH_3C_6H_5^{\oplus}{<}^{C(Cl)(R){-}O{-}\bar{A}lCl_3}_{H} \right]$$

transition state

$$\longrightarrow CH_3C_6H_4^{\oplus}{=}C(R){-}O{-}AlCl_3^{-} + HCl \longleftrightarrow CH_3C_6H_4{-}C(R){=}\overset{+}{O}{-}\overset{-}{A}lCl_3$$

$$\longrightarrow CH_3C_6H_4{\cdot}CO{\cdot}R + AlCl_3$$

It has been suggested that the S_N2 mechanism is general and that the ionic mechanism operates in such cases where either the aromatic compound or the acyl halide is sterically hindered, *e.g.*, Baddeley *et al.* (1954) have provided evidence that with substituted benzoyl halides the acyl cation is the acylating agent. On the other hand, Tedder (1954) has suggested that acylations with acyl chloride and aluminium chloride take place by both ionic and substitution mechanisms. Reactive aromatic hydrocarbons are acylated by both processes simultaneously, but less activated hydrocarbons proceed through more of the S_N2 mechanism, and benzene itself almost exclusively through the S_N2 mechanism.

Wurtz–Fittig reaction (1863). Homologues of benzene may be prepared by warming an ethereal solution of an alkyl and aryl halide with sodium (*cf.* Wurtz reaction):

$$C_6H_5Br + C_2H_5Br + 2Na \longrightarrow C_6H_5{\cdot}C_2H_5 + 2NaBr \quad (60\%)$$

Diphenyl and *n*-butane (and some other compounds) are obtained as by-products.

The advantages of the Wurtz–Fittig method over the Friedel–Crafts are that the structure of the product is known and that long *n*-side-chains can be easily introduced:

$$C_6H_5Br + CH_3{\cdot}(CH_2)_2{\cdot}CH_2Br \xrightarrow{Na} C_6H_5{\cdot}(CH_2)_3{\cdot}CH_3 \quad (62\text{–}72\%)$$

The mechanism of the Wurtz–Fittig reaction is uncertain Two have been suggested, and there is evidence for both (*cf.* Wurtz reaction):

I. The reaction proceeds via the formation of organic-metallic compounds:

(i) $C_6H_5Br + 2Na \longrightarrow C_6H_5^{-}Na^{+} + NaBr$

(ii) $C_6H_5^{-}Na^{+} + C_2H_5Br \longrightarrow C_6H_5 - C_2H_5 + NaBr$

(iii) $C_2H_5Br + 2Na \longrightarrow C_2H_5^{-}Na^{+} + NaBr$

(iv) $C_2H_5^{-}Na^{+} + C_2H_5Br \longrightarrow C_2H_5 - C_2H_5 + NaBr$

(v) $C_2H_5^{-}Na^{+} + C_6H_5Br \longrightarrow C_6H_5{\cdot}C_2H_5 + NaBr$

(vi) $C_6H_5^{-}Na^{+} + C_2H_5Br \longrightarrow C_6H_5{\cdot}C_2H_5 + NaBr$

Since reaction (i) proceeds very much faster than (iii), (vi) will be the main reaction.

II. The reaction proceeds via the formation of free radicals:

$$C_6H_5Br + Na\cdot \longrightarrow C_6H_5\cdot + NaBr$$
$$2C_6H_5\cdot \longrightarrow C_6H_5 - C_6H_5$$
$$C_2H_5Br + Na\cdot \longrightarrow C_2H_5\cdot + NaBr$$
$$2C_2H_5\cdot \longrightarrow C_2H_5 - C_2H_5$$
$$C_6H_5\cdot + C_2H_5\cdot \longrightarrow C_6H_5{\cdot}C_2H_5$$

In addition to diphenyl, other by-products are also obtained in the Wurtz–Fittig reaction, *viz.*, benzene, *o*-diphenylbenzene and triphenylene. The formation of these is readily explained by the free-radical mechanism, disproportionation of the free radicals taking place as follows:

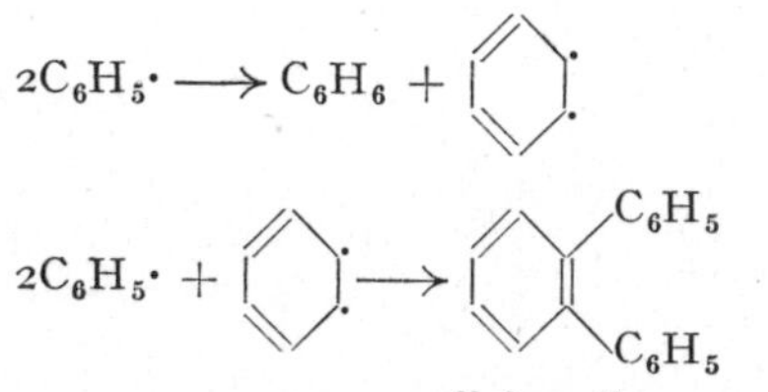

$$2C_6H_5\cdot \longrightarrow C_6H_6 + C_6H_4{:}$$

$$2C_6H_5\cdot + C_6H_4{:} \longrightarrow C_6H_4(C_6H_5)_2$$

o-diphenylbenzene

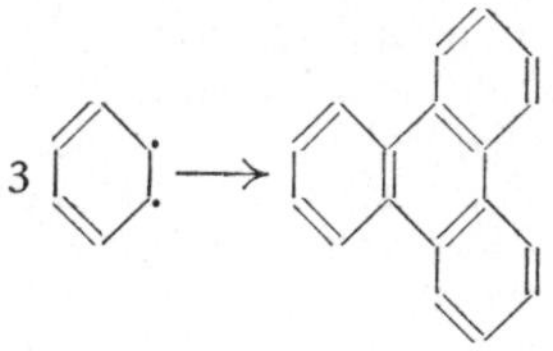

$$3\,C_6H_4{:} \longrightarrow C_{18}H_{12}$$

triphenylene

The formation of these polyphenyl compounds has, however, also been explained by non-radical mechanisms (*cf.* Wurtz reaction, p. 46). It is also possible that the action of sodium on bromobenzene leads to the formation of *benzyne* (p. 521); this has been reported to trimerise to triphenylene (Lüttringhaus *et al.*, 1955).

Method using a Grignard reagent. Homologues of benzene may be prepared by the action of an alkyl halide on phenylmagnesium bromide:

$$C_6H_5Br \xrightarrow{Mg} C_6H_5{\cdot}MgBr \xrightarrow{CH_3I} C_6H_5{\cdot}CH_3 \quad (v.g.)$$

For the introduction of a methyl or ethyl group, the corresponding alkyl sulphate may be used instead of the alkyl halide (*cf.* p. 335).

Benzene homologues with branched side-chains may be prepared by the action of alkyl-magnesium halide on an aromatic ketone, *e.g.*, *iso*propylbenzene from acetophenone:

$$C_6H_5{\cdot}CO{\cdot}CH_3 + CH_3{\cdot}MgI \longrightarrow C_6H_5{\cdot}C(OMgI)(CH_3){-}CH_3 \xrightarrow{H_2O} C_6H_5{\cdot}C(OH)(CH_3){-}CH_3$$

$$\xrightarrow[-H_2O]{heat} C_6H_5{\cdot}C(CH_3){=}CH_2 \xrightarrow{H_2/Ni} C_6H_5{\cdot}CH(CH_3)_2$$

Decarboxylation of aromatic acids. Many aromatic acids are readily decarboxylated when heated with soda-lime, *e.g.*, toluene from *p*-toluic acid:

$$p\text{-}CH_3\cdot C_6H_4\cdot CO_2H \xrightarrow{NaOH(CaO)} C_6H_5\cdot CH_3$$

Removal of oxygen from phenols. When distilled with zinc dust, phenols are converted (in poor yield) into the corresponding hydrocarbons, *e.g.*, *p*-cresol gives toluene:

$$p\text{-}CH_3\cdot C_6H_4\cdot OH + Zn \longrightarrow C_6H_5\cdot CH_3 + ZnO$$

Method of chloromethylation. This is the process whereby a hydrogen atom (generally of an aromatic compound) is replaced by a *chloromethyl group*, CH_2Cl. The reaction may be carried out by heating the aromatic hydrocarbon with formalin or paraformaldehyde and hydrochloric acid in the presence of zinc chloride as catalyst, *e.g.*, benzyl chloride from benzene:

$$C_6H_6 + CH_2O + HCl \xrightarrow{ZnCl_2} C_6H_5\cdot CH_2Cl + H_2O \quad (79\%)$$

Chloromethyl ether and dichloromethyl ether may be used instead of formalin or paraformaldehyde, but unlike the latter, do not require the presence of a catalyst. Many catalysts may be used with formalin (or paraformaldehyde), the most useful being zinc chloride, aluminium chloride, stannic chloride, acetic acid and sulphuric acid.

The introduction of a chloromethyl group is very useful, since this group is readily converted into other groups such as CH_3, CH_2OH, CHO, $CH_2\cdot CN$.

Chloromethylation is generally applicable to aromatic hydrocarbons such as benzene, naphthalene, anthracene, phenanthrene, diphenyl, and to many of their derivatives. Monoalkylbenzenes are converted mainly into the *p*-chloromethyl derivatives, together with a small amount of the *o*-compound. In certain cases it is possible to introduce a second chloromethyl group (see, *e.g.*, p. 686). The yields of the chloromethylated compounds are variable, usually lying between 50–80 per cent. The presence of a halogen atom in the ring reduces the yield of the chloromethylated derivative. A nitro-group behaves in a similar manner, and the presence of two nitro-groups inhibits the reaction altogether, *e.g.*, nitrobenzene gives only a small yield of the chloromethylated compound; *m*-dinitrobenzene gives none. Ketones of the type Ar·CO·R give very poor yields, and those of the type Ar·CO·Ar do not react at all. Phenols, however, are very reactive, so much so that polymers are often obtained.

General properties of the benzene homologues. The benzene homologues are usually colourless liquids, insoluble in water, but miscible in all proportions with organic solvents. All burn with smoky flames.

Toluene (*methylbenzene*), $C_6H_5\cdot CH_3$, is obtained commercially from coal-tar, or by catalytically dehydrogenating *n*-heptane or methyl*cyclo*hexane (both obtained from petroleum; see p. 476):

$$CH_3\cdot(CH_2)_5\cdot CH_3 \longrightarrow C_6H_5\cdot CH_3 + 4H_2$$

Toluene is also prepared by reaction between benzene and methane at high temperature.

Toluene is a colourless liquid, b.p. 111°, resembling benzene in many of its chemical properties. Since, however, it contains a side-chain, it undergoes some further reactions, *e.g.*, the side-chain may be oxidised in stages, first to give benzaldehyde and then to give benzoic acid:

$$C_6H_5{\cdot}CH_3 \xrightarrow{[O]} C_6H_5{\cdot}CHO \xrightarrow{[O]} C_6H_5{\cdot}CO_2H$$

When toluene is nitrated or sulphonated, a mixture of the three possible isomers is obtained, mainly consisting of the *o*- and *p*- and very little of the *m*-isomer. Chlorine and bromine react with toluene in one of two ways, according to the conditions; the halogen may enter the nucleus or the side chain (see p. 518).

Xylenes, C_8H_{10}. Four isomers of the formula C_8H_{10} are known:

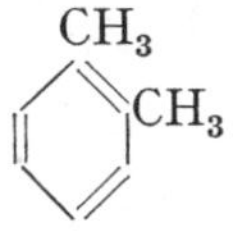

o-xylene	*m*-xylene	*p*-xylene	ethylbenzene
b.p. 144°	b.p. 139°	b.p. 138°	b.p. 136°

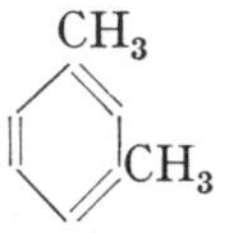

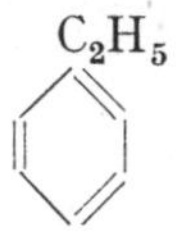

All of these isomers are present in the light oil fraction of coal-tar, and are difficult to separate because their boiling points are close together (see p. 584). The methyl groups in the xylenes may be oxidised by dilute nitric acid, one at a time, to give carboxylic acids; the *m*-isomer is not so easily oxidised as the *o*- and *p*-isomers:

$$\underset{}{CH_3{\cdot}C_6H_4{\cdot}CH_3} \xrightarrow{[O]} \underset{\text{a toluic acid}}{CH_3{\cdot}C_6H_4{\cdot}CO_2H} \xrightarrow{[O]} \underset{\text{a phthalic acid}}{HO_2C{\cdot}C_6H_4{\cdot}CO_2H}$$

Potassium permanganate acts in a similar manner to nitric acid, but chromic acid oxidises the *o*-isomer to carbon dioxide and water.

Hydrocarbons of formula C_9H_{12}. There are eight isomeric hydrocarbons of formula C_9H_{12}, *viz.*, three trimethylbenzenes, three methylethylbenzenes, one *n*-propylbenzene, and one *iso*propylbenzene. The three trimethylbenzenes occur in coal-tar:

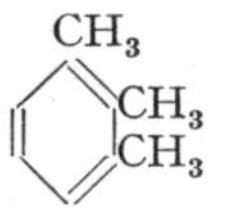

hemimellitene	*ψ-cumene*	*mesitylene*
b.p. 175°	b.p. 169°	b.p. 164°

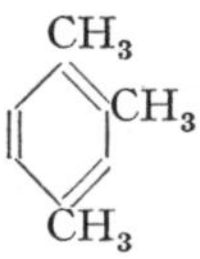

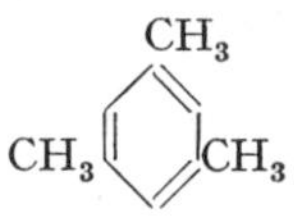

Mesitylene is the most important of these, and is usually prepared by distilling acetone with sulphuric acid (p. 158).

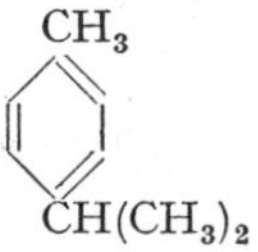

***iso*Propylbenzene** (*cumene*), $C_6H_5{\cdot}CH(CH_3)_2$, b.p. 153°, also occurs in coal-tar.

***p*-Cymene** (*cymene*, *p*-methyl*iso*propylbenzene), b.p. 177°, occurs in oil of thyme and eucalyptus oil, and is related to camphor and other terpenes.

Aromatic hydrocarbons with unsaturated side-chains. The only important unsaturated aromatic hydrocarbon is **styrene** (*phenylethylene, vinylbenzene*), $C_6H_5{\cdot}CH{=}CH_2$. This occurs in storax (a balsam) and in coal-tar (distilling with the xylenes). Styrene may be prepared as follows:

(i) By heating methylphenylmethanol with sulphuric acid:

$$C_6H_5\cdot MgBr + CH_3\cdot CHO \longrightarrow C_6H_5\cdot \underset{\cdot CH_3}{CH}OMgBr \xrightarrow{H_2O}$$

$$C_6H_5\cdot CHOH\cdot CH_3 \xrightarrow[- H_2O]{heat} C_6H_5\cdot CH{=}CH_2$$

(ii) By heating 2-phenylethanol with alkali:

$$C_6H_5\cdot CH_2\cdot CH_2OH \longrightarrow C_6H_5\cdot CH{=}CH_2 + H_2O$$

(iii) The most convenient laboratory preparation is to heat cinnamic acid with a small amount of quinol:

$$C_6H_5\cdot CH{=}CH\cdot CO_2H \longrightarrow C_6H_5\cdot CH{=}CH_2 + CO_2$$

A small amount of quinol is also placed in the receiving vessel to prevent the polymerisation of the styrene.

Styrene is manufactured by dehydrogenating ethylbenzene catalytically:

$$C_6H_5\cdot C_2H_5 \xrightarrow[600^\circ]{ZnO} C_6H_5\cdot CH{=}CH_2 + H_2$$

Ethylbenzene is prepared industrially by the action between benzene and ethylene in the presence of aluminium chloride.

Styrene is a colourless liquid, b.p. 145°. It adds on bromine to form the dibromide, and is readily reduced to ethylbenzene. It polymerises slowly to a solid on standing, and rapidly when exposed to sunlight or in the presence of sodium. This polymer, which is known as *metastyrene*, $(C_8H_8)_n$, may be depolymerised by heating. Styrene is used for making plastics and synthetic rubbers.

Substitution in the side-chain of styrene gives rise to two possibilities:

$C_6H_5\cdot CCl{=}CH_2$	$C_6H_5\cdot CH{=}CHCl$
α-chlorostyrene	β- or ω-chlorostyrene

Phenylacetylene, $C_6H_5\cdot C{\equiv}CH$, may be prepared by decarboxylating phenylpropiolic acid, $C_6H_5\cdot C{\equiv}C\cdot CO_2H$, or by heating ω-bromostyrene with ethanolic potassium hydroxide.

Phenylacetylene is a liquid, b.p. 142°, with acidic properties, *e.g.*, it forms metallic derivatives (*cf.* acetylene, p. 89). It is reduced to styrene by zinc dust and acetic acid, and in the presence of sulphuric acid, phenylacetylene adds on a molecule of water to form acetophenone:

$$C_6H_5\cdot C{\equiv}CH + H_2O \longrightarrow C_6H_5\cdot CO\cdot CH_3$$

Oxidation of aromatic hydrocarbons. The benzene ring is usually very resistant to oxidation, and so when benzene homologues are oxidised, it is the side-chain which is attacked. Whatever the length of the side-chain, the ultimate oxidation product is benzoic acid; sometimes the intermediate products can be isolated, but it is usually difficult to control the oxidation. Cullis *et al.* (1955) have shown that when *n*- and *iso*propyl-benzene are oxidised with potassium permanganate, the initial attack is at the α-carbon, *e.g.*,

$$C_6H_5\cdot CH_2\cdot CH_2\cdot CH_3 \xrightarrow{[O]} C_6H_5\cdot CO_2H + CH_3\cdot CO_2H + H_2O$$

Furthermore, these authors found that as the size of the alkyl group increased in a monoalkylbenzene, the extent of ring rupture decreases. The oxidations of toluene and ethylbenzene proceed as follows:

$$C_6H_5\cdot CH_3 \longrightarrow [C_6H_5\cdot CH_2OH] \longrightarrow C_6H_5\cdot CHO \longrightarrow C_6H_5\cdot CO_2H$$

$$C_6H_5\cdot CH_2\cdot CH_3 \longrightarrow C_6H_5\cdot CO\cdot CH_3 \longrightarrow C_6H_5\cdot CO_2H$$

When two side-chains are present, it is possible to oxidise them one at a time, *e.g.*, the xylenes may be oxidised first to a toluic acid and then to a phthalic acid. When the two side-chains are of unequal length, it is the longer one which is usually attacked first:

$$CH_3\text{-}C_6H_4\text{-}CH_2{\cdot}CH_2{\cdot}CH_3 \xrightarrow[HNO_3]{\text{dilute}} CH_3\text{-}C_6H_4\text{-}CH_2{\cdot}CH_2{\cdot}CO_2H$$

The usual oxidising agents for side-chains are dilute nitric acid, acid or alkaline permanganate, dichromate-sulphuric acid mixture, and chromic acid which may be chromium trioxide in either glacial acetic acid or concentrated sulphuric acid. All except permanganate usually attack the longer side-chain first. Recently, it has been found that selenium dioxide at 250–340° will oxidise a methyl side-chain to a mixture of aldehyde and carboxylic acid (Sultanov *et al.*, 1946):

$$Ar{\cdot}CH_3 \xrightarrow{SeO_2} Ar{\cdot}CHO + Ar{\cdot}CO_2H$$

Oxidation with chromic acid is selective, the *p*-isomer being more easily oxidised than the *m*-; the *o*-isomer is often completely oxidised to carbon dioxide, or the ring may be opened to give an aliphatic compound. Oxidation of *o*-compounds, however, is usually successful with permanganate (*i.e.*, no breakdown of the ring). When negative groups such as a halogen, nitro-, carboxyl or sulphonic acid group are attached to the ring, they are unaffected by oxidising agents, the result of oxidation being a substituted benzoic acid; this therefore offers a means of preparing such compounds. The presence of a negative group, however, in the *o*-position to the side-chain generally makes oxidation difficult with *acidic* oxidising agents. The best oxidising agent for such *o*-compounds is probably alkaline permanganate. If there are two side-chains present as well as a negative group, then alkaline permanganate usually attacks the one *ortho* to the negative group.

An interesting oxidising agent is potassium ferricyanide. This will oxidise a methyl group to a carboxyl group only if there is a nitro-group *ortho* to the methyl group.

If a hydroxyl or amino-group is attached to the ring, the ring becomes very sensitive to oxidising agents, the ring usually breaking down completely, whatever the oxidising agent used. If, however, these groups are "protected" by acetylation, oxidation of side-chains may be effected without breakdown of the ring, but it is then best to use a *neutral* oxidising agent, *e.g.*, permanganate in the presence of magnesium sulphate, to prevent hydrolysis of the acetyl derivative. On the other hand, if the arylsulphonyl derivative, $Ar{\cdot}SO_2$—, is prepared instead of the acetyl derivative, oxidation of side-chains may be carried out in acid media, since the sulphonyl derivative is much more difficult to hydrolyse than the acetyl derivative.

Metalation of aromatic compounds. Metallic derivatives of aromatic compounds may be prepared by various methods; *e.g.*, benzene heated with an alkyl-sodium forms phenylsodium:

$$C_6H_6 + R^-Na^+ \longrightarrow C_6H_5^-Na^+ + RH$$

Phenylsodium may also be prepared by heating diphenylmercury with sodium:

$$(C_6H_5)_2Hg + 2Na \longrightarrow 2C_6H_5^-Na^+ + Hg$$

Diphenylmercury may be prepared by refluxing a mixture of bromobenzene, sodium amalgam, xylene and a small amount of ethyl acetate:

$$2C_6H_5Br + Na_2/Hg \longrightarrow (C_6H_5)_2Hg + 2NaBr \quad (32\text{–}37\%)$$

Phenyl-lithium may conveniently be prepared by the action of lithium on bromo- or iodobenzene in ethereal solution:

$$C_6H_5Br + 2Li \longrightarrow C_6H_5Li + LiBr$$

All these metalated aromatic compounds (*i.e.*, organo-metallic compounds) undergo the general reactions of the Grignard reagents. In practice, the lithium compound is generally used, since it is so readily prepared (see also p. 344).

A very important case of metalation is **mercuration**. Aromatic compounds containing almost all the common functional groups have been mercurated, and in general mercuration proceeds easily with the formation of mono-, di- and even polymercurated compounds. Mercuration is becoming an increasingly important substitution reaction, and aromatic mercurated compounds are increasing in importance in medicine and as intermediates in the preparation of other compounds (see text).

Aromatic mercuration is carried out in two ways:

(i) **Direct mercuration.** This is the reaction in which a hydrogen atom of benzene, a polynuclear hydrocarbon, or a heterocyclic compound, is replaced by the *mercuri-acid group*, the most common one being the *acetoxymercuri-group*, $-Hg{\cdot}O{\cdot}CO{\cdot}CH_3$. This group is usually introduced by heating the hydrocarbon with mercuric acetate, or with the equivalent of mercuric oxide in glacial acetic acid, at 90–160°, for one or more hours, *e.g.*, *acetoxymercuribenzene* (*phenylmercury acetate*):

$$C_6H_6 + Hg(O{\cdot}CO{\cdot}CH_3)_2 \longrightarrow C_6H_5{-}Hg{\cdot}O{\cdot}CO{\cdot}CH_3 + CH_3{\cdot}CO_2H$$

The monomercurated derivative is the main product, and is accompanied by a varying amount of polymercurated derivatives.

Mercuration may be effected by heating the aromatic compound with the mercury salt only, or together with acetic anhydride or with solvents such as methanol or ethanol.

The most important aromatic compounds that can be mercurated are the aromatic hydrocarbons, aryl chlorides, nitro-compounds, amino-compounds, phenols, acids and acid anhydrides. The aryl halides and nitro-compounds are mercurated with difficulty, whereas compounds containing a hydroxyl or an amino-group (activating groups) are mercurated more readily than the parent hydrocarbon.

The orienting influence of substituent groups may be unusual. With an *o*-*p*-orienting group the reaction is usually normal, *e.g.*, aniline and phenol give the expected *o*- and *p*-derivatives, but toluene gives about 20 per cent. of the *m*-compound. On the other hand, a *m*-orienting group may behave abnormally, *e.g.*, Klapproth *et al.* (1950) have shown that mercuration of nitrobenzene with mercuri perchlorate in aqueous perchloric acid at 23° gives 11 per cent. of *o*- and *p*-, and 89 per cent. of *m*-compound, whereas mercuration with mercuric acetate at 150° gives 57 per cent. of *o*- and *p*-, and 43 per cent. of *m*-. The reason offered for this is that in the former case the mercuric salt is ionised and so the reaction is heterolytic, *i.e.*, electrophilic, and consequently the usual orientation is observed. In the latter case the salt is unionised, and so this reaction proceeds largely through a homolytic process, *i.e.*, by a free-radical mechanism (*cf.* p. 500).

The position of the actoxymercuri-group can be found by treating the mercurated compound with halogen, whereupon the group is replaced by a halogen atom:

$$Ar—Hg·O·CO·CH_3 + Br_2 \longrightarrow ArBr + HgBr(O·CO·CH_3)$$

This reaction is the most characteristic reaction of mercurated compounds. On the other hand, if a mercurated compound is treated with sodium halide, the *acetyl group* is replaced by a halogen atom to form a *halogenomercuri*-compound (*phenylmercury halide*):

$$Ar—Hg·O·CO·CH_3 + NaCl \longrightarrow Ar—HgCl + CH_3·CO_2Na$$

Mercuric nitrate readily reacts with excess benzene to form phenylmercury nitrate $C_6H_5·HgNO_3$. The nitric acid liberated (from the mercuric nitrate) during the reaction decomposes the mercurated compound, but this can be avoided by using a mixture of mercuric nitrate and mercuric oxide (the latter neutralising the liberated nitric acid). If instead of mercuric nitrate, a solution of mercuric nitrate in nitric acid is used, the benzene is oxidised and nitrated to dinitrophenol and picric acid. In this case the reaction is known as *oxynitration* (see p. 601).

(ii) **Indirect mercuration.** This is the reaction in which a functional group is replaced by a mercuri-acid group, usually the *chloromercuri-group*, —HgCl. Mostly used for this purpose are the diazonium salts, sulphinic acids and aryl halides (see text).

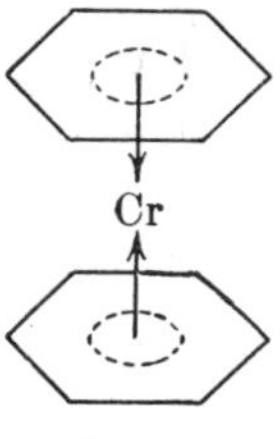

The advantage of indirect over direct mercuration is that the former may be used to prepare a particular isomer, whereas the latter usually produces a mixture of isomers.

Cr

It has now been found that benzene (and various other aromatics) forms metallic complexes similar to the ferrocenes (p. 458), *e.g.*, when benzene, chromic chloride, aluminium chloride and powdered aluminium are heated at 180°, a product containing the $(C_6H_6)_2Cr^+$ cation is obtained. This, on reduction with, *e.g.*, hypophosphorous acid, gives dibenzenechromium (O), $(C_6H_6)_2Cr$, a dark brown solid (Zeiss *et al.*, 1956).

Synthesis of aromatic compounds from aliphatic compounds. Many methods are available for the conversion of aliphatic compounds into aromatic, *e.g.*,

(i) From acetylenic compounds, *e.g.*, acetylene passed through a red hot tube forms benzene:

$$3C_2H_2 \longrightarrow C_6H_6$$

When methylacetylene or bromoacetylene is treated with a small amount of concentrated sulphuric acid, the *s*-trisubstituted benzene derivative is formed:

$$3CH_3·C⋮CH \xrightarrow{H_2SO_4} \text{(1,3,5-trimethylbenzene: } CH_3, CH_3, CH_3)$$

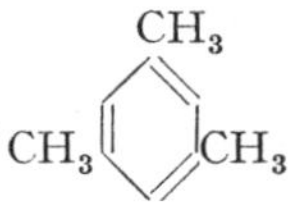

$$3CH⋮CBr \xrightarrow{H_2SO_4} \text{(1,3,5-tribromobenzene: } Br, Br, Br)$$

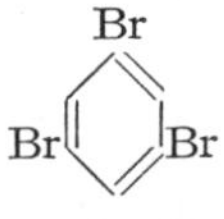

(ii) When acetone is distilled with sulphuric acid, mesitylene is formed (p. 158). Similarly, butanone forms *s*-triethylbenzene (and other products).

(iii) When carbon monoxide is passed over heated potassium, the potassium salt of hexahydroxybenzene is formed:

$$6CO + 6K \longrightarrow C_6(OK)_6$$

(iv) Phloroglucinol (*s*-trihydroxybenzene) may be prepared from sodiomalonic ester as follows:

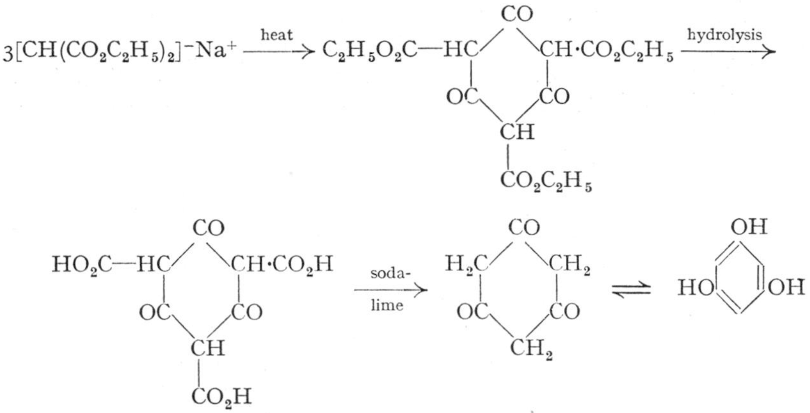

$$3[CH(CO_2C_2H_5)_2]^-Na^+ \xrightarrow{\text{heat}} C_2H_5O_2C—HC\begin{matrix} CO \\ \diagup \quad \diagdown \\ \quad \\ OC \quad\quad CO \\ \diagdown \quad \diagup \\ CH \\ | \\ CO_2C_2H_5 \end{matrix}CH·CO_2C_2H_5 \xrightarrow{\text{hydrolysis}}$$

$$HO_2C—HC\begin{matrix} CO \\ \diagup \quad \diagdown \\ \quad \\ OC \quad\quad CO \\ \diagdown \quad \diagup \\ CH \\ | \\ CO_2H \end{matrix}CH·CO_2H \xrightarrow[\text{lime}]{\text{soda-}} H_2C\begin{matrix} CO \\ \diagup \quad \diagdown \\ \quad \\ OC \quad\quad CO \\ \diagdown \quad \diagup \\ CH_2 \end{matrix}CH_2 \rightleftharpoons \text{1,3,5-}C_6H_3(OH)_3$$

(v) *cyclo*Hexane derivatives (prepared by the Diels–Alder reaction, p. 450) can be dehydrogenated to give aromatic compounds. Dehydrogenation may be carried out by heating the compound with sulphur, selenium, or a palladium–charcoal catalyst:

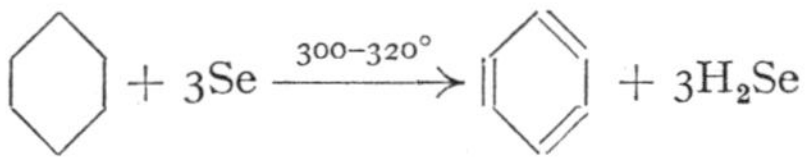

$$C_6H_{12} + 3Se \xrightarrow{300–320°} C_6H_6 + 3H_2Se$$

(vi) By means of hydroforming, and high-temperature cracking (p. 476).

Conversion of aromatic compounds into aliphatic compounds. Many methods are available for the conversion of aromatic compounds into aliphatic, but care must be exercised, since opening of the ring often results in its complete breakdown.

(i) By ozonolysis, *e.g.*, *o*-xylene (see p. 481).

(ii) When phenol is carefully oxidised, *meso*tartaric is formed (p. 400).

(iii) When benzene is oxidised by air in the presence of vanadium pentoxide as catalyst, maleic anhydride is formed. On the other hand, oxidation of benzene with hydrogen peroxide in *t*.-butanol in the presence of a little osmium tetroxide gives allomucic, *meso*tartaric and oxalic acids (p. 400).

(iv) When phenol is oxidised with peracetic acid, muconic acid is formed (p. 410).

(v) Phenol may be reduced to *cyclo*hexanol, which, on oxidation with concentrated nitric acid, gives adipic acid (p. 361).

(vi) A curious example of the opening of the benzene ring is the reduction of salicylic acid to give pimelic acid (see p. 653).

Difference in reactions between aromatic and aliphatic compounds. As will be seen in the text, many differences exist between aromatic and aliphatic compounds. These differences constitute " aromatic character," a term which cannot be defined precisely. A molecule is generally understood to possess aromatic character when it is stabilised by a large resonance energy arising from the geometry of the molecule being such as to permit all the ring atoms to be embraced by one M.O. Thus aromatic character is limited to molecules (or regions of molecules) which are planar or nearly planar (see p. 485). The following summary includes the more important differences between aromatic and aliphatic compounds:

(i) The stability of the nucleus towards additive reagents.
(ii) The ease of substitution in the nucleus.
(iii) The stability of the nucleus and the ease of oxidation of side-chains.

(iv) The Friedel–Crafts reaction.
(v) Chloromethylation.
(vi) Mercuration reactions.
(vii) The stability of aryl halides.
(viii) The weaker basic properties of aromatic amines.
(ix) The formation of diazonium salts from primary aromatic amines.
(x) The acidic properties of phenols (as compared with the alcohols).

QUESTIONS

1. How are the following compounds prepared commercially: (*a*) C_6H_6, (*b*) PhMe, (*c*) PhEt, (*d*) $PhCH{=}CH_2$?
2. Write out the structures and names of the isomers of each of the following formulæ: (*a*) $C_6H_4Cl_2$, (*b*) C_6H_4ClBr, (*c*) $C_6H_3(NO_2)_3$, (*d*) $C_6H_3Cl_2(NO_2)$, (*e*) $C_7H_6Cl(NH_2)$.
3. Write an account of the methods of orientation.
4. Discuss the structure of benzene.
5. Write an essay on aromatic substitution.
6. Starting with benzene and any other chemical you like, show how you would synthesise:—(*a*) PhMe, (*b*) PhEt, (*c*) *p*-$C_6H_4Me_2$, (*d*) *m*-$C_6H_4Et_2$, (*e*) $Ph{\cdot}CH_2{\cdot}CH_2{\cdot}CH_3$, (*f*) $Ph{\cdot}CH_2{\cdot}CN$, (*g*) $Ph{\cdot}CH_2OH$, (*h*) $Ph{\cdot}CH_2{\cdot}CH_2{\cdot}OH$, (*i*) $Ph{\cdot}CHBr{\cdot}CH_3$, (*j*) $Ph{\cdot}CMe_3$, (*k*) *p*-$MeC_6H_4{\cdot}CH_2OH$, (*l*) $Ph{\cdot}CH{=}CH_2$, (*m*) $Ph{\cdot}C{\equiv}CH$, (*n*) PhLi, (*o*) PhHgOAc, (*p*) PhHgBr.
7. Name the compounds and state the conditions under which they may be obtained when each of the following compounds is oxidised:

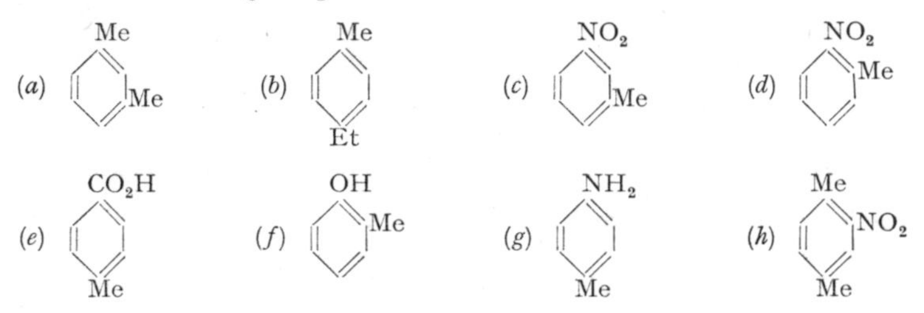

8. Define and give examples of :—(*a*) the Friedel–Crafts reaction, (*b*) the Wurtz–Fittig reaction, (*c*) Chloromethylation, (*d*) Mercuration, (*e*) Metalation.
9. Describe a number of methods whereby aliphatics may be converted into aromatics, and vice-versa.
10. Discuss methods that have been used for studying organic reactions.
11. Write as essay on the problem of the *ortho-para* ratio.
12. Give an account of hyperconjugation.
13. Discuss the problem of " aromatic character."

READING REFERENCES

Newell, Faraday's Discovery of Benzene, *J. Chem. Educ.*, 1926, **3**, 1248.
Schorlemmer, *Rise and Development of Organic Chemistry*, Macmillan (1894). Ch. IX, The Structure of Benzene.
Gilman, *Advanced Organic Chemistry*, Wiley (1942, 2nd ed.), Vol. I, Ch. 3, Aromatic Character.
Thomas, Anhydrous Aluminium Chloride in Organic Chemistry, Reinhold Publishing Co.
Organic Reactions, Wiley. (i) Vol. I (1942), Ch. 3, Chloromethylation of Aromatic Compounds. (ii) Vol. III (1946), Ch. 1, The Alkylation of Aromatic Compounds by the Friedel–Crafts Method.
Kobe and Doumani, Aromatic Mercuration, *Ind. Eng. Chem.*, 1941, **33**, 170.
Badger, The Aromatic Bond, *Quart. Reviews* (*Chem. Soc.*), 1951, **5**, 147.
Brown, Molecular Orbitals and Organic Reactions, *ibid.*, 1952, **6**, 63.
Bunnet and Zahler, Aromatic Nucleophilic Substitution Reactions, *Chem. Reviews*, 1951, **49**, 273.
Ingold, *Structure and Mechanism in Organic Chemistry*, Bell and Sons (1953). Chh. IV, V, VI, XV.
Wheland, *Resonance in Organic Chemistry*, Wiley (1955), Ch. 8, p. 476. Orientation of Substituents in Aromatic Systems.

Hammett, *Physical Organic Chemistry*, McGraw–Hill (1940), Ch. 7. The Effect of Structure on Reactivity.
Nelson, Aromatic Substitution by Free Radicals, *J. Chem. Educ.*, 1955, **32**, 606.
Nelson, Directive Effects in Electrophilic Aromatic Substitution, *J. Org. Chem.*, 1956, **21**, 145.
Baker, *Hyperconjugation*, Oxford Press (1952).
Dewar, *The Electronic Theory of Organic Chemistry*, Oxford Press (1949), Ch. IX. Aromatic Compounds.
Newman (Ed.), *Steric Effects in Organic Chemistry*, Wiley (1956), Ch. 3. Steric Effects in Aromatic Substitution.
Badger, *The Structures and Reactions of Aromatic Compounds*, Cambridge Press (1954).
Baddeley, Modern Aspects of the Friedel–Crafts Reaction, *Quart. Reviews* (*Chem. Soc.*), 1954, **8**, 355.
Gore, The Friedel–Crafts Acylation Reaction, *Chem. Reviews*, 1955, **55**, 229.
Green, Some Applications of Valence-bond Theory to Aromatic Substitution, *J.C.S.*, **1954**, 3538.
de la Mare and Harvey, The Kinetics and Mechanisms of Aromatic Halogen Substitution, *ibid.*, **1956**, 36.
Brown *et al.*, Mechanism of the Alkylation Reaction, *J. Amer. Chem. Soc.*, 1956, **78**, 2185.

CHAPTER XXI

AROMATIC HALOGEN COMPOUNDS

THERE are three types of aromatic halogen compounds, the *addition* compounds, the *nuclear substitution* products, and the *side-chain* substitution products.

Addition compounds. When treated with chlorine or bromine in the presence of sunlight, benzene forms the benzene hexahalides, $C_6H_6Cl_6$ and $C_6H_6Br_6$, respectively. The addition probably takes place by a chain mechanism:

$$Cl_2 \xrightarrow{h\nu} 2Cl\cdot$$

$$C_6H_6 + Cl\cdot \longrightarrow C_6H_6Cl\cdot \xrightarrow{Cl_2} C_6H_6Cl_2 \xrightarrow[\text{etc.}]{Cl\cdot} (CHCl)_6$$

Benzene hexachloride (1 : 2 : 3 : 4 : 5 : 6-hexachloro*cyclo*hexane), $C_6H_6Cl_6$, theoretically can exist in eight stereoisomeric forms (*cf.* inositol, p. 460). Until recently only five of these were known: α, β, γ, δ, ε; but Kolka *et al.* (1954) have now prepared two others, η and θ. The γ-isomer is a powerful insecticide; it is very stable and acts more quickly than D.D.T. All of the isomers have been shown to exist in the chair form, and the α-isomer has been identified as the (±)-form (Cristol, 1949). The following conformations have been assigned respectively to the α- and γ-isomers: *aaeeee* and *aaaeee*. γ-Hexachloro*cyclo*hexane is prepared commercially by treating benzene with chlorine in the presence of ultra-violet light. The α-, β-, γ- and δ-isomers are produced, the γ- to the extent of 12–14 per cent.; this is the only one that has insecticidal properties. It is very difficult to separate the isomers, but it may be done by fractional crystallisation from various organic solvents.

Mullins (1955) has suggested that molecular size and shape are critical for the action of chlorinated hydrocarbon insecticides. According to Mullins, the molecule of γ-BHC is smaller than those of the other stereoisomers and so can penetrate more readily.

Nuclear substitution products (aryl halides). These compounds may be prepared by the following methods:

1. **Direct halogenation.** *Low temperature and the presence of a halogen carrier favour nuclear substitution.* Chlorination and bromination may be very conveniently carried out at ordinary temperature in the presence of an iron or aluminium amalgam catalyst; the extent of the substitution depends on the amount of halogen used, *e.g.*, chlorobenzene is formed when benzene is treated with chlorine (1 molecule) in the presence of iron:

$$C_6H_6 + Cl_2 \xrightarrow{Fe} C_6H_5Cl + HCl \quad (90\%)$$

If 2 molecules of chlorine are used, then a mixture of *o*- and *p*-dichlorobenzenes is obtained, the latter predominating:

$$C_6H_5Cl + Cl_2 \xrightarrow{Fe} \underset{o-\,+\,p-}{C_6H_4Cl_2} + HCl$$

When toluene is brominated in the presence of iron (using 1 molecule of bromine), a mixture of *o*- and *p*-bromotoluenes (*tolyl bromides*) is obtained:

$$C_6H_5{\cdot}CH_3 + Br_2 \xrightarrow{Fe} \underset{o- \; + \; p-}{CH_3{\cdot}C_6H_4Br} + HBr$$

To obtain the *o*-, *m*- and *p*-toluene derivatives pure, it is best to prepare them from the corresponding toluidines (*cf.* method 3).

The mechanism of aromatic halogenation is not certain. Kinetic studies have shown that the order of the reaction with respect to the halogen varies from one to five, depending on the halogen concentration (Robertson *et al.*, 1943–1954). According to Robertson (1954), the general mechanism of aromatic bromination in *acetic acid* is:

$$ArH + Br_2 \rightleftharpoons ArH{\cdot}Br_2 \xrightarrow{slow} ArHBr^+ + Br^-$$

$$ArHBr^+ \xrightarrow{fast} ArBr + H^+$$

$$H^+ + Br^- \xrightarrow{fast} HBr$$

The structure of the intermediate (*i.e.*, transition state) is not certain; Yeddanapalli *et al.* (1956) have suggested it is:

$$C_6H_5{-}H + Br{-}Br \longrightarrow {}^+C_6H_5(H)(\bar{Br}{-}Br)$$

When the halogenation is carried out in the presence of a catalyst (the *usual* procedure for *nuclear* halogenation), the problem is made more complicated since the halogen acid liberated also acts as a catalyst. A possible mechanism for the chlorination of benzene in the presence of ferric chloride is:

$$Cl_2 + FeCl_3 \rightleftharpoons Cl^+ + FeCl_4^-$$

$$C_6H_6 + Cl^+ \rightleftharpoons [C_6H_6Cl]^+ \longrightarrow C_6H_5Cl + H^+$$

$$H^+ + FeCl_4^- \longrightarrow HCl + FeCl_3$$

Nuclear chlorination can be carried out with sulphuryl chloride in the presence of a catalyst, a most effective one being a mixture of sulphur monochloride and aluminium chloride; *e.g.*, sulphuryl chloride in the presence of 1 per cent. of this catalyst chlorinates benzene in the cold. Toluene can be similarly chlorinated, and the *side-chain is not attacked in the absence of organic peroxides*. Chlorination with sulphuryl chloride is stepwise, and the final product depends on the amount of this reagent used:

$$C_6H_5CH_3 \rightarrow o\text{- and } p\text{-}CH_3C_6H_4Cl \rightarrow 2,4\text{-}CH_3C_6H_3Cl_2 \rightarrow 2,3,4\text{- and } 2,4,5\text{-}CH_3C_6H_2Cl_3 \rightarrow 2,3,4,6\text{- and } 2,3,4,5\text{-}CH_3C_6HCl_4 \rightarrow CH_3C_6Cl_5$$

2. Treatment of nuclear hydroxy-compounds with phosphorus pentachloride results in the formation of nuclear-chlorinated compounds:

$$C_6H_5OH + PCl_5 \longrightarrow C_6H_5Cl + POCl_3 + HCl$$

The yield of chlorobenzene, however, is poor, the main product being triphenyl phosphate, $(C_6H_5O)_3PO$.

Rydon *et al.* (1957), however, have shown that aryl chlorides may be prepared from phenols as follows:

$$3ArOH + PCl_5 \xrightarrow{\text{heat}} 3HCl + (ArO)_3PCl_2 \xrightarrow[\text{heat}]{\text{Ar'OH}}$$

$$HCl + (ArO)_3(Ar'O)PCl \xrightarrow{\text{heat}} Ar'X + (ArO_3)PO$$

In these reactions Ar′ contains a more powerful electron-attracting group than does Ar, *e.g.*, when Ar = C_6H_5 and Ar′ = *p*-$NO_2{\cdot}C_6H_4$—, the product is *p*-$NO_2{\cdot}C_6H_4Cl$ (91%).

Bromides and iodides may also be prepared as follows:

$$(ArO)_3(Ar'O)PCl + RX \xrightarrow{\text{heat}} RCl + (ArO)_3(Ar'O)PX$$

$$\xrightarrow{\text{heat}} Ar'X + (ArO)_3PO$$

3. The decomposition of diazonium salts under suitable conditions is generally the most satisfactory method of preparing nuclear derivatives (see p. 559); *e.g.*, benzenediazonium chloride, in the presence of cuprous chloride, produces chlorobenzene:

$$C_6H_5{\cdot}N_2Cl \xrightarrow{\text{CuCl}} C_6H_5Cl + N_2$$

4. The silver salts of many aromatic acids react with bromine to form aryl bromides (*cf.* p. 96), *e.g.*,

$$C_6H_5{\cdot}CO_2Ag + Br_2 \longrightarrow C_6H_5Br + CO_2 + AgBr \quad (53\%)$$

$$p\text{-}NO_2{\cdot}C_6H_4{\cdot}CO_2Ag + Br_2 \longrightarrow p\text{-}NO_2{\cdot}C_6H_4Br + CO_2 + AgBr \quad (79\%)$$

Iodine compounds. Iodination is reversible, very little iodo-compound being present in the equilibrium mixture (*cf.* p. 35):

$$C_6H_6 + I_2 \rightleftharpoons C_6H_5I + HI$$

If, however, the iodination is carried out in the presence of an oxidising agent, *e.g.*, nitric acid, mercuric oxide, etc., the yield of iodo-compound is usually very good:

$$2C_6H_6 + I_2 \xrightarrow[HNO_3]{[O]} 2C_6H_5I + H_2O \quad (86\text{–}87\%)$$

Iodine compounds are generally most conveniently prepared via the diazonium salts (method 3), but if an activating group (hydroxyl or amino-) is present in the ring, then iodine monochloride, or even iodine without the presence of an oxidising agent, may be used (see aniline, p. 544).

Fluorine compounds. Fluorination of benzene in the vapour phase in the presence of a metallic catalyst results in the formation of *no aromatic fluorine products*; instead, a complex mixture of aliphatic and alicyclic fluoro-compounds is obtained: CF_4, C_2F_6, C_3F_8, C_4F_{10}, C_5F_{12}, C_6F_{12} (in greatest amount), C_6HF_{11}, $C_{12}F_{22}$ (Bigelow *et al.*).

Perfluorobenzene, C_6F_6, may be prepared by treating perchlorobenzene with bromine trifluoride (other products are also obtained):

$$C_6Cl_6 \xrightarrow{BrF_3} C_6F_6$$

If, however, perchlorobenzene is treated with antimony pentafluoride, not all the chlorine atoms are replaced, and an *alicylic* compound results:

$$C_6Cl_6 \xrightarrow{SbF_5} C_6Cl_2F_8 \xrightarrow{KMnO_4} CO_2H{\cdot}(CF_2)_4{\cdot}CO_2H$$

This compound, when oxidised with permanganate, yields octafluoroadipic acid.

Fluorinated aromatic compounds are always prepared indirectly, the most convenient method of introducing a fluorine atom into the ring being via the diazonium salt (see p. 560).

General properties of the nuclear halogen derivatives. Nuclear halogen derivatives are colourless oils or crystalline solids, insoluble in water but soluble in organic solvents; their densities are all greater than 1. **The halogen atom is firmly attached to the nucleus, and is not easily displaced by OH(NaOH), $NH_2(NH_3)$, CN(KCN), etc.** The aryl halides thus differ very much from the alkyl halides, but resemble the vinyl halides (p. 251). Under special conditions, however, the halogen atom in the aryl halides may be replaced:

(i) If an aryl halide is heated with aqueous sodium hydroxide under pressure at 300°, the halogen atom is replaced by hydroxyl:

$$C_6H_5Cl + NaOH \longrightarrow C_6H_5OH + NaCl$$

Phenol is also produced when chlorobenzene and steam are passed over a silica-gel catalyst at 500° (Chiba, 1953).

(ii) When an aryl chloride is heated with aqueous ammonia in the presence of cuprous oxide at 200° under pressure, the amino-compound is formed:

$$2C_6H_5Cl + 2NH_3 + Cu_2O \longrightarrow 2C_6H_5{\cdot}NH_2 + 2CuCl + H_2O \quad (90\%)$$

Chlorobenzene also reacts with potassamide in liquid ammonia at low temperatures to form aniline. Roberts *et al.* (1953), using the isotope ^{14}C to label the carbon of the C—Cl group, showed that the amino-group entered partly at the labelled carbon and partly at the *ortho*-carbon. This behaviour has been explained by postulating a **benzyne** intermediate.

$$C_6H_5^{*}Cl \xrightarrow{NH_2^-} Cl^- + NH_3 + C_6H_4^{*} \xrightarrow{NH_3} \text{(I)} + \text{(II)}$$

(I) (II)

Bunnett and Zahler (1951) have proposed the name **cine-substitution** for reactions of this kind, *i.e.*, for the formation of (II) where nucleophilic aromatic substitution occurs in which the ring position taken up by the entering group is not the same as that of the displaced group.

(iii) An aryl bromide reacts with anhydrous cuprous cyanide when heated in the presence of pyridine or quinoline, *e.g.*, bromobenzene forms phenyl cyanide:

$$C_6H_5Br + CuCN \xrightarrow[200^\circ]{\text{pyridine}} C_6H_5{\cdot}CN + CuBr$$

Pyridine or quinoline is not always necessary, and sodium cyanide may be used instead of cuprous cyanide provided a small amount of the latter is also present. Aryl chlorides may be used if the chlorine atom is activated by a nitro-group in the *o*- or *p*-position (see below).

(iv) If a strongly negative group, *e.g.*, the nitro-group, is in the *o*- or *p*-position to the halogen atom, replacement of the latter halogen atom is fairly easy, *e.g.*, *o*- and *p*-chloronitrobenzenes may be converted, at about 150–200°, by ethanolic potassium hydroxide, and ethanolic ammonia into the corresponding nitrophenols and nitroanilines. These are examples of activated nucleophilic aromatic substitution, and the activation of the halogen atom is believed to be due to the electron-withdrawing (—I) effect of the nitro-group.

$$o\text{-}ClC_6H_4NO_2 + OH^- \longrightarrow [C_6H_4(Cl)(OH)\overset{+}{N}O_2^{--}] \longrightarrow o\text{-}C_6H_4(OH)NO_2 + Cl^-$$

A very interesting reaction of the halogenonitro-benzenes is the **von Richter reaction** (1871). In this reaction, when the compound is heated with potassium cyanide at 150°, the nitro-group is expelled and a cyano group enters the ring *ortho* to the position occupied by the former (this is an example of cine-substitution).

$$p\text{-}BrC_6H_4NO_2 \xrightarrow[C_2H_5OH]{KCN} m\text{-}BrC_6H_4CN; \quad o\text{-}BrC_6H_4NO_2 \xrightarrow[C_2H_5OH]{KCN} m\text{-}BrC_6H_4CN$$

(v) An aryl halide may be converted into the parent hydrocarbon by reducing it with a nickel-aluminium alloy in the presence of alkali (Schwenk *et al.*, 1944):

$$C_6H_5Cl + 2[H] \xrightarrow[NaOH]{Ni/Al} C_6H_6 + HCl$$

Aryl bromides and aryl iodides form Grignard reagents, and undergo the Ullmann reaction (p. 551). The aryl chlorides, however, form Grignard reagents under special conditions (Ramsden *et al.*, 1958). The aryl halides do not react with sodioacetoacetic ester or with sodiomalonic ester, but they undergo the Wurtz–Fittig (p. 507) and Fittig reactions (p. 669). Ketones, however, may be directly phenylated with bromobenzene as follows, the reaction proceeding via a benzyne intermediate (Leake *et al.*, 1955):

$$C_6H_5Br \xrightarrow[\text{liq. } NH_3]{NaNH_2} C_6H_4 \text{ (benzyne)} \xrightarrow{[C_2H_5{\cdot}CO{\cdot}CH{\cdot}CH_3]^-Na^+} C_6H_5{\cdot}CH(CH_3){\cdot}CO{\cdot}C_2H_5 \quad (60\%)$$

As will be seen later, side-chain substituted halogen derivatives behave like the alkyl halides in most ways and therefore are better not to be regarded as aryl halides but as aryl-substituted alkyl halides.

The aryl halides are difficult to mercurate, but they may be mercurated by refluxing them with mercuric acetate until a test portion gives no precipitate of mercuric oxide with aqueous sodium hydroxide. On the other hand, chloromercuri-derivatives may be prepared from aryl bromides or iodides as follows:

$$ArBr + Mg \longrightarrow Ar{\cdot}MgBr \xrightarrow{HgCl_2} Ar{\cdot}HgCl + MgClBr$$

The lack of reactivity of the halogen atom in aryl chlorides is not easily explained, and none of the explanations that have been suggested is certain. One suggestion is that resonance stabilises the molecule and gives the halogen atom some " double-bond character "; this is not possible in alkyl halides but is in vinyl halides which are also unreactive.

The same explanation may be offered from the M.O. point of view. The lone pair of $3p_z$ electrons on the chlorine atom can conjugate with the π-electrons of the benzene ring, and hence the binding of the chlorine atom to the benzene ring is increased by delocalisation of this lone pair (*cf.* vinyl chloride, p. 251).

Chlorobenzene (*phenyl chloride*), C_6H_5Cl, is produced commercially by the Raschig process: a mixture of benzene vapour, air and hydrogen chloride is passed over a catalyst (copper chloride):

$$C_6H_6 + HCl + \tfrac{1}{2}O_2 \longrightarrow C_6H_5Cl + H_2O$$

Chlorobenzene is a liquid, b.p. 132°. It is used for the manufacture of aniline, phenol, and D.D.T. D.D.T. is a contraction for *p* : *p*′-dichlorodiphenyltrichloroethane [1 : 1 : 1-trichloro-2 : 2-bis(*p*-chlorophenyl)-ethane]. It is a solid, m.p. 109–110°, and is manufactured by heating chlorobenzene and chloral with concentrated sulphuric acid:

$$2C_6H_5Cl + CCl_3{\cdot}CHO \xrightarrow{H_2SO_4} CCl_3{\cdot}CH(C_6H_4Cl)_2$$

Good commercial D.D.T. contains about 75 per cent. *p* : *p*′-D.D.T., 20 per cent. *o* : *p*′-D.D.T. (m.p. 74–75°), and 5 per cent. of other substances as impurities; it is a powerful insecticide.

Side-chain substituted compounds. Side-chain substitution is favoured by high temperature and light, and the *absence* of halogen carriers; *e.g.*, when chlorinated at its boiling point in the presence of light, toluene is converted into benzyl chloride (see also below):

$$C_6H_5{\cdot}CH_3 + Cl_2 \longrightarrow C_6H_5{\cdot}CH_2Cl + HCl$$

It is generally believed that side-chain substitution proceeds by a chain reaction (*cf.* p. 95):

$$Cl_2 \xrightarrow{h\nu} 2Cl{\cdot}$$

$$C_6H_5{\cdot}CH_3 + Cl{\cdot} \longrightarrow C_6H_5{\cdot}CH_2{\cdot} + HCl$$

$$C_6H_5{\cdot}CH_2{\cdot} + Cl_2 \longrightarrow C_6H_5{\cdot}CH_2Cl + Cl{\cdot}; \text{ etc.}$$

Side-chain substitution may be readily effected by sulphuryl chloride in the *presence* of organic peroxides. Excess of sulphuryl chloride will introduce no more than two chlorine atoms on the same carbon atom; *e.g.*, toluene gives benzylidene chloride as the final product:

$$C_6H_5{\cdot}CH_3 \xrightarrow{SO_2Cl_2} C_6H_5{\cdot}CH_2Cl \xrightarrow{SO_2Cl_2} C_6H_5{\cdot}CHCl_2$$

In these reactions it is believed that the peroxide provides traces of free radicals which then set up the chain reaction (*cf.* p. 64).

When the side-chain is larger than a methyl group, its halogenation is more complicated, *e.g.*, chlorination of ethylbenzene at its boiling point in the presence of light first produces a mixture of α- and β-chloroethylbenzenes, and finally pentachloroethylbenzene:

$$C_6H_5{\cdot}CH_2{\cdot}CH_3 \xrightarrow{Cl_2} \underset{\alpha\text{-isomer}}{C_6H_5{\cdot}CHCl{\cdot}CH_3} + \underset{\beta\text{-isomer}}{C_6H_5{\cdot}CH_2{\cdot}CH_2Cl} \xrightarrow{Cl_2} C_6H_5{\cdot}CCl_2{\cdot}CCl_3$$

The monochloro-derivatives can be isolated (using 1 molecule of chlorine), but it is extremely difficult to isolate any of the other intermediates (when chlorine is used in excess). If, however, chlorination is carried out in the cold and in the presence of light, then the main product of substitution is the α-isomer:

$$C_6H_5{\cdot}CH_2{\cdot}CH_3 \xrightarrow{Cl_2} C_6H_5{\cdot}CHCl{\cdot}CH_3 \xrightarrow{Cl_2} C_6H_5{\cdot}CCl_2{\cdot}CH_3$$

If two side-chains are present, both may be halogenated, *e.g.*,

$$CH_3{\cdot}C_6H_4{\cdot}CH_3 \xrightarrow{Cl_2} \underset{\text{methylbenzyl chloride}}{CH_3{\cdot}C_6H_4{\cdot}CH_2Cl} \xrightarrow{Cl_2}$$

$$\underset{\text{xylylene chloride}}{CH_2Cl{\cdot}C_6H_4{\cdot}CH_2Cl} \xrightarrow{Cl_2} \underset{\text{bis-(trichloromethyl)-benzene}}{C_6H_4(CCl_3)_2}$$

A curious feature of this reaction is that the fully chlorinated product cannot be obtained with *o*-xylene, but can with the *m*- and *p*-isomers. The explanation may be the spatial effect.

When a hydroxyl or an amino-group (activating groups) is present in the ring, side-chain halogenation is very difficult, if not impossible; *e.g.*, bromination of *p*-cresol gives 2 : 6-dibromo-*p*-cresol:

CH₃-C₆H₄-OH $\xrightarrow{Br_2}$ 2,6-Br₂-4-CH₃-C₆H₂OH (ring structures: CH$_3$ … OH $\xrightarrow{Br_2}$ CH$_3$, Br, Br … OH)

Introduction of fluorine into the side-chain may be carried out by heating the corresponding chloro-derivative with hydrogen fluoride under pressure, or with antimony pentafluoride; *e.g.*, trifluoromethylbenzene (benzotrifluoride) from benzotrichloride and antimony pentafluoride:

$$C_6H_5{\cdot}CH_3 \xrightarrow{Cl_2} C_6H_5{\cdot}CCl_3 \xrightarrow{SbF_5} C_6H_5{\cdot}CF_3$$

The trifluoromethyl group is very resistant to attack, *e.g.*, oxidation of trifluoromethylbenzene results in the formation of trifluoroacetic acid:

$$C_6H_5{\cdot}CF_3 \xrightarrow{[O]} CF_3{\cdot}CO_2H$$

Benzyl chloride, $C_6H_5{\cdot}CH_2Cl$, may be prepared by passing chlorine into boiling toluene until the theoretical increase in weight for benzyl chloride is obtained:

$$C_6H_5{\cdot}CH_3 + Cl_2 \longrightarrow C_6H_5{\cdot}CH_2Cl + HCl \quad (60\%)$$

Benzyl chloride may also be prepared by the chloromethylation of benzene.

Benzyl chloride is a liquid, b.p. 179°, and chemically it behaves like an alkyl halide, *e.g.*, when heated with aqueous alkali, aqueous potassium cyanide, or ethanolic ammonia, it is converted into benzyl alcohol, $C_6H_5{\cdot}CH_2OH$, benzyl cyanide, $C_6H_5{\cdot}CH_2{\cdot}CN$, and benzylamine, $C_6H_5{\cdot}CH_2{\cdot}NH_2$, respectively. Actually, the chlorine atom in benzyl chloride is more reactive than in methyl chloride. One suggestion that has been put forward to account for this is hyperconjugation:

$$\overset{Cl}{H_2\ddot{C}}{-}C_6H_5 \longleftrightarrow \overset{\bar{Cl}}{H_2C}{=}C_6H_5^{+} \longleftrightarrow \overset{\bar{Cl}}{H_2C}{=}C_6H_5^{+}$$

This shows that the chlorine is largely ionised, but does not account for the fact that the $—CH_2Cl$ group is mainly *o*-*p*-orienting and not *m*- (*cf.* p. 497).

From the M.O. point of view, ionisation of the chlorine atom would leave the carbon atom with a positive charge. The " closed circuit " of the benzene ring can now extend itself to cover this carbon atom, *i.e.*, the resulting positive ion is stabilised by delocalisation (Fig. 1). It is this extension of conjugation that acts as the " driving force " in the ionisation of the chlorine atom. Conjugation is not possible in alkyl halides.

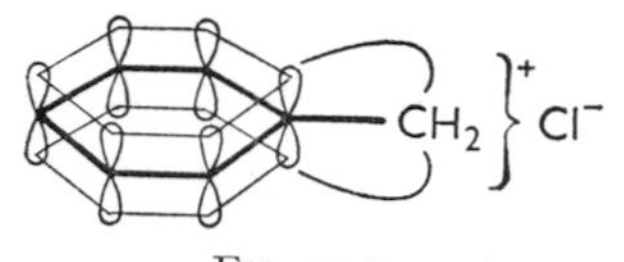

FIG. 21.1.

Benzylidene chloride (*benzal chloride*), $C_6H_5{\cdot}CHCl_2$, may be prepared by passing chlorine into boiling toluene in the presence of light until the weight increase corresponds to $C_6H_5{\cdot}CHCl_2$:

$$C_6H_5{\cdot}CH_3 + 2Cl_2 \longrightarrow C_6H_5{\cdot}CHCl_2 + 2HCl \quad (g.)$$

It may also be prepared by the action of phosphorus pentachloride on benzaldehyde:

$$C_6H_5{\cdot}CHO + PCl_5 \longrightarrow C_6H_5{\cdot}CHCl_2 + POCl_3$$

Benzylidene chloride is a liquid, b.p. 207°; it is hydrolysed by calcium hydroxide solution to benzaldehyde, and is used industrially for this purpose.

$$C_6H_5{\cdot}CHCl_2 + Ca(OH)_2 \longrightarrow C_6H_5{\cdot}CHO + CaCl_2 + H_2O$$

The conversion of toluene into benzaldehyde via benzylidene chloride is an example of *indirect* oxidation.

Benzotrichloride, $C_6H_5{\cdot}CCl_3$, may be prepared by the continued action of chlorine on boiling toluene in the presence of light:

$$C_6H_5{\cdot}CH_3 + 3Cl_2 \longrightarrow C_6H_5{\cdot}CCl_3 + 3HCl$$

It is a liquid, b.p. 214°. When heated with calcium hydroxide solution, it is converted into benzoic acid; it is used industrially for this purpose. This is another example of indirect oxidation:

$$C_6H_5{\cdot}CCl_3 + 2H_2O \xrightarrow{Ca(OH)_2} C_6H_5{\cdot}CO_2H + 3HCl$$

It can be seen from the foregoing that the properties of the side-chain halogen derivatives are very much different from those of the nuclear halogen derivatives. The former closely resemble the alkyl halides but, in general, possess a pungent smell and are lachrymatory (provided the halogen atom is on the α-carbon); they have been used in warfare.

Polyvalent iodine compounds. When a well-cooled chloroform solution of iodobenzene is treated with chlorine, a precipitate of **iodobenzene dichloride** (*phenyliodochloride*) is formed:

$$C_6H_5I + Cl_2 \longrightarrow C_6H_5{\cdot}ICl_2 \quad (87–94\%)$$

This is a yellow crystalline solid: its structure is uncertain. When exposed to light or heated to 110°, it is converted into *p*-chloroiodobenzene:

$$C_6H_5{\cdot}ICl_2 \longrightarrow p\text{-}Cl{\cdot}C_6H_4{\cdot}I + HCl$$

When treated with alkali, iodobenzene dichloride is converted into **iodosobenzene,** $C_6H_5I{\rightarrow}O$:

$$C_6H_5{\cdot}ICl_2 + 2NaOH \longrightarrow C_6H_5{\cdot}IO + 2NaCl + H_2O \quad (60\text{–}62\%)$$

Iodosobenzene is a yellow solid which is basic, *e.g.*, with hydrochloric acid it forms iodobenzene dichloride, and with nitric acid, iodobenzene dinitrate:

$$C_6H_5{\cdot}IO + 2HNO_3 \longrightarrow C_6H_5{\cdot}I(NO_3)_2 + H_2O$$

Iodosobenzene has been used to oxidise sulphides to sulphoxides (Ford-Moore, 1949), and iodobenzene (iodosobenzene) diacetate oxidises primary aromatic amines to azo-compounds (Pausacker, 1953).

When steam distilled, iodosobenzene is converted into **iodoxybenzene**:

$$2C_6H_5{\cdot}IO \longrightarrow C_6H_5{\cdot}IO_2 + C_6H_5I \quad (92\text{–}95\%)$$

This is also obtained when iodobenzene dichloride is treated with an alkaline solution of sodium hypochlorite:

$$C_6H_5{\cdot}ICl_2 + NaOCl + H_2O \longrightarrow C_6H_5{\cdot}IO_2 + NaCl + 2HCl \quad (87\text{–}92\%)$$

Iodoxybenzene is a solid which does not melt or vaporise when heated to 230°; all iodoxy-compounds exhibit this refractory property. The structure of iodoxybenzene is not known with certainty; it may be $C_6H_5{-}I{\lessgtr}^{\,{=}O}_{\,{\rightarrow}O}$. It forms salts with inorganic acids, *e.g.*, $C_6H_5{\cdot}IO_2{\cdot}H_2SO_4$, but although these salts are fairly stable in the solid state, they are readily hydrolysed in solution. Iodoxybenzene also forms salts with alkalis, but these have not yet been isolated.

When a mixture of iodoso- and iodoxybenzene is treated with aqueous sodium hydroxide, **diphenyliodonium iodate** is formed, and this, on treatment with potassium iodide, forms **diphenyliodonium iodide**:

$$C_6H_5{\cdot}IO + C_6H_5{\cdot}IO_2 \xrightarrow{NaOH} [(C_6H_5)_2I]^+IO_3^- \xrightarrow{KI} [(C_6H_5)_2I]^+I^- \quad (70\text{–}72\%)$$

Diphenyliodonium iodide readily changes to iodobenzene on heating; the mechanism of this reaction is obscure. Diphenyliodonium iodide is the salt of the base *diphenyliodonium hydroxide* which may be prepared, in solution, by the action of " silver hydroxide " on a mixture of iodoso- and iodoxybenzene:

$$C_6H_5{\cdot}IO + C_6H_5{\cdot}IO_2 + \text{“ AgOH ”} \longrightarrow [(C_6H_5)_2I]^+OH^- + AgIO_3$$

QUESTIONS

1. Name the compounds and state the conditions under which they are formed when each of the following compounds is treated with chlorine: (*a*) C_6H_6, (*b*) PhMe, (*c*) *o*-$C_6H_4Me_2$, (*d*) PhEt, (*e*) *p*-Me·C_6H_4·Et.
2. Discuss the general methods of preparing:—(*a*) nuclear halogen derivatives, (*b*) side-chain halogen derivatives, and write an account of the general properties of these two types of halogen compounds.
3. Starting with benzene and any other compound you like, how would you prepare:—(*a*) PhCl, (*b*) PhI, (*c*) D.D.T., (*d*) $PhCH_2Br$, (*e*) $PhCHMeCO_2H$, (*f*) $PhCH_2{\cdot}CH_2{\cdot}NH_2$, (*g*) *o*-$C_6H_4(CH_2Br)_2$, (*h*) 2 : 4 : 6-tribromophenol, (*i*) *p*-nitrophenol, (*j*) $PhCH_2F$, (*k*) PhCHO, (*l*) $PhCO_2H$?
4. Discuss the use of sulphuryl chloride as a chlorinating agent.
5. Write an account of the aromatic polyvalent iodine compounds.
6. How would you distinguish between:—(*a*) $PhCH_2Cl$ and *p*-MeC_6H_4Cl; (*b*) PhCOCl and *p*-$ClC_6H_4CO_2H$?
7. Write an account of cine-substitution.

READING REFERENCES

Brown, Sulphuryl Chloride in Organic Chemistry, *Ind. Eng. Chem.*, 1944, **36**, 785.
Haller, Insecticides, *ibid.*, 1947, **39**, 469.
Bigelow, The Action of Fluorine on Organic Compounds, *Chem. Reviews*, 1947, **40**, 51.
Fluorine Symposium, *Ind. Eng. Chem.*, 1947, **39**, 237.
Masson, Race and Pounder, The Iodoxy-group and its Relations, *J.C.S.*, **1935**, 1669.
Ann. Reports, 1949, **46**, pp. 137–140. Aromatic Halogenation.
Bunnett and Zahler, Aromatic Nucleophilic Substitution Reactions, *Chem. Reviews*, 1951, **49**, 273.
Everard and Sutton, The Polar Effect of the Halogens and Other Groups, *J.C.S.*, **1951**, 2821.

CHAPTER XXII

AROMATIC NITRO-COMPOUNDS

AROMATIC nitro-compounds are almost invariably prepared by direct nitration, using one of the following reagents:

(i) *Concentrated nitric acid,* density about 1·5.

(ii) *Fuming nitric acid* (6–12 per cent. nitrogen dioxide).

(iii) *Mixed acid.* This is a mixture of nitric acid (concentrated or fuming) and various amounts of concentrated sulphuric acid (sometimes fuming sulphuric acid is used). Mixed acid is by far the most important nitrating agent. Occasionally other acids besides sulphuric acid are used, *e.g.*, glacial acetic acid.

Boron trifluoride is a very effective catalyst for nitration (Thomas *et al.*, 1940). One equivalent of catalyst must be used:

$$ArH + HNO_3 + BF_3 \longrightarrow Ar{\cdot}NO_2 + BF_3{\cdot}H_2O$$

The yields are better and the products purer than by the above methods. Furthermore, boron trifluoride is particularly useful for nitrating compounds containing a negative group, *e.g.*,

$$C_6H_5{\cdot}NO_2 + HNO_3 \xrightarrow{BF_3} m\text{-}C_6H_4(NO_2)_2 \quad (87\%)$$

Oláh *et al.* (1956) have shown that nitronium tetrafluoroborate (a stable compound) is a useful nitrating agent.

$$ArH + (NO_2^+)(BF_4^-) \longrightarrow Ar{\cdot}NO_2 + HF + BF_3 \quad (g.\text{–}ex.)$$

This method of nitration gives direct preparative proof of the electrophilic character of nitration through the nitronium cation (see below).

(iv) *Acetyl nitrate,* $CH_3{\cdot}CO{\cdot}O{\cdot}NO_2$, is useful as a nitrating agent in certain cases, since it introduces a nitro-group into the *o*-position, and produces almost only the mononitro-derivative. Acetyl nitrate, however, is somewhat dangerous to use, since it tends to explode when heated.

The nitrating agent used depends on the nature of the compound to be nitrated and the object in view, *i.e.*, the introduction of one or more nitro-groups. In any case, whichever reagent is used, it is usually difficult to stop the nitration process at one nitro-group (except with acetyl nitrate).

As an outcome of a great deal of experimental work, it has been shown that nitration with mixed acid, *i.e.*, nitration in sulphuric acid, is due to some substance produced from the nitric acid and not the nitric acid itself. According to Bennett *et al.* and Ingold *et al.* (1946), the active nitrating agent is the *nitronium cation*, NO_2^+, which, they believe, is formed as follows:

$$HNO_3 + 2H_2SO_4 \longrightarrow NO_2^+ + H_3O^+ + 2HSO_4^-$$

The evidence for the existence of the nitronium cation is shown:

(i) By electrolysis experiments, *e.g.*, it has been found that nitric acid in oleum migrates to the cathode.

(ii) By cryoscopic experiments in which it has been shown that *i* (the van't Hoff factor) is 4; this value satisfies the equation given above.

(iii) By the isolation of salts of the nitronium ion, *e.g.*, nitronium perchlorate, $(NO_2^+)(ClO_4^-)$, and nitronium tetrafluoroborate, $(NO_2^+)(BF_4^-)$ [see (iii) above].

(iv) By spectroscopic analysis (which has shown the existence of the nitronium ion).

Nitration (with mixed acid) thus possibly proceeds as follows:

$$C_6H_6 + NO_2^+ \rightleftharpoons [C_6H_6NO_2]^+ \longrightarrow C_6H_5NO_2 + H^+$$

$$H^+ + HSO_4^- \longrightarrow H_2SO_4$$

Nitration in concentrated aqueous nitric acid and in organic solvents is also believed to be via the nitronium ion:

$$2HNO_3 \longrightarrow NO_2^+ + H_2O + NO_3^-$$

On the other hand, in more dilute nitric acid solutions, it is probably the *nitracidium cation* that is involved in nitration:

$$2HNO_3 \rightleftharpoons H_2NO_3^+ + NO_3^-$$

General properties of the nitro-compounds. Most nitro-compounds are yellow crystalline solids; a few, including nitrobenzene, are yellow liquids. Many are steam-volatile, and except for a few mononitro-derivatives, cannot be distilled under atmospheric pressure because, when strongly heated, they decompose, often with explosive violence. All the nitro-compounds are denser than water, in which they are insoluble; they are, however, readily soluble in organic solvents. The nitro-group is firmly attached to the nucleus and may be replaced only under certain conditions (see later). Nitro-compounds form addition products with many aromatic compounds; their most important reaction is their reduction by various reducing agents.

Nitrobenzene (*oil of mirbane*), $C_6H_5{\cdot}NO_2$, may be prepared by the action of cold mixed acid on benzene, and then warming to complete the reaction:

$$C_6H_6 + HNO_3 \longrightarrow C_6H_5{\cdot}NO_2 + H_2O \quad (85\%)$$

It is a pale yellow oil, b.p. 211°, with a smell like benzaldehyde. It is almost insoluble in water, but is steam-volatile; its vapour is poisonous. It is used for scenting cheap soaps, in the manufacture of floor polishes, aniline, benzidine and some azo-dyes, etc. It is used as a solvent, and is used occasionally as an oxidising agent in organic chemistry, *e.g.*, in the preparation of quinoline.

When heated with solid potassium hydroxide, nitrobenzene produces a mixture of *o*- and *p*-nitrophenols and some azoxybenzene.

Dinitrobenzenes. When nitrobenzene is heated with mixed acid (fuming nitric acid and concentrated sulphuric acid), the main product is *m*-dinitrobenzene:

$$C_6H_5NO_2 + HNO_3 \xrightarrow{H_2SO_4} m\text{-}C_6H_4(NO_2)_2 + H_2O \quad (75\text{–}87\%)$$

Nitric acid alone may be used to introduce one nitro-group; mixed acid must be used to introduce the second nitro-group into nitrobenzene.

m-Dinitrobenzene is a pale yellow solid, m.p. 90°, practically insoluble in water, but is steam-volatile. It may be reduced stepwise by, *e.g.*, sodium sulphide, to *m*-nitroaniline, and then to *m*-phenylenediamine:

$$m\text{-}C_6H_4(NO_2)_2 \xrightarrow{Na_2S} m\text{-}NH_2C_6H_4NO_2 \xrightarrow{Na_2S} m\text{-}C_6H_4(NH_2)_2$$

The hydrogen atom *o*- or *o*-*p*- to two nitro-groups is easily displaced by oxidation, but not by substitution; *e.g.*, *m*-dinitrobenzene is oxidised by an alkaline solution of potassium ferricyanide to a mixture of 2 : 4-dinitrophenol (mainly) and 2 : 6-dinitrophenol (small amount):

$$C_6H_4(NO_2)_2 \xrightarrow[NaOH]{K_3Fe(CN)_6} C_6H_3(NO_2)_2OH + C_6H_3(NO_2)_2OH$$

***o*-Dinitrobenzene** can be isolated after removing the *m*-isomer when nitrobenzene is nitrated. Nitration of acetanilide gives a mixture of *o*- and *p*-nitroacetanilides:

$$C_6H_5{\cdot}NH{\cdot}CO{\cdot}CH_3 \xrightarrow{HNO_3} o\text{-}NO_2{\cdot}C_6H_4{\cdot}NH{\cdot}CO{\cdot}CH_3 + p\text{-}NO_2{\cdot}C_6H_4{\cdot}NH{\cdot}CO{\cdot}CH_3$$

These isomers are separated; each is deacetylated, and by replacing the amino-group by a nitro-group (see p. 560), the *o*- and *p*-dinitrobenzenes may be obtained pure, *e.g.*,

$$p\text{-}NO_2{\cdot}C_6H_4{\cdot}NH{\cdot}CO{\cdot}CH_3 \xrightarrow{H_2O} p\text{-}NO_2{\cdot}C_6H_4{\cdot}NH_2 \xrightarrow[HBF_4]{NaNO_2} p\text{-}NO_2{\cdot}C_6H_4{\cdot}N_2BF_4 \xrightarrow[Cu]{NaNO_2} p\text{-}C_6H_4(NO_2)_2$$

It is necessary to " protect " compounds with a hydroxyl or amino-group in the ring, since these compounds are very easily oxidised instead of nitrated by nitric acid.

An alternative method for preparing *o*- and *p*-dinitrobenzenes is to oxidise the corresponding nitroaniline with Caro's acid, and then to oxidise the product, the nitro-nitroso-derivative, with a mixture of nitric acid and hydrogen peroxide:

$$p\text{-}NO_2{\cdot}C_6H_4{\cdot}NH_2 \xrightarrow{H_2SO_5} p\text{-}NO_2{\cdot}C_6H_4{\cdot}NO \xrightarrow{HNO_3/H_2O_2} p\text{-}C_6H_4(NO_2)_2 \quad (v.g.)$$

On the other hand, peroxytrifluoroacetic acid oxidises the amino-group directly to the nitro-group (Emmons *et al.*, 1953), *e.g.*,

$$NH_2{\cdot}C_6H_4{\cdot}NH_2 \xrightarrow{CF_3{\cdot}CO_3H} NO_2{\cdot}C_6H_4{\cdot}NO_2 \quad (86\%)$$

***p*-Dinitrobenzene** may also be prepared by oxidising *p*-benzoquinone dioxime (p. 643) with nitric acid:

$$HON{=}C_6H_4{=}NOH \xrightarrow[HNO_3]{[O]} p\text{-}C_6H_4(NO_2)_2$$

o- and *p*-Dinitrobenzenes are colourless solids, melting points 118° and 173°, respectively. They resemble the *m*-isomer in many ways, but differ in the following respects.

(i) When *o*- and *p*-dinitrobenzenes are boiled with aqueous sodium hydroxide, one nitro-group is replaced by hydroxyl to give the corresponding nitrophenol:

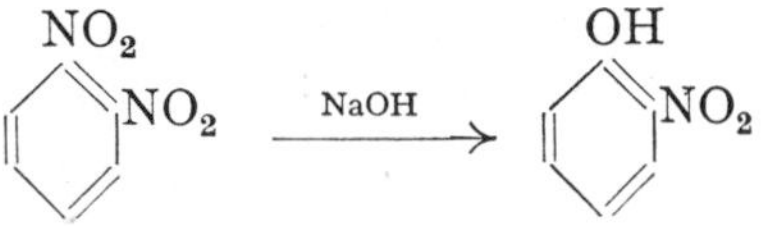

NO_2, NO_2 $\xrightarrow{NaOH}$ OH, NO_2

This reaction is used to separate *m*-dinitrobenzene from its *o*- and *p*-isomers in the industrial preparation of *m*-dinitrobenzene.

(ii) When boiled with ethanolic ammonia, *o*- and *p*-dinitrobenzenes are converted into the corresponding nitroanilines, one nitro-group being displaced by an amino-group:

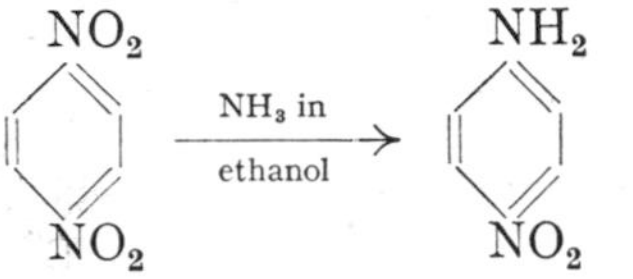

NO_2, NO_2 $\xrightarrow[\text{ethanol}]{NH_3 \text{ in}}$ NH_2, NO_2

(iii) When boiled with methanolic sodium methoxide, *o*- and *p*-dinitrobenzenes are converted into the corresponding nitroanisoles, one nitro-group being replaced by a methoxyl group:

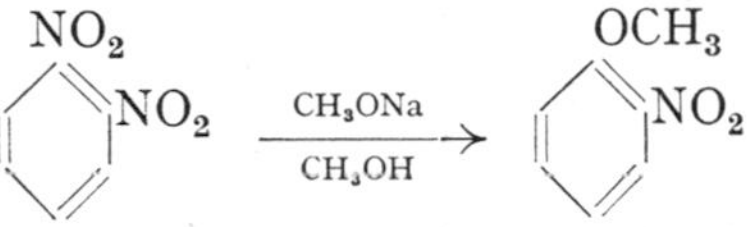

NO_2, NO_2 $\xrightarrow[CH_3OH]{CH_3ONa}$ OCH_3, NO_2

These reactions are characteristic of polynitro-compounds in which two nitro-groups are in the *o*- or *p*-positions, one nitro-group being replaced by a hydroxyl, amino-, or methoxyl group.

s-Trinitrobenzene may be prepared by the nitration of *m* dinitrobenzene with mixed acid consisting of fuming nitric acid and fuming sulphuric acid. This reaction takes five days to complete; it is very difficult to introduce the third nitro-group, and it is impossible to introduce more than three nitro-groups by direct nitration. A better method of preparing *s*-trinitrobenzene is to oxidise 2 : 4 : 6-trinitrotoluene, and to decarboxylate the trinitrobenzoic acid so produced by heating it in acetic acid solution:

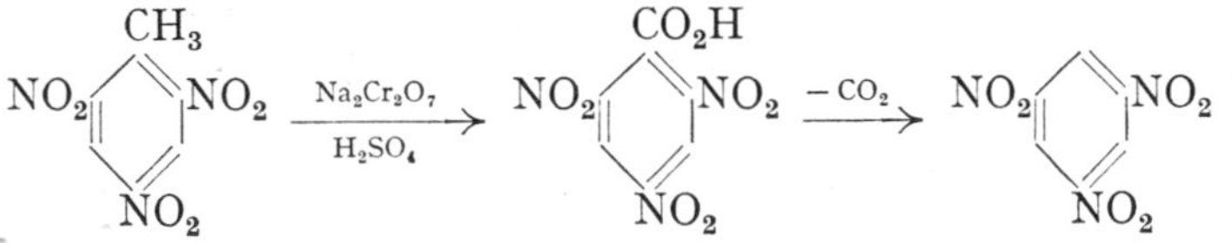

CH_3, NO_2, NO_2, NO_2 $\xrightarrow[H_2SO_4]{Na_2Cr_2O_7}$ CO_2H, NO_2, NO_2, NO_2 $\xrightarrow{-CO_2}$ NO_2, NO_2, NO_2 (43–46%)

It may also be prepared by the removal of the chlorine atom in picryl chloride by means of hydrogen iodide generated from sodium iodide and acetic acid in acetone solution (Blatt *et al.*, 1952):

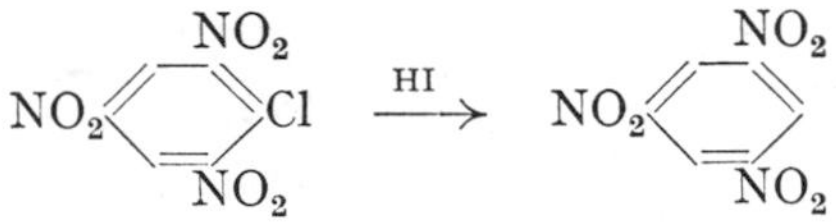

NO_2, NO_2, Cl, NO_2 $\xrightarrow{HI}$ NO_2, NO_2, NO_2 (70%)

s-Trinitrobenzene is a colourless solid, m.p. 122°. It forms well-defined addition compounds with many aromatic compounds such as hydrocarbons, phenols, etc. It has been suggested that the two components in these molecular compounds are held together by a chemical link. On the other hand, it has also been suggested that the binding may be physical association due to, *e.g.*, dipole induction effects.

When three nitro-groups are present in the ring as in *s*-trinitrobenzene, one may be removed by the reagents which attack the *o*- and *p*-dinitro-compounds; *e.g.*, when heated with methanolic sodium methoxide, *s*-trinitrobenzene forms 3 : 5-dinitroanisole:

$$C_6H_3(NO_2)_3 \xrightarrow[CH_3OH]{CH_3ONa} C_6H_3(OCH_3)(NO_2)_2 \quad (63\text{–}77\%)$$

Benzene may be oxidised and nitrated simultaneously to dinitrophenol and picric acid by mercuric nitrate in nitric acid solution (see p. 601).

Nitrotoluenes. Benzene homologues are more readily nitrated than benzene itself, due to the activating effect of the alkyl group. When nitrated with mixed acid, toluene forms a mixture of *o*- and *p*-nitrotoluenes:

$$C_6H_5CH_3 \xrightarrow[H_2SO_4]{HNO_3} o\text{-}CH_3C_6H_4NO_2\ (65\text{–}70\%) + p\text{-}CH_3C_6H_4NO_2\ (30\%)$$

These isomers may readily be separated by fractional distillation under reduced pressure: *o*-isomer, m.p. −4°, b.p. 222°; *p*-isomer, m.p. 54°, b.p. 238°.

A larger yield of *o*-nitrotoluene may be obtained by nitrating toluene with acetyl nitrate:

$$C_6H_5CH_3 \xrightarrow{CH_3\cdot CO\cdot O\cdot NO_2} o\text{-}CH_3C_6H_4NO_2\ (85\text{–}90\%) + p\text{-}CH_3C_6H_4NO_2\ (10\text{–}15\%) + CH_3\cdot CO_2H$$

m-Nitrotoluene, m.p. 16°, b.p. 227°, may be prepared by reducing the *p*-isomer, acetylating the *p*-toluidine, nitrating the acetyl derivative, deacetylating, and replacing the amino-group by hydrogen (see p. 557):

$$p\text{-}CH_3C_6H_4NO_2 \xrightarrow{[H]} p\text{-}CH_3C_6H_4NH_2 \xrightarrow{(CH_3\cdot CO)_2O} p\text{-}CH_3C_6H_4NH\cdot CO\cdot CH_3 \xrightarrow{HNO_3} CH_3C_6H_3(NO_2)NH\cdot CO\cdot CH_3 \xrightarrow{H_2O}$$

$$CH_3C_6H_3(NO_2)NH_2 \xrightarrow{NaNO_2/H_2SO_4} CH_3C_6H_3(NO_2)N_2HSO_4 \xrightarrow{C_2H_5OH} m\text{-}CH_3C_6H_4NO_2$$

All the nitrotoluenes may be reduced to the corresponding toluidines. A very interesting oxidising effect of a nitro-group is the internal oxidation of *o*-nitrotoluene to *o*-aminobenzoic acid when heated with ethanolic sodium hydroxide:

$$o\text{-}CH_3C_6H_4NO_2 \xrightarrow{NaOH/C_2H_5OH} o\text{-}NaO_2CC_6H_4NH_2$$

Dinitrotoluenes. Nitration of any of the nitrotoluenes gives a mixture of 2 : 4- and 2 : 6-dinitrotoluenes.

2 : 4 : 6-Trinitrotoluene (T.N.T.), m.p. 81°, may be prepared by nitrating toluene with mixed acid consisting of fuming nitric and fuming sulphuric acids. This reaction takes place far more readily than with benzene because of the activation of the ring by the methyl group.

Trinitrotoluene is used as an explosive; mixed with ammonium nitrate, it forms the explosive *amatol*.

Artificial musks. Polynitro-derivatives of benzene containing a tertiary butyl group, possess odours resembling musk, and are used in perfumery, *e.g.*,

[Structures: CH_3, NO_2, NO_2, $C(CH_3)_3$, NO_2 — "toluene-musk"; CH_3, $(CH_3)_3C$, NO_2, OCH_3, NO_2 — "musk ambrette"; $CO{\cdot}CH_3$, $(CH_3)_3C$, CH_3, NO_2, NO_2, CH_3 — "musk ketone"]

"toluene-musk" "musk ambrette" "musk ketone"

Halogeno-nitrobenzenes. Nitration of phenyl halides produces a mixture of the *o*- and *p*-halogeno-nitrobenzenes; these may be separated by freezing and filtration, the *p*-isomer having the higher melting point. The halogen atom *o*- or *p*- to a nitro group is fairly reactive, and is replaced when heated with alkali, ethanolic ammonia, etc., to form respectively nitrophenols, nitroanilines, etc. Smith *et al.* (1953) have shown that the halogen atom in halogenonitro-compounds may be removed by heating with copper powder and benzoic acid. Chlorine and bromine may be removed when *o*- or *p*- to a nitro-group, iodine is removed from *any* position, and fluorine not at all, *e.g.*,

$$o\text{-}BrC_6H_4NO_2 \xrightarrow[C_6H_5{\cdot}CO_2H]{Cu} C_6H_5NO_2 \xleftarrow[C_6H_5{\cdot}CO_2H]{Cu} m\text{-}IC_6H_4NO_2$$

When two nitro-groups are present in the *o*- and *p*-positions (with respect to the halogen atom), the halogen atom is more reactive, and when three nitro-groups are present in the *p*- and two *o*-positions, the halogen atom is so reactive that it can be replaced by hydroxyl merely by warming with water, *e.g.*, picryl chloride forms picric acid:

$$2,4,6\text{-}(NO_2)_3C_6H_2Cl \xrightarrow{H_2O} 2,4,6\text{-}(NO_2)_3C_6H_2OH$$

It is also interesting to note that the fluorine atom in 1-fluoro-2 : 4-dinitrobenzene is strongly activated. This compound condenses with amino-groups to form *N*-2 : 4-dinitrophenyl derivatives. This reaction has been used in protein and peptide studies (Sanger, 1945).

A methyl group is also made reactive by a nitro-group in the *o*- or *p*-

position, *e.g.*, trinitrotoluene condenses with benzaldehyde in the presence of ethanolic potassium hydroxide to form *trinitrostilbene*:

$$NO_2C_6H_2(NO_2)_2\text{-}CH_3 + OCH\text{-}C_6H_5 \xrightarrow{KOH} NO_2C_6H_2(NO_2)_2\text{-}CH{=}CH\text{-}C_6H_5 + H_2O$$

Halogenation of nitrobenzene produces mainly the *m*-derivative:

$$C_6H_5NO_2 + Br_2 \xrightarrow[heat]{Fe} m\text{-}BrC_6H_4NO_2 + HBr \quad (85\%)$$

A halogen atom *m*- to a nitro-group shows the same unreactivity as the halogen atom in a phenyl halide.

Phenylnitromethane, $C_6H_5{\cdot}CH_2{\cdot}NO_2$, may be prepared by heating toluene with dilute nitric acid in a sealed tube at 100°, or by heating benzyl chloride with aqueous ethanolic silver nitrite:

$$C_6H_5{\cdot}CH_3 + HNO_3 \longrightarrow C_6H_5{\cdot}CH_2{\cdot}NO_2 + H_2O \quad (p.)$$
$$C_6H_5{\cdot}CH_2Cl + Ag{\cdot}O{\cdot}NO \longrightarrow C_6H_5{\cdot}CH_2{\cdot}NO_2 + AgCl \quad (f.g.).$$

Phenylnitromethane is best prepared as follows:

$$C_6H_5{\cdot}CH_2{\cdot}CN + CH_3{\cdot}O{\cdot}NO_2 + C_2H_5ONa \longrightarrow$$
$$\underset{\text{(I)}}{C_6H_5{\cdot}C(CN){=}NO_2Na} + CH_3OH + C_2H_5OH \xrightarrow[heat]{aq.\ NaOH} \underset{\text{(II)}}{C_6H_5{\cdot}C(CO_2Na){=}NO_2Na} \xrightarrow{HCl}$$
$$\left[C_6H_5{\cdot}C(CO_2H){=}NO_2H\right] \xrightarrow{-CO_2} C_6H_5{\cdot}CH{:}NO_2H \xrightarrow[\text{(3 days)}]{\text{isomerises}} C_6H_5{\cdot}CH_2{\cdot}NO_2 \quad (50\text{–}55\%)$$

(I) is sodio-phenyl*aci*nitroacetonitrile, and (II) is the sodium salt of phenylnitroacetic acid.

Phenylnitromethane behaves as a true primary aliphatic nitro-compound; both the nitro- and *aci*nitro-forms have been isolated (*cf.* p. 287):

$$\underset{\substack{\text{yellow oil}\\ \text{b.p. }226°}}{C_6H_5{\cdot}CH_2{\cdot}NO_2} \rightleftharpoons \underset{\substack{\text{solid}\\ \text{m.p. }84°}}{C_6H_5{\cdot}CH{=}NO_2H}$$

Abnormal nitration. When nuclear-substituted aromatic compounds are nitrated, there are many cases where an alkyl, halogen, alkoxyl, acyl, carboxyl, or sulphonic acid group is replaced by a nitro-group; in some cases, a hydrogen atom in the side-chain is replaced by the *nitrate* group. Generally, abnormal nitration is more likely to occur in the nitration of polysubstituted benzene compounds, particularly the polyalkylbenzenes. Mono-, di- and trialkylbenzenes (where the alkyl group is methyl or ethyl) give the expected nitro-compounds. Polyalkylbenzenes containing three or more alkyl groups in some cases give normal products, and in others, abnormal; *e.g.*, ethylmesitylene, when nitrated with mixed acid (fuming nitric and sulphuric), gives 3 : 5 : 6-trinitro-4-ethyl-*o*-xylene:

$$C_6H_2(CH_3)_3(C_2H_5) \longrightarrow 1,2\text{-}(CH_3)_2\text{-}3,5,6\text{-}(NO_2)_3\text{-}4\text{-}C_2H_5\text{-}C_6$$

AROMATIC NITROSO-COMPOUNDS

The simplest aromatic nitroso-compound is **nitrosobenzene,** $C_6H_5{\cdot}NO$. This may be prepared by oxidising phenylhydroxylamine with dichromate-sulphuric acid mixture, or by oxidising aniline with Caro's acid:

$$C_6H_5{\cdot}NHOH \xrightarrow[H_2SO_4]{K_2Cr_2O_7} C_6H_5{\cdot}NO \xleftarrow{H_2SO_5} C_6H_5{\cdot}NH_2$$

Nitrosobenzene may also be prepared by the electrolytic reduction of nitrobenzene (see later).

Nitroso-compounds containing certain other groups in the ring may be prepared directly by the action of nitrous acid on the compound, *e.g.*, dimethylaniline forms *p*-nitrosodimethylaniline:

$$C_6H_5{\cdot}N(CH_3)_2 + HNO_2 \longrightarrow p\text{-}ON{\cdot}C_6H_4{\cdot}N(CH_3)_2 + H_2O$$

Nitrosobenzene, in the solid state, exists as colourless crystals, m.p. 68°; this is the dimer. In the liquid (fused) state, in solution, or in the gaseous state, nitrosobenzene is green; this is the monomer (*cf.* p. 290).

Reactions of nitrosobenzene. Nitrosobenzene is reduced by hydrogen in the presence of palladium (on a calcium carbonate support) to *azobenzene*:

$$2C_6H_5{\cdot}NO + 2H_2 \xrightarrow{Pd} C_6H_5{\cdot}N{:}N{\cdot}C_6H_5 + 2H_2O \quad (100\%)$$

When reduced with concentrated hydriodic acid-red phosphorus, nitrosobenzene gives phenylhydroxylamine:

$$C_6H_5{\cdot}NO + 2HI \xrightarrow{P} C_6H_5{\cdot}NH{\cdot}OH + I_2$$

Reduction with metal and acid gives aniline:

$$C_6H_5{\cdot}NO + 4[H] \xrightarrow{Fe/HCl} C_6H_5{\cdot}NH_2 + H_2O$$

Reduction of nitroso-compounds with sulphur dioxide or sodium hydrogen sulphite is often accompanied by the simultaneous introduction of a sulphonic acid group, *e.g.*, *p*-nitrosophenol forms 2-amino-5-hydroxybenzene-1 : 3-disulphonic acid:

$$p\text{-}HO{\cdot}C_6H_4{\cdot}NO \xrightarrow{H_2SO_3} 5\text{-}HO\text{-}2\text{-}H_2N\text{-}C_6H_2(SO_3H)_2\text{-}1,3$$

Nitrosobenzene is oxidised by alkaline hydrogen peroxide, dilute nitric acid, or a mixture of nitric acid and hydrogen peroxide, to nitrobenzene:

$$C_6H_5{\cdot}NO + H_2O_2 \xrightarrow{NaOH} C_6H_5{\cdot}NO_2 + H_2O$$

Nitrosobenzene condenses with aniline to form azobenzene:

$$C_6H_5{\cdot}NO + C_6H_5{\cdot}NH_2 \longrightarrow C_6H_5{\cdot}N{:}N{\cdot}C_6H_5 + H_2O$$

It will also condense with compounds containing a reactive methylene group, *e.g.*,

$$C_6H_5{\cdot}NO + C_6H_5{\cdot}CH_2{\cdot}CN \longrightarrow C_6H_5{\cdot}C(CN){:}N{\cdot}C_6H_5 + H_2O$$

The orienting influence of the nitroso-group has been discussed on p. 497.

Phenylhydroxylamine, $C_6H_5{\cdot}NH{\cdot}OH$, may be prepared by reducing nitrobenzene with zinc dust and aqueous ammonium chloride (yield: 62–68 per cent.), or by the electrolytic reduction of nitrobenzene in an aqueous solution of acetic acid containing sodium acetate.

Phenylhydroxylamine is a white solid, m.p. 81°, soluble in water, ethanol and ether. It is a powerful reducing agent, *e.g.*, it reduces ammoniacal silver nitrate and Fehling's solution. It readily absorbs oxygen from the air to form nitrosobenzene; this can react with unchanged phenylhydroxylamine to give *azoxybenzene*:

$$C_6H_5{\cdot}NH{\cdot}OH + C_6H_5{\cdot}NO \longrightarrow C_6H_5{\cdot}\overset{\overset{\displaystyle O}{\uparrow}}{N}{:}N{\cdot}C_6H_5 + H_2O$$

In dilute acid solution, phenylhydroxylamine rearranges to *p*-aminophenol. According to Hughes and Ingold (1951), the mechanism is possibly:

$$H{-}C_6H_4{-}NHOH \xrightarrow{H^+} H{-}C_6H_4{-}\overset{+}{N}H{\cdot}OH_2 \xrightarrow{-H_2O} H{\overset{+}{-}}C_6H_4{=}NH$$

$$H{-}C_6H_4{-}\overset{+}{N}H{\cdot}OH_2 \xrightarrow[(-H_2O)]{H_2O} \overset{+}{H_2O}(H)C_6H_4{=}NH \qquad H{\overset{+}{-}}C_6H_4{=}NH \xrightarrow{H_2O} \overset{+}{H_2O}(H)C_6H_4{=}NH$$

$$HO{-}C_6H_4{-}NH_2 \xleftarrow{-H^+} H_2\overset{+}{O}{-}C_6H_4{-}NH_2 \longleftarrow \overset{+}{H_2O}(H)C_6H_4{=}NH$$

If the *p*-position is occupied by a methyl group, the rearrangement can still take place, but in this case ammonia is eliminated and a methylquinol is formed; this methylquinol then readily rearranges to a quinol:

$$CH_3{-}C_6H_4{-}NH{\cdot}OH \xrightarrow{acid} (CH_3)(OH)C_6H_4{=}NH \xrightarrow[-NH_3]{H_2O\ (acid)} (CH_3)(OH)C_6H_4{=}O \longrightarrow CH_3C_6H_3(OH)_2$$

Phenylhydroxylamine is used to prepare **cupferron**; an ethereal solution of phenylhydroxylamine is treated with dry ammonia gas, and then *n*-butyl nitrite is added:

$$C_6H_5{\cdot}NH{\cdot}OH + C_4H_9{\cdot}O{\cdot}NO + NH_3 \longrightarrow C_6H_5{\cdot}N(NO){\cdot}ONH_4 + C_4H_9OH \quad (85\text{–}90\%)$$

Cupferron is the ammonium salt of *N*-nitrosophenylhydroxylamine, and was originally used for the quantitative estimation of copper and iron (hence its name). Cupferron is a colourless solid, and the structure of its metallic complexes is uncertain.

Reduction products of the nitro-compounds. The course of the reduction of nitro-compounds has been shown to take place through the following stages:

$$C_6H_5{\cdot}NO_2 \longrightarrow C_6H_5{\cdot}NO \longrightarrow C_6H_5{\cdot}NH{\cdot}OH \longrightarrow C_6H_5{\cdot}NH_2$$

The nature of the final product, however, depends mainly on the *p*H of the solution in which the reduction is carried out.

(i) In acid solution (metal and acid), aniline is obtained:

$$C_6H_5{\cdot}NO_2 + 6[H] \xrightarrow{metal/acid} C_6H_5{\cdot}NH_2 + 2H_2O$$

In acid solution, the intermediate products nitrosobenzene and phenylhydroxylamine are reduced far more rapidly than nitrobenzene, and so these intermediates are never isolated.

(ii) In neutral solution, *e.g.*, with zinc dust and ammonium chloride solution, the main product of the reduction is phenylhydroxylamine.

(iii) In alkaline solution the compound obtained depends on the nature of the reducing agent used (see p. 572). The complex compounds that may be obtained are:

(*a*) *Azoxybenzene.* This is believed to be formed by interaction of the intermediate products nitrosobenzene and phenylhydroxylamine:

$$C_6H_5{\cdot}NO + C_6H_5{\cdot}NH{\cdot}OH \longrightarrow C_6H_5{\cdot}\overset{\overset{O}{\uparrow}}{N}{:}N{\cdot}C_6H_5 + H_2O$$

(*b*) *Azobenzene.* This is believed to be formed by reaction between two molecules of phenylhydroxylamine:

$$2C_6H_5{\cdot}NH{\cdot}OH \longrightarrow C_6H_5{\cdot}N{:}N{\cdot}C_6H_5 + 2H_2O$$

(*c*) *Hydrazobenzene.* This is apparently formed by the reduction of azobenzene:

$$C_6H_5{\cdot}N{:}N{\cdot}C_6H_5 + 2[H] \longrightarrow C_6H_5{\cdot}NH{\cdot}NH{\cdot}C_6H_5$$

Thus by choosing a suitable alkaline reducing agent, it is possible to isolate (*a*), (*b*), or (*c*).

Electrolytic reduction of nitro-compounds in acid or alkaline solution also takes place through the stages:

$$C_6H_5{\cdot}NO_2 \longrightarrow C_6H_5{\cdot}NO \longrightarrow C_6H_5{\cdot}NH{\cdot}OH \longrightarrow C_6H_5{\cdot}NH_2$$

In weakly acid solution, the main product is aniline; but in strongly acid solution, the product is *p*-aminophenol, formed by the rearrangement of phenylhydroxylamine. On the other hand, aromatic nitro-compounds are reduced to azo-compounds by lithium aluminium hydride.

The course of catalytic reduction (with Raney nickel) has not been investigated in detail. It is quite likely that it takes place in the same way as those discussed above; the final product is often almost a quantitative yield of amine.

QUESTIONS

1. Write an account of the mechanism of nitration with (*a*) mixed acid, (*b*) with concentrated aqueous nitric acid.

2. Starting with benzene or toluene, how would you prepare each of the following:—(*a*) $PhNO_2$, (*b*) *o*-, *m*- and *p*-$C_6H_4(NO_2)_2$, (*c*) *s*-$C_6H_3(NO_2)_3$, (*d*) *o*-, *m*- and *p*-$MeC_6H_4{\cdot}NO_2$, (*e*) T.N.T., (*f*) *o*-, *m*- and *p*-$ClC_6H_4{\cdot}NO_2$, (*g*) $Ph{\cdot}CH_2{\cdot}NO_2$?
In each case indicate the principles upon which you have based your method.

3. What are the important differences in behaviour between *o*-, *m*- and *p*-dinitrobenzene? Which of these isomers resemble *s*-trinitrobenzene in chemical properties?

4. Discuss the effect of a nitro-group on the reactivity of:—(*a*) a halogen atom, (*b*) a methyl group, (*c*) another nitro-group, in aromatic compounds.

5. Write an account of the preparation and properties of:—
(*a*) PhNO, (*b*) *p*-$Me_2N{\cdot}C_6H_4{\cdot}NO$, (*c*) Ph·NH·OH.

6. Write an account of the reduction products of nitrobenzene.

7. A compound has the formula $C_7H_7O_2N$. Write out the structures of the possible isomers and show how you would distinguish between them.

READING REFERENCES

Gillespie and Millen, Aromatic Nitration, *Quart. Reviews (Chem. Soc.)*, 1948, **2**, 277.
Nightingale, Anomalous Nitration Reactions, *Chem. Reviews*, 1927, **40**, 117.
Sidgwick, *The Organic Chemistry of Nitrogen*, Oxford Press (New Ed. by Taylor and Baker, 1937), Ch. 7. Nitroso-compounds. Ch. 8. Aromatic Nitro-compounds.
Blackall, Hughes and Ingold, Kinetics and Mechanism of Aromatic Nitration, Part IX, *J.C.S.*, **1952**, 28.
Vanderzee and Edgell, The Kinetics of the Reduction of Aromatic Nitro Compounds with Tin and Hydrochloric Acid, *J. Amer. Chem. Soc.*, 1950, **72**, 2916.

CHAPTER XXIII

AROMATIC AMINO-COMPOUNDS

AROMATIC amines are of two types, one in which the amino-group is attached directly to the ring, and the other in which the amino-group is in the side-chain. The latter behave very much like the aliphatic amines, and so may be regarded as aryl-substituted aliphatic amines.

Nuclear amino-compounds fall into the same three classes as the aliphatic amines, *viz.*, *primary amines*, $Ar{\cdot}NH_2$; *secondary amines*, Ar_2NH and $Ar{\cdot}NH{\cdot}R$; and *tertiary amines*, Ar_3N, $Ar_2N{\cdot}R$ and $Ar{\cdot}NR_2$.

Purely aromatic quaternary compounds, *i.e.*, compounds of the type $Ar_4\overset{+}{N}\}X^-$, have not yet been prepared; compounds of the type $Ar_3\overset{+}{N}{\cdot}R\}X^-$, however, are known.

General methods of preparation of primary amines. 1. Primary aromatic amines are nearly always prepared by the reduction of the corresponding nitro-compound. Various reducing reagents may be used, *e.g.*, tin, iron, or zinc, with hydrochloric or acetic acid:

$$Ar{\cdot}NO_2 + 6[H] \xrightarrow{\text{metal/acid}} Ar{\cdot}NH_2 + 2H_2O \quad (v.g.\text{–}ex.)$$

Zinc and hydrochloric acid often produce the chloroamino-compound as well as the desired amino-compound. Acetic acid is very useful for compounds which contain a group that is attacked by inorganic acid; *e.g.*, reduction of *p*-nitro-acetanilide in hydrochloric acid solution leads to some hydrolysis of the acetyl group; use of acetic acid prevents this deacetylation.

Titanous chloride in hydrochloric acid reduces nitro-compounds to amines, and may be used for the quantitative estimation of nitro-groups in a compound:

$$Ar{\cdot}NO_2 + 6TiCl_3 + 6HCl \longrightarrow Ar{\cdot}NH_2 + 6TiCl_4 + 2H_2O$$

By means of aqueous ethanolic ammonium hydrogen sulphide, aqueous sodium sulphide, or stannous chloride in hydrochloric acid, nitro-groups in a polynitro-compound can be reduced one at a time, *e.g.*, *m*-nitroaniline from *m*-dinitrobenzene:

$$C_6H_4(NO_2)_2 + 3NH_4HS \longrightarrow C_6H_4(NH_2)(NO_2) + 3NH_3 + 3S + 2H_2O \quad (70\text{–}80\%)$$

It appears that ammonium hydrogen sulphide and sodium sulphide will not reduce a nitro-group in the *o*-position to an alkyl group, whereas stannous chloride in hydrochloric acid reduces this nitro-group preferentially:

$$\underset{\text{3-nitro-}p\text{-toluidine}}{CH_3C_6H_3(NO_2)(NH_2)} \xleftarrow{NH_4HS} CH_3C_6H_3(NO_2)_2 \xrightarrow{SnCl_2/HCl} \underset{\text{5-nitro-}o\text{-toluidine}}{CH_3C_6H_3(NH_2)(NO_2)}$$

Sulphur dioxide or sodium hydrogen sulphite may also be used to reduce one nitro-group in polynitro-compounds, but in certain cases the reduction is accompanied by the introduction of a sulphonic acid group, *e.g.*,

$$m\text{-}C_6H_4(NO_2)_2 \xrightarrow{NaHSO_3} \text{4-}NO_2\text{-2-}NH_2\text{-}C_6H_3\text{-1-}SO_3H$$

4-nitro-orthanilic acid

Nitro-compounds may be reduced catalytically to the corresponding amine at 200–400°; if Raney nickel or platinum is used as catalyst, the reduction may be carried out at room temperature. Catalytic reduction is particularly useful for compounds which contain a group that is hydrolysable in acid solution, *e.g.*, *p*-nitroacetanilide, $p\text{-}NO_2{\cdot}C_6H_4{\cdot}NH{\cdot}CO{\cdot}CH_3$. Although organic sulphur compounds poison the Raney nickel catalyst, nitro-compounds containing a thiol, sulphide, etc., linkage can nevertheless still be reduced by using a large excess of the catalyst (Fel'dman, 1949). The reduction of nitro-compounds may also be effected with hydrazine hydrate. The reaction is slow, but is catalysed by Raney nickel (Balcom *et al.*, 1953). Dewar *et al.* (1956) have shown that palladised charcoal is a more convenient catalyst, the yields of amine varying from 60—81 per cent.

Nitro-compounds may also be reduced by means of *cyclo*hexene and palladium, and if more than one nitro-group is present, it is possible to reduce only one (see p. 460).

Certain nitro-compounds may be reduced to the corresponding amine in liquid ammonia solution by sodium and methanol, or sodium and ammonium bromide (Watt *et al.*, 1947), *e.g.*,

$$C_6H_5{\cdot}NO_2 \xrightarrow{Na/CH_3OH} C_6H_5{\cdot}NH_2 \quad (92\%)$$

If a nitro-compound contains an unsaturated chain or an aldehyde group in the nucleus, alkaline ferrous sulphate may be used as the reducing agent to avoid reduction of these other groups. If only an aldehyde group is present, then stannous chloride may be used as the reducing agent; *e.g.*, *m*-nitrobenzaldehyde may be reduced to *m*-aminobenzaldehyde:

$$m\text{-}NO_2{\cdot}C_6H_4{\cdot}CHO \xrightarrow{SnCl_2/HCl} m\text{-}NH_2{\cdot}C_6H_4{\cdot}CHO$$

2. Amino-compounds may be prepared by reduction of nitroso-compounds:

$$C_6H_5{\cdot}NO + 4[H] \xrightarrow{Sn/HCl} C_6H_5{\cdot}NH_2 + H_2O$$

3. Reduction of azo- and hydrazo-compounds, usually with sodium hyposulphite (dithionite), gives very good yields of amino-compound:

$$Ar{\cdot}N{:}N{\cdot}Ar' + 2Na_2S_2O_4 + 4H_2O \longrightarrow Ar{\cdot}NH_2 + Ar'{\cdot}NH_2 + 4NaHSO_3$$

Reduction of azo-compounds is very useful in certain cases (see, *e.g.*, p. 572).

4. Amino-compounds may be prepared by the Hofmann reaction (p. 192); *e.g.*, benzamide gives aniline:

$$C_6H_5{\cdot}CO{\cdot}NH_2 \xrightarrow{Br_2/KOH} C_6H_5{\cdot}NH_2$$

5. The Schmidt reaction may be used to prepare amines (*cf.* p. 294):

$$Ar{\cdot}CO_2H + HN_3 \xrightarrow{H_2SO_4} Ar{\cdot}NH_2 + CO_2 + N_2$$

6. Ammonolysis of halogeno- and hydroxy-compounds may be used in certain cases to prepare amino-compounds (see, *e.g.*, aniline).

7. Many amino-compounds may be prepared by means of rearrangement reactions (see, *e.g.*, p. 577).

Aniline (*aminobenzene*), $C_6H_5{\cdot}NH_2$, was discovered by Unverdorben (1826), who obtained it by distilling indigo; this name was given to it by Fritzsche (1841), who derived it from *anil*, the Portuguese word for indigo.

In the laboratory, aniline is prepared by the reduction of nitrobenzene with metal and acid, *e.g.*, tin and hydrochloric acid:

$$C_6H_5{\cdot}NO_2 + 6[H] \longrightarrow C_6H_5{\cdot}NH_2 + 2H_2O \quad (80\%)$$

The aniline remains in solution as aniline stannichloride $(C_6H_5{\cdot}NH_2)_2{\cdot}H_2SnCl_6$; when the solution is made alkaline and steam distilled, the aniline comes over in the distillate.

Commercially, aniline is prepared:

(i) By the reduction of nitrobenzene with iron, water and a small amount of hydrochloric acid (one fortieth of the theoretical amount).

The mechanism of the reduction is uncertain, but there is some evidence to show it may be as follows:

$$Fe + 2HCl \longrightarrow FeCl_2 + 2[H]$$
$$C_6H_5{\cdot}NO_2 + 6[H] \longrightarrow C_6H_5{\cdot}NH_2 + 2H_2O$$
$$FeCl_2 + 2H_2O \longrightarrow Fe(OH)_2 + 2HCl$$
$$C_6H_5{\cdot}NO_2 + 6Fe(OH)_2 + 4H_2O \longrightarrow C_6H_5{\cdot}NH_2 + 6Fe(OH)_3$$

(ii) By the catalytic reduction (nickel catalyst) of nitrobenzene.

(iii) By heating chlorobenzene with excess aqueous ammonia in the presence of cuprous oxide at 200° under pressure. The cuprous oxide renders the reaction irreversible by decomposing the ammonium chloride formed in the reaction:

$$2C_6H_5Cl + 2NH_3 + Cu_2O \longrightarrow 2C_6H_5{\cdot}NH_2 + 2CuCl + H_2O \quad (90\%)$$

Aniline (whose properties are characteristic of primary aromatic amines in general) is, when freshly prepared, a colourless liquid, b.p. 184°; it has an unpleasant odour and is poisonous. When exposed to air, it rapidly darkens, since it is very sensitive to oxidation. It is practically insoluble in water, but is steam-volatile; it is readily soluble in organic solvents.

Aniline forms crystalline salts with strong inorganic acids, and these salts are considerably hydrolysed in solution. Aniline is a weaker base than the primary aliphatic amines, and this may be explained by resonance (which is not possible in aliphatic primary amines):

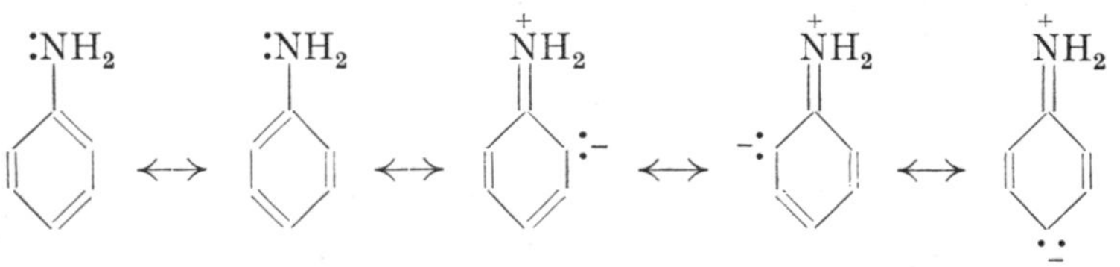

In aniline, owing to resonance, the lone pair of electrons on the nitrogen atom is less available for co-ordinating with a proton; at the same time, the small positive charge on the nitrogen atom would tend to repel a proton. Alternatively, since there are more resonating structures possible for aniline itself than for the cation $C_6H_5{\cdot}\overset{+}{N}H_3$, the former will be stabilised with respect to the latter.

The decreased basicity of aniline may be explained from M.O. theory as follows. The lone pair of $2p$ electrons on the nitrogen atom conjugate with the

p_z electrons of the benzene ring, thereby reducing their availability for accepting a proton owing to partial delocalisation (see Fig. 20.4, p. 501).

Hydrogen atoms of the amino-group are replaceable by halogen when aniline is treated with hypohalous acid. When aniline is heated with sodium or potassium, the metal dissolves with the evolution of hydrogen:

$$C_6H_5{\cdot}NH_2 + K \longrightarrow [C_6H_5{\cdot}NH]^-K^+ + \tfrac{1}{2}H_2$$

Aniline combines with alkyl halides to give finally a quaternary ammonium compound:

$$C_6H_5{\cdot}NH_2 + 3CH_3Cl \longrightarrow [C_6H_5{\cdot}N(CH_3)_3]^+Cl^-$$

Aniline gives the iso*cyanide reaction* when heated with chloroform and ethanolic potassium hydroxide:

$$C_6H_5{\cdot}NH_2 + CHCl_3 + 3KOH \longrightarrow C_6H_5{\cdot}NC + 3KCl + 3H_2O$$

Aniline is readily acetylated, and condenses with aromatic aldehydes to form anils or Schiff bases; *e.g.*, when warmed with benzaldehyde, it forms benzylideneaniline:

$$C_6H_5{\cdot}NH_2 + C_6H_5{\cdot}CHO \longrightarrow C_6H_5{\cdot}N{:}CH{\cdot}C_6H_5 + H_2O \quad (84\text{–}87\%)$$

These Schiff bases are easily hydrolysed to the free amine, and so their formation offers a means of "protecting" an amino-group, *e.g.*, during nitration. Schiff bases may also be used to prepare secondary amines:

$$C_6H_5{\cdot}N{:}CH{\cdot}Ar \xrightarrow[Ni]{H_2} C_6H_5{\cdot}NH{\cdot}CH_2{\cdot}Ar$$

On the other hand, benzylideneaniline undergoes reductive cleavage to aniline by hydrogen transfer with *cyclo*hexene and palladium (Braude *et al.*, 1954; see also p. 460).

When refluxed with ethanolic carbon disulphide and solid potassium hydroxide, aniline forms **s-diphenylthiourea** (*thiocarbanilide*), m.p. 154°, which is used as a rubber accelerator:

$$CS_2 + 2C_6H_5{\cdot}NH_2 + 2KOH \longrightarrow S{:}C(NH{\cdot}C_6H_5)_2 + K_2S + 2H_2O \quad (70\%)$$

When treated with concentrated hydrochloric acid, diphenylthiourea is converted into phenyl *iso*thiocyanate:

$$S{:}C(NH{\cdot}C_6H_5)_2 + HCl \longrightarrow C_6H_5{\cdot}NCS + C_6H_5{\cdot}NH_2{\cdot}HCl$$

Phenyl *iso*thiocyanate may be conveniently prepared by running aniline into a cooled mixture of carbon disulphide and concentrated aqueous ammonium hydroxide, and decomposing the precipitated ammonium phenyldithiocarbamate with lead nitrate solution:

$$C_6H_5{\cdot}NH_2 + CS_2 + NH_4OH \longrightarrow C_6H_5{\cdot}NH{\cdot}CS_2NH_4 + H_2O \xrightarrow{Pb(NO_3)_2}$$
$$C_6H_5{\cdot}NCS + NH_4NO_3 + HNO_3 + PbS \quad (74\text{–}78\%)$$

Baxter *et al.* (1956) have shown that aryl *iso*thiocyanates may be prepared by heating arylthioureas in chlorobenzene solution at 150°, *e.g.*,

$$C_6H_5{\cdot}N{\cdot}CS{\cdot}NH_2 \longrightarrow C_6H_5{\cdot}NCS + NH_3 \quad (44\%)$$

The oxidation products of aniline are far more complex than those obtained from primary aliphatic amines (p. 300). Nitrosobenzene, nitrobenzene, phenylhydroxylamine, *p*-benzoquinone, azobenzene, azoxybenzene, aniline black (a dye), etc., may be isolated, the actual substance obtained depending on the nature of the oxidising agent used, *e.g.*, Caro's acid oxidises aniline to a mixture of nitroso- and nitrobenzene; peroxytrifluoroacetic acid oxidises aniline to nitrobenzene (89%; Emmons, 1954); chromic acid gives *p*-benzoquinone; sodium hypochlorite gives a purple coloration—this reaction is characteristic of aniline.

Aniline may be easily mercurated with an aqueous ethanolic solution of mercuric acetate in the cold or on warming.

The most important difference between aniline and primary aliphatic amines is their behaviour towards nitrous acid; aliphatic amines liberate nitrogen (see p. 299), whereas aniline (and all other primary aromatic monoamines) forms *diazonium salts*, which are stable in cold aqueous solution:

$$C_6H_5{\cdot}NH_2 + HNO_2 + HCl \longrightarrow \underset{\text{benzenediazonium chloride}}{C_6H_5{\cdot}N_2Cl} + 2H_2O$$

Acetanilide (N-*phenylacetamide*), $C_6H_5{\cdot}NH{\cdot}CO{\cdot}CH_3$, may be readily prepared, in very good yield, by heating aniline with acetyl chloride, acetic anhydride, or glacial acetic acid. It is a white crystalline solid, m.p. 114°, almost insoluble in cold water but readily soluble in hot. It is hydrolysed by strong acids or alkalis to aniline. It is used in medicine, under the name of *antifebrin*, as a febrifuge. It is a useful intermediate in various reactions of aniline in which it is desirable to "protect" the amino-group, *e.g.*, in nitration, halogenation, etc.; the acetamido-group is predominantly *p*-orienting. The *N*-phenyl derivative of the amide of any acid is known as an *anilide*.

Halogenated anilines. The amino-group in aniline activates the *o*- and *p*-positions to a very large degree; *e.g.*, when aniline is treated with excess chlorine- or bromine-water, an immediate precipitate of the 2 : 4 : 6-*trihalogeno-derivative* is obtained:

$$C_6H_5NH_2 + 3Br_2 \longrightarrow 2,4,6\text{-}Br_3C_6H_2NH_2 + 3HBr$$

The yield is quantitative, and so this reaction is used to estimate aniline.

In order to introduce only one chlorine or bromine atom, the activating effect of the amino-group must be lowered; this may be done by acetylation:

$$C_6H_5{\cdot}NH{\cdot}CO{\cdot}CH_3 \xrightarrow{Br_2/CH_3{\cdot}CO_2H} \underset{(80\%)}{p\text{-}BrC_6H_4{\cdot}NH{\cdot}CO{\cdot}CH_3} + \underset{\text{(small amount)}}{o\text{-}BrC_6H_4{\cdot}NH{\cdot}CO{\cdot}CH_3}$$

These, on hydrolysis, yield the corresponding bromoanilines, which may be separated by steam distillation (the *o*-compound being steam volatile).

The deactivating effect of the acetyl group may be due to the inductive effect of the carbonyl group, thereby inhibiting, to a certain extent, the lone pair entering into resonance.

An interesting method of preparing *p*-chloroaniline is to heat *p*-chlorobromobenzene with ammonia in the presence of cuprous oxide:

$$p\text{-}ClC_6H_4Br + NH_3 \xrightarrow{Cu_2O} p\text{-}ClC_6H_4NH_2$$

This is possible due to the more ready displacement of bromine compared with chlorine.

Aniline is readily chlorinated by sulphuryl chloride, in the *absence* of catalysts, to form the mono-, di- and trichloroanilines, *e.g.*,

$$C_6H_5NH_2 + SO_2Cl_2 \longrightarrow p\text{-}ClC_6H_4NH_2 + SO_2 + HCl$$

***p*-Iodoaniline** may be prepared by the action of iodine on aniline in the presence of aqueous sodium hydrogen carbonate (*cf.* p. 520). Oxidising agents cannot be used to remove the hydrogen iodide, since they will oxidise the aniline; hence the use of sodium hydrogen carbonate.

m-Chloro- and bromo-anilines may be prepared by reducing the corresponding halogeno-nitrobenzenes. They are also formed by the halogenation of aniline in concentrated sulphuric acid, the *m*-orienting effect being due to the presence of the $-\overset{+}{N}H_3$ group (see p. 495).

2 : 6-Dichloroaniline may be prepared by first blocking the *p*-position of aniline with a sulphonamide group, refluxing the sulphanilamide with hydrochloric acid and hydrogen peroxide, and subsequently refluxing the product, 3 : 5-dichlorosulphanilamide, with 70 per cent. sulphuric acid, thereby removing the sulphonamide group:

$$p\text{-}NH_2C_6H_4SO_2NH_2 \xrightarrow{HCl/H_2O_2} 4\text{-}NH_2\text{-}3,5\text{-}Cl_2C_6H_2SO_2NH_2 \xrightarrow{H_2SO_4} 2,6\text{-}Cl_2C_6H_3NH_2 \quad (50\text{–}55\%)$$

The presence of a halogen atom, particularly in the *o*- or *p*-position, decreases the basic properties of aniline; *e.g.*, the salts of the trihalogeno-anilines are completely hydrolysed in aqueous solution (*cf.* nitroanilines, below).

An interesting point about trihalogeno-anilines is their anomalous nitration:

$$2,4,6\text{-}Br_3C_6H_2NH_2 \xrightarrow[\text{in } CH_3CO_2H]{\text{fuming } HNO_3} 2,6\text{-}Br_2\text{-}4\text{-}NO_2C_6H_2NH_2$$

Nitroanilines. Direct treatment of aniline with nitric acid gives a complex mixture of mono-, di- and trinitro-compounds, and oxidation products. If, however, the amino-group is protected (and deactivated) by acetylation or by the formation of the benzylidene derivative, the main product on nitration is the *p*-nitro-derivative:

$$C_6H_5NH{\cdot}CO{\cdot}CH_3 \xrightarrow{HNO_3} p\text{-}NO_2C_6H_4NH{\cdot}CO{\cdot}CH_3 \ (90\%) + o\text{-}NO_2C_6H_4NH{\cdot}CO{\cdot}CH_3 \ (1\text{–}2\%)$$

The nitroacetanilides may be separated by digesting the mixture with chloroform in which the *o*-derivative is soluble and the *p*-, insoluble. Alternatively, they may be separated by keeping the *o*-compound liquid (m.p. 93°) and filtering off the solid *p*-isomer (m.p. 215°); or by chromatographic adsorption, since the *o*-compound chelates. After separation, the nitro-anilines may be obtained by hydrolysis with alkali.

Nitration of aniline derivatives is accelerated by nitrous acid. This is believed to be due to the formation of the nitroso-compound, followed by its oxidation to the nitro-compound (see phenol, p. 600).

o- and p-Nitroanilines may be prepared by heating *o*- and *p*-chloronitro-benzenes with ammonia (*cf.* p. 533). The *o*-isomer, however, is best prepared as follows:

$$C_6H_5NH\cdot CO\cdot CH_3 \xrightarrow{H_2SO_4} p\text{-}HO_3S\cdot C_6H_4\cdot NH\cdot CO\cdot CH_3 \xrightarrow{HNO_3} (NH\cdot CO\cdot CH_3)(NO_2)C_6H_3(SO_3H) \xrightarrow{H_2SO_4} o\text{-}NO_2\cdot C_6H_4\cdot NH_2$$

m-Nitroaniline (m.p. 114°) may be prepared by the partial reduction of *m*-dinitrobenzene with ammonium hydrogen sulphide (yield: 70–80 per cent.), sodium sulphide (yield: 70 per cent.), or stannous chloride in hydro-chloric acid. *m*-Nitroaniline may also be prepared by the direct nitration of aniline *in the presence of concentrated sulphuric acid* (*cf. m*-chloroaniline, above). Industrially, it is prepared by reducing *m*-dinitrobenzene with the calculated quantity of iron (for one nitro-group) and a small amount of hydrochloric acid.

All three nitroanilines may be reduced by metal and acid to the correspond-ing diamines. All can be halogenated in the *o*-position; iodine mono-chloride in boiling acetic acid is used to prepare the iodo-compound:

$$p\text{-}NO_2\cdot C_6H_4\cdot NH_2 + 2ICl \longrightarrow 2,6\text{-}I_2\text{-}4\text{-}NO_2\cdot C_6H_2\cdot NH_2 + 2HCl \quad (56\text{–}64\%)$$

o- and *p*-Nitroanilines, but not *m*-, react with boiling aqueous sodium hydroxide to give the corresponding nitrophenol (*cf.* chloronitrobenzenes, p. 533):

$$p\text{-}NO_2\cdot C_6H_4\cdot NH_2 \xrightarrow{NaOH} p\text{-}NO_2\cdot C_6H_4\cdot OH + NH_3$$

All the nitroanilines are weaker bases than aniline. This may be due to the inductive effect of the nitro-group tending to withdraw electrons from the ring, thereby decreasing the availability of the lone pair on the nitrogen atom of the amino-group; the net result is an increased contribution of the charged state, due to resonance, to the actual state of the molecule:

$$:NH_2\text{-}C_6H_4\text{-}NO_2 \longleftrightarrow \overset{+}{N}H_2{=}C_6H_4{=}\overset{+\,-}{NO_2}$$

This explanation is supported by the fact that the dipole moment of *p*-nitroaniline is greater than the sum of the dipole moments of the amino- and nitro-groups.

Increasing the number of nitro-groups decreases the basic properties of the compound due to an increase in resonance. A nitro-group in the *o*- or *p*-position has a much greater effect than one in the *m*-position.

From the point of view of M.O. theory, the decreased basicity may be accounted for by the fact that in nitroanilines, the nitrogen atoms of both nitro- and amino-groups enter into conjugation with the benzene ring. Also, since the nitrogen atom of the nitro-group has a positive charge and consequently attracts the electron cloud, partial delocalisation of the lone pair on the amino-group will be greater than had the nitro-group been absent. Calculation shows that this effect of the nitro-group is greater in the *o*- and *p*-positions than in the *m*-position.

2 : 4-Dinitroaniline, m.p. 180°, may be prepared by passing ammonia gas into a heated mixture of 1-chloro-2 : 4-dinitrobenzene and ammonium acetate:

$$C_6H_3Cl(NO_2)_2 + 2NH_3 \xrightarrow{CH_3\cdot CO_2NH_4} C_6H_3(NH_2)(NO_2)_2 + NH_4Cl \quad (61\text{–}68\%)$$

Aminobenzenesulphonic acids (see p. 590).

Toluidines (*tolylamines*). These may be obtained by reduction of the corresponding nitrotoluenes. *o*- and *m*-Toluidines are oils, b.p. 201° and 200°, respectively; *p*-toluidine is a solid, m.p. 45°, b.p. 200°.

Nitration of toluene gives a mixture of *o*- and *p*-nitrotoluenes, and this, when reduced with iron and dilute hydrochloric acid, gives a mixture of the corresponding toluidines.

When the reaction mixture is steam distilled, both pass over; when the distillate is cooled, the hydrate of the *p*-isomer crystallises out, the *o*-compound remaining as an oil (yield of *o*- and *p*-isomers is 90–95 per cent.). Both isomers are used in the preparation of dyes.

m-Nitrotoluene is prepared via a diazonium salt (p. 558).

***N*-Alkylanilines.** The commonest *N*-alkylanilines are mono- and dimethylaniline. These may be prepared by heating aniline with methyl iodide:

$$C_6H_5\cdot NH_2 + CH_3I \longrightarrow C_6H_5\cdot NH\cdot CH_3\cdot HI$$

$$C_6H_5\cdot NH\cdot CH_3 + CH_3I \longrightarrow C_6H_5\cdot N(CH_3)_2\cdot HI$$

Commercially, these methylanilines are prepared by heating a mixture of aniline, methanol and sulphuric acid under pressure at 230°. No quaternary compound is formed under these conditions (*cf.* p. 292). Monomethylaniline is the main product (50 per cent.) when about 1·2 molecules of methanol are used; dimethylaniline and unchanged aniline are also present. Dimethylaniline is obtained as the main product (95 per cent.) by using a large excess of methanol; monomethylaniline and unchanged aniline are also present, but these are removed by acetylating the mixture and distilling off the dimethylaniline.

To prepare higher *N*-alkyl derivatives of aniline, hydrochloric acid is used instead of sulphuric, since the latter tends to dehydrate the alcohol to olefin.

An interesting example of *reductive methylation* is the conversion of aniline into dimethylaniline; aniline and formaldehyde, in aqueous ethanolic sulphuric acid, is hydrogenated in the presence of platinum as catalyst (Pearson *et al.*, 1951).

$$C_6H_5{\cdot}NH_2 + 2CH_2O + 2H_2 \xrightarrow{Pt} C_6H_5{\cdot}N(CH_3)_2 + 2H_2O \quad (74\%)$$

Mono- and dimethylaniline are liquids, b.p. 196° and 193°, respectively, and, due to the closeness of their boiling points, cannot be readily separated by fractional distillation. They can be separated, however, by acetylating the monomethyl derivative (as indicated above).

Pure monomethylaniline may be prepared by treating the sodium derivative of acetanilide with methyl iodide in toluene solution:

$$[C_6H_5{\cdot}N{\cdot}CO{\cdot}CH_3]^-Na^+ + CH_3I \longrightarrow C_6H_5{\cdot}N(CH_3){\cdot}COCH_3 + NaI \xrightarrow{KOH} C_6H_5{\cdot}NH{\cdot}CH_3 \quad (90\%)$$

Pure monomethylaniline may also be prepared as follows:

$$C_6H_5{\cdot}NH_2 + C_6H_5{\cdot}SO_2Cl \longrightarrow C_6H_5{\cdot}NH{\cdot}SO_2{\cdot}C_6H_5 \xrightarrow[NaOH]{(CH_3)_2SO_4} C_6H_5{\cdot}N(CH_3){\cdot}SO_2{\cdot}C_6H_5 \xrightarrow{H_2O} C_6H_5{\cdot}NH{\cdot}CH_3$$

Secondary amines, particularly those in which one group is of the type $Ar{\cdot}CH_2$—, may be readily prepared by the catalytic reduction of the corresponding anil (p. 296).

Mono- and dimethylaniline are slightly *weaker* bases than aniline itself. The reason for this is not certain, but it may be due to the electron-releasing property of an alkyl group. This would tend to increase resonance and consequently the lone pair on the nitrogen atom would be less available for proton co-ordination in these bases than in aniline. On the other hand, phenyltrimethylammonium hydroxide $\{C_6H_5{\cdot}\overset{+}{N}(CH_3)_3\}OH^-$, is strongly basic.

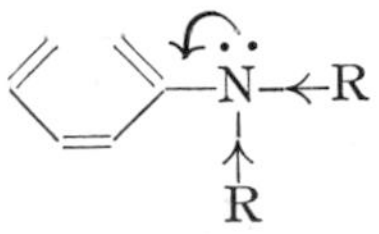

Mono- and dimethylaniline resemble secondary and tertiary aliphatic amines in many ways, but differ in that they can also undergo substitution reactions (in the *o*- and *p*-positions) due to the presence of the benzene ring. Monoalkylanilines form pale yellow *N*-nitrosoamines with nitrous acid, and these give Liebermann's nitroso-reaction (p. 300):

$$C_6H_5{\cdot}NH{\cdot}CH_3 + HNO_2 \longrightarrow C_6H_5{\cdot}N(NO){\cdot}CH_3 + H_2O \quad (87\text{–}93\%)$$

This may be converted into the original compound by heating with hydrochloric acid:

$$C_6H_5{\cdot}N(NO){\cdot}CH_3 + H_2O \xrightarrow{HCl} C_6H_5{\cdot}NH{\cdot}CH_3 + HNO_2$$

The nitroso-compound may also be reduced by nascent hydrogen to *as*-methylphenylhydrazine:

$$C_6H_5{\cdot}N(NO){\cdot}CH_3 + 4[H] \xrightarrow{Zn/CH_3{\cdot}CO_2H} C_6H_5{\cdot}N(CH_3){\cdot}NH_2 + H_2O \quad (52\text{–}56\%)$$

***N*-Methylformanilide,** $C_6H_5{\cdot}N(CH_3){\cdot}CHO$, may be prepared by distilling a mixture of methylaniline, formic acid and toluene:

$$C_6H_5{\cdot}NH{\cdot}CH_3 + H{\cdot}CO_2H \longrightarrow C_6H_5{\cdot}N(CH_3){\cdot}CHO + H_2O \quad (93\text{–}97\%)$$

It is a liquid, b.p. 253°, and is used as a formylating agent in the preparation of aldehydes (see p. 629).

Dialkylanilines form *p*-nitroso-compounds with nitrous acid, *e.g.*, dimethylaniline forms *p*-nitrosodimethylaniline (green flakes):

$$C_6H_5N(CH_3)_2 + HNO_2 \longrightarrow p\text{-}ON\cdot C_6H_4N(CH_3)_2 + H_2O \quad (80\text{–}90\%)$$

If the *p*-position is occupied, the *o*-nitroso-compound is formed:

$$p\text{-}CH_3C_6H_4N(CH_3)_2 \xrightarrow{HNO_2} \text{2-nitroso-4-methyl-}N(CH_3)_2 \text{ compound}$$

The nitroso-group activates the dimethylamino-group, *e.g.*, when boiled with aqueous sodium hydroxide, *p*-nitrosodimethylaniline forms *p*-nitrosophenol; the mechanism is possibly:

$$p\text{-}Me_2N\cdot C_6H_4\cdot N{=}O + OH^- \longrightarrow \text{(}Me_2N,\ \bar{O}\text{ adduct; } {=}N{-}\bar{O}^-\text{)} \longrightarrow \text{(}Me_2NH,\ \bar{O};\ {=}N{-}\bar{O}\text{)} \longrightarrow p\text{-}\bar{O}\cdot C_6H_4\cdot N{=}O + Me_2NH$$

p-Nitrosodimethylaniline is readily oxidised by permanganate to *p*-nitrodimethylaniline, and may be reduced to *p*-aminodimethylaniline.

When dimethylaniline is dissolved in concentrated sulphuric acid and then nitrated with nitric acid at 40–55°, a tetranitro-derivative is obtained in which one methyl group has been replaced by a nitro-group:

$$C_6H_5N(CH_3)_2 \xrightarrow{HNO_3/H_2SO_4} CH_3\cdot N\cdot NO_2 \text{ on } C_6H_2(NO_2)_3 \ (2,4,6)$$

The dimethylamino-group activates the *p*-hydrogen atom so much that dimethylaniline will condense with formaldehyde and carbonyl chloride to form diphenylmethane derivatives, and with aromatic aldehydes to form triphenylmethane derivatives; *e.g.*, with carbonyl chloride, it forms *Michler's ketone*:

$$COCl_2 + 2C_6H_5N(CH_3)_2 \longrightarrow CO[C_6H_4N(CH_3)_2]_2 + 2HCl$$

A remarkable property of the mono- and dialkylanilines (and the quaternary compounds) is the ability of their hydrochlorides (or hydrobromides) to undergo rearrangement on strong heating, an alkyl group migrating from the nitrogen atom and entering preferentially the *p*-position, or, if this is occupied, the *o*-; *e.g.*, when trimethylphenylammonium chloride is heated under pressure, the following rearrangement takes place:

$$\overset{+}{N}(CH_3)_3\}Cl^- \text{ (benzene ring)} \xrightarrow{300^\circ} N(CH_3)_2\cdot HCl \text{ (ring, } p\text{-}CH_3) \longrightarrow NH\cdot CH_3\cdot HCl \text{ (ring, } o\text{-}CH_3, p\text{-}CH_3) \longrightarrow NH_2\cdot HCl \text{ (ring, } o,o'\text{-}CH_3, p\text{-}CH_3)$$

This reaction is known as the **Hofmann–Martius rearrangement** (1871); it may be used to prepare aniline homologues.

Many mechanisms have been proposed for the Hofmann–Martius rearrangement. Hughes and Ingold (1952) have proposed the following, based largely on the suggestion of Hickinbottom (1934) that the rearrangement occurs via the formation of an alkyl carbonium ion:

$$C_6H_5\cdot\overset{+}{N}H_2\cdot C_2H_5\}Cl^- \rightleftharpoons C_6H_5\cdot NH_2 + C_2H_5Cl$$

$$C_2H_5Cl \rightleftharpoons C_2H_5^+ + Cl^-$$

$$C_6H_5\cdot NH_2 + C_2H_5^+ \rightleftharpoons C_6H_5\cdot NH_3^+ + C_2H_4$$

$$C_2H_5^+ + C_6H_5\cdot NH_2 \longrightarrow p\text{-}C_2H_5\cdot C_6H_4\cdot NH_2 + H^+$$

$$H^+ + C_6H_5\cdot NH_2 \rightleftharpoons C_6H_5\cdot NH_3^+$$

Rearrangements of this kind have been observed to take place with aniline derivatives of the type $C_6H_5\cdot\overset{|}{N}\text{—}Z$, where Z is R, X, NH_2, NO, or NO_2, *e.g.*,

$$NH\cdot NH_2\cdot HCl \text{ (benzene ring)} \xrightarrow{250^\circ} NH_2\cdot HCl \text{ (ring, } p\text{-}NH_2) + NH_2\cdot HCl \text{ (ring, } o\text{-}NH_2)$$

(main product)

When Z is NO, *i.e.*, the compound is the *N*-nitroso-derivative of a secondary aromatic amine, the rearrangement is known as the **Fischer–Hepp rearrangement** (1886).

The main product in the Fischer–Hepp rearrangement is the *p*-isomer, and the mechanism is believed to be *intermolecular* and possibly as follows:

$$NR\cdot NO \text{ (benzene ring)} + HCl \rightleftharpoons NH\cdot R \text{ (benzene ring)} + NOCl \longrightarrow NH\cdot R \text{ (ring, } p\text{-}NO) + HCl$$

Hughes *et al.* (1956) have studied the rearrangement of phenylnitramine in sulphuric acid in the presence of enriched ^{15}N tracer. The products were *o*- and *p*-nitroaniline and they contained the normal amount of ^{15}N, thus showing that the rearrangement is *intramolecular*. According to Hughes and Ingold (1952), the mechanism is:

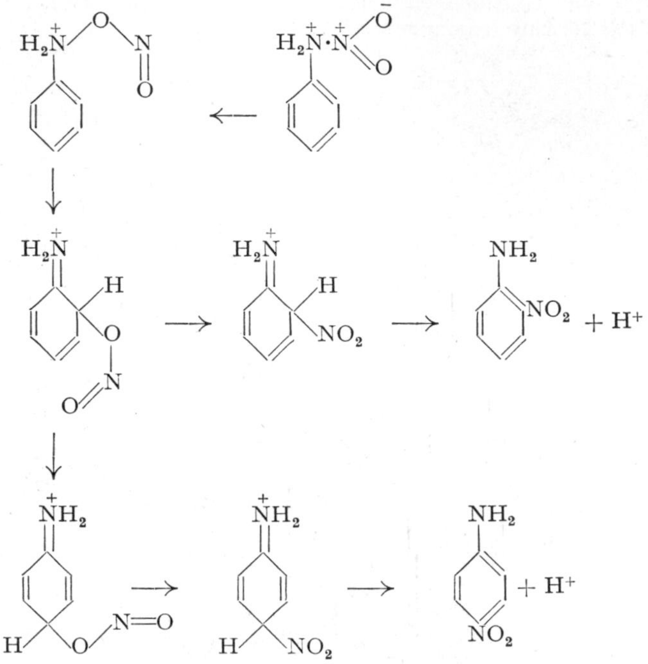

The mechanism of the rearrangement of *N*-chloroacetanilide in hydrochloric acid (which acts as a catalyst) is believed to be:

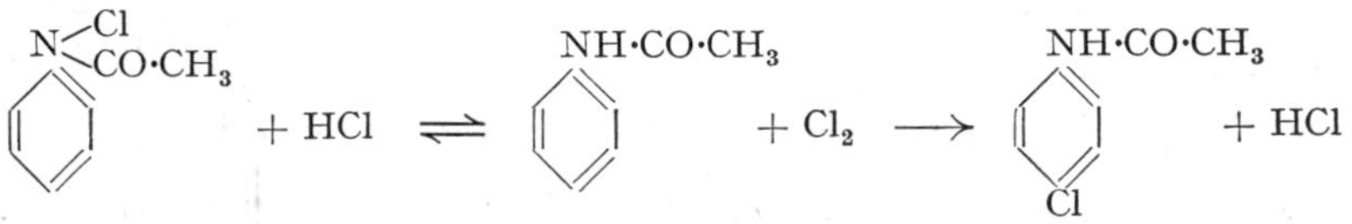

This is an example of the **Orton rearrangement** (1909), which is the rearrangement of *N*-halogenoacylanilides in which the halogen migrates to the *p*-position and sometimes to the *o*-position. The rearrangement may be effected:

(i) By means of halogen acids as catalysts; the intermolecular mechanism given above was proposed by Orton and is supported by Olson *et al.* (1936–1938) who used hydrochloric acid containing radioactive chlorine, some of which appeared in the chloroacetanilide produced.

(ii) By the action of heat or photochemically; these reactions probably occur by a free-radical mechanism. Hickinbottom *et al.* (1955) have shown that this rearrangement is also effected by benzoyl peroxide in the absence of light. Thus the rearrangement in this case is a homolytic intermolecular chlorination.

(iii) With carboxylic acids or phenols in aprotic solvents. The mechanism of the rearrangement under these conditions is not certain; some workers (Soper *et al.*, 1945) believe it to be intermolecular, and others (Bell *et al.*, 1934–1939) intramolecular. According to Soper, the mechanism is:

$$C_6H_5\cdot NX\cdot CO\cdot CH_3 + HOY \longrightarrow C_6H_5\cdot NH\cdot CO\cdot CH_3 + XOY \longrightarrow p\text{-}X\cdot C_6H_4\cdot NH\cdot CO\cdot CH_3 + HOY$$

where X is the halogen and HOY the acid catalyst. Dewar *et al.* (1957) have obtained definite evidence that this reaction takes place in stages, and believe their work supports the Soper mechanism.

The rearrangement of phenylhydroxylamine in acid solution to *p*-aminophenol (p. 536) may be regarded as the case where Z is OH.

Diphenylamine $(C_6H_5)_2NH$, may be prepared by heating phenol with aniline in the presence of zinc chloride at 260°:

$$C_6H_5OH + C_6H_5{\cdot}NH_2 \xrightarrow{ZnCl_2} (C_6H_5)_2NH + H_2O$$

It may also be prepared by the **Ullmann reaction**; this is carried out by refluxing acetanilide, potassium carbonate, bromobenzene and a little copper powder in nitrobenzene solution (copper accelerates the reaction):

$$C_6H_5{\cdot}NH{\cdot}CO{\cdot}CH_3 + C_6H_5Br + K_2CO_3 \xrightarrow{Cu} (C_6H_5)_2NH + CO_2 + CH_3{\cdot}CO_2K + KBr \quad (60\%)$$

Commercially, diphenylamine is prepared by heating aniline with aniline hydrochloride at 140° under pressure:

$$C_6H_5{\cdot}NH_2 + C_6H_5{\cdot}NH_2{\cdot}HCl \longrightarrow (C_6H_5)_2NH + NH_4Cl \quad (85\%)$$

Diphenylamine is a colourless, pleasant-smelling solid, m.p. 54°. It is a weaker base than aniline, and its salts are completely hydrolysed in solution. It forms an *N*-nitroso-derivative with nitrous acid. A solution of diphenylamine in phosphoric acid gives a blue colour with oxidising agents; this reaction is used as a test for nitric acid. When melted with sulphur, diphenylamine forms *phenothiazine* (*thiodiphenylamine*):

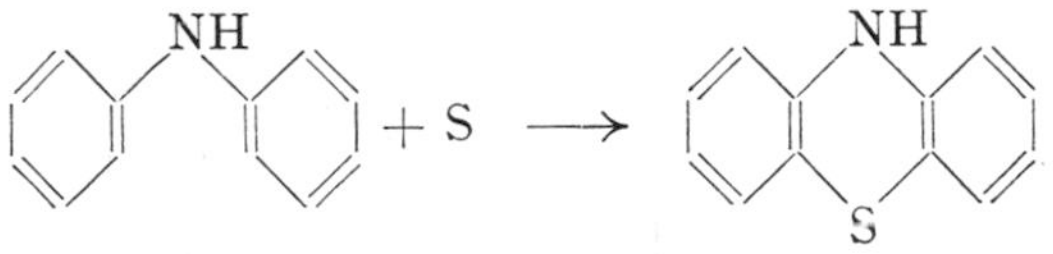

NH + S ⟶ NH, S

Diphenylamine is used for making certain dyes.

When heated with sodium or sodamide, diphenylamine is converted into the sodium salt:

$$(C_6H_5)_2NH + Na \longrightarrow [(C_6H_5)_2N]^-Na^+ + \tfrac{1}{2}H_2$$

When treated with iodine, sodiodiphenylamine forms *tetraphenylhydrazine*:

$$2(C_6H_5)_2N^-Na^+ + I_2 \longrightarrow (C_6H_5)_2N{\cdot}N(C_6H_5)_2 + 2NaI$$

Tetraphenylhydrazine is best prepared by oxidising diphenylamine with potassium permanganate in acetone solution. It is a colourless crystalline solid, but in benzene solution (or any other non-ionising solvent) it produces a green colour due to the formation of the free hydrazine radical, *diphenylnitrogen*, in which the nitrogen is bivalent:

$$(C_6H_5)_2N{-}N(C_6H_5)_2 \rightleftharpoons 2(C_6H_5)_2N{\cdot}$$

When the solution is diluted, the colour deepens, thereby showing increased dissociation; the colour also deepens on warming and fades on cooling. That we are dealing with a free radical is shown, apart from the colour phenomena (the colour intensity does not obey Beer's law), by the immediate reaction of the substance (in solution) with *e.g.*, nitric oxide, a reaction which is characteristic of free radicals:

$$(C_6H_5)_2N{\cdot} + NO \longrightarrow (C_6H_5)_2N{-}NO$$

The stability of this free hydrazine radical is believed to be due to its being a resonance hybrid (*cf.* triphenylmethyl, p. 675).

Triphenylamine $(C_6H_5)_3N$, may be prepared by the reaction between sodiophenylamine and bromobenzene:

$$(C_6H_5)_2N^-Na^+ + C_6H_5Br \longrightarrow (C_6H_5)_3N + NaBr$$

A better method of preparation is the Ullmann reaction; diphenylamine, iodobenzene, potassium carbonate and a little copper powder are heated in nitrobenzene solution:

$$2(C_6H_5)_2NH + 2C_6H_5I + K_2CO_3 \xrightarrow{Cu} 2(C_6H_5)_3N + CO_2 + 2KI + H_2O \quad (82–85\%)$$

Triphenylamine is a colourless crystalline solid, m.p. 127°, and is too weak a base to combine with acids. The decreasing basic character of aniline, diphenylamine and triphenylamine may be explained by the increasing number of resonating structures (reaching a maximum in triphenylamine), thereby decreasing the availability of the lone pair on the nitrogen atom (*cf.* aniline, p. 541).

Triphenylamine dissolves in concentrated sulphuric acid to give a blue solution.

Benzylamine (*α-aminotoluene*), $C_6H_5{\cdot}CH_2{\cdot}NH_2$, may be prepared by the reduction of phenyl cyanide or benzaldoxime:

$$C_6H_5{\cdot}CN \xrightarrow{Na/C_2H_5OH} C_6H_5{\cdot}CH_2{\cdot}NH_2 \xleftarrow{Na/C_2H_5OH} C_6H_5{\cdot}CH{:}N{\cdot}OH$$

It may also be prepared by heating benzyl chloride with ammonia under pressure, or by the Hofmann reaction on phenylacetamide (*cf.* p. 192):

$$C_6H_5{\cdot}CH_2{\cdot}CO{\cdot}NH_2 \xrightarrow{Br_2/KOH} C_6H_5{\cdot}CH_2{\cdot}NH_2 + CO_2$$

Benzylamine is a colourless liquid, b.p. 185°, which resembles the aliphatic amines, and is best regarded (as far as the amino-group is concerned) as a phenyl-substituted methylamine; *e.g.*, it differs from the primary aromatic amines in that it is soluble in water, basic (more so than aniline), and with nitrous acid does not form a diazonium salt but gives benzyl alcohol:

$$C_6H_5{\cdot}CH_2{\cdot}NH_2 + HNO_2 \longrightarrow C_6H_5{\cdot}CH_2OH + N_2 + H_2O$$

Diamines

The aromatic diamines may be prepared:

1. By reduction of dinitro-compounds.
2. By the reduction of nitroamines.
3. By the reduction of *C*-nitrosoamines.
4. By reducing an aminoazo-compound with sodium hyposulphite;

e.g., reduction of aminoazobenzene gives aniline and *p*-phenylenediamine:

$$C_6H_5{\cdot}N{:}N{-}C_6H_4{-}NH_2 \xrightarrow{Na_2S_2O_4} C_6H_5{\cdot}NH_2 + NH_2{-}C_6H_4{-}NH_2$$

The diamines are colourless or white crystalline solids which turn brown when exposed to the air. They are " diacid " bases, and their reactions are characterised by those of the three phenylenediamines.

***o*-Phenylenediamine** (*benzene-1 : 2-diamine, 1 : 2-diaminobenzene*) is best prepared by reducing *o*-nitroaniline with zinc dust and aqueous ethanolic sodium hydroxide:

$$C_6H_4(NH_2)(NO_2) + 3Zn + H_2O \xrightarrow{NaOH} C_6H_4(NH_2)_2 + 3ZnO \quad (74–85\%)$$

It is a white crystalline solid, m.p. 102°. The most characteristic property of *o*-diamines is the ease with which they form heterocyclic compounds.

(i) When *o*-phenylenediamine is treated with ferric chloride solution, a dark red colour is produced due to the formation of 2 : 3-*diaminophenazine*:

$$C_6H_4(NH_2)_2 + C_6H_4(NH_2)_2 \xrightarrow{FeCl_3} C_{12}H_6N_2(NH_2)_2$$

(ii) *Benziminazoles* are formed when *o*-phenylenediamine is heated with organic acids, *e.g.*,

$$C_6H_4(NH_2)_2 + H{\cdot}CO_2H \xrightarrow{-H_2O} \left[C_6H_4(NH{\cdot}CHO)(NH_2)\right] \xrightarrow{-H_2O} C_6H_4{<}^{NH}_{N}{>}CH \quad (83–85\%)$$

benziminazole

(iii) When *o*-phenylenediamine is treated with nitrous acid (a solution of the diamino-compound in acetic acid is treated with aqueous sodium nitrite), *benztriazole* is formed:

$$C_6H_4(NH_2)_2 + HNO_2 \xrightarrow{-H_2O} \left[C_6H_4(N{:}N{\cdot}OH)(NH_2)\right] \xrightarrow{-H_2O} C_6H_4{<}^{N}_{NH}{>}N \quad (75–81\%)$$

(iv) *o*-Phenylenediamine condenses with α-dicarbonyl compounds to form *quinoxalines*; *e.g.*, with glyoxal, quinoxaline is formed:

$$C_6H_4(NH_2)_2 + \begin{matrix} O{=}CH \\ | \\ O{=}CH \end{matrix} \longrightarrow C_6H_4{<}^{N=CH}_{N=CH} + 2H_2O$$

This reaction is used to identify *o*-diamines; the α-dicarbonyl compound employed for this purpose is phenanthraquinone, resulting in the formation of a sparingly soluble phenazine derivative:

$$C_6H_4(NH_2)_2 + C_{14}H_8O_2 \longrightarrow C_{20}H_{12}N_2 + 2H_2O$$

***m*-Phenylenediamine** (*benzene*-1 : 3-*diamine*, 1 : 3-*diaminobenzene*) is best prepared by the reduction of *m*-dinitrobenzene with iron and hydrochloric acid:

$$C_6H_4(NO_2)_2 + 12[H] \xrightarrow{Fe/HCl} C_6H_4(NH_2)_2 + 4H_2O \quad (90\%)$$

It is a white crystalline solid, m.p. 63°. The most characteristic reaction of *m*-phenylenediamine is the formation of brown dyes—*Bismarck Brown*—when it is treated with nitrous acid; a monazo- and a bisazo-compound are formed:

$$H_2N\cdot C_6H_4-N{=}N-C_6H_3(NH_2)_2 \qquad (NH_2)_2C_6H_3-N{=}N-C_6H_4-N{=}N-C_6H_3(NH_2)_2$$

This reaction is used as a colorimetric method for the determination of nitrites in water; even when nitrites are present in traces, a yellow colour is produced. On the other hand, by dissolving *m*-phenylenediamine in concentrated hydrochloric acid, and by keeping the nitrous acid always in excess, both amino-groups may be diazotised to give the tetrazo-compound:

$$C_6H_4(NH_2)_2 + 2HNO_2 + 2HCl \longrightarrow C_6H_4(N_2Cl)_2 + 4H_2O$$

m-Phenylenediamine is used in the preparation of dyes.

***p*-Phenylenediamine** (*benzene*-1 : 4-*diamine*, 1 : 4-*diaminobenzene*) may be prepared by the reduction of *p*-nitroaniline or aminoazobenzene. It is a white crystalline solid, m.p. 147°. On vigorous oxidation it forms *p*-benzoquinone:

$$C_6H_4(NH_2)_2 \xrightarrow[H_2SO_4]{K_2Cr_2O_7} O{=}C_6H_4{=}O$$

p-Phenylenediamine can be diazotised in the ordinary way, and is used in the preparation of dyes.

QUESTIONS

1. Compare and contrast the reactions of $PhNH_2$ and $EtNH_2$.
2. How may primary aromatic amines be prepared? In your answer, discuss the advantages and disadvantages of the various reducing agents that may be used.
3. Starting with C_6H_6 or PhMe, how would you prepare:—(*a*) *o*-, *m*- and *p*-nitroaniline, (*b*) *o*-, *m*- and *p*-nitrotoluidine, (*c*) *p*-aminobenzaldehyde, (*d*) PhNCS, (*e*) *o*-, *m*- and *p*-bromoaniline, (*f*) 2 : 6-dibromoaniline, (*g*) 2 : 6-dibromo-*p*-phenylenediamine, (*h*) 2 : 4-dinitroaniline, (*i*) $PhMeN{\cdot}NH_2$, (*j*) PhNMe·CHO, (*k*) *s*-trimethylaniline, (*l*) 3-bromo-4-aminotoluene?

4. How are the following compounds prepared commercially and what are their uses:—(*a*) $PhNH_2$, (*b*) $PhNH{\cdot}CO{\cdot}CH_3$, (*c*) *m*-$NO_2{\cdot}C_6H_2{\cdot}NH_2$, (*d*) *o*- and *p*-toluidines, (*e*) PhNHMe, (*f*) $PhNMe_2$, (*g*) Ph_2NH?

5. Write an essay on the basic properties of aniline and its halogeno-, nitro-, and halogeno-nitro-derivatives.

6. Write an account of the rearrangement of the *N*-substituted aniline compounds.

7. Name the compounds and state the conditions under which they are formed when $PhNH_2$, PhNHMe and $PhNMe_2$, are respectively treated with:—(*a*) HNO_2, (*b*) MeI, (*c*) $Ar{\cdot}SO_2Cl$, (*d*) Ac_2O, (*e*) CS_2, (*f*) $CHCl_3$, (*g*) chromic acid, (*h*) Ph·CHO, (*i*) $H{\cdot}CO_2H$, (*j*) Br_2, (*k*) HNO_3, (*l*) $COCl_2$, (*m*) HCl and heat.

8. Write an account of the preparation and properties of (*a*) Ph_2NH, (*b*) Ph_3N, (*c*) $PhCH_2{\cdot}NH_2$.

9. Define and give examples of:—(*a*) the Schmidt reaction, (*b*) the Hofmann reaction, (*c*) the Hofmann rearrangement, (*d*) the Fischer–Hepp rearrangement, (*e*) the Ullmann reaction, (*f*) an anilide, (*g*) the Orton rearrangement.

10. Write an account of the preparation and properties of the three isomeric phenylenediamines.

11. How would you distinguish between PhNHEt, $PhNMe_2$, (Me / NHMe) and (Me / NH_2 / Me)?

12. Discuss the various methods for distinguishing between primary, secondary and tertiary aromatic amines.

READING REFERENCES

Olson *et al.*, The Rearrangement of N-Chloroacetanilide, *J. Amer. Chem. Soc.*, 1937, **59**, 1613.

Spring, Reactions of Aldehydes with Amines, *Chem. Reviews*, 1940, **26**, 297.

Sidgwick, *The Organic Chemistry of Nitrogen*, Oxford Press (New Ed. by Taylor and Baker, 1937), Ch. 3, Aromatic Amines.

Gilman, *Advanced Organic Chemistry*, Wiley (1942, 2nd Ed.). Vol. I, Ch. 12, Rearrangements.

Dewar, The Mechanism of Benzidine-type Rearrangements and the Role of π-Electrons in Organic Chemistry, *J.C.S.*, **1946**, 406.

Hughes and Ingold, Aromatic Rearrangements, *Quart. Reviews* (*Chem. Soc.*), 1952, **6**, 34.

Werner, Amination by Reduction, *Ind. Eng. Chem.*, 1950, **42**, 1661.

Dewar and Scott, The Orton Rearrangement, *J.C.S.*, **1957**, 2676.

CHAPTER XXIV

DIAZONIUM SALTS AND THEIR RELATED COMPOUNDS

WHEN a primary aliphatic amine is treated with nitrous acid, the nature of the product depends on the amine used (see p. 299); nitrogen is always evolved quantitatively:

$$R{\cdot}NH_2 + HNO_2 \longrightarrow ROH + N_2 + H_2O$$

When, however, a primary aromatic amine is treated with nitrous acid in a well-cooled solution, the product is an unstable compound known as a **diazonium salt**:

$$Ar{\cdot}NH_2 + HNO_2 + HCl \longrightarrow Ar{\cdot}N_2Cl + H_2O$$

Diazo-compounds may be obtained with primary aliphatic amines provided that the amino-group is attached to a carbon atom which is adjacent to a negative group such as acyl, carbalkoxy, or cyano; *e.g.*, aminoacetic ester forms diazoacetic ester (p. 312):

$$CH_2(NH_2){\cdot}CO_2C_2H_5 \xrightarrow{HNO_2} CHN_2{\cdot}CO_2C_2H_5$$

The formation of a diazonium compound by the interaction of sodium nitrite, an inorganic acid (usually) and a primary aromatic amine, in ice-cold solution, is known as *diazotisation*. This reaction was discovered by Griess in 1858.

The diazonium compounds are salts of the strong base *diazonium hydroxide*, $Ar{\cdot}N_2OH$, which has not yet been isolated, but is known in aqueous solution. Most diazonium salts of the inorganic acids are colourless solids, extremely soluble in water, and many, particularly the nitrate, are explosive (in the solid state). They form complex salts with many metallic salts, of which one of the most important is zinc chloride, $(Ar{\cdot}N_2)_2{}^{2+}ZnCl_4{}^{2-}$. These complex salts are stable in solution, and hence offer a means of stabilising a diazonium salt solution.

The diazonium salts are very important synthetic reagents, being the starting point in the preparation of various aromatic compounds, dyes and drugs. As pointed out previously, the preparation of a diazonium salt in the solid state is usually a hazardous process. Fortunately, however, the aqueous solutions of the diazonium salts undergo practically all the necessary reactions (*cf.* the Grignard reagents).

There are various methods of preparing a solution of a diazonium salt, but the usual procedure is to dissolve (or suspend) the amine in excess dilute inorganic acid (usually hydrochloric or sulphuric) cooled in ice and to add slowly, with stirring, a cooled aqueous solution of sodium nitrite, the addition of which is completed when the reaction mixture produces a blue colour with potassium iodide-starch paper, thereby showing the presence of free nitrous acid.

When dealing with a mono-*o*- or *p*-substituted amine, *e.g.*, nitro- or chloro-amine, it is necessary to use a more concentrated acid (than for the unsubstituted amine) because of the weakened basic character of the amino-group (p. 545). An alternative method is to mix the amine and sodium nitrite in aqueous solution and to pour this on to a mixture of cracked ice and concentrated hydrochloric acid. When dealing with di-(*o* : *o*′- or *o* : *p*-) or tri-(*o* : *o*′ : *p*-)substituted amines, diazotisation may usually be effected by dissolving the amine in concentrated sulphuric acid and adding solid sodium nitrite, concentrated aqueous sodium nitrite, or sodium nitrite dissolved in concentrated sulphuric acid.

The mechanism of diazotisation is still not settled, but it seems certain that the rate-determining step involves the *free* base. One possibility is:

$$Ar{-}\ddot{N}H_2 + HO{-}N{=}O \rightleftharpoons \begin{matrix} Ar{-}\overset{+}{N}H{-}H \\ | \\ HO{-}N{-}\bar{O} \end{matrix} \rightleftharpoons \begin{matrix} Ar{-}\ddot{N}{-}H \\ | \\ N{=}O \end{matrix} + H_2O$$

$$\underset{}{\overset{HOH}{\rightleftharpoons}} \begin{matrix} Ar{-}\ddot{N} \\ \| \\ N{-}OH \end{matrix} \overset{HCl}{\rightleftharpoons} [Ar{-}N{\equiv}N]^{+}Cl^{-} + H_2O$$

Nomenclature. The name of the diazonium salt is obtained by adding diazonium chloride, diazonium sulphate, etc., to the name of the parent hydrocarbon, *e.g.*, $C_6H_5{\cdot}N_2Cl$, benzenediazonium chloride; *p*-$CH_3{\cdot}C_6H_4{\cdot}N_2HSO_4$, *p*-toluenediazonium sulphate.

Reactions of the diazonium salts. These may be divided into two groups: those which involve the liberation of nitrogen gas and the displacement of the diazo-group, $—N_2X$, by another univalent group, and those in which the two nitrogen atoms are retained.

REPLACEMENT REACTIONS

1. **Replacement by hydroxyl.** When a diazonium sulphate solution is boiled or steam distilled, the diazo-group is replaced by hydroxyl, *e.g.*,

$$C_6H_5{\cdot}N_2HSO_4 + H_2O \longrightarrow C_6H_5OH + N_2 + H_2SO_4 \quad (g.)$$

The solution should be fairly strongly acid in order to avoid coupling (p. 562) which leads to tar formation. The hydrolysis of diazonium salts has been improved by running the aqueous solution down a chilled tube in a vessel containing boiling 20 per cent. sulphuric acid through which steam is passing, *e.g.*, *o*-toluenediazonium chloride gives *o*-cresol in 89 per cent. yield (Lambooy, 1950).

2. **Replacement by hydrogen.** Replacement of the diazo-group by hydrogen offers a means of preparing substituted aromatic compounds in which the substituents are in positions which they would not take up by direct substitution. According to Kornblum (1944, 1949), the most reliable method of replacing the diazo-group by hydrogen is by means of hypophosphorous acid. Furthermore, Kornblum *et al.* (1949) have shown that the aromatic primary amino-group may be selectively replaced by hydrogen in aliphatic-aromatic diamines by dissolving the diamine in hypophosphorous acid and adding sodium nitrite at 0–5°, *e.g.*,

$$NH_2{-}C_6H_4{-}CH_2{\cdot}NH_2 \xrightarrow[NaNO_2]{H_3PO_2} C_6H_5{-}CH_2{\cdot}NH_2 \quad (84\%)$$

Another common method of replacing the diazo-group by hydrogen is to dissolve the amine in a mixture of ethanol and concentrated sulphuric acid, add sodium nitrite and then warm (sometimes in the presence of copper as catalyst). According to Griess (1864), benzenediazonium sulphate reacted as follows:

$$C_6H_5{\cdot}N_2HSO_4 + C_2H_5OH \longrightarrow C_6H_6 + CH_3{\cdot}CHO + N_2 + H_2SO_4$$

Remsen *et al.* (1887), however, showed that this was incorrect; the main product was shown to be phenetole together with a small amount of benzene.

This was confirmed by Hantzsch *et al.* (1901) who obtained the following results in absolute ethanol:

$$C_6H_5{\cdot}N_2Cl + C_2H_5OH \longrightarrow \underset{(61\%)}{C_6H_5{\cdot}O{\cdot}C_2H_5} + \underset{(5\%)}{C_6H_6}$$

When methanol was used instead of ethanol, no benzene was obtained at all; the product was anisole, $C_6H_5{\cdot}O{\cdot}CH_3$ (70%). As a result of much work it appears that the amount of side-reactions, *i.e.*, formation of ether, depends on the structure of the diazonium salt and the nature of the alcohol used; *e.g.*, if a negative group is in the *o*-position, the diazo-group is replaced in good yield by hydrogen when ethanol is used. On the other hand, if methanol is used instead of ethanol, the main product is an aryl methyl ether; this offers a means of preparing methyl ethers:

m-*Bromotoluene*

$$\text{(CH}_3\text{, Br, NH}_2\text{ benzene)} \xrightarrow[H_2SO_4]{NaNO_2} \text{(CH}_3\text{, Br, N}_2\text{HSO}_4\text{ benzene)} \xrightarrow[Cu]{C_2H_5OH} \text{(CH}_3\text{, Br benzene)} \quad (54\text{–}59\%)$$

m-*Nitrotoluene*

$$\text{(CH}_3\text{, NO}_2\text{, NH}_2\text{ benzene)} \xrightarrow[H_2SO_4]{NaNO_2} \text{(CH}_3\text{, NO}_2\text{, N}_2\text{HSO}_4\text{ benzene)} \xrightarrow[\text{(warm)}]{C_2H_5OH} \text{(CH}_3\text{, NO}_2\text{ benzene)} \quad (62\text{–}72\%)$$

s-*Tribromobenzene*

$$\text{(NH}_2\text{, Br, Br, Br benzene)} \xrightarrow[H_2SO_4]{NaNO_2} \text{(N}_2\text{HSO}_4\text{, Br, Br, Br benzene)} \xrightarrow[\text{(let stand)}]{C_2H_5OH} \text{(Br, Br, Br benzene)} \quad (64\text{–}71\%)$$

The mechanism of the decomposition of diazonium salts with alcohols is uncertain. According to Hey and Waters (1937), the reaction takes place by a free-radical mechanism:

$$C_6H_5{-}N{=}N{-}Cl \longrightarrow C_6H_5{\cdot} + N_2 + Cl{\cdot}$$
$$C_6H_5{\cdot} + CH_3{\cdot}CH_2OH \longrightarrow C_6H_6 + CH_3{\cdot}\dot{C}HOH$$
$$CH_3{\cdot}\dot{C}HOH + Cl{\cdot} \longrightarrow CH_3{\cdot}CHO + HCl$$

Side-reaction

$$C_6H_5{\cdot} + C_2H_5{-}O{-}H \longrightarrow C_6H_5{-}O{-}C_2H_5 + H{\cdot}$$
$$H{\cdot} + Cl{\cdot} \longrightarrow HCl$$

or

$$C_2H_5{-}O{-}H + Cl{\cdot} \longrightarrow C_2H_5O{\cdot} + HCl$$
$$C_6H_5{\cdot} + C_2H_5O{\cdot} \longrightarrow C_6H_5{\cdot}O{\cdot}C_2H_5$$

Hey and Waters believe, however, that this free-radical decomposition is *not* generally produced in *aqueous* solution, but that their formation is possible in *non-ionising* solvents, *e.g.*, ethanol, acetone, ethyl acetate, etc. When diazonium salts are decomposed in these solvents in the presence of metals, the metal is attacked to form an organo-metallic compound. This has been used to prepare aromatic derivatives of mercury, antimony, arsenic and tellurium.

Many reagents have been used to replace the diazo-group by hydrogen; the two usual methods have been described above. Roe *et al.* (1952) have now shown that this reaction can be carried out in reasonable yields by decomposing the fluoroborate in ethanol in the presence of zinc dust.

$$Ar{\cdot}NH_2 \longrightarrow Ar{\cdot}N_2BF_4 \xrightarrow[Zn]{C_2H_5OH} ArH \quad (47\text{–}85\%)$$

3. **Replacement by halogen.** (i) **Sandmeyer reaction** (1884). When a diazonium salt solution is run into a solution of cuprous halide dissolved in the corresponding halogen acid, the diazo-group is replaced by a halogen atom, *e.g.*,

m-*Chloronitrobenzene*

$$C_6H_4(NH_2)(NO_2) \xrightarrow[HCl]{NaNO_2} C_6H_4(N_2Cl)(NO_2) \xrightarrow{CuCl/HCl} C_6H_4(Cl)(NO_2) \quad (68\text{–}71\%)$$

p-*Bromotoluene*

$$CH_3{\cdot}C_6H_4{\cdot}NH_2 \xrightarrow[H_2SO_4]{NaNO_2} CH_3{\cdot}C_6H_4{\cdot}N_2HSO_4 \xrightarrow{CuBr/HBr} CH_3{\cdot}C_6H_4{\cdot}Br \quad (70\text{–}73\%)$$

The diazotisation may be carried out with hydrobromic acid, but in practice sulphuric acid is used, since it is cheaper and only slightly affects the yield of aryl bromide.

The important point to note in the Sandmeyer reaction is that it is the *halogen joined to the copper that enters the nucleus.* The mechanism of the reaction is uncertain. Cowdrey and Davies (1949) have investigated the reaction kinetics of the Sandmeyer reaction and suggest that the mechanism is (*a*) slow co-ordination of the terminal N atom of $Ar{\cdot}N_2^+$ to the copper in the $CuCl_2^-$ ion to form the complex $Ar{\cdot}N_2{\cdot}CuCl_2$, (*b*) decomposition of this to ArCl, or (*c*) further fast addition to it of $Ar{\cdot}N_2^+$ to give $[(Ar{\cdot}N_2)_2CuCl_2]^+$, which either (*d*) decomposes to ArCl or (*e*) reacts with $CuCl_2^-$ to give $Ar{\cdot}N{:}N{\cdot}Ar$.

Pfeil *et al.* (1949) have obtained *p*-chloronitrobenzene in 98 per cent. yield by treating *p*-nitrobenzenediazonium chloride with *cupric* chloride in hydrochloric acid. It appears that cupric chloride is effective only if the diazotised amine contains a *negative* group.

(ii) **Gattermann reaction** (1890). This reaction is carried out by dissolving the amine in hydrochloric or hydrobromic acid, cooling, adding cooled aqueous sodium nitrite, and then warming the diazonium salt solution in the presence of copper powder, *e.g.*,

$$CH_3{\cdot}C_6H_4{\cdot}NH_2 \xrightarrow{NaNO_2/HBr} CH_3{\cdot}C_6H_4{\cdot}N_2Br \xrightarrow{Cu} CH_3{\cdot}C_6H_4{\cdot}Br \quad (43\text{–}47\%)$$

Iodo-compounds may be prepared by boiling the diazonium salt solution with aqueous potassium iodide:

$$C_6H_5{\cdot}N_2Cl + KI \longrightarrow C_6H_5I + KCl + N_2 \quad (74\text{–}76\%)$$

This is usually the best method for introducing iodine into the benzene ring.

Fluoro-compounds may be prepared by the **Balz–Schiemann reaction** (1927). When borofluoric acid is added to a diazonium salt solution, the insoluble diazonium borofluoride is precipitated. This is collected by filtration, dried and heated gently:

$$C_6H_5{\cdot}N_2Cl + HBF_4 \longrightarrow C_6H_5{\cdot}N_2BF_4 + HCl \longrightarrow C_6H_5F + N_2 + BF_3 \quad (51\text{–}57\%)$$

Borofluoric acid may be prepared by adding hydrochloric acid to sodium borofluoride, or by dissolving boric acid in 50 per cent. hydrofluoric acid (contained in a lead vessel); the latter usually gives better yields.

Fluoro-compounds may also be prepared by dissolving the amine in cold anhydrous hydrofluoric acid, adding solid sodium nitrite and then allowing the solution to stand until the excess acid has evaporated; the residue consists of a mixture of aryl fluoride and sodium fluoride (Aelony, 1934):

$$Ar{\cdot}NH_2 \xrightarrow{NaNO_2/HF} Ar{\cdot}N_2F \longrightarrow Ar{\cdot}F + N_2$$

4. **Replacement by a cyano-group.** This is a special case of the Sandmeyer and Gattermann reactions, and is carried out by treating a diazonium salt solution with cuprous cyanide dissolved in aqueous potassium cyanide or with aqueous potassium cyanide in the presence of copper powder:

$$C_6H_5{\cdot}N_2Cl \xrightarrow{K_3Cu(CN)_4} C_6H_5{\cdot}CN + N_2 \quad (65\%)$$

$$C_6H_5{\cdot}N_2HSO_4 + KCN \xrightarrow{Cu} C_6H_5{\cdot}CN + KHSO_4 + N_2 \quad (60\%)$$

5. **Replacement by a nitro-group.** This was originally carried out by treating a diazonium salt solution with an equivalent amount of nitrous acid in the presence of cuprous oxide:

$$C_6H_5{\cdot}N_2Cl + HNO_2 \xrightarrow{Cu_2O} C_6H_5{\cdot}NO_2 + N_2 + HCl$$

A better method is to decompose the diazonium borofluoride with aqueous sodium nitrite containing copper powder:

$$p\text{-}NO_2C_6H_4NH_2 \xrightarrow{NaNO_2/HBF_4} p\text{-}NO_2C_6H_4N_2BF_4 \xrightarrow[Cu]{NaNO_2} p\text{-}C_6H_4(NO_2)_2 + NaBF_4 + N_2 \quad (67\text{–}82\%)$$

Hodgson and Marsden (1944) have found that the decomposition of a diazonium cobaltinitrite $(Ar{\cdot}N_2)_3{}^{3+}Co(NO_2)_6{}^{3-}$, in the cold, by aqueous sodium nitrite in the presence of cuprous oxide and copper sulphate gives nitro-compounds in yields higher than 60 per cent. The diazonium cobaltinitrite is prepared by adding sodium cobaltinitrite to a diazonium salt solution previously neutralised with calcium carbonate; the yield is almost quantitative.

6. **Replacement by an arsonic acid group, AsO_3H_2.** One method is **Bart's reaction** (1910). This is carried out by decomposing a diazonium salt with sodium arsenite in the presence of a copper salt, *e.g.*, phenylarsonic acid:

$$C_6H_5{\cdot}N_2Cl + Na_3AsO_3 \xrightarrow{CuSO_4} C_6H_5{\cdot}AsO_3Na_2 + N_2 + NaCl \xrightarrow{HCl} C_6H_5{\cdot}AsO_3H_2 \quad (39\text{–}45\%)$$

The yield may be increased by buffering the solution with sodium carbonate (Blas, 1940).

An alternative method to the Bart reaction is to add a suspension of a diazonium borofluoride to an aqueous solution of sodium meta-arsenite in the presence of a small amount of cuprous chloride (Ruddy *et al.*, 1942):

$$C_6H_5{\cdot}N_2BF_4 + NaAsO_2 + H_2O \xrightarrow{CuCl} C_6H_5{\cdot}AsO_3H_2 + NaF + N_2 + BF_3 \quad (58\%)$$

7. **Replacement by an aryl group.** This may be carried out by treating a diazonium sulphate with ethanol and copper powder, *e.g.*, diphenyl from benzenediazonium sulphate:

$$2C_6H_5{\cdot}N_2HSO_4 \xrightarrow[Cu]{C_2H_5OH} C_6H_5{\cdot}C_6H_5 + 2N_2 + 2H_2SO_4 \quad (25\%)$$

This is really a special case of the Gattermann reaction. Alternatively, a diaryl may be prepared by adding an aromatic compound to an *alkaline* solution of a diazonium salt, *e.g.*, *p*-bromodiphenyl from *p*-bromobenzenediazonium chloride and benzene:

$$Br{-}C_6H_4{-}N_2Cl + C_6H_6 \xrightarrow{NaOH} Br{-}C_6H_4{-}C_6H_5 + N_2 + NaCl + H_2O \quad (34\text{–}35\%)$$

This method of preparation is known as the **Gomberg reaction** (1924), and experiment has shown that whatever is the nature of a substituent in the second component, *o*- or *p*-substitution always occurs; *e.g.*, benzenediazonium chloride forms *p*-nitrodiphenyl when treated with nitrobenzene:

$$C_6H_5{-}N_2Cl + C_6H_5{-}NO_2 \xrightarrow{NaOH} C_6H_5{-}C_6H_4{-}NO_2$$

This anomalous orienting effect of the nitro-group led Hey *et al.* (1934) to suggest that the reaction takes place by a free-radical mechanism:

$$C_6H_5{\cdot}N_2Cl \longrightarrow C_6H_5{\cdot} + N_2 + Cl{\cdot}$$

$$C_6H_5{\cdot} + C_6H_5{\cdot}NO_2 \longrightarrow C_6H_5{-}C_6H_4{-}NO_2 + H{\cdot}$$

$$H{\cdot} + Cl{\cdot} \longrightarrow HCl$$

The Gomberg reaction is very useful for closing rings.

8. **Replacement by a chloromercuri-group.** This is an example of indirect mercuration (*cf.* p. 514), and may be carried out by heating the double compound of a diazonium chloride and mercuric chloride in acetone or ethanol solution with copper powder:

$$Ar{\cdot}N_2Cl{\cdot}HgCl_2 + 2Cu \longrightarrow Ar{\cdot}HgCl + N_2 + 2CuCl \quad (40\%)$$

By this means it is possible to prepare the mercuri-compounds of aromatic hydrocarbons, aryl halides, nitro-compounds, amines, phenols, acids and esters. If the double compound is heated in acetone solution with copper powder and then with copper powder in aqueous ammonia, the diaryl mercury compound is obtained:

$$2Ar{\cdot}N_2Cl{\cdot}HgCl_2 + 6Cu \longrightarrow Ar_2Hg + Hg + 6CuCl + N_2$$

The diazo-group may be replaced by many other groups, *e.g.*,

(i) $Ar{\cdot}N_2Cl \xrightarrow{CuSCN} Ar{\cdot}SCN$

(ii) $Ar{\cdot}N_2Cl \xrightarrow{KNCO/Cu} Ar{\cdot}NCO$

(iii) $2Ar{\cdot}N_2Cl \xrightarrow{(NH_4)_2S} Ar_2S$

(iv) $Ar{\cdot}N_2HSO_4 + SO_2 + Cu \longrightarrow Ar{\cdot}SO_2H + N_2 + CuSO_4$

(v) $Ar{\cdot}N_2Cl + S{:}C\begin{smallmatrix}\diagup SK \\ \diagdown OC_2H_5\end{smallmatrix} \longrightarrow S{:}C\begin{smallmatrix}\diagup SAr \\ \diagdown OC_2H_5\end{smallmatrix} \xrightarrow{H_2O} ArSH$

(vi) Beech (1954) has shown that formaldoxime reacts with diazonium salts to give products which, on hydrolysis, yield aldehydes. Other oximes, under similar conditions, give alkyl aryl ketones (R = H or R):

$$Ar{\cdot}N_2Cl + R{\cdot}CH = NOH \xrightarrow{NaOH} Ar{\cdot}CR = NOH \xrightarrow{H_2O} Ar{\cdot}CO{\cdot}R$$

In certain cases, diazotisation may lead to abnormal reactions; *e.g.*,

(i) Diazotisation of *o*-diamines produces triazoles (p. 553).
(ii) Treatment of *m*-phenylenediamine with nitrous acid gives Bismarck Brown (p. 554).

REACTIONS OF THE DIAZONIUM SALTS IN WHICH THE NITROGEN ATOMS ARE RETAINED

1. When bromine and hydrobromic acid are added to a diazonium salt solution, a crystalline precipitate of *diazonium perbromide*, $Ar{\cdot}N_2Br_3$, is obtained. This, on heating, forms the aryl bromide. On the other hand, if the perbromide is treated with aqueous ammonia, the azide, $Ar{\cdot}N_3$, is produced.

Phenyl azide may also be prepared by the action of hydrazoic acid on nitrosobenzene (Maffei *et al.*, 1954):

$$C_6H_5{\cdot}NO + 2HN_3 \longrightarrow C_6H_5{\cdot}N_3 + H_2O + 2N_2 \quad (92\%)$$

2. When reduced with stannous chloride and hydrochloric acid, or with sodium sulphite, diazonium salts form phenylhydrazines:

$$Ar{\cdot}N_2Cl + 4[H] \xrightarrow{SnCl_2/HCl} Ar{\cdot}NH{\cdot}NH_2{\cdot}HCl$$

If vigorous reducing agents are used, *e.g.*, zinc and hydrochloric acid, the product is an aromatic amine:

$$Ar{\cdot}N_2Cl \xrightarrow{Zn/HCl} [Ar{\cdot}NH{\cdot}NH_2] \xrightarrow{Zn/HCl} Ar{\cdot}NH_2 + NH_3$$

3. Diazonium salts readily undergo *coupling* reactions. This is the reaction between a diazonium salt and another substance containing a labile hydrogen, the result being the formation of an *azo-compound.*

The most important group of compounds that couple with diazonium salts are phenols, naphthols and primary, secondary and tertiary aromatic amines; *e.g.*, benzenediazonium chloride couples with phenol to form *p*-hydroxyazobenzene:

$$C_6H_5N_2Cl + C_6H_5OH \longrightarrow C_6H_5{-}N{=}N{-}C_6H_4OH + HCl$$

With primary and secondary amines, coupling may take place at the nitrogen atom to form *diazoamino-compounds* (*N*-azo-compounds), or directly with the nucleus to form *aminoazo-compounds* (*C*-azo-compounds). Generally, the nature of the amino-compound and the *p*H of the solution decide which type of coupling takes place (see p. 569).

Compounds containing an active methylene group, *e.g.*, acetoacetic ester, and certain hydrocarbons, *e.g.*, mesitylene, *iso*durene, butadiene, also couple with diazonium salts. According to Dimroth (1907), coupling with acetoacetic ester (and other keto-enol tautomers) takes place via the formation of the *O*-azo-compound, which then rearranges to the *C*-azo-compound, and this, in turn, rearranges to the hydrazone:

$$CH_3\text{—}C(OH){=}CH\text{—}CO_2C_2H_5 \xrightarrow[NaOH]{C_6H_5 \cdot N_2Cl} \left[CH_3\text{—}C(O \cdot N_2 \cdot C_6H_5){=}CH\text{—}CO_2C_2H_5\right] \longrightarrow \left[CH_3\text{—}C({=}O)\text{—}CH \cdot N_2 \cdot C_6H_5\text{—}CO_2C_2H_5\right] \longrightarrow CH_3\text{—}C({=}O)\text{—}C({=}N \cdot NH \cdot C_6H_5)\text{—}CO_2C_2H_5$$

This coupling reaction is often used to detect the presence of the enolic form in the keto-enol mixtures, and is then referred to as the **Japp–Klingermann reaction** (1887).

Simple diazonium salts do not couple with hydrocarbons, but the nitro-derivatives couple readily; *e.g.*, diazotised picramide (*s*-trinitroaniline) couples with mesitylene:

$$C_6H_3(CH_3)_3 + ClN_2 \cdot C_6H_2(NO_2)_3 \xrightarrow{NaOH} (CH_3)_3C_6H_2\text{—}N{=}N\text{—}C_6H_2(NO_2)_3$$

With phenols, coupling is best carried out in faintly alkaline solution; with amines, in faintly acid solution. The azo-group enters mainly the *p*-position to the hydroxyl or amino-group, but if this position is occupied, coupling takes place in the *o*-position; it never occurs in the *m*-position; *e.g.*, *p*-cresol gives the *o*-azo-compound:

$$p\text{-}HO \cdot C_6H_4 \cdot CH_3 + C_6H_5 \cdot N_2Cl \xrightarrow{NaOH} HO \cdot C_6H_3(CH_3)\text{—}N{:}N \cdot C_6H_5$$

It has also been found that the rate of coupling is increased if the diazonium salt contains a negative group such as nitro-, sulphonic acid, or chlorine (*cf.* coupling with hydrocarbons, above).

When an excess of diazonium salt is used, the *bisazo-* (*o-* and *p-*) and the *trisazo-compound* may be formed:

$$C_6H_5OH \xrightarrow{Ar \cdot N_2Cl} p\text{-}HO \cdot C_6H_4 \cdot N_2 \cdot Ar \longrightarrow HO \cdot C_6H_3(N_2 \cdot Ar)_2 \longrightarrow HO \cdot C_6H_2(N_2 \cdot Ar)_3$$

Experiment has shown that the introduction of a second azo-group is facilitated by the presence of an alkyl group in the *p*-position to the hydroxyl group, or by two hydroxyl groups in the *m*-positions; *e.g.*, resorcinol readily forms the trisazo-derivative:

$$C_6H_4(OH)_2 \xrightarrow{C_6H_5 \cdot N_2Cl} (HO)_2C_6H_3 \cdot N_2 \cdot C_6H_5 \longrightarrow (HO)_2C_6H_2(N_2 \cdot C_6H_5)_2 \longrightarrow (HO)_2C_6H(N_2 \cdot C_6H_5)_3$$

The introduction of the second (and third) azo-group takes place more slowly than the first, and so it is possible to introduce two (or three) different azo-groups.

When a compound contains a hydroxyl and an amino-group in the *p*-positions, the amino-group directs coupling to the *o*-position in acid solution and the hydroxyl group to the *o*-position in alkaline solution:

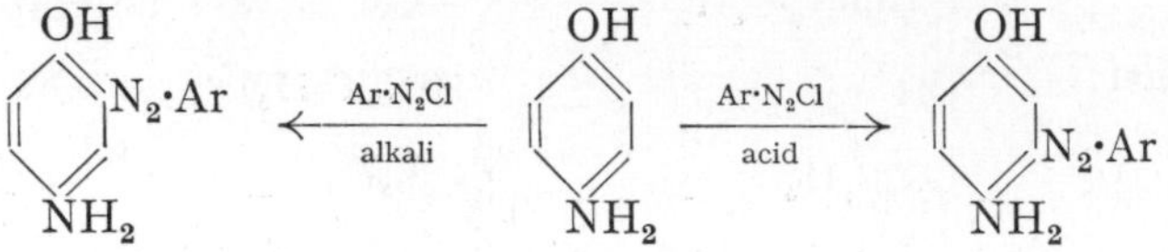

$$\text{HO-C}_6\text{H}_3(\text{N}_2\cdot\text{Ar})\text{-NH}_2 \xleftarrow[\text{alkali}]{\text{Ar}\cdot\text{N}_2\text{Cl}} \text{HO-C}_6\text{H}_4\text{-NH}_2 \xrightarrow[\text{acid}]{\text{Ar}\cdot\text{N}_2\text{Cl}} \text{HO-C}_6\text{H}_3(\text{N}_2\cdot\text{Ar})\text{-NH}_2$$

Unusual cases of coupling may occur when the phenol contains a carboxyl or a sulphonic acid group in the *p*-position to the hydroxyl group, the carboxyl or sulphonic acid group being replaced by an azo-group; *e.g.*,

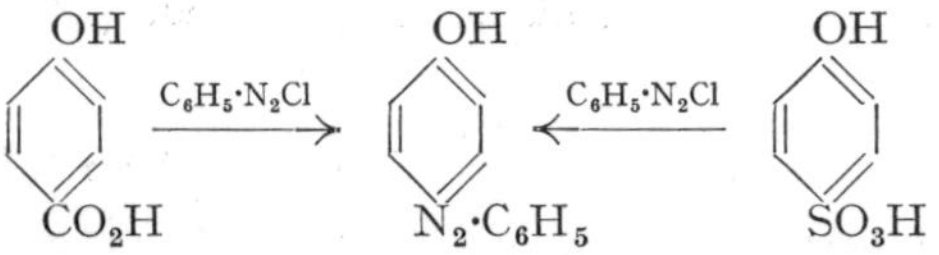

$$\text{HO-C}_6\text{H}_4\text{-CO}_2\text{H} \xrightarrow{\text{C}_6\text{H}_5\cdot\text{N}_2\text{Cl}} \text{HO-C}_6\text{H}_4\text{-N}_2\cdot\text{C}_6\text{H}_5 \xleftarrow{\text{C}_6\text{H}_5\cdot\text{N}_2\text{Cl}} \text{HO-C}_6\text{H}_4\text{-SO}_3\text{H}$$

The coupling reaction with 2-naphthol is used to detect the presence of a primary aromatic amine. The compound is treated with sodium nitrite in acid solution, and this solution is added to an alkaline solution of 2-naphthol. A red precipitate of azo-2-naphthol (insoluble in alkali) shows that the original compound was a primary aromatic amine; *e.g.*, benzenediazonium chloride forms 1-phenylazo-2-naphthol:

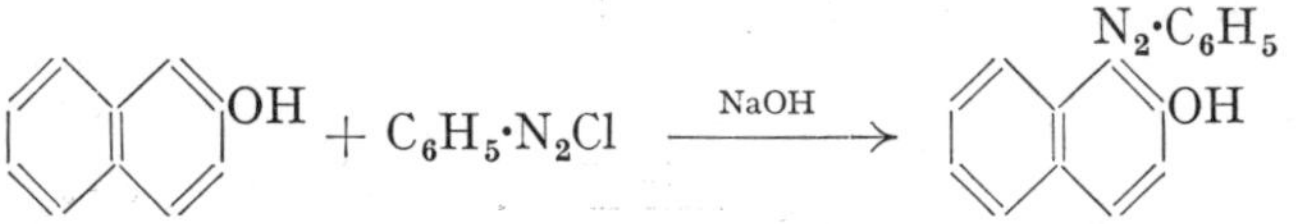

$$\text{C}_{10}\text{H}_7\text{OH} + \text{C}_6\text{H}_5\cdot\text{N}_2\text{Cl} \xrightarrow{\text{NaOH}} \text{C}_{10}\text{H}_6(\text{OH})\text{N}_2\cdot\text{C}_6\text{H}_5$$

The mechanism of coupling is still a subject of discussion. One of the early theories was that the *O*-azo-compound (in phenols) and the *N*-azo-compound (in primary and secondary amines) were formed first, and that these then rearranged to the *C*-azo-compound (p. 563). Recent work, however, indicates that coupling takes place by direct attack at the carbon atom, the active components in the coupling reaction being the diazonium cation and the free amine or the phenoxide ion (Wistar and Bartlett, 1941; Hauser and Breslow, 1941):

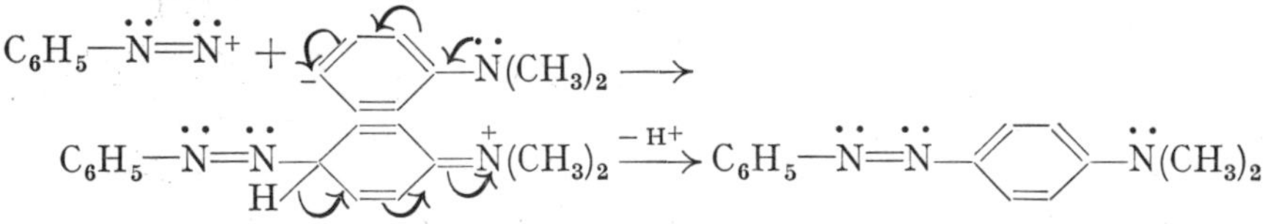

$$\text{C}_6\text{H}_5\text{—}\ddot{\text{N}}\text{=}\ddot{\text{N}}^+ + {}^-\text{C}_6\text{H}_4\text{=}\overset{+}{\text{N}}(\text{CH}_3)_2 \longrightarrow$$

$$\text{C}_6\text{H}_5\text{—}\ddot{\text{N}}\text{=}\ddot{\text{N}}\text{—C}_6\text{H}_4(\text{H})\text{=}\overset{+}{\text{N}}(\text{CH}_3)_2 \xrightarrow{-\text{H}^+} \text{C}_6\text{H}_5\text{—}\ddot{\text{N}}\text{=}\ddot{\text{N}}\text{—C}_6\text{H}_4\text{—}\ddot{\text{N}}(\text{CH}_3)_2$$

The phenoxide ion also undergoes the electromeric effect in a similar manner:

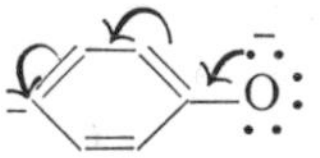

$${}^-\text{C}_6\text{H}_4\text{=}\ddot{\text{O}}\text{:}$$

Structure of the diazonium salts. Griess (1864) believed that each nitrogen atom in benzenediazonium chloride was attached to the benzene ring, and he proposed the formula $\text{C}_6\text{H}_4\text{—N=N}\langle^{\text{H}}_{\text{Cl}}$. Kekulé (1866), however, believed that only one of the two nitrogen atoms was directly attached to the ring, his reason being that diazonium salts are converted into *mono-substituted* derivatives of benzene, *e.g.*, *mono*hydric phenols, *mono*halogen derivatives, etc., *i.e.*, the N_2Cl group is replaced by a *univalent* radical. Kekulé also suggested that the structure of benzenediazonium chloride was similar to its best-known derivatives, the azo-compounds, the structure of which was known to be Ar—N=N—Ar′. Kekulé therefore proposed the formula $C_6H_5—\overset{a}{N}=\overset{b}{N}—Cl$, arguing that the attachment of the chlorine atom to $\overset{b}{N}$ was shown by the fact that the coupling reaction of benzenediazonium chloride produced the azo-compounds.

The attachment of only one nitrogen atom to the benzene ring was proved by Langfurth (1878), who showed that the tetrabromo-sulphonic acid of aniline yields a diazo-compound in which the four bromine atoms and the sulphonic acid group are still present.

In 1869, Blomstrand suggested the formula $C_6H_5 \cdot \overset{Cl}{N} \vdots N$, his reason being that since the diazonium salts closely resembled the ammonium salts (in basic character, solubility in water, etc.), both must contain quinquevalent nitrogen. Blomstrand also thought that this formula readily explained the formation of a diazonium salt from a primary aromatic amine:

$$C_6H_5—\underset{\underset{Cl}{|}}{N}\begin{matrix} H \\ H \\ H \end{matrix} + \begin{matrix} O \\ \\ HO \end{matrix}\!>\!N \longrightarrow C_6H_5—\underset{\underset{Cl}{|}}{N}\equiv N + 2H_2O$$

In modern terminology this formula is written $C_6H_5—\overset{+}{N}\equiv N{:}\}Cl^-$.

Electrical conductivity measurements by Goldschmidt (1890) showed that diazonium salts dissociated into two ions, thus supporting Blomstrand's formula. Strecker (1871) upheld Blomstrand's formula on the grounds of dissimilarity between the properties of the diazonium compounds and the azo-compounds. The former are unstable (and explosive in the solid state), whereas the latter are very stable; hence the structures of the two compounds must be completely different. Le Fèvre *et al.* (1955) have obtained evidence from the infrared absorption spectra of diazonium salts that a triple bond is present.

In 1892, von Pechmann proposed the nitrosamine structure, Ar·NH·NO, for the diazonium hydroxides, basing his arguments on the fact that toluenediazonium chloride gave nitrosobenztoluidide when treated with benzoyl chloride and aqueous sodium hydroxide:

$$CH_3 \cdot C_6H_4 \cdot NH \cdot NO + C_6H_5 \cdot COCl \xrightarrow{NaOH} CH_3 \cdot C_6H_4 \cdot N(NO) \cdot CO \cdot C_6H_5 + HCl$$

In 1894, the problem of the structure of the diazonium compounds was further complicated by the discovery of two forms of the *diazoates* (*diazotates*); one was called the *n*-diazoate, and the other the *iso*diazoate. Von Pechmann proposed structural isomerism to account for their existence, suggesting that the *n*-diazoate was the salt of *normal* diazohydroxide, Ar·N⁚N·OH, and that the *iso*diazoate was the salt of *iso*diazohydroxide, which he believed to have the nitrosamine structure, Ar·NH·NO.

In 1895, Hantzsch, who was influenced by his work on the aromatic oximes (p. 637), proposed geometrical isomerism to account for the existence of the two forms of the diazoates. He adopted the Kekulé formula, since this can give rise to geometrical isomerism (assuming there is no free rotation about an N=N double bond). Geometrical isomerism is not possible with the Blomstrand formula (*cf.* the acetylenic dicarboxylic acids, p. 406).

According to Hantzsch, the " diazo-compounds " (the name originally given to them by Griess) have the Blomstrand formula in acid solution, and these Hantzsch called the *diazonium salts, i.e.*, diazonium salts have the formula $[Ar—N{\equiv}N]^+X^-$, where X is Cl, Br, HSO_4, NO_3, etc. These are the salts of *diazonium hydroxide*, $[Ar—N{\equiv}N]^+OH^-$, which has never been isolated. When a diazonium salt solution is made alkaline, the diazonium hydroxide liberated rapidly rearranges to the *diazohydroxide*, the salts of which Hantzsch called the *diazoates* (*diazotates*). The mechanism of these changes may be as follows:

$$[Ar—N{\equiv}N\!:]^+Cl^- \xrightarrow{NaOH} [Ar—N{\equiv}N\!:]^+OH^-$$

$$Ar—\overset{+}{N}{\equiv}N\!: \longleftrightarrow Ar—\ddot{N}{=}\overset{+}{N}\!: \underset{}{\overset{OH^-}{\rightleftharpoons}} Ar—\ddot{N}{=}\ddot{N}—OH \xrightarrow{NaOH} [Ar—\ddot{N}{=}\ddot{N}—\ddot{\underset{..}{O}}\!:]^-Na^+$$

These diazoates exist in two geometrical isomeric forms, the *syn*-(*cis*-) and *anti*-(*trans*-):

$$\begin{matrix} Ar—N \\ \| \\ NaO—N \end{matrix} \qquad\qquad \begin{matrix} Ar—N \\ \| \\ N—ONa \end{matrix}$$

sodium *n*-diazoate *syn*-form — sodium *iso*diazoate *anti*-form

The *syn*-form, the *n*-diazoate, is produced in weakly alkaline solution and is unstable, slowly changing into the *anti*-form, the *iso*diazoate; this change is accelerated by making the solution strongly alkaline. Hantzsch found that one form produces dyes with phenols and amines far more readily than the other, and assumed that the *syn*-isomer was the reactive form (*cis*-isomers contain more internal energy than the *trans*).

This led to a controversy between Hantzsch and Bamberger, who supported the theory of structural isomerism (of von Pechmann). Hantzsch supported his contentions by making use of physico-chemical methods, a procedure rarely used before in organic chemistry; and in 1912, Bamberger agreed with Hantzsch.

In 1926, Angeli reopened the question by proposing structural isomerism for the existence of the two diazoates, suggesting that the *n*-diazohydroxide was $Ar—\overset{\overset{O}{\uparrow}}{N}{=}NH$ and the *iso*diazohydroxide, $Ar—N{=}N{\cdot}OH$. Hantzsch once again attempted to defend his theory of geometrical isomerism, but this time he was not so successful as against Bamberger. At the present time, chemists have reverted to the two original schools of thought, the geometrical isomerism of Hantzsch and the structural isomerism of either von Pechmann or Angeli; *e.g.*, Hodgson and Marsden (1945) believe:

(i) that the solid *syn*-(*n*-) diazoates are represented by the formula $Ar{\cdot}N{=}NOM$ (where M is a metal), and in aqueous solution hydrolyse to give an equilibrium mixture of diazohydroxide and diazonium hydroxide:

$$Ar{\cdot}N{=}NOM \xrightarrow{H_2O} Ar{\cdot}N{=}NOH \rightleftharpoons Ar{\cdot}N_2^+ + OH^-$$

(ii) that the *anti*-(*iso*-) diazoates are either nitrosamines $Ar{\cdot}\bar{N}(NO)\}\overset{+}{M}$, or equilibrium mixtures in alkaline solution of the ionised *n*-diazoate and nitrosamine:

$$Ar{\cdot}N{=}N\bar{O}\}\overset{+}{M} \rightleftharpoons Ar{\cdot}\bar{N}(NO)\}\overset{+}{M}$$

The strongest evidence brought forward by Hantzsch in favour of geometrical isomerism was the existence of two *diazosulphonates* and two *diazocyanides*.

The diazosulphonates. When a solution of a diazonium salt is treated with a cold alkaline solution of potassium sulphite, an orange or red precipitate is obtained. This compound couples immediately with phenols, is oxidised by iodine to the diazonium sulphate, and liberates sulphur dioxide when treated with inorganic acids. On standing in solution, this reactive form changes to a stable form which is paler in colour, does not couple with phenols, is not oxidised by iodine, and does not liberate sulphur dioxide when treated with inorganic acids.

Bamberger (1874) suggested that the labile and stable forms were *structural* isomers, the former being the *sulphite*, $Ar{\cdot}N_2{\cdot}O{\cdot}SO_2K$, and the latter the *sulphonate*, $Ar—N{=}N—SO_3K$. Hantzsch found that the absorption spectra of both compounds were similar, and therefore believed that the labile and stable forms were geometrical isomers, the former being the *syn*- and the latter the *anti*-.

Marsden and Hodgson (1943), however, have reopened the question. These authors argue that it is difficult to explain the ease of coupling of the *syn*- and the impossibility of coupling of the *anti*-diazosulphonate if they are stereoisomers. On the other hand, if the compounds are structural isomers, then the difference in coupling power is explained by the ready rupture of the N—O bond in the *syn*-form (sulphite) and the non-rupture of the N—S bond in the anti-form (sulphonate). Furthermore, these authors argue that the liberation of nitrogen from the *syn*- but not from the *anti*-form by copper sulphate is in accord with the sulphite formula for the *syn*-form; it is oxidised to the diazonium sulphate, followed by decomposition by the cuprous salt thereby produced.

The diazocyanides. When a diazonium salt solution is treated with potassium cyanide in slightly acid solution at temperatures below − 5°, a yellow precipitate is obtained. The physical properties of these compounds, *e.g.*, insolubility, colour and non-electrolytes, appear to indicate that they cannot be diazonium salts. Hantzsch therefore believed these compounds to have the structure Ar—N=N—CN (this azo-structure would account for their physical properties).

When allowed to stand in the solid state or in ethanolic solution, the yellow precipitate turns red. This red form may also be prepared by adding potassium cyanide to a diazonium salt solution at temperatures above 0°.

Hantzsch and Schultze (1895) prepared two forms of *p*-chloro- and *p*-nitro-benzenediazocyanides and showed that one form, the *labile* yellow form, coupled with 2-naphthol, and was decomposed into aryl cyanide by copper powder. The other form, the *stable* red form, did not couple with 2-naphthol, and was not attacked by copper. Hantzsch proposed geometrical isomerism to explain the existence of the two forms, the labile being the *syn*-, and the stable, the *anti*-:

```
ClC6H4—N              ClC6H4—N
       ||                    ||
  N≡C—N                     N—C≡N
(syn-form)               (anti-form)
```

Orton (1903) believed that the labile form was the cyanide Ar—N=N—CN, and the stable form the *iso*cyanide, Ar—N=N—NC. This, however, could not be reconciled with the work of Hantzsch and Schultze, who had shown that the labile and stable diazocyanides, on boiling with acid, both gave the same acid amide and same carboxylic acid. These hydrolytic products are characteristic of cyanides; *iso*cyanides give amines.

$$Ar{\cdot}N{=}N{\cdot}CN \xrightarrow{H_2O} Ar—N{=}N—CO{\cdot}NH_2 \xrightarrow{H_2O} Ar—N{=}N—CO_2H$$

Le Fèvre *et al.* (1938, 1947, 1949) examined the dipole moments, refractivities, magnetic optical rotatory powers, diamagnetic susceptibilities and ultraviolet spectra of the diazocyanides, and believe that their results agree with geometrical isomerism. Sheppard and Sutherland (1947), from an examination of the vibrational spectra of some pairs of diazocyanides, also believe that the diazo-cyanides are geometrical isomers (both forms being the cyanide).

In 1939, Stephenson and Waters claimed that the reactivity, *i.e.*, the coupling power, of the *syn*-diazocyanide is associated with the fact that in ionising solvents, the covalent diazocyanide (I) exists in equilibrium with the diazonium cyanide (II) to which the ionic reactivity (*i.e.*, coupling) is due, whereas the *anti*-diazocyanides do not yield (II) in this way:

$$\begin{matrix} Ar-N \\ \| \\ NC-N \end{matrix} \rightleftharpoons \begin{matrix} Ar-N^+ \\ ||| \\ N \end{matrix} + CN^-$$
(I) (II)

Hydrazines. The most important substituted hydrazine is **phenylhydrazine,** $C_6H_5 \cdot NH \cdot NH_2$. This may be prepared by the reduction of benzenediazonium chloride with stannous chloride and hydrochloric acid:

$$C_6H_5 \cdot N_2Cl + 4[H] \xrightarrow{SnCl_2/HCl} C_6H_5 \cdot NH \cdot NH_2 \cdot HCl \quad (90\%)$$

The reduction may also be carried out with sodium sulphite; the benzenediazonium chloride is poured into aqueous sodium sulphite, concentrated hydrochloric acid is added, and the solution is then heated on a water-bath. The mechanism of the reduction may be as follows, sodium benzene-*anti*-diazosulphonate, (III), and the sodium salt of phenylhydrazine sulphonate, (IV), being intermediate products:

$$[C_6H_5 \cdot N \vdots N]^+Cl^- \xrightarrow{Na_2SO_3} \begin{matrix} C_6H_5-N \\ \| \\ N-SO_3Na \end{matrix} \ (III) \xrightarrow{H_2SO_3}$$

$$\left[\begin{matrix} C_6H_5 \cdot N \cdot NH \cdot SO_3Na \\ | \\ SO_3H \end{matrix}\right] \xrightarrow{H_2O} \underset{(IV)}{C_6H_5 \cdot NH \cdot NH \cdot SO_3Na} + H_2SO_4 \xrightarrow{HCl}$$

$$C_6H_5 \cdot NH \cdot NH_2 \cdot HCl \xrightarrow{NaOH} C_6H_5 \cdot NH \cdot NH_2 \quad (80\text{–}84\%)$$

Phenylhydrazine is a colourless liquid when freshly distilled, b.p. 241°. It is readily oxidised when exposed to the air. It is very slightly soluble in water but is very soluble in organic solvents. Phenylhydrazine is strongly basic and forms well-defined salts, *e.g.*, phenylhydrazine hydrochloride, $C_6H_5 \cdot NH \cdot NH_2 \cdot HCl$; these salts are relatively stable to atmospheric oxidation. Phenylhydrazine is a powerful reducing agent, reducing Fehling's solution in the cold:

$$C_6H_5 \cdot NH \cdot NH_2 + 2CuO \longrightarrow C_6H_6 + Cu_2O + N_2 + H_2O$$

Hardie *et al.* (1957) have described a new method of phenylation by oxidising phenylhydrazine with metallic oxides (preferably silver) in an aromatic solvent, *e.g.*,

$$C_6H_5 \cdot NH \cdot NH_2 \xrightarrow{Ag_2O} [C_6H_5 \cdot N{=}NH] \longrightarrow C_6H_5 \cdot + N_2 + H \cdot$$

$C_6H_5\cdot$ + ArH ⟶ $C_6H_5 \cdot Ar$; $C_6H_5 \cdot C_6H_5$ (by-product); C_6H_6 (by-product)

When reduced with vigorous reducing agents, *e.g.*, zinc and hydrochloric acid, phenylhydrazine gives aniline and ammonia; this shows the structure of phenylhydrazine:

$$C_6H_5 \cdot NH \cdot NH_2 + 2[H] \xrightarrow{Zn/HCl} C_6H_5 \cdot NH_2 + NH_3$$

The most important reaction of phenylhydrazine is with carbonyl compounds to form *phenylhydrazones,* and with simple sugars to form *osazones.* These derivatives are usually well-defined crystalline solids, and so are useful for the identification of carbonyl compounds. Many phenylhydrazones are decomposed by strong inorganic acids to reform the carbonyl compound. When reduced with zinc and acetic acid, phenylhydrazones form primary amines:

$$C_6H_5{\cdot}NH{\cdot}N{:}CH{\cdot}R + 4[H] \longrightarrow C_6H_5{\cdot}NH_2 + R{\cdot}CH_2{\cdot}NH_2$$

Phenylhydrazine is used for making antipyrine (p. 724).

Various derivatives of phenylhydrazine are used instead of phenylhydrazine, since these produce compounds which crystallise more readily, *e.g.*, *p*-nitro-, 2 : 4-dinitro- and *p*-bromophenylhydrazine. Of these, 2 : 4-dinitrophenylhydrazine is most commonly used, and this is prepared by the action of hydrazine sulphate and potassium acetate on 1-chloro-2 : 4-dinitrobenzene (*cf.* p. 533):

$$\text{Cl-}C_6H_3(NO_2)_2\text{ (2,4)} + NH_2{\cdot}NH_2{\cdot}H_2SO_4 \xrightarrow{CH_3\cdot CO_2K} NH_2{\cdot}NH{\cdot}C_6H_3(NO_2)_2\text{ (2,4)} \quad (80\%)$$

It is a red crystalline solid, m.p. 194°.

DIAZOAMINO- AND AMINOAZO-COMPOUNDS

Diazo-compounds have the structure Ar—N=N—Y, where Y is a group that is not attached to the nitrogen atom by carbon, **Azo-compounds,** on the other hand, have the structure Ar—N=N—Ar, each aryl group being attached to a nitrogen atom by carbon.

Diazoaminobenzene, $C_6H_5{\cdot}N{=}N{\cdot}NH{\cdot}C_6H_5$, is formed by the interaction of benzenediazonium chloride and aniline. It may be prepared by treating aniline hydrochloride solution with sodium nitrite just sufficient to diazotise *half* of the aniline, and then adding sodium acetate:

$$C_6H_5{\cdot}N_2Cl + C_6H_5{\cdot}NH_2 + CH_3{\cdot}CO_2Na \longrightarrow C_6H_5{\cdot}N{=}N{\cdot}NH{\cdot}C_6H_5 + NaCl + CH_3{\cdot}CO_2H \quad (82\text{–}85\%)$$

Diazoaminobenzene is often formed during the diazotisation of aniline, especially when the solution is only weakly acid. It exists in two forms, one as golden-yellow prisms, m.p. 98°, and the other, yellow prisms, m.p. 80°. Diazoaminobenzene explodes when heated rapidly, and is insoluble in water but soluble in ethanol. It is feebly basic and does not form stable salts. When boiled with dilute sulphuric acid, diazoaminobenzene liberates nitrogen forming phenol and aniline:

$$C_6H_5{\cdot}N{:}N{\cdot}NH{\cdot}C_6H_5 + H_2O \xrightarrow{H_2SO_4} C_6H_5OH + N_2 + C_6H_5{\cdot}NH_2$$

When boiled with concentrated hydrobromic acid, diazoaminobenzene forms bromobenzene and aniline, and when treated with sodium nitrite and hydrochloric acid, it forms benzenediazonium chloride.

When 1 molecule of aniline, in ethanol solution, is treated with 2 molecules of benzenediazonium chloride, bisdiazoaminobenzene is formed:

$$C_6H_5{\cdot}NH_2 + 2C_6H_5{\cdot}N_2Cl \longrightarrow C_6H_5{\cdot}N({-}N{=}N{\cdot}C_6H_5)_2 + 2HCl$$

A very important property of diazoaminobenzene is its tendency to rearrange to aminoazobenzene (see below).

Tautomerism of the diazoamino compounds. When benzenediazonium chloride is added to *p*-toluidine, the product obtained is the same as that formed by adding *p*-toluenediazonium chloride to aniline:

A. $C_6H_5N_2Cl + NH_2C_6H_4CH_3 \longrightarrow$

$C_6H_5{-}N{=}N{-}NH{-}C_6H_4CH_3 + HCl$

B. $CH_3C_6H_4N_2Cl + NH_2C_6H_5 \longrightarrow$

$CH_3C_6H_4{-}N{=}N{-}NH{-}C_6H_5 + HCl$

Since the same product is obtained in reactions *A* and *B*, the explanation may be either that only one form, the *stable* form, is present, the other, the *labile* form, changing into the stable form; or that both forms are present in equilibrium, thereby forming a tautomeric system. Two compounds have been shown to be present as follows:

(i) By reduction with tin and hydrochloric acid. Reduction of *A* would (presumably) give aniline and *p*-tolylhydrazine, and *B*, *p*-toluidine and phenylhydrazine:

$C_6H_5{-}N{=}N{-}NH{-}C_6H_4CH_3 \xrightarrow{Sn/HCl}$

$C_6H_5NH_2 + NH_2{\cdot}NHC_6H_4CH_3$

$CH_3C_6H_4{-}N{=}N{-}NH{-}C_6H_5 \xrightarrow{Sn/HCl}$

$CH_3C_6H_4NH_2 + NH_2{\cdot}NHC_6H_5$

In practice, all four compounds are obtained.

(ii) By hydrolysis with sulphuric acid. Hydrolysis of *A* would give phenol and *p*-toluidine, and *B*, *p*-cresol and aniline:

$C_6H_5{-}N{=}N{-}NH{-}C_6H_4CH_3 \xrightarrow{H_2O}$

$C_6H_5OH + N_2 + NH_2C_6H_4CH_3$

$CH_3C_6H_4{-}N{=}N{-}NH{-}C_6H_5 \xrightarrow{H_2O}$

$CH_3C_6H_4OH + N_2 + NH_2C_6H_5$

Again, in practice, all four compounds are obtained.

These results therefore show that both *A* and *B* are present:

$$\underset{A.}{C_6H_5{-}N{=}N{-}NH{-}C_6H_4CH_3} \rightleftharpoons \underset{B.}{C_6H_5{-}NH{-}N{=}N{-}C_6H_4CH_3}$$

This tautomeric system is known as the *diazoamino triad system*, the *three nitrogen system*, or the *triazene* system.

Further support for the existence of this tautomeric system may be obtained from a consideration of the cyclic diazoamino-compound, *methylbenztriazole* (*cf.* p. 553):

$$CH_3C_6H_3(NH_2)_2 \xrightarrow{HNO_2} \text{(I)} \quad or \quad \text{(II)}$$

(I) (II)

Only *one* product is obtained and this, on acetylation, gives two acetyl derivatives which, on hydrolysis, give the same product. These results are readily explained if (I) and (II) exist in equilibrium.

***p*-Aminoazobenzene** is formed when diazoaminobenzene is warmed at 30–40° with a small amount of aniline hydrochloride:

$$C_6H_5{\cdot}N{=}N{-}NH{-}C_6H_5 \longrightarrow C_6H_5{\cdot}N{=}N{-}C_6H_4{-}NH_2 \quad (80\%)$$

This isomeric change also takes place when the precipitate of diazoaminobenzene is left in contact with its mother liquor for several days.

If the *p*-position in the anilino-group is occupied, then the isomeric change occurs more slowly, the azo-group taking up the *o*-position to the amino-group:

$$C_6H_5{\cdot}N{=}N{-}NH{-}C_6H_4{-}CH_3 \longrightarrow C_6H_5{\cdot}N{=}N{-}C_6H_3(NH_2)CH_3$$

The mechanism of diazoamino-aminoazo rearrangement is still uncertain; one proposed recently is that the diazoamino-compound accepts a proton from the catalyst (amine salt), and this intermediate breaks down into a diazonium cation and amine, these two then coupling in the *p* position:

$$C_6H_5{-}\ddot{N}H{-}\ddot{N}{=}N{-}C_6H_5 + C_6H_5{\cdot}\overset{+}{N}H_3 \rightleftharpoons \left[C_6H_5{-}NH_2{-}\ddot{N}{=}N{-}C_6H_5\right]^+ + C_6H_5{\cdot}NH_2$$

$$\Downarrow\Uparrow$$

$$C_6H_5{\cdot}NH_2 + [C_6H_5{-}N{\equiv}N]^+ \longrightarrow C_6H_5{-}N{=}N{-}C_6H_4{-}NH_2$$

Evidence for this mechanism is to be found in the fact that if the amine salt, $Ar{\cdot}\overset{+}{N}H_3\}Cl^-$, is used as the catalyst instead of aniline hydrochloride, the product of the rearrangement consists of two azo-compounds, $C_6H_5{\cdot}N{=}N{-}C_6H_4{\cdot}NH_2$ and $C_6H_5{\cdot}N{=}N{-}Ar'{\cdot}NH_2$ (Ar′ is Ar less a hydrogen atom). This shows that the rearrangement is *intermolecular* (*i.e.*, separates into parts), the $C_6H_5{\cdot}NH_2$ and $Ar{\cdot}NH_2$ molecules competing for the diazonium cation (Kidd, 1937). This intermolecular mechanism is supported by Clusius *et al.* (1952) who worked with diazoaminoazobenzene containing ^{15}N.

Aminoazobenzene forms brilliant orange-red plates, m.p. 126°. It is insoluble in water but may be rendered soluble by sulphonation (*cf.* p. 743). Aminoazobenzene is manufactured in large quantities for the preparation of bisazo-dyes and indulenes. Aminoazobenzene forms two series of salts with acids. When one equivalent of hydrochloric acid is used, the salt formed is yellow and unstable, and probably has the structure (I) (since this

$$C_6H_5{\cdot}N{=}N{\cdot}C_6H_4{\cdot}\overset{+}{N}H_3\}Cl^- \quad \text{(I)} \qquad C_6H_5{\cdot}NH{-}N{=}C_6H_4{=}\overset{+}{N}H_2\}Cl^- \quad \text{(II)}$$

has the same type of spectrum as azobenzene). When, however, a large excess of hydrochloric acid is used, the salt produced is dark violet and stable, and its structure is probably (II), *i.e.*, the salt of the quinone-iminohydrazone (see p. 745); the spectrum of this salt is different from that of azobenzene.

On vigorous reduction, aminoazobenzene is converted into aniline and *p*-phenylenediamine:

$$C_6H_5{-}N{=}N{-}C_6H_4{\cdot}NH_2 \xrightarrow{Sn/HCl} C_6H_5{\cdot}NH_2 + NH_2{\cdot}C_6H_4{\cdot}NH_2$$

If titanous chloride is used as the reducing agent, the reaction is quantitative, and so may be used for the volumetric determination of aminoazo-dyes.

Aminoazobenzene is oxidised by manganese dioxide and sulphuric acid to *p*-benzoquinone.

Secondary amines behave similarly to aniline in their reaction towards diazonium salts; *e.g.*, methylaniline couples with benzenediazonium chloride to form methyldiazoaminobenzene:

$$C_6H_5{\cdot}N_2Cl + C_6H_5{\cdot}NH{\cdot}CH_3 \longrightarrow C_6H_5{\cdot}N{=}N{-}N(CH_3){\cdot}C_6H_5 + HCl$$

At the same time, however, *C*-azo-coupling takes place, some methylaminoazobenzene being formed:

$$C_6H_5{\cdot}N_2Cl + C_6H_5{\cdot}NH{\cdot}CH_3 \longrightarrow C_6H_5{\cdot}N{=}N{\cdot}C_6H_4{\cdot}NH{\cdot}CH_3 + HCl$$

This is also formed by the rearrangement of methyldiazoaminobenzene.

With tertiary amines, the formation of a diazoamino-compound is impossible; the aminoazo-compound is always formed by direct coupling in the *p*-position; *e.g.*, dimethylaminoazobenzene from dimethylaniline and benzenediazonium chloride:

$$C_6H_5{\cdot}N_2Cl + C_6H_5{\cdot}N(CH_3)_2 \longrightarrow C_6H_5{\cdot}N{=}N{\cdot}C_6H_4{\cdot}N(CH_3)_2 + HCl$$

Reduction of azo-compounds with sodium hyposulphite, or stannous chloride and hydrochloric acid offers a relatively simple method of preparing diamines (or amino-phenols) in a pure state; *e.g.*, 2 : 5-diaminotoluene from *m*-toluidine:

$$C_6H_5{\cdot}N_2Cl + CH_3{\cdot}C_6H_4{\cdot}NH_2 \xrightarrow{NaOH} C_6H_5{-}N{=}N{-}C_6H_3(CH_3){\cdot}NH_2$$

$$\xrightarrow{Na_2S_2O_4} C_6H_5{\cdot}NH_2 + NH_2{\cdot}C_6H_3(CH_3){\cdot}NH_2$$

It should be noted that the azo-compound, 4-amino-2-methylazobenzene, is formed by direct coupling with the nucleus. Generally, the diazoamino-compound (*N*-coupling) is formed by reaction between diazonium salts and primary aromatic amines (*cf.* p. 569); *m*-toluidine and the naphthylamines always form the *C*-azo-compound.

Azoxybenzene may be prepared by reducing nitrobenzene with methanolic sodium methoxide (which is oxidised to sodium formate). It may be conveniently prepared by refluxing nitrobenzene with alkaline sodium arsenite:

$$4C_6H_5{\cdot}NO_2 + 3As_2O_3 + 18NaOH \longrightarrow$$

$$2C_6H_5{\cdot}\overset{O}{\overset{\uparrow}{N}}{=}N{\cdot}C_6H_5 + 6Na_3AsO_4 + 9H_2O \quad (85\%)$$

Reduction of nitro-compounds with glucose in alkaline solution gives azoxy-compounds, *e.g.*, nitrobenzene gives azoxybenzene (83 per cent. yield; Galbraith *et al.*, 1951). Metallic thallium also reduces nitro-compounds in ethanolic solution to the corresponding azoxy-compounds (McHatton *et al.*, 1953), *e.g.*,

$$2C_6H_5 \cdot NO_2 + 6Tl + 6C_2H_5OH \longrightarrow C_6H_5 \cdot N{=}N(O) \cdot C_6H_5 + 6TlOC_2H_5 + 3H_2O \quad (84\%)$$

Oxidation of aniline with peracetic acid also gives an 85 per cent. yield of azoxybenzene (Greenspan, 1947).

Azoxybenzene is a yellow crystalline solid, m.p. 36°, insoluble in water but soluble in ethanol and ether. When warmed with iron filings, it is reduced to azobenzene. When reduced with ammonium sulphide, azoxybenzene gives hydrazobenzene, and with metal and acid it gives aniline.

When warmed with concentrated sulphuric acid, azoxybenzene rearranges to hydroxyazobenzene; this is an example of the **Wallach transformation** (1880). Gore *et al.* (1950) have shown that azoxybenzene gives 65 per cent. of *p*-hydroxyazobenzene when heated at 90° for 30 minutes with 83 per cent. sulphuric acid.

$$C_6H_5-N(\rightarrow O){=}N-C_6H_5 \longrightarrow HO-C_6H_4-N{=}N-C_6H_5$$

With 98 per cent. sulphuric acid at 25°, however, only 9·5 per cent. of *p*-hydroxyazobenzene was obtained, together with 58 per cent. of azobenzene and some other products. It was found that high temperatures increase the yield of the hydroxyazo-compound, and high concentrations of sulphuric acid increase the yield of the àzo-compound. On the other hand, Badger *et al.* (1954) have isomerised a number of azoxy derivatives to *o*-hydroxyazo-derivatives exclusively (or almost exclusively) by exposure to sunlight. An intramolecular mechanism has been proposed for this *ortho*-rearrangement.

$$C_6H_5-\overset{+}{N}(O^-){=}N-C_6H_5 \longrightarrow C_6H_5-\overset{+}{\ddot{N}}-N{=}C_6H_4(O^-)H \longrightarrow C_6H_5-\ddot{N}{=}N-C_6H_4-OH\ (o)$$

Formerly, the formula of azoxybenzene was believed to contain a three-membered ring (*cf.* V). This was shown to be incorrect by Angeli (1913), who obtained two bromoazoxybenzenes when *p*-bromoazobenzene was oxidised with hydrogen peroxide in acetic acid:

$$Br-C_6H_4-N{=}N-C_6H_5 \xrightarrow{H_2O_2} Br-C_6H_4-N(\rightarrow O){=}N-C_6H_5\ \text{(III)} + Br-C_6H_4-N{=}N(\rightarrow O)-C_6H_5\ \text{(IV)}$$

If the structure of *p*-bromoazoxybenzene were (V), it would make no difference whether the bromine atom was in one ring or the other. If, however, the oxygen is attached to one or other nitrogen atom by a co-ordinate link, the structure is unsymmetrical and therefore two isomers are possible (III and IV).

$$\text{Br-}C_6H_4\text{-N(-O-)N-}C_6H_5$$

(V)

Azoxybenzene exists in two forms which are geometrical isomers:

$$\begin{array}{c} C_6H_5\text{—N} \\ \| \\ C_6H_5\text{—N}\rightarrow O \end{array} \qquad \begin{array}{c} C_6H_5\text{—N} \\ \| \\ O\leftarrow\text{N—}C_6H_5 \end{array}$$

cis, m.p. 86° *trans*, m.p. 36°

This *trans*-isomer is " ordinary " azoxybenzene.

Azobenzene may be prepared by carefully warming azoxybenzene with three times its weight of iron filings, or by the reaction between nitrosobenzene and aniline:

$$C_6H_5\cdot NO + C_6H_5\cdot NH_2 \longrightarrow C_6H_5\cdot N{=}N\cdot C_6H_5 + H_2O$$

It may be conveniently prepared by reducing nitrobenzene with sodium amalgam, alkaline sodium stannite, or best with zinc dust and methanolic sodium hydroxide:

$$2C_6H_5\cdot NO_2 + 8[H] \xrightarrow{Zn/NaOH} C_6H_5\cdot N{:}N\cdot C_6H_5 + 4H_2O \quad (84\text{–}86\%)$$

Lithium aluminium hydride also reduces nitrobenzene to azobenzene. Another convenient preparation is to gently reflux hydrazobenzene (yield is 50 per cent. of each compound):

$$2C_6H_5\cdot NH\cdot NH\cdot C_6H_5 \longrightarrow C_6H_5\cdot N{:}N\cdot C_6H_5 + 2C_6H_5\cdot NH_2$$

Azobenzene crystallises in orange-red plates, m.p. 68°, insoluble in water but soluble in organic solvents. According to Hartley (1938), azobenzene exists as geometrical isomers, the *trans*-form being " ordinary " azobenzene:

$$\begin{array}{c} C_6H_5\text{—N} \\ \| \\ C_6H_5\text{—N} \end{array} \qquad \begin{array}{c} C_6H_5\text{—N} \\ \| \\ \text{N—}C_6H_5 \end{array}$$

cis, m.p. 71·4° *trans*, m.p. 68°

It is of interest to note that the reduction of *cis*-azoxybenzene with lithium aluminium hydride gives *trans*-azobenzene (Badger *et al.*, 1953).

Azobenzene is reduced by zinc dust and aqueous sodium hydroxide to hydrazobenzene, and by stannous chloride or titanous chloride in acid solution, and by alkaline sodium hyposulphite, to aniline. Azobenzene is not reduced by sodium sulphide. Sodium hydrogen sulphite adds on to azobenzene to form a bisulphite compound:

$$C_6H_5\cdot N{=}N\cdot C_6H_5 + NaHSO_3 \longrightarrow C_6H_5\cdot NH\cdot N(C_6H_5)\cdot SO_3Na$$

Azobenzene is oxidised by hydrogen peroxide in acetic acid to azoxybenzene. Oxidation of *cis*-azobenzene with perbenzoic acid gives *cis*-azoxybenzene. The *trans*-compound gives *trans*-azoxybenzene on oxidation in the dark, but in sunlight some *cis*-isomer is also obtained (Badger *et al.*, 1953). The most outstanding property of the azo-compounds is their colour, and this is used to great advantage in the manufacture of azo-dyes.

Hydroxyazo-compounds (azophenols). Hydroxyazo-compounds may be obtained by coupling diazonium salts with monohydric phenols (or with *m*-dihydric phenols), *e.g.*, *p*-hydroxyazobenzene (I):

$$C_6H_5{\cdot}N_2Cl + C_6H_5OH \xrightarrow{NaOH} C_6H_5{\cdot}N{=}N{-}C_6H_4{-}OH \quad (I)$$

On the other hand, certain hydroxyazo-compounds may be obtained by the reaction between quinones and phenylhydrazine (or its derivatives). This gives

$$C_6H_5{\cdot}NH{\cdot}N{=}C_6H_4{=}O \quad (II)$$

rise to the possibility of structure (II) for *p*-hydroxyazobenzene, *i.e.*, p-*benzoquinone monophenylhydrazone*. In practice, however, (II) cannot be prepared by the action of phenylhydrazine on *p*-benzoquinone, since the latter is reduced to quinol, but with, *e.g.*, *o*-nitrophenylhydrazine, the monophenylhydrazine derivative of *p*-benzoquinone has been prepared. This would correspond to structure (II), and has been shown to be identical with *o*-nitrohydroxyazobenzene obtained by coupling phenol with diazotised *o*-nitroaniline (a reaction which indicates a structure corresponding to I). Furthermore, both the *O*- and *N*-alkyl derivatives of (I) and (II) have been prepared.

4-Phenylazo-1-naphthol has been prepared both ways, *i.e.*, by direct coupling between 1-naphthol and benzenediazonium chloride (corresponding to III), and by reaction between 1 : 4-naphthaquinone and phenylhydrazine (corresponding to IV):

$$\text{1-OH-4-}(N{:}N{\cdot}C_6H_5)\text{-naphthalene} \quad (III) \qquad \text{1-}(O{=})\text{-4-}(={N{\cdot}NH{\cdot}C_6H_5})\text{-naphthalene} \quad (IV)$$

The question that now arises is: Which is the correct structure, or do both exist together in equilibrium (tautomeric mixture)? Goldschmidt (1891) attempted to find the answer by benzoylating hydroxyazo-compounds (or quinone monophenylhydrazones), and reducing the products. He obtained benzoylated amines, and explained their formation by assuming that since the benzoyl group appeared finally as the *N*-derivative and not the *O*-derivative, the introduction of the benzoyl group into the original compound must have taken place by replacement of hydrogen on the N atom, thereby indicating that the structure was the phenylhydrazone type (II) and not the hydroxyazo-type (I). Thus:

$$C_6H_5{\cdot}NH{-}N{=}C_6H_4{=}O \xrightarrow{C_6H_5COCl} C_6H_5{\cdot}N(CO{\cdot}C_6H_5){-}N{=}C_6H_4{=}O \xrightarrow{[H]}$$

$$C_6H_5{\cdot}N(CO{\cdot}C_6H_5){-}NH{-}C_6H_4{-}OH \xrightarrow{[H]} C_6H_5{\cdot}NH{\cdot}CO{\cdot}C_6H_5 + NH_2{-}C_6H_4{-}OH$$

On the other hand, Jacobsen *et al.* (1903), when they reduced the alkyl derivatives of hydroxyazo-compounds, always found the alkyl group attached to the oxygen. This indicates the hydroxyazo-structure, and contradicts the evidence of Goldschmidt.

Auwers (1908) then showed that *N*-acylated *p*-quinone monophenylhydrazones readily change into the isomeric *O*-acylated hydroxyazo-compounds, *e.g.*,

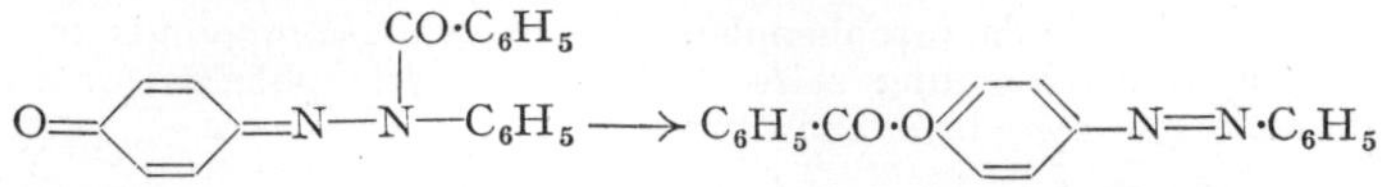

$$O{=}C_6H_4{=}N{-}N(CO{\cdot}C_6H_5){-}C_6H_5 \longrightarrow C_6H_5{\cdot}CO{\cdot}O{-}C_6H_4{-}N{=}N{\cdot}C_6H_5$$

He also found that it was not possible to prepare the *N*-benzoyl derivatives of the *O*-quinone monophenylhydrazones, the migration to the oxygen atom taking place so readily.

Thus, as far as the *p*-compounds are concerned, it is not possible to be certain which benzoyl derivative is the starting material. Moreover, further work showed that since primary amines react very readily with esters, the acyl group is likely to be found with the nitrogen atom, whether the starting material is the *O*- or *N*-derivative; *e.g.*, when aniline is warmed with *p*-aminophenyl benzoate, benzanilide and *p*-aminophenol are produced:

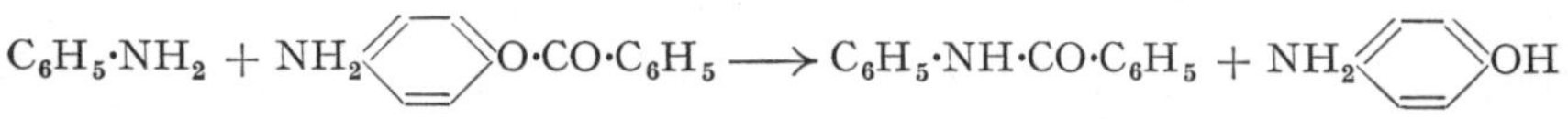

$$C_6H_5{\cdot}NH_2 + NH_2{-}C_6H_4{-}O{\cdot}CO{\cdot}C_6H_5 \longrightarrow C_6H_5{\cdot}NH{\cdot}CO{\cdot}C_6H_5 + NH_2{-}C_6H_4{-}OH$$

It can therefore be seen that the interpretation of the reduction products of acylated hydroxyazo-compounds is difficult and uncertain.

Another approach to settle the question of structure has been by studying the properties of the *m*-hydroxyazo-compounds. It has been found that the behaviour of these compounds is similar to that of the *o*- and *p*-isomers, and since the *m*-hydroxy-compounds cannot form a quinonoid structure (see p. 639), a quinone phenylhydrazone structure cannot be used for *m*-compounds. Thus, by analogy, the hydroxyazo-structure may be assumed for the *o*- and *p*-compounds. This, however, is not conclusive (or satisfactory).

p-Hydroxyazo-compounds are soluble in dilute alkali, and since phenols are readily soluble in alkali, this suggests that the *p*-compounds have the hydroxy-azo-structure. On the other hand, *o*-hydroxyazo-compounds (except *o*-hydroxy-azobenzene) are insoluble in dilute alkali; this suggests the quinonoid structure. Mason (1932), however, suggested that this insolubility in alkali was due to chelation (V), which is impossible in the *p*-series. This suggestion has been confirmed by infrared absorption studies (Hadži, 1956). Kuhn *et al.* (1935)

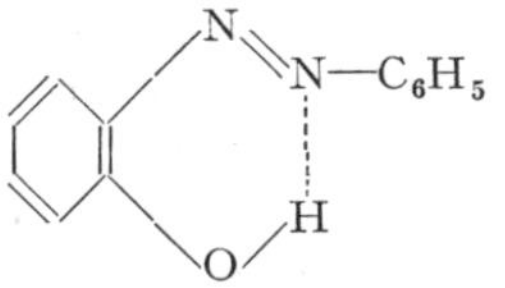

(V) 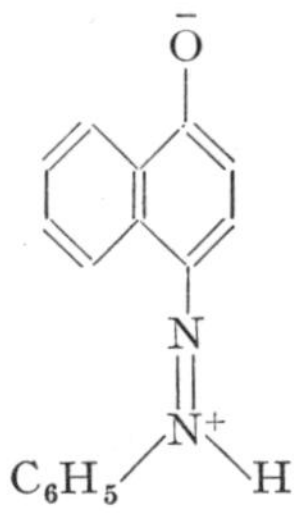 (VI)

have shown from electronic spectral investigations that both *o*- and *p*-azophenol exist in the azo-form only, irrespective of solvent. This is also the case for the *solid* state of these two compounds, as has been shown from infrared and electronic spectral studies (Hadži, 1956). On the other hand, investigation of the electronic spectra of the 1-arylazo-2-naphthols has shown that these compounds exist in equilibrium as a tautomeric mixture of hydroxyazo and hydrazone forms (Burawoy *et al.*, 1953). Furthermore, it was shown that the equilibrium depends on the nature and position of substituents in the *aryl* nucleus, and also on the nature of the solvent. Hadži has found from an investigation of the infrared and electronic spectra of a mixture of *solid* phenyl-azonaphthols that these compounds exist either as pure phenylhydrazones or as a mixture of both tautomeric forms. It also appears that structure (VI) plays an important part in the state of 4-phenylazo-1-naphthol.

Another problem of structure is that of the diazo-oxides. When *o*-hydroxy-benzenediazonium chloride (*o*-diazophenol) is treated with alkali, the diazo-oxide is formed, the structure of which was thought to be an oxide ring:

$$C_6H_4(OH)N_2Cl \xrightarrow{NaOH} C_6H_4 \langle O \cdot N{=}N \rangle$$

A quinonoid structure has also been suggested. It now appears that the properties of *o*-diazophenol are best explained on the basis of a resonance hybrid (involving the quinonoid structure):

$$O{=}C_6H_4{=}\overset{+}{N}{=}\overset{-}{N}: \longleftrightarrow \overset{-}{O}{-}C_6H_4{-}\overset{+}{N}{\equiv}N:$$

Similarly, *p*-diazophenol is also believed to be a resonance hybrid (the oxide ring structure is extremely unlikely):

$$O{=}C_6H_4{=}\overset{+}{N}{=}\ddot{N}: \longleftrightarrow \overset{-}{O}{-}C_6H_4{-}\overset{+}{N}{\equiv}N:$$

Hydrazobenzene (s-*diphenylhydrazine*), $C_6H_5{\cdot}NH{\cdot}NH{\cdot}C_6H_5$, may be prepared by reducing nitrobenzene or azobenzene with zinc dust and aqueous sodium hydroxide. It is also formed when azoxybenzene is reduced electrolytically; azobenzene has never been isolated as an intermediate product in this reduction.

Hydrazobenzene is a colourless crystalline solid, m. p. 126°. It is slowly oxidised by atmospheric oxygen to azobenzene; this oxidation is rapid with sodium hypobromite. Hydrazobenzene is reduced by stannous chloride and hydrochloric acid to aniline, and when heated, forms azobenzene and aniline (see azobenzene, above).

The most important reaction of hydrazobenzene is its rearrangement to *benzidine* (4 : 4′-*diaminodiphenyl*) when warmed with hydrochloric acid:

$$C_6H_5{\cdot}NH{-}NH{\cdot}C_6H_5 \xrightarrow{HCl} NH_2{\cdot}C_6H_4{-}C_6H_4{\cdot}NH_2 \quad (90\%)$$

This is known as the **benzidine transformation.** The rearrangement, however, is not completely in the *p* : *p*′-positions; some *diphenyline* (2 : 4′-*diaminodiphenyl*) is also formed (30%):

$$C_6H_5{\cdot}NH{-}NH{\cdot}C_6H_5 \xrightarrow{HCl} NH_2{\cdot}C_6H_4{-}C_6H_4{\cdot}NH_2\ (o)$$

When the *p*-position of one nucleus is occupied, *o* : *p*′-coupling (*i.e.*, diphenyline formation) or the *o*- and ***p*-semidine transformations** take place, according to the nature of the group in the *p*-position. When a methyl, methoxyl, or an ethoxyl group is in the *p*-position, the main product is an *o*-semidine, accompanied by a small amount of the *p*-semidine (in the case of the methyl group, apparently only the *o*-semidine is formed); *e.g.*, *p*-methoxyhydrazobenzene gives mainly anilinomethoxyaniline (I) (the *o*-semidine), together with some methoxyanilinoaniline (II) (the *p*-semidine):

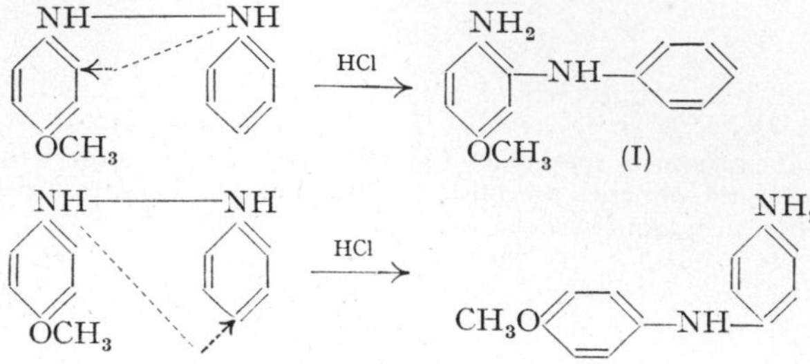

On the other hand, if the *p*-position is occupied by Cl, Br, I, or $N(CH_3)_2$, the main product is a diphenyline derivative, accompanied by a small amount of *o*- and *p*-semidines; *e.g.*, *p*-chlorohydrazobenzene gives chlorodiphenyline (III), anilinochloroaniline (IV) (the *o*-semidine), and chloroanilinoaniline (V) (the *p*-semidine):

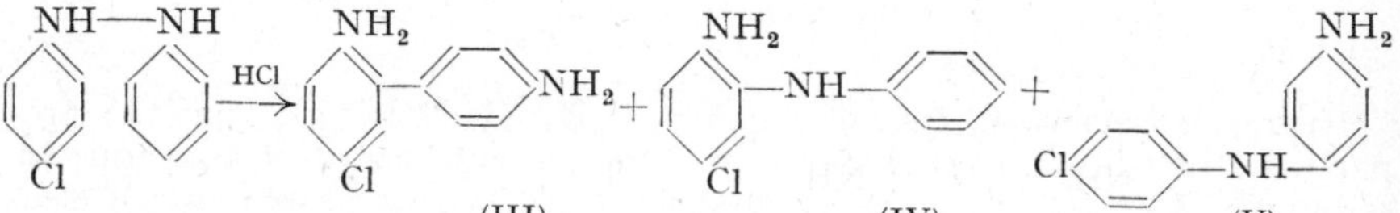

When both *p*-positions are occupied, then only the *o*-semidine transformation takes place (the *p*-rearrangement is now impossible); *e.g.*, *p*-hydrazotoluene gives *o*-amino-(4 : 3′-)-ditolylamine:

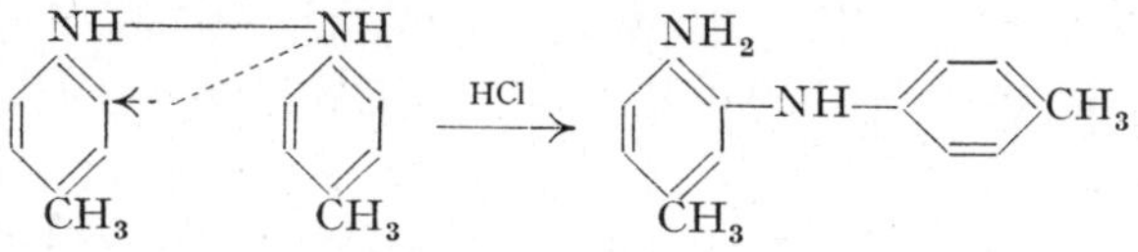

According to Večeřa *et al.* (1956), in the rearrangement of hydrazobenzene, not only benzidine and diphenyline are formed, but also 2 : 2′-diaminodiphenyl, 2-aminodiphenylamine, and 4-aminodiphenylamine. All of these products were identified by means of paper chromatography. Thus the semidine transformation also occurs to some extent even though the *p*-positions of *both* rings are unoccupied.

Carlin *et al.* (1956) have carried out the benzidine rearrangement on 3 : 3′-dibromo-5 : 5′-dimethylhydrazobenzene in sulphuric acid and obtained the following products.

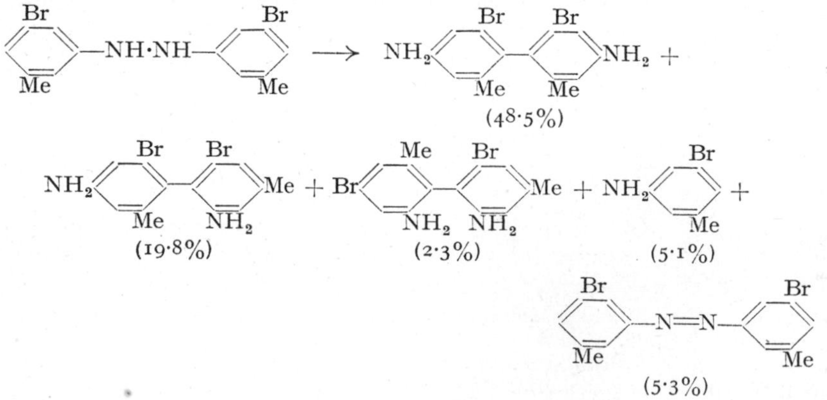

(48·5%)

(19·8%) (2·3%) (5·1%)

(5·3%)

Clemo *et al.* (1954) have shown that an *N*-methylhydrazobenzene also undergoes the normal benzidine rearrangement:

$$C_6H_5\text{—NMe—NH—}C_6H_4(NO_2) \xrightarrow{HCl} MeNH\text{—}C_6H_4\text{—}C_6H_3(NO_2)\text{—}NH_2$$

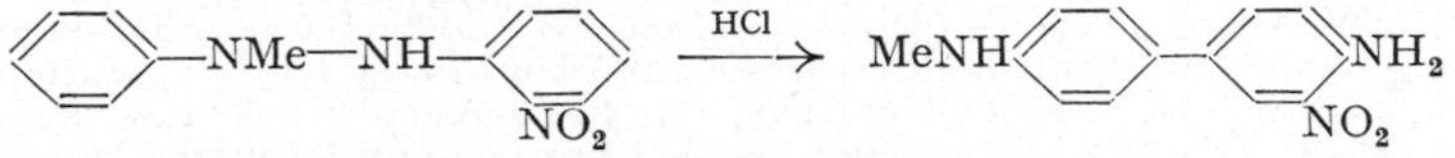

The mechanism of the above transformations is still uncertain. The benzidine transformation has been shown to be intramolecular; *e.g.*, Ingold and Kidd (1933) found that when a mixture of the hydrazobenzenes ANH·NHA and BNH·NHB rearranged, the result always was a mixture of NH_2–A–A–NH_2 and NH_2–B–B–NH_2; the compound NH_2–A–B–NH_2 was never formed. Thus there are no " free parts " formed during the rearrangement, since if there were, some of the A–B compound would have been expected. This is also supported by Wheland *et al.* (1952) who prepared (VI) and (VII) ($\overset{*}{C} = {}^{14}C$), and carried out the rearrangement with the mixture. Compounds (VIII) and (IX) were obtained, and since (VIII) contained almost all of the tracer atom, the mechanism is thus intramolecular. (Actually IX did contain about 0·3 per cent. of the tracer atom.)

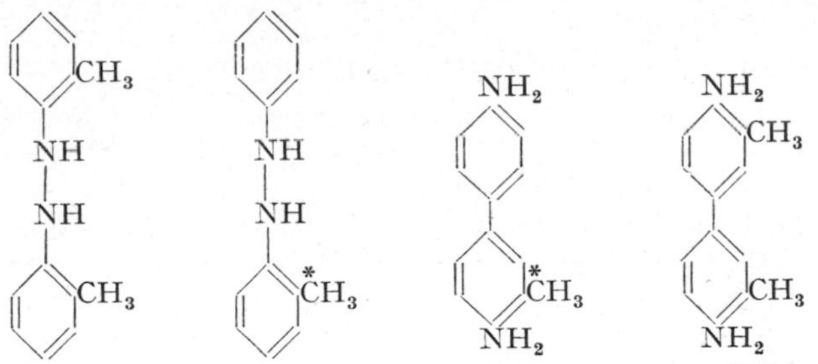

(VI) (VII) (VIII) (IX)

Hammond and Shine (1950) have shown that the velocity of the benzidine rearrangement is proportional to the square of the hydrogen ion concentration. Thus it has been suggested that the rearrangement proceeds via a transition state which contains two protons. Hughes *et al.* (1956), on the basis of their study of the rearrangement of phenylnitramine (p. 549), have proposed the following mechanism (in the transition state the two benzene rings lie in approximately parallel planes):

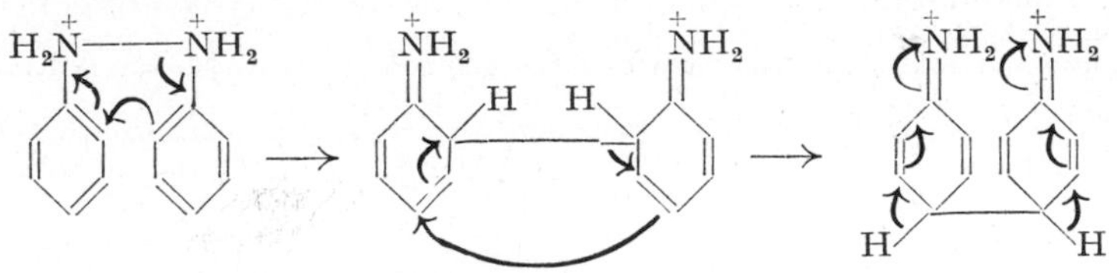

(X)

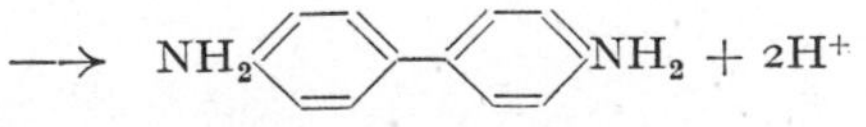

$$\longrightarrow NH_2\text{—}C_6H_4\text{—}C_6H_4\text{—}NH_2 + 2H^+$$

In a similar way, the left-hand ring in (X) can use its nitrogen atom to link either with the *p*- or the remaining *o*-position of the right-hand ring, thereby giving a semidine rearrangement.

QUESTIONS

1. Starting with benzene or toluene, show how you would prepare:—(*a*) *m*-bromotoluene, (*b*) *m*-nitrotoluene, (*c*) *s*-tribromobenzene, (*d*) *p*-iodotoluene, (*e*) *m*-fluoronitrobenzene, (*f*) *o*-tolunitrile, (*g*) *p*-dinitrobenzene, (*h*) phenylarsonic acid, (*i*) *m*-nitrophenylmercuric chloride, (*j*) 2 : 4-diaminophenol, (*k*) 3 : 4-diaminophenol, (*l*) 2 : 5-diaminotoluene, (*m*) 1 : 2 : 3-tribromobenzene, (*n*) 4-chloro-1 : 3-dinitrobenzene, (*o*) 3 : 4-dinitrotoluene, (*p*) 1 : 3-dinitro-4-hydroxybenzene, (*q*) 3-amino-4-hydroxytoluene, (*r*) *p*-methylazobenzene.
2. Write an account of the synthetic uses of the diazonium salts.
3. Describe the preparation and properties of:—(*a*) phenylhydrazine, (*b*) 2 : 4-dinitrophenylhydrazine, (*c*) diazoaminobenzene, (*d*) aminoazobenzene, (*e*) methylaminoazobenzene, (*f*) methyldiazoaminobenzene, (*g*) dimethylaminoazobenzene, (*h*) azoxybenzene, (*i*) azobenzene, (*j*) hydrazobenzene, (*k*) benzidine, (*l*) diphenyline.
4. Write an account of the coupling reactions of the diazonium salts.
5. Write an essay on the structure of the " diazo-compounds ".
6. Discuss the rearrangements of compounds with the structures Ar–N=N–NHAr′ and Ar–NH·NH–Ar′.
7. Write an account of the structure of the hydroxyazo-compounds.
8. Define and give examples of:—(*a*) diazotisation, (*b*) Sandmeyer reaction, (*c*) Gattermann reaction, (*d*) Balz–Schiemann reaction, (*e*) Bart's reaction, (*f*) benzidine transformation, (*g*) semidine transformation, (*h*) Wallach transformation.

READING REFERENCES

Cowdrey and Davies, Sandmeyer and Related Reactions, *Quart. Reviews* (*Chem. Soc.*), 1952, **6**, 358.
Hey and Waters, Free-radical Reactions of the Diazo-compounds, *J.C.S.*, **1948**, 882.
Saunders, *Aromatic Diazo Compounds*, Arnold (1949, 2nd Ed).
Sidgwick, *The Organic Chemistry of Nitrogen*, Oxford Press (New Ed. by Taylor and Baker, 1937), Ch. 13. Aromatic Diazo-Compounds. Ch. 14. Azoxy- and Azo-Compounds.
Coupling of Diazonium Salts.
(i) Wistar and Bartlett, *J. Amer. Chem. Soc.*, 1941, **63**, 413.
(ii) Hauser and Breslow, *ibid.*, 1941, **63**, 418.
Moore, The Hantzsch Memorial Lecture, *J.C.S.*, **1936**, 1055.
Hughes and Ingold, Aromatic Rearrangements, *Quart. Reviews* (*Chem. Soc.*), 1952, **6**, 53.
Organic Reactions, Wiley.
(i) Vol. II (1944), Ch. 10. The Bart Reaction.
(ii) Vol. V (1949), Ch. 4. Preparation of Aromatic Fluorine Compounds from Diazonium Fluoroborates.
Campbell and Day, The Structure of the Aromatic Triazenes, *Chem. Reviews*, 1951, **48**, 299.
Gillis, The Mechanism of Diazotisation, *J. Chem. Educ.*, 1954, **31**, 344.
Hadži, Absorption Spectra and Structure of Some Solid Hydroxyazo-compounds, *J.C.S.*, **1956**, 2143.
Kornblum and Kelly, The Reaction of Diazonium Salts with Alcohols, *Science*, 1953, **117**, 379.
Ingold *et al.*, Kinetic Form of the Benzidine and Semidine Rearrangements, *J.C.S.*, **1957**, 1906.

CHAPTER XXV

SULPHONIC ACIDS

ONE of the most characteristic properties of the aromatic hydrocarbons and their derivatives is the ease with which they can be sulphonated with concentrated or fuming sulphuric acid, or with chlorosulphonic acid. The saturated aliphatic hydrocarbons are not so readily sulphonated, and so this reaction can be used to separate saturated aliphatic hydrocarbons from aromatic hydrocarbons.

Aromatic sulphonic acids are usually prepared by direct sulphonation, since this is far more convenient than indirect methods. The usual sulphonating agents are:

(i) *Concentrated sulphuric acid* (98 per cent.); *e.g.*, benzene readily forms benzenesulphonic acid (note the reversibility of the reaction):

$$C_6H_6 + H_2SO_4 \rightleftharpoons C_6H_5{\cdot}SO_3H + H_2O$$

(ii) *Sulphur trioxide* in an inert solvent such as sulphuric acid, *i.e.*, *oleum* (*fuming sulphuric acid*), or as an addition product with pyridine or dioxan. Oleum with a free sulphur trioxide content up to about 70 per cent. is particularly useful for those cases where sulphonation is difficult, *e.g.*, the sulphonation of compounds containing *m*-orienting groups in the ring (nitro-compounds, sulphonic acids, etc.).

(iii) *Chlorosulphonic acid.* This results in the formation of either a sulphonic acid by carrying out the reaction in carbon tetrachloride solution (using one molecule of reagent), or a sulphonyl chloride (using excess of reagent):

$$ArH + ClSO_3H \longrightarrow Ar{\cdot}SO_3H + HCl$$

$$Ar{\cdot}SO_3H + ClSO_3H \longrightarrow Ar{\cdot}SO_2Cl + H_2SO_4$$

(iv) *Sulphuryl chloride* in the presence of aluminium chloride sulphonates aromatic compounds in the cold to form a sulphonyl chloride:

$$ArH + SO_2Cl_2 \longrightarrow Ar{\cdot}SO_2Cl + HCl$$

An example of indirect sulphonation is the replacement of an "activated" halogen atom by sulphonic acid group, *e.g.*, *o*-chloronitrobenzene reacts with sodium sulphite to form *o*-nitrobenzenesulphonic acid:

$$C_6H_4(Cl)(NO_2) + Na_2SO_3 \longrightarrow C_6H_4(SO_3Na)(NO_2) + NaCl$$

Another example of indirect sulphonation is the reduction of nitro- or nitroso-compounds with sulphur dioxide (see p. 539).

When a compound containing an *o*-*p*-orienting group is sulphonated with sulphuric acid or oleum, the temperature at which the reaction is carried out affects the ratio of the *o*- and *p*-isomers. Generally, lower temperatures favour *o*-substitution and higher temperatures, *p*-substitution; both isomers, however, are always obtained.

Lauer (1935) found that the presence of water also influenced the *o*-*p* ratio. When concentrated sulphuric acid (98 per cent.) is used, the product is mainly a mixture of the *o*- and *p*-isomers, together with a small amount of the *m*-isomer;

or vice-versa. When sulphur trioxide (gaseous or in oleum) is used, 100 per cent. *o-p-* or *m*-substitution is obtained; *e.g.*,

$$p\text{-}BrC_6H_4SO_3H\ (100\%) \xleftarrow{SO_3} C_6H_5Br \xrightarrow{H_2SO_4} p\text{-}BrC_6H_4SO_3H\ (96\%) + o\text{-}BrC_6H_4SO_3H\ (4\%)$$

$$m\text{-}NO_2C_6H_4SO_3H\ (100\%) \xleftarrow{SO_3} C_6H_5NO_2 \xrightarrow{H_2SO_4} m\text{-}NO_2C_6H_4SO_3H\ (97\%) + o\text{-}NO_2C_6H_4SO_3H\ (3\%)$$

Very few catalysts are known for sulphonation; the salts of mercury, silver and vanadium, and iodine, seem the best. It has also been found that a mercury catalyst may change the orientation of sulphonation (see anthraquinone, p. 703).

Chlorosulphonic acid, at low temperatures, usually gives a high yield of the *o*-isomer when the compound contains an *o-p*-orienting group (see p. 586).

Many mechanisms have been suggested for sulphonation with sulphuric acid or sulphur trioxide, but none is certain. It is certain, however, that sulphonation with these reagents is *reversible*. According to Price (1941), sulphonation with sulphuric acid takes place as follows:

$$(HO)_2SO_2 + H_2SO_4 \rightleftharpoons [(H_2O^+)(HO)SO_2] + HSO_4^- \underset{+H_2O}{\overset{-H_2O}{\rightleftharpoons}} HO\text{—}\overset{+}{S}O_2$$

$$C_6H_6 + {}^{+}SO_2\text{—}OH \rightleftharpoons [C_6H_6^{\oplus}(H)\text{—}SO_2{\cdot}OH] \underset{+H^+}{\overset{-H^+}{\rightleftharpoons}} C_6H_5SO_2{\cdot}OH$$

This mechanism is supported by the work of Hinshelwood *et al.* (1948). These authors have carried out some kinetic experiments on sulphonation of aromatic compounds, and they suggest that their results may be explained by assuming that the ion $SO_2{\cdot}OH^+$ is the sulphonating agent.

According to some authors, the mechanism of sulphonation in *fuming* sulphuric acid involves direct attack by *free* sulphur trioxide, *e.g.*,

$$C_6H_6 + SO_3 \rightleftharpoons [C_6H_6^{\oplus}(H)\text{—}SO_2\text{—}\bar{O}] \rightleftharpoons [C_6H_5\text{—}SO_2\text{—}\bar{O} + H^+] \rightleftharpoons C_6H_5SO_2{\cdot}OH$$

On the other hand, Brand *et al.* (1952) have shown that the sulphonation of nitrobenzene in fuming sulphuric acid is consistent with the following mechanism:

$$H_2SO_4 + SO_3 \rightleftharpoons H_2S_2O_7 \overset{H^+}{\rightleftharpoons} H_2SO_4 + SO_2{\cdot}OH^+$$

$$ArH + SO_2{\cdot}OH^+ \rightleftharpoons Ar{\cdot}SO_2{\cdot}OH + H^+$$

Benzenesulphonic acid, $C_6H_5{\cdot}SO_3H$, may be readily prepared by heating benzene with concentrated sulphuric acid at 80°:

$$C_6H_6 + H_2SO_4 \rightleftharpoons C_6H_5{\cdot}SO_3H + H_2O \quad (75\text{–}80\%)$$

Owing to the reversibility of this reaction, the accumulation of water tends to regenerate the benzene by desulphonation of the sulphonic acid. Hence to obtain the maximum yield of sulphonic acid, it is necessary to remove the water from the reaction mixture as the reaction proceeds. The simplest way in which this may be done is by using oleum, the water being removed chemically by combination with free sulphur trioxide:

$$SO_3 + H_2O \longrightarrow H_2SO_4$$

Alternatively, the water may be removed by carrying out the reaction at high temperature or under reduced pressure, or by passing an inert gas, *e.g.*, nitrogen, through the mixture, or by forming a constant-boiling mixture with an inert liquid, *e.g.*, kerosene. On the other hand, Thomas *et al.* (1940) have shown that boron trifluoride (one equivalent) is an effective catalyst in aromatic sulphonation, *e.g.*,

$$C_6H_6 + H_2SO_4 + BF_3 \longrightarrow C_6H_5{\cdot}SO_3H + BF_3{\cdot}H_2O \quad (98\%)$$

During sulphonation a small amount of sulphone is produced as a by-product, *e.g.*, *diphenylsulphone*:

$$2C_6H_6 + H_2SO_4 \longrightarrow (C_6H_5)_2SO_2 + 2H_2O$$

Since these sulphones are insoluble in water, they may be readily separated from the sulphonic acid by filtration.

Properties of benzenesulphonic acid. Benzenesulphonic acid is a colourless crystalline deliquescent solid, m.p. 44°. It is very soluble in water and the solution is strongly acid (about as strong as sulphuric acid). Benzenesulphonic acid and other aromatic sulphonic acids are useful catalysts in esterification and dehydration, being better than sulphuric acid, since they attack the reaction constituents far less than does sulphuric acid. The sulphonic acids are valuable as synthetic reagents because of the ease with which the sulphonic group can be replaced by a hydrogen, amino, hydroxyl, cyano, thiol, or a nitro-group. Furthermore, since the presence of a sulphonic acid group makes the compound soluble in water, sulphonation is an extremely important process in the preparation of dyes and drugs (converting them into soluble derivatives).

Reactions of benzenesulphonic acid. The following reactions are typical of all sulphonic acids.

1. As pointed out above, sulphonation is a reversible reaction, but the ease of desulphonation depends on the nature of the aromatic nucleus. Benzenesulphonic acid may be desulphonated by heating with dilute hydrochloric acid under pressure at 150–200°:

$$C_6H_5{\cdot}SO_3H + H_2O \xrightarrow[150^\circ]{HCl} C_6H_6 + H_2SO_4 \quad (v.g.)$$

With some sulphonic acids the sulphonic acid group may be eliminated merely by steam distillation. This desulphonation is very useful for preparing certain isomers, *e.g.*, *o*-chlorotoluene may be prepared as follows:

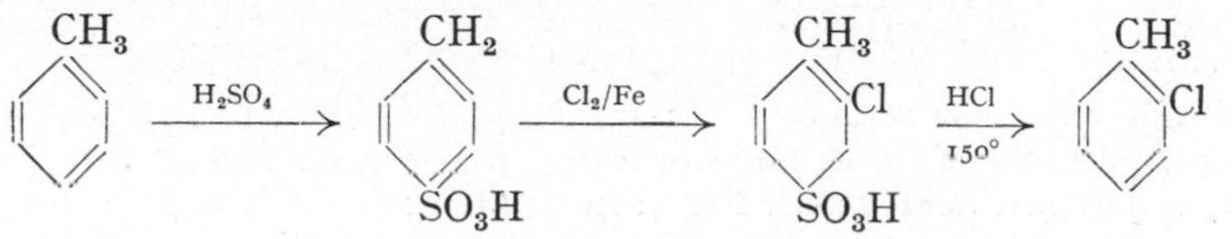

$$C_6H_5{\cdot}CH_3 \xrightarrow{H_2SO_4} p\text{-}CH_2{\cdot}C_6H_4{\cdot}SO_3H \xrightarrow{Cl_2/Fe} CH_3{\cdot}C_6H_3Cl{\cdot}SO_3H \xrightarrow[150^\circ]{HCl} o\text{-}CH_3{\cdot}C_6H_4Cl$$

Desulphonation may also be used to separate certain isomers, *e.g.*, the three xylenes. The xylene fraction from coal tar may be treated with cold 80 per cent. sulphuric acid. Under these conditions, the *m*-isomer is readily sulphonated to *m*-xylene-4-sulphonic acid, the *o*- and *p*-isomers remaining unaffected:

$$C_6H_4(CH_3)_2 + H_2SO_4 \longrightarrow C_6H_3(CH_3)_2SO_3H + H_2O$$

Thus only the *m*-isomer dissolves, and hence may be separated from the other two. The mixture of *o*- and *p*-xylenes is then sulphonated with concentrated sulphuric acid (98 per cent.), and the resulting *o*-xylene-4-sulphonic acid and *p*-xylene-2-sulphonic acid may be separated by fractional crystallisation from the diluted sulphonated mixture; the *p*-derivative is less soluble than the *o*-. The xylenes are then regenerated by heating their sulphonic acid derivatives with dilute hydrochloric acid under pressure.

2. When sodium benzenesulphonate is fused with sodamide, aniline is obtained:

$$C_6H_5{\cdot}SO_3Na + NaNH_2 \longrightarrow C_6H_5{\cdot}NH_2 + Na_2SO_3 \quad (f.g.\text{–}g.)$$

3. Fusion with sodium hydroxide converts sodium benzenesulphonate into sodium phenoxide:

$$C_6H_5{\cdot}SO_3Na + NaOH \longrightarrow Na_2SO_3 + C_6H_5OH \xrightarrow{NaOH} C_6H_5ONa \quad (g.\text{–}v.g.)$$

4. When sodium benzenesulphonate is fused with sodium cyanide, phenyl cyanide is formed:

$$C_6H_5{\cdot}SO_3Na + NaCN \longrightarrow C_6H_5{\cdot}CN + Na_2SO_3 \quad (f.g.)$$

5. When the potassium salt of benzenesulphonic acid is fused with potassium hydrogen sulphide, thiophenol is formed:

$$C_6H_5{\cdot}SO_3K + KSH \longrightarrow C_6H_5SH + K_2SO_3 \quad (f.g.)$$

6. The sulphonic acid group is often readily replaced by a nitro-group. This offers a means of preparing nitro-derivatives of compounds that are easily oxidised by nitric acid, since the sulphonic acid derivatives are not easily oxidised; *e.g.*, picric acid from phenol:

$$C_6H_5OH \xrightarrow{H_2SO_4} o\text{-}HO{\cdot}C_6H_4{\cdot}SO_3H \xrightarrow{HNO_3} HO{\cdot}C_6H_2(NO_2)_2{\cdot}SO_3H \xrightarrow{HNO_3} HO{\cdot}C_6H_2(NO_2)_3$$

$$C_6H_5OH \xrightarrow{H_2SO_4} p\text{-}HO{\cdot}C_6H_4{\cdot}SO_3H \xrightarrow{HNO_3} HO{\cdot}C_6H_2(NO_2)_2{\cdot}SO_3H \xrightarrow{HNO_3} HO{\cdot}C_6H_2(NO_2)_3$$

Halogen may also replace a sulphonic acid group which is either *o*- or *p*- to a hydroxyl or to an amino-group; *e.g.*, when treated with bromine water, sulphanilic acids forms *s*-tribromoaniline:

$$\text{(sulphanilic acid, } NH_2\text{ and } SO_3H\text{ para)} \xrightarrow{Br_2/H_2O} \text{2,4,6-tribromoaniline (} NH_2\text{, Br, Br, Br)}$$

Sulphonic acids form many derivatives that are analogous to those of the carboxylic acids, *e.g.*, salts, esters, acid chlorides, amides, etc. The acid chloride may be prepared by treating a sulphonic acid or its sodium salt with phosphorus pentachloride, *e.g.*, benzenesulphonyl chloride:

$$C_6H_5{\cdot}SO_3H + PCl_5 \longrightarrow C_6H_5{\cdot}SO_2Cl + HCl + POCl_3 \quad (g.\text{–}ex.)$$
$$C_6H_5{\cdot}SO_3Na + PCl_5 \longrightarrow C_6H_5{\cdot}SO_2Cl + NaCl + POCl_3 \quad (75\text{–}80\%)$$

The aromatic sulphonyl chlorides, however, are usually best prepared by treating an aromatic compound with excess of chlorosulphonic acid:

$$C_6H_6 + 2ClSO_3H \longrightarrow C_6H_5{\cdot}SO_2Cl + HCl + H_2SO_4 \quad (75\text{–}77\%)$$

The sulphonyl chlorides are decomposed very slowly by water but rapidly by alkali; they react with alcohols in the presence of alkali to form esters:

$$Ar{\cdot}SO_2Cl + ROH + NaOH \longrightarrow Ar{\cdot}SO_3R + NaCl + H_2O$$

It is important to note that the esters of the sulphonic acids *cannot* be prepared by direct esterification. The sulphonic acid esters are very good alkylating agents for alcohols and amines:

$$ROH + Ar{\cdot}SO_3R' \longrightarrow R{\cdot}O{\cdot}R' + Ar{\cdot}SO_3H$$
$$R{\cdot}NH_2 + Ar{\cdot}SO_3R' + NaOH \longrightarrow R{\cdot}NH{\cdot}R' + Ar{\cdot}SO_3Na + H_2O$$

Benzenesulphonyl chloride is reduced to benzenesulphinic acid or thiophenol by lithium aluminium hydride, depending on the conditions (Field *et al.*, 1951).

When shaken with concentrated ammonia, the sulphonyl chlorides form sulphonamides; *e.g.*, benzenesulphonamide from benzenesulphonyl chloride:

$$C_6H_5{\cdot}SO_2Cl + 2NH_3 \longrightarrow C_6H_5{\cdot}SO_2{\cdot}NH_2 + NH_4Cl$$

These sulphonamides are well-defined crystalline solids, and so are used to characterise the sulphonic acids. Better derivatives for characterising the sulphonic acids are their *S*-benzyl*iso*thiouronium salts:

$$\left[C_6H_5{\cdot}CH_2{\cdot}S{\cdot}C\begin{matrix}\nearrow \overset{+}{N}H_2 \\ \searrow NH_2\end{matrix}\right]Cl^- + Ar{\cdot}SO_3Na \longrightarrow \left[C_6H_5{\cdot}CH_2{\cdot}S{\cdot}C\begin{matrix}\nearrow \overset{+}{N}H_2 \\ \searrow NH_2\end{matrix}\right]SO_3{\cdot}Ar^- + NaCl$$

Sulphonyl chlorides also react with primary and secondary amines to form *N*-substituted sulphonamides. These derivatives may be used to separate the three classes of amines (see the Hinsberg separation, p. 292), and for this purpose it is better to use *p*-toluenesulphonyl chloride than benzenesulphonyl chloride, since the former is a solid (m.p 69°) and the latter a liquid (b.p. 246°, with decomp.).

Sulphonic acid anhydrides have been prepared by heating the acid with excess of phosphorus pentoxide (Field *et al.*, 1952), *e.g.*,

$$2C_6H_5{\cdot}SO_3H \xrightarrow[(-H_2O)]{P_2O_5} (C_6H_5{\cdot}SO_2)_2O \quad (70\%)$$

Benzenedisulphonic acids. When heated with excess of fuming sulphuric acid at 200°, benzene forms benzene-*m*-disulphonic acid as the main product and the *p*-isomer in a small amount:

$$C_6H_6 \xrightarrow{\text{oleum}} m\text{-}C_6H_4(SO_3H)_2 + p\text{-}C_6H_4(SO_3H)_2$$

Continued heating of the *m*-isomer in sulphuric acid causes it to rearrange to the *p*-isomer. Benzene-*o*-disulphonic acid may be prepared by sulphonating *m*-aminobenzenesulphonic acid, and then replacing the amino-group by hydrogen (diazotising, etc.).

When fused with potassium hydroxide, *m*- and *p*-benzenedisulphonic acids both form resorcinol (*m*-dihydroxybenzene); benzene-*o*-disulphonic acid forms catechol (*o*-dihydroxybenzene).

s-Benzenetrisulphonic acid may be prepared by heating benzene-*m*-disulphonic acid with fuming sulphuric acid.

Toluenesulphonic acids. When toluene is treated with concentrated sulphuric acid, the *o*- and *p*-toluenesulphonic acids are formed, low temperatures (below 100°) favouring the formation of the *o*-isomer, and high temperatures (above 100°) the *p*-:

$$C_6H_5CH_3 \xrightarrow[\text{(below 100°)}]{H_2SO_4} o\text{-}CH_3C_6H_4SO_3H\ (50\%) + p\text{-}CH_3C_6H_4SO_3H\ (45\%)$$

Both isomers are crystalline solids, the *o*- melting at 67·5°, and the *p*- at 106°. They may be separated by treating the mixture of the isomers with phosphorus pentachloride and then filtering; *p*-toluenesulphonyl chloride is a solid, m.p. 69°, whereas the *o*-compound is an oil.

A much better yield of *o*-toluenesulphonic acid may be obtained by treating toluene with chlorosulphonic acid at low temperatures:

$$C_6H_5CH_3 \xrightarrow{ClSO_3H} o\text{-}CH_3C_6H_4SO_2Cl\ (85\%) + p\text{-}CH_3C_6H_4SO_2Cl\ \text{(small amount)}$$

These are separated by filtration and converted into the sulphonic acids by heating with alkali, and then acidifying the solution.

o-Toluenesulphonyl chloride is used in the preparation of saccharin (p. 651); *p*-toluenesulphonic acid is used in the preparation of antiseptics, chloroamine T and dichloramine T. **Chloramine T** is the sodium salt of *N*-chloro-*p*-toluenesulphonamide (*toluene*-p-*sulphonsodiochloramide*), and may be prepared as follows:

$$p\text{-}CH_3C_6H_4SO_3H \xrightarrow{PCl_5} p\text{-}CH_3C_6H_4SO_2Cl \xrightarrow{NH_3} p\text{-}CH_3C_6H_4SO_2{\cdot}NH_2 \xrightarrow[NaOH]{NaOCl} p\text{-}CH_3C_6H_4SO_2{\cdot}NCl\}^-Na^+$$

In addition to being used as an antiseptic, chloramine T is also used as a laboratory reagent instead of hypochlorite salts, since it is stable and liberates hypochlorous acid when acidified:

$$CH_3C_6H_4SO_2\cdot NCl\}Na \xrightarrow{HCl} CH_3C_6H_4SO_2\cdot NHCl \xrightarrow{H_2O} CH_3C_6H_4SO_2\cdot NH_2 + HOCl$$

When treated with a large excess of sodium hypochlorite solution, *p*-toluenesulphonamide forms **dichloramine T** (N : N-*dichloro*-p-*toluenesulphonamide*):

$$CH_3C_6H_4SO_2\cdot NH_2 \xrightarrow{NaOCl} CH_3C_6H_4SO_2\cdot NCl_2$$

m-*Toluenesulphonic acid* (an oil) may be prepared by replacing the amino-group in *p*-toluidine-*m*-sulphonic acid by hydrogen:

$$CH_3C_6H_3(SO_3H)NH_2 \xrightarrow{\text{diazotise, etc.}} CH_3C_6H_4SO_3H$$

Isolation of the sulphonic acids. It is usually difficult to isolate the sulphonic acids due to their great solubility in water and their non-volatility. Generally, the isolation of the acids is not attempted, since their salts undergo the desired synthetic reactions. The sulphonic acids (or their salts) may be isolated by any one of the following methods, the actual method used depending on the properties of the acid under investigation:

(i) When the sulphonic acid is not very soluble, the sulphonating mixture is cooled and filtered (through glass wool).

(ii) The sulphonating mixture is allowed to flow into a saturated solution of sodium chloride; in many cases the sodium sulphonate is precipitated.

(iii) The usual method for isolating the sulphonic acids is to dilute the sulphonating mixture and neutralise the liquid with the carbonate of calcium, barium or lead. The insoluble sulphate is collected by filtration, and the filtrate, which contains the soluble salt of the sulphonic acid, is evaporated to dryness under reduced pressure; this gives the dry salt. To obtain the sulphonic acid the solution of the lead salt is decomposed with hydrogen sulphide, filtered and the filtrate evaporated to dryness under reduced pressure. The sodium salt of a sulphonic acid may readily be prepared by adding aqueous sodium carbonate to the calcium or barium sulphonate solution until all the calcium or barium has been precipitated. The liquid is filtered and evaporated to dryness under reduced pressure.

Since the free sulphonic acids are hygroscopic liquids or solids, they are very difficult to purify; some sulphonic acids have not yet been isolated in a pure state.

The separation of a mixture of isomeric sulphonic acids is usually difficult. The method to be employed must be found by experiment. Many are used, *e.g.*, fractional crystallisation of the acids from water or from organic solvents; fractional crystallisation of the salts from suitable solvents; conversion of the sulphonic acids into their sulphonyl chlorides, which are then separated.

Jacobsen rearrangement (1886). During sulphonation polyalkylbenzenes, halogenated polyalkylbenzenes, or polyhalogenated benzenes fairly readily undergo isomerisation due to the migration of an alkyl group or a halogen atom. This is known as the *Jacobsen rearrangement*, and two types of migrations are possible: intramolecular (no " free parts "), in which a group moves from one position to another in the *same* molecule; and intermolecular (involving " free parts "), in which one or more groups are transferred from one molecule to another. Experiment has shown that both types of migrations usually occur simultaneously in the Jacobsen rearrangement, and that an alkyl group always migrates to the vicinal position. Thus the Jacobsen rearrangement offers a means of preparing *vic*-compounds from non-*vic*-compounds; *e.g.*, sulphonation of durene gives 70 per cent. *prehnitenesulphonic acid* (I) and very small amounts of 5-*ψ-cumenesulphonic acid* (II) and *hexamethylbenzene* (III); sulphur dioxide, carbon dioxide and about 30 per cent. of a brown amorphous material are also obtained (Smith and Cass, 1932). The reaction possibly takes place as follows:

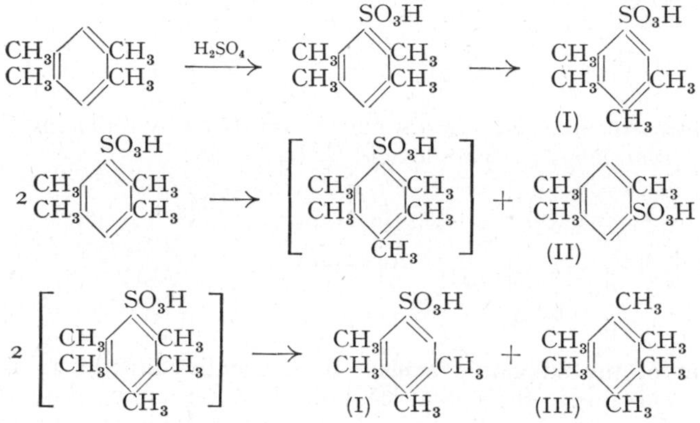

CH_3, CH_3, CH_3, CH_3 (durene) $\xrightarrow{H_2SO_4}$ SO_3H; CH_3, CH_3, CH_3, CH_3 $\longrightarrow$ SO_3H; CH_3, CH_3, CH_3, CH_3 (I)

2 [SO_3H; CH_3, CH_3, CH_3, CH_3] $\longrightarrow$ [SO_3H; CH_3, CH_3, CH_3, CH_3, CH_3] + CH_3, CH_3, CH_3, SO_3H (II)

2 [SO_3H; CH_3, CH_3, CH_3, CH_3, CH_3] $\longrightarrow$ SO_3H; CH_3, CH_3, CH_3, CH_3 (I) + CH_3; CH_3, CH_3, CH_3, CH_3, CH_3 (III)

An example of the migration of a halogen atom is the rearrangement of 5-chloro-ψ-cumene- to 3-chloro-ψ-cumene-sulphonic acid:

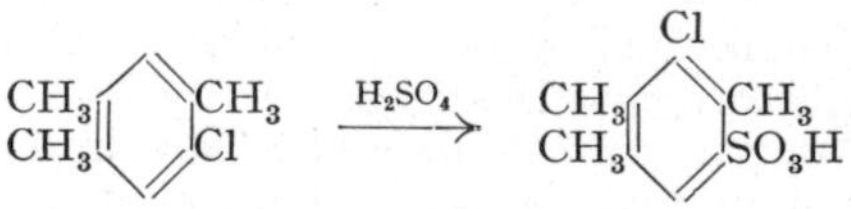

CH_3, CH_3, CH_3, Cl $\xrightarrow{H_2SO_4}$ Cl; CH_3, CH_3, CH_3, SO_3H

The mechanism of the Jacobsen rearrangement is uncertain; the only certain thing appears to be that it is the sulphonic acid, and not the hydrocarbon, that rearranges. It has also been found (so far) that the Jacobsen rearrangement does not take place when the compound contains an amino-, nitro-, methoxyl, or a carboxyl group.

Sulphinic acids, ArSO·OH. The general methods of preparing the aromatic sulphinic acids may be illustrated by the preparation benzenesulphinic acid:

(i) By warming benzenesulphonyl chloride with zinc dust and water, and then acidifying the liquid:

$$C_6H_5{\cdot}SO_2Cl \xrightarrow{Zn/H_2O} (C_6H_5{\cdot}SO_2)_2Zn \xrightarrow{HCl} 2C_6H_5{\cdot}SO_2H \quad (g.)$$

Alternatively, the reduction of the sulphonyl chloride may be effected by means of a hot aqueous solution of sodium sulphide:

$$C_6H_5{\cdot}SO_2Cl + 2Na_2S \longrightarrow C_6H_5{\cdot}SO_2Na + NaCl + Na_2S_2 \quad (g.)$$

Alkaline sodium sulphite is also widely used:

$$C_6H_5{\cdot}SO_2Cl + Na_2SO_3 + 2NaOH \longrightarrow C_6H_5{\cdot}SO_2Na + NaCl + Na_2SO_4 + H_2O$$

Aryl esters of sulphonic acids are reduced by lithium aluminium hydride to sulphinic acids.

$$C_6H_5{\cdot}SO_3Ar \xrightarrow{LiAlH_4} C_6H_5{\cdot}SO_2H + ArOH$$

Alkyl esters, on the other hand, usually give the sulphonic acid.

$$C_6H_5{\cdot}SO_3R \xrightarrow{LiAlH_4} C_6H_5{\cdot}SO_3H + RH$$

(ii) By the action of copper powder on a solution of a diazonium salt saturated with sulphur dioxide:

$$C_6H_5{\cdot}N_2HSO_4 + SO_2 + Cu \longrightarrow C_6H_5{\cdot}SO_2H + N_2 + CuSO_4 \quad (g.)$$

(iii) By the action of sulphur dioxide on benzene in the presence of anhydrous aluminium chloride:

$$C_6H_6 + SO_2 \xrightarrow{AlCl_3} C_6H_5{\cdot}SO_2H \quad (g.)$$

(iv) By the action of sulphur dioxide on an arylmagnesium bromide.

$$C_6H_5MgBr + SO_2 \xrightarrow{-40^\circ} C_6H_5{\cdot}SO_2MgBr \xrightarrow{H_2O} C_6H_5{\cdot}SO_2H \quad (g.)$$

The usual by-product in this reaction is the sulphoxide.

$$C_6H_5{\cdot}SO_2MgBr + C_6H_5MgBr \longrightarrow (C_6H_5)_2SO + (MgBr)_2O$$

(v) Sulphinic acids may be prepared by fusion of sulphones with potassium hydroxide at 200° (see p. 321).

The sulphinic acids are unstable solids which readily oxidise in the air to sulphonic acids. They are reduced by zinc and hydrochloric acid to thiols; *e.g.*, benzenesulphinic acid gives *thiophenol*:

$$C_6H_5{\cdot}SO_2H + 4[H] \xrightarrow{Zn/HCl} C_6H_5SH + 2H_2O$$

The sulphinic acids are decomposed when warmed with water, forming the sulphonic acid and the *disulphoxide*, Ar·SO·SO·Ar. The most useful reaction of the sulphinic acids is the ease with which the sulphinic acid group is replaced by a chloromercuri-group (this is an example of indirect mercuration); *e.g.*, *p*-tolylmercuric chloride may be prepared by boiling an aqueous solution of sodium *p*-toluenesulphinate with mercuric chloride:

$$CH_3{-}C_6H_4{-}SO_2Na + HgCl_2 \longrightarrow CH_3{-}C_6H_4{-}HgCl + SO_2 + NaCl \quad (51\text{–}57\%)$$

Thiophenol, C_6H_5SH, is the simplest aryl thiol, and may be prepared by the action of phosphorus pentasulphide on phenol:

$$5C_6H_5OH + P_2S_5 \longrightarrow 5C_6H_5SH + P_2O_5 \quad (v.p.)$$

A far better method of preparation is to reduce benzenesulphonyl chloride with zinc and sulphuric acid:

$$C_6H_5{\cdot}SO_2Cl + 6[H] \longrightarrow C_6H_5SH + HCl + 2H_2O \quad (96\%)$$

This reaction shows that in the sulphonic acids the sulphur atom is directly attached to a carbon atom in the ring. Lithium aluminium hydride also reduces sulphonyl chlorides to thiols (Marvel *et al.*, 1950).

Thiophenol is a colourless liquid, b.p. 170°, with a nauseating odour. It undergoes the usual reactions of the thiols, and is a stronger acid than phenol (*cf.* the aliphatic thiols, p. 316).

Sulphanilic acid (p-*aminobenzenesulphonic acid*), p-$NH_2 \cdot C_6H_4 \cdot SO_3H$, is formed as the main product when aniline is sulphonated with oleum (containing 10 per cent. sulphur trioxide) at 180°; some metanilic and a little orthanilic acid are also produced. With excess of oleum, a second sulphonic acid group may be introduced into the *o*-position (to the amino-group), and a third into the *o'*-position. Sulphanilic acid is prepared commercially by the " baking process "; the acid sulphate of aniline (prepared by mixing about equal weights of aniline and concentrated sulphuric acid) is heated for some time at 200°; again, the other two isomers are produced, but less of the metanilic acid in this case.

The mechanism of the baking process is uncertain. According to Bamberger (1897), the acid sulphate of aniline is converted into *phenylsulphamic acid* (I), which then rearranges to *orthanilic acid* (II), which, in turn, rearranges to sulphanilic acid (*cf.* the Hofmann–Martius rearrangement, p. 549):

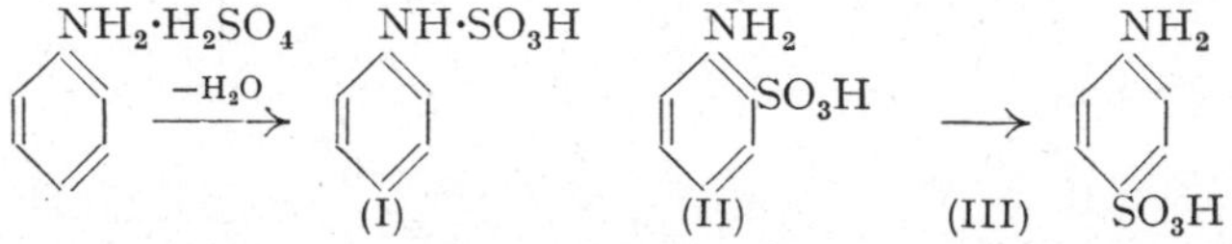

$$C_6H_5NH_2 \cdot H_2SO_4 \xrightarrow{-H_2O} C_6H_5NH \cdot SO_3H \text{ (I)} \quad o\text{-}NH_2 \cdot C_6H_4 \cdot SO_3H \text{ (II)} \longrightarrow p\text{-}NH_2 \cdot C_6H_4 \cdot SO_3H \text{ (III)}$$

In support of this mechanism, Bamberger prepared phenylsulphamic acid (which, however, has not been isolated as an intermediate in the above reaction), and showed that when carefully heated, it formed orthanilic acid which, on heating at 180°, rearranged to sulphanilic acid. On the other hand, sulphonation in oleum is believed to occur by *direct* sulphonation, and the formation of a larger amount of metanilic acid may be accounted for by the sulphonation of the anilinium ion (p. 495).

Sulphanilic acid is a white solid, m.p. 288° (with decomp.), almost insoluble in cold water but fairly easily soluble in hot. It forms salts with bases but does not combine with acids. The latter may be due to sulphanilic acid existing as an inner salt, p-$H_3\overset{+}{N} \cdot C_6H_4 \cdot SO_3^-$ (sulphonic acids are as strong as the inorganic acids). When sulphanilic acid is treated with nitric acid, the sulphonic acid group is replaced by a nitro-group to form *p*-nitroaniline. Similarly, bromine water attacks sulphanilic acid to form *s*-tribromoaniline. Sulphanilic acid may be diazotised, but there is reason to believe that the diazonium salt may be an inner salt, p-$N{\vdots}\overset{+}{N} \cdot C_6H_4 \cdot SO_3^-$. Sulphanilic acid is a very important intermediate in dye chemistry, and its substituted amides form the sulphanilamide drugs.

Orthanilic acid (o-*aminobenzenesulphonic acid*) may be prepared by refluxing *o*-chloronitrobenzene with sodium sulphide and sulphur in ethanol solution, heating the product di-*o*-nitrophenyl sulphide with concentrated nitric acid in the presence of chlorine (which is passed in), refluxing the *o*-nitrobenzenesulphonyl chloride with aqueous sodium carbonate, and finally reducing the *o*-nitrobenzenesulphonic acid with iron and acetic acid:

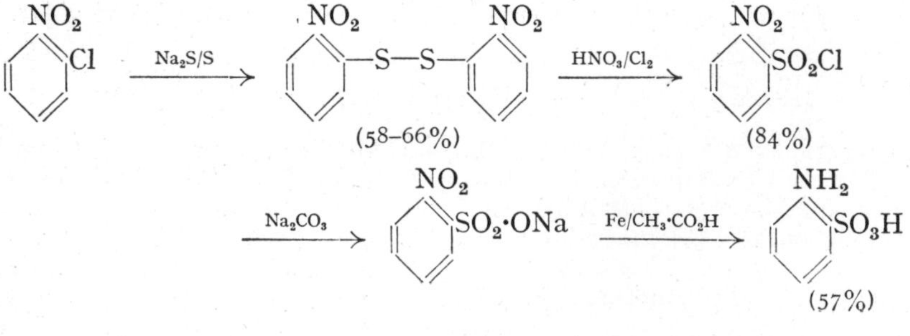

$$o\text{-}NO_2 \cdot C_6H_4Cl \xrightarrow{Na_2S/S} o\text{-}NO_2 \cdot C_6H_4\text{—S—S—}C_6H_4 \cdot NO_2\text{-}o \ (58\text{–}66\%) \xrightarrow{HNO_3/Cl_2} o\text{-}NO_2 \cdot C_6H_4 \cdot SO_2Cl \ (84\%)$$

$$\xrightarrow{Na_2CO_3} o\text{-}NO_2 \cdot C_6H_4 \cdot SO_2 \cdot ONa \xrightarrow{Fe/CH_3 \cdot CO_2H} o\text{-}NH_2 \cdot C_6H_4 \cdot SO_3H \ (57\%)$$

Orthanilic acid may also be prepared by sulphonating *p*-bromoaniline, and then removing the bromine atom with zinc dust and aqueous sodium hydroxide:

$$p\text{-}NH_2C_6H_4Br \xrightarrow{H_2SO_4} NH_2(SO_3H)C_6H_3Br \xrightarrow{Zn/NaOH} o\text{-}NH_2C_6H_4SO_3H$$

Orthanilic acid is a crystalline solid which, on heating with concentrated sulphuric acid, isomerises to sulphanilic acid (see above).

Metanilic acid (m-*aminobenzenesulphonic acid*) may be prepared by reducing *m*-nitrobenzenesulphonic acid. It is a crystalline solid, and is used in the manufacture of dyes.

QUESTIONS

1. Write an account of the sulphonating agents that may be used in aromatic chemistry and discuss, where possible, the mechanism of their action.
2. Starting with benzene or toluene, show how you would prepare:—(*a*) $PhSO_3H$, (*b*) *p*-MeC_6H_4SH, (*c*) picric acid, (*d*) $PhSO_2Cl$, (*e*) *p*-$MeC_6H_4{\cdot}SO_2{\cdot}NH_2$, (*f*) *o*-, *m*- and *p*-$C_6H_4(SO_3H)_2$, (*g*) *o*-, *m*- and *p*-$MeC_6H_4{\cdot}SO_3H$, (*h*) chloramine T, (*i*) $PhSO_2H$, (*j*) *m*-$MeC_6H_4{\cdot}SO_2H$, (*k*) *p*-$MeC_6H_4{\cdot}HgCl$, (*l*) PhSH, (*m*) sulphanilic acid, (*n*) orthanilic acid, (*o*) metanilic acid, (*p*) *o*-$NO_2{\cdot}C_6H_4{\cdot}SO_3H$, (*q*) *p*-$NO_2$-toluene-*o*-sulphonic acid, (*r*) 5-NO_2–2-NH_2-benzenesulphonic acid.
3. Write an account of the isolation of the sulphonic acids, and discuss their use as synthetic reagents.
4. Compare and contrast the reactions of the sodium salts, acid chlorides, ammonium salts, amides and esters of the sulphonic acids and the carboxylic acids.
5. Write notes on:—(*a*) the Jacobsen rearrangement, (*b*) the sulphonation of aniline.
6. Show how you would distinguish between the following compounds:

   p-$MeC_6H_4{\cdot}SO_2Cl$, *p*-$CH_2Cl{\cdot}C_6H_4{\cdot}SO_3H$ and *o*-Cl-*p*-toluenesulphonic acid.
7. Discuss the preparation and properties of the aromatic sulphonic acids.

READING REFERENCES

Stubbs, Williams and Hinshelwood, Sulphonation by Sulphuric Acid in Nitrobenzene Solution, *J.C.S.*, **1948**, 1065.

Suter, *Organic Compounds of Sulphur*, Wiley (1944).

Organic Reactions, Wiley. Vol. III (1946), Ch. 4. Direct Sulphonation of Aromatic Hydrocarbons and their Halogen Derivatives.

Ibid., Vol. I (1942), Ch. 1. The Jacobsen Reaction.

Brown, Sulphuryl Chloride in Organic Chemistry, *Ind. Eng. Chem.*, 1944, **36**, 788.

Gilman, *Advanced Organic Chemistry*, Wiley (1942, 2nd ed.). Vol. I, Ch. 10. Organic Sulphur Compounds.

Alexander, The Mechanism of Sulphonation of Aromatic Amines, *J. Amer. Chem. Soc.*, 1946, **68**, 969; 1947, **69**, 1599.

Ann. Reports, 1949, **46**, pp. 135–137. Aromatic Sulphonation.

Fisk, Sulphonation, *Ind. Eng. Chem.*, 1950, **42**, 1746.

Truce and Murphy, The Preparation of Sulphinic Acids, *Chem. Reviews*, 1951, **48**, 69.

Hughes and Ingold, Aromatic Rearrangements, *Quart. Reviews* (*Chem. Soc.*), 1952, **6**, 51.

Gold *et al.*, The Mechanism of Aromatic Sulphonation and Desulphonation in Aqueous Sulphuric Acid, *J.C.S.*, **1956**, 1635.

CHAPTER XXVI

PHENOLS

PHENOLS are aromatic compounds containing hydroxyl groups directly attached to the nucleus, and they are classified as monohydric, dihydric, trihydric phenols, etc., according as they contain one, two, three, etc., hydroxyl groups.

MONOHYDRIC PHENOLS

General methods of preparation. 1. A number of monohydric phenols occur in coal-tar and their extraction from this source is very important commercially.

(i) *Middle oil* (p. 475) is cooled, whereupon naphthalene crystallises out (43 per cent.). The oil is pressed free from the naphthalene and then treated with aqueous sodium hydroxide, which dissolves the phenols. The alkaline liquor is drawn off, boiled, and air is blown through; this removes naphthalene (that remained after cooling the oil), pyridine, etc. The liquid is allowed to cool and then carbon dioxide is blown through, thereby decomposing the sodium phenoxides into the free phenols and sodium carbonate, the latter dissolving in the aqueous layer. This aqueous layer is drawn off, and the crude phenols (the yield of which is about 12 per cent. of the middle oil) are fractionated. Three fractions are collected: *phenol*, b.p. 182° (20 per cent.), *cresols*, b.p. 190–203° (43 per cent.) and *xylenols*, b.p. 211–225° (26 per cent.); the residue is *pitch*.

(ii) *Heavy oil* is treated in the same manner as above. After being pressed to remove naphthalene, the residual oil contains cresols, higher phenols, naphthol, etc. (heavy oil contains about 7 per cent. of the phenols).

2. Phenols may be prepared by fusion of sodium sulphonates with sodium hydroxide:

$$Ar{\cdot}SO_3Na + NaOH \longrightarrow ArOH + Na_2SO_3$$

3. When a diazonium sulphate solution is steam distilled, a phenol is produced:

$$Ar{\cdot}N_2HSO_4 + H_2O \longrightarrow ArOH + N_2 + H_2SO_4$$

4. Phenols are formed when compounds containing an "activated" halogen atom are heated with aqueous sodium hydroxide (p. 533); *e.g.*, *p*-nitrophenol from *p*-chloronitrobenzene:

$$p\text{-}ClC_6H_4NO_2 + NaOH \longrightarrow p\text{-}HOC_6H_4NO_2 + NaCl$$

5. Distillation of phenolic acids with soda-lime produces phenols; *e.g.*, sodium salicylate gives phenol:

$$o\text{-}HOC_6H_4CO_2Na + NaOH(CaO) \longrightarrow C_6H_5OH + Na_2CO_3$$

6. Phenols may be prepared by means of a Grignard reagent (see p. 335):

$$Ar{\cdot}MgBr \xrightarrow{O_2} Ar{\cdot}O{\cdot}MgBr \xrightarrow{acid} ArOH$$

Phenol (*carbolic acid, hydroxybenzene*), C_6H_5OH, may be prepared by any of the general methods; commercially, it is prepared from coal tar (see above). The supply from this source is now insufficient to give the amount of phenol required for industry, and so it is also prepared synthetically. Various methods are used. The oldest synthetic method is the fusion of sodium benzenesulphonate with sodium hydroxide:

$$C_6H_5{\cdot}SO_3Na \xrightarrow{NaOH} C_6H_5ONa \xrightarrow{HCl} C_6H_5OH$$

A more recent method is to heat chlorobenzene with 10 per cent. solution of sodium carbonate or sodium hydroxide under pressure at about 300°:

$$\text{(i)}\ C_6H_5Cl + Na_2CO_3 + H_2O \longrightarrow C_6H_5OH + NaCl + NaHCO_3$$
$$\text{(ii)}\ C_6H_5Cl + C_6H_5OH + Na_2CO_3 \longrightarrow (C_6H_5)_2O + NaCl + NaHCO_3$$

By adding about 10 per cent. of diphenyl ether to the reaction mixture, the further formation of this ether is prevented in reaction (ii).

In addition to diphenyl ether, some *o*- and *p*-hydroxydiphenyls are obtained:

OH

o-compound

HO

p-compound

The *o*-compound is used as an antiseptic, and the *p*- for making resins.

One of the newest methods of preparing phenol synthetically is to heat chlorobenzene (prepared by the Raschig method, p. 523) with steam at 425° in the presence of a catalyst:

$$C_6H_6 + HCl + \tfrac{1}{2}O_2 \longrightarrow C_6H_5Cl + H_2O$$
$$C_6H_5Cl + H_2O \longrightarrow C_6H_5OH + HCl$$

The hydrochloric acid formed in the second reaction is returned for use in the first. Another new method is the oxidation of cumene to the hydroperoxide which is then decomposed into phenol and acetone by means of acid:

$$C_6H_6 + CH_3{\cdot}CH{=}CH_2 \xrightarrow{AlCl_3} C_6H_5{\cdot}CH(CH_3)_2 \xrightarrow{O_2} C_6H_5{\cdot}C(CH_3)_2{-}O{\cdot}OH$$
$$\xrightarrow{acid} C_6H_5OH + CH_3{\cdot}CO{\cdot}CH_3$$

Properties of phenol—these are characteristic of monohydric phenols. Phenol is a colourless crystalline solid, m.p. 43°, b.p. 182°, which turns pink on exposure to air and light. It is moderately soluble in cold water, but is readily soluble in ethanol and ether. Phenol undergoes the *Liebermann reaction* (*cf*. p. 300); when phenol is dissolved in concentrated sulphuric acid and a few drops of aqueous sodium nitrite added, a red colour is obtained on dilution, and turns green when made alkaline with aqueous sodium hydroxide.

Phenol is used as an antiseptic and disinfectant, and in the preparation of dyes, drugs, bakelite, etc.

Reactions. 1. Phenol gives a violet colour with ferric chloride; this reaction is characteristic of all compounds containing the grouping —C(OH)=C< (*cf.* enols, p. 206).

2. Phenol behaves as a weak acid, forming *phenoxides* with strong alkalis:

$$C_6H_5OH + NaOH \longrightarrow C_6H_5ONa + H_2O$$

Since phenol is a weaker acid than carbonic acid, it may be separated from carboxylic acids by making the solution alkaline with sodium hydroxide, and then passing in carbon dioxide. Phenol is liberated from its sodium salt and so may be extracted with ether; the carboxylic acid salts are *not* decomposed by carbon dioxide.

Phenols are stronger acids than the alcohols, one possible explanation being that the former exist as resonance hybrids whereas the latter do not:

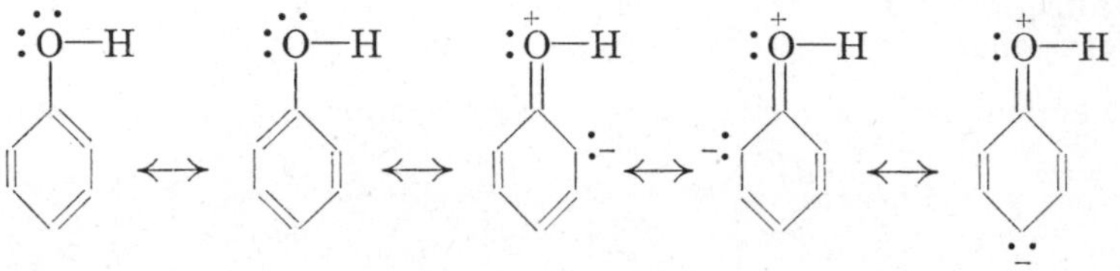

:Ö—H ↔ :Ö—H ↔ :Ö⁺—H ↔ :Ö⁺—H ↔ :Ö⁺—H

Thus the oxygen atom acquires a positive charge, and so attracts the electron pair of the O—H bond, thereby facilitating the release of a proton. Since resonance is impossible in alcohols, the hydrogen atom is more firmly linked to the oxygen. Support for this argument is to be found in the fact that the resonance energy of phenol is greater than that of the benzene ring (this indicates that the presence of the hydroxyl group has given rise to a larger number of resonating structures); and it has also been shown that the C—OH bond has about 16 per cent. double bond character. At the same time, the negative phenoxide ion is stabilised by resonance.

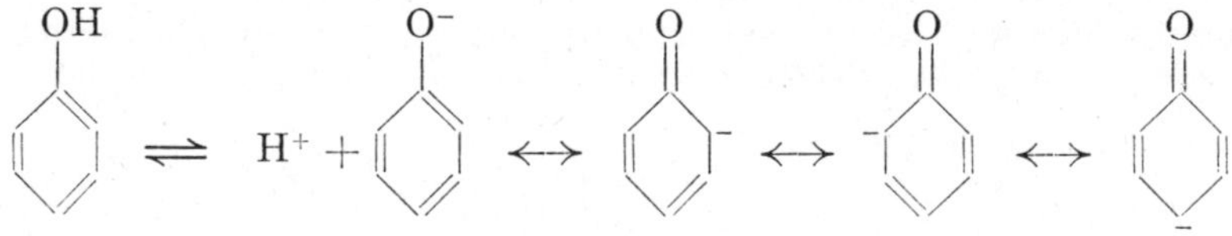

OH ⇌ H^+ + O⁻ ↔ O ↔ O ↔ O

Furthermore, since this ion carries only one charge and the undissociated phenol molecule two, the former will be more stable than the latter. Thus this tendency to form the more stable phenoxide ion may be considered as the " driving force " for dissociation.

3. Phenol can be halogenated, nitrated, and sulphonated to give *o*- and *p*-derivatives (the hydroxyl group is *o*-*p*-orienting; *cf.* 2 above).

4. Phenol reacts with phosphorus pentachloride to form only a very small amount of chlorobenzene, the main product being triphenyl phosphate, $(C_6H_5O)_3PO$ (see p. 520). Phenol does *not* react with hydrogen chloride.

5. When distilled with zinc dust, phenol is converted into benzene:

$$C_6H_5OH + Zn \longrightarrow C_6H_6 + ZnO$$

Phenol may also be converted into benzene by treating with hydrogen at atmospheric pressure in the presence of molybdenum oxide as catalyst (Fischer *et al.*, 1932):

$$C_6H_5OH + H_2 \longrightarrow C_6H_6 + H_2O$$

6. When heated with the double compounds of ammonia and zinc or calcium chloride, phenol forms aniline:

$$C_6H_5OH + NH_3 \xrightarrow{ZnCl_2} C_6H_5{\cdot}NH_2 + H_2O$$

Aniline is also produced when phenol is heated with ammonia under pressure.

7. The alkali phenoxides react with alkyl halides to form phenolic ethers; *e.g.*, sodium phenoxide and methyl iodide form *anisole*:

$$C_6H_5ONa + CH_3I \longrightarrow C_6H_5{\cdot}O{\cdot}CH_3 + NaI$$

8. Phenol can be hydrogenated in the presence of a nickel catalyst at 160° to *cyclo*hexanol (*cf.* reaction 5, above):

$$C_6H_5OH + 3H_2 \xrightarrow{Ni} C_6H_{11}OH \quad (ex.)$$

When phenol is oxidised with potassium permanganate, the ring is broken down (most phenols behave in a similar manner). Homologues of phenol can, however, be oxidised to the corresponding phenolic acid *provided the hydroxyl group is protected by alkylation or acylation.* The best means of protection is the formation of the benzenesulphonate, *e.g.*,

$$CH_3C_6H_4OH + C_6H_5{\cdot}SO_2Cl \xrightarrow{NaOH} CH_3C_6H_4O{\cdot}SO_2{\cdot}C_6H_5 \xrightarrow{KMnO_4} CO_2HC_6H_4O{\cdot}SO_2{\cdot}C_6H_5 \xrightarrow{H_2O} CO_2HC_6H_4OH$$

Phenol also undergoes the **Elbs persulphate oxidation** (1893). In this reaction, monohydric phenols are oxidised to dihydric phenols with potassium persulphate in alkaline solution. If the *p*-position to the hydroxyl group is free, the quinol is formed; if the *p*-position is occupied, the catechol derivative is formed. The yields of dihydric phenol are often low, but the products can readily be isolated pure.

9. Phenol undergoes the Friedel–Crafts reaction to form mainly the *p*-derivative and a small amount of the *o*- (see also p. 505):

$$C_6H_5OH + CH_3Cl \xrightarrow{AlCl_3} p\text{-}CH_3C_6H_4OH + o\text{-}CH_3C_6H_4OH$$

10. Phenol couples in the *p*-position with diazonium salts in alkaline solution to form hydroxyazo-compounds (p. 575).

11. When sodium or potassium phenoxide is heated with carbon dioxide, a phenolic acid is formed (see p. 652), *e.g.*, salicylic acid:

$$C_6H_5ONa + CO_2 \longrightarrow o\text{-}HOC_6H_4CO_2Na$$

12. Phenol is chloromethylated (p. 509) so readily that usually polymers are obtained.

The presence of a negative group, however, decreases the activating effect of the hydroxyl group; *e.g.*, *p*-nitrophenol may be successfully chloromethylated to give 2-hydroxy-5-nitrobenzyl chloride.

On the other hand, phenol may be chloromethylated successfully by first converting it into an ester (usually the ethyl phenyl carbonate by means of chloroformic ester), and chloromethylating this.

13. Phenol can be readily mercurated, *e.g.*, when refluxed with aqueous mercuric acetate, *o*-acetoxymercuriphenol is formed (together with some dimercurated compound):

$$C_6H_5OH + (CH_3{\cdot}CO_2)_2Hg \longrightarrow o\text{-}HO{\cdot}C_6H_4{\cdot}Hg{\cdot}O{\cdot}CO{\cdot}CH_3 + CH_3{\cdot}CO_2H$$

14. Phenol undergoes the *Reimer–Tiemann reaction* (p. 627), and the *Gattermann reaction* (p. 618).

15. When treated with acid chlorides, phenol forms phenyl esters:

$$C_6H_5OH + R{\cdot}COCl \longrightarrow R{\cdot}CO_2C_6H_5 + HCl$$

These phenyl esters, under suitable conditions, undergo the **Fries rearrangement** (1908). This consists of the conversion of a phenyl ester into an *o*- or *p*-hydroxyketone, or a mixture of both, by treatment with anhydrous aluminium chloride:

$$C_6H_5{\cdot}O{\cdot}CO{\cdot}R \xrightarrow{AlCl_3} o\text{-}HO{\cdot}C_6H_4{\cdot}CO{\cdot}R + p\text{-}HO{\cdot}C_6H_4{\cdot}CO{\cdot}R$$

Generally low temperatures (60° or less) favour the formation of the *p*-isomer, whereas high temperatures (above 160°), favour the *o*-isomer. In either case, the yield of phenolic ketone is better than that obtained by means of a Friedel–Crafts reaction. Cullinane *et al.* (1956) have found that the rearrangement of *o*-tolyl acetate in the presence of titanium tetrachloride in nitrobenzene gives almost entirely the *p*-substituted hydroxyketone and *o*-cresol. Cullinane *et al.* (1957) have also found that *p*-tolyl acetate gives mainly 2-hydroxy-5-methylacetophenone and some *p*-cresol under the same conditions.

Many theories have been suggested for the Fries rearrangement, but none is certain. According to Baltzly *et al.* (1955), the mechanism is:

$$C_6H_5{\cdot}O{\cdot}CO{\cdot}R + AlCl_3 \rightleftharpoons C_6H_5{\cdot}(Cl_3Al{:}O\text{ - - - }CO{\cdot}R) \longrightarrow (O{:}AlCl_3,\ \text{H},\ CO{\cdot}R) \longrightarrow o\text{-}HO{\cdot}C_6H_4{\cdot}CO{\cdot}R + AlCl_3$$

It is also possible for an *intermolecular* process to occur, *i.e.*, the complex acylates *another* molecule, the usual rules of orientation being followed (see p. 506). *Intramolecular* rearrangement, however, gives only the *o*-hydroxyketone.

On the other hand, Cullinane *et al.* (1956, 1957) have proposed the following mechanism:

$$p\text{-}CH_3{\cdot}C_6H_4{\cdot}O{\cdot}CO{\cdot}CH_3 + TiCl_4 \longrightarrow p\text{-}CH_3{\cdot}C_6H_4{\cdot}O{\cdot}CO{\cdot}CH_3,\ TiCl_4 \rightleftharpoons p\text{-}CH_3{\cdot}C_6H_4{\cdot}O{\cdot}TiCl_4^- \text{ - - - } CO{\cdot}CH_3^+ \longrightarrow 2\text{-}CH_3{\cdot}CO\text{-}4\text{-}CH_3{\cdot}C_6H_3{\cdot}O{\cdot}TiCl_4 + HCl$$

16. Phenol condenses with aliphatic and aromatic aldehydes in the *o*- and *p*-positions, the most important example being the condensation with formaldehyde. At low temperature, in the presence of dilute acid or alkali, and using formalin (40 per cent. aqueous formaldehyde), the main product is *p*-hydroxybenzyl alcohol, together with a small amount of the *o*-isomer.

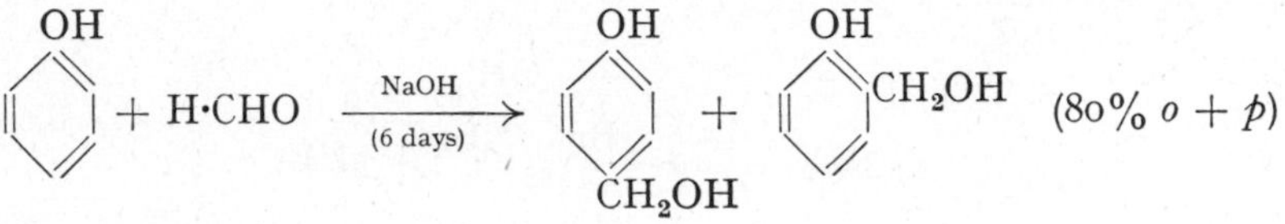

$$C_6H_5OH + H{\cdot}CHO \xrightarrow[\text{(6 days)}]{\text{NaOH}} p\text{-}HOC_6H_4CH_2OH + o\text{-}HOC_6H_4CH_2OH \quad (80\%\ o + p)$$

This is known as the **Lederer–Manasse reaction** (1894); its mechanism may be:

Acid catalysis

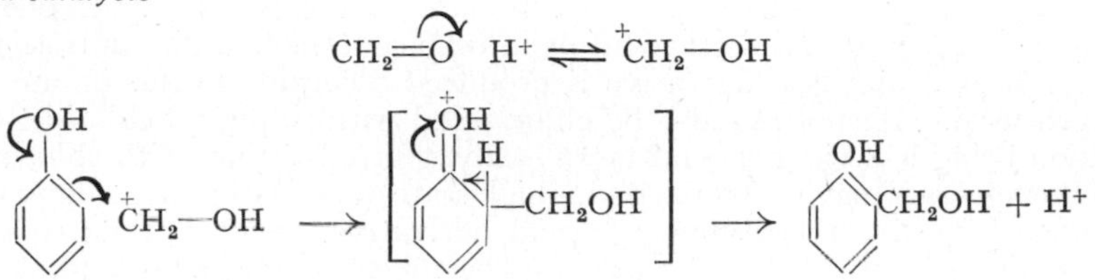

$$CH_2{=}O \quad H^+ \rightleftharpoons \overset{+}{C}H_2{-}OH$$

$$C_6H_5OH + \overset{+}{C}H_2{-}OH \longrightarrow \left[\overset{+}{O}H{=}C_6H_5(H){-}CH_2OH\right] \longrightarrow o\text{-}HOC_6H_4CH_2OH + H^+$$

Base catalysis

$$C_6H_5\bar{O} + H_2C{=}O \longrightarrow \left[O{=}C_6H_5(H){-}CH_2{-}\bar{O}\right] \longrightarrow o\text{-}\bar{O}C_6H_4CH_2OH$$

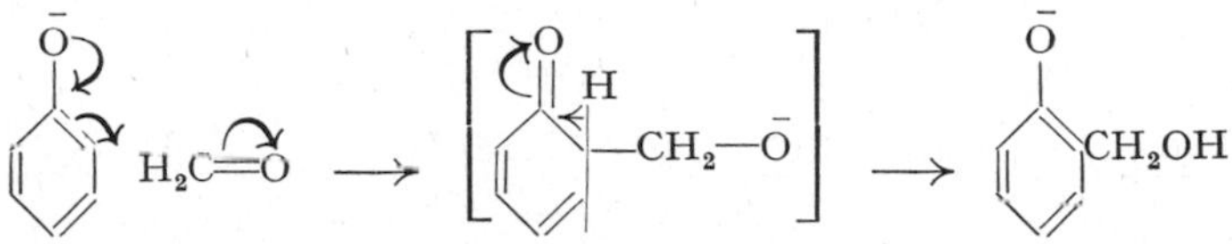

When larger amounts of formaldehyde are used, bishydroxymethylphenol and *p* : *p*′-dihydroxydiphenylmethane are obtained:

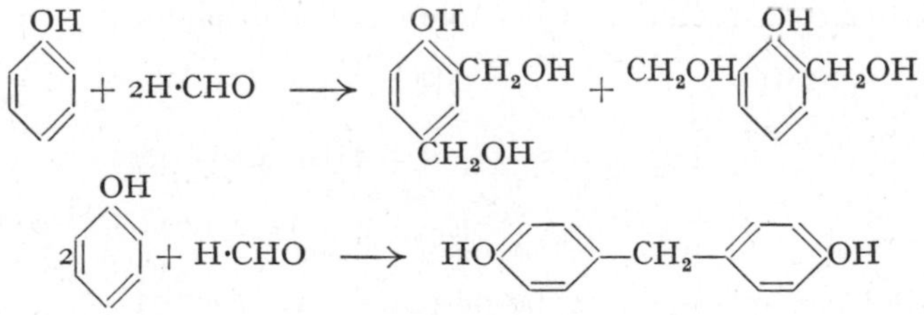

$$C_6H_5OH + 2H{\cdot}CHO \longrightarrow 2,4\text{-}(CH_2OH)_2C_6H_3OH + 2,6\text{-}(CH_2OH)_2C_6H_3OH$$

$$2C_6H_5OH + H{\cdot}CHO \longrightarrow HO{-}C_6H_4{-}CH_2{-}C_6H_4{-}OH$$

These condensations are the basis of the preparation of phenol-formaldehyde resins; phenol and excess formaldehyde, in the presence of dilute sodium hydroxide, slowly form a three-dimensional polymer of the possible structure:

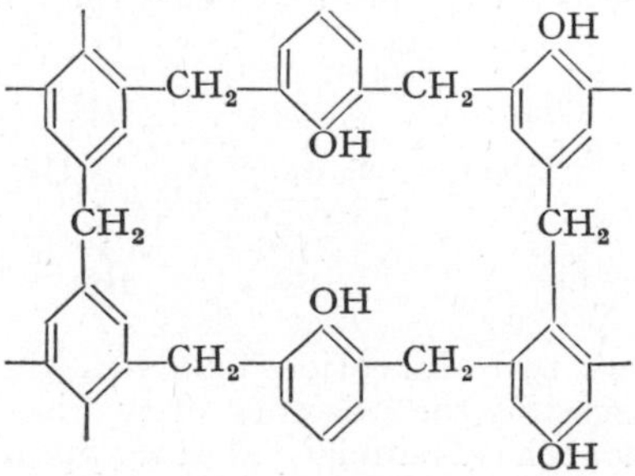

OH
—CH₂— —CH₂—
OH
CH₂ CH₂
OH
—CH₂— —CH₂—
OH

Substituted Phenols

Halogenated Phenols. The presence of the hydroxyl group activates the *o*- and *p*-positions to such an extent that phenol, on treatment with chlorine or bromine water, gives an immediate precipitate of the 2 : 4 : 6-trihalogen derivative:

$$C_6H_5OH + 3Br_2 \xrightarrow{H_2O} C_6H_2Br_3OH\ (2{:}4{:}6\text{-tribromophenol}) + 3HBr$$

This reaction may be used to estimate phenol quantitatively.

Gaseous chlorine or bromine at 150–180° attacks phenol to give mainly the *o*-halogen derivative and a small amount of the *p*-isomer. If phenol is halogenated in glacial acetic acid or in carbon tetrachloride solution, the mono-, di- or trihalogen derivative is produced according to the amount of halogen used. Phenol can also be chlorinated with sulphuryl chloride, the reaction being less vigorous and more easily controlled than with chlorine.

o-*Bromophenol* may be obtained in a high state of purity by first sulphonating phenol to give the disulphonic acid derivative, which is then treated with sodium hydroxide and bromine. The mixture is acidified and steam distilled, whereupon the sulphonic acid groups are eliminated, the resulting *o*-bromophenol distilling over:

$$C_6H_5OH \xrightarrow{H_2SO_4} C_6H_3(OH)(SO_3H)_2 \xrightarrow{Br_2/NaOH} C_6H_2Br(OH)(SO_3H)_2 \xrightarrow{acid} o\text{-}BrC_6H_4OH \quad (40\text{–}43\%)$$

p-*Bromophenol* may be prepared by adding bromine dissolved in carbon disulphide to a cooled solution of phenol in carbon disulphide:

$$C_6H_5OH + Br_2 \xrightarrow{CS_2} p\text{-}BrC_6H_4OH + HBr \quad (80\text{–}84\%)$$

o- and *p*-Halogeno-phenols may be prepared pure from the corresponding halogeno-anilines.

If the hydroxyl group is in the *o*- or *p*-position to a negative group such as NO_2, CO_2H, or SO_3H, then on treatment with *aqueous* halogen, the negative group is often displaced, the product being the trihalogen derivative of phenol; *e.g.*,

$$o\text{-}NO_2C_6H_4OH \xrightarrow{Br_2/H_2O} 2{:}4{:}6\text{-}Br_3C_6H_2OH$$

o-*Bromophenol* shows two absorption bands in the infrared; this has been explained by suggesting the existence of two isomers due to hydrogen bonding. *o*-Iodophenol behaves similarly, but it appears that *o*-chlorophenol exists almost entirely in the *cis* form (hydrogen bonding is much stronger for chlorine than for bromine or iodine).

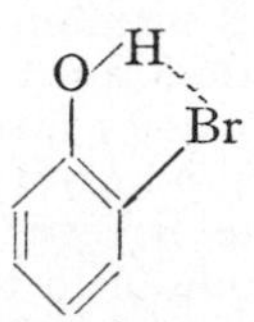

cis-form 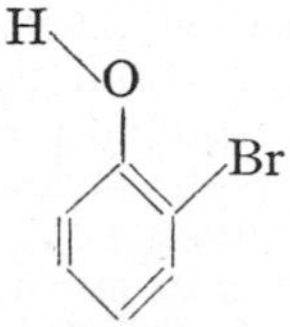 *trans*-form

o-*Iodophenol* is best prepared by heating phenol with mercuric acetate, converting the *o*-acetoxymercuriphenol into the corresponding chloromercuri-derivative by heating with aqueous sodium chloride, and replacing the chloromercuri-group by treatment with iodine in chloroform solution:

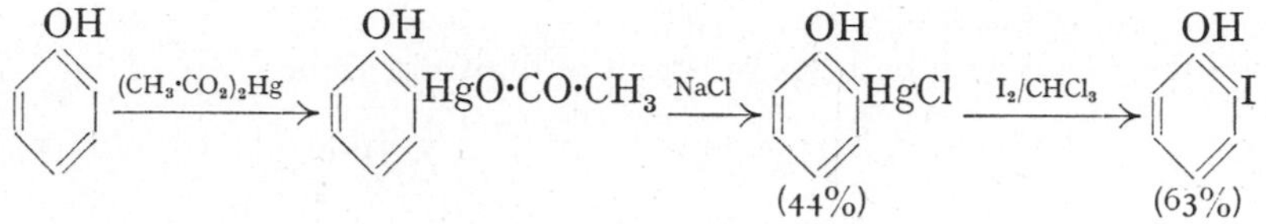

$$C_6H_5OH \xrightarrow{(CH_3\cdot CO_2)_2Hg} o\text{-}HOC_6H_4HgO\cdot CO\cdot CH_3 \xrightarrow{NaCl} o\text{-}HOC_6H_4HgCl \xrightarrow{I_2/CHCl_3} o\text{-}HOC_6H_4I$$

(44%) (63%)

p-*Iodophenol* may be prepared as follows:

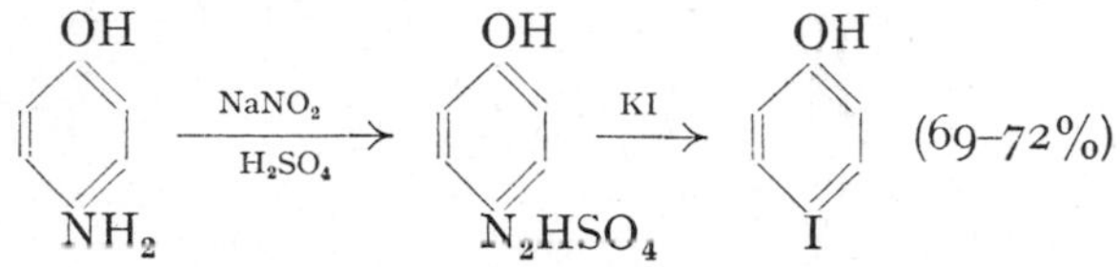

$$p\text{-}NH_2C_6H_4OH \xrightarrow[H_2SO_4]{NaNO_2} p\text{-}HOC_6H_4N_2HSO_4 \xrightarrow{KI} p\text{-}IC_6H_4OH \quad (69\text{–}72\%)$$

The halogenated phenols, particularly the *o*- and *p*-derivatives, are stronger acids than phenol itself, *e.g.*, tribromophenol decomposes carbonates. This may be due to the inductive effect of the halogen atom which enhances resonance, thereby increasing the tendency for proton release in the hydroxyl group.

When the halogenated phenols are fused with potassium hydroxide, halogen is replaced by hydroxyl, but the positions do not always remain the same, *e.g.*, all three isomeric chlorophenols give resorcinol (*m*-dihydroxybenzene).

Nitrophenols. Treatment of phenol with cold dilute nitric acid gives a mixture of *o*- and *p*-nitrophenols, the latter predominating; oxidation products are also obtained. These isomers may be separated by steam distillation. As we have seen (p. 48), solubility in hydroxylic solvents depends on, among other things, the power to form hydrogen bonds with the solvent. Phenol can form these bonds and hence a certain solubility in water can be expected. This argument also applies to substituted phenols since the hydroxyl group is still present, but in the *o*-compounds, however, because chelation is possible, hydrogen bonding with the solvent water molecules is hindered and hence the solubility is lowered. Furthermore, since chelation causes the *o*-compound to behave as a " monomer," this isomer will be more volatile than the corresponding *m*- and *p*-isomers. Thus the effects of chelation are lower solubility and greater volatility in the *o*-compounds, thereby enabling these to be separated from their *m*- and *p*-isomers by steam distillation. The *o*-isomer may also be separated from the *p*- by crystallisation or by chromatography.

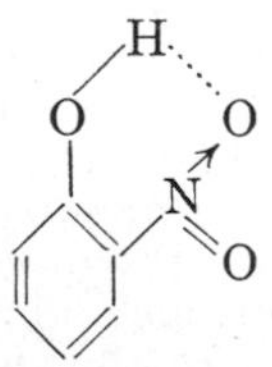

It has been found that the nitration of phenol (and of aniline) is accelerated by the presence of nitrous acid, and it appears that the mechanism of the reaction is different from that of ordinary nitration. Evidence for this is based on the observation that when phenol is nitrated in the presence of very little nitrous acid, *o*- and *p*-nitrophenols are formed in the ratio of 7 : 3. When nitrated in the presence of a large amount of nitrous acid, the ratio becomes 1 : 9, which is the ratio in which *o*- and *p*-nitrosophenols are formed if the nitric acid is omitted. It is therefore believed that the nitroso-compound is formed first, and this is then oxidised to the nitro-compound (Hughes *et al.*, 1946). This scheme may be used to prepare pure *p*-nitrophenol in very good yield; phenol is treated with nitrous acid and the product, *p*-nitrosophenol, is oxidised to *p*-nitrophenol.

o- and *p*-Nitrophenols are prepared commercially by direct nitration of phenol, and by hydrolysis of *o*- and *p*-chloronitrobenzenes with aqueous sodium hydroxide.

o- and *p*-Nitrophenols are also formed when nitrobenzene is heated with solid potassium hydroxide (*cf.* p. 500).

m-Nitrophenol may be prepared from *m*-dinitrobenzene:

$$C_6H_4(NO_2)_2 \xrightarrow{NH_4HS} C_6H_4(NH_2)NO_2 \xrightarrow[H_2SO_4]{NaNO_2} C_6H_4(N_2HSO_4)NO_2 \xrightarrow{H_2O} C_6H_4(OH)NO_2$$

(81–86% on the nitroaniline)

o-Nitrophenol is a yellow solid, m.p. 45°; the *m*- and *p*-isomers are colourless solids, m.ps. 97° and 114°, respectively. The *o*- and *p*-derivatives are stronger acids than the *m*-, and all are stronger acids than phenol (*cf.* chlorophenols, above). All three are readily reduced to the corresponding aminophenols, and the nitro-group in the *o*- and *p*-compounds is displaced on treatment with bromine water, 2 : 4 : 6-tribromophenol being formed. The salts of the three nitrophenols are highly coloured (yellow to red), and *o*- and *p*-nitrophenols give rise to two series of ethers, one colourless and the other coloured. The colour of the latter series is believed to be due to the presence of the *quinonoid* structure:

$$HO-C_6H_4-N{\overset{\nearrow O}{\underset{\searrow O}{}}} \rightleftharpoons O{=}C_6H_4{=}N{\overset{\nearrow OH}{\underset{\searrow O}{}}}$$

n-form — *aci*-form

$$RO-C_6H_4-N{\overset{\nearrow O}{\underset{\searrow O}{}}} \qquad O{=}C_6H_4{=}N{\overset{\nearrow OR}{\underset{\searrow O}{}}}$$

colourless ether — coloured ether

Only one form of the nitrophenols is known, but the existence of two series of ethers suggests that the nitrophenols are tautomeric. The colourless ethers are stable, and are only very slowly hydrolysed to the nitrophenol: the coloured ethers are unstable, and are easily hydrolysed. The *n*-ethers are produced by alkylating the nitrophenyl in the usual way (*e.g.*, with alkyl halide and alkali). If, however, the silver salt of the nitrophenol is treated with alkyl iodide, a mixture of the *n*- and *aci*-ethers is obtained.

The ethers of *m*-nitrophenol exist only in one form—colourless. This agrees with the fact that the *m*-compound cannot form the quinonoid structure.

On the other hand, it is difficult to explain the colour of the salts of *m*-nitrophenol on this theory. One suggestion is that the ion can resonate more than the undissociated phenol, and this gives rise to colour.

Phenol *Ion*

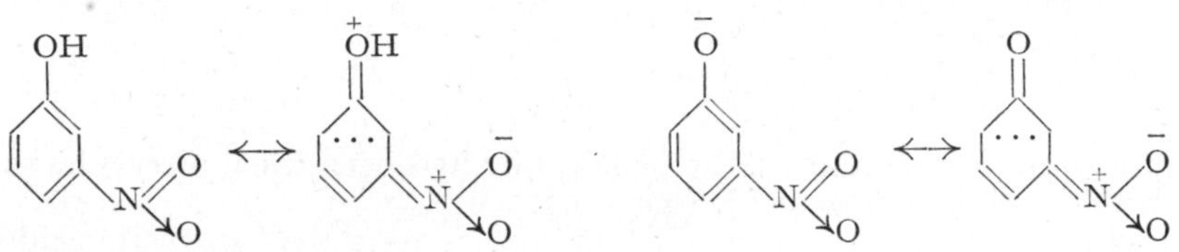

Owing to the negative charge on the oxygen atom, more of the other resonating structure is present. This also explains why *m*-nitrophenol is a stronger acid than phenol.

When *o*- and *p*-nitrophenols are nitrated, 2 : 4-dinitrophenol is formed, and this, in turn, can be further nitrated to 2 : 4 : 6-trinitrophenol (*picric acid*). The yield of picric acid is poor due to large losses by oxidation. Picric acid is prepared commercially by first sulphonating phenol and then nitrating the product (see p. 584). Another commercial method is as follows:

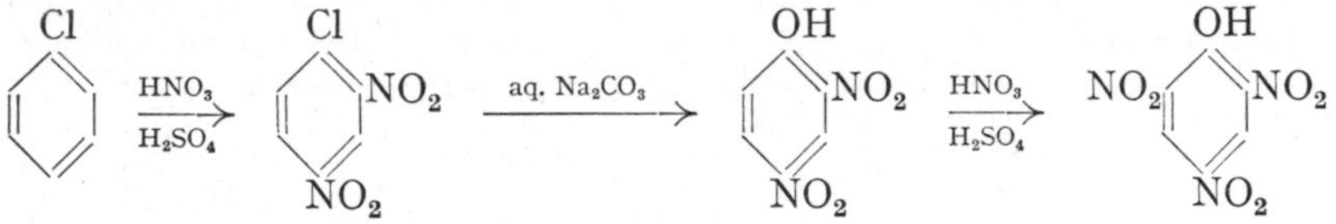

$$C_6H_5Cl \xrightarrow[H_2SO_4]{HNO_3} C_6H_3Cl(NO_2)_2 \xrightarrow{aq.\ Na_2CO_3} C_6H_3(OH)(NO_2)_2 \xrightarrow[H_2SO_4]{HNO_3} C_6H_2(OH)(NO_2)_3$$

The interesting point to note about this method is that the presence of the negative nitro-group protects, to a large extent, the hydroxyl group from oxidation. It is in the nitration of phenol to the *o*- and *p*-nitrophenols that the loss by oxidation is greatest.

Picric acid may be obtained in the laboratory by oxidising *s*-trinitrobenzene with potassium ferricyanide.

When benzene is subjected to *oxynitration, i.e.*, simultaneous oxidation and nitration by means of a solution of mercuric nitrate in nitric acid, 2 : 4-dinitrophenol and picric acid are formed. This is often referred to as the **Wolffenstein–Böters reaction** (1906).

Picric acid is a yellow crystalline solid, m.p. 122°, with a bitter taste (Greek: *pikros*, bitter). It is almost insoluble in cold water, but is soluble in hot water and in ether. It is a fairly strong acid, decomposing carbonates; the three nitro-groups in the *p*- and two *o*-positions create the maximum enhancement of resonance. The yellow colour is probably due to the presence of a large amount of the quinonoid structure. Picric acid forms crystalline molecular compounds known as *picrates*, with aromatic hydrocarbons, amines and phenols; their picrates are frequently used to identify these classes of compounds. When treated with bleaching powder, picric acid forms chloropicrin (p. 107) as one of the products. Picric acid forms *picryl chloride* when treated with phosphorus pentachloride. Although phenol gives a very poor yield of chlorobenzenes with phosphorus pentachloride, the nitrophenols (*o*-, *p*-, and *o* : *p*-derivatives) give fairly good yields of chloro-compound (the nitrophenols are relatively strongly acidic). The chlorine atom in picryl chloride is very reactive (owing to the presence of the three nitro-groups in the *p*- and two *o*-positions); *e.g.*, when boiled with water, picryl chloride forms picric acid, and when shaken with concentrated ammonia, *picramide*:

$$C_6H_2(NO_2)_3OH \xleftarrow{H_2O} C_6H_2(NO_2)_3Cl \xrightarrow{NH_3} C_6H_2(NO_2)_3NH_2$$

The chlorine atom is also readily replaced by hydrogen when picryl chloride is treated with hydrogen iodide (see p. 531).

Picramic acid (2-*amino*-4 : 6-*dinitrophenol*) is formed when picric acid is reduced with sodium sulphide (*cf.* p. 539):

$$C_6H_2(OH)(NO_2)_3 \xrightarrow{Na_2S} C_6H_2(OH)(NH_2)(NO_2)_2 \quad (90\%)$$

Picric acid is used in the manufacture of explosives, and is a dye for wool and silk.

Aminophenols. These may be prepared by reducing the corresponding nitrophenols with metal and acid, or catalytically. *m*-Aminophenol (used in the manufacture of dyes) is prepared commercially by heating resorcinol with ammonia and ammonium chloride under pressure at 200°:

$$C_6H_4(OH)_2 + NH_3 \xrightarrow{NH_4Cl} C_6H_4(OH)NH_2 + H_2O$$

This replacement reaction is only satisfactory for the preparation of the *m*-isomer.

o- and *p*-Aminophenols are more weakly acidic than phenol, possibly due to the amino-group inhibiting resonance of the hydroxyl group with the benzene ring; thus they do not form phenoxides with alkalis. On the other hand, they form salts with strong inorganic acids. The *o*- and *p*-derivatives are readily oxidised to the corresponding quinones; the *m*-compound is not easily oxidised (and does not give a quinone). *o*-Aminophenol has a marked tendency to form cyclic compounds (*cf.* *o*-phenylenediamines, p. 553); *e.g.*, with acetic acid it forms 2-methylbenzoxazole:

$$C_6H_4(OH)NH_2 + HO{-}C(=O){-}CH_3 \longrightarrow C_6H_4{<}^{O}_{N}{>}C{\cdot}CH_3 + 2H_2O$$

The amino-group in aminophenols is more readily acetylated than the hydroxyl group; *e.g.*, when *p*-aminophenol hydrochloride is acetylated with one equivalent of acetic anhydride in the presence of aqueous sodium acetate, *p*-acetamidophenol is formed:

$$HO{\cdot}C_6H_4{\cdot}NH_2{\cdot}HCl + (CH_3{\cdot}CO)_2O \xrightarrow{CH_3{\cdot}CO_2Na} HO{\cdot}C_6H_4{\cdot}NH{\cdot}CO{\cdot}CH_3$$

p-*Aminophenol*, m.p. 186°, is very important as a photographic developer. It may be prepared by boiling phenylhydroxylamine with sulphuric acid (see p. 536), or by reducing hydroxyazobenzene with sodium hyposulphite:

$$C_6H_5N_2Cl + C_6H_5OH \xrightarrow{NaOH} C_6H_5\text{—N:N—}C_6H_4OH \xrightarrow{Na_2S_2O_4} C_6H_5NH_2 + NH_2C_6H_4OH$$

It is prepared industrially by the electrolytic reduction of nitrobenzene in sulphuric acid (see p. 536).

p-Aminophenol is readily oxidised to *p*-benzoquinone (p. 639).

Two other important photographic developers are *amidol*, m.p. 78°, and *metol*, m.p. 87°:

amidol: $C_6H_3(OH)(NH_2)_2$ (OH at 1, NH_2 at 2 and 4)

metol: $HOC_6H_4\cdot NH\cdot CH_3$ (para)

Phenolsulphonic acids. When phenol is treated with concentrated sulphuric acid, *o*- and *p*-phenolsulphonic acids are formed, the former being the main product at ordinary temperatures, and the latter at higher temperatures (110°); the *o*-compound rearranges to the *p*- on heating. *m*-Phenolsulphonic may be obtained by the controlled potassium hydroxide fusion of benzene-*m*-disulphonic acid at about 180°:

$$m\text{-}C_6H_4(SO_3K)_2 \xrightarrow{KOH} m\text{-}KOC_6H_4SO_3K$$

When *o*- or *p*- to a hydroxyl group (or an amino-group), a sulphonic acid group is often displaced by halogen when the sulphonic acid is halogenated in aqueous solution (*cf.* nitrophenols):

$$p\text{-}HOC_6H_4SO_3H \xrightarrow{Br_2/H_2O} 2,4,6\text{-}Br_3C_6H_2OH + H_2SO_4$$

Nitrosophenols. When treated with nitrous acid, phenol forms mainly *p*-nitrosophenol, and a small amount of the *o*-compound:

$$C_6H_5OH \xrightarrow{HNO_2} p\text{-}HOC_6H_4NO \quad (90\%)$$

p-Nitrosophenol is also formed when *p*-nitrosodimethylaniline is boiled with alkali (p. 548):

$$p\text{-}(CH_3)_2NC_6H_4NO + H_2O \longrightarrow p\text{-}HOC_6H_4NO + (CH_3)_2NH \quad (90\%)$$

p-Nitrosophenol crystallises from hot water in pale yellow needles which readily turn brown. On the other hand, it crystallises from ether in brownish-green flakes. This colour suggests that *p*-nitrosophenol may have a quinonoid structure, *i.e.*, the following tautomeric system is present (*cf.* nitrophenols):

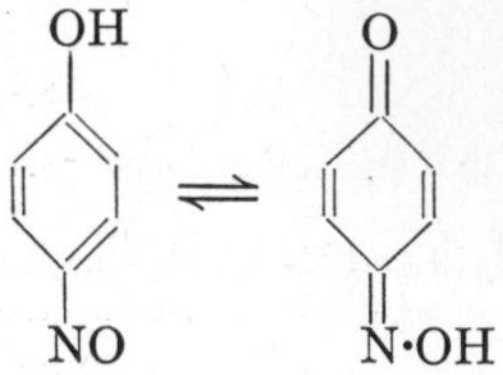

This is supported by the fact that *p*-nitrosophenol has been shown to be identical with the monoxime of *p*-benzoquinone, which may be prepared by the action of hydroxylamine on *p*-benzoquinone:

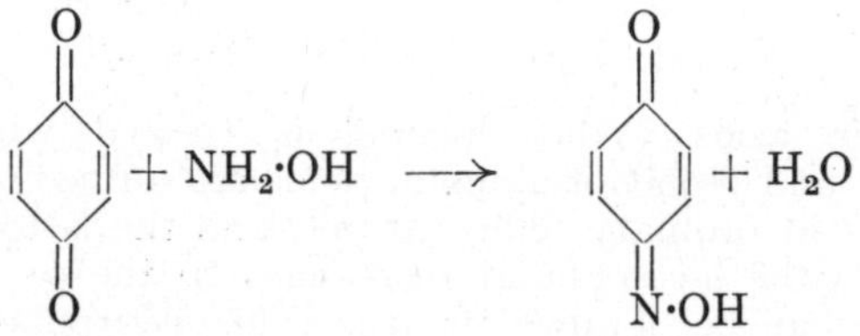

Havinga *et al.* (1955) have shown, from a study of ultraviolet spectra, that *p*-nitrosophenol exists in solution as the phenol together with the quinone oxime, but in the solid state it appears that only the latter form is present. Hadži (1956), from an examination of the infrared spectrum of the monoxime of benzoquinone, concludes that the oxime structure is correct for the compound in the solid state, and that this form predominates in chloroform solution.

o-*Nitrosophenol* may be prepared by the **Baudisch reaction** (1913), which uses the *nitrosyl radical* NOH and an oxidising agent; a nitroso- and a hydroxyl group are introduced into the ring (*cf.* oxynitration, p. 601):

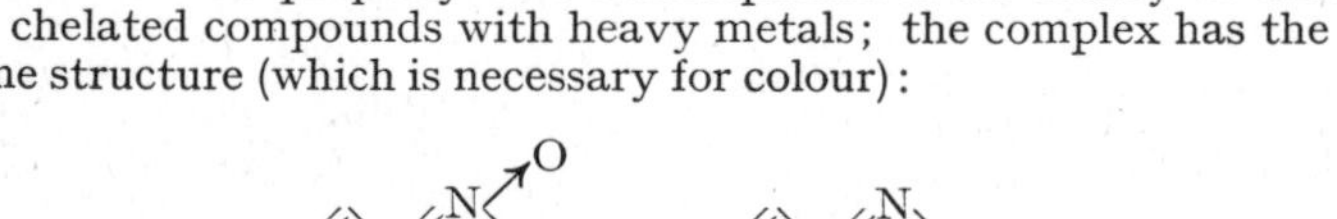

The nitrosyl radical is formed by the reduction of nitrous acid or the oxidation of hydroxylamine; the presence of a copper salt is essential, both to stabilise the nitrosyl radical and to ensure that *o*-, and not *p*-nitrosophenol, is formed.

The characteristic property of *o*-nitrosophenol is its ability to form highly-coloured chelated compounds with heavy metals; the complex has the quinone-monoxime structure (which is necessary for colour):

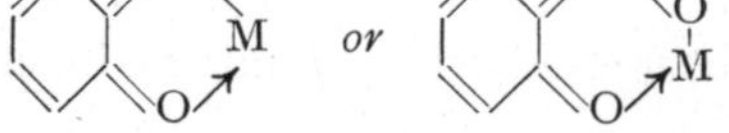

M = metal

Homologues of Phenol

Cresols (*hydroxytoluenes*), $CH_3{\cdot}C_6H_4OH$. The cresols occur in the middle and heavy oil fractions of coal-tar (p. 424). The mixture of the three cresols (together with a little phenol) is known as *cresylic acid* or *creosote*, and is used for preserving purposes, *e.g.*, timber, railway sleepers, etc. A solution of cresols in soapy water is known as *lysol*, which is used as a disinfectant.

The boiling points of the cresols are: *o*-, 191°; *m*-, 201°; *p*-, 202·5°. By means of a very good fractionating column it is possible to separate the *o*-isomer from the other two. Each isomer can be obtained pure from the corresponding toluidine.

When either *o*- or *m*-chlorotoluene is heated with aqueous sodium hydroxide at about 300–320° under pressure, a certain amount of *m*-cresol is obtained.

The methyl group in the cresols is *not* oxidised to a carboxyl group by chromic acid; nor is the ring attacked (*cf.* p. 512). If, however, the hydroxyl group is acetylated or alkylated, the methyl group can then be oxidised.

m- and *p*-Cresols are used in the manufacture of resins, plasticisers, etc.

Two higher homologues of phenol are the isomers *thymol* (3-hydroxy-4-*iso*-propyltoluene), and *carvacrol* (2-hydroxy-4-*iso*propyltoluene):

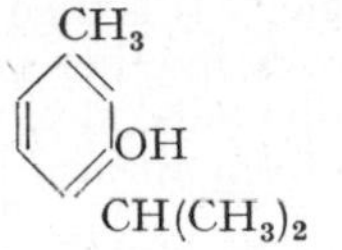

CH_3 / OH / $CH(CH_3)_2$
thymol, m.p. 51°

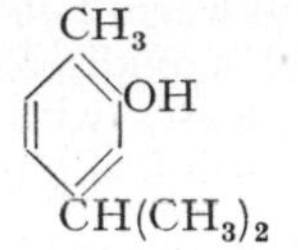

CH_3 / OH / $CH(CH_3)_2$
carvacrol, b.p. 237°

Thymol occurs in the essential oil, oil of thyme, but is prepared commercially by heating *m*-cresol and *iso*propanol with sulphuric acid; it is used in perfumery and as an antiseptic. Carvacrol also occurs in some essential oils, but is prepared by heating camphor with iodine:

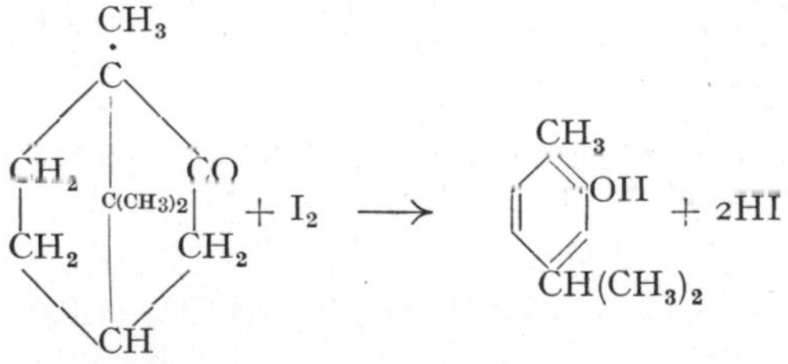

CH_3 · C; CH_2, CO; $C(CH_3)_2$; CH_2, CH_2; CH $+ I_2 \longrightarrow$ CH_3 / OH / $CH(CH_3)_2$ $+ 2HI$

It is used in perfumery and as an antiseptic.

A number of monochloro-derivatives of monohydric phenols are also very good disinfectants, *e.g.*, 2-chloro-5-hydroxytoluene.

DIHYDRIC PHENOLS

There are three possible dihydroxybenzenes, and all are known:

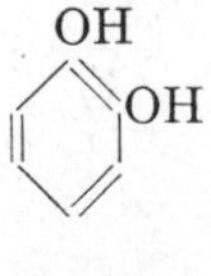

OH / OH — catechol

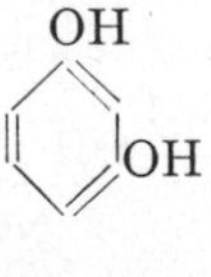

OH / OH — resorcinol

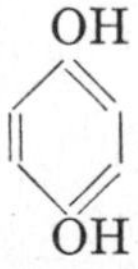

OH / OH — quinol

Catechol (o-*dihydroxybenzene*) occurs in certain plants. It may be prepared by the alkaline fusion of *o*-phenolsulphonic acid; commercially, it is prepared by heating *o*-chlorophenol or *o*-dichlorobenzene with 20 per cent.

aqueous sodium hydroxide and a trace of copper sulphate at 190° under pressure:

$$C_6H_4(OH)Cl \xrightarrow{H_2O} C_6H_4(OH)_2 \xleftarrow{H_2O} C_6H_4Cl_2$$

Catechol may be conveniently prepared in the laboratory by the action of alkaline hydrogen peroxide on salicylaldehyde:

$$C_6H_4(CHO)(OH) + H_2O_2 \xrightarrow{NaOH} C_6H_4(OH)_2 + H{\cdot}CO_2Na \quad (69–73\%)$$

This reaction is characteristic of *o*- and *p*-hydroxyaldehydes; it is known as the **Dakin reaction** (1909).

Catechol is a colourless solid, m.p. 105°, soluble in water, ethanol and ether. With ferric chloride it gives a green coloration which turns red on the addition of sodium carbonate. Catechol is a powerful reducing agent: its aqueous solution darkens on exposure to air due to oxidation; it reduces cold silver nitrate and warm Fehling's solution. It is used as a photographic developer. Catechol is oxidised by silver oxide in ether solution to *o*-benzoquinone, and it condenses with many compounds, *e.g.*, with phthalic anhydride in the presence of sulphuric acid to form alizarin (p. 776).

Two curious reactions of catechol are its oxidation with nitrous acid in ether solution to dihydroxytartaric acid, and its easy carboxylation to protocatechuic acid by heating with aqueous ammonium carbonate at 140° under pressure:

$$CO_2H{\cdot}C(OH)_2{\cdot}C(OH)_2{\cdot}CO_2H \xleftarrow{HNO_2} C_6H_4(OH)_2 \xrightarrow{(NH_4)_2CO_3} C_6H_3(OH)_2CO_2H$$

Important derivatives of catechol are *guaiacol* and *adrenaline* (the hormone secreted by the adrenal glands):

$$(HO)_2C_6H_3{\cdot}CHOH{\cdot}CH_2{\cdot}NH{\cdot}CH_3$$

adrenaline

Resorcinol (m-*dihydroxybenzene*) is prepared industrially by the alkaline fusion of benzene-*m*-disulphonic acid.

Resorcinol is also formed when benzene-*p*-disulphonic acid or all three bromobenzenesulphonic acids are fused with alkali.

Resorcinol is a colourless crystalline solid, m.p. 110°, very soluble in water, ethanol and ether. Its aqueous solution gives a violet coloration with ferric chloride. It is not so powerful a reducing agent as the *o*- and *p*-isomers, but it will reduce silver nitrate and Fehling's solution on warming. With nitrous acid it forms dinitrosoresorcinol:

$$C_6H_4(OH)_2 \xrightarrow{HNO_2} C_6H_2(OH)_2(NO)_2 \rightleftharpoons C_6H_2O_2(N{\cdot}OH)_2$$

This is known as *Fast Green* O, and is used as a dye.

When nitrated, resorcinol forms **styphnic acid** (2 : 4 : 6-*trinitroresorcinol*), m.p. 180°:

$$C_6H_4(OH)_2 \xrightarrow[H_2SO_4]{HNO_3} C_6H(NO_2)_3(OH)_2$$

Styphnates are used to identify certain compounds by molecular complex formation (*cf.* picrates, p. 601).

A number of reactions of resorcinol are best explained on the assumption that resorcinol behaves as a tautomeric substance:

dienol form $\rightleftharpoons$ diketo form

Resorcinol is used for making dyes.

Orcinol (3 : 5-*dihydroxytoluene*), $CH_3C_6H_3(OH)_2$, m.p. 290°, is found in many lichens, and is chemically related to litmus.

Quinol (*hydroquinone*, p-*dihydroxybenzene*) occurs in the glucoside *arbutin*. It may be prepared by diazotising *p*-aminophenol (yield 30 per cent.), or by reducing *p*-benzoquinone with sulphurous acid:

$$O{=}C_6H_4{=}O + H_2SO_3 + H_2O \longrightarrow HOC_6H_4OH + H_2SO_4 \quad (ex.)$$

It is made commercially as follows:

$$C_6H_5NH_2 \xrightarrow[H_2SO_4]{MnO_2} O{=}C_6H_4{=}O \xrightarrow[H_2O]{Fe} HOC_6H_4OH$$

Quinol is a colourless solid, m.p. 170°, very soluble in water, ethanol and ether. It is a powerful reducing agent and hence is used as a photographic developer. It is oxidised by ferric chloride to *p*-benzoquinone; it is also oxidised by diazonium salts, no coupling taking place at all. In both cases, the oxidation takes place via the intermediate formation of *quinhydrone* (p. 641). Quinol behaves as a tautomeric compound.

$$HOC_6H_4OH \rightleftharpoons O{=}C_6H_4(H_2)(H_2){=}O$$

Cookson *et al.* (1955) have shown that quinol forms an adduct with maleic anhydride.

HO–C₆H₄–OH + CH·CO–O–CH·CO (maleic anhydride) —heat→ adduct

This is particularly interesting since it is the first example of an adduct being formed from a *monocyclic* hydrocarbon (see Diels–Alder reaction, p. 450.)

Clathrates. When quinol is crystallised from a solution in water saturated with sulphur dioxide, a quinol-sulphur dioxide complex is obtained. These inclusion complexes are also formed with hydrogen sulphide, methanol, etc., and have a molecular formula of the type $3C_6H_4(OH)_2.Z$ (where Z is one molecule of the second component). Powell *et al.* (1948), using X-ray analysis, found that in these complexes the quinol molecules were linked together through hydrogen bonds to form giant molecules the cavities in which enclosed the second component. Powell named these complexes **clathrates,** and showed that the " cages " must be large enough to contain the molecule of the second component and that they must be so arranged that the enclosed molecules do not escape. These clathrates are stable, but the imprisoned molecules may be released either by melting or by means of an organic solvent which dissolves quinol.

Clathrates differ from channel complexes (p. 369) in that each molecule of the second component is enclosed in a separate molecular cage of limited size, and thus the possible variations of this second component depend on *molecular size.* Hence clathrates may be used to separate certain homologues, *e.g.*, quinol forms a clathrate with methanol but not with any other homologue of this alcohol series.

TRIHYDRIC PHENOLS

There are three possible trihydroxybenzenes, and all are known:

pyrogallol (1,2,3-trihydroxy) hydroxyquinol (1,2,4-trihydroxy) phloroglucinol (1,3,5-trihydroxy)

Pyrogallol (vic-*trihydroxybenzene*) may be prepared by heating solid gallic acid in a stream of carbon dioxide, or by heating an aqueous solution of gallic acid at 210° under pressure:

$HO_2C–C_6H_2(OH)_3$ —(solid)→ $C_6H_3(OH)_3 + CO_2$ (40%)

Pyrogallol is a colourless solid, m.p. 133°, soluble in water, ethanol and ether; its aqueous solution gives a red coloration with ferric chloride. Alkaline solutions of pyrogallol oxidise very rapidly on exposure to air, and hence are used in gas analysis for the absorption of oxygen (and carbon dioxide); the pyrogallol is oxidised to a complex mixture containing, among other things, carbon monoxide, carbon dioxide, acetic and oxalic acids.

Pyrogallol also reduces the salts of silver, gold, platinum and mercury to their metals. It is used as a photographic developer.

Hydroxyquinol (as-*trihydroxybenzene*), m.p. 140°, may be prepared by the alkaline fusion of quinol in air. It is best prepared by hydrolysing its triacetate, which is obtained by heating *p*-benzoquinone with acetic anhydride and concentrated sulphuric acid:

$$C_6H_4O_2 + 2(CH_3{\cdot}CO)_2O \xrightarrow{H_2SO_4} C_6H_3(O{\cdot}CO{\cdot}CH_3)_3 + CH_3{\cdot}CO_2H \xrightarrow{H_2O} C_6H_3(OH)_3$$

Phloroglucinol (s-*trihydroxybenzene*) is obtained when many plant resins are fused with alkalis. It may be prepared by fusing resorcinol with sodium hydroxide in the air, but a convenient laboratory method is to reduce s-trinitrobenzoic acid, and heat the resulting amino-derivative with hydrochloric acid (yield: 46–53 per cent. as dihydrate):

$$C_6H_2(NO_2)_3{\cdot}CO_2H \xrightarrow{Sn/HCl} C_6H_2(NH_2)_3{\cdot}CO_2H \xrightarrow{HCl} C_6H_3(OH)_3 + CO_2 + 3NH_4Cl$$

It should be noted that this decarboxylation and replacement of amino-groups by hydroxyl merely by boiling with hydrochloric acid is *not* a general reaction.

Phloroglucinol is a colourless solid, m.p. 218°, fairly soluble in water, its aqueous solution giving a bluish-violet coloration with ferric chloride. Its alkaline solutions rapidly darken on exposure to air due to oxidation. Phloroglucinol behaves as a tautomeric compound; *e.g.*, when warmed with acetic anhydride, it forms the triacetate, and when treated with hydroxylamine, the trioxime:

$$C_6H_3(OH)_3 \rightleftharpoons \text{cyclohexane-1,3,5-trione } (C_6H_6O_3,\ 3\ CH_2 \text{ groups})$$

This tautomeric system was formerly supported by the statement that phloroglucinol could be prepared from acetone and malonyl chloride, but according to Elvidge *et al.* (1952), these two compounds do *not* give phloroglucinol.

Infrared spectra studies have shown that *all* phenols are entirely enolic in the solid state and also in solution. Of all the phenols mentioned in the foregoing account, the tendency to react as a ketone is most pronounced in phloroglucinol. Further evidence for the existence of tautomerism in phenols is the formation of two types of alkyl derivatives when alkylated with alkyl halide in the presence of alkali, *viz.*, *O*- and *C*-alkyl derivatives; *e.g.*, resorcinol gives a mixture of three methylated products:

$$C_6H_4(OH)_2 \rightleftharpoons \text{keto form} \xrightarrow[KOH]{CH_3I} C_6H_4(O{\cdot}CH_3)_2 + \text{2,2-dimethyl diketone} + \text{(CH}_3)_2\text{, O}{\cdot}CH_3\text{, CH}_3 \text{ derivative}$$

Phloroglucinol forms only the *C*-alkyl derivatives:

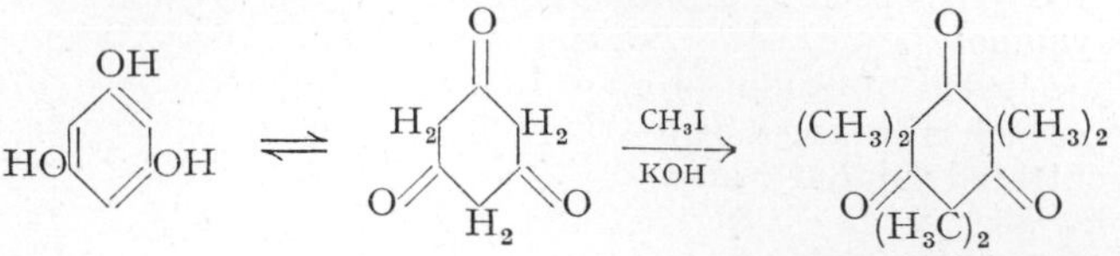

C-hexamethylphloroglucinol

These alkylations, however, may be explained, not by the existence of a keto-enol system, but by attack of alkyl carbonium ions at negative points in the system. This is a reasonable assumption since alkylations are always carried out in alkaline solution, and so one can expect the presence of a resonance hybrid ion (Thomson, 1956), *e.g.*,

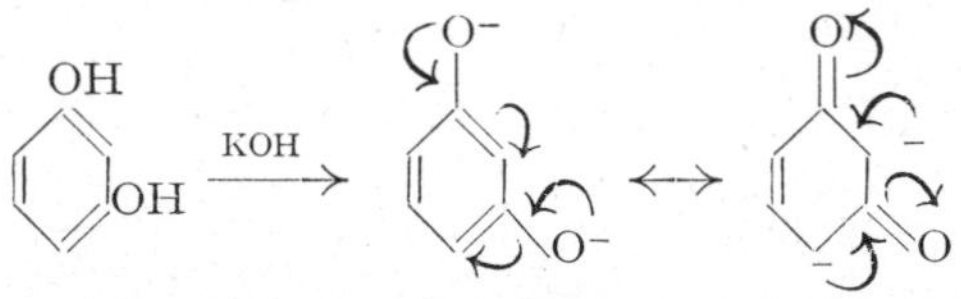

In addition to the phenols described above, three tetrahydric, one pentahydric, and one hexahydric phenol are known.

AROMATIC ETHERS

The aromatic ethers may be divided into two groups, the *phenolic ethers*, which are of the type Ar·O·R, and the ethers of the type Ar_2O (the diaryl ethers).

Phenolic ethers. These may be prepared by heating sodium phenoxide with alkyl halide in ethanol solution, or by treating an alkaline solution of a phenol with alkyl sulphate:

$$\mathrm{ArONa + RX \longrightarrow Ar{\cdot}O{\cdot}R + NaX} \quad (v.g.)$$

$$\mathrm{ArONa + R_2SO_4 \longrightarrow Ar{\cdot}O{\cdot}R + RNaSO_4} \quad (v.g.\text{–}ex.)$$

Phenolic methyl ethers may be obtained in excellent yield by the action of diazomethane on a phenol:

$$\mathrm{ArOH + CH_2N_2 \longrightarrow Ar{\cdot}O{\cdot}CH_3 + N_2} \quad (ex.)$$

Two important phenolic ethers are **anisole** (*methyl phenyl ether, methoxybenzene*), $C_6H_5{\cdot}O{\cdot}CH_3$, b.p. 155°, and **phenetole** (*ethyl phenyl ether, ethoxybenzene*), $C_6H_5{\cdot}O{\cdot}C_2H_5$, b.p. 172°. These ethers are prepared industrially by the alkylation of phenol with methyl or ethyl sulphate, or with the methyl and ethyl esters of *p*-toluenesulphonic acid.

Anisole and phenetole are used as the starting point for the preparation of various derivatives. They are stable liquids; they are unaffected by most acids and alkalis, but are decomposed by concentrated hydriodic acid (or hydrobromic acid) into phenol and alkyl iodide (or bromide):

$$\mathrm{C_6H_5{\cdot}O{\cdot}CH_3 + HI \longrightarrow C_6H_5OH + CH_3I}$$

The alkyl iodide can be absorbed by an ethanolic solution of silver nitrate, and the silver iodide so formed, weighed. This is the basis of the **Zeisel method** for the estimation of methoxyl and ethoxyl groups.

Phenolic ethers may be decomposed by refluxing with aluminium chloride, or better, with aluminium bromide, in benzene solution, using one equivalent of aluminium halide for each alkoxyl group present. The mechanism of the reaction is uncertain; according to Pfeiffer and Loewe (1936), the reaction takes place as follows:

$$C_6H_5{\cdot}O{\cdot}R + AlCl_3 \longrightarrow \left[C_6H_5{-}\overset{\overset{AlCl_3}{|}}{O}{-}R\right] \longrightarrow RCl + C_6H_5{\cdot}O{\cdot}AlCl_2 \xrightarrow{H_2O} C_6H_5OH + HOAlCl_2$$

Phenolic ethers may also be decomposed by refluxing in pyridine solution with sodium:

$$C_6H_5{\cdot}O{\cdot}R + 2Na \longrightarrow C_6H_5Na + RONa \xrightarrow{H_2O} C_6H_6 + ROH$$

Formation of an ether provides a means of protecting the hydroxyl group in many reactions; *e.g.*, in the Friedel–Crafts reaction, due to acidic character of the hydroxyl group, aluminium chloride is attacked with the liberation of hydrogen chloride:

$$C_6H_5OH + AlCl_3 \longrightarrow C_6H_5{\cdot}OAlCl_2 + HCl$$

Thus to carry out a successful Friedel–Crafts reaction with phenol, it is necessary to use a large amount of aluminium chloride. This, however, may be avoided by carrying out the reaction with the methyl ether, but the temperature must be kept as low as possible to prevent the catalyst decomposing the ether.

Catechol ethers. Guaiacol (o-*hydroxyanisole*), m.p. 32°, b.p. 205°, occurs in beech-wood tar from which it may be obtained by fractional distillation. Guaiacol is prepared synthetically from *o*-anisidine:

$$o\text{-}C_6H_4(O{\cdot}CH_3)(NH_2) \xrightarrow[\text{boil}]{NaNO_2/H_2SO_4} o\text{-}C_6H_4(O{\cdot}CH_3)(OH)$$

When refluxed with constant boiling hydrobromic acid, or heated with hydriodic acid at 130°, guaiacol is converted into catechol.

Guaiacol is used in medicine, and as the starting material in the preparation of vanillin (see p. 631).

Veratrole (1 : 2-*dimethoxybenzene*), b.p. 207°, may be prepared by methylating catechol with methyl sulphate in alkaline solution:

$$o\text{-}C_6H_4(OH)(OH) \xrightarrow[NaOH]{(CH_3)_2SO_4} o\text{-}C_6H_4(O{\cdot}CH_3)(O{\cdot}CH_3) \quad (95\%)$$

Eugenol (4-*allylguaiacol*), b.p. 254°, occurs in oil of cloves and in many other essential oils. When heated with ethanolic potassium hydroxide, or better, with potassium hydroxide in diethyleneglycol at 180°, eugenol isomerises to ***iso*-eugenol** (4-*propenylguaiacol*):

$$\underset{\text{eugenol}}{C_6H_3(OH)(OCH_3)(CH_2{\cdot}CH{:}CH_2)} \longrightarrow \underset{iso\text{eugenol}}{C_6H_3(OH)(OCH_3)(CH{:}CH{\cdot}CH_3)}$$

This migration of the double bond in the allyl side-chain, under the influence of alkali, is general; this is an example of prototropy.

*iso*Eugenol, b.p. 267·5°, also occurs naturally, and gives vanillin on gentle oxidation.

Anethole (p-*methoxypropenylbenzene*), m.p. 22–23°, b.p. 235°, is one of the chief constituents of aniseed oil, from which it is obtained. It is also prepared synthetically by the interaction of *p*-methoxyphenylmagnesium bromide and allyl bromide, and isomerising the product, **estragole** (*methyl-chavicol*), with alkali:

$$p\text{-}CH_3O\cdot C_6H_4\cdot MgBr + CH_2{:}CH\cdot CH_2Br \longrightarrow p\text{-}CH_3O\cdot C_6H_4\cdot CH_2\cdot CH{:}CH_2 \xrightarrow{KOH} p\text{-}CH_3O\cdot C_6H_4\cdot CH{:}CH\cdot CH_3$$

estragole, b.p. 215°

Safrole (4-*allyl*-1 : 2-*methylenedioxybenzene*), b.p. 232°, occurs in camphor oil and sassafras oil. When heated in ethanolic potassium hydroxide solution, or better, in a concentrated solution of potassium hydroxide in cellosolve (p. 237), safrole isomerises to ***iso*safrole**:

$$CH_2O_2{:}C_6H_3\cdot CH_2\cdot CH{:}CH_2 \xrightarrow{KOH} CH_2O_2{:}C_6H_3\cdot CH{:}CH\cdot CH_3$$

safrole *iso*safrole

*iso*Safrole, b.p. 252°, also occurs naturally, and gives piperonal on gentle oxidation (p. 631).

Aromatic ethers of the type Ar_2O. These are most conveniently prepared by means of the *Ullmann reaction* (*cf.* p. 552); *e.g.*, **diphenyl ether** may be prepared by refluxing a mixture of bromobenzene, phenol, potassium hydroxide with a small amount of copper as catalyst:

$$C_6H_5Br + C_6H_5OH + KOH \xrightarrow{Cu} (C_6H_5)_2O + KBr + H_2O \quad (90\%)$$

Diphenyl ether may also be prepared by heating phenol with aluminium chloride:

$$2C_6H_5OH \xrightarrow{AlCl_3} (C_6H_5)_2O + H_2O$$

Diphenyl ether is a solid, m.p. 28°, with a geranium odour. It is *not* decomposed by hydriodic acid, and is valuable as a high temperature heat transfer medium.

Ethers of aminophenols. The methyl ethers of *o*- and *p*-aminophenol are known as *o*-anisidine and *p*-anisidine, respectively, and each may be prepared by reducing its corresponding nitroanisole, *e.g.*, *o*-anisidine from *o*-nitroanisole:

$$o\text{-}CH_3O\cdot C_6H_4\cdot NO_2 \xrightarrow{Sn/HCl} o\text{-}CH_3O\cdot C_6H_4\cdot NH_2$$

The anisidines are used in the preparation of azo-dyes.

The ethyl ethers of the aminophenols are known as **phenetidines**; these are also used in the preparation of azo-dyes. The acetyl derivative of *p*-phenetidine is known as **phenacetin,** and is prepared commercially as follows:

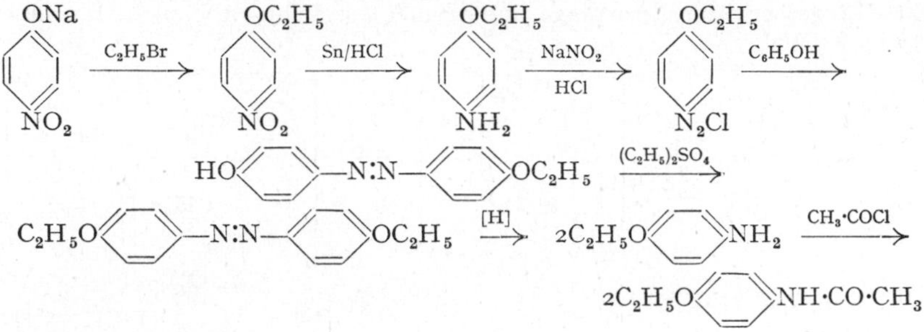

$$C_6H_4(ONa)(NO_2) \xrightarrow{C_2H_5Br} C_6H_4(OC_2H_5)(NO_2) \xrightarrow{Sn/HCl} C_6H_4(OC_2H_5)(NH_2) \xrightarrow[HCl]{NaNO_2} C_6H_4(OC_2H_5)(N_2Cl) \xrightarrow{C_6H_5OH}$$

$$HO{-}C_6H_4{-}N{:}N{-}C_6H_4{-}OC_2H_5 \xrightarrow{(C_2H_5)_2SO_4}$$

$$C_2H_5O{-}C_6H_4{-}N{:}N{-}C_6H_4{-}OC_2H_5 \xrightarrow{[H]} 2C_2H_5O{-}C_6H_4{-}NH_2 \xrightarrow{CH_3{\cdot}COCl}$$

$$2C_2H_5O{-}C_6H_4{-}NH{\cdot}CO{\cdot}CH_3$$

Phenacetin is replacing acetanilide in medicine; it is a very good analgesic (*i.e.*, promotes relief from pain) and antipyretic (*i.e.*, fever-reducing).

Dulcin is the carbamyl derivative of *p*-phenetidine, and is prepared by heating *p*-phenetidine with urea:

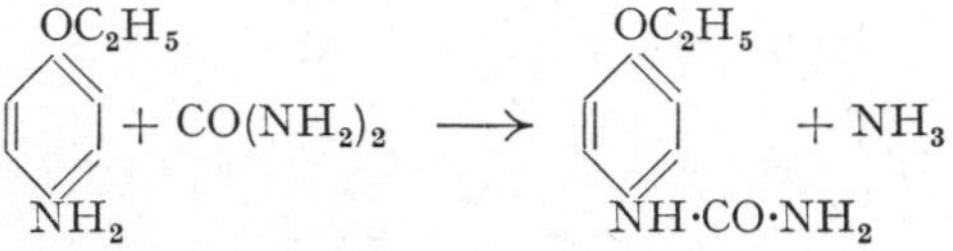

$$C_6H_4(OC_2H_5)(NH_2) + CO(NH_2)_2 \longrightarrow C_6H_4(OC_2H_5)(NH{\cdot}CO{\cdot}NH_2) + NH_3$$

Dulcin is a solid, m.p. 171°, and is about 200 times as sweet as sugar; it is used commercially as a sweetening agent.

Claisen rearrangement. When heated to about 200°, allyl ethers of phenols rearrange to form the corresponding *o*-allylphenols, *e.g.*,

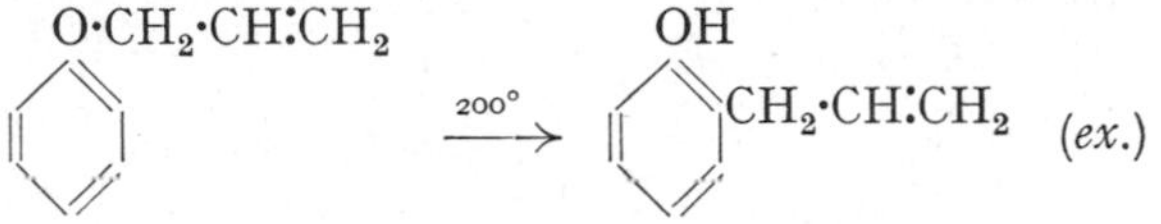

$$C_6H_5{\cdot}O{\cdot}CH_2{\cdot}CH{:}CH_2 \xrightarrow{200^\circ} o\text{-}C_6H_4(OH)(CH_2{\cdot}CH{:}CH_2) \quad (ex.)$$

This is known as the *Claisen rearrangement* The starting material may be readily prepared by heating phenol with allyl bromide in acetone solution in the presence of potassium carbonate:

$$C_6H_5OH + CH_2{=}CH{\cdot}CH_2Br \xrightarrow{K_2CO_3} C_6H_5{\cdot}O{\cdot}CH_2{\cdot}CH{=}CH_2 + HBr \quad (86\text{–}97\%)$$

In the Claisen rearrangement the allyl group migrates to the *o*-position preferably, but if both *o*-positions are occupied, it migrates to the *p*-position:

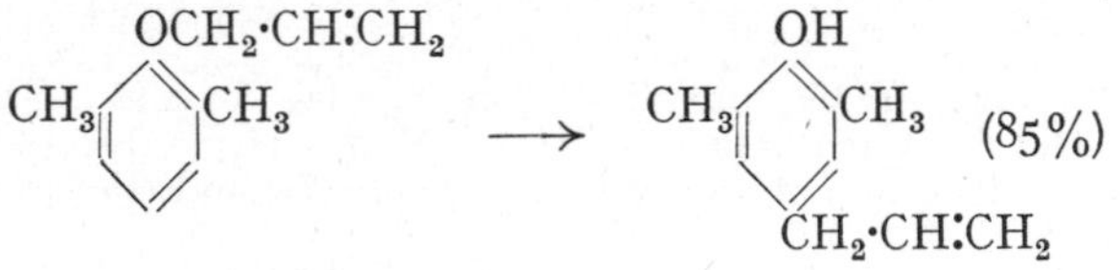

$$C_6H_3(CH_3)_2{\cdot}OCH_2{\cdot}CH{:}CH_2 \longrightarrow C_6H_2(CH_3)_2(OH)(CH_2{\cdot}CH{:}CH_2) \quad (85\%)$$

The Claisen rearrangement also takes place with allyl ethers of enols; actually, the rearrangement was originally discovered by Claisen (1912), while working on *O*-allylacetoacetic ester:

$$CH_3{\cdot}C(O{\cdot}CH_2{\cdot}CH{=}CH_2){=}CH{\cdot}CO_2C_2H_5 \longrightarrow CH_3{\cdot}CO{-}CH(CH_2{\cdot}CH{=}CH_2){\cdot}CO_2C_2H_5$$

This reaction further shows the resemblance between phenols and enols.

The mechanism of the Claisen rearrangement has been the subject of a great deal of work. It is now generally accepted that the *o*-rearrangement occurs by an intramolecular cyclic mechanism. The intramolecular nature of the rearrangement has been demonstrated by the fact that if two different ethers are heated together, they rearrange independently. Thus the *o*-rearrangement may be written:

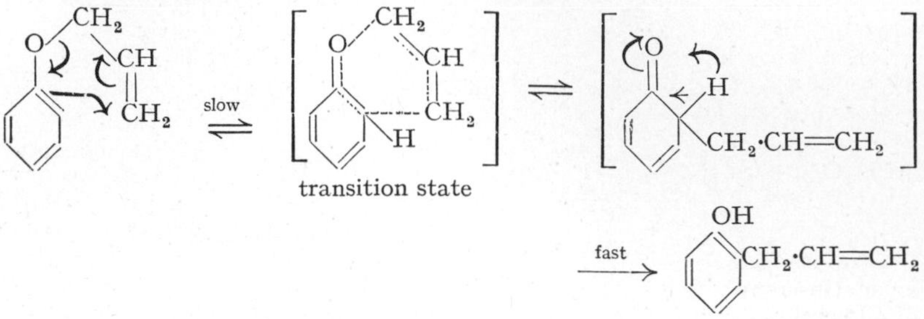

transition state

This is supported by many experiments, *e.g.*, Kistiakowsky *et al.* (1942), using deuterium as a tracer atom, showed that an *o*-D atom migrated to the oxygen atom:

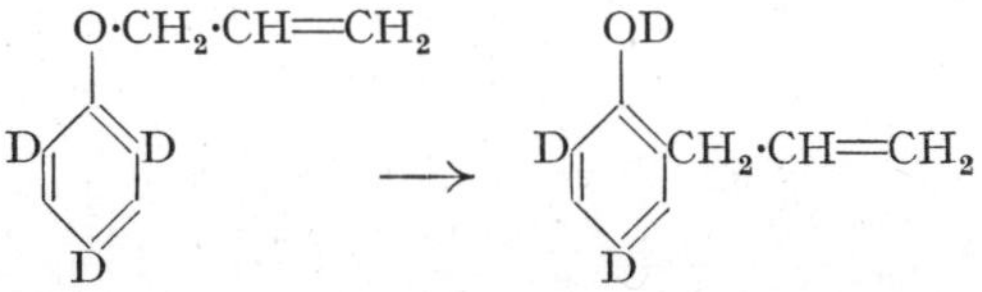

Schmid *et al.* (1953) carried out the rearrangement with the allyl radical labelled with ^{14}C and found that all of the tracer atom of the allyl group in the product was contained in the carbon attached to the nucleus; this supports the intramolecular cyclic mechanism.

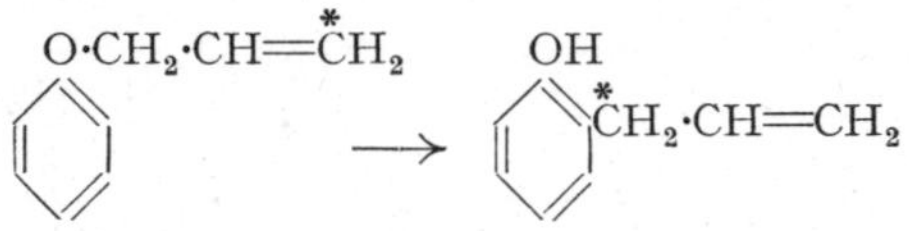

The mechanism of the *p*-rearrangement is believed to occur in two stages, each one with " inversion ", and thus the final product will *not* be " inverted ". Schmid *et al.* (1953) showed the following rearrangement occurred with labelled allyl 2 : 6-dimethylphenyl ether:

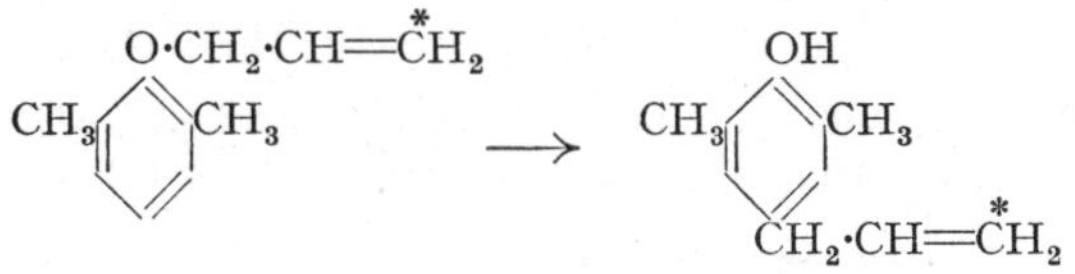

Curtin *et al.* (1954, 1956) prepared compounds (I) and (II) (A = allyl, $—CH_2·CH{=}CH_2$; M = methallyl, $—CH_2·C(CH_3){=}CH_2$), subjected each to the Claisen rearrangement, and obtained a mixture of (III) and (IV) from each:

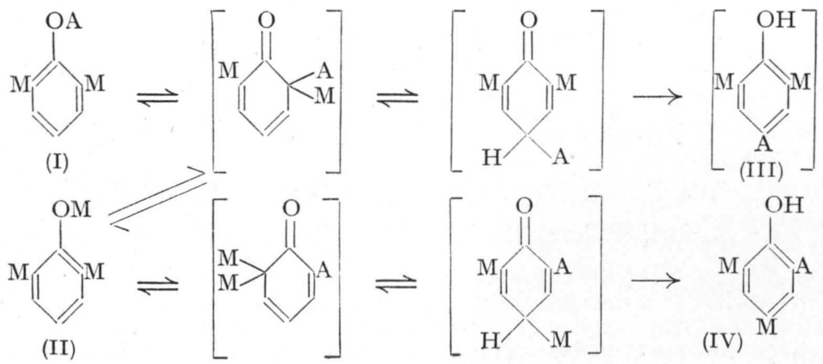

It will be seen that, apart from the two-step mechanism, it has been proposed that the rearrangement proceeds via the formation of a dienone (this also applies to the *o*-rearrangement). Evidence for the existence of this dienone in the *p*-rearrangement has been obtained by Curtin *et al.* (the above results can only be explained satisfactorily on the assumption that dienones are intermediates), and also by Conroy *et al.* (1956). Furthermore, the reversibility of both stages has been proved by Schmid *et al.* (1956) who used isotopically labelled allyl radicals.

QUESTIONS

1. Describe how each of the following compounds is prepared commercially:—(*a*) Phenol, (*b*) *o*- and *p*-nitrophenols, (*c*) picric acid, (*d*) *m*- and *p*-aminophenols, (*e*) catechol, (*f*) resorcinol, (*g*) anisole, (*h*) phenetole, (*i*) phenacetin, (*j*) dulcin.

2. Name the compounds and state under what conditions they are formed when phenol is treated with:—(*a*) $FeCl_3$, (*b*) NaOH, (*c*) Na_2CO_3, (*d*) Br_2, (*e*) HNO_3, (*f*) H_2SO_4, (*g*) Zn, (*h*) NH_3, (*i*) H_2, (*j*) EtI, (*k*) $KMnO_4$, (*l*) $Ph{\cdot}N_2Cl$, (*m*) CO_2, (*n*) AcCl, (*o*) H·CHO, (*p*) SO_2Cl_2, (*q*) PCl_5, (*r*) HNO_2, (*s*) $AlCl_3$.

3. Discuss the *differences* between the properties of PhOH and EtOH and attempt to account for them.

4. Starting with benzene or toluene, show how you would prepare:–(*a*) phenol, (*b*) 5-nitro-2-hydroxybenzyl alcohol, (*c*) *o*-nitrosophenol, (*d*) *p*-hydroxyacetophenone, (*e*) *p*-hydroxybenzyl chloride, (*f*) *o*-, *m*- and *p*-bromophenols, (*g*) *o*- and *p*-iodophenols, (*h*) *m*-nitrophenol, (*i*) picramide, (*j*) picramic acid, (*k*) *N*-acetylaminophenol, (*l*) *m*-phenolsulphonic acid, (*m*) *o*-, *m*- and *p*-cresols, (*n*) thymol, (*o*) *s*-trinitrobenzoic acid.

5. Write an account of:—(*a*) displacement of groups in phenol derivatives, (*b*) hydrogen bonding in phenol derivatives, (*c*) acid or basic strengths of phenol derivatives, (*d*) nitration of phenol, (*e*) the colour of nitrophenol ethers.

6. Describe the preparation and the more important properties of:—(*a*) the three dihydroxybenzenes, (*b*) the three trihydroxybenzenes.

7. Starting with any phenol you like, show how you would synthesise:—(*a*) guaiacol, (*b*) veratrole, (*c*) eugenol, (*d*) anethole, (*e*) diphenyl ether, (*f*) *o*-anisidine, (*g*) *p*-phenetidine.

8. Define and give examples of:—(*a*) Chloromethylation, (*b*) mercuration, (*c*) Fries reaction, (*d*) Lederer–Manasse reaction, (*e*) oxynitration, (*f*) Baudisch reaction, (*g*) Zeisel method, (*h*) Ullmann reaction, (*i*) Claisen rearrangement, (*j*) Elbs persulphate oxidation.

9. How would you show, by means of analytical and synthetic evidence, that the structure of a compound is (benzene ring: CH_3 at top, Br on the lower right, OC_2H_5 at bottom)?

10. Discuss the mechanisms of (*a*) the Fries reaction, (*b*) the Claisen rearrangement.

11. Give an account of the principles involved in the separation of isomeric substituted phenols.

12. Write an essay on clathrates.

READING REFERENCES

Organic Reactions, Wiley. Vol. I (1942), Ch. II. The Fries Reaction.
Vol. II (1944), Ch. 1. The Claisen Rearrangement.
Weiss, Molecular Compounds, *J.C.S.*, **1942**, 245.
Oxynitration.
(i) Westheimer *et al.*, *J. Amer. Chem. Soc.*, 1947, **69**, 773.
(ii) Carmack *et al.*, *ibid.*, 1947, **69**, 785.
(iii) Aristoff *et al.*, *Ind. Eng. Chem.*, 1948, **40**, 1281.
Cronheim, *o*-Nitrosophenols, *J. Org. Chem.*, 1947, **12**, 1, 7, 20.
Sidgwick, *The Organic Chemistry of Nitrogen.* Oxford Press (New Ed. by Taylor and Baker, 1937). (ii) p. 221. Nitrosophenols. (ii) p. 265. Nitrophenols.
Kenyon and Boehmer, Phenol by Sulphonation, *Ind. Eng. Chem.*, 1950, **42**, 1446.
Sethna, The Elbs Persulphate Oxidation, *Chem. Reviews*, 1951, **49**, 91.
Thomson, Phenol Tautomerism, *Quart. Reviews* (*Chem. Soc.*), 1956, **10**, 27.
Salt, Synthetic Phenol Manufacture, *Chem. and Ind.*, **1953**, S46.
Truter, Sorting Molecules by Size and Shape, *Research*, 1953, **6**, 320.

CHAPTER XXVII

ALCOHOLS, ALDEHYDES, KETONES AND QUINONES

AROMATIC ALCOHOLS

AROMATIC alcohols are compounds containing a hydroxyl group in a *side-chain*, and may be regarded as aryl derivatives of the aliphatic alcohols. Aromatic alcohols may be classified as primary, secondary, or tertiary alcohols, and their methods of preparation are similar to those used for aliphatic alcohols (p. 113). Only primary alcohols will be discussed in this section; secondary and tertiary aromatic alcohols are dealt with in the section on polynuclear hydrocarbons (see, *e.g.*, pp. 673, 676).

Benzyl alcohol (*phenylcarbinol*), $C_6H_5{\cdot}CH_2OH$, may be prepared:

(i) By hydrolysing benzyl chloride with aqueous sodium hydroxide:

$$C_6H_5{\cdot}CH_2Cl + NaOH \longrightarrow C_6H_5{\cdot}CH_2OH + NaCl \quad (70\%)$$

This method is used commercially:

(ii) By reducing benzaldehyde with zinc and hydrochloric acid:

$$C_6H_5{\cdot}CHO + 2[H] \longrightarrow C_6H_5{\cdot}CH_2OH$$

(iii) By means of the Cannizzaro reaction:

$$2C_6H_5{\cdot}CHO + NaOH \longrightarrow C_6H_5{\cdot}CH_2OH + C_6H_5{\cdot}CO_2Na \quad (90\%)$$

It may also be prepared by means of a crossed Cannizzaro reaction (p. 154):

$$C_6H_5{\cdot}CHO + H{\cdot}CHO + NaOH \longrightarrow C_6H_5{\cdot}CH_2OH + H{\cdot}CO_2Na$$

Benzyl alcohol (which is isomeric with the cresols) is a colourless liquid, b.p. 205°, sparingly soluble in water but readily soluble in organic solvents. Its reactions are similar to those of the primary aliphatic alcohols; *e.g.*, on oxidation, it forms benzaldehyde and finally benzoic acid:

$$C_6H_5{\cdot}CH_2OH \xrightarrow{[O]} C_6H_5{\cdot}CHO \xrightarrow{[O]} C_6H_5{\cdot}CO_2H$$

Benzyl alcohol forms esters, many of which are used in perfumery, *e.g.*, benzyl acetate (prepared from benzyl alcohol and acetic anhydride) occurs in oil of jasmine. Benzyl alcohol reacts with sodium to form sodium benzyl oxide.

In addition to the above reactions, benzyl alcohol exhibits aromatic properties due to the presence of the ring, *e.g.*, it can be nitrated, sulphonated, etc. Care, however, must be taken to avoid reaction with the hydroxyl group; it is therefore generally better, when preparing nuclear-substituted derivatives of benzyl alcohol, to use benzyl chloride (the CH_2Cl and CH_2OH groups are both *o-p*-orienting), and then hydrolyse to the alcohol.

Benzyl alcohol may be catalytically (palladium) reduced to toluene:

$$C_6H_5{\cdot}CH_2OH + H_2 \xrightarrow{Pd} C_6H_5{\cdot}CH_3 + H_2O$$

This reaction occurs when the benzyl group is attached to O, N, or S, and may also be effected by sodium amalgam or lithium aluminium hydride. *Debenzylation* is a very useful reaction since a benzyl group may be introduced into a compound to protect a sensitive group and then removed at the end of the reaction.

Hydroxybenzyl alcohols may be prepared by the Lederer–Manasse reaction (p. 597). **o-Hydroxybenzyl alcohol, salicyl alcohol** (*saligenin*), o-$HO{\cdot}C_6H_4{\cdot}CH_2OH$, occurs in the glucoside *salicin*. It is a crystalline solid, m.p. 87°, and is used in medicine as an antipyretic.

2-Phenylethanol (β-*phenylethyl alcohol*), $C_6H_5{\cdot}CH_2{\cdot}CH_2OH$, may be prepared by reducing phenylacetic ester with sodium and ethanol:

$$C_6H_5{\cdot}CH_2{\cdot}CO_2C_2H_5 + 4[H] \longrightarrow C_6H_5{\cdot}CH_2{\cdot}CH_2OH + C_2H_5OH$$

It is prepared industrially by the action of ethylene oxide on phenylmagnesium bromide:

$$C_6H_5{\cdot}MgBr + \overset{\diagup O \diagdown}{CH_2{\cdot}CH_2} \longrightarrow C_6H_5{\cdot}CH_2{\cdot}CH_2{\cdot}OMgBr \xrightarrow{H_2O} C_6H_5{\cdot}CH_2{\cdot}CH_2OH$$

2-Phenylethanol is a colourless oil, b.p. 220°, and is the chief constituent of rose oil. When heated with alkali, it forms styrene.

2-Phenylethanol and its esters are used in perfumery.

AROMATIC ALDEHYDES

Aromatic aldehydes fall into two groups: those in which the aldehyde group is directly attached to the nucleus, and those in which it is attached to the side-chain. The former group comprises the aromatic aldehydes; the latter, which behave as aliphatic aldehydes, are best regarded as aryl-substituted aliphatic aldehydes.

Benzaldehyde (*benzenecarbonal*), $C_6H_5{\cdot}CHO$, is also known as *oil of bitter almonds*, since it is found in the glucoside *amygdalin* which occurs in bitter almonds. Amygdalin may be hydrolysed by dilute acids or the enzyme emulsin to benzaldehyde, glucose and hydrogen cyanide:

$$C_{20}H_{27}O_{11}N + 2H_2O \longrightarrow C_6H_5{\cdot}CHO + 2C_6H_{12}O_6 + HCN$$

Benzaldehyde may be prepared by any of the following methods which are general for its homologues as well.

1. By the hydrolysis of benzylidene chloride with water at 100°, in the presence of iron powder as catalyst:

$$C_6H_5{\cdot}CHCl_2 + H_2O \longrightarrow C_6H_5{\cdot}CHO + 2HCl \quad (76\%)$$

Benzylidene chloride usually contains benzyl chloride and benzotrichloride, and consequently the product of hydrolysis is contaminated with benzyl alcohol and benzoic acid. If, however, hydrolysis is carried out with boric acid, then only benzylidene chloride is hydrolysed, the other two being unaffected under these conditions (the Makarov–Zemlianskii–Prokin method, 1936).

2. By boiling benzyl chloride with aqueous copper or lead nitrate in a current of carbon dioxide. The mechanism of the reaction is unknown; the equation usually given is:

$$2C_6H_5{\cdot}CH_2Cl + Pb(NO_3)_2 \longrightarrow 2C_6H_5{\cdot}CHO + PbCl_2 + 2HNO_2 \quad (40\%)$$

3. *By the oxidation of toluene.* This may be done in the vapour phase or in the liquid phase. In *vapour-phase oxidation*, toluene is catalytically oxidised with air diluted with nitrogen to prevent complete oxidation of the hydrocarbon. The temperature may be as high as 500°, and the catalyst is the oxide of metals such as manganese, molybdenum, zirconium, etc.:

$$C_6H_5{\cdot}CH_3 + O_2 \longrightarrow C_6H_5{\cdot}CHO + H_2O$$

Oxidation of hydrocarbons containing a side-chain of two or more carbon atoms gives mainly a ketone since only the α-carbon atom is readily oxidised, *e.g.*, ethylbenzene forms acetophenone:

$$C_6H_5{\cdot}CH_2{\cdot}CH_3 \xrightarrow[ZrO_2]{O_2} C_6H_5{\cdot}CO{\cdot}CH_3$$

In *liquid phase oxidation,* toluene is oxidised with manganese dioxide and 65 per cent. sulphuric acid at 40°. This method is used commercially.

Benzaldehyde may be conveniently prepared in the laboratory by oxidising toluene with chromium trioxide in acetic anhydride. As the benzaldehyde is formed, it is converted into benzylidene acetate, thereby preventing further oxidation of the benzaldehyde. Hydrolysis of the acetate with dilute sulphuric or hydrochloric acid gives benzaldehyde:

$$C_6H_5{\cdot}CH_3 \xrightarrow[(CH_3{\cdot}CO)_2O]{CrO_3} C_6H_5{\cdot}CH(O{\cdot}CO{\cdot}CH_3)_2 \xrightarrow{H_2O} C_6H_5{\cdot}CHO + CH_3{\cdot}CO_2H \quad (40\text{–}50\%)$$

A better yield of benzaldehyde may be obtained by oxidising benzyl alcohol with chromium trioxide in acetic anhydride (yield 90 per cent.) or with acid dichromate (yield 80–95 per cent.).

An interesting oxidising agent is chromyl chloride (**Étard's reaction,** 1877). In this method the hydrocarbon is treated with chromyl chloride in carbon tetrachloride solution and the complex, which is precipitated, is decomposed with water:

$$C_6H_5{\cdot}CH_3 + 2CrO_2Cl_2 \longrightarrow C_6H_5{\cdot}CH_3{\cdot}2CrO_2Cl_2 \xrightarrow{H_2O} C_6H_5{\cdot}CHO \quad (80\%)$$

Side-chains larger than methyl are oxidised at the *terminal* carbon atom, *e.g.*, ethylbenzene gives phenylacetaldehyde:

$$C_6H_5{\cdot}CH_2{\cdot}CH_3 \longrightarrow C_6H_5{\cdot}CH_2{\cdot}CHO$$

4. **Gattermann–Koch aldehyde synthesis** (1897). Benzaldehyde may be synthesised by bubbling a mixture of carbon monoxide and hydrogen chloride through a solution of nitrobenzene or ether containing benzene and a catalyst consisting of aluminium chloride and a small amount of cuprous chloride:

$$C_6H_6 + CO + HCl \xrightarrow{AlCl_3} C_6H_5{\cdot}CHO + HCl$$

In the absence of cuprous chloride the yield is very poor: in its presence, and under normal pressure, the yield is 30–50 per cent.; under high pressure, the yield is 80–90 per cent. Benzaldehyde can also be prepared from benzene and carbon monoxide under a pressure of 90 atmospheres in the presence of aluminium chloride. The reaction, however, must be carried out in the presence of a small amount of water which, presumably, produces hydrogen chloride by hydrolysis of aluminium chloride:

$$C_6H_6 + CO \xrightarrow[H_2O]{AlCl_3} C_6H_5{\cdot}CHO \quad (g.)$$

This method is used commercially.

When there are substituents in the ring, *e.g.*, a methyl group, the aldehyde group is introduced into the *p*-position only. The Gattermann–Koch aldehyde synthesis is not applicable to phenols and their ethers.

5. **Gattermann aldehyde synthesis** (1906). When benzene is treated with a mixture of hydrogen cyanide and hydrogen chloride in the presence of aluminium chloride, and the complex so produced decomposed with water, benzaldehyde is produced (in low yield).

Two mechanisms have been proposed for this reaction:

(i) *Formamidine hydrochloride* (*iminoformyl chloride*) is formed as an intermediate:

$$HCl + HCN \xrightarrow{AlCl_3} HN{=}CHCl$$

$$C_6H_6 + HN{:}CHCl \xrightarrow{AlCl_3} HCl + \underset{\text{aryl imine}}{C_6H_5{\cdot}CH{:}NH} \xrightarrow{H_2O} C_6H_5{\cdot}CHO + NH_3$$

(ii) *Chloromethyleneformamidine* is formed as an intermediate (Hinkel *et al.*, 1935):

$$2HCN + HCl \xrightarrow{AlCl_3} ClCH{:}N{\cdot}CH{:}NH$$

$$C_6H_6 + ClCH{:}N{\cdot}CH{:}NH \xrightarrow{AlCl_3} HCl + \underset{\text{aryl methyleneformamidine}}{C_6H_5{\cdot}CH{:}N{\cdot}CH{:}NH} \xrightarrow{H_2O}$$

$$C_6H_5{\cdot}CH{:}NH + NH_3 + H{\cdot}CO_2H \xrightarrow{H_2O} C_6H_5{\cdot}CHO + NH_3$$

There is evidence in support of each of these mechanisms, but it appears that (i) is more widely accepted.

The Gattermann reaction is applicable to phenols and phenolic ethers (see also phenolic aldehydes, p. 627).

6. **Sommelet's Reaction** (1913). Benzaldehyde is produced when benzyl chloride is refluxed with hexamethylenetetramine in aqueous ethanolic solution, followed by acidification and steam distillation:

$$C_6H_5{\cdot}CH_2Cl + (CH_2)_6N_4 \longrightarrow C_6H_5{\cdot}CHO \quad (60\text{–}70\%)$$

The mechanism of this reaction is uncertain. According to Angyal *et al.* (1953), the mechanism is:

(i) $C_6H_5{\cdot}CH_2Cl + C_6H_{12}N_4 \longrightarrow [C_6H_5{\cdot}CH_2{\cdot}C_6H_{12}N_4]^+Cl^- \longrightarrow$

$$C_6H_5{\cdot}CH_2{\cdot}N{=}CH_2 \xrightleftharpoons{H^+} C_6H_5{\cdot}CH_2{\cdot}\overset{+}{N}H{=}CH_2$$

(ii) $C_6H_5{\cdot}CH_2{\cdot}\overset{+}{N}H{=}CH_2 + C_6H_5{\cdot}\underset{H}{CH}{-}NH_2 \rightleftharpoons$

$$C_6H_5{\cdot}CH_2{\cdot}NH{\cdot}CH_3 + C_6H_5{\cdot}CH{=}\overset{+}{N}H_2 \xrightleftharpoons{H_2O} C_6H_5{\cdot}CHO + NH_3$$

Methylenebenzylamine, formed by hydrolysis of the quaternary compound, adds on a proton, and the ion thus formed reacts with benzylamine (formed as an intermediate) with transfer of a *hydride* ion from the latter to the former.

7. **Rosenmund reduction** (1918). Benzaldehyde is produced by bubbling hydrogen through benzoyl chloride in xylene solution in the presence of a palladium catalyst until the theoretical amount of hydrogen chloride has been evolved. The liquid is then acidified and steam distilled. To stop the reaction at the aldehyde stage, a quinoline-sulphur poison is added:

$$C_6H_5{\cdot}COCl + H_2 \xrightarrow{Pd} C_6H_5{\cdot}CHO + HCl \quad (v.g.)$$

This method may be used to prepare hydroxybenzaldehydes, provided the hydroxyl group is protected, *e.g.*, by acetylation.

8. **Stephen's method** (1925). When phenyl cyanide is reduced with stannous chloride and hydrochloric acid in ethereal solution, and then the product hydrolysed with water, benzaldehyde is formed (*cf.* p. 139):

$$C_6H_5{\cdot}CN \xrightarrow[\text{(ii) } H_2O]{\text{(i) } SnCl_2/HCl} C_6H_5{\cdot}CHO \quad (v.g.)$$

This method is a general one except for *o*-substituted cyanides, *e.g.*, *o*-tolyl cyanide, in which the yields are negligible due, possibly, to steric hindrance.

9. Benzaldehyde may be prepared by the reaction between phenylmagnesium bromide and ethyl formate:

$$C_6H_5{\cdot}MgBr + H{\cdot}CO_2C_2H_5 \longrightarrow C_6H_5{\cdot}CHO + MgBr(OC_2H_5)$$

10. Benzaldehyde may be obtained from aniline via the diazonium salt and formaldoxime (Beech, 1954):

$$C_6H_5{\cdot}N_2Cl \xrightarrow{CH_2=NOH} C_6H_5{\cdot}CH{=}NOH \xrightarrow{H_2O} C_6H_5{\cdot}CHO \quad (40\%)$$

Benzaldehyde is a colourless liquid, b.p. 179°. with a smell of almonds. It is only slightly soluble in water, but is readily soluble in ethanol and ether; it is steam-volatile. It is used for flavouring purposes, in perfumery and in the dye industry.

Benzaldehyde (and aromatic aldehydes in general) resembles aliphatic aldehydes in the following reactions:

(i) It gives the Schiff's reaction (p. 148).

(ii) It is readily oxidised, *i.e.*, it is a strong reducing agent; *e.g.*, it reduces ammoniacal silver nitrate to silver, itself being oxidised to benzoic acid. Benzaldehyde oxidises to benzoic acid when exposed to air. Baeyer and Villiger (1900) suggested that this oxidation took place by autoxidation via the formation of perbenzoic acid:

$$C_6H_5{\cdot}\overset{\overset{O}{\|}}{C}{-}H + O_2 \longrightarrow C_6H_5{\cdot}\overset{\overset{O}{\|}}{C}{-}O{-}OH \xrightarrow{C_6H_5\cdot CHO} 2C_6H_5{\cdot}CO_2H$$

Later work, however, has indicated that this mechanism is incomplete, and that autoxidation proceeds first via the free peroxide radical.

According to Bäckström (1934), the mechanism of the reaction is:

$$C_6H_5{\cdot}CHO \xrightarrow{h\nu} C_6H_5{\cdot}\dot{C}H{-}\dot{O}$$

$$C_6H_5{\cdot}\dot{C}H{-}\dot{O} + C_6H_5{\cdot}CHO \longrightarrow C_6H_5{\cdot}\dot{C}{=}O + C_6H_5{\cdot}\dot{C}HOH$$

$$C_6H_5{\cdot}\dot{C}{=}O + O_2 \longrightarrow C_6H_5{\cdot}C\begin{cases}O{-}O\cdot\\ {=}O\end{cases}$$

$$C_6H_5{\cdot}C\begin{cases}O{-}O\cdot\\ {=}O\end{cases} + C_6H_5{\cdot}CHO \longrightarrow C_6H_5{\cdot}C\begin{cases}O{-}OH\\ {=}O\end{cases} + C_6H_5{\cdot}\dot{C}{=}O$$

$$C_6H_5{\cdot}C\begin{cases}O{-}OH\\ {=}O\end{cases} + C_6H_5{\cdot}CHO \longrightarrow 2C_6H_5{\cdot}CO_2H$$

(iii) Benzaldehyde forms a bisulphite compound, and may be prepared pure via this compound:

$$C_6H_5{\cdot}CHO + NaHSO_3 \longrightarrow C_6H_5{\cdot}CH(OH){\cdot}SO_3Na$$

(iv) Benzaldehyde forms a cyanohydrin (*mandelonitrile*), $C_6H_5{\cdot}CH(OH){\cdot}CN$, with hydrogen cyanide, and an oxime (and phenylhydrazone) with hydroxylamine (and phenylhydrazine). The latter compounds exist in two geometrical isomeric forms, *e.g.*, benzaldoxime:

$$\begin{array}{c} C_6H_5-C-H \\ \| \\ N-OH \end{array} \qquad \begin{array}{c} C_6H_5-C-H \\ \| \\ HO-N \end{array}$$

syn-form *anti*-form

With hydrazine, benzaldehyde forms benzylideneazine, $C_6H_5{\cdot}CH{:}N{\cdot}N{:}CH{\cdot}C_6H_5$.

(v) Benzaldehyde reacts with phosphorus pentachloride to form benzylidene chloride:

$$C_6H_5{\cdot}CHO + PCl_5 \longrightarrow C_6H_5{\cdot}CHCl_2 + POCl_3$$

(vi) Benzaldehyde readily undergoes condensation with many aromatic and aliphatic compounds (see below).

Benzaldehyde (and other aromatic aldehydes) differs from aliphatic aldehydes in the following ways:

(i) It does not reduce Fehling's solution.

(ii) It does not readily polymerise; *e.g.*, it does not resinify with sodium hydroxide, but undergoes the Cannizzaro reaction due to its not having an α-hydrogen atom:

$$2C_6H_5{\cdot}CHO + NaOH \longrightarrow C_6H_5{\cdot}CH_2OH + C_6H_5{\cdot}CO_2Na$$

The mechanism of the Cannizzaro reaction is uncertain. Haber and Willstätter (1931) suggested a chain mechanism. Kharasch and Foy (1935) showed that the yield of benzyl alcohol and benzoic acid in the *heterogeneous* Cannizzaro reaction is lowered or even completely inhibited by employing peroxide-free benzaldehyde. This implies a free radical mechanism, which is supported by work of Weiss (1941).

On the other hand, several ionic mechanisms have been proposed; *e.g.*, according to Geissman the mechanism of the reaction may be:

$$C_6H_5{\cdot}\overset{H}{\overset{|}{C}}{=}O + \bar{O}H \rightleftharpoons C_6H_5{\cdot}\overset{H}{\overset{|}{\underset{OH}{\underset{|}{C}}}}{-}O^-$$

$$C_6H_5{\cdot}\overset{H}{\overset{|}{\underset{OH}{\underset{|}{C}}}}{-}O^- + C_6H_5{\cdot}\overset{O}{\overset{\|}{\underset{H}{\underset{|}{C}}}} \rightleftharpoons C_6H_5{\cdot}\overset{H}{\overset{|}{\underset{OH}{\underset{|}{C}}}}{\cdot}O{\cdot}\overset{O^-}{\overset{|}{\underset{H}{\underset{|}{C}}}}{\cdot}C_6H_5 \longrightarrow$$

$$C_6H_5{\cdot}\overset{H}{\overset{|}{\underset{H}{\underset{|}{C}}}}{\cdot}O{\cdot}\overset{O}{\overset{\|}{C}}{\cdot}C_6H_5 + \bar{O}H \longrightarrow C_6H_5{\cdot}CH_2OH + C_6H_5{\cdot}CO_2^-$$

This mechanism postulates the intermediate formation of benzyl benzoate (which has been isolated by Lachman, 1923) by the displacement of a hydroxyl ion and the intramolecular shift of a *hydride ion*, H:–. Recent work of Alexander (1947, 1948) supports this mechanism, and this author has shown that the Cannizzaro reaction with benzaldehyde in a *homogeneous* medium gives the same results in the presence or absence of peroxides.

(iii) Benzaldehyde does not yield a simple addition product with ammonia, but forms a complex product, *hydrobenzamide*.

$$3C_6H_5{\cdot}CHO + 2NH_3 \longrightarrow C_6H_5{\cdot}CH({-}N{:}CH{\cdot}C_6H_5)_2 + 3H_2O \quad (90\%)$$

Benzaldehyde also reacts with primary aromatic amines to form *anils* or *Schiff bases*; *e.g.*, with aniline it forms benzylideneaniline:

$$C_6H_5{\cdot}CHO + C_6H_5{\cdot}NH_2 \longrightarrow C_6H_5{\cdot}CH{:}N{\cdot}C_6H_5 + H_2O \quad (85\%)$$

Aliphatic aldehydes tend to form compounds of the type

$$R{\cdot}CH(NH{\cdot}C_6H_5)_2.$$

(iv) Reduction of benzaldehyde with zinc and hydrochloric acid or with sodium amalgam gives *hydrobenzoin* as well as benzyl alcohol (*cf.* pinacol, p. 239):

$$2C_6H_5{\cdot}CHO + 2[H] \longrightarrow C_6H_5{\cdot}CHOH{\cdot}CHOH{\cdot}C_6H_5$$

(v) When chlorinated in the absence of a halogen carrier, benzaldehyde forms benzoyl chloride (no α-hydrogen present):

$$C_6H_5{\cdot}CHO + Cl_2 \longrightarrow C_6H_5{\cdot}COCl + HCl$$

(vi) Benzaldehyde behaves as a base in concentrated sulphuric acid (see p. 633).

Condensation Reactions of Benzaldehyde

1. **Claisen reaction** (see also p. 147). Benzaldehyde, in the presence of dilute alkali, condenses with aliphatic aldehydes or ketones containing α-hydrogen; *e.g.*, with acetaldehyde it forms *cinnamaldehyde*:

$$C_6H_5{\cdot}CHO + CH_3{\cdot}CHO \xrightarrow{NaOH} C_6H_5{\cdot}CH{:}CH{\cdot}CHO + H_2O$$

With acetone, benzaldehyde forms benzylideneacetone (m.p. 42°; used in perfumery):

$$C_6H_5{\cdot}CHO + CH_3{\cdot}CO{\cdot}CH_3 \xrightarrow{NaOH} C_6H_5{\cdot}CH{:}CH{\cdot}CO{\cdot}CH_3 + H_2O \quad (65\text{–}78\%)$$

If the reaction is carried out in aqueous ethanolic sodium hydroxide, *dibenzylideneacetone* (m.p. 112°) is produced by interaction of benzylideneacetone and another molecule of benzaldehyde:

$$C_6H_5{\cdot}CH{:}CH{\cdot}CO{\cdot}CH_3 + C_6H_5{\cdot}CHO \longrightarrow C_6H_5{\cdot}CH{:}CH{\cdot}CO{\cdot}CH{:}CH{\cdot}C_6H_5 + H_2O \quad (90\text{–}94\%)$$

Benzaldehyde also condenses with acetophenone to form *phenyl styryl ketone* (*benzylideneacetophenone*):

$$C_6H_5{\cdot}CHO + CH_3{\cdot}CO{\cdot}C_6H_5 \xrightarrow{NaOH} C_6H_5{\cdot}CH{:}CH{\cdot}CO{\cdot}C_6H_5 + H_2O \quad (85\%)$$

Derivatives of phenyl styryl ketone are known as *chalkones*. Phenyl styryl ketone may be reduced catalytically (platinum) in ethyl acetate solution to *benzylacetophenone*:

$$C_6H_5{\cdot}CH{:}CH{\cdot}CO{\cdot}C_6H_5 + H_2 \xrightarrow{Pt} C_6H_5{\cdot}CH_2{\cdot}CH_2{\cdot}CO{\cdot}C_6H_5 \quad (81\text{–}95\%)$$

The above condensation reactions, apart from their synthetic value, illustrate the use of benzaldehyde to detect the presence of a $—CH_2{\cdot}CO$- group in carbonyl compounds (*cf.* p. 152).

Benzaldehyde condenses with crotonaldehyde, in the presence of pyridine acetate, to form 5-phenylpentadienal:

$$C_6H_5{\cdot}CHO + CH_3{\cdot}CH{:}CH{\cdot}CHO \longrightarrow C_6H_5{\cdot}CH{:}CH{\cdot}CH{:}CH{\cdot}CHO + H_2O$$

This reaction is an example of vinylogy (p. 269), and was introduced by Kuhn (1929).

Benzaldehyde also condenses with nitromethane to form ω-nitrostyrene; the methylene group is made "active" by the adjacent nitro-group:

$$C_6H_5\cdot CHO + CH_3\cdot NO_2 \xrightarrow{NaOH} C_6H_5\cdot CH{:}CH\cdot NO_2 + H_2O \quad (80\text{–}83\%)$$

2. **Perkin reaction** (1877). When benzaldehyde (or any other aromatic aldehyde) is heated with the anhydride of an aliphatic acid (containing two α-hydrogen atoms) in the presence of its sodium salt, condensation takes place to form a β-arylacrylic acid; *e.g.*, with acetic anhydride and sodium acetate, cinnamic acid is formed:

$$C_6H_5\cdot CHO + (CH_3\cdot CO)_2O \xrightarrow{CH_3\cdot CO_2Na} C_6H_5\cdot CH{:}CH\cdot CO_2H$$

With propionic anhydride and sodium propionate, α-methylcinnamic acid is formed:

$$C_6H_5\cdot CHO + (CH_3\cdot CH_2\cdot CO)_2O \xrightarrow{CH_3\cdot CH_2\cdot CO_2Na} C_6H_5\cdot CH{:}C(CH_3)\cdot CO_2H$$

The mechanism of the Perkin reaction has been the subject of much discussion. Perkin believed that the anhydride was involved, whereas Fittig believed it was the salt. The general feeling now is that it is the anhydride that is the addendum; the actual steps involved, however, are uncertain. The mechanism may be as follows (*cf.* the aldol condensation):

$$CH_3\cdot CO\cdot O\cdot CO\cdot CH_3 + CH_3\cdot CO_2^- \rightleftharpoons \bar{C}H_2\cdot CO\cdot O\cdot CO\cdot CH_3 + CH_3\cdot CO_2H$$

$$C_6H_5\cdot\underset{H}{\overset{O}{\overset{\|}{C}}} + \bar{C}H_2\cdot CO\cdot O\cdot CO\cdot CH_3 \rightleftharpoons C_6H_5\cdot\underset{H}{\overset{\bar{O}}{C}}\cdot CH_2\cdot CO\cdot O\cdot CO\cdot CH_3 \overset{H^+}{\rightleftharpoons}$$

$$C_6H_5\cdot\underset{H}{\overset{OH}{C}}\cdot CH_2\cdot CO\cdot O\cdot CO\cdot CH_3 \xrightarrow{-H_2O} C_6H_5\cdot CH{:}CH\cdot CO\cdot O\cdot CO\cdot CH_3 \xrightarrow{H_2O} C_6H_5\cdot CH{:}CH\cdot CO_2H + CH_3\cdot CO_2H$$

It should be noted that only the α-hydrogen atoms of the anhydride are involved in the condensation.

Experiment has shown that the Perkin reaction proceeds more readily when the aldehyde contains a halogen atom or a nitro-group in the ring.

Benzaldehyde undergoes the Knoevenagel reaction with malonic acid in ethanolic ammonia to form cinnamic acid:

$$C_6H_5\cdot CHO + CH_2(CO_2H)_2 \longrightarrow C_6H_5\cdot CH{:}CH\cdot CO_2H + CO_2 + H_2O$$

A special case of the Perkin reaction is the condensation of benzaldehyde with cyclic anhydrides, *e.g.*, succinic anhydride (see p. 264).

3. **Benzoin condensation.** When refluxed with aqueous ethanolic potassium cyanide, benzaldehyde forms benzoin (see also p. 677):

$$2C_6H_5\cdot CHO \xrightarrow{KCN} C_6H_5\cdot CHOH\cdot CO\cdot C_6H_5 \quad (83\%)$$

4. Benzaldehyde condenses with phenols and tertiary aromatic amines in the presence of sulphuric acid or zinc chloride to form triphenylmethane derivatives; *e.g.*, with dimethylaniline it forms *malachite green*:

$$C_6H_5\cdot CHO + 2\,C_6H_5\cdot N(CH_3)_2 \xrightarrow{H_2SO_4} C_6H_5\cdot CH\left[C_6H_4\cdot N(CH_3)_2\right]_2$$

Derivatives of benzaldehyde

A large variety of substituted benzyl alcohols can be oxidised to the corresponding aldehydes by means of dinitrogen tetroxide solutions (yields: 91–98 per cent.). The benzyl alcohols (except the nitro-compounds) may be obtained by reduction of acid chloride or methyl esters with lithium aluminium hydride (Field *et al.*, 1955), *e.g.*,

$$C_6H_4(OCH_3)(COCl) \xrightarrow[93\%]{LiAlH_4} C_6H_4(OCH_3)(CH_2OH) \xrightarrow[96\%]{N_2O_4} C_6H_4(OCH_3)(CHO)$$

Various substituted benzaldehydes may also be obtained via diazonium salts (Beech, 1954), *e.g.*,

$$C_6H_4(NH_2)(NO_2) \quad C_6H_4(N_2Cl)(NO_2) \xrightarrow[(ii)\ H_2O]{(i)\ CH_2{=}NOH} C_6H_4(CHO)(NO_2) \quad (33\%)$$

Nitrobenzaldehydes. Curiously enough, nitrating mixture nitrates benzaldehyde to a large extent instead of oxidising it (as might have been expected). The main product is the *m*-isomer, m.p. 58° (about 50 per cent.), together with the *o*-isomer (about 20 per cent.).

o-*Nitrobenzaldehyde* may be prepared by oxidising *o*-nitrocinnamic acid with cold aqueous potassium permanganate:

$$C_6H_4(CH{:}CH{\cdot}CO_2H)(NO_2) \xrightarrow{KMnO_4} C_6H_4(CHO)(NO_2)$$

Alternatively, it may be prepared by dissolving *o*-nitrotoluene in glacial acetic acid containing acetic anhydride, and adding chromium trioxide and sulphuric acid. The product is the diacetate and this, on hydrolysis, gives the aldehyde:

$$C_6H_4(CH_3)(NO_2) \longrightarrow C_6H_4(CH(O{\cdot}CO{\cdot}CH_3)_2)(NO_2) \longrightarrow C_6H_4(CHO)(NO_2)$$

(23–24%) (74%)

A better yield may be obtained by oxidising the *o*-nitrotoluene with manganese dioxide and sulphuric acid.

o-Nitrobenzaldehyde is a yellow solid, m.p. 44°. Its most important reaction is its conversion into indigotin when heated with acetone and sodium hydroxide:

$$2C_6H_4(NO_2)(CHO) + 2CH_3{\cdot}CO{\cdot}CH_3 \xrightarrow{NaOH} C_6H_4{<}^{NH}_{CO}{>}C{=}C{<}^{CO}_{NH}{>}C_6H_4$$

p-*Nitrobenzaldehyde* (m.p. 106°) may be prepared by oxidising *p*-nitrocinnamic acid or *p*-nitrotoluene; it may also be prepared by oxidising *p*-nitrobenzyl chloride with aqueous lead nitrate.

All three nitrobenzaldehydes may be reduced to the corresponding aminobenzaldehydes by shaking a mixture of nitrobenzaldehyde and solid sodium carbonate with ferrous sulphate solution (*cf.* p. 540). The reduction may also be effected by stannous chloride and hydrochloric acid. On the other hand, sodium borohydride reduces nitrobenzaldehydes to the corresponding nitrobenzyl alcohols.

o-*Aminobenzaldehyde* readily condenses with compounds containing a —CH_2·CO—group to form quinoline compounds; *e.g.*, with acetaldehyde it forms *quinoline*:

$$C_6H_4(CHO)(NH_2) + CH_3\text{—}CHO \longrightarrow \text{quinoline} + 2H_2O$$

m- and p-*Aminobenzaldehydes* are used in the preparation of dyes. *o*- and *p*-Aminobenzaldehydes are prepared commercially by the oxidation of the corresponding aminobenzyl alcohols (see method 3, p. 628).

2:4-*Dinitrobenzaldehyde* (m.p. 72°) may be prepared by dissolving dimethylaniline in concentrated hydrochloric acid and adding sodium nitrite. The *p*-nitroso-compound so produced is heated with 2:4-dinitrotoluene in the presence of sodium carbonate, and the condensation product is then heated with hydrochloric acid (*cf.* p. 533):

$$C_6H_5N(CH_3)_2 \xrightarrow{HNO_2} p\text{-}ON\cdot C_6H_4N(CH_3)_2$$

$$(CH_3)_2N\text{—}C_6H_4\text{—}NO + CH_3\text{—}C_6H_3(NO_2)_2 \xrightarrow{Na_2CO_3}$$

$$(CH_3)_2N\text{—}C_6H_4\text{—}N{:}CH\text{—}C_6H_3(NO_2)_2 \xrightarrow{HCl} p\text{-}H_2N\cdot C_6H_4N(CH_3)_2 + 2{:}4\text{-}(NO_2)_2C_6H_3CHO \quad (24\text{–}32\%)$$

Halogen derivatives of benzaldehyde. *m*-Halogenobenzaldehydes may be prepared from *m*-nitrobenzaldehyde by reduction and subsequent replacement of the diazo-group by halogen (Sandmeyer reaction), *e.g.*, *m*-chlorobenzaldehyde:

$$m\text{-}NO_2C_6H_4CHO \xrightarrow{SnCl_2/HCl} m\text{-}NH_2C_6H_4CHO \xrightarrow[HCl]{NaNO_2} m\text{-}N_2ClC_6H_4CHO \xrightarrow[HCl]{CuCl} m\text{-}ClC_6H_4CHO \quad (75\text{—}79\%)$$

o- and *p*-Halogeno-benzaldehydes may be prepared by brominating the corresponding halogeno-toluenes at their boiling points in the presence of light to give the benzylidene bromide derivative, and hydrolysing this with calcium hydroxide; *e.g.*, *p*-bromobenzaldehyde from *p*-bromotoluene:

$$p\text{-}BrC_6H_4CH_3 \xrightarrow{Br_2} p\text{-}BrC_6H_4CHBr_2 \xrightarrow{H_2O} p\text{-}BrC_6H_4CHO \quad (60\text{–}69\%)$$

Alternatively, the halogeno-toluene may be oxidised with manganese dioxide and sulphuric acid.

2 : 6-*Dichlorobenzaldehyde* (m.p. 72°) is important in the preparation of triphenylmethane dyes; it may be prepared as follows:

$$o\text{-}CH_3C_6H_4NO_2 \xrightarrow[Fe]{Cl_2} Cl(CH_3)C_6H_3NO_2 \xrightarrow{Fe/HCl} Cl(CH_3)C_6H_3NH_2 \xrightarrow[HCl]{NaNO_2} Cl(CH_3)C_6H_3N_2Cl \xrightarrow[HCl]{CuCl}$$

$$Cl_2C_6H_3CH_3 \xrightarrow[\text{(at b.p.)}]{Cl_2} Cl_2C_6H_3CHCl_2 \xrightarrow[\text{(con. } H_2SO_4)]{H_2O} Cl_2C_6H_3CHO$$

Concentrated sulphuric acid must be used to hydrolyse the *o* : *o'*-dichlorobenzylidene chloride; alkali has very little effect (this is an example of steric hindrance). The overall yield of 2 : 6-dichlorobenzaldehyde is very small; this is to be expected from the large number of steps involved. This method illustrates the important point that although a particular method gives a small yield of the desired product, it may be the only worthwhile method to use. It is therefore important that the reader should realise that many syntheses, although very complicated, may nevertheless be the best in practice (*cf.* 2 : 4-dinitrobenzaldehyde, above).

Benzaldehydesulphonic acids. Sulphonation of benzaldehyde gives mainly the *m*-derivative. The *o*- and *p*-isomers are prepared indirectly.

Cinnamaldehyde (3-*phenylpropenal*), $C_6H_5{\cdot}CH{:}CH{\cdot}CHO$, is the chief constitutent of cinnamon oil, from which it may be isolated by means of its bisulphite compound. It may be prepared synthetically by the Claisen reaction between benzaldehyde and acetaldehyde:

$$C_6H_5{\cdot}CHO + CH_3{\cdot}CHO \xrightarrow{NaOH} C_6H_5{\cdot}CH{:}CH{\cdot}CHO + H_2O$$

Cinnamaldehyde is an oil, b.p. 252°, which slowly oxidises in air to cinnamic acid. This acid may also be obtained by oxidising cinnamaldehyde with ammoniacal silver nitrate:

$$C_6H_5{\cdot}CH{:}CH{\cdot}CHO + [O] \longrightarrow C_6H_5{\cdot}CH{:}CH{\cdot}CO_2H$$

Vigorous oxidising agents, *e.g.*, acid permanganate, convert cinnamaldehyde into benzoic acid.

Cinnamaldehyde forms the normal bisulphite compound with sodium hydrogen sulphite, but on prolonged treatment with this reagent, the sodium salt of a disulphonic acid is formed, possibly as follows (*cf.* p. 261):

$$C_6H_5{\cdot}CH{:}CH{\cdot}CHO + NaHSO_3 \rightleftharpoons C_6H_5{\cdot}CH{:}CH(OH){\cdot}SO_3Na$$

$$\downarrow$$

$$\underset{\text{(1 : 4-addition)}}{C_6H_5{\cdot}CH(SO_3Na){\cdot}CH_2{\cdot}CHO} \xrightleftharpoons{NaHSO_3} C_6H_5{\cdot}CH(SO_3Na){\cdot}CH_2{\cdot}CH(OH){\cdot}SO_3Na$$

The normal addition is reversible; the 1 : 4-addition is irreversible, and hence all the cinnamaldehyde is gradually converted into the disulphonic acid. Cinnamaldehyde adds on bromine to the double bond to form the dibromide, $C_6H_5{\cdot}CHBr{\cdot}CHBr{\cdot}CHO$, and is reduced by aluminium *iso*propoxide to cinnamyl alcohol, $C_6H_5{\cdot}CH{:}CH{\cdot}CH_2OH$.

PHENOLIC ALDEHYDES

Phenolic aldehydes (*hydroxyaldehydes*) are very important compounds, and contain an aldehyde group and one or more hydroxyl groups directly attached to the nucleus.

General methods of preparation. 1. **Gattermann's aldehyde synthesis** (*cf.* benzaldehyde, p. 618). When phenol or a phenolic ether is treated with a mixture of hydrogen cyanide and hydrogen chloride in the presence of aluminium chloride, and the complex produced then decomposed with water, *p*-hydroxy-(or alkoxy)benzaldehyde is the main product:

$$HOC_6H_4 + ClCH{:}NH \xrightarrow{AlCl_3} HOC_6H_4CH{:}NH + HCl \xrightarrow{H_2O} HOC_6H_4CHO + NH_3$$

When one hydroxyl group is present in the ring, aluminium chloride is used as catalyst; but with *m*-substituted di- or trihydric phenols, zinc chloride is a better catalyst.

Instead of a mixture of hydrogen cyanide and hydrogen chloride, zinc cyanide and hydrogen chloride may be used (Adams *et al.*, 1923). Pure zinc cyanide, however, is ineffective; a trace of potassium or sodium chloride is necessary. Hinkel (1937) has shown that zinc cyanide may be used for hydrocarbons, and Niedzielski and Nord (1941) have found that sodium cyanide may be used for any aromatic hydrocarbon except benzene.

2. **Reimer–Tiemann reaction** (1876). This reaction is carried out by refluxing an alkaline solution of phenol with chloroform at 60°, distilling off the excess chloroform, acidifying the residual liquid with sulphuric acid, and then steam-distilling it. Unchanged phenol and *o*-hydroxybenzaldehyde distil over, leaving behind *p*-hydroxybenzaldehyde.

The mechanism of the Reimer–Tiemann reaction is uncertain. According to Wynberg (1954) it is:

$$C_6H_5OH \xrightarrow{NaOH} C_6H_5O^- + {:}CCl_2 \longrightarrow \text{(cyclohexadienone with H and } {:}CCl_2^- \text{)} \longrightarrow o\text{-}^-OC_6H_4CHCl_2 \xrightarrow[H_2O]{OH^-} o\text{-}^-OC_6H_4CHO$$

Hine (1950) has obtained kinetic evidence to show that carbon dichloride is the reactive species rather than chloroform itself.

$$CHCl_3 + OH^- \underset{}{\overset{fast}{\rightleftharpoons}} H_2O + CCl_3^- \xrightarrow{slow} Cl^- + CCl_2$$

These compounds containing bivalent carbon are known as *carbenes*; thus CCl_2 is called dichlorocarbene.

When *o*- or *p*-cresol is used instead of phenol, a ketonic by-product containing the dichloromethyl group is always obtained, *e.g.*,

$$p\text{-}CH_3C_6H_4OH \xrightarrow[CHCl_3]{NaOH} \text{2-}OH\text{-5-}CH_3C_6H_3CHO + \text{4-}CH_3\text{-4-}CHCl_2\text{-cyclohexa-2,5-dienone}$$

A large amount of phenol always remains unreacted in the Reimer–Tiemann reaction. To account for this, Armstrong and Richardson (1933) suggested:

$$C_6H_5OH + CHCl_3 \xrightarrow{NaOH} [o\text{-}O^-C_6H_4CHCl_2] \xrightarrow{2C_6H_5ONa} o\text{-}\bar{O}C_6H_4CH(OC_6H_5)_2 \xrightarrow{H_2SO_4} o\text{-}HOC_6H_4CHO + 2C_6H_5OH$$

These authors obtained evidence for the existence of the diphenylacetal derivative in the alkaline solution. Another interesting point about the Reimer–Tiemann reaction is that the nature of the *cation* affects the *o*/*p* ratio, *e.g.*, with sodium hydroxide, the ratio is 2 : 1; with cæsium hydroxide, 1 : 1 (Brady *et al.*, 1950).

In the Reimer–Tiemann reaction, phenols react with chloroform and alkali to give *o*- and *p*-phenolic aldehydes, the *o*-isomer predominating. The yields are not usually above 50 per cent., and the presence of a negative group such as NO_2, CN, CO_2H, or SO_3H (*m*-orienting) decreases the yield to less than 25 per cent. If one of the *o*-positions is occupied, the aldehyde group tends to go to the *p*-position; *e.g.*, guaiacol forms vanillin:

$$o\text{-}HOC_6H_4OCH_3 \xrightarrow[NaOH]{CHCl_3} 4\text{-}HO\text{-}3\text{-}CH_3OC_6H_3CHO$$

If carbon tetrachloride is used instead of chloroform, the product of the reaction is a phenolic acid (see p. 652).

3. *o*- and *p*-Hydroxybenzyl alcohols may be prepared by the Lederer–Manasse reaction (p. 597). These alcohols may be oxidised to the corresponding hydroxyaldehydes (aminobenzaldehydes may be prepared similarly from aniline). This method is used industrially, the oxidation being carried out with nitrosobenzene or phenylhydroxylamine, in the presence of copper as catalyst:

$$p\text{-}HOC_6H_4CH_2OH + C_6H_5{\cdot}NO \xrightarrow{Cu} p\text{-}HOC_6H_4CH{:}N{\cdot}C_6H_5 \xrightarrow{H_2O} p\text{-}HOC_6H_4CHO \quad (40\text{–}50\%)$$

An extension of the above method is the *chloral condensation.* This is a modified Lederer–Manasse reaction, chloral being used instead of formaldehyde, *e.g.*,

$$C_6H_5OH + CCl_3{\cdot}CHO \xrightarrow{aq.\ K_2CO_3} p\text{-}HOC_6H_4CHOH{\cdot}CCl_3 \xrightarrow[NaOH]{Na_2Cr_2O_7} p\text{-}HOC_6H_4CHO \quad (40\text{–}60\%)$$

In this reaction, the chloral always enters the *p*-position unless it is occupied, in which case *o*-substitution takes place, but to a lesser extent.

4. **Duff's reaction** (1932). When phenol is heated with a mixture of hexamethylenetetramine, glycerol and boric acid, the mixture then acidified with sulphuric acid and steam distilled, *o*-hydroxybenzaldehyde is formed:

$$C_6H_5OH \xrightarrow{(CH_2)_6N_4} o\text{-}HO\cdot C_6H_4\cdot CH{:}N\cdot CH_3 \xrightarrow{H_2O} o\text{-}HO\cdot C_6H_4\cdot CHO \quad (15\text{–}20\%)$$

This method gives only the *o*-compound, and is hindered by the presence of a negative group in the ring.

5. **Formylation with *N*-methylformanilide** (Vilsmeier and Haack, 1927). Provided the aromatic compound has a labile hydrogen atom in the nucleus it can be formylated, *i.e.*, an aldehyde group can be introduced, by means of *N*-methylformanilide. The method works well for the *o*- and *p*-positions of phenolic ethers (and dialkyl anilines); it does not work with hydrocarbons, except with anthracene, in which case the aldehyde group enters the 9-position (see p. 702). The formylation is carried out by treating the compound with *N*-methylformanilide and phosphoryl chloride, and when the reaction is complete, adding aqueous sodium acetate and steam distilling:

$$C_6H_5\cdot OCH_3 + C_6H_5\cdot N(CH_3)\cdot CHO \longrightarrow p\text{-}CH_3O\cdot C_6H_4\cdot CHO + C_6H_5\cdot NH\cdot CH_3$$

Dimethylformamide, $H\cdot CO\cdot N(CH_3)_2$, may be used instead of *N*-methylformanilide.

N-Methylformanilide (and, in general, disubstituted formamides) reacts with Grignard reagents to form aldehydes (Bouveault, 1904; Smith *et al.*, 1941), *e.g.*,

$$o\text{-}CH_3\cdot C_6H_4\cdot Br \xrightarrow{Mg} o\text{-}CH_3\cdot C_6H_4\cdot MgBr \xrightarrow{C_6H_5\cdot NMe\cdot CHO} o\text{-}CH_3\cdot C_6H_4\cdot CHO \quad (50\%)$$

6. **By means of organo-lithium compounds.** When a substituted phenyllithium compound is heated with ethyl orthoformate or *N*-methylformanilide, an intermediate compound is obtained which, on hydrolysis with acid, gives a substituted benzaldehyde in 70 per cent. yield, *e.g.*,

$$p\text{-}CH_3O\cdot C_6H_4\cdot Li + H\cdot C(OC_2H_5)_3 \longrightarrow p\text{-}CH_3O\cdot C_6H_4\cdot CH(OC_2H_5)_2 \xrightarrow{H_2O} p\text{-}CH_3O\cdot C_6H_4\cdot CHO$$

Salicylaldehyde (o-*hydroxybenzaldehyde*) occurs in certain essential oils. It may be prepared by any of the general methods applicable to *o*-hydroxyaldehydes. It is manufactured by the oxidation of *o*-hydroxybenzyl alcohol (obtained by method 3, above), and by the oxidation of *o*-cresylbenzenesulphonate with manganese dioxide and sulphuric acid:

$$o\text{-}(C_6H_5\cdot SO_2\cdot O)C_6H_4\cdot CH_3 \xrightarrow{[O]} o\text{-}(C_6H_5\cdot SO_2\cdot O)C_6H_4\cdot CHO \xrightarrow{H_2O} o\text{-}HO\cdot C_6H_4\cdot CHO$$

Salicylaldehyde is an oil, b.p. 197°, soluble in water and alkalis to give a yellow solution. The aqueous solution gives a violet coloration with ferric chloride. Salicylaldehyde may be oxidised to salicylic acid and reduced to *o*-hydroxybenzyl alcohol. Oxidation with alkaline hydrogen peroxide converts it into catechol (see p. 606).

The hydroxyl group of salicylaldehyde is not so reactive as that in the *m*- and *p*-isomers. This is probably due to hydrogen bonding, which also accounts for the high volatility of salicylaldehyde (compared with the *m*- and *p*-compounds).

Salicylaldehyde (and other *o*-hydroxy-aldehydes) condenses with ketones to form unsaturated ketones which, under the influence of hydrochloric acid, form ring compounds known as **pyrylium compounds,** in which the oxygen is tercovalent unielectrovalent:

$$C_6H_4(CHO)(OH) + CH_3{\cdot}CO{\cdot}R \longrightarrow C_6H_4(CH{:}CH{\cdot}CO{\cdot}R)(OH) \xrightarrow{HCl} \text{pyrylium chloride } (R, \overset{+}{O}\ Cl^-)$$

Anisaldehyde (p-*methoxybenzaldehyde*) occurs in various essential oils. It is prepared industrially by oxidising anethole (by ozonolysis or with acid dichromate):

$$p\text{-}CH_3O{\cdot}C_6H_4{\cdot}CH{:}CH{\cdot}CH_3 \xrightarrow[H_2SO_4]{K_2Cr_2O_7} p\text{-}CH_3O{\cdot}C_6H_4{\cdot}CHO$$

Anisaldehyde may be prepared synthetically by methylating *p*-hydroxybenzaldehyde with methyl sulphate and aqueous sodium hydroxide or with methyl iodide and ethanolic potassium hydroxide. It may also be prepared synthetically by introducing an aldehyde group into the *p*-position of anisole (*e.g.*, methods 1, 5 and 6), or by oxidation of the corresponding alcohols (*cf.* p. 624, derivatives of benzaldehyde).

Anisaldehyde is an oil, b.p. 248°, which may be oxidised to anisic acid and reduced to anisyl alcohol.

Protocatechualdehyde (3 : 4-*dihydroxybenzaldehyde*) may be prepared by heating vanillin with hydrochloric acid:

$$C_6H_3(OH)(OCH_3)(CHO) \xrightarrow{HCl} C_6H_3(OH)(OH)(CHO)$$

It may also be prepared by adding phosphorus pentachloride to piperonal, then treating the product with cold water, and finally boiling the solution:

$$C_6H_3(O{-}CH_2{-}O)(CHO) \xrightarrow{PCl_5} C_6H_3(O{-}CCl_2{-}O)(CHO) \xrightarrow{H_2O} C_6H_3(O{-}CO{-}O)(CHO) \xrightarrow{H_2O} C_6H_3(OH)(OH)(CHO)\ (61\%)$$

Protocatechualdehyde may be prepared synthetically by means of the Reimer–Tiemann reaction using catechol:

$$(HO)_2C_6H_4 + CHCl_3 \xrightarrow{NaOH} (HO)_2C_6H_3{\cdot}CHO$$

Protocatechualdehyde is a crystalline solid, m.p. 153°, soluble in water. Its aqueous solution gives a green coloration with ferric chloride, and reduces ammoniacal silver nitrate. When methylated with approximately one equivalent of methyl sulphate, protocatechualdehyde gives a mixture of vanillin (I), and *iso*vanillin (II); excess methyl sulphate gives veratraldehyde (III):

$$\text{C}_6\text{H}_3(\text{OH})(\text{OH})\text{CHO} \xrightarrow[\text{NaOH}]{(\text{CH}_3)_2\text{SO}_4} \underset{\text{(I)}}{\text{C}_6\text{H}_3(\text{OH})(\text{OCH}_3)\text{CHO}} + \underset{\text{(II)}}{\text{C}_6\text{H}_3(\text{OCH}_3)(\text{OH})\text{CHO}} \longrightarrow \underset{\text{(III)}}{\text{C}_6\text{H}_3(\text{OCH}_3)(\text{OCH}_3)\text{CHO}}$$

Vanillin (***m*-methoxy-*p*-hydroxybenzaldehyde**) occurs in many substances of plant origin, *e.g.*, the vanilla bean. It may be prepared synthetically from guaiacol (p. 611) by means of the Reimer–Tiemann or the Gattermann reaction. Industrially, it is prepared:

(i) By oxidising *iso*eugenol (from eugenol) with nitrobenzene:

$$\text{C}_6\text{H}_3(\text{OH})(\text{OCH}_3)\text{CH}_2\cdot\text{CH:CH}_2 \xrightarrow{\text{KOH}} \text{C}_6\text{H}_3(\text{OH})(\text{OCH}_3)\text{CH:CH}\cdot\text{CH}_3 \xrightarrow{[\text{O}]} \text{C}_6\text{H}_3(\text{OH})(\text{OCH}_3)\text{CHO}$$

If the oxidation is carried out with acid dichromate, it is necessary to protect the hydroxyl group (by acetylation, etc.). On the other hand, ozonolysis may be used without protecting the hydroxyl group.

(ii) By the Lederer–Manasse reaction as follows:

$$\text{C}_6\text{H}_4(\text{OH})(\text{OCH}_3) + \text{H}\cdot\text{CHO} \xrightarrow{\text{NaOH}} \text{C}_6\text{H}_3(\text{OH})(\text{OCH}_3)\text{CH}_2\text{OH} \xrightarrow{\text{C}_6\text{H}_5\cdot\text{NH}\cdot\text{OH}} \text{C}_6\text{H}_3(\text{OH})(\text{OCH}_3)\text{CH:N}\cdot\text{C}_6\text{H}_5 \xrightarrow{\text{H}_2\text{O}} \text{C}_6\text{H}_3(\text{OH})(\text{OCH}_3)\text{CHO}$$

(iii) The liquors from the extraction of lignin from wood-pulp contain vanillin, and are now used as a source of vanillin.

Vanillin is a crystalline solid, m.p. 81°. When heated with hydrochloric acid, it forms protocatechualdehyde; with methyl sulphate it forms veratraldehyde. Ethylation converts vanillin into ethylvanillin (a synthetic compound), which is three times as strong as vanillin:

$$\text{C}_6\text{H}_3(\text{OH})(\text{OCH}_3)\text{CHO} \xrightarrow[\text{NaOH}]{(\text{C}_2\text{H}_5)_2\text{SO}_4} \text{C}_6\text{H}_3(\text{OC}_2\text{H}_5)(\text{OCH}_3)\text{CHO}$$

Piperonal (*heliotropin, 3 : 4-methylenedioxybenzaldehyde*) is the methylene ether of protocatechualdehyde, and is obtained when piperic acid (from the alkaloid piperine) is oxidised. It may be prepared synthetically by treating protocatechualdehyde with methylene iodide and sodium hydroxide:

$$\text{C}_6\text{H}_3(\text{OH})(\text{OH})\text{CHO} + \text{CH}_2\text{I}_2 + 2\text{NaOH} \longrightarrow \text{C}_6\text{H}_3(\text{O}{-}\text{CH}_2{-}\text{O})\text{CHO} + 2\text{NaI} + 2\text{H}_2\text{O}$$

It is manufactured by the oxidation of *iso*safrole (from safrole) by ozonolysis or with acid dichromate:

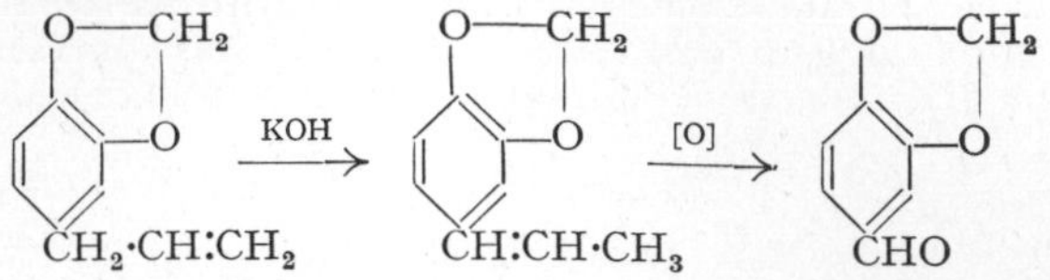

$$\underset{CH_2\cdot CH{:}CH_2}{\overset{O—CH_2}{\text{—O}}} \xrightarrow{KOH} \underset{CH{:}CH\cdot CH_3}{\overset{O—CH_2}{\text{—O}}} \xrightarrow{[O]} \underset{CHO}{\overset{O—CH_2}{\text{—O}}}$$

Piperonal is a solid, m.p. 37°, with the smell of heliotrope. It may be oxidised to piperonylic acid and reduced to piperonyl alcohol. When treated with phosphorus pentachloride and then with water, piperonal forms protocatechualdehyde (see above). This aldehyde is also obtained, together with formaldehyde or methanol, when piperonal is heated with dilute hydrochloric acid at 200° under pressure.

AROMATIC KETONES

Aromatic ketones may be either aryl-alkyl ketones or diaryl ketones.

Acetophenone (*methyl phenyl ketone, acetylbenzene*), $C_6H_5\cdot CO\cdot CH_3$, may be prepared by distilling a mixture of calcium benzoate and calcium acetate:

$$(C_6H_5\cdot CO_2)_2Ca + (CH_3\cdot CO_2)_2Ca \longrightarrow 2C_6H_5\cdot CO\cdot CH_3 + 2CaCO_3$$

It may also be prepared by the catalytic oxidation of ethylbenzene (p. 618), but it is best prepared by means of the Friedel–Crafts reaction:

$$C_6H_6 + CH_3\cdot COCl \xrightarrow{AlCl_3} C_6H_5\cdot CO\cdot CH_3 + HCl \quad (50\%)$$

The yield is improved (to 60 per cent.) by using a mixture of aluminium and mercury chlorides as catalyst.

Alkyl aryl ketones may be prepared from diazonium salts and aldoximes other than formaldoxime (see p. 562), and by the phenylation of ketones (see p. 522).

Acetophenone is a solid, m.p. 20°; it is used as an hypnotic (under the name of hypnone) and in perfumery. When reduced with sodium and ethanol, acetophenone gives *methylphenylmethanol*, $C_6H_5\cdot CHOH\cdot CH_3$; reduction by Clemmensen's method gives ethylbenzene. Oxidation with cold potassium permanganate gives *phenylglyoxylic acid* (*benzoylformic acid*) which, on further oxidation, is converted into benzoic acid:

$$C_6H_5\cdot CO\cdot CH_3 \xrightarrow{[O]'} C_6H_5\cdot CO\cdot CO_2H \xrightarrow{[O]} C_6H_5\cdot CO_2H$$

Acetophenone is oxidised by selenium dioxide to *phenylglyoxal*:

$$C_6H_5\cdot CO\cdot CH_3 + SeO_2 \longrightarrow C_6H_5\cdot CO\cdot CHO + Se + H_2O \quad (69\text{–}72\%)$$

Acetophenone can be chloromethylated (p. 509), and it is readily halogenated in the ω-position; *e.g.*, *phenacyl bromide* (ω-bromoacetophenone) is formed when acetophenone is treated with bromine in ether at 0° in the presence of a small amount of aluminium chloride:

$$C_6H_5\cdot CO\cdot CH_3 + Br_2 \longrightarrow C_6H_5\cdot CO\cdot CH_2Br + HBr \quad (64\text{–}66\%)$$

Phenacyl bromide (m.p. 51°) is used to identify acids, with which it forms well-defined crystalline esters.

When treated with two equivalents of bromine, acetophenone forms ω : ω-dibromoacetophenone (*phenacylidene bromide*). This compound undergoes rearrangement on treatment with alkali to form *mandelic acid* :

$$C_6H_5\cdot CO\cdot CHBr_2 \xrightarrow[\text{(ii) HCl}]{\text{(i) KOH}} [C_6H_5\cdot CO\cdot CH(OH)_2] \longrightarrow C_6H_5\cdot CHOH\cdot CO_2H$$

This rearrangement does not take place if both *o*-positions are occupied, *e.g.*, in the ω : ω-dibromo-derivative of acetomesitylene.

Phenacyl chloride, m.p. 59°, may be conveniently prepared by the Friedel–Crafts condensation between chloroacetyl chloride and benzene:

$$C_6H_6 + CH_2Cl{\cdot}COCl \xrightarrow{AlCl_3} C_6H_5{\cdot}CO{\cdot}CH_2Cl + HCl$$

(Structure: benzene ring with $CO{\cdot}CH_3$ at top, CH_3 at both *o*-positions and CH_3 at *p*-position — acetomesitylene)

Acetophenone forms an oxime, phenylhydrazone and cyanohydrin, but does not form a bisulphite compound (*cf.* p. 141). It reacts with ammonia to form acetophenone-ammonia, $(C_6H_5{\cdot}C{\cdot}CH_3)_3N_2$ (*cf.* benzaldehyde and ammonia), and with Grignard reagents in the usual way. When, however, both *o*-positions in acetophenone are occupied, the compound exhibits steric hindrance; *e.g.*, acetomesitylene does not form an oxime, and does not react with Grignard reagents in the usual way.

The acetyl group is *m*-orienting, and so when acetophenone undergoes nuclear substitution, the main product is the *m*-derivative.

In the presence of aluminium *tert.*-butoxide, acetophenone undergoes condensation to form **dypnone** (b.p. 340–345°):

$$C_6H_5{\cdot}\overset{\overset{\displaystyle CH_3}{|}}{C}{=}O + CH_3{\cdot}CO{\cdot}C_6H_5 \longrightarrow C_6H_5{\cdot}\overset{\overset{\displaystyle CH_3}{|}}{C}{=}CH{\cdot}CO{\cdot}C_6H_5 + H_2O \quad (77\text{–}82\%)$$

In the presence of hydrochloric acid, *s*-triphenylbenzene (m.p. 172°) is formed:

$$3C_6H_5{\cdot}CO{\cdot}CH_3 \longrightarrow$$ (benzene ring with C_6H_5 at positions 1, 3 and 5)

Acetophenone condenses with acetic anhydride in the presence of boron trifluoride to form *benzoylacetone*, m.p. 61° (Meerwein *et al.*, 1934):

$$C_6H_5{\cdot}CO{\cdot}CH_3 + (CH_3{\cdot}CO)_2O \xrightarrow{BF_3} C_6H_5{\cdot}CO{\cdot}CH_2{\cdot}CO{\cdot}CH_3 + CH_3{\cdot}CO_2H \quad (83\%)$$

This is also formed by the condensation of acetophenone with ethyl acetate in the presence of sodium ethoxide:

$$C_6H_5{\cdot}CO{\cdot}CH_3 + CH_3{\cdot}CO_2C_2H_5 \xrightarrow{C_2H_5ONa} C_6H_5{\cdot}CO{\cdot}CH_2{\cdot}CO{\cdot}CH_3 \quad (66\%)$$

Acetophenone condenses with ethyl benzoate in the presence of sodium ethoxide to form *dibenzoylmethane*, m.p. 77°.

$$C_6H_5{\cdot}CO_2C_2H_5 + CH_3{\cdot}CO{\cdot}C_6H_5 \xrightarrow{C_2H_5ONa} C_6H_5{\cdot}CO{\cdot}CH_2{\cdot}CO{\cdot}C_6H_5 \quad (62\text{–}71\%)$$

Acetophenone undergoes the Mannich reaction (see p. 289):

$$C_6H_5{\cdot}CO{\cdot}CH_3 + H{\cdot}CHO + (CH_3)_2NH{\cdot}HCl \longrightarrow C_6H_5{\cdot}CO{\cdot}CH_2{\cdot}CH_2{\cdot}N(CH_3)_2{\cdot}HCl \quad (60\%)$$

Aromatic aldehydes and ketones generally behave as bases in concentrated sulphuric acid; cryoscopic experiments show that *i* (van't Hoff factor) is 2, and this value agrees with the following equation (R = H or R):

$$Ar{\cdot}CO{\cdot}R + H_2SO_4 \rightleftharpoons [Ar{\cdot}C({=}\overset{+}{O}H){\cdot}R][HSO_4^-]$$

The carbonyl compound may be recovered by dilution with water.

On the other hand, certain *unsaturated* ketones behave differently. Gillespie *et al.* (1954) found that all but two of the fourteen unsaturated carbonyl compounds investigated by them gave freezing point depressions in sulphuric acid which increase with time and only reach a constant limiting value after a long period. These stable values varied up to 6. These results have been attributed to sulphonation, and sulphonic acids have been isolated in certain cases, *e.g.*, benzylideneacetophenone gives first a value of $i = 2$, and finally $i = 4$.

$$Ph{\cdot}CH{=}CH{\cdot}CO{\cdot}Ph + H_2SO_4 \rightleftharpoons Ph{\cdot}CH{=}CH{\cdot}C(={\overset{+}{O}}H){\cdot}Ph + HSO_4^- \quad (i = 2)$$

$$Ph{\cdot}CH{=}CH{\cdot}C(={\overset{+}{O}}H){\cdot}Ph + 2H_2SO_4 \longrightarrow HO_3S{\cdot}C_6H_4{\cdot}CH{=}CH{\cdot}C(={\overset{+}{O}}H){\cdot}Ph + H_3\overset{+}{O} + HSO_4^- \quad (i = 4)$$

The solutions of these oxonium salts are much deeper in colour than the ketone or the solution of the ketone in an organic solvent, *e.g.*, benzylideneacetophenone is a very pale yellow solid, and its solution in ethanol is also pale yellow, but its solution in concentrated sulphuric acid is deep yellow. These deep-coloured oxonium salts have therefore been named *halochromic* salts.

Willgerodt reaction (1887). This is the name given to those reactions in which a carbonyl compound is converted into an amide with the same number of carbon atoms. The Willgerodt reaction was originally carried out by heating an aryl alkyl ketone with an aqueous solution of yellow ammonium polysulphide; *e.g.*, acetophenone forms the amide of phenylacetic acid, together with a small amount of the ammonium salt:

$$C_6H_5{\cdot}CO{\cdot}CH_3 \xrightarrow{(NH_4)_2S_x} C_6H_5{\cdot}CH_2{\cdot}CO{\cdot}NH_2 + C_6H_5{\cdot}CH_2{\cdot}CO_2NH_4$$

The amido-group is always formed at the end of the chain whatever the size of the R group in $C_6H_5{\cdot}CO{\cdot}R$; *e.g.*, butyrophenone forms γ-phenylbutyramide:

$$C_6H_5{\cdot}CO{\cdot}CH_2{\cdot}CH_2{\cdot}CH_3 \longrightarrow C_6H_5{\cdot}CH_2{\cdot}CH_2{\cdot}CH_2{\cdot}CO{\cdot}NH_2$$

The Willgerodt reaction is very useful for preparing aryl-substituted aliphatic acids.

A modified technique of carrying out the Willgerodt reaction is to heat the ketone with approximately equimolecular amounts of sulphur and a dry amine (Kindler, 1923, 1927); a particularly useful amine is morpholine, NH⟨ ⟩O (ring). The final product is a thioamide and this, on acid or alkaline hydrolysis, gives an acid; or alternatively, on electrolytic reduction, the thioamide gives an amine, *e.g.*,

$$C_6H_5{\cdot}CO{\cdot}CH_3 + (CH_3)_2NH + S \longrightarrow C_6H_5{\cdot}CH_2{\cdot}C({=}S){\cdot}N(CH_3)_2$$

$$C_6H_5{\cdot}CH_2{\cdot}CH_2{\cdot}N(CH_3)_2 \xleftarrow{[H]} C_6H_5{\cdot}CH_2{\cdot}C({=}S){\cdot}N(CH_3)_2 \xrightarrow{acid} C_6H_5{\cdot}CH_2{\cdot}CO_2H$$

Thus, by means of the Kindler procedure, bases containing the nitrogen atom on the terminal carbon atom of the side-chain can be synthesised.

The Willgerodt reaction was originally limited to ketones, but it has now been shown to be applicable to olefins, acetylenes, alcohols, halides, amines, etc.

Phenolic ketones may be prepared by the **Houben–Hoesch synthesis** (1927). This is the condensation of cyanides with polyhydric phenols, particularly *m*-compounds, in the presence of zinc chloride and hydrogen chloride; *e.g.*, phloroglucinol condenses with methyl cyanide to form *phloroacetophenone* (m.p. 219°):

$$C_6H_3(OH)_3 + CH_3{\cdot}CN \xrightarrow[HCl]{ZnCl_2} \left[C_6H_2(OH)_3{\cdot}C(=NH){\cdot}CH_3 \right] \xrightarrow{H_2O} C_6H_2(OH)_3{\cdot}CO{\cdot}CH_3 \quad (74\text{–}87\%)$$

This method is really an extension of Gattermann's phenolic aldehyde synthesis. It is not applicable to phenol itself.

Phenolic ketones may also be prepared by the Fries rearrangement (p. 596), and by heating polyhydric phenols with aliphatic acids in the presence of fused zinc chloride; *e.g.*, pyrogallol and acetic acid form *gallacetophenone* (m.p. 173°):

$$C_6H_3(OH)_3 + CH_3{\cdot}CO_2H \xrightarrow{ZnCl_2} C_6H_2(OH)_3{\cdot}CO{\cdot}CH_3 + H_2O$$

Many phenolic ketones occur naturally, free or as glycosides.

Benzophenone (*diphenyl ketone*), $C_6H_5{\cdot}CO{\cdot}C_6H_5$, may be prepared in a similar manner to acetophenone, *e.g.*,

(i) By heating calcium benzoate:

$$(C_6H_5{\cdot}CO_2)_2Ca \longrightarrow C_6H_5{\cdot}CO{\cdot}C_6H_5 + CaCO_3 \quad (30\%)$$

(ii) By the Friedel–Crafts condensation between benzoyl chloride and benzene:

$$C_6H_6 + C_6H_5{\cdot}COCl \xrightarrow{AlCl_3} C_6H_5{\cdot}CO{\cdot}C_6H_5 + HCl \quad (80\%)$$

Carbonyl chloride may be used instead of benzoyl chloride:

$$2C_6H_6 + COCl_2 \xrightarrow{AlCl_3} C_6H_5{\cdot}CO{\cdot}C_6H_5 + 2HCl$$

The Friedel–Crafts reaction may also be carried out with carbon tetrachloride, followed by steam distillation of the dichloro-compound produced:

$$2C_6H_6 + CCl_4 \xrightarrow{AlCl_3} (C_6H_5)_2CCl_2 \xrightarrow{H_2O} (C_6H_5)_2CO \quad (80\text{–}89\%)$$

(iii) By heating *o*-benzoylbenzoic acid with copper powder at 260°:

$$C_6H_5{\cdot}CO{\cdot}C_6H_4{\cdot}CO_2H \xrightarrow[260^\circ]{Cu} C_6H_5{\cdot}CO{\cdot}C_6H_5 + CO_2$$

Benzophenone exists in two solid forms, a stable, m.p. 49°, and an unstable form, m.p. 26°. It cannot be chloromethylated (*cf.* acetophenone). It is reduced by zinc and ethanolic potassium hydroxide to **benzhydrol** (*diphenylcarbinol*, m. p. 68°) and by zinc and acetic acid to **benzopinacol** (m.p. 188°):

$$\underset{(90\%)}{(C_6H_5)_2C(OH){\cdot}C(OH)(C_6H_5)_2} \xleftarrow[CH_3{\cdot}CO_2H]{Zn} (C_6H_5)_2CO \xrightarrow{Zn/KOH} \underset{(90\%)}{(C_6H_5)_2CHOH}$$

When benzophenone, dissolved in *iso*propanol to which a drop of acetic acid has been added, is exposed to bright sunlight, benzopinacol is formed:

$$2(C_6H_5)_2CO + (CH_3)_2CHOH \xrightarrow{h\nu} (C_6H_5)_2C(OH){\cdot}C(OH)(C_6H_5)_2 + (CH_3)_2CO \quad (93\text{–}94\%)$$

When benzophenone is dissolved in *iso*propanol and a small amount of sodium added, benzhydrol is formed. This compound is believed to be formed via benzopinacol which is first produced and then decomposed by sodium *iso*propoxide to benzophenone and benzhydrol. Evidence in favour of this mechanism is afforded by the fact that benzopinacol is decomposed into benzophenone and benzhydrol by sodium hydroxide:

$$(C_6H_5)_2C(OH){\cdot}C(OH)(C_6H_5)_2 \xrightarrow{NaOH} (C_6H_5)_2CO + (C_6H_5)_2CHOH$$

Benzopinacol is also obtained by the reduction of benzophenone with a mixture of magnesium and magnesium iodide, which appears to behave as magnesious iodide, MgI (Gomberg and Bachmann, 1927):

$$2(C_6H_5)_2CO + 2MgI \longrightarrow \underset{\substack{| \quad\quad |\\ IMgO \quad OMgI}}{(C_6H_5)_2C{-}C(C_6H_5)_2} \xrightarrow{-MgI_2} \underset{\substack{| \quad\quad |\\ O \quad\quad O\\ \diagdown \; \diagup\\ Mg}}{(C_6H_5)_2C{-}{-}C(C_6H_5)_2}$$

$$\xrightarrow{H_2O} (C_6H_5)_2C(OH){\cdot}C(OH)(C_6H_5)_2$$

When heated in acetic acid solution in the presence of iodine as catalyst, benzopinacol undergoes the pinacol–pinacolone rearrangement (p. 159) to form *benzopinacolone* (m.p. 179°):

$$(C_6H_5)_2C(OH){\cdot}C(OH)(C_6H_5)_2 \longrightarrow (C_6H_5)_3C{\cdot}CO{\cdot}C_6H_5 + H_2O \quad (98\text{–}99\%)$$

When distilled with zinc dust, benzophenone forms diphenylmethane, and when fused with potassium hydroxide, benzene and potassium benzoate:

$$(C_6H_5)_2CO + KOH \longrightarrow C_6H_6 + C_6H_5{\cdot}CO_2K$$

Benzophenone forms an oxime, but does not form a cyanohydrin or a bisulphite compound. The explanation for the latter is not clear; it may be due entirely to the spatial effect.

Benzophenone dissolves sodium without the evolution of hydrogen, forming a compound (blue or green) which reacts rapidly with iodine or oxygen, and consequently is believed to be a free radical:

$$(C_6H_5)_2CO + Na \longrightarrow (C_6H_5)_2\dot{C}{-}\bar{O}\overset{+}{Na}$$

There is also present the following equilibrium (*cf.* acyloins, p. 180):

$$2(C_6H_5)_2\dot{C}{-}\bar{O}\overset{+}{Na} \rightleftharpoons \begin{array}{l}(C_6H_5)_2C{-}\bar{O}\overset{+}{Na}\\ \quad\quad\quad\;\, |\\ (C_6H_5)_2C{-}\bar{O}\overset{+}{Na}\end{array}$$

The sodium salts of the free radicals are known as **metallic ketyls.** They are decomposed by water into benzophenone and benzhydrol (possibly via the dimer; *cf.* benzopinacol above). Aromatic ketones with a primary or secondary alkyl group evolve hydrogen when treated with sodium; *i.e.*, they enolise, and so will not form a metallic ketyl.

A very important derivative of benzophenone is **Michler's ketone,** which may be prepared by treating dimethylaniline with carbonyl chloride:

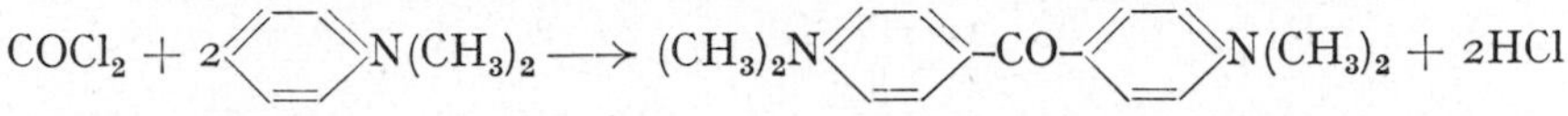

$$COCl_2 + 2C_6H_5N(CH_3)_2 \longrightarrow (CH_3)_2NC_6H_4\text{-CO-}C_6H_4N(CH_3)_2 + 2HCl$$

Michler's ketone is used in the preparation of certain triphenylmethane dyes (p. 758).

Elbs reaction (1884). This is the reaction whereby a polynuclear hydrocarbon is formed by the pyrolysis of a diaryl ketone containing a methyl or a methylene group in the *o*-position to the carbonyl group; *e.g.*, *o*-methylbenzophenone forms anthracene (see also p. 698):

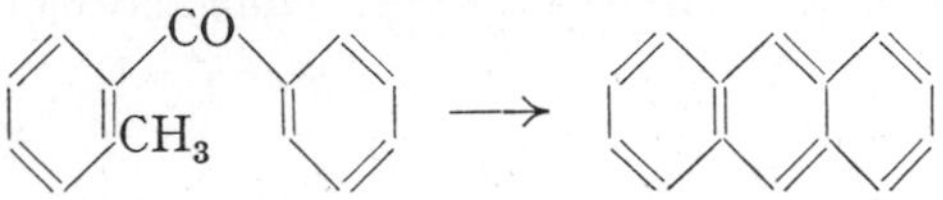

$$o\text{-}CH_3C_6H_4\text{-CO-}C_6H_5 \longrightarrow \text{anthracene}$$

The mechanism of the Elbs reaction is uncertain; according to Badger *et al.* (1953) it proceeds via free radicals. Hurd *et al.* (1951), using deuterium as tracer, have shown that hydrogen in the 9-position (in anthracene) does not come from the *o*-methyl group but from the *o*-hydrogen of the benzene ring, *e.g.*,

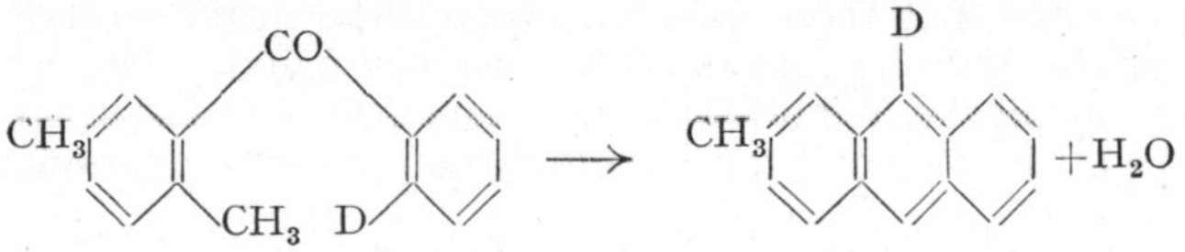

$$CH_3C_6H_3(CH_3)\text{-CO-}C_6H_4D \longrightarrow CH_3C_{14}H_8D + H_2O$$

STEREOCHEMISTRY OF ALDOXIMES AND KETOXIMES

Many aromatic aldoximes and ketoximes exist in two isomeric forms. Structural isomerism was first suggested to account for the existence of this isomerism, two of the following four structures corresponding to the two isomers (where R is an alkyl or an aryl group):

Ar—C—R ‖ N—OH	Ar—C—R ‖ H—N→O	Ar—C—R │ ╲H N═O	Ar—C—R │ ╲O H—N
(I)	(II)	(III)	(IV)

Hantzsch and Werner (1890), however, suggested that the isomerism of the oximes was geometrical and not structural. According to these authors, nitrogen is tervalent (in oximes), and is situated at one corner of a tetrahedron with its three valencies directed towards the other three corners; consequently the three valencies are not coplanar. These authors also assumed that there was no free rotation about the C═N double bond (*cf.* geometrical isomerism of the C═C compounds, p. 405). They therefore proposed configurations (V) and (VI) for the two isomers:

Ar—C—R ‖ N—OH	Ar—C—R ‖ HO—N
(V)	(VI)

Many facts are in favour of geometrical isomerism, *e.g.*,

(i) If Ar = R, then isomerism disappears.

(ii) (III) and (IV) would be optically active; this is not found to be so in practice.

On the other hand, (II) would also exhibit geometrical isomerism, and recent work has shown that it may also be present, since methylation (with methyl sulphate) may produce four methyl derivatives corresponding to (VII–X) (Semper and Lichtenstadt, 1918):

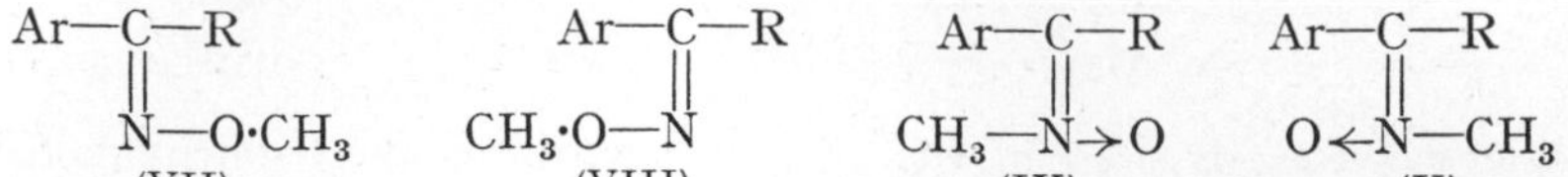

$$\underset{\text{(VII)}}{\begin{array}{l}Ar—C—R\\ \quad\ \|\\ \quad N—O·CH_3\end{array}} \qquad \underset{\text{(VIII)}}{\begin{array}{r}Ar—C—R\\ \|\quad\ \\ CH_3·O—N\quad\ \end{array}} \qquad \underset{\text{(IX)}}{\begin{array}{c}Ar—C—R\\ \|\\ CH_3—N\rightarrow O\end{array}} \qquad \underset{\text{(X)}}{\begin{array}{c}Ar—C—R\\ \|\\ O\leftarrow N—CH_3\end{array}}$$

Thus it appears that the oximes can exist in forms (I) and (II). Brady (1916) considered that oximes in solution are a tautomeric mixture of (I) and (II) (*oximino-nitrone diad system*). Absorption spectra studies of oximes and their methyl derivatives indicate that if oximes are tautomeric mixtures of (I) and (II), the equilibrium must be almost completely on the oxime side, *i.e.*,

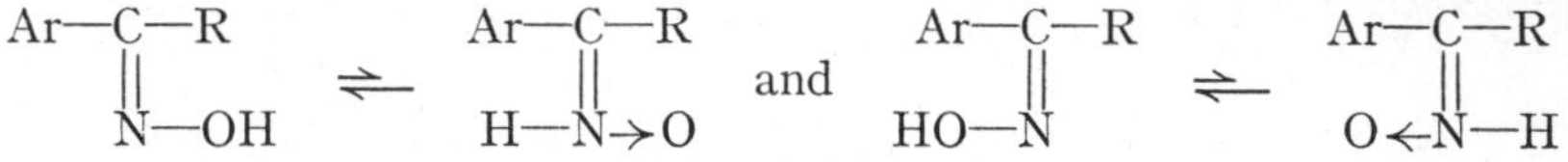

$$\begin{array}{l}Ar—C—R\\ \quad\ \|\\ \quad N—OH\end{array} \rightleftharpoons \begin{array}{c}Ar—C—R\\ \|\\ H—N\rightarrow O\end{array} \quad \text{and} \quad \begin{array}{r}Ar—C—R\\ \|\quad\ \\ HO—N\quad\ \end{array} \rightleftharpoons \begin{array}{c}Ar—C—R\\ \|\\ O\leftarrow N—H\end{array}$$

It is possible, however, that none of the nitrone form is actually present, but its methyl derivative is formed during the process of methylation. If we assume that methyl sulphate provides methyl carbonium ions, $\overset{+}{C}H_3$, then it is possible that these ions may attack the nitrogen atom (with its lone pair) or the oxygen atom (with its two lone pairs). This would result in the formation of the *N*- and *O*-methyl ethers, without having to postulate the presence of the nitrone form in equilibrium with the oxime form.

Determination of Configuration

Aldoximes. The two isomeric aldoximes may be distinguished by the behaviour of their acetyl derivatives towards aqueous sodium carbonate; one gives the oxime back again, and the other forms the cyanide Ar·CN. Detailed experiments of Brady and Bishop (1925) have shown that elimination reactions take place in the *trans*-position (*cf.* p. 408). Thus the acetylated oxime which regenerates the oxime is the *syn*- (*cis*-) form, and the other, which produces the cyanide, the *anti*- (*trans*-) form:

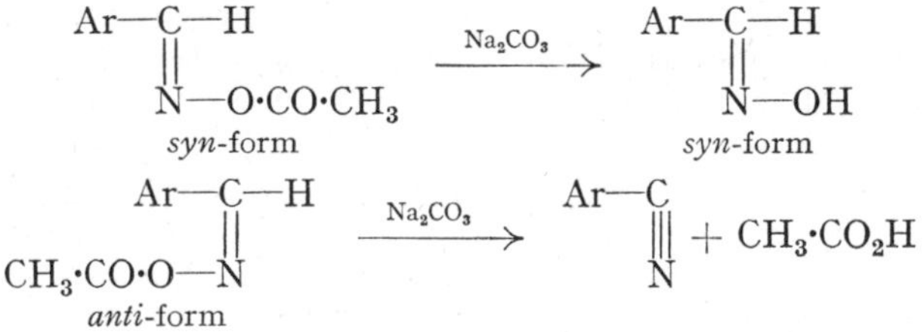

$$\underset{syn\text{-form}}{\begin{array}{l}Ar—C—H\\ \quad\ \|\\ \quad N—O·CO·CH_3\end{array}} \xrightarrow{Na_2CO_3} \underset{syn\text{-form}}{\begin{array}{l}Ar—C—H\\ \quad\ \|\\ \quad N—OH\end{array}}$$

$$\underset{anti\text{-form}}{\begin{array}{r}Ar—C—H\\ \|\quad\ \\ CH_3·CO·O—N\quad\ \end{array}} \xrightarrow{Na_2CO_3} \begin{array}{l}Ar—C\\ \quad\ \ |||\\ \quad\ \ N\end{array} + CH_3·CO_2H$$

Ketoximes. Beckmann transformation (1886). When treated with certain reagents such as sulphuric acid, hydrochloric acid, or phosphorus pentachloride, ketoximes undergo molecular rearrangement to form an acid amide. This phenomenon is known as the *Beckmann transformation* (or *rearrangement*). A detailed study by Meisenheimer (1921) showed that the Beckmann transformation takes place in the *anti*-position, *i.e.*,

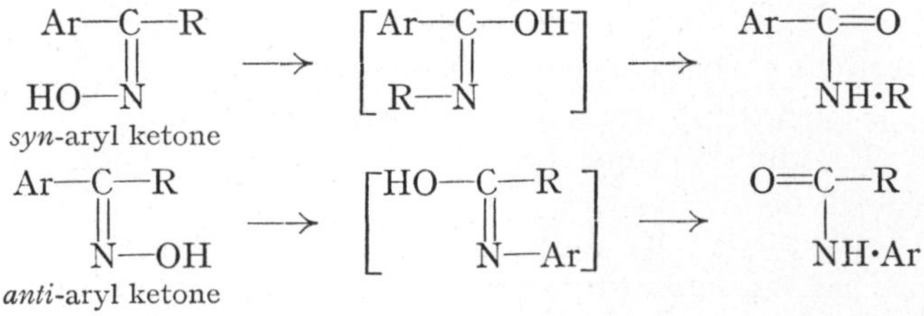

$$\underset{syn\text{-aryl ketone}}{\begin{array}{r}Ar—C—R\\ \|\quad\ \\ HO—N\quad\ \end{array}} \longrightarrow \left[\begin{array}{r}Ar—C—OH\\ \|\quad\ \ \\ R—N\quad\ \ \end{array}\right] \longrightarrow \begin{array}{l}Ar—C{=}O\\ \quad\ \ |\\ \quad NH·R\end{array}$$

$$\underset{anti\text{-aryl ketone}}{\begin{array}{l}Ar—C—R\\ \quad\ \|\\ \quad N—OH\end{array}} \longrightarrow \left[\begin{array}{l}HO—C—R\\ \qquad\ \|\\ \qquad N—Ar\end{array}\right] \longrightarrow \begin{array}{l}O{=}C—R\\ \quad\ \ |\\ \quad NH·Ar\end{array}$$

Thus by identifying the acid amide produced after the Beckmann transformation, and using the fact that the rearrangement takes place in the *anti*-position, the configuration of the ketoxime can be determined.

The mechanism of the Beckmann transformation is still a subject of much discussion.

QUINONES

Quinones are compounds which are formed by the replacement of two hydrogen atoms in the nucleus by two oxygen atoms. Two quinones of benzene are possible: *o*-benzoquinone and *p*-benzoquinone:

m-Benzoquinone has not been prepared; it is impossible to arrange two carbonyl oxygen atoms in the ring in the *m*-position and still maintain a valency of four for carbon (*cf.*, however, *m*-nitrophenol, p. 601).

***p*-Benzoquinone** (p-*quinone*) may be prepared by the oxidation of quinol with ferric chloride, manganese dioxide and sulphuric acid, or acid dichromate; the best oxidising agent is sodium chlorate in dilute sulphuric acid in the presence of vanadium pentoxide as catalyst:

$$\text{quinol (OH, OH)} \xrightarrow[V_2O_5]{NaClO_3/H_2SO_4} \text{p-benzoquinone} \quad (92\text{–}96\%)$$

Quinol may also be oxidised to quinone by lead tetra-acetate.

$$\text{quinol} + (CH_3{\cdot}CO_2)_4Pb \longrightarrow \text{quinone} + 2CH_3{\cdot}CO_2H + (CH_3{\cdot}CO_2)_2Pb$$

p-Benzoquinone is usually prepared in the laboratory by the oxidation of aniline with potassium dichromate and sulphuric acid.

In general, *p*-quinones may be prepared by the oxidation (using dichromate-sulphuric acid) of *p*-dihydroxy-, *p*-diamino- or *p*-aminohydroxy-compounds, *e.g.*,

$$\text{p-}C_6H_4(NH_2)_2 \xrightarrow{[O]} \underset{(I)}{HN{=}C_6H_4{=}NH} \xrightarrow{[O]} O{=}C_6H_4{=}O \xleftarrow{[O]} \underset{(II)}{O{=}C_6H_4{=}NH} \xleftarrow{[O]} \text{p-}HO{\cdot}C_6H_4{\cdot}NH_2$$

The intermediate products I (p-*benzoquinonedi-imine*) and II (p-*benzoquinoneimine*) can be isolated under certain conditions (see p. 643).

p-Benzoquinone crystallises in yellow prisms, m.p. 116°; it has a sharp smell, sublimes when heated, is slightly soluble in water, and is steam-volatile. On exposure to light, *p*-benzoquinone turns brown.

The yellow colour of *p*-benzoquinone is due to the presence of the quinonoid structure =⟨⟩=. This structure is also known as a *crossed conjugated system*; it contains three (or more) conjugated double bonds which are not arranged in a continuous chain. *p*-Benzoquinone behaves in many ways as an αβ-unsaturated ketone rather than as an aromatic compound; *e.g.*, it adds on bromine in the 3 : 4-positions to give the dibromo-derivative; with excess bromine, it adds on two more bromine atoms in the 3′ : 4′-positions to give the tetra-bromo-derivative. It also adds on hydrogen chloride to form mainly *chloroquinol* (*chlorohydroquinone*), m.p. 106°; the mechanism of this addition is possibly 1 : 4-addition first, followed by enolisation:

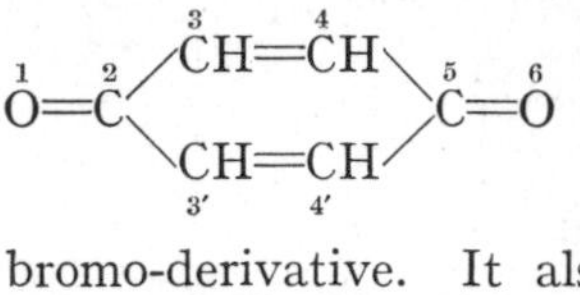

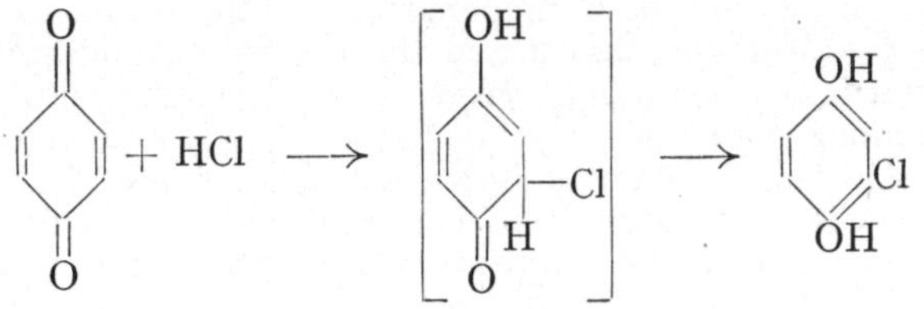

Chloroquinol, on oxidation, gives chloro-*p*-benzoquinone. By repeating the process of adding hydrogen chloride and then oxidising, the final product obtained is *tetrachloro*-p-*benzoquinone* (*chloranil*):

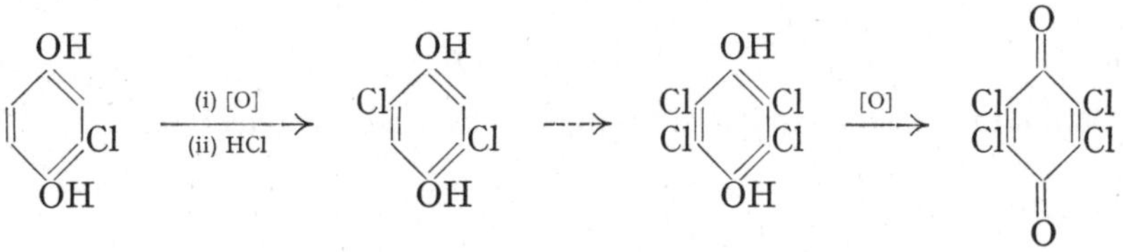

(i) [O]
(ii) HCl
[O]

Chloranil is used as a fungicide and as an oxidising agent (see below).

As can be seen from the above equation, chloro-*p*-benzoquinone adds on hydrogen chloride to form 2 : 5-dichloroquinol; this is to be expected by 1 : 4-addition (other dichloro-derivatives, however, are also possible by 1 : 4-addition, but only the 2 : 5-appears to be formed). In the same way, *p*-benzoquinone forms 2 : 5-addition compounds with primary or secondary amines in ethanolic solution, but in this case the quinone, and not the quinol derivative, is obtained. This is believed to be formed as follows (via 1 : 4-addition), *e.g.*, with aniline, the final product is 2 : 5-dianilino-*p*-benzoquinone:

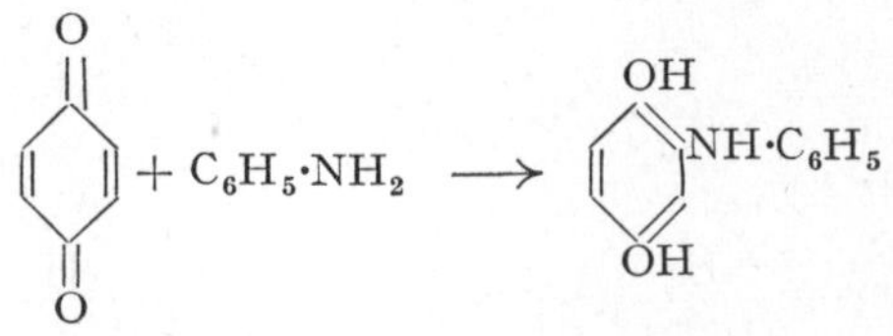

$+ C_6H_5{\cdot}NH_2 \longrightarrow$ $NH{\cdot}C_6H_5$

$$C_6H_3(OH)_2(NH\cdot C_6H_5) + O{=}C_6H_4{=}O \longrightarrow O{=}C_6H_3(NH\cdot C_6H_5){=}O + C_6H_4(OH)_2 \xrightarrow{C_6H_5\cdot NH_2}$$

$$C_6H_5\cdot NH\cdot C_6H_2(OH)_2\cdot NH\cdot C_6H_5 \xrightarrow{p\text{-}O{:}C_6H_4{:}O} C_6H_5\cdot NH\cdot C_6H_2(O)_2\cdot NH\cdot C_6H_5$$

p-Benzoquinone is a fairly strong oxidising agent, but although it is not strong enough to oxidise chloroquinol, it can oxidise anilino-compounds (itself being reduced to quinol).

In a similar way, primary alcohols, in the presence of zinc chloride, form 2 : 5-dialkoxy-p-benzoquinones with p-benzoquinone.

The addition of hydrogen cyanide to p-benzoquinone is exceptional in that 2 : 3-dicyanoquinol is formed:

$$O{=}C_6H_4{=}O + 2HCN \longrightarrow C_6H_2(OH)_2(CN)_2$$

When treated with acetic anhydride in the presence of sulphuric acid, p-benzoquinone forms hydroxyquinol triacetate; this is known as the **Thiele acetylation** (1898).

$$O{=}C_6H_4{=}O \xrightarrow[H_2SO_4]{(CH_3\cdot CO)_2O} C_6H_3(O\cdot CO\cdot CH_3)_3 \quad (86–87\%)$$

p-Benzoquinone is easily reduced to quinol (1 : 6-addition) by sulphurous acid, hydrogen sulphide, or sodium hyposulphite (yield: 80 per cent.). An intermediate product of this reduction, in acid solution, is **quinhydrone** (green prisms, m.p. 171°). This is believed to be a complex formed by hydrogen bonding between one molecule of p-benzoquinone and one of quinol:

$$O{=}C_6H_4{=}O\cdots H{-}O{-}C_6H_4{-}O{-}H\cdots \quad \textit{or} \quad O{=}C_6H_4{=}O\cdots H{-}O{-}C_6H_4{-}OH$$

This is a characteristic property of p-benzoquinone; *e.g.*, with two molecules of phenol, *phenoquinone* is formed; this may be:

$$C_6H_5{-}O{-}H\cdots O{=}C_6H_4{=}O\cdots H{-}O{-}C_6H_5$$

p-Benzoquinone is so easily reduced that it is used as an oxidising agent—generally chloranil is more satisfactory—in reactions where inorganic oxidising agents must be avoided. It liberates iodine from acidified potassium iodide solution, and is oxidised by silver oxide to maleic acid (and other products). It forms a monoxime and a dioxime (see below), and can act as a dienophile in the Diels–Alder reaction, *e.g.*, with butadiene it forms a hydrogenated anthraquinone derivative (see p. 698).

It has been suggested that the oxidising property of benzoquinone is due to the fact that when the quinone adds on two electrons, the benzenoid structure (with a large resonance energy) is obtained:

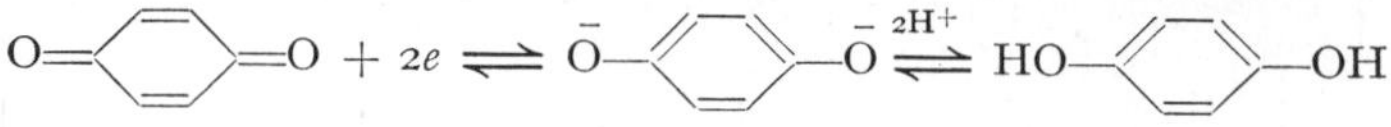

$$O{=}C_6H_4{=}O + 2e \rightleftharpoons \bar{O}{-}C_6H_4{-}\bar{O} \overset{2H^+}{\rightleftharpoons} HO{-}C_6H_4{-}OH$$

Benzoquinone dehydrogenates many hydroaromatic compounds, and the hydrogen transfer has been shown to take place with the transfer of hydride ions:

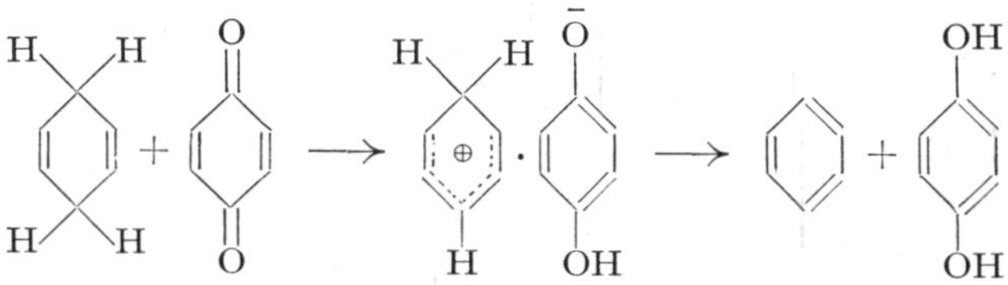

$$C_6H_8 + O{=}C_6H_4{=}O \longrightarrow C_6H_7^{\oplus} \cdot {}^{-}O{-}C_6H_4{-}OH \longrightarrow C_6H_6 + HO{-}C_6H_4{-}OH$$

An interesting point about this dehydrogenation is that, on the basis of this mechanism, it might be anticipated that *gem.*-dialkylhydroaromatic compounds would be converted into aromatic compounds with a migration of the "blocking" group (*cf.* the Wagner rearrangement, p. 120). Such reactions have been effected in practice by using high-potential quinones, *e.g.*,

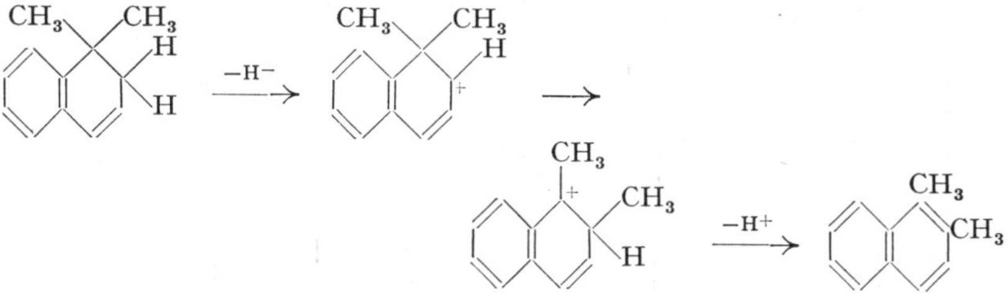

$$\xrightarrow{-H^-} \quad \longrightarrow \quad \xrightarrow{-H^+}$$

Structure of *p*-benzoquinone. Analysis and molecular-weight determinations show that the molecular formula of *p*-benzoquinone is $C_6H_4O_2$. On reduction, *p*-benzoquinone gives quinol, which is known to be *p*-dihydroxybenzene. Thus *p*-benzoquinone contains two oxygen atoms in the *p*-positions; this is supported by the fact that on mild oxidation, quinol forms *p*-benzoquinone. Using these facts Fittig (1863) proposed the formula $O{=}C_6H_4{=}O$ for *p*-benzoquinone.

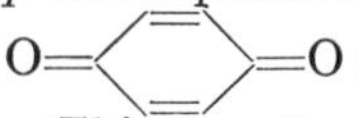

This structure, however, did not appear to agree with certain other properties of *p*-benzoquinone; *e.g.*, on treatment with phosphorus pentachloride, *p*-dichlorobenzene is formed. This reaction appears to indicate that oxygen is linked to carbon by a *single* bond. Graebe (1867) therefore suggested

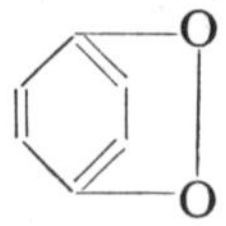

or (*writing this in another way*)

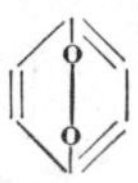

This structure was supported by the argument that *p*-benzoquinone is a strong oxidising agent (comparable to hydrogen peroxide, the structure of which is H—O—O—H).

Many other properties of *p*-benzoquinone, however, do not agree with Graebe's formula, but do agree with Fittig's; *e.g.*,

(i) *p*-Benzoquinone forms a monoxime and a dioxime. This indicates the presence of two carbonyl groups.

(ii) *p*-Benzoquinone behaves as an unsaturated cyclic ketone rather than as an aromatic compound; *e.g.*, its addition of halogens, halogen acids, etc., is not characteristic of aromatic compounds.

(iii) *p*-Benzoquinone behaves as a dienophile in the Diels–Alder reaction; this indicates the presence of the grouping O═C—C═C.

(iv) Infrared measurements of benzoquinone have shown that a carbonyl group is present.

(v) If Graebe's formula were correct, there appears to be no reason why *m*-benzoquinone should not exist.

It can therefore be seen from the foregoing that Fittig's formula agrees better with the properties of *p*-benzoquinone and consequently is the accepted one.

***p*-Benzoquinone oximes.** *p*-Benzoquinone forms two oximes with hydroxylamine. With one equivalent of hydroxylamine the monoxime is formed, and this is tautomeric with *p*-nitrosophenol (p. 604). The dioxime is a yellow crystalline solid.

***p*-Benzoquinoneimine,** $NH{:}C_6H_4{:}O$, and ***p*-benzoquinonedi-imine,** $NH{:}C_6H_4{:}NH$, may be prepared by the careful oxidiation of *p*-aminophenol and *p*-phenylenediamine, respectively, with silver oxide in ethereal solution. The mono-imine is a bright yellow crystalline solid; the di-imine is colourless and unstable. When warmed with inorganic acids, both compounds form *p*-benzoquinone and ammonia.

Indophenol may be prepared by condensing *p*-nitrosophenol with phenol in the presence of 70 per cent. sulphuric acid or concentrated hydrochloric acid:

$$O{=}C_6H_4{=}NOH + C_6H_5OH \xrightarrow{H_2SO_4} O{=}C_6H_4{=}N{-}C_6H_4{-}OH + H_2O$$

It is a brown solid, m.p. 160°, giving a red solution in ethanol; it was formerly used as a dye.

***o*-Benzoquinone** may be prepared by the oxidation of catechol with silver oxide in dry ethereal solution in the presence of anhydrous sodium sulphate. The latter is necessary to remove the water formed during the reaction, since *o*-benzoquinone is readily oxidised by silver oxide in the presence of water:

$$C_6H_4(OH)_2 \xrightarrow{Ag_2O} C_6H_4O_2$$

o-Benzoquinone exists in two forms, one as unstable green needles, and the other, stable light-red crystalline plates. It is odourless, not steam volatile, and is reduced to catechol by sulphurous acid. It is a strong oxidising agent, *e.g.*, it liberates iodine from acidified potassium iodide.

The alternative structure (benzene ring with O—O bridge across the ortho positions) has been rejected on grounds similar to those used for the *p*-compound.

Many benzoquinone compounds occur naturally, and are the cause of the colour in the pigments in which they are found.

Quinols are compounds with the structure

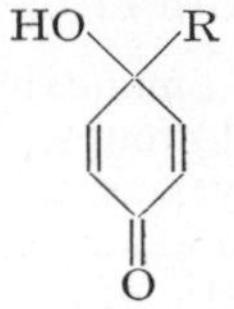

They may be prepared by oxidising *p*-alkylphenols with Caro's acid; *e.g.*, *p*-cresol gives p-*toluquinol* (4-*methylquinol*):

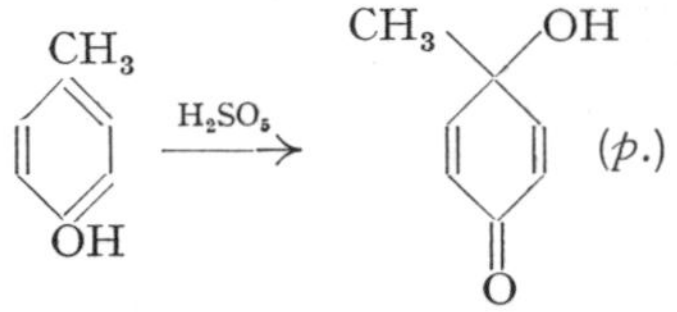

Quinols may also be prepared by treating *p*-alkylphenylhydroxylamines with dilute sulphuric acid. Rearrangement to the imine first takes place (*cf.* phenylhydroxylamine, p. 536), and this is then hydrolysed to the quinol; *e.g.*, *p*-tolylhydroxylamine gives first iminotoluquinone and then *p*-toluquinol:

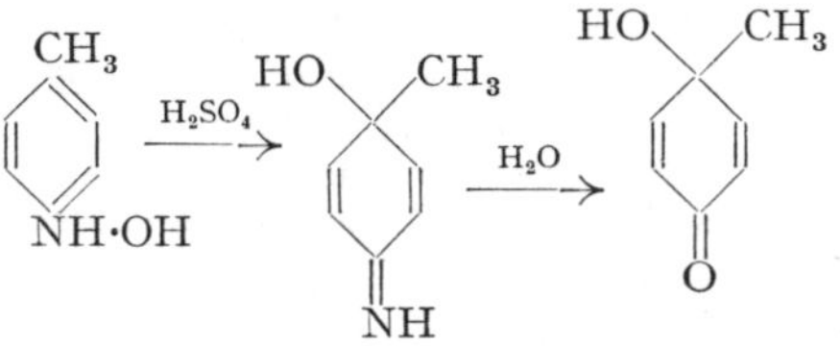

Quinols are colourless solids, soluble in alkalis, readily acetylated and readily reduced to the *p*-alkyl-phenol. Their most characteristic reaction is their great tendency to rearrange to the aromatic structure; *e.g.*, 2 : 4-dimethylquinol, under the influence of dilute sulphuric acid, rearranges to 2 : 5-dimethylquinol:

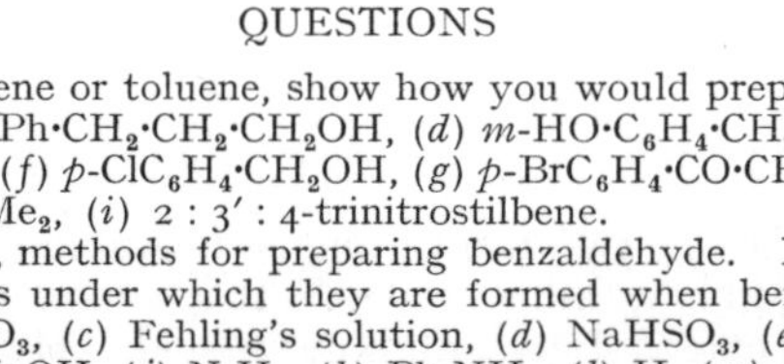

QUESTIONS

1. Starting with benzene or toluene, show how you would prepare:—(*a*) $Ph{\cdot}CH_2OH$, (*b*) $Ph{\cdot}CH_2{\cdot}CH_2OH$, (*c*) $Ph{\cdot}CH_2{\cdot}CH_2{\cdot}CH_2OH$, (*d*) *m*-$HO{\cdot}C_6H_4{\cdot}CH_2OH$, (*e*) *o*-$NO_2{\cdot}C_6H_4{\cdot}CH_2OH$, (*f*) *p*-$ClC_6H_4{\cdot}CH_2OH$, (*g*) *p*-$BrC_6H_4{\cdot}CO{\cdot}CH_2Br$, (*h*) $Ph{\cdot}CH_2{\cdot}CH_2{\cdot}CH_2{\cdot}NMe_2$, (*i*) 2 : 3′ : 4-trinitrostilbene.

2. Describe, in detail, methods for preparing benzaldehyde. Name the compounds and state the conditions under which they are formed when benzaldehyde is treated with:—(*a*) O_2, (*b*) $AgNO_3$, (*c*) Fehling's solution, (*d*) $NaHSO_3$, (*e*) HCN, (*f*) $NH_2{\cdot}OH$, (*g*) NH_3, (*h*) PCl_5, (*i*) NaOH, (*j*) N_2H_4, (*k*) $Ph{\cdot}NH_2$, (*l*) H, (*m*) Cl_2, (*n*) $CH_3{\cdot}CHO$, (*o*) Me_2CO, (*p*) $H{\cdot}CHO$, (*q*) $MeNO_2$, (*r*) $Ph{\cdot}CO{\cdot}CH_3$, (*s*) Ac_2O, (*i*) succinic anhydride, (*u*) PhOH, (*v*) $Ph{\cdot}NMe_2$, (*w*) HNO_3, (*x*) H_2SO_4.

3. Describe how each of the following compounds may be prepared:—(*a*) *o*-, *m*- and *p*-nitrobenzaldehydes, (*b*) 2 : 4-dinitrobenzaldehyde, (*c*) *m*- and *p*-chlorobenzaldehydes, (*d*) 2 : 6-dichlorobenzaldehyde, (*e*) anisaldehyde, (*f*) protocatechualdehyde, (*g*) vanillin, (*h*) veratraldehyde, (*i*) piperonal, (*j*) benzoylacetone, (*k*) 4-*n*-hexyl-resorcinol, (*l*) benzhydrol, (*m*) benzopinacol, (*n*) chloranil, (*o*) quinhydrone.

4. Write a detailed account of the general methods of preparing phenolic aldehydes. Discuss the properties of salicylaldehyde.

5. How may cinnamaldehyde, acetophenone and benzophenone be prepared? Name the compounds and state the conditions under which they are formed when each of these compounds is treated with:—(*a*) oxidising agents, (*b*) reducing agents, (*c*) Br_2, (*d*) HCN, (*e*) $NH_2{\cdot}OH$, (*f*) $NaHSO_3$, (*g*) NH_3, (*h*) HNO_3, (*i*) HCl, (*j*) Ac_2O, (*k*) EtOAc, (*l*) $(NH_4)_2S_x$, (*m*) Me_2NH + S.

6. Write an account of the isomerism of the aromatic aldoximes and ketoximes.

7. Describe the preparation and properties of *o*- and *p*-benzoquinones. Outline the evidence for the accepted structures of these compounds.

8. A compound has the molecular formula C_7H_8O. Write out all the possible isomers and show how you would distinguish between them.

9. Define and give examples of:—(*a*) Étard's reaction, (*b*) Gattermann–Koch aldehyde synthesis, (*c*) Gattermann aldehyde synthesis, (*d*) Sommelet's reaction, (*e*) Rosenmund reduction, (*f*) Stephen's method, (*g*) Cannizzaro reaction, (*h*) Claisen reaction, (*i*) Perkin reaction, (*j*) vinylogy, (*k*) Knoevenagel reaction, (*l*) Reimer–Tiemann reaction, (*m*) Duff's reaction, (*n*) Mannich reaction, (*o*) Willgerodt reaction, (*p*) Houben–Hoesch synthesis, (*q*) Elbs reaction, (*r*) Beckmann rearrangement.

READING REFERENCES

Ferguson, Synthesis of Aromatic Aldehydes, *Chem. Reviews*, 1946, **38**, 227.
Sprung, Reactions of Aldehydes with Amines, *ibid.*, 1940, **26**, 297.
Organic Reactions, Wiley. (i) Vol. I (1942), Ch. 8. The Perkin Reaction. (ii) Vol. II (1944), Ch. 2. The Willgerodt reaction.
Organic Reactions, Wiley, Vol. II (1944), Ch. 3. The Cannizzaro Reaction.
Vol. V (1949), Ch. 6. The Gattermann–Koch Reaction.
Vol. V. (1949), Ch. 9. The Hoesch Reaction.
Vol. VIII (1954), Ch. 4. The Sommelet Reaction.
Vol. IX (1957), Ch. 2. The Gattermann Synthesis of Aldehydes.
Alexander, Studies of the Mechanism of the Cannizzaro Reaction, *J. Amer. Chem. Soc.*, 1947, **69**, 89; 1948, **70**, 2592.
Stempel, Rearrangement of Substituted Benzopinacols, *J. Chem. Educ.*, 1946, **23**, 434.
Allen and Wilson, Mechanism of the Addition of Hydrogen Cyanide to Quinone, *J. Amer. Chem. Soc.*, 1941, **63**, 1756.
McEwen *et al.*, The Schmidt Reaction Applied to Several Unsymmetrical Diarylethylenes, *ibid.*, 1950, **72**, 3212.
Angyal *et al.*, The Sommelet Reaction, *J.C.S.*, **1953**, 1737, 1740, 1742.
Mannich Reaction, *Ann. Reports* (*Chem. Soc.*), 1949, **46**, pp. 151–153.
Willgerodt–Kindler Reaction, *ibid.*, 1949, **46**, pp. 210–213.
Dauben *et al.*, Mechanism of the Willgerodt Reaction, *J. Amer. Chem. Soc.*, 1956, **78**, 4135.
Sanders *et al.*, Acetophenone, *Ind. Eng. Chem.*, 1953, **45**, 2.
Field and Grundy, The Preparation of Aromatic Aldehydes by Means of the Dinitrogen Tetroxide Reagent, *J.C.S.*, **1955**, 1110.
Wynberg, Some Observations on the Mechanism of the Reimer–Tiemann Reaction, *J. Amer. Chem. Soc.*, 1956, **78**, 4135.
Finar, *Organic Chemistry*, Vol. II (1956), Longmans, Green, Ch.VI (section 2d). Oximes.

CHAPTER XXVIII

AROMATIC ACIDS

AROMATIC acids are compounds containing one or more carboxyl groups which are directly attached to the nucleus. Those acids in which the carboxyl group occurs in the side-chain may be regarded as aryl-substituted aliphatic acids, but they are also classified as aromatic acids, since they exhibit aromatic properties due to the presence of a benzene ring.

MONOBASIC ACIDS WITH THE CARBOXYL GROUP ATTACHED TO THE RING

General methods of preparation. 1. By the oxidation of the corresponding alcohol or aldehyde; *e.g.*, benzaldehyde gives benzoic acid:

$$C_6H_5\cdot CHO \xrightarrow{KMnO_4} C_6H_5\cdot CO_2H \quad (v.g.)$$

2. By the hydrolysis of the corresponding cyanide, *e.g.*, *o*-tolyl cyanide gives *o*-toluic acid:

$$o\text{-}CH_3\cdot C_6H_4\cdot CN + 2H_2O \xrightarrow{H_2SO_4} o\text{-}CH_3\cdot C_6H_4\cdot CO_2H + NH_3 \quad (g.\text{–}v.g.)$$

3. By means of a Grignard reagent, *e.g.*,

$$C_6H_5\cdot MgBr + CO_2 \longrightarrow C_6H_5\cdot CO_2MgBr \xrightarrow{HCl} C_6H_5\cdot CO_2H \quad (90\%)$$

4. By means of the Friedel–Crafts reaction; *e.g.*, treatment of benzene with carbonyl chloride in the presence of anhydrous aluminium chloride gives benzoyl chloride which, on hydrolysis, forms benzoic acid:

$$C_6H_6 + COCl_2 \xrightarrow{AlCl_3} C_6H_5\cdot COCl \longrightarrow C_6H_5\cdot CO_2H \quad (55\text{–}58\%)$$

Excess of carbonyl chloride must be used in this method; otherwise benzophenone will be the main product (p. 635).

5. By the oxidation of benzene homologues with dilute nitric acid, dichromate and sulphuric acid, alkaline permanganate, or chromium trioxide in glacial acetic acid. In some cases it may be more convenient to chlorinate the hydrocarbon, and then oxidise the chloro-derivative, *e.g.*,

$$C_6H_5\cdot CH_3 \xrightarrow{Cl_2} C_6H_5\cdot CH_2Cl \xrightarrow[KMnO_4]{Na_2CO_3} [C_6H_5\cdot CH_2OH] \xrightarrow{[O]} C_6H_5\cdot CO_2H \quad (80\%)$$

In this way the oxidation of the side-chain is much easier, since the intermediate alcohol is much more readily oxidised than the hydrocarbon itself.

General properties. In general, the aromatic acids are slightly stronger acids than the aliphatic, less soluble in water, and less volatile. They are fairly easily soluble in hot water, and are readily decarboxylated by heating with soda-lime.

Benzoic acid (*benzenecarboxylic acid*), $C_6H_5\cdot CO_2H$, is present in certain resins, particularly gum-benzoin; it is also present in balsams. Benzoic acid is also found as *hippuric acid* (*benzoylglycine*) in the urine of horses.

Benzoic acid may be prepared in the laboratory by any of the general methods. Commercially, it is prepared as follows:

(i) By the hydrolysis of benzotrichloride with aqueous calcium hydroxide in the presence of iron powder as catalyst (this is an example of indirect oxidation):

$$C_6H_5{\cdot}CCl_3 + 2H_2O \xrightarrow[Fe]{Ca(OH)_2} C_6H_5{\cdot}CO_2H + 3HCl$$

(ii) By the catalytic oxidation of toluene with air and stannic vanadate as catalyst:

$$2C_6H_5{\cdot}CH_3 + 3O_2 \longrightarrow 2C_6H_5{\cdot}CO_2H + 2H_2O$$

(iii) By the hydrolysis of benzoyl chloride prepared from benzene and carbonyl chloride (see method 4 above).

(iv) When phthalic anhydride and steam are passed over a metal phthalate catalyst, *e.g.*, zinc, chromium or nickel salt at 200–300°, some of the resulting phthalic acid is decarboxylated to benzoic acid:

$$C_6H_4(CO)_2O + H_2O \longrightarrow C_6H_4(CO_2H)_2 \longrightarrow C_6H_5{\cdot}CO_2H + CO_2$$

Benzoic acid is a white crystalline solid, m.p. 122°, sparingly soluble in cold water but readily soluble in hot water, ethanol and ether. It is steam-volatile. It forms salts in the usual way; the silver salt (white) and the ferric salt (buff-coloured) are insoluble. Benzoic acid readily forms esters when it is refluxed with an alcohol in the presence of a small amount of concentrated sulphuric acid or hydrogen chloride. Benzoic esters are pleasant-smelling liquids which are denser than water. Phenyl benzoate, which may be prepared by the action of benzoyl chloride on an alkaline solution of phenol, is a solid, m.p. 71°. In general, it has been found that benzoic acid containing a substituent in the *o*-position does not esterify as easily as the *m*- or *p*-isomer. If both *o*-positions (with respect to the carboxyl group) are occupied, then esterification occurs with the greatest difficulty, if at all. Furthermore, once the ester is formed from these di-*ortho*-substituted benzoic acids, it is very difficult to hydrolyse them. The explanation for these abnormal reactions is not yet complete (see the *ortho*-effect, p. 657, for further details).

Benzoyl chloride (*benzenecarbonyl chloride*), $C_6H_5{\cdot}COCl$, was the first acid chloride to be discovered. It may be readily prepared by distilling benzoic acid with phosphorus pentachloride or with thionyl chloride:

$$C_6H_5{\cdot}CO_2H + SOCl_2 \longrightarrow C_6H_5{\cdot}COCl + HCl + SO_2 \quad (75\text{–}80\%)$$

It is prepared commercially by chlorinating benzaldehyde in the cold (benzaldehyde contains no α-hydrogen atom):

$$C_6H_5{\cdot}CHO + Cl_2 \longrightarrow C_6H_5{\cdot}COCl + HCl \quad (ex.)$$

Another commercial method is to heat benzoic acid with benzotrichloride:

$$C_6H_5{\cdot}CO_2H + C_6H_5{\cdot}CCl_3 \longrightarrow 2C_6H_5{\cdot}COCl + HCl$$

Benzoyl chloride is a colourless fuming liquid, b.p. 197°, with an irritating odour. It is only very slowly decomposed by water or by dilute sodium hydroxide (*cf.* acetyl chloride), and because of this, compounds containing an active hydrogen atom can be benzoylated in the presence of dilute aqueous sodium hydroxide. This method of benzoylation is known as the **Schotten–Baumann reaction,** *e.g.*,

$$C_6H_5{\cdot}COCl + C_6H_5{\cdot}NH_2 + NaOH \longrightarrow C_6H_5{\cdot}CO{\cdot}NH{\cdot}C_6H_5 + NaCl + H_2O$$

p-Nitrobenzoyl and 3:5-dinitrobenzoyl derivatives of the alcohols are usually well-defined crystalline substances, and so are used to characterise the alcohols.

Hippuric acid (*benzoylglycine*) may be readily prepared by the action of benzoyl chloride on glycine:

$$C_6H_5{\cdot}COCl + NH_2{\cdot}CH_2{\cdot}CO_2H \longrightarrow C_6H_5{\cdot}CO{\cdot}NH{\cdot}CH_2{\cdot}CO_2H + HCl$$

It is a white solid, m.p. 188°, almost insoluble in water. Its most important reaction is its condensation with aromatic aldehydes to form **azlactones;** *e.g.*, when heated with benzaldehyde, acetic anhydride and sodium acetate, hippuric acid forms benzoyl-α-aminocinnamic azlactone (*2-phenyl-4-benzylideneoxazol-5-one*):

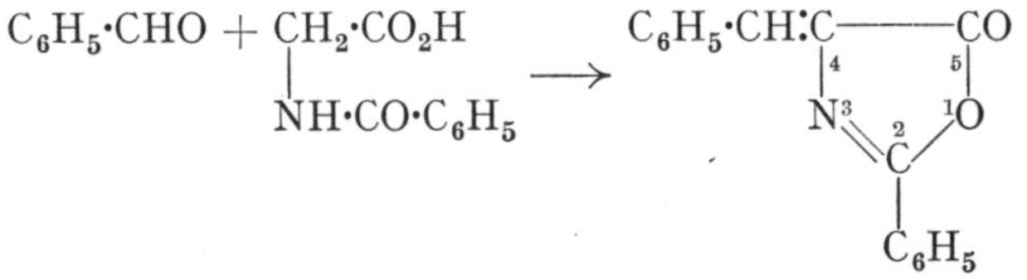

$$C_6H_5{\cdot}CHO + \underset{\textstyle NH{\cdot}CO{\cdot}C_6H_5}{CH_2{\cdot}CO_2H} \longrightarrow \begin{array}{ccc} C_6H_5{\cdot}CH{:}\overset{}{C}_4 & \text{---} & \overset{}{C}O_5 \\ | & & | \\ N^3 & & O^1 \\ & \diagdown\!\!\diagdown C^2 \diagup & \\ & | & \\ & C_6H_5 & \end{array}$$

This reaction is usually referred to as the **Erlenmeyer azlactone synthesis** (1893). Azlactones are very important as intermediates in the preparation of amino- and ketoacids; *e.g.*, *phenylalanine* may be prepared from the above azlactone as follows:

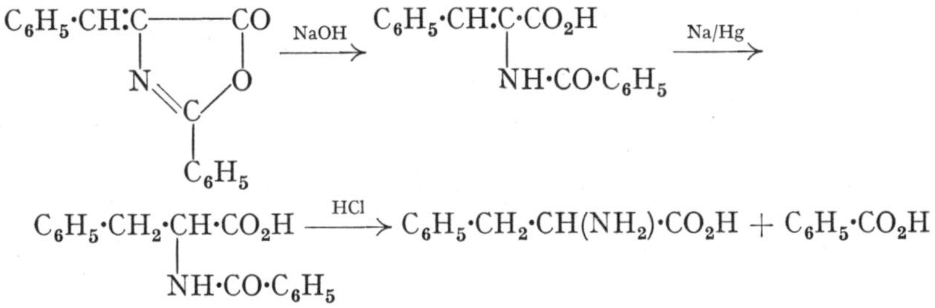

$$\begin{array}{ccc} C_6H_5{\cdot}CH{:}C & \text{---} & CO \\ | & & | \\ N & & O \\ & \diagdown\!\!\diagdown C \diagup & \\ & | & \\ & C_6H_5 & \end{array} \xrightarrow{NaOH} \underset{\textstyle NH{\cdot}CO{\cdot}C_6H_5}{C_6H_5{\cdot}CH{:}C{\cdot}CO_2H} \xrightarrow{Na/Hg}$$

$$\underset{\textstyle NH{\cdot}CO{\cdot}C_6H_5}{C_6H_5{\cdot}CH_2{\cdot}CH{\cdot}CO_2H} \xrightarrow{HCl} C_6H_5{\cdot}CH_2{\cdot}CH(NH_2){\cdot}CO_2H + C_6H_5{\cdot}CO_2H$$

See also p. 655 for another synthetic use of azlactones.

Benzamide (*benzenecarbonamide*), $C_6H_5{\cdot}CO{\cdot}NH_2$, may be prepared by the action of concentrated aqueous ammonia on benzoyl chloride or by hydrolysing phenyl cyanide with warm alkaline 3 per cent. hydrogen peroxide:

$$C_6H_5{\cdot}COCl + 2NH_3 \longrightarrow C_6H_5{\cdot}CO{\cdot}NH_2 + NH_4Cl \quad (v.g.)$$

$$C_6H_5{\cdot}CN \xrightarrow{H_2O_2} C_6H_5{\cdot}CO{\cdot}NH_2 \quad (ex.)$$

Benzamide is a white crystalline solid, m.p. 130°. It undergoes most of the usual reactions of an aliphatic acid amide; *e.g.*, it is readily hydrolysed by dilute acids or alkalis to benzoic acid and ammonia; it forms mercury benzamide, $(C_6H_5{\cdot}CO{\cdot}NH)_2Hg$, with mercuric oxide. Benzamide forms two types of ethers, *N*- and *O*- (*cf.* p. 191); *e.g.*, when the *silver salt* of benzamide is treated with ethyl iodide, *O*-ethylbenzamide, $C_6H_5{\cdot}C(OC_2H_5){:}NH$, is formed (hydrolysis gives benzoic acid, ethanol and ammonia). On the other hand, when the *sodium salt* is treated with ethyl iodide, *N*-ethylbenzamide, $C_6H_5{\cdot}CO{\cdot}NH{\cdot}C_2H_5$, is formed (hydrolysis gives benzoic acid and ethylamine).

Benzoic anhydride, $(C_6H_5{\cdot}CO)_2O$, may be prepared by heating a mixture of sodium benzoate and benzoyl chloride:

$$C_6H_5{\cdot}CO_2Na + C_6H_5{\cdot}COCl \longrightarrow (C_6H_5{\cdot}CO)_2O + NaCl \quad (g.)$$

A better method is to slowly distil a mixture of benzoic acid and acetic anhydride (*cf.* p. 188):

$$2C_6H_5\cdot CO_2H + (CH_3\cdot CO)_2O \longrightarrow (C_6H_5\cdot CO)_2O + 2CH_3\cdot CO_2H \quad (72\text{–}74\%)$$

McGookin *et al.* (1951) have prepared benzoic anhydride by the action of dry silver oxide or yellow mercuric oxide on benzoyl chloride in benzene:

$$2C_6H_5\cdot COCl + Ag_2O \longrightarrow (C_6H_5\cdot CO)_2O + 2AgCl$$

Benzoic anhydride is a white solid, m.p. 42°. It is only very slowly decomposed by water (*cf.* acetic anhydride); it may be used in the Schotten–Baumann reaction, but is not so convenient as benzoyl chloride.

Benzoyl peroxide, $C_6H_5\cdot CO\cdot O\cdot O\cdot CO\cdot C_6H_5$, may be prepared by the action of sodium peroxide on benzoyl chloride:

$$2C_6H_5\cdot COCl + Na_2O_2 \longrightarrow (C_6H_5\cdot CO)_2O_2 + 2NaCl$$

A more convenient method is to add a mixture of benzoyl chloride and aqueous sodium hydroxide to cool hydrogen peroxide with vigorous shaking:

$$2C_6H_5\cdot COCl + 2NaOH + H_2O_2 \longrightarrow (C_6H_5\cdot CO)_2O_2 + 2NaCl + 2H_2O \quad (80\text{–}95\%)$$

Benzoyl peroxide is a fairly stable solid, m.p. 104°. It is used as a bleaching agent for white flour.

Perbenzoic acid, $C_6H_5\cdot CO\cdot O\cdot OH$, may be prepared by adding a solution of benzoyl peroxide in chloroform to a cooled solution of sodium methoxide in methanol and extracting the product, sodium perbenzoate, with ice-cold water. When the aqueous solution is acidified with cold concentrated sulphuric acid, extracted with chloroform, and then the chloroform removed under reduced pressure, perbenzoic acid (m.p. 41°) remains:

$$(C_6H_5\cdot CO)_2O_2 + CH_3ONa \longrightarrow C_6H_5\cdot CO\cdot O_2Na + C_6H_5\cdot CO_2CH_3 \quad (82\%)$$

Kergomard *et al.* (1956) have prepared perbenzoic acid by reaction between benzoyl chloride and an aqueous ethanolic solution of sodium peroxide, or better, hydrogen peroxide and sodium carbonate.

Perbenzoic acid is a fairly active oxidising agent; *e.g.*, it converts the ethylenic bond quantitatively into the ethylene oxide derivative:

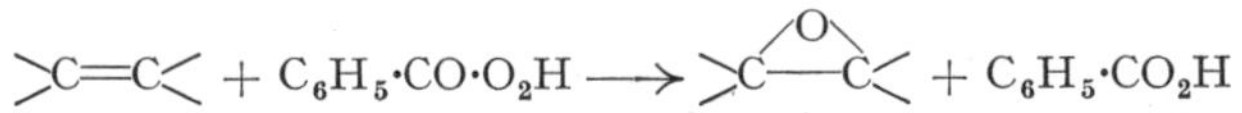

$$>C{=}C< + C_6H_5\cdot CO\cdot O_2H \longrightarrow >C\overset{O}{\frown}C< + C_6H_5\cdot CO_2H$$

Perbenzoic acid is therefore used for the detection and estimation of ethylenic bonds (Prileschaiev reaction; *cf.* p. 68). It is far less troublesome to handle than peracetic acid, and so is used preferably (often as its sodium salt).

Phenyl cyanide (*benzonitrile, benzenecarbonitrile*) may be prepared by heating benzamide with phosphorus pentoxide, by means of the Sandmeyer reaction with benzenediazonium chloride (p. 559), or by fusing sodium benzenesulphonate with sodium cyanide (p. 584). It is a colourless oil, b.p. 191°, and behaves similarly to the aliphatic cyanides.

There are many homologues of benzoic acid, but only the **toluic acids** need be mentioned:

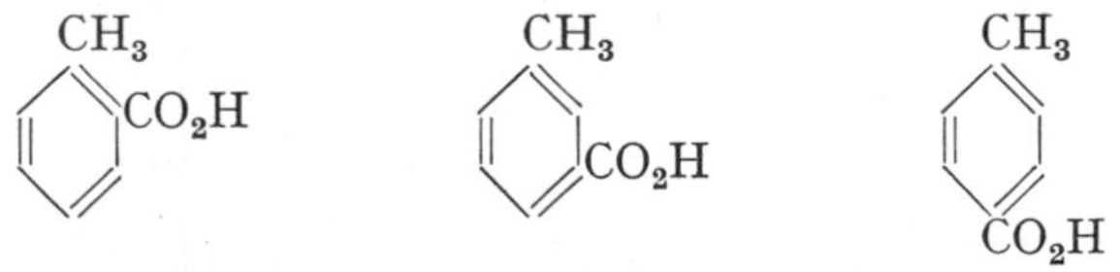

CH_3, CO_2H (ortho)	CH_3, CO_2H (meta)	CH_3, CO_2H (para)
o-toluic acid, m.p. 105°	*m*-toluic acid, m.p. 111°	*p*-toluic acid, m.p. 180°

Each may be prepared by oxidising the corresponding xylene with dilute nitric acid, or from the corresponding toluidine (via the cyanide).

Substituted derivatives of benzoic acid. Benzoic acid is attacked by the usual electrophilic reagents chlorine, bromine, nitric and sulphuric acids, to give mainly the *m*-derivatives; *e.g.*, *m*-bromobenzoic acid may be obtained by heating benzoic acid, bromine and water under pressure:

$$C_6H_5CO_2H + Br_2 \longrightarrow m\text{-}BrC_6H_4CO_2H + HBr \quad (80\%)$$

Waters *et al.* (1950) have prepared *m*-iodobenzoic acid (75% yield) by adding iodine to a solution of benzoic acid in concentrated sulphuric acid containing silver sulphate.

o- and *p*-Substituted benzoic acids may be obtained by oxidising the corresponding toluene derivatives, *e.g.*,

(i) $$o\text{-}ClC_6H_4CH_3 \xrightarrow{KMnO_4} o\text{-}ClC_6H_4CO_2H \quad (76\text{–}78\%)$$

(ii) $$p\text{-}ClHgC_6H_4CH_3 \xrightarrow{KMnO_4} p\text{-}ClHgC_6H_4CO_2H \ (61\text{–}74\%) \xrightarrow{I_2/C_2H_5OH} p\text{-}IC_6H_4CO_2H \ (72\text{–}81\%)$$

Many substituted benzoic acids may also be prepared from the corresponding aminobenzoic acids (via the diazonium salts). *o*- and *p*-Substituted benzoic acids may be obtained directly by using, *e.g.*, the sodium salt of benzoic acid (see p. 495).

Nitrobenzoic acids. *o*- and *p*-Nitrobenzoic acids may be prepared by oxidising the corresponding nitrotoluenes with acid dichromate:

$$p\text{-}O_2NC_6H_4CH_3 \xrightarrow{[O]} p\text{-}O_2NC_6H_4CO_2H \quad (82\text{–}86\%)$$

m-Nitrobenzoic acid may be prepared by direct nitration of methyl benzoate:

$$C_6H_5CO_2CH_3 \xrightarrow{HNO_3/H_2SO_4} m\text{-}O_2NC_6H_4CO_2CH_3 \xrightarrow[\text{(ii) HCl}]{\text{(i) NaOH}} m\text{-}O_2NC_6H_4CO_2H \quad (81\text{–}85\%)$$

3 : 5-Dinitrobenzoic acid, m.p. 204°, is formed when benzoic acid is nitrated with a mixture of fuming nitric and sulphuric acids:

$$C_6H_5CO_2H \xrightarrow{HNO_3/H_2SO_4} 3,5\text{-}(NO_2)_2C_6H_3CO_2H \quad (60\%)$$

It is used to characterise alcohols.

2 : 5-Dinitrobenzoic acid may be prepared by treating 2-amino-5-nitrotoluene with potassium persulphate and sulphuric acid (*i.e.*, Caro's acid) and further oxidising the product, 5-nitro-2-nitrosotoluene, with potassium dichromate and sulphuric acid:

$$\text{NO}_2\text{-C}_6\text{H}_3(\text{CH}_3)\text{NH}_2 \longrightarrow \text{NO}_2\text{-C}_6\text{H}_3(\text{CH}_3)\text{NO} \longrightarrow \text{NO}_2\text{-C}_6\text{H}_3(\text{CO}_2\text{H})\text{NO}_2 \quad (55\text{–}66\%)$$

Aminobenzoic acids. All three aminobenzoic acids may be obtained by reduction of the corresponding nitrobenzoic acids.

Anthranilic acid (o-*aminobenzoic acid*) may be prepared by reducing *o*-nitrobenzoic acid. An interesting preparation is by the internal oxidation of *o*-nitrotoluene (p. 533).

Commercially, anthranilic acid is prepared by oxidising phthalimide with aqueous sodium hydroxide and sodium hypochlorite (the Hofmann reaction):

$$\text{C}_6\text{H}_4(\text{CO})_2\text{NH} \xrightarrow{\text{NaOH}} \text{C}_6\text{H}_4(\text{CO}_2\text{Na})\text{CO·NH}_2 \xrightarrow{\text{NaOCl}} \text{C}_6\text{H}_4(\text{CO}_2\text{Na})\text{NH}_2 \xrightarrow{\text{HCl}} \text{C}_6\text{H}_4(\text{CO}_2\text{H})\text{NH}_2$$

Anthranilic acid is a white solid, m.p. 145°, soluble in water, ethanol and ether; it behaves as an acid and as an amine; it does not exist as an inner salt in the solid state (*cf.* sulphanilic acid). When distilled, anthranilic acid is decarboxylated to aniline.

Methyl anthranilate is used in perfumery, since it is the characteristic constituent of jasmine and orange blossoms. Anthranilic acid is used in the industrial preparation of indigotin (p. 772).

***m*-Aminobenzoic acid,** m.p. 174°, is used in the preparation of azo-dyes.

***p*-Aminobenzoic acid,** m.p. 186°, is one of the substances comprising the vitamin B complex. It has been claimed that it is an anti-grey hair factor; it is also said to be essential for the growth of chicks. Certain derivatives of *p*-aminobenzoic acid are used as local anaesthetics, *e.g.*, *novocaine*, $\text{NH}_2\text{C}_6\text{H}_4\text{CO}_2\text{CH}_2\text{·CH}_2\text{·N}(\text{C}_2\text{H}_5)_2$.

Sulphobenzoic acids. Sulphonation of benzoic acid gives *m*-sulphobenzoic acid. The *o*- and *p*-isomers may be prepared by oxidising the corresponding toluenesulphonic acids.

Saccharin (o-*sulphobenzoic imide*) may be prepared by treating toluene with chlorosulphonic acid and separating the *o*- and *p*-toluenesulphonyl chlorides (p. 586). The *o*-compound is then treated with ammonia, and the resulting amide oxidised with permanganate to *o*-sulphamide benzoic acid; this, on heating, forms saccharin:

$$\text{C}_6\text{H}_4(\text{CH}_3)\text{SO}_2\text{Cl} \xrightarrow{\text{NH}_3} \text{C}_6\text{H}_4(\text{CH}_3)\text{SO}_2\text{·NH}_2 \xrightarrow{\text{KMnO}_4} \text{C}_6\text{H}_4(\text{CO}_2\text{H})\text{SO}_2\text{·NH}_2 \xrightarrow{\text{heat}} \text{C}_6\text{H}_4\lt{}^{\text{CO}}_{\text{SO}_2}\gt\text{NH}$$

Pure saccharin, in high yield, may be obtained by oxidising *o*-toluenesulphonamide with dichromate and sulphuric acid (Matveev, 1946).

The method described above was one of the first to be used industrially. Many other industrial methods are now employed; *e.g.*, one starts with anthranilic acid; this is diazotised and treated with liquid sulphur dioxide in the presence of copper as catalyst. The sulphinic acid derivative thereby obtained is treated with chlorine in alkaline solution, and the sulphonyl chloride so produced is treated with ammonia and heated:

$$\text{C}_6\text{H}_4(\text{CO}_2\text{H})\text{NH}_2 \xrightarrow[\text{H}_2\text{SO}_4]{\text{NaNO}_2} \text{C}_6\text{H}_4(\text{CO}_2\text{H})\text{N}_2\text{HSO}_4 \xrightarrow[\text{Cu}]{\text{SO}_2}$$

$$\text{C}_6\text{H}_4(\text{CO}_2\text{H})\text{SO}_2\text{H} \xrightarrow[\text{Cl}_2]{\text{NaOH}} \text{C}_6\text{H}_4(\text{CO}_2\text{H})\text{SO}_2\text{Cl} \xrightarrow[\text{(ii) heat}]{\text{(i) NH}_3} \text{C}_6\text{H}_4\lt{}^{\text{CO}}_{\text{SO}_2}\gt\text{NH}$$

Saccharin is a crystalline solid, m.p. 224°, about 550 times as sweet as sugar. It is almost insoluble in water, and hence is sold as its sodium salt, which is very soluble. Saccharin is very sweet in dilute but is bitter in concentrated solutions. It is used instead of sugar for many purposes, *e.g.*, sweetening preserves, drinks, etc. It is also used by diabetics and obese persons.

Phenolic Acids. There are three hydroxybenzoic acids; only the *o*-isomer, *salicylic acid*, is important.

Salicylic acid (o-*hydroxybenzoic acid*) occurs as its methyl ester in many essential oils. It may be obtained by the oxidation of salicylaldehyde or salicyl alcohol; or fusing *o*-sulphobenzoic acid with sodium hydroxide. Salicylic acid may be prepared by replacing the amino-group in anthranilic acid by hydroxyl (via the diazonium salt), and also by the Reimer–Tiemann reaction using an alkaline solution of phenol and carbon tetrachloride (*cf.* p. 627):

$$C_6H_5OH \xrightarrow[CCl_4]{NaOH} o\text{-}C_6H_4(OH)CO_2H$$

The original industrial method of preparing salicylic acid was the **Kolbe synthesis** (1859), and this was slightly modified by Schmitt (1885) to give the method (the **Kolbe–Schmitt reaction**) used now. This process is carried out by heating sodium phenoxide with carbon dioxide at 120–140° under pressure.

$$C_6H_5ONa + CO_2 \longrightarrow o\text{-}C_6H_4(OH)CO_2Na \xrightarrow{HCl} o\text{-}C_6H_4(OH)CO_2H$$

A small amount of the *p*-derivative is formed at the same time, and if the temperature rises above 140°, the *p*-isomer is the main product. A by-product in the Kolbe–Schmitt reaction is 4-hydroxy*iso*phthalic acid (3–5 per cent.).

The mechanism of the Kolbe–Schmitt reaction is uncertain. Schmitt believed that sodium phenyl carbonate was formed as an intermediate and that this rearranged to salicylic acid:

$$C_6H_5ONa + CO_2 \longrightarrow C_6H_5O\cdot CO_2Na \longrightarrow o\text{-}C_6H_4(OH)CO_2Na$$

There is, however, much experimental evidence against this mechanism. Jones *et al.* (1954), by an examination of the infrared absorption spectrum of the product obtained in the Kolbe–Schmitt reaction, have been led to suggest the following intramolecular mechanism involving a sodium phenoxide-carbon dioxide complex and a π-complex:

$$C_6H_5ONa + O{=}C{=}O \longrightarrow \underset{\text{complex}}{C_6H_5O\cdots Na\leftarrow O\text{-}\overset{+}{C}{=}O} \longrightarrow \underset{\pi\text{-complex}}{[C_6H_5(O\cdots Na\text{-}O)\rightarrow\overset{+}{C}{=}O]} \longrightarrow \underset{\pi\text{-complex}}{[C_6H_5(\bar{O})(C(=O)ONa)\rightarrow H^+]} \longrightarrow o\text{-}C_6H_4(OH)C(=O)ONa$$

Salicylic acid is a white crystalline solid, m.p. 159°, sparingly soluble in cold water but readily soluble in hot water, ethanol and ether. It is used as an antiseptic, in medicine, and in the preparation of azo-dyes.

Salicylic acid behaves as a phenol and as an acid. Its aqueous solutions give a violet coloration with ferric chloride. When heated quickly, salicylic acid sublimes; but when heated slowly, it undergoes decarboxylation:

$$o\text{-}HO \cdot C_6H_4 \cdot CO_2H \longrightarrow C_6H_5OH + CO_2$$

On the other hand, when heated to about 200°, it forms phenyl salicylate:

$$2\,o\text{-}HO \cdot C_6H_4 \cdot CO_2H \longrightarrow o\text{-}HO \cdot C_6H_4 \cdot CO_2C_6H_5 + CO_2 + H_2O$$

This is possibly formed by combination of phenol (the first decomposition product) with unchanged salicylic acid.

It has been found that as the number of hydroxyl groups in the *o*- and *p*-positions with respect to the carboxyl group increases, so the ease of decarboxylation (and carboxylation) increases. In any case, decarboxylation is always readily effected by heating with soda-lime. When the potassium salt of salicylic acid is heated at 230°, *p*-hydroxybenzoic acid is formed (see below). When reduced with sodium and *iso*pentanol, salicylic acid is converted into pimelic acid. The mechanism of this reaction is uncertain; one that has been proposed is:

$$o\text{-}HO \cdot C_6H_4 \cdot CO_2H \xrightarrow{[H]} \text{(tetrahydro: } H_2, H_2, H_2, H_2\text{; } CO_2H, OH) \rightleftharpoons \text{(cyclohexanone: } H, CO_2H, =O\text{)} \xrightarrow[\text{(acid)}]{H_2O} CO_2H \cdot CH_2 \cdot CH_2 \cdot CH_2 \cdot CH_2 \cdot CH_2 \cdot CO_2H$$

When treated with bromine water, salicylic acid forms *s*-tribromophenol, the carboxyl group being displaced by bromine:

$$o\text{-}HO \cdot C_6H_4 \cdot CO_2H \xrightarrow{Br_2} 2,4,6\text{-}Br_3C_6H_2OH$$

This reaction is characteristic of the carboxyl group when it is *o*- or *p*- to a hydroxyl or an amino-group (*cf.* p. 590). Similarly, the carboxyl group is displaced by a nitro-group when salicylic acid is treated with fuming nitric acid:

$$o\text{-}HO \cdot C_6H_4 \cdot CO_2H \xrightarrow{HNO_3} 2,4,6\text{-}(NO_2)_3C_6H_2OH$$

The reason for this ready displacement of the carboxyl group by bromine or by the nitro-group is not certain, but it may possibly occur by the following mechanism:

$$HO-C_6H_4-CO_2^- + Br-Br \longrightarrow Br^- + HO^+{=}C_6H_4{<}^{CO_2^-}_{Br} \longrightarrow HO-C_6H_4-Br + CO_2$$

Decarboxylation in alkaline solution may be explained similarly (a proton is the attacking agent instead of Br^+).

When treated with carbonates, only the carboxyl group in salicylic acid forms salts; with alkali, both the carboxyl and hydroxyl groups form salts. Sodium salicylate is used in the treatment of rheumatism. Salicylic acid is a stronger acid than its *m*- and *p*-isomers (see the *ortho*-effect, below).

Methyl salicylate, *o*-$HO{\cdot}C_6H_4{\cdot}CO_2CH_3$, b.p. 224°, is the principal constituent of oil of wintergreen. It may be prepared by direct esterification, and is used in perfumery and as a flavouring material. *Salol* (*phenyl salicylate*), *o*-$HO{\cdot}C_6H_4{\cdot}CO_2C_6H_5$, m.p. 43°, may be prepared by heating salicylic acid with phenol in the presence of phosphoryl chloride. It is used as an internal antiseptic. *Aspirin* (*acetylsalicylic acid*), *o*-$CH_3{\cdot}CO{\cdot}O{\cdot}C_6H_4{\cdot}CO_2H$, m.p. 135°, may be prepared by acetylating salicylic acid with a mixture of acetic anhydride and glacial acetic acid. Aspirin behaves in a number of unusual ways, and Davidson *et al.* (1953) have suggested that the assumption of an equilibrium between aspirin (I) and salicyloylacetic anhydride (II) offers an explanation for several of the unusual properties of aspirin as well as its pronounced acetylating action.

$$\text{(I)}\ o\text{-}C_6H_4(O{\cdot}CO{\cdot}CH_3)(CO_2H) \underset{}{\overset{\text{base}}{\rightleftharpoons}} o\text{-}C_6H_4(OH)(CO{\cdot}O{\cdot}CO{\cdot}CH_3)\ \text{(II)}$$

***m*-Hydroxybenzoic acid,** m.p. 201°, may be prepared from *m*-aminobenzoic acid:

$$m\text{-}C_6H_4(CO_2H)NH_2 \xrightarrow[H_2SO_4]{NaNO_2} m\text{-}C_6H_4(CO_2H)N_2HSO_4 \xrightarrow{H_2O} m\text{-}C_6H_4(CO_2H)OH \quad (60\%)$$

It does *not* give a coloration with ferric chloride.

***p*-Hydroxybenzoic acid,** m.p. 214°, may be prepared by heating potassium salicylate at 230°:

$$2\ o\text{-}C_6H_4(OH)CO_2K \longrightarrow p\text{-}C_6H_4(OK)CO_2K + C_6H_5OH + CO_2 \xrightarrow{HCl} p\text{-}C_6H_4(OH)CO_2H \quad (70\text{–}80\%)$$

It may also be prepared by oxidising the methyl group in *p*-cresol (with protection of the hydroxyl group during the oxidation):

$$p\text{-}CH_3C_6H_4OH \xrightarrow[NaOH]{C_6H_5{\cdot}SO_2Cl} p\text{-}CH_3C_6H_4O{\cdot}SO_2{\cdot}C_6H_5 \xrightarrow{KMnO_4} p\text{-}HO_2CC_6H_4O{\cdot}SO_2{\cdot}C_6H_5 \xrightarrow{H_2O} p\text{-}HO_2CC_6H_4OH \quad (90\%)$$

p-Hydroxybenzoic acid is formed when *p*-chlorobenzoic acid is heated with aqueous sodium hydroxide:

$$p\text{-}ClC_6H_4CO_2H + NaOH \longrightarrow p\text{-}HOC_6H_4CO_2H + NaCl$$

Many esters of *p*-hydroxybenzoic acid have antiseptic properties. The acid gives a red coloration with ferric chloride.

Anisic acid (*p-methoxybenzoic acid*), *p*-$CH_3O{\cdot}C_6H_4{\cdot}CO_2H$, m.p. 184°, may be prepared by the oxidation of anethole (p. 612). When heated with concentrated hydriodic acid, anisic acid forms *p*-hydroxybenzoic acid and methyl iodide, and on distillation with calcium oxide it forms anisole (p. 610).

Protocatechuic acid (3 : 4-*dihydroxybenzoic acid*) occurs in various plants, and is formed when certain resins (catechin, gum-benzoin, etc.) are fused with alkali. It may be prepared by heating catechol with aqueous ammonium carbonate at 140° under pressure (p. 605), or from vanillin as follows (note the demethylation):

$$\text{CHO}(OCH_3)(OH)C_6H_3 \xrightarrow[240^\circ]{KOH} CO_2K(OK)(OK)C_6H_3 \xrightarrow{HCl} CO_2H(OH)(OH)C_6H_3 \quad (89\text{–}99\%)$$

Protocatechuic acid crystallises with one molecule of water of crystallisation; the anhydrous acid melts at 199° with decomposition into catechol and carbon dioxide.

Veratric acid (3 : 4-*dimethoxybenzoic acid*), m.p. 181°, may be prepared by methylating protocatechuic acid with methyl sulphate in the presence of aqueous sodium hydroxide:

$$CO_2H(OH)(OH)C_6H_3 \xrightarrow[NaOH]{(CH_3)_2SO_4} CO_2H(OCH_3)(OCH_3)C_6H_3$$

Homoprotocatechuic acid (3 : 4-*dihydroxyphenylacetic acid*), m.p. 127°, may be prepared by treating veratraldehyde with hydrogen cyanide and boiling the product, 3 : 4-dimethoxymandelonitrile, with hydriodic acid (Pictet and Gams, 1909):

$$(CH_3O)_2C_6H_3{\cdot}CHO \xrightarrow{HCN} (CH_3O)_2C_6H_3{\cdot}CH(OH){\cdot}CN \xrightarrow{HI} (HO)_2C_6H_3{\cdot}CH_2{\cdot}CO_2H$$

It should be noted that the prefix *homo* indicates that the compound contains one more carbon atom than the parent substance.

Homoveratric acid (3 : 4-*dimethoxyphenylacetic acid*), m.p. 99°, may be prepared by methylating homoprotocatechuic acid with methyl sulphate in the presence of aqueous sodium hydroxide. It may be prepared via the azlactone synthesis as follows:

$$(CH_3O)_2C_6H_3{\cdot}CHO + CH_2(CO_2H){\cdot}NH{\cdot}CO{\cdot}C_6H_5 \xrightarrow[CH_3{\cdot}CO_2Na]{(CH_3{\cdot}CO)_2O} (CH_3O)_2C_6H_3{-}CH{:}C{-}CO\ (N{=}C(C_6H_5){-}O) \xrightarrow[reflux]{NaOH}$$

$$(CH_3O)_2C_6H_3{\cdot}CH_2{\cdot}CO{\cdot}CO_2Na \xrightarrow[NaOH]{H_2O_2} (CH_3O)_2C_6H_3{\cdot}CH_2{\cdot}CO_2Na$$

Homoveratric acid may also be prepared by chloromethylating veratrole, treating the product with potassium cyanide, and hydrolysing the homoveratronitrile so produced (Bide and Wilkinson, 1945):

$$(CH_3O)_2C_6H_4 \xrightarrow[HCl]{H\cdot CHO} (CH_3O)_2C_6H_3\cdot CH_2Cl \xrightarrow{KCN} (CH_3O)_2C_6H_3\cdot CH_2\cdot CN \xrightarrow{H_2O} (CH_3O)_2C_6H_3\cdot CH_2\cdot CO_2H$$

Piperonylic acid (3 : 4-*methylenedioxybenzoic acid*), m.p. 229°, may be prepared by the oxidation of piperonal (p. 631), or by heating protocatechuic acid with methylene iodide and aqueous sodium hydroxide:

$$(OH)_2C_6H_3\cdot CO_2H + CH_2I_2 + 2NaOH \longrightarrow CH_2O_2C_6H_3\cdot CO_2H + 2NaI + 2H_2O$$

Piperonal and piperonylic acid are oxidation products of piperic acid, which occurs in the alkaloid piperine. Veratric acid is one of the products of oxidation of the alkaloid papaverine. The orientation of the groups in these acids (and in the corresponding homo-acids) may be shown as follows. Sulphonation of *p*-hydroxybenzoic acid (the orientation of which is known) produces a sulphonic acid derivative in which, according to the rules of directing power, the sulphonic acid group is *o*- to the hydroxyl group. This derivative, on fusion with potassium hydroxide, produces the dihydroxybenzoic acid in which the two hydroxyl groups are *o*- to each other. This is confirmed by the fact that the acid, *viz.*, protocatechuic acid, gives catechol (orientation known) when heated to its melting point:

$$HO\cdot C_6H_4\cdot CO_2H \xrightarrow{H_2SO_4} HO(SO_3H)C_6H_3\cdot CO_2H \xrightarrow{KOH} (HO)_2C_6H_3\cdot CO_2H \xrightarrow{heat} C_6H_4(OH)_2$$

Thus protocatechuic acid must be 3 : 4-dihydroxybenzoic acid. Hence the dimethoxy-derivative, veratric acid, must be 3 : 4-dimethoxybenzoic acid. At the same time, the orientations of the corresponding aldehydes, protocatechualdehyde and veratraldehyde, are established. Similarly, since piperonylic acid is the methylene ether of protocatechuic acid (shown by analytical and synthetic evidence), its orientation is also established. Finally, since homoprotocatechuic acid (and its methylated derivative, homoveratric acid) can be synthesised from veratraldehyde (see above), its orientation is thus ascertained.

Gallic acid (3 : 4 : 5-*trihydroxybenzoic acid*), m.p. 253°, occurs in the free state in tea and in many plants. It is best prepared by boiling tannin (tannic acid) with dilute acids. When heated at its melting point, it forms pyrogallol and carbon dioxide (p. 608). It is a powerful reducing agent and hence is used as a photographic developer. It is readily soluble in water, and its aqueous solution gives a bluish-black precipitate with ferric chloride. This property is used in the manufacture of ink.

Depsides. These are esters of aromatic hydroxyacids with hydroxyacids. They are known as di-depsides, tri-depsides, etc., according to the number of molecules in the ester ; *e.g.*, the simplest di-depside is that formed from two molecules of *p*-hydroxybenzoic acid:

$$HO\cdot C_6H_4\cdot CO\cdot O\cdot C_6H_4\cdot CO_2H$$

Depsides are related to certain types of tannins,

The *ortho*-effect. As we have already seen, the properties of *o*-compounds usually differ very much from those of the corresponding *m*- and *p*-isomers. The effect of *o*-substituents was first observed in 1872 when Hofmann found that aminopentamethylbenzene gave little or no quaternary ammonium compound on heating with methyl iodide. This was soon followed by many other cases in which reaction was slowed down, or completely inhibited by the presence of substituents in the *o*-positions; *e.g.*,

(i) Benzamide is readily hydrolysed, whereas pentamethylbenzamide cannot be hydrolysed.

(ii) Benzaldehyde forms an anil with aniline but not with *s*-tribromoaniline.

(iii) Benzoic acid and *o*-substituted benzoic acids form methyl esters with methanol and hydrogen chloride (Fischer–Speier method, p. 176), but di-*ortho*-substituted benzoic acids do not form methyl esters under the same conditions (Victor Meyer, 1874).

Victor Meyer (1894) attempted to explain these abnormalities by **steric hindrance**, *i.e.*, the *o*-groups mechanically interfered in the reaction of the carboxyl group, tending to shield it from the attacking reagent. This seemed to be supported by the fact that if the carboxyl group was removed from the ring by one carbon atom, esterification was normal; *e.g.*, mesitylacetic acid, (I), esterifies readily, whereas mesitoic acid, (II), does not esterify at all (by the Fischer–Speier method):

CO_2H · CH_2 · [ring with CH_3, CH_3, CH_3] (I)

CO_2H · [ring with CH_3, CH_3, CH_3] (II)

On the other hand, Kellas (1897) found that esterification of *o*-substituted benzoic acids is slower than that of the *m*- and *p*-isomers, and that the *m*-isomer is esterified more rapidly than the *p*-. This latter observation is contrary to Victor Meyer's explanation. On the basis of a purely spatial effect, the *m*- and *p*-substituted benzoic acids would have been expected to have esterified at the same rate, since in both acids the substituent groups do not mechanically interfere. Kellas also found that the nitro-group hindered esterification more effectively than the iodine atom, and since the former group has a smaller volume than the latter, the reverse results would have been expected.

A detailed study of the reactivity and strength of *o*-substituted benzoic acids and *o*-substituted amines, and the abnormal effects of *o*-substituents on the hydrolysis of esters, amides and cyanides, has shown that the effects cannot be explained by mechanical interference alone. In fact, in many cases, it is doubtful whether the *spatial factor* (*i.e.*, mechanical interference) operates at all. It is the polar influence of the substituents (and other factors) which usually plays a prominent part in the abnormal reactions of these *o*-substituted compounds. Thus the term steric hindrance, originally intended by Victor Meyer to denote a spatial effect, is misleading. Hence there is now a tendency to call the general phenomenon (of abnormal behaviour) the **proximity effect**, a term which denotes the special influence of groups near the reacting group. The ***ortho*-effect** is a special case of the proximity effect, being used only in connection with *nuclear* substituents. The term steric hindrance is, however, often used to denote the proximity effect (as defined above). On the other hand, there is a tendency to reserve the use of the term steric hindrance for an effect connected with the energy of activation of the molecule.

It can be seen that the term steric hindrance originally considered the geometry of the molecule as such. When, however, a molecule undergoes chemical reaction, it does so via a transition state. Consequently the geometry of both the initial and transition states must be taken into consideration. Furthermore, since the transition state involves more atoms than the initial state, and also the state of hybridisation at the attacked carbon atom is not necessarily the same as in the initial state, steric hindrance is involved more in the transition than in the initial state (see also p. 99), and therefore also depends on the mechanism of the reaction. Thus a study of the effects of steric hindrance requires a knowledge of reaction mechanisms. S_N1 reactions will not be affected by steric hindrance unless large groups are present, when steric acceleration will result (p. 99). In S_N2 reactions, however, the attacked carbon atom has to " accommodate " the attacking agent, thereby resulting in crowding in the transition state. Consequently S_N2 reactions are very much affected by steric hindrance.

Spatial factors (a term which will be used in this book to denote steric hindrance in its original sense) play a part in the *ortho*-effect, but other contributing factors are chelation and the steric inhibition of resonance. These factors, particularly chelation, are also partly responsible for a number of proximity effects in general.

The *ortho*-effect due to chelation is exhibited by the *o*-nitrohalogeno- and hydroxy-benzoic acids; *e.g.*, salicylic acid is stronger than its corresponding *m*- and *p*-isomers. Owing to chelation there is an increased inductive effect (as shown), thereby facilitating the release of the proton. It should be noted that negative substituents in benzoic acid may be expected to change

O=C-←O-←H

O H O C O-←H

NO$_2$

the strength of the acid; *e.g.*, it can be anticipated that *p*-nitrobenzoic acid should be stronger than benzoic acid due to the polar influence of the nitro-group transmitted through the ring. The nitro-group, however, behaves in the same way in the *o*-position, but the *o*-derivative is a stronger acid than the *p*-. Hence some other factor operates in the case of the *o*-compound, and is absent in the *p*-. Chelation is possible in the *o*-derivative but impossible in the *p*-. Chelation may also be used to explain the volatility of *o*-halogenophenols (p. 598), *o*-nitrophenol (p. 599), etc.

An alternative explanation for this *ortho*-effect in *o*-hydroxybenzoic acids is as follows. The carboxylate ion (IV), because of the equivalence of its

HO C O ⇌ H$^+$ + $O^{-\frac{1}{2}}$ C $O^{-\frac{1}{2}}$; $O^{-\frac{1}{2}}$ C $O^{-\frac{1}{2}}$ H O ; H O $O^{-\frac{1}{2}}$ C $O^{-\frac{1}{2}}$ H O

(III) (IV) (V) (VI)

two resonating structures, has a greater resonance energy than the undissociated acid (III) and so is more stable (p. 172). Any structural change in the molecule that will stabilise the anion, *i.e.*, increases its contribution, will therefore increase the strength of the acid. An *o*-hydroxyl group can stabilise the anion by intramolecular hydrogen bonding (V), and so this *o*-hydroxyacid is stronger than the corresponding *m*- and *p*-isomers (where chelation is not possible). Furthermore, *two* *o*-hydroxyl groups should stabilise the anion even more (VI) and so 2 : 6-dihydroxybenzoic acid should be a much stronger acid than *o*-hydroxybenzoic acid; this has been found to be so in practice.

The dipole moment of *p*-nitroaniline is greater than the sum of the dipoles of the nitro- and amino-groups. This is attributed to increased resonance of both of these groups:

O←N=O | NH_2 O←N—O⁻ | $\overset{+}{N}H_2$ (planar) NO_2 | CH_3 CH_3 CH_3 CH_3 | NH_2

On the other hand, the dipole moment of nitroaminodurene is the sum of the dipoles of the nitro- and amino-groups (Birtles and Hampson, 1937). This may be explained by the non-existence of any charged structures. These must be planar, and this is impossible in nitroaminodurene due to the spatial effect of the methyl groups. This is an example of the *steric inhibition of resonance*.

A very interesting case of steric inhibition of resonance is the following. When methyl benzoate is dissolved in concentrated sulphuric acid and the solution then poured into water, the ester is recovered unchanged. When, however, methyl mesitoate is treated in the same manner, mesitoic acid is obtained (Hammett *et al.*, 1937). The reverse has also been shown to be true, *i.e.*, when a solution of benzoic acid in concentrated sulphuric acid is poured into methanol, benzoic acid is recovered; but with mesitoic acid methyl mesitoate is obtained (Newman, 1941). These results have been explained as follows. Methyl benzoate in sulphuric acid adds on a proton, and the ion is stabilised by resonance.

O OMe C + H^+ ⇌ $\overset{+}{H}O$ OMe C ⟷ HO OMe $\overset{+}{C}$ ⟷ HO OMe C + ⟷ etc.

In the case of methyl mesitoate we have:

O OMe C Me Me Me + H^+ ⇌ $\overset{+}{H}O$ OMe C Me Me Me ⟶

MeOH + O C⁺ Me Me Me ⟷ O C Me + Me Me ⟷ etc.

In this case resonance of the ester ion is not possible since planarity cannot be achieved. If, however, methanol is eliminated, the *resulting ion* can now be stabilised by resonance.

MONOBASIC ACIDS WITH THE CARBOXYL GROUP IN THE SIDE-CHAIN

Phenylacetic acid (*α-toluic acid*), $C_6H_5{\cdot}CH_2{\cdot}CO_2H$, occurs in certain esters; it may be prepared from benzyl chloride as follows:

$$C_6H_5{\cdot}CH_2Cl \xrightarrow{KCN} C_6H_5{\cdot}CH_2{\cdot}CN \xrightarrow[(H_2SO_4)]{H_2O} C_6H_5{\cdot}CH_2{\cdot}CO_2H \quad (60\text{–}70\%)$$

It may also be prepared by reducing mandelonitrile with hydriodic acid and red phosphorus:

$$C_6H_5{\cdot}CH(OH){\cdot}CN \xrightarrow{HI/P} C_6H_5{\cdot}CH_2{\cdot}CO_2H \quad (90\%)$$

Phenylacetic acid is a white crystalline solid, m.p. 77°, soluble in hot water. Since it contains two α-hydrogen atoms, it is reactive in the side-chain as well as in the ring, *e.g.*, chlorination in the cold in the presence of a halogen carrier, gives *o*- and *p*-nuclear substitution; chlorination at the boiling point of the acid, in the absence of a halogen carrier, gives replacement of the α-hydrogen (*cf.* toluene, p. 523). When oxidised with chromic acid, phenylacetic acid is converted into benzoic acid.

Mandelic acid (*phenylglycollic acid*), $C_6H_5{\cdot}CHOH{\cdot}CO_2H$, may be obtained from the glucoside amygdalin by regulated hydrolysis (*cf.* benzaldehyde, p. 617). It may be prepared by adding a saturated solution of sodium hydrogen sulphite to a mixture of aqueous sodium cyanide and benzaldehyde, separating the layer of mandelonitrile, and hydrolysing this with cold concentrated hydrochloric acid:

$$C_6H_5{\cdot}CHO \xrightarrow{NaHSO_3} C_6H_5{\cdot}CH(OH){\cdot}SO_3Na \xrightarrow{NaCN}$$
$$C_6H_5{\cdot}CH(OH){\cdot}CN \xrightarrow[(HCl)]{H_2O} C_6H_5{\cdot}CH(OH){\cdot}CO_2H \quad (50\text{–}52\%)$$

Mandelic acid may also be prepared by the hydrolysis of phenacylidene chloride (*cf.* p. 632):

$$C_6H_5{\cdot}CO{\cdot}CH_3 \xrightarrow[(CH_3{\cdot}CO_2H)]{Cl_2} C_6H_5{\cdot}CO{\cdot}CHCl_2 \xrightarrow[(ii)\ HCl]{(i)\ NaOH}$$
$$C_6H_5{\cdot}CHOH{\cdot}CO_2H \quad (76\text{–}87\%)$$

Mandelic acid is a white crystalline solid, fairly soluble in water. It behaves as a hydroxyacid, and is optically active. The acid obtained from amygdalin is lævorotatory, m.p. 133°; the m.p. of the DL-acid is 118°. On vigorous oxidation, mandelic acid gives benzoic acid.

Hydratropic acid (*α-phenylpropionic acid*), $C_6H_5{\cdot}CH(CH_3){\cdot}CO_2H$, b.p. 265°, may be prepared by the reduction of *atropic acid*, $C_6H_5{\cdot}C(:CH_2){\cdot}CO_2H$, obtained by heating *tropic acid*, $C_6H_5{\cdot}CH(CH_2OH){\cdot}CO_2H$, which occurs in the alkaloid atropine.

β-**Phenylpropionic acid** (*hydrocinnamic acid*), $C_6H_5{\cdot}CH_2{\cdot}CH_2{\cdot}CO_2H$, may be prepared by reducing cinnamic acid with sodium amalgam:

$$C_6H_5{\cdot}CH{:}CH{\cdot}CO_2H + 2[H] \longrightarrow C_6H_5{\cdot}CH_2{\cdot}CH_2{\cdot}CO_2H \quad (85\%)$$

The reduction may also be carried out electrolytically, using a lead anode (yield: 80–90 per cent.). β-Phenylpropionic acid may be synthesised from benzyl chloride and malonic ester:

$$C_6H_5 \cdot CH_2Cl + [CH(CO_2C_2H_5)_2]^-Na^+ \longrightarrow C_6H_5 \cdot CH_2 \cdot CH(CO_2C_2H_5)_2 + NaCl$$

$$\xrightarrow[\text{(ii) boil}]{\text{(i) acidity}} C_6H_5 \cdot CH_2 \cdot CH_2 \cdot CO_2H + CO_2 + 2C_2H_5OH$$

β-Phenylpropionic acid is a white crystalline solid, m.p. 47°, soluble in hot water. It is oxidised by chromic acid to benzoic acid.

Cinnamic acid, $C_6H_5 \cdot CH{:}CH \cdot CO_2H$, is the *trans*-isomer, and hence is also known as **trans-β-phenylacrylic acid.** The *cis*-isomer (cis-β-*phenylacrylic acid*) is usually called **allocinnamic acid:**

$$\begin{array}{c} C_6H_5—C—H \\ \| \\ H—C—CO_2H \end{array} \qquad\qquad \begin{array}{c} C_6H_5—C—H \\ \| \\ HO_2C—C—H \end{array}$$

cinnamic acid — allocinnamic acid

Cinnamic acid is the form that occurs naturally (free and as esters) in balsams and resins. It may be prepared:

(i) *By Perkin's reaction* (p. 623):

$$C_6H_5 \cdot CHO + (CH_3 \cdot CO)_2O \xrightarrow{CH_3 \cdot CO_2Na} C_6H_5 \cdot CH{:}CH \cdot CO_2H \quad (85\%)$$

(ii) *By Knoevenagel's reaction* (p. 263):

$$C_6H_5 \cdot CHO + CH_2(CO_2H)_2 \xrightarrow[\text{heat}]{NH_3/C_2H_5OH} C_6H_5 \cdot CH{:}CH \cdot CO_2H \quad (80\%)$$

(iii) By the *Claisen condensation* between benzaldehyde and ethyl acetate in the presence of sodium ethoxide (since benzaldehyde is one of the reactants, this is also referred to as a *Claisen reaction*; see p. 147):

$$C_6H_5 \cdot CHO + CH_3 \cdot CO_2C_2H_5 \xrightarrow{C_2H_5ONa} C_6H_5 \cdot CH{:}CH \cdot CO_2C_2H_5 \xrightarrow[\text{(acid)}]{H_2O}$$

$$C_6H_5 \cdot CH{:}CH \cdot CO_2H + C_2H_5OH \quad (68\text{–}74\%)$$

(iv) By heating benzylidene chloride with sodium acetate:

$$C_6H_5 \cdot CHCl_2 + CH_3 \cdot CO_2Na \longrightarrow C_6H_5 \cdot CH{:}CH \cdot CO_2Na + 2HCl$$

(v) By the oxidation of benzylideneacetone with sodium hypochlorite (*cf.* the haloform reaction):

$$C_6H_5 \cdot CH{:}CH \cdot CO \cdot CH_3 \xrightarrow{NaOCl} C_6H_5 \cdot CH{:}CH \cdot CO_2H$$

Methods (iv) and (v) are used industrially.

Cinnamic acid is a crystalline solid, m.p. 133°. It behaves as an αβ-unsaturated acid, and as a benzene derivative. It is reduced by sodium amalgam to γ-phenylpropionic acid; reduction of its ethyl ester, however, leads to the formation of the bimolecular product, ethyl β : β′-diphenyladipate (*cf.* p. 261):

$$2C_6H_5 \cdot CH{:}CH \cdot CO_2C_2H_5 \xrightarrow{[H]} \begin{array}{l} C_6H_5 \cdot CH \cdot CH_2 \cdot CO_2C_2H_5 \\ \quad\;\; | \\ C_6H_5 \cdot CH \cdot CH_2 \cdot CO_2C_2H_5 \end{array}$$

When a phenyl group is attached to the β-carbon atom of an α : β-unsaturated carbonyl compound, both the double bond and carbonyl group are reduced by lithium aluminium hydride (*cf.* p. 259):

$$C_6H_5{\cdot}CH{=}CH{\cdot}CO_2H \xrightarrow{LiAlH_4} C_6H_5{\cdot}CH_2{\cdot}CH_2{\cdot}CH_2OH$$

By using the inverse addition at $-10°$, the double bond is left intact, *e.g.*,

$$C_6H_5{\cdot}CH{=}CH{\cdot}CO_2C_2H_5 \xrightarrow[-10°]{LiAlH_4} C_6H_5{\cdot}CH{=}CH{\cdot}CH_2OH$$

When oxidised with chromic acid, cinnamic acid forms a mixture of benzaldehyde and benzoic acid. Concentrated nitric acid nitrates it to a mixture of *o*- and *p*-nitrocinnamic acids, the latter predominating.

When distilled with soda-lime, cinnamic acid forms styrene:

$$C_6H_5{\cdot}CH{:}CH{\cdot}CO_2Na + NaOH \longrightarrow C_6H_5{\cdot}CH{:}CH_2 + Na_2CO_3$$

Styrene is also obtained when cinnamic acid is heated for some time just above its melting point. When exposed to sunlight, cinnamic acid dimerises to a mixture of *truxinic acid* (3 : 4-*diphenyl*cyclo*butane*-1 : 2-*dicarboxylic acid*), (I), and *truxillic acid* (2 : 4-*diphenyl*cyclo*butane*-1 : 3-*dicarboxylic acid*), (II):

$$2C_6H_5{\cdot}CH{:}CH{\cdot}CO_2H \longrightarrow \underset{\text{(I)}}{\begin{array}{l}C_6H_5{\cdot}CH{-}CH{\cdot}CO_2H\\ \quad\;\;|\qquad\;\;|\\ C_6H_5{\cdot}CH{-}CH{\cdot}CO_2H\end{array}} + \underset{\text{(II)}}{\begin{array}{l}C_6H_5{\cdot}CH{-}CH{\cdot}CO_2H\\ \quad\;\;|\qquad\;\;|\\ HO_2C{\cdot}CH{-}CH{\cdot}C_6H_5\end{array}}$$

Allocinnamic acid is believed to occur in four allotropic forms, m.ps 32°, 42°, 58°, and 68°; all are unstable, the form melting at 32° being the least stable. Allocinnamic acid may be prepared in one or other of its forms by exposing cinnamic acid to ultraviolet light, or by the partial reduction of phenylpropiolic acid with hydrogen and colloidal platinum as catalyst:

$$C_6H_5{\cdot}C{:}C{\cdot}CO_2H + H_2 \xrightarrow{Pt} C_6H_5{\cdot}CH{:}CH{\cdot}CO_2H$$

Allocinnamic acid readily changes into cinnamic acid, and under the influence of light dimerises to truxinic acid.

Phenylpropiolic acid (*phenylpropynoic acid*), $C_6H_5{\cdot}C{:}C{\cdot}CO_2H$, may be prepared by boiling the ethyl ester of cinnamic acid dibromide with ethanolic potassium hydroxide:

$$C_6H_5{\cdot}CH{:}CH{\cdot}CO_2C_2H_5 \xrightarrow[(CCl_4)]{Br_2} C_6H_5{\cdot}CHBr{\cdot}CHBr{\cdot}CO_2C_2H_5 \xrightarrow[\text{(ii) acid}]{\text{(i) }KOH/C_2H_5OH} C_6H_5{\cdot}C{:}C{\cdot}CO_2H \quad (77\text{–}81\%)$$

Phenylpropiolic acid is a crystalline solid, m.p. 136°. On catalytic reduction (using colloidal platinum), phenylpropiolic acid forms allocinnamic acid. Reduction with zinc and acetic acid gives cinnamic acid, and with sodium amalgam, β-phenylpropionic acid. When refluxed with barium hydroxide solution, phenylpropiolic acid is converted into phenylacetylene:

$$C_6H_5{\cdot}C{:}C{\cdot}CO_2H \longrightarrow C_6H_5{\cdot}C{:}CH + CO_2$$

***o*-Coumaric acid** (*o-hydroxycinnamic acid*), m.p. 108°, may be prepared by boiling coumarin (see below) with sodium ethoxide, or by diazotising *o*-aminocinnamic acid and then heating the diazonium sulphate solution.

When exposed to ultraviolet light, *o*-coumaric acid (the stable *trans*-form) is converted into *coumarinic acid* (the unstable *cis*-form):

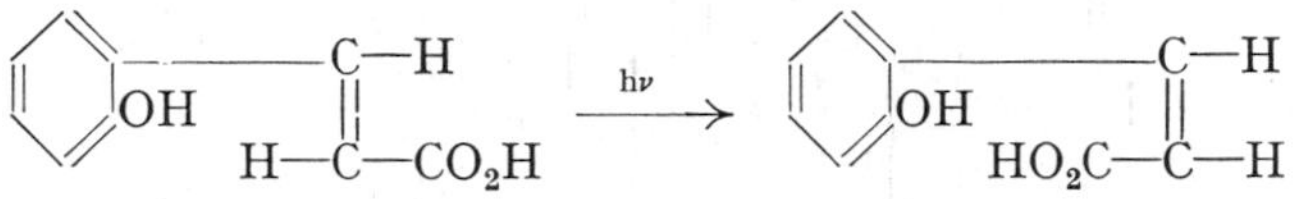

$$o\text{-}C_6H_4(OH)\text{–}CH{=}CH\text{–}CO_2H \ (\text{coumaric acid}) \xrightarrow{h\nu} o\text{-}C_6H_4(OH)\text{–}CH{=}CH\text{–}CO_2H \ (\text{coumarinic acid})$$

coumaric acid — coumarinic acid

Coumarinic acid (o-*hydroxyallocinnamic acid*) is unstable, spontaneously forming its δ-lactone as soon as it is set free from its salts; the lactone is known as *coumarin* (benzo-α-pyrone), m.p. 67°:

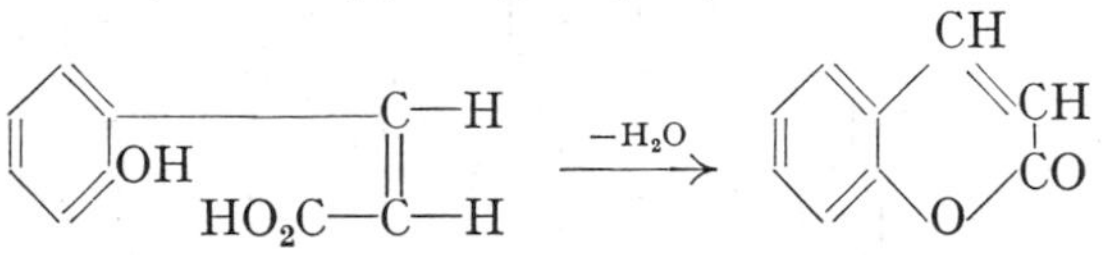

$$o\text{-}C_6H_4(OH)\text{–}CH{=}CH\text{–}CO_2H \xrightarrow{-H_2O} \text{coumarin}$$

Coumarin may be prepared by the Perkin reaction.

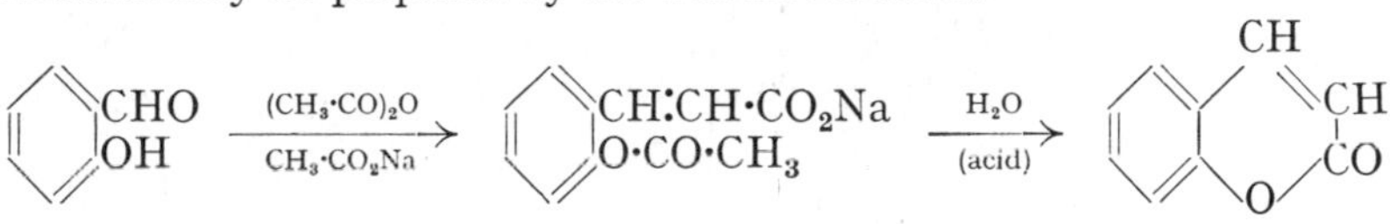

$$o\text{-}C_6H_4(CHO)(OH) \xrightarrow[CH_3\cdot CO_2Na]{(CH_3\cdot CO)_2O} o\text{-}C_6H_4(CH{:}CH\cdot CO_2Na)(O\cdot CO\cdot CH_3) \xrightarrow[(acid)]{H_2O} \text{coumarin}$$

One of the most convenient methods for synthesising coumarins is the **Pechmann reaction** (1883) which is the condensation of a phenol with a β-keto-ester. The usual condensing reagents are sulphuric acid, phosphorus pentoxide, etc., but Koo (1955) has shown that polyphosphoric acid is very effective, *e.g.*, resorcinol and ethyl acetoacetate give 7-hydroxy-4-methylcoumarin:

$$m\text{-}C_6H_4(OH)_2 + CH_2(CO\cdot CH_3)(CO_2C_2H_5) \longrightarrow \text{7-hydroxy-4-methylcoumarin} \quad (98\%)$$

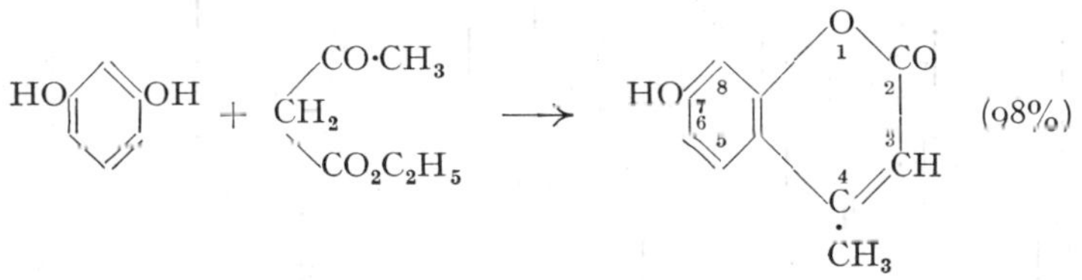

Coumarin is a natural perfume, and is also used as an artificial flavour. When heated with sodium ethoxide, it is converted into coumaric acid.

Crawford *et al.* (1956) have shown that *free* coumarinic acids can be isolated from 8-nitrocoumarins but not from other nitrocoumarins. The stability of these acids is attributed to chelation of the nitro-group with the neighbouring hydroxyl group, *e.g.*,

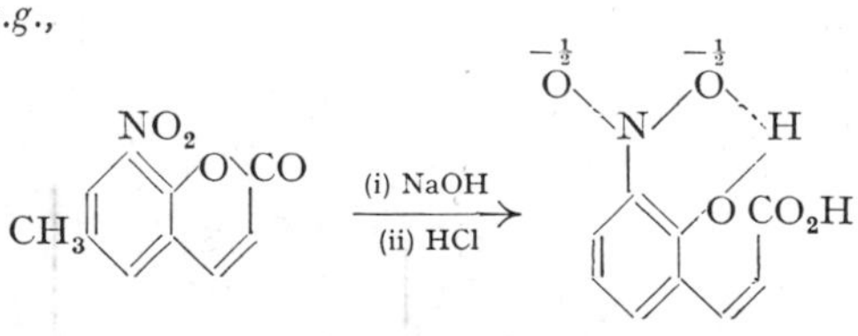

$$\text{6-methyl-8-nitrocoumarin} \xrightarrow[\text{(ii) HCl}]{\text{(i) NaOH}} \text{chelated coumarinic acid } (O^{-\frac{1}{2}}\text{–}N\text{–}O^{-\frac{1}{2}}\cdots H\text{–}O)$$

DIBASIC AROMATIC ACIDS

There are three benzenedicarboxylic acids possible, and all are known:

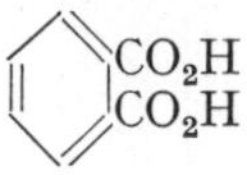

phthalic acid (1,2-$C_6H_4(CO_2H)_2$); *iso*phthalic acid (1,3-$C_6H_4(CO_2H)_2$); terephthalic acid (1,4-$C_6H_4(CO_2H)_2$)

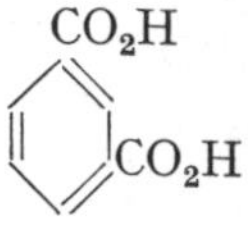

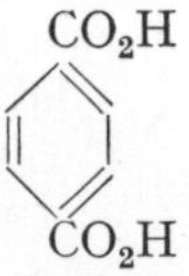

Phthalic acid (*benzene*-1 : 2-*dicarboxylic acid*) may be prepared by the oxidation of any benzene derivative having only two side-chains in the *o*-positions; permanganate or dilute nitric acid is used as the oxidising agent (chromic acid brings about ring rupture; see p. 512):

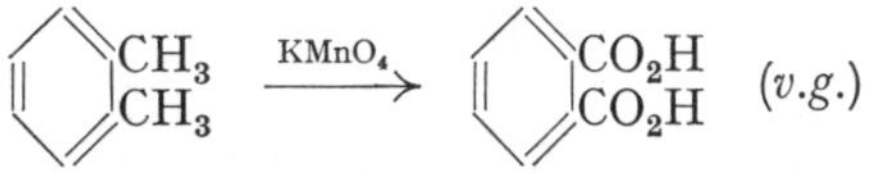

$$C_6H_4(CH_3)_2 \xrightarrow{KMnO_4} C_6H_4(CO_2H)_2 \quad (v.g.)$$

Industrially, phthalic acid is prepared by the oxidation of naphthalene with concentrated sulphuric acid and mercuric sulphate as a catalyst at a temperature of 200° (the yield varies between 25–60 per cent.). This method is almost obsolete, the oxidation being now carried out by passing naphthalene vapour mixed with air over vanadium pentoxide as catalyst at 400–500°:

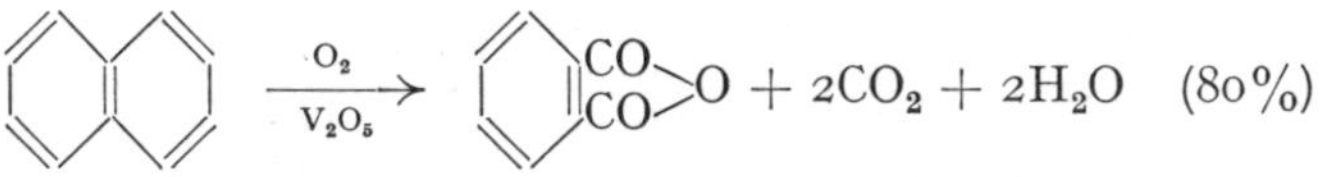

$$C_{10}H_8 \xrightarrow[V_2O_5]{O_2} C_6H_4(CO)_2O + 2CO_2 + 2H_2O \quad (80\%)$$

Maleic acid is obtained as a by-product. A more recent method is to use *o*-xylene as the starting material instead of naphthalene.

In all the above methods, the product of oxidation is phthalic anhydride. This is readily converted into the acid by heating it with alkali, and then acidifying:

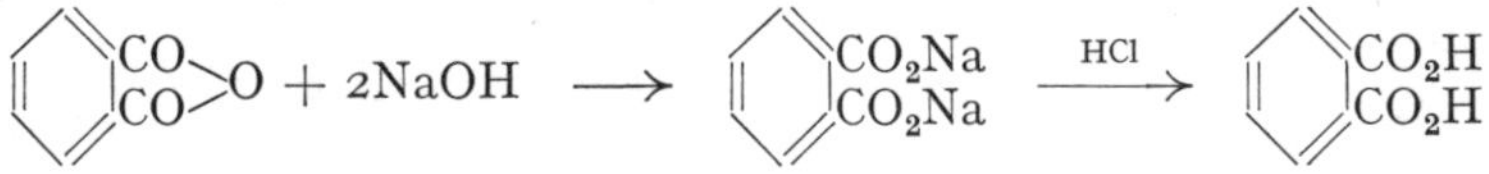

$$C_6H_4(CO)_2O + 2NaOH \longrightarrow C_6H_4(CO_2Na)_2 \xrightarrow{HCl} C_6H_4(CO_2H)_2$$

Phthalic acid is a white crystalline solid, m.p. 231° (rapid heating), with conversion into its anhydride. It is almost insoluble in cold water, but is fairly readily soluble in hot water. It undergoes most of the typical reactions of a dicarboxylic acid. When heated with potassium hydroxide, it is decarboxylated to benzene. It is reduced by sodium amalgam to di-, tetra- and hexahydrophthalic acids. Mercuration of phthalic acid is usually carried out by refluxing the sodium salt with aqueous mercuric acetate containing sodium acetate, until no ionic mercury remains in the solution. Phthalic acid may also be mercurated by fusing it with mercuric acetate, or by heating the mercury salt of phthalic acid until the mercury has been transferred to the nucleus:

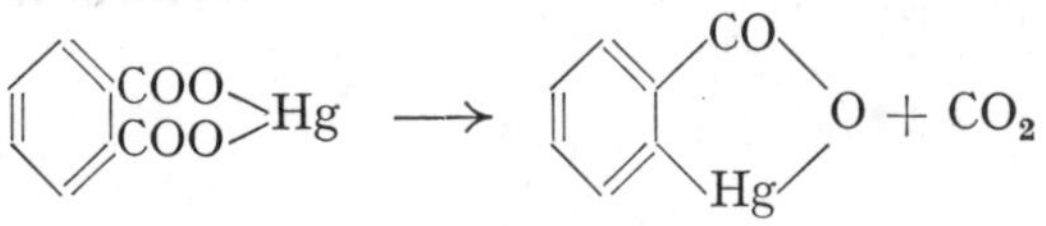

$$C_6H_4(COO)_2Hg \longrightarrow C_6H_4\begin{matrix}CO\\Hg\end{matrix}\!\!>O + CO_2$$

Phthalic anhydride is prepared industrially by the oxidation of naphthalene or *o*-xylene (see above). It is a white solid, m.p. 128°, slowly hydrolysed by water but rapidly by alkalis or acids. When nitrated, phthalic anhydride forms a mixture of 3- and 4-nitrophthalic acids. When these are reduced, their corresponding aminophthalic acids spontaneously decarboxylate to form *m*-aminobenzoic acid:

$$\text{3-}NH_2C_6H_3(CO_2H)_2 \xrightarrow{-CO_2} \text{m-}NH_2C_6H_4CO_2H \xleftarrow{-CO_2} \text{4-}NH_2C_6H_3(CO_2H)_2$$

It is the carboxyl group *o*- or *p*- to the amino-group that is lost. The esters of these aminophthalic acids are quite stable.

Phthalic anhydride undergoes a large number of condensation reactions (see text). Phthalic anhydride and phthalic acid are used industrially in the preparation of dyes, plastics (glyptals), plasticisers, benzoic acid, etc.

Phthalide may be prepared by reducing phthalic anhydride with zinc dust and aqueous sodium hydroxide:

$$C_6H_4{<}^{CO}_{CO}{>}O + 4[H] \longrightarrow C_6H_4{<}^{CH_2}_{CO}{>}O + H_2O$$

It is also formed when the anhydride is reduced catalytically with nickel at 200°, but is accompanied by varying amounts of toluic acid and ring-hydrogenated compounds, *e.g.*, hexahydrophthalic acid. Phthalide may also be prepared by reducing phthalimide with a zinc-copper alloy and aqueous sodium hydroxide:

$$C_6H_4{<}^{CO}_{CO}{>}NH \xrightarrow{[H]} C_6H_4{<}^{CO_2Na}_{CH_2OH} \xrightarrow{HCl} C_6H_4{<}^{CO}_{CH_2}{>}O \quad (66\text{–}71\%)$$

Phthalide is a white crystalline solid, m.p. 75°. It may be converted into *homophthalic acid*, m.p. 175°, by fusing it with potassium cyanide at 180° and hydrolysing the product with boiling 50 per cent. sulphuric acid:

$$C_6H_4{<}^{CH_2}_{CO}{>}O \xrightarrow{KCN} C_6H_4{<}^{CH_2\cdot CN}_{CO_2K} \; (67\text{–}83\%) \xrightarrow[(H_2SO_4)]{H_2O} C_6H_4{<}^{CH_2\cdot CO_2H}_{CO_2H} \; (71\text{–}75\%)$$

Phthalimide may be prepared by heating phthalic anhydride with dry ammonia at about 200° under pressure:

$$C_6H_4{<}^{CO}_{CO}{>}O + NH_3 \longrightarrow C_6H_4{<}^{CO}_{CO}{>}NH + H_2O \quad (90\%)$$

It is a white solid, m.p. 238°. It is weakly acidic; *e.g.*, with ethanolic potassium hydroxide it forms potassio-phthalimide:

$$C_6H_4{<}^{CO}_{CO}{>}NH + KOH \longrightarrow C_6H_4{<}^{CO}_{CO}{>}N\}K + H_2O \quad (68\%)$$

This salt is used in Gabriel's synthesis of primary amines (p. 294), and for preparing many α-aminoacids. The salt is decomposed into phthalimide by carbon dioxide.

Treatment of phthalimide with alkaline sodium hypochlorite results in the formation of anthranilic acid (p. 651). When hydrolysed with warm aqueous sodium hydroxide, phthalimide forms phthalic acid. If, however, phthalimide is allowed to stand in cold aqueous potassium hydroxide, or if warmed with barium hydroxide solution, it is converted into *phthalamic acid*:

$$C_6H_4(CO)_2NH + H_2O \longrightarrow C_6H_4(CO_2H)(CO{\cdot}NH_2)$$

Phthalimide may be reduced to phthalide.

Phthaloyl chloride (phthalyl chloride) may be prepared by heating phthalic acid or phthalic anhydride with phosphorus pentachloride at 150°. It may also be prepared by heating phthalic acid with thionyl chloride in the presence of zinc chloride at 220° (*cf.* p. 359):

$$\underset{(92\%)}{C_6H_4(COCl)_2} \xleftarrow{PCl_5} C_6H_4(CO_2H)_2 \xrightarrow[ZnCl_2]{SOCl_2} \underset{(86\%)}{C_6H_4(COCl)_2}$$

Phthaloyl chloride is a colourless oily liquid, m.p. 15–16°. When heated with aluminium chloride for some time, it is converted into *as*-phthaloyl chloride, m.p. 89° (*cf.* succinyl chloride):

$$C_6H_4(COCl)_2 \xrightarrow{AlCl_3} C_6H_4{<}^{CCl_2}_{CO}{>}O \quad (72\%)$$

When reduced with zinc and hydrochloric acid, phthaloyl chloride is converted into phthalide.

Phthalaldehydic acid (o-*formylbenzoic acid*), m.p. 100·5°, may be prepared by oxidising naphthalene with alkaline permanganate and decomposing the product, *phthalonic acid*, by boiling it in xylene solution:

$$C_{10}H_8 \xrightarrow{[O]} \underset{(40\text{–}50\%)}{C_6H_4(CO{\cdot}CO_2H)(CO_2H)} \longrightarrow \underset{(65\%)}{C_6H_4(CHO)(CO_2H)} + CO_2$$

Phthalaldehydic acid may be prepared by passing bromine vapour into phthalide and heating the product, 2-bromophthalide, with water:

$$C_6H_4{<}^{CO}_{CH_2}{>}O \xrightarrow{Br_2} \underset{(82\text{–}83\%)}{C_6H_4{<}^{CO}_{CHBr}{>}O} \xrightarrow{H_2O} \underset{(65\text{–}68\%)}{C_6H_4(CO_2H)(CHO)} + HBr$$

Opianic acid (5 : 6-*dimethoxyphthalaldehydic acid*), m.p. 150°, is one of the

$$(CH_3O)_2C_6H_2(CHO)(CO_2H)$$

products obtained by heating *narcotine* (an alkaloid of opium) with water.

Phthalaldehyde, m.p. 56°, may be prepared by ozonolysis of naphthalene (p. 683), or by the reduction of phthalobisdimethylamide with lithium aluminium hydride (Weygand *et al.*, 1951).

$$C_6H_4[CO{\cdot}N(CH_3)_2]_2 \xrightarrow{LiAlH_4} C_6H_4(CHO)_2 \quad (70\%)$$

Monoperphthalic acid may be prepared by adding phthalic acid to a cooled alkaline solution of hydrogen peroxide, acidifying, and extracting with ether:

$$C_6H_4(CO)_2O + H_2O_2 + 2NaOH \longrightarrow C_6H_4(CO{\cdot}O_2Na)(CO_2Na) + 2H_2O \xrightarrow{H_2SO_4} C_6H_4(CO{\cdot}O_2H)(CO_2H) \quad (65\text{–}70\%)$$

Monoperphthalic acid resembles perbenzoic acid in its properties, but is more stable.

***iso*Phthalic acid** (*benzene*-1 : 3-*dicarboxylic acid*) may be prepared by oxidising *m*-xylene with permanganate. It is a crystalline solid, m.p. 346°. It does *not* form an anhydride.

Terephthalic acid (*benzene*-1 : 4-*dicarboxylic acid*) may be prepared by oxidising *p*-xylene with permanganate, or by oxidising *p*-methylacetophenone with concentrated nitric acid at about 300°:

$$p\text{-}CH_3{\cdot}C_6H_4{\cdot}CO{\cdot}CH_3 \xrightarrow{HNO_3} p\text{-}C_6H_4(CO_2H)_2 \quad (84\text{–}88\%)$$

It is a white powder which sublimes without melting when heated. It does *not* form an anhydride. It forms polyesters with glycol, and the plastic so obtained is known as *terylene*.

Polycarboxylic acids. Three isomeric tri- and three isomeric tetracarboxylic acids are known; one penta- and one hexacarboxylic acid are also known.

Mellitic acid (*benzenehexacarboxylic acid*) may be prepared by oxidising hexamethylbenzene with permanganate. It is also formed when graphite or wood-charcoal is oxidised with fuming nitric acid.

Mellitic acid is stable solid, m.p. 288° (with decomposition). It occurs as its aluminium salt in peat and lignite.

QUESTIONS

1. Describe the methods for preparing benzoic acid in the laboratory and industrially.
2. How may each of the following compounds be prepared:—(*a*) Ph·COCl, (*b*) $Ph{\cdot}CO{\cdot}NH_2$, (*c*) $Ph{\cdot}CO{\cdot}NH{\cdot}CH_2{\cdot}CO_2H$, (*d*) $(Ph{\cdot}CO)_2O$, (*e*) $(Ph{\cdot}CO)_2O_2$, (*f*) $PhCO{\cdot}O_2H$, (*g*) *o*-, *m*- and *p*-$CH_3{\cdot}C_6H_4{\cdot}CO_2H$, (*h*) *m*-$BrC_6H_4{\cdot}CO_2H$, (*i*) *o*-, *m*- and *p*-$NO_2{\cdot}C_6H_4{\cdot}CO_2H$, (*j*) *p*-$IC_6H_4{\cdot}CO_2H$, (*k*) *o*-$HO_3S{\cdot}C_6H_4{\cdot}CO_2H$, (*l*) 3 : 5-$(NO_2)_2C_6H_3{\cdot}CO_2H$, (*m*) 2 : 5-$(NO_2)_2C_6H_3{\cdot}CO_2H$, (*n*) *o*-$NH_2{\cdot}C_6H_4{\cdot}CO_2H$, (*o*) novocaine, (*p*) saccharin?
3. Write an account of the laboratory and industrial methods of preparing salicylic acid. Name the compounds and state the conditions under which they are formed when salicylic acid is treated with:—(*a*) heat, (*b*) NaOH/CaO, (*c*) H, (*d*) Br_2, (*e*) Na_2CO_3, (*f*) NaOH, (*g*) HNO_3, (*h*) MeOH, (*i*) PhOH, (*j*) Ac_2O.
4. Starting with benzene or toluene, show how you would prepare:—(*a*) *m*- and *p*-$HOC_6H_4{\cdot}CO_2H$, (*b*) anisic acid, (*c*) protocatechuic acid, (*d*) veratric acid, (*e*) homoprotocatechuic acid, (*f*) homoveratric acid, (*g*) piperonylic acid, (*h*) gallic acid, (*i*) $PhCH_2{\cdot}CO_2H$, (*j*) $PhCH(OH){\cdot}CO_2H$, (*k*) hydratropic acid, (*l*) $PhCH_2{\cdot}CH_2{\cdot}CO_2H$, (*m*) $PhC{\vdots}C{\cdot}CO_2H$, (*n*) coumaric acid, (*o*) coumarinic acid, (*p*) coumarin.
5. Discuss the methods for determining the orientation of the groups in the acids (*a*)—(*h*) in question 4.
6. Write an essay on the ortho-effect.
7. Write an account of the preparation and properties of cinnamic and allocinnamic acids.
8. Define and give examples of:—(*a*) the Schotten–Baumann reaction, (*b*) Erlenmeyer's azlactone synthesis, (*c*) the Prileschaiev reaction, (*d*) Kolbe–Schmitt reaction, (*e*) Pechmann reaction.
9. Describe the preparation and some important reactions of:—(*a*) phthalic acid, (*b*) phthalic anhydride, (*c*) phthalide, (*d*) phthalimide, (*e*) homophthalic acid, (*f*) phthaloyl

chloride, (*g*) phthalaldehydic acid, (*h*) monoperphthalic acid, (*i*) *iso*phthalic acid, (*j*) terephthalic acid.

10. Write an account of the analytical and synthetic evidence (i) for the structure of opianic acid, (ii) for the orientation of 3- and 4-nitrophthalic acids.

READING REFERENCES

Downs, The Oxidation of Aromatic Hydrocarbons, *Ind. Eng. Chem.*, 1940, **32**, 1294.
Organic Reactions, Wiley. Vol. III (1946), Ch. 5. Azlactones. Vol. VII (1953), Ch. 1. The Pechmann Reaction.
Hughes, Steric Hindrance, *Quart. Reviews* (*Chem. Soc.*), 1948, **2**, 107.
Ingold, *Structure and Mechanism in Organic Chemistry*, Bell & Sons (1953), Ch. 7. Nucleophilic Aliphatic Substitution.
Steric Strain, *Ann. Reports* (*Chem. Soc.*), 1955, **52**, pp. 137–151.
Dippy *et al.*, Steric Effects in Substituted Nitrobenzoic Acids, *J.C.S.*, **1956**, 2995.
Brown, Chemical Effects of Steric Strains, *ibid.*, **1956**, 1248.
Ingold, Quantitative Study of Steric Hindrance, *Quart. Reviews* (*Chem. Soc.*), 1957, **11**, 1.
Newman (Ed.), *Steric Effects in Organic Chemistry*, Wiley (1956).
Jones *et al.*, Mechanism of the Kolbe–Schmitt Reaction, *J.C.S.*, **1954**, 3145.

CHAPTER XXIX

POLYNUCLEAR HYDROCARBONS AND THEIR DERIVATIVES

POLYNUCLEAR hydrocarbons may be divided into two groups, those in which the rings are isolated, *e.g.*, diphenyl, diphenylmethane, etc.; and those in which two or more rings are fused together in the *o*-positions, *e.g.*, naphthalene, anthracene, etc.

ISOLATED SYSTEMS

Diphenyl (*biphenyl*), $C_6H_5{\cdot}C_6H_5$, occurs in small quantities in coal-tar. It may be prepared:

(i) **By Fittig's reaction** (1863). This is carried out by treating bromobenzene with sodium in ethereal solution:

$$2C_6H_5Br + 2Na \longrightarrow C_6H_5{\cdot}C_6H_5 + 2NaBr \quad (20\text{–}30\%)$$

Benzene, *o*-diphenylbenzene and triphenylene are obtained as by-products (*cf.* p. 508). It should be noted that the Fittig reaction is analogous to the Wurtz reaction. The former, however, involves the use of aryl halide only, the latter, alkyl halide. The Wurtz–Fittig reaction involves the use of both alkyl and aryl halides.

(ii) When bromobenzene in ethanolic solution is made alkaline and refluxed with hydrazine in the presence of a palladium catalyst on a calcium carbonate support, diphenyl is obtained (Busch *et al.*, 1936):

$$2C_6H_5Br + 2[H] \longrightarrow C_6H_5{\cdot}C_6H_5 + 2HBr \quad (80\%)$$

(It is the hydrazine which supplies the hydrogen.)

(iii) (*a*) By warming benzenediazonium sulphate in ethanol with copper powder:

$$2C_6H_5{\cdot}N_2HSO_4 \xrightarrow[C_2H_5OH]{Cu} C_6H_5{\cdot}C_6H_5 + 2N_2 + 2H_2SO_4 \quad (25\%)$$

(*b*) By diazotising benzidine and allowing the diazonium salt solution to stand in contact with hypophosphorous acid:

$$NH_2\text{–}C_6H_4\text{–}C_6H_4\text{–}NH_2 \xrightarrow{NaNO_2/HCl} ClN_2\text{–}C_6H_4\text{–}C_6H_4\text{–}N_2Cl \xrightarrow{H_3PO_2} C_6H_5\text{–}C_6H_5 \quad (60\%)$$

(iv) By the **Ullmann diaryl synthesis** (1903). Iodobenzene is heated with copper powder in a sealed tube:

$$2C_6H_5I + 2Cu \longrightarrow C_6H_5{\cdot}C_6H_5 + 2CuI \quad (80\%)$$

Aryl chlorides and bromides do not usually react unless there is a negative group *o*- or *p*- to the halogen atom, *e.g.*, *o*-chloronitrobenzene forms 2 : 2′-dinitrodiphenyl:

$$2\ o\text{-}NO_2C_6H_4Cl \xrightarrow{Cu} (o\text{-}NO_2C_6H_4)_2 \quad (52\text{–}61\%)$$

Aryl iodides react readily, but aryl fluorides are not sufficiently reactive for the Ullmann diaryl synthesis.

By choosing suitable starting materials, it is possible to prepare many diphenyl derivatives by the Ullmann synthesis, *e.g.*, 4 : 4′-dimethyldiphenyl from *p*-iodotoluene:

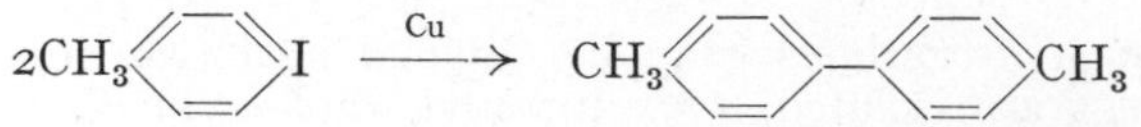

$$2CH_3C_6H_4I \xrightarrow{Cu} CH_3C_6H_4{-}C_6H_4CH_3$$

Kornblum *et al.* (1952) have shown that dimethylformamide is a good solvent for this synthesis, and the yields obtained are higher.

There is a large amount of evidence to support a free-radical mechanism for the Ullmann diaryl synthesis (Rapson, 1941; Bell, 1954; Nursten, 1955).

(v) Arylmagnesium halides do not react with aryl halides. Reaction, however, will take place in the presence of small quantities of metal halides such as $CoCl_2$, $NiCl_2$, $FeCl_3$, etc. (Kharasch and Fields, 1941); *e.g.*, diphenyl is formed by reaction between phenylmagnesium bromide and bromobenzene in the presence of a small amount of cobaltous chloride:

$$C_6H_5{\cdot}MgBr + C_6H_5Br \xrightarrow{CoCl_2} C_6H_5{\cdot}C_6H_5 + MgBr_2 \quad (g.)$$

Traces of benzene, terphenyl, etc. are also formed. The mechanism of the reaction is uncertain; Kharasch believes it takes place via free radicals:

$$C_6H_5{\cdot}MgBr + CoCl_2 \longrightarrow C_6H_5{\cdot}CoCl + MgClBr$$
$$2C_6H_5{\cdot}CoCl \longrightarrow C_6H_5{\cdot}C_6H_5 + 2{\cdot}CoCl$$
$${\cdot}CoCl + C_6H_5Br \longrightarrow CoClBr + C_6H_5{\cdot}$$
$$C_6H_5{\cdot} \longrightarrow C_6H_6,\ C_6H_5{\cdot}C_6H_5, \text{ etc.}$$

Industrially, diphenyl is prepared by passing benzene vapour through a red-hot tube, preferably packed with pumice (600–800°):

$$2C_6H_6 \longrightarrow C_6H_5{\cdot}C_6H_5 + H_2$$

A more recent method is to mix benzene vapour (preheated to 650°) with superheated steam (1000–1100°), and passing the mixture into steel vessels coated internally with a film of Fe_3O_4.

Diphenyl is a colourless crystalline solid, m.p. 71°, insoluble in water but soluble in ethanol and ether. It is increasing in use as a heat transfer medium; chlorinated diphenyls are used as plasticisers.

Diphenyl undergoes the usual nuclear substitution reactions, the phenyl group being *o*- and *p*-orienting (one phenyl group behaving as an electron-releasing group and the other as an electron-acceptor). The first substituent enters mainly the 4-position, and to a lesser extent the 2-position. Introduction of a second substituent usually takes place in the *unsubstituted* ring; *e.g.*, on nitration, the main product is 4-nitrodiphenyl, together with

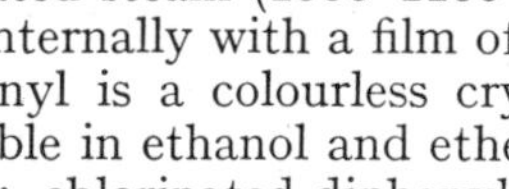

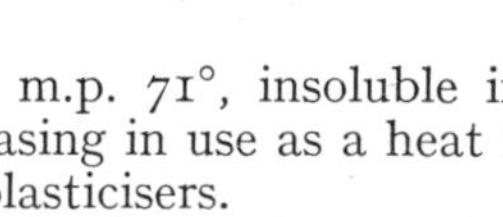

δ+ δ− δ−

m′ o′ o m
p′ 4′ 3′2′ 1′ 5′6′ 1 2 3 4 6 5 p
m′ o′ o m

a small amount of 2-nitrodiphenyl. Further nitration gives 4 : 4′-dinitrodiphenyl (and some 2 : 4′- and 2 : 2′-dinitrodiphenyls). Diphenyl behaves similarly on halogenation and sulphonation.

When oxidised with chromic acid, diphenyl forms a small amount of benzoic acid, most of the hydrocarbon being oxidised completely to carbon dioxide and water.

Benzidine (4 : 4'-*diaminodiphenyl*) may be prepared by the *benzidine transformation* (p. 577); hydrazobenzene, on warming with hydrochloric acid, rearranges to benzidine:

$$C_6H_5\text{—NH·NH—}C_6H_5 \xrightarrow{HCl} NH_2C_6H_4\text{—}C_6H_4NH_2 \quad (90\%)$$

The structure of benzidine may be shown by its formation on the reduction of 4 : 4'-dinitrodiphenyl (which may be prepared by the Ullmann synthesis starting with *p*-bromonitrobenzene).

Benzidine is a colourless solid, m.p. 127°. Its hydrochloride is soluble, but its sulphate is sparingly soluble in water. It is very important commercially since its used in the preparation of azo-dyes, *e.g.*, congo red (p. 753).

***o*-Tolidine** (4 : 4'-*diamino*-3 : 3'-*dimethyldiphenyl*), m.p. 129°, and **dianisidine** (4 : 4'-*diamino*-3 : 3'-*dimethoxydiphenyl*), m.p. 138°, are manufactured on a large scale as intermediates in the preparation of azo-dyes.

Diphenic acid (*diphenyl*-2 : 2'-*dicarboxylic acid*) may be readily prepared by oxidising phenanthraquinone with potassium dichromate and sulphuric acid, or by the direct oxidation of phenanthrene with 50 per cent. hydrogen peroxide in glacial acetic (68% yield; O'Connor *et al.*, 1951).

$$\text{phenanthraquinone (O O)} \xrightarrow{[O]} \text{diphenic acid } (CO_2H\ CO_2H)$$

It may also be prepared by the action of ammoniacal cuprous oxide on diazotised anthranilic acid:

$$2\ C_6H_4(CO_2H)N_2Cl \xrightarrow{Cu_2O} \text{diphenic acid } (CO_2H\ CO_2H) \quad (72\text{–}84\%)$$

The methyl ester may be obtained by heating methyl *o*-iodobenzoate with copper powder (Ullmann synthesis):

$$2\ C_6H_4(CO_2CH_3)I \xrightarrow{Cu} \text{dimethyl diphenate } (CO_2CH_3\ CO_2CH_3)$$

Diphenic acid is a solid, m.p. 229°. When heated with acetic anhydride, it forms diphenic anhydride, and when heated with concentrated sulphuric acid, fluorenone-4-carboxylic acid:

$$\text{fluorenone-4-carboxylic acid } (CO_2H,\ CO) \xleftarrow{H_2SO_4} \text{diphenic acid } (CO_2H\ CO_2H) \xrightarrow{(CH_3\cdot CO)_2O} \text{diphenic anhydride } (CO\text{—}O\text{—}CO)$$

When the calcium salt of diphenic acid is distilled, fluorenone is obtained:

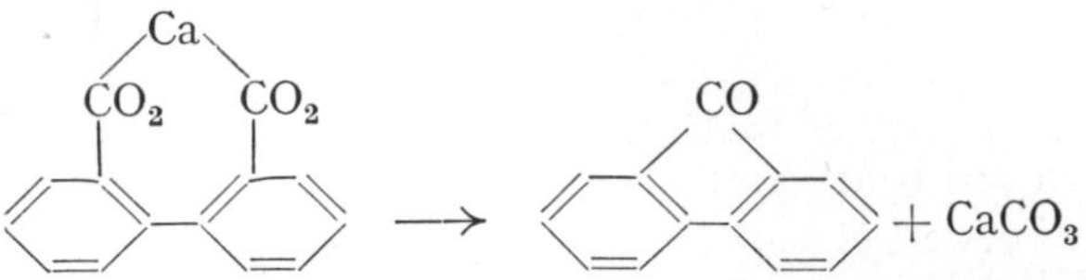

$$(C_6H_4CO_2)_2Ca \longrightarrow C_{6}H_4\text{-}CO\text{-}C_6H_4 + CaCO_3$$

When oxidised with potassium permanganate, diphenic acid forms phthalic acid. Distillation with soda-lime gives diphenyl.

If at least three of the positions 2, 2′, 6 and 6′ are occupied by sufficiently large groups, free rotation about the single bond joining the two phenyl groups is no longer possible Provided each ring has not a vertical plane of symmetry, this restricted rotation gives rise to optical activity due to the molecule being *asymmetric as a whole* (p. 385); *e.g.*, 6-*nitrodiphenyl*-2 : 2′-*dicarboxylic acid*, (I), and 6 : 6′-*diamino*-2 : 2′-*dimethyldiphenyl*, (II), have been resolved. If the substituent group is large enough, then only two groups

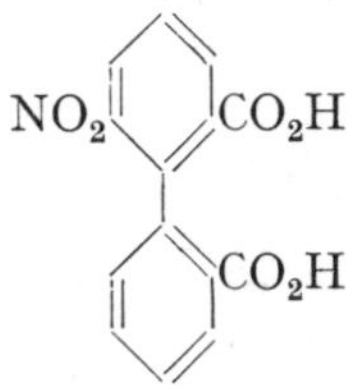

(I) 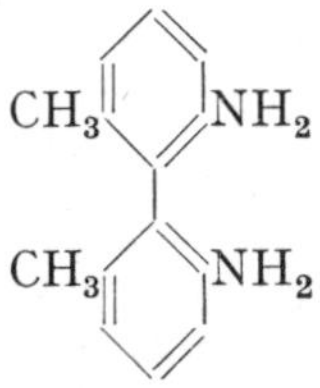 (II) 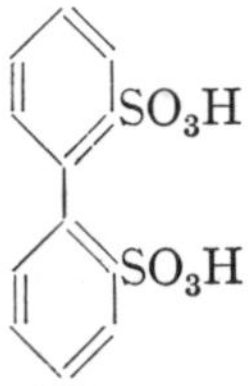 (III)

in the *o*- and *o*′-positions will cause restricted rotation, *e.g.*, *diphenyl*-2 : 2′-*disulphonic* acid, (III), has been resolved.

The cause of the restricted rotation is believed to be due mainly to the spatial effects of the groups in the *o*- and *o*′-positions.

A number of polyphenyls and some of their derivatives have been prepared, *e.g.*, *terphenyl*, *quaterphenyl*, *quinquephenyl*, and *sexiphenyl*.

Diphenylmethane. Some related compounds of diphenylmethane have

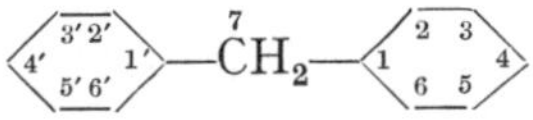

$$C_6H_5\text{—}\overset{7}{C}H_2\text{—}C_6H_5$$

already been discussed, *e.g.*, benzophenone (p. 635). Diphenylmethane may be prepared:

(i) By the Friedel–Crafts condensation between benzyl chloride and benzene:

$$C_6H_5{\cdot}CH_2Cl + C_6H_6 \xrightarrow{AlCl_3} C_6H_5{\cdot}CH_2{\cdot}C_6H_5 + HCl \quad (50\%)$$

(ii) By the condensation between one molecule of formaldehyde and two molecules of benzene in the presence of concentrated sulphuric acid:

$$2C_6H_6 + CH_2O \xrightarrow{H_2SO_4} C_6H_5{\cdot}CH_2{\cdot}C_6H_5 + H_2O$$

(iii) By heating benzophenone with hydriodic acid and red phosphorus at 160° under pressure:

$$C_6H_5{\cdot}CO{\cdot}C_6H_5 \xrightarrow{HI/P} C_6H_5{\cdot}CH_2{\cdot}C_6H_5 \quad (95\%)$$

(iv) By allowing a mixture of benzyl alcohol, benzene, acetic and sulphuric acids to stand for 6 hours:

$$C_6H_5{\cdot}CH_2OH + C_6H_6 \longrightarrow C_6H_5{\cdot}CH_2{\cdot}C_6H_5 + H_2O \quad (25\%)$$

Diphenylmethane is a crystalline solid, m.p. 26°. Its reactions are similar to those of diphenyl, *e.g.*, on nitration, the nitro-group enters mainly the 4-position; the second nitro-group then enters the 4′-position (the benzyl group is *o-p*-orienting). Since the hydrogen of the methylene group is very active (due to each ring being electron-attracting, *i.e.*, each ring behaves as a negative group), bromination of diphenylmethane gives rise to substitution at the methylene carbon atom, and not in the ring, to form, *e.g.*, diphenylmethyl bromide:

$$C_6H_5{\cdot}CH_2{\cdot}C_6H_5 + Br_2 \longrightarrow C_6H_5{\cdot}CHBr{\cdot}C_6H_5 + HBr$$

When oxidised with chromic acid, diphenylmethane forms benzophenone. When its vapour is passed through a red hot tube, diphenylmethane forms fluorene:

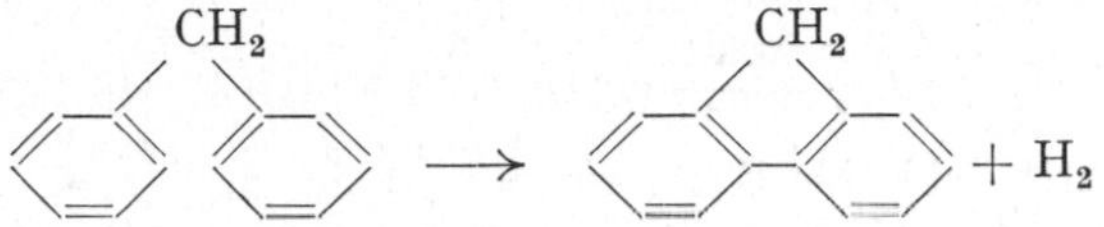

CH_2 (diphenylmethane) $\longrightarrow$ CH_2 (fluorene) $+ H_2$

Triphenylmethane may be prepared by the Friedel–Crafts condensation between benzene and either benzylidene chloride or chloroform:

$$2C_6H_6 + C_6H_5{\cdot}CHCl_2 \xrightarrow{AlCl_3} (C_6H_5)_3CH + 2HCl$$

$$3C_6H_6 + CHCl_3 \xrightarrow{AlCl_3} (C_6H_5)_3CH + 3HCl \quad (33\%)$$

It may also be prepared by condensing benzaldehyde with benzene in the presence of zinc chloride:

$$C_6H_5{\cdot}CHO + 2C_6H_6 \xrightarrow{ZnCl_2} (C_6H_5)_3CH + H_2O$$

Triphenylmethane is a colourless crystalline solid, m.p. 93°. It is the parent substance of the triphenylmethane dyes (p. 756). When brominated, it forms triphenylmethyl bromide, $(C_6H_5)_3CBr$ (*cf.* diphenylmethane, above). Oxidation with chromium trioxide in acetic acid converts triphenylmethane into *triphenylcarbinol*, m.p. 165°:

$$(C_6H_5)_3CH + [O] \longrightarrow (C_6H_5)_3COH \quad (85\%)$$

This compound may also be prepared by reaction between phenylmagnesium bromide and benzophenone or ethyl benzoate:

$$(C_6H_5)_2CO + C_6H_5{\cdot}MgBr \longrightarrow (C_6H_5)_3COMgBr \xrightarrow{H_2O} (C_6H_5)_3COH \quad (75\%)$$

$$C_6H_5{\cdot}CO_2C_2H_5 + 2C_6H_5{\cdot}MgBr \longrightarrow (C_6H_5)_3COMgBr \xrightarrow{H_2O} (C_6H_5)_3COH \quad (89\text{–}93\%)$$

Triphenylcarbinol reacts almost instantaneously with hydrochloric acid in acetic acid or with acetyl chloride to form triphenylmethyl chloride (*cf.* tertiary alcohols, p. 119):

$$(C_6H_5)_3COH + CH_3{\cdot}COCl \longrightarrow (C_6H_5)_3CCl + CH_3{\cdot}CO_2H \quad (93\text{–}95\%)$$

In the presence of hydrochloric acid, triphenylcarbinol forms ethers with alcohols, *e.g.*,

$$(C_6H_5)_3COH + CH_3OH \xrightarrow{HCl} (C_6H_5)_3C{\cdot}O{\cdot}CH_3 + H_2O$$

It condenses with aniline hydrochloride to form *p*-aminotetraphenylmethane, and when refluxed with formic acid, it forms triphenylmethane.

When treated with sodium in ethereal solution (or in liquid ammonia), triphenylmethane forms triphenylmethylsodium:

$$(C_6H_5)_3CH + Na \longrightarrow (C_6H_5)_3\bar{C}Na^+ + \tfrac{1}{2}H_2$$

This compound forms the sodium salt of triphenylacetic acid when heated with carbon dioxide.

Derivatives of triphenylmethane are best prepared synthetically (see, *e.g.*, p. 756).

Triphenylmethyl chloride may be prepared from triphenylcarbinol and acetyl chloride (see above), or by the Friedel–Crafts condensation between benzene and carbon tetrachloride; tetraphenylmethane is *not* formed:

$$3C_6H_6 + CCl_4 \xrightarrow{AlCl_3} (C_6H_5)_3CCl + 3HCl \quad (68\text{–}84\%)$$

Triphenylmethyl chloride is a crystalline solid, m.p. 112°. The halogen atom is extremely reactive, *e.g.*, when boiled with water, triphenylmethyl chloride forms the corresponding alcohol, and with ethanol it forms the ethyl ether:

$$(C_6H_5)_3C{\cdot}O{\cdot}C_2H_5 \xleftarrow{C_2H_5OH} (C_6H_5)_3CCl \xrightarrow{H_2O} (C_6H_5)_3COH$$

Triphenylmethyl chloride may be converted into triphenylmethane as follows:

$$(C_6H_5)_3CCl \xrightarrow{Mg} (C_6H_5)_3C{\cdot}MgCl \xrightarrow{H_2O} (C_6H_5)_3CH$$

This reaction is particularly interesting since the preparation of the Grignard reagent from triphenylmethyl bromide was shown to be via a free-radical mechanism (Gomberg and Bachmann, 1930). These authors showed that when half the total amount of magnesium had reacted, the solution contained triphenylmethyl and hexaphenylethane, *but no Grignard reagent*:

$$2(C_6H_5)_3CBr + Mg \longrightarrow 2(C_6H_5)_3C{\cdot} + MgBr_2$$
$$Mg + MgBr_2 \rightleftharpoons 2{\cdot}MgBr$$
$$(C_6H_5)_3C{\cdot} + {\cdot}MgBr \longrightarrow (C_6H_5)_3C{\cdot}MgBr$$

When triphenylmethyl chloride is dissolved in liquid sulphur dioxide, the solution shows a conductivity of the same order of magnitude as a solution of a strong electrolyte. This is due to the presence of triphenylmethyl carbonium ions, $(C_6H_5)_3C^+$, and chloride ions.

Tetraphenylmethane may be prepared by the action of phenylmagnesium bromide on triphenylmethyl chloride:

$$(C_6H_5)_3CCl + C_6H_5{\cdot}MgBr \longrightarrow (C_6H_5)_4C + MgClBr \quad (v.p.)$$

It may also be prepared by diazotising *p*-aminotetraphenylmethane in ethanolic solution and then boiling (see also triphenylcarbinol, above):

$$(C_6H_5)_3COH + C_6H_5{\cdot}NH_2{\cdot}HCl \longrightarrow (C_6H_5)_3C{\cdot}C_6H_4{\cdot}NH_2{\cdot}HCl \xrightarrow[C_2H_5OH]{NaNO_2} (C_6H_5)_4C$$

Tetraphenylmethane *cannot* be prepared by reaction between benzene and carbon tetrachloride in the presence of aluminium chloride (see triphenylmethyl chloride, above). The reason for this is not certain, but it is likely that the spatial effect plays a large part in hindering the reaction.

Tetraphenylmethane is a very stable crystalline solid, m.p. 282°.

Hexaphenylethane may be prepared by the action of silver, zinc or mercury on triphenylmethyl chloride in benzene solution *in the absence of air*:

$$2(C_6H_5)_3CCl \xrightarrow{Ag} (C_6H_5)_3C{\cdot}C(C_6H_5)_3 + 2AgCl$$

It is a colourless solid, m.p. 145–147°, but when dissolved in a non-ionising solvent such as benzene or *cyclo*hexane, it forms a *yellow* solution. This yellow colour is due to the dissociation of hexaphenylethane into the free radical triphenylmethyl (Gomberg, 1900):

$$(C_6H_5)_3C{-}C(C_6H_5)_3 \rightleftharpoons 2(C_6H_5)_3C\cdot$$

The stability of this free radical is attributed to resonance, a large number of resonating structures contributing to the resonance hybrid:

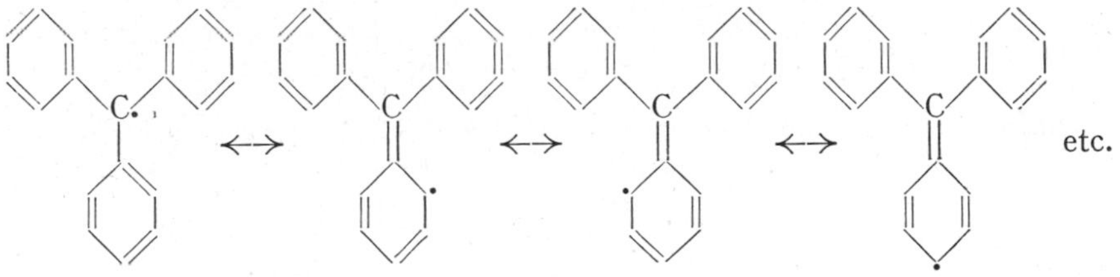

C· ↔ C ↔ C ↔ C etc.

The reason for the colour of this free radical is uncertain.

Triphenylmethyl reacts immediately with a number of reagents to form triphenylmethyl derivatives, *e.g.*, with oxygen, it forms a colourless peroxide:

$$2(C_6H_5)_3C\cdot + O_2 \longrightarrow (C_6H_5)_3C{\cdot}O{\cdot}O{\cdot}C(C_6H_5)_3$$

With iodine it forms triphenylmethyl iodide, and with nitric oxide, nitrosotriphenylmethane:

$$2(C_6H_5)_3C\cdot + I_2 \rightleftharpoons 2(C_6H_5)_3CI$$
$$(C_6H_5)_3C\cdot + NO \longrightarrow (C_6H_5)_3C{\cdot}NO$$

It also combines with sodium to form triphenylmethylsodium, a brick-red solid and an electrical conductor:

$$(C_6H_5)_3C\cdot + Na \longrightarrow (C_6H_5)_3\bar{C}Na^+$$

None of these reactions is typical of a hydrocarbon, and the dissociation of hexaphenylethane was finally proved by molecular weight determinations (freezing point and elevation of boiling point). Triphenylmethyl was the first free radical to be discovered.

In addition to the above reactions, triphenylmethyl can act as a powerful reducing agent, and will reduce the salts of silver, gold and mercury to the metals, *e.g.*,

$$(C_6H_5)_3C\cdot + AgCl \longrightarrow (C_6H_5)_3CCl + Ag$$

It will also reduce ferric chloride to ferrous chloride, and this reaction may be used as a test for the presence of a free radical. Yellow solutions of triphenylmethyl are slowly decolorised on exposure to sunlight, triphenylmethane and diphenyl-bisdiphenylene-ethane being formed due to disproportionation:

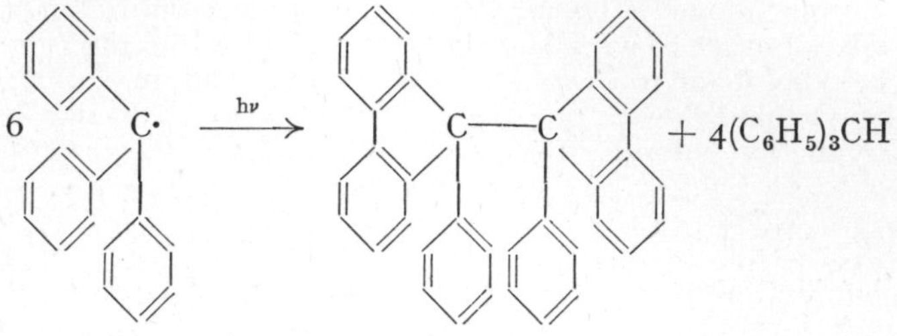

$$6\,(C_6H_5)_3C\cdot \xrightarrow{h\nu} \text{(diphenyl-bisdiphenylene-ethane)} + 4(C_6H_5)_3CH$$

This hexa-arylethane can also dissociate into free radicals, but does so to a much smaller extent than hexaphenylethane.

When dissolved in liquid sulphur dioxide, the solution shows a high conductivity (Walden, 1903), and this was explained by assuming that the hexaphenylethane dissociates into positive and negative ions:

$$(C_6H_5)_3C—C(C_6H_5)_3 \rightleftharpoons (C_6H_5)_3C^+ + (C_6H_5)_3C^-$$

According to Anderson (1935), however, the dissociation is probably:

$$(C_6H_5)_6C_2 + 2SO_2 \rightleftharpoons 2(C_6H_5)_3C^+ + 2\dot{S}O_2^-$$

Dibenzyl (1 : 2-*diphenylethane*), $C_6H_5\cdot CH_2\cdot CH_2\cdot C_6H_5$, may be prepared by the Friedel–Crafts condensation between benzene and ethylene chloride:

$$2C_6H_6 + ClCH_2\cdot CH_2Cl \xrightarrow{AlCl_3} C_6H_5\cdot CH_2\cdot CH_2\cdot C_6H_5 + 2HCl$$

Another method of preparation is by the action of sodium or copper on benzyl bromide:

$$2C_6H_5\cdot CH_2Br \xrightarrow{Na} C_6H_5\cdot CH_2\cdot CH_2\cdot C_6H_5$$

Dibenzyl is a white solid, m.p. 52°. It is oxidised by permanganate or chromic acid to benzoic acid.

Stilbene (*trans-s*-diphenylethylene), $C_6H_5\cdot CH{:}CH\cdot C_6H_5$, may be prepared:

(i) By heating benzylidene chloride with sodium:

$$2C_6H_5\cdot CHCl_2 + 4Na \longrightarrow C_6H_5\cdot CH{=}CH\cdot C_6H_5 + 4NaCl$$

(ii) By treating benzylmagnesium bromide with benzaldehyde and dehydrating the product, benzylphenylmethanol:

$$C_6H_5\cdot CHO + C_6H_5\cdot CH_2\cdot MgBr \longrightarrow C_6H_5\cdot CH\begin{cases}OMgBr\\CH_2\cdot C_6H_5\end{cases} \xrightarrow{H_2O}$$

$$C_6H_5\cdot CHOH\cdot CH_2\cdot C_6H_5 \xrightarrow[\text{(heat)}]{-H_2O} C_6H_5\cdot CH{=}CH\cdot C_6H_5$$

(iii) By reducing benzoin with amalgamated zinc and an ethanolic solution of hydrogen chloride:

$$C_6H_5\cdot CHOH\cdot CO\cdot C_6H_5 \longrightarrow C_6H_5\cdot CH{=}CH\cdot C_6H_5 \quad (53\text{–}57\%)$$

Stilbene, m.p. 124°, is the stable *trans*-isomer; *iso*stilbene, b.p. 145° (13 mm.), is the unstable *cis*-isomer:

$$\begin{array}{c}C_6H_5—C—H\\ \|\\ H—C—C_6H_5\end{array} \qquad \begin{array}{c}C_6H_5—C—H\\ \|\\ C_6H_5—C—H\end{array}$$

stilbene *iso*stilbene

iso*Stilbene* may be prepared by reducing tolan with zinc dust and ethanol:

$$C_6H_5{\cdot}C{\equiv}C{\cdot}C_6H_5 + 2[H] \longrightarrow C_6H_5{\cdot}CH{=}CH{\cdot}C_6H_5$$

This result is unexpected since addition to a triple bond (to form an ethylenic compound) usually takes place in the *trans*-position (*cf.* p. 408). *iso*Stilbene may also be prepared by irradiating stilbene with ultra-violet light.

*iso*Stilbene is readily converted into stilbene under the catalytic influence of traces of hydrogen bromide and peroxides.

Stilbene is reduced by sodium and ethanol to dibenzyl. It adds on bromine to form stilbene bromide which, on heating with ethanolic potassium hydroxide, forms **tolan** (*diphenylacetylene*), m.p. 62°:

$$C_6H_5{\cdot}CH{=}CH{\cdot}C_6H_5 \xrightarrow{Br_2} C_6H_5{\cdot}CHBr{\cdot}CHBr{\cdot}C_6H_5 \xrightarrow{KOH} C_6H_5{\cdot}C{\vdots}C{\cdot}C_6H_5$$

Stilbene bromide reacts with silver acetate to form two isomeric diacetates. These, on hydrolysis, form hydrobenzoin and *iso*hydrobenzoin (see later):

$$C_6H_5{\cdot}CH(O{\cdot}CO{\cdot}CH_3){\cdot}CH(O{\cdot}CO{\cdot}CH_3){\cdot}C_6H_5 \xrightarrow{H_2O} C_6H_5{\cdot}CHOH{\cdot}CHOH{\cdot}C_6H_5$$

Benzoin, $C_6H_5{\cdot}CHOH{\cdot}CO{\cdot}C_6H_5$, is usually prepared by the *benzoin condensation,* this reaction being carried out by refluxing benzaldehyde with aqueous ethanolic potassium cyanide:

$$2C_6H_5{\cdot}CHO \xrightarrow{KCN} C_6H_5{\cdot}CHOH{\cdot}CO{\cdot}C_6H_5 \quad (83\%)$$

The cyanide ion is a specific catalyst in the benzoin condensation, the mechanism of which is still uncertain. Weiss (1941) has proposed a chain mechanism. On the other hand, Lapworth (1903) proposed an ionic mechanism:

$$C_6H_5{\cdot}\overset{\overset{O}{\|}}{\underset{H}{C}} + {:}CN^- \rightleftharpoons \left[C_6H_5{\cdot}\overset{\overset{\bar{O}}{|}}{\underset{H}{C}}{-}CN\right] \rightleftharpoons \left[C_6H_5{-}\overset{\overset{OH}{|}}{\underset{\bullet\bullet}{\bar{C}}}{-}CN\right] \xrightleftharpoons{C_6H_5{\cdot}CHO}$$

$$\left[C_6H_5{\cdot}\overset{\overset{OH}{|}}{\underset{CN}{C}}{-}\overset{\overset{\bar{O}}{|}}{\underset{H}{C}}{-}C_6H_5\right] \rightleftharpoons C_6H_5{\cdot}\overset{\overset{O}{\|}}{C}{-}\overset{\overset{OH}{|}}{\underset{H}{C}}{\cdot}C_6H_5 + {:}CN^-$$

This mechanism does not explain the specificity of the cyanide ion as catalyst.

When a mixture of aldehydes is treated with aqueous ethanolic potassium cyanide, " mixed " benzoins (as well as the " single " benzoins) are obtained:

$$Ar{\cdot}CHO + Ar'{\cdot}CHO \xrightarrow{KCN} Ar{\cdot}CHOH{\cdot}CO{\cdot}Ar' + Ar'{\cdot}CHOH{\cdot}CO{\cdot}Ar$$

Furthermore, the reversibility of the benzoin condensation is indicated by the fact that when the benzoin Ar·CHOH·CO·Ar is heated with the aldehyde Ar′·CHO in the presence of potassium cyanide, a mixed benzoin is obtained (Buck and Ide, 1933):

$$Ar{\cdot}CHOH{\cdot}CO{\cdot}Ar + 2Ar'{\cdot}CHO \rightleftharpoons 2Ar{\cdot}CHOH{\cdot}CO{\cdot}Ar'$$

Aliphatic aldehydes do not undergo the benzoin condensation.

Benzoin is a colourless solid, m.p. 137°. It contains an asymmetric carbon atom and both the (+)- and (—)-forms have been prepared (Mackenzie and Wren, 1908, 1913). Benzoin is reduced to **deoxybenzoin** (*desoxybenzoin*), $C_6H_5{\cdot}CH_2{\cdot}CO{\cdot}C_6H_5$, m.p. 60°, which may also be prepared by the following Friedel–Crafts reaction:

$$C_6H_5{\cdot}CH_2{\cdot}COCl + C_6H_6 \xrightarrow{AlCl_3} C_6H_5{\cdot}CH_2{\cdot}CO{\cdot}C_6H_5 + HCl \quad (82\text{–}83\%)$$

The prefix *deoxy-* (formerly *desoxy-*) indicates the replacement of a hydroxyl group by hydrogen. Deoxybenzoin contains an active methylene group; *e.g.*, it forms a sodio-derivative, condenses with aldehydes in the presence of piperidine, and adds on to αβ-unsaturated carbonyl compounds (*cf.* ethyl malonate).

Benzoin is an α-hydroxyketone; hence it reduces Fehling's solution and forms an osazone. When reduced by sodium amalgam, benzoin forms mainly **hydrobenzoin,** and a small amount of ***iso*hydrobenzoin:**

$$C_6H_5{\cdot}CHOH{\cdot}CO{\cdot}C_6H_5 + 2[H] \longrightarrow C_6H_5{\cdot}CHOH{\cdot}CHOH{\cdot}C_6H_5$$

This formula (tolylene glycol) contains two identical asymmetric carbon atoms, and hence the compound can exist in the *dextro*, *laevo*, and *meso*-forms (*cf.* tartaric acid). The racemic modification is known as hydrobenzoin (m.p. 139°), and the *meso*-form as *iso*hydrobenzoin (m.p. 121°). Both forms give benzoic acid on oxidation.

Benzoin is oxidised by chromic acid to a mixture of benzaldehyde and benzoic acid, and by nitric acid to **benzil**:

$$C_6H_5{\cdot}CHOH{\cdot}CO{\cdot}C_6H_5 \xrightarrow[HNO_3]{[O]} C_6H_5{\cdot}CO{\cdot}CO{\cdot}C_6H_5 \quad (96\%)$$

Benzil is a yellow crystalline solid, m.p. 95°. It behaves as a typical α-diketone, *e.g.*, it is oxidised by hydrogen peroxide in acetic acid to benzoic acid, forms a monoxime and dioxime, etc.

Two monoximes of benzil are known: α-(*cis*-), m.p. 134°, and β-(*trans*-), m.p. 113°. Three dioximes are possible and all are known: α-(*cis–cis*-), m.p. 237°, β-(*trans–trans*-) m.p. 207°, and γ- or *amphi-* (*cis–trans*-), m.p. 166° (*cf.* p. 638).

Benzil condenses with *o*-phenylenediamine to form 2 : 3-*diphenylquinoxaline*:

$$\begin{array}{l} C_6H_5{\cdot}C{=}O \\ \quad\;\; | \\ C_6H_5{\cdot}C{=}O \end{array} + C_6H_4(NH_2)_2 \longrightarrow \begin{array}{l} C_6H_5{-}C{=}N \\ C_6H_5{-}C{=}N \end{array} \!\!\! > C_6H_4 \quad (ex.)$$

The nature of the reduction products of benzil depends on the reducing agent used. Thus reduction with sodium amalgam gives hydrobenzoin (and some *iso*hydrobenzoin); amalgamated zinc and hydrogen chloride in ethanol, stilbene; sodium hyposulphite in ethanol, benzoin; amalgamated tin and hydrogen chloride in ethanol, deoxybenzoin; and catalytic reduction using nickel at 230°, dibenzyl.

When heated with ethanolic potassium hydroxide, benzil undergoes the **benzilic acid rearrangement:**

$$C_6H_5{\cdot}CO{\cdot}CO{\cdot}C_6H_5 + KOH \longrightarrow (C_6H_5)_2C(OH){\cdot}CO_2K \quad (77\text{–}79\%)$$

The mechanism of this rearrangement is uncertain. The rearrangement has been shown to be of the first order with respect to both benzil and hydroxide ion (Westheimer, 1936), and it has also been shown that when benzil is heated for a very short time with sodium hydroxide in water containing ^{18}O—methanol solution, the benzil recovered contained ^{18}O (Roberts and Urey, 1938). This is in keeping with the first step being the addition of hydroxide ion, and on the basis of these experiments, the latter authors proposed the following mechanism:

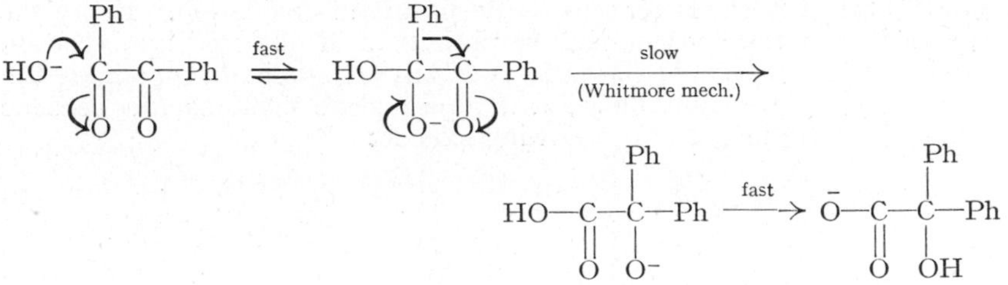

$$HO^- + Ph{-}CO{-}CO{-}Ph \xrightleftharpoons{\text{fast}} HO{-}C(Ph)(O^-){-}CO{-}Ph \xrightarrow[\text{(Whitmore mech.)}]{\text{slow}} HO{-}CO{-}C(Ph)(O^-){-}Ph \xrightarrow{\text{fast}} {}^-O{-}CO{-}C(Ph)(OH){-}Ph$$

According to Clark *et al.* (1955), the specific accelerating influence of the

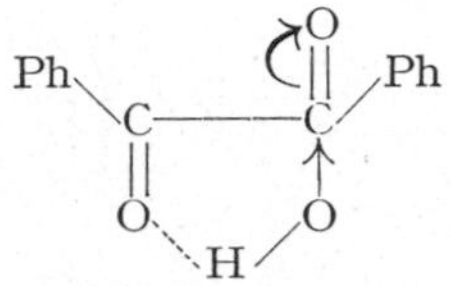

$$Ph{-}C(=O){-}C(=O)(O^-)(Ph) \quad (\text{O}\cdots\text{H}{-}\text{O hydrogen-bonded})$$

hydroxide ion on this rearrangement can be attributed to the ready nucleophilic attack (the rate-determining step) provided by hydrogen-bonding.

It has now been shown that barium and thallous hydroxide are much more effective reagents than potassium or sodium hydroxide (Pfeil *et al.*, 1956). Furthermore, it has also been shown that the hydroxide ion is *not* a specific catalyst for the rearrangement: potassium methoxide and *t.*-butoxide produce the corresponding esters of benzilic acid (von Doering *et al.*, 1956). Benzilic acid (m.p. 150°) forms diphenylacetic acid when refluxed in acetic acid solution with hydriodic acid and red phosphorus:

$$(C_6H_5)_2C(OH){\cdot}CO_2H + 2[H] \longrightarrow (C_6H_5)_2CH{\cdot}CO_2H + H_2O \quad (94\text{–}97\%)$$

When oxidised with chromic acid, benzilic acid forms benzophenone.

CONDENSED SYSTEMS

NAPHTHALENE

Naphthalene, $C_{10}H_8$, is the largest single constituent of coal-tar (6 per cent.). It is obtained by cooling the middle and heavy oils (p. 475), whereupon naphthalene crystallises out. The oil is pressed free from the naphthalene, the crude naphthalene cake melted, treated with concentrated sulphuric acid (to remove basic impurities), washed with water, and then treated with aqueous sodium hydroxide (to remove acidic impurities). Finally the naphthalene is distilled to give the pure product. It is interesting to note that naphthalene does *not* occur in low-temperature carbonisation tar.

Structure of naphthalene. Erlenmeyer (1866) proposed the symmetrical formula, (I), for naphthalene, and Graebe (1869) proved that it did consist of two benzene rings fused together in the *o*-positions. He used several methods, but the line of approach was the same, *e.g.*, he found that on oxidation, naphthalene gave phthalic acid. Thus naphthalene contains the group (II), *i.e.*, a benzene ring with two side-chains in the *o*-positions. When nitrated, naphthalene gave nitronaphthalene which, on oxidation, gave *o*-nitrophthalic acid. This indicates that the nitro-group is in the benzene ring,

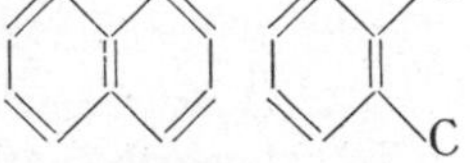

(I) (II)

and that it is the side-chains which are oxidised. When nitronaphthalene was reduced and the corresponding aminonaphthalene oxidised, phthalic acid was obtained. As we have seen (p. 512), an amino-group attached to the nucleus renders the latter extremely sensitive to oxidation. Hence the inference is that the benzene ring in phthalic acid obtained by oxidation of aminonaphthalene is not the same ring as that originally containing the nitro-group in nitronaphthalene, *i.e.*, naphthalene contains *two* benzene rings. The above facts fit the following scheme:

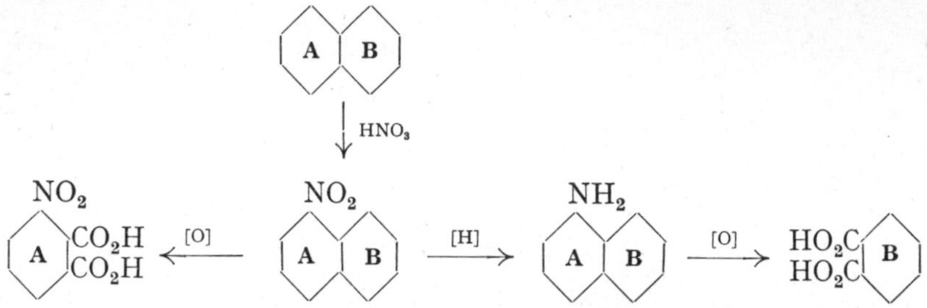

A B
HNO_3
NO_2 A CO_2H CO_2H ← [O] — NO_2 A B — [H] → NH_2 A B — [O] → HO_2C HO_2C B

This structure for naphthalene has been confirmed by many syntheses, *e.g.*,

(i) When 4-phenylbut-1-ene is passed over red-hot calcium oxide, naphthalene is formed:

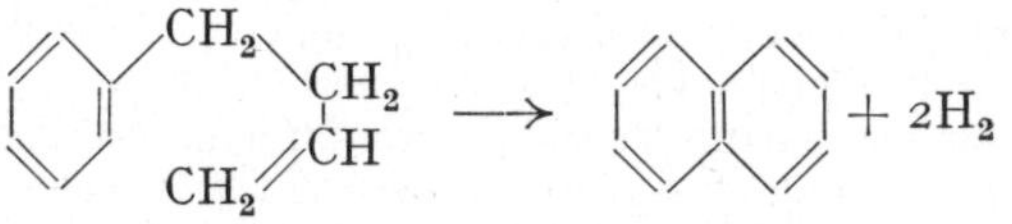

$C_6H_5 \cdot CH_2 \cdot CH_2 \cdot CH{=}CH_2 \longrightarrow C_{10}H_8 + 2H_2$

(ii) When 4-phenylbut-3-enoic acid is heated, 1-naphthol is formed and this, on distillation with zinc dust, gives naphthalene:

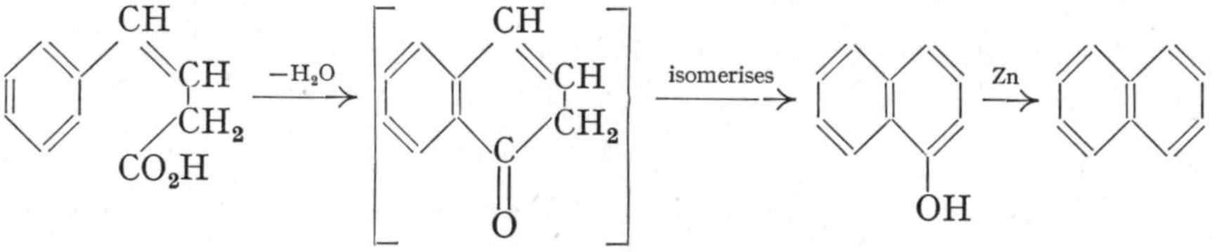

$C_6H_5 \cdot CH{=}CH \cdot CH_2 \cdot CO_2H \xrightarrow{-H_2O}$ [keto form: CH, CH, CH_2, C=O] $\xrightarrow{\text{isomerises}}$ 1-naphthol (OH) $\xrightarrow{Zn}$ naphthalene

(iii) *o*-Xylylene bromide combines with disodioethanetetracarboxylic ester to form tetrahydronaphthalenetetracarboxylic ester and this, when refluxed in acid solution, gives tetrahydronaphthalenedicarboxylic acid. When the silver salt of this acid is heated, naphthalene is formed:

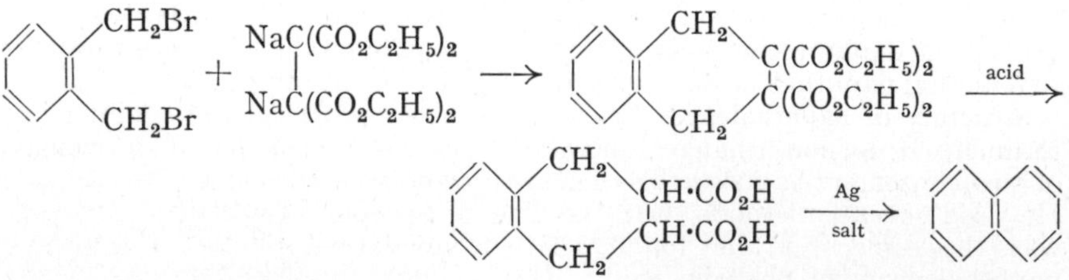

$C_6H_4(CH_2Br)_2 + \begin{matrix} NaC(CO_2C_2H_5)_2 \\ | \\ NaC(CO_2C_2H_5)_2 \end{matrix} \longrightarrow C_6H_4 \begin{matrix} CH_2 - C(CO_2C_2H_5)_2 \\ CH_2 - C(CO_2C_2H_5)_2 \end{matrix} \xrightarrow{\text{acid}}$

$C_6H_4 \begin{matrix} CH_2 - CH \cdot CO_2H \\ CH_2 - CH \cdot CO_2H \end{matrix} \xrightarrow[\text{salt}]{\text{Ag}}$ naphthalene

(iv) **Haworth synthesis** (1932). Benzene is treated with succinic anhydride in the presence of aluminium chloride, and the ketonic acid produced (Burcker, 1882) is reduced by the Clemmensen method. The ring is closed by heating with concentrated sulphuric acid and the product, α-tetralone, reduced to tetrahydronaphthalene by the Clemmensen method. This compound is then dehydrogenated to naphthalene by distilling it with selenium:

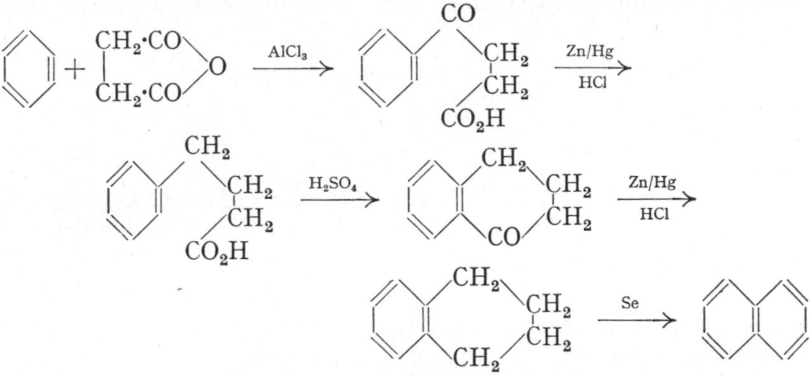

It should be noted that ring closure may also be effected by means of a Friedel–Crafts reaction on the acid chloride as follows:

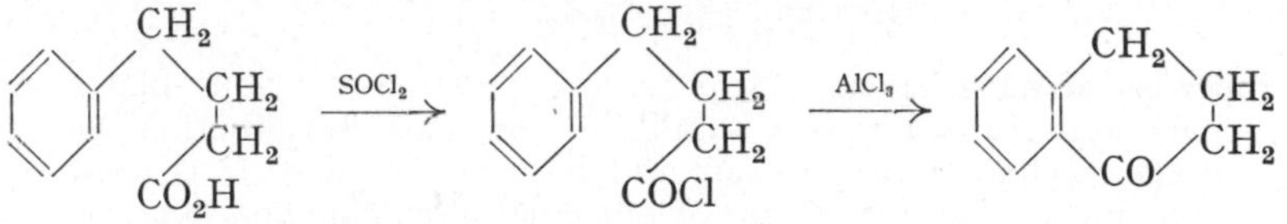

It should be noted here that the formation of cyclic ketones by *intramolecular* acylation is a very important synthetic process. Sulphuric, phosphoric, and hydrofluoric acid are commonly used as catalysts for ring-closure of acids, and aluminium or stannic chlorides for acid chlorides.

Positions of the double bonds in naphthalene. Many suggestions have been made regarding the fourth valency of each carbon atom in naphthalene, but only two formulæ need be considered, the symmetrical formula (I), and the unsymmetrical, (II) (and III). Physico-chemical evidence, *e.g.*, heat of combustion, etc., points towards naphthalene being a resonance hybrid of mainly three resonating structures, (I), (II) and (III):

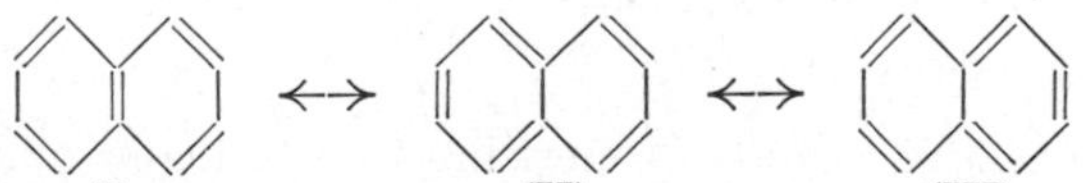

(I) (II) (III)

It should be noted that there are $n + 1$ principal resonating structures for a polynuclear hydrocarbon containing n benzene rings fused together in a *linear* manner.

The resonance energy of naphthalene is 75 k. cal./mole. This value is larger than that for benzene and is to be expected, since in the case of the latter only two resonating structures contribute to the resonance hybrid.

Fries rule (1935). Fries compared the possible arrangements of double bonds in polynuclear compounds with benzoquinones. Structures (II) and (III) have arrangements corresponding to *o*-benzoquinone. Since quinones are far more reactive than a purely aromatic compound, Fries believed that the *stable* form of a polynuclear compound did not contain this quinonoid arrangement. He therefore formulated the following rule: *the most stable arrangement of a polynuclear compound is that form which has the maximum number of rings in the benzenoid condition*, i.e., *three double bonds in each individual ring*. Thus, according to the Fries rule, naphthalene tends to behave as structure (I) (with two benzenoid rings) rather than as (II) or (III) (with one benzenoid ring).

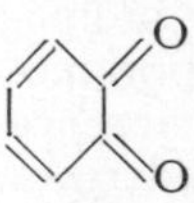

Isomerism and nomenclature of naphthalene derivatives. Positions 1, 4, 5 and 8 are identical (α- positions), as are positions 2, 3, 6 and 7 (β- positions). In the old literature, the positions 1 : 2- were known as *o*-; 1 : 3-, *m*-; 1 : 4-, *p*-; 1 : 5-, *ana*; 1 : 6-, *epi*; 1 : 7-, *kata*; 1 : 8- *peri*; 2 : 6- *amphi*; and 2 : 7-, *pros*. Some of these prefixes are still used, but it is best to use numbers; the Greek letters α- and β- are still frequently used to indicate the position of a single substituent.

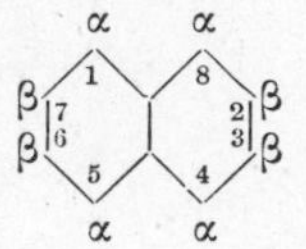

Monosubstitution products.	$C_{10}H_7X$	Two: 1- and 2-
Disubstitution products.	$C_{10}H_6X_2$	10 isomers
	$C_{10}H_6XY$	14 isomers

There are 14 possible isomers for $C_{10}H_5X_3$, 22 for $C_{10}H_4X_4$, 14 for $C_{10}H_3X_5$, 10 for $C_{10}H_2X_6$, 2 for $C_{10}HX_7$, and 1 for $C_{10}X_8$.

Properties of naphthalene. Naphthalene exists as lustrous plates, m.p. 80°, insoluble in water but very soluble in hot ethanol, cold ether, benzene, etc. It has a characteristic odour and is very volatile. It is used as an insecticide and in the preparation of phthalic anhydride and dyes.

Naphthalene resembles benzene in many of its reactions but is more reactive, forming addition and substitution products more readily than benzene and is more readily oxidised and reduced (especially in the 1 : 4-positions).

Addition compounds of naphthalene. A number of reduction products of naphthalene can be isolated, the nature of the product depending on the reducing agent used. When reduced with sodium and ethanol, naphthalene gives 1 : 4-*dihydronaphthalene* (1 : 4-*dialin*), m. p. 25°:

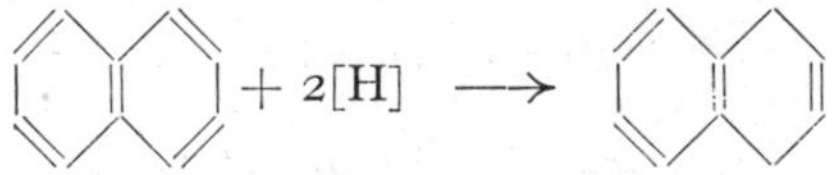

+ 2[H] ⟶

1 : 4-dialin is unstable, readily isomerising to 1 : 2-dialin (m.p. −8°) when heated with ethanolic sodium ethoxide. 1 : 2-Dialin is also unstable, fairly readily eliminating hydrogen to form naphthalene.

When reduced with sodium and *iso*pentanol, naphthalene gives 1 : 2 : 3 : 4-*tetrahydronaphthalene* (*tetralin*), b.p. 206–208°:

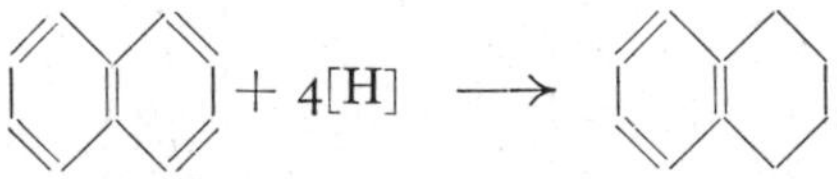

+ 4[H] ⟶

Tetralin is used as a solvent for varnishes, lacquers, etc. When treated with bromine in the presence of light, tetralin forms the mono- and dibromo-derivatives, substitution occurring in the *alicyclic* ring. When these bromo-derivatives are heated, hydrogen bromide is eliminated, the monobromo-compound forming dialin, and the dibromo-, naphthalene. In the absence of light and in the presence of iron as halogen carrier, tetralin undergoes substitution in the aromatic ring to form 5- and 6-bromo-1 : 2 : 3 : 4-tetrahydronaphthalenes.

α-**Tetralone,** b.p. 129·4°/12 mm., may be prepared by synthesis (iv), p. 680, or by heating tetralin with air for 50 hours at 70° and decomposing the peroxide with dilute sodium hydroxide:

$$\text{tetralin} + O_2 \longrightarrow \text{tetralin hydroperoxide (H, O·OH)} \xrightarrow{NaOH} \text{1-tetralone} \quad (44\text{–}56\%)$$

When naphthalene is catalytically reduced using nickel, tetralin and then *decahydronaphthalene* (*decalin*) are obtained:

$$\text{naphthalene} \xrightarrow{H_2/Ni} \text{tetralin} \longrightarrow \text{decalin}$$

Decalin exists in two geometrical isomeric forms, *cis*- (b.p. 193°) and *trans*- (b.p. 185°). With nickel as catalyst, the main product is the *trans*-isomer; with platinum, *cis*- (see also p. 468). The commercial product is a mixture of the two forms, and is used as a solvent for varnishes, lacquers, etc.

Dry chlorine adds on to solid naphthalene to give naphthalene di- and tetrachlorides, $C_{10}H_8Cl_2$ and $C_{10}H_8Cl_4$. In both of these compounds the chlorine atoms are in the same ring (shown by the fact that on oxidation, both form phthalic acid). When naphthalene dichloride is heated at 40°, hydrogen chloride is eliminated and 1-chloronaphthalene is produced. When naphthalene tetrachloride is treated with alkali, a mixture of dichloronaphthalenes is formed, the 1 : 3-isomer predominating.

Naphthalene adds on sodium to give 1 : 4-disodionaphthalene; this, on treatment with carbon dioxide, forms the sodium salt of 1 : 4-dihydronaphthalene-1 : 4-dicarboxylic acid:

$$\text{naphthalene} \xrightarrow{Na} \text{1:4-disodio-1:4-dihydronaphthalene (H, Na)} \xrightarrow{CO_2} \text{1:4-dihydronaphthalene-1:4-di}(CO_2Na)$$

Oxidation of naphthalene. Naphthalene is oxidised by concentrated sulphuric acid and mercuric sulphate or by air in the presence of vanadium pentoxide, to phthalic anhydride (p. 664). It is oxidised by acid permanganate to phthalic acid, and by alkaline permanganate to phthalonic acid (p. 666). Chromic acid oxidises it to 1 : 4-naphthaquinone (p. 692). When treated with ozone, naphthalene forms the *diozonide* and this, on treatment with water, gives *phthalaldehyde*:

$$\text{naphthalene} \xrightarrow{O_3} \text{diozonide } (2\,O_3) \xrightarrow{H_2O} C_6H_4(CHO)_2$$

Substitution products of naphthalene. Orientation in the naphthalene nucleus is more complicated than in the benzene nucleus, due to the presence of two rings in the former. The first group always enters the 1-position in naphthalene except in two cases, when the 2-derivative is the main product: (i) sulphonation at high temperature, and (ii) in the Friedel–Crafts reaction. Introduction of a second substituent can give rise to *homonuclear* (*isonuclear*) substitution (the second substituent entering the *same* ring as the first), or to *heteronuclear* substitution (the second substituent entering the *other* ring). The following empirical generalisations are useful for predicting the position taken up by the second substituent:

(*a*) When Cl, Br, OH, CH_3, NH·R or NH·CO·CH_3 is in the 1-position, homonuclear substitution takes place mainly in position 4, and to a lesser extent in 2.

(*b*) When OH, CH_3, NH·R or NH·CO·CH_3 is in the 2-position, homonuclear substitution usually takes place in the 1-position (the introduction of the SO_3H group is an exception; this group enters position 6).

It is worth noting that homonuclear substitution usually occurs when the group already present is *o*-*p*-orienting.

(*c*) When NO_2 or SO_3H is in the 1- or 2-position, heteronuclear substitution occurs in position 5 or 8; if halogen or NH_2 is in the 2-position, heteronuclear substitution also occurs in position 5 or 8.

It is relatively easy to determine the orientation of monosubstitution products of naphthalene by oxidation to the phthalic acid derivative or by synthesis. It is, however, not always easy for disubstituted derivatives. It can be readily ascertained by means of oxidation (to phthalic acid derivatives) whether both substituents are in the same ring or not. 1 : 8-Compounds, if the substituents are of the right type, *e.g.*, carboxyl groups, readily form cyclic derivatives, and hence these positions (1 : 8-) may be determined. In some cases it is possible to synthesise disubstituted derivatives by *unambiguous syntheses*; *e.g.*, 1 : 5-dichloronaphthalene may be synthesised from *o*-chlorobenzaldehyde and succinic anhydride as follows (*cf.*, p. 264):

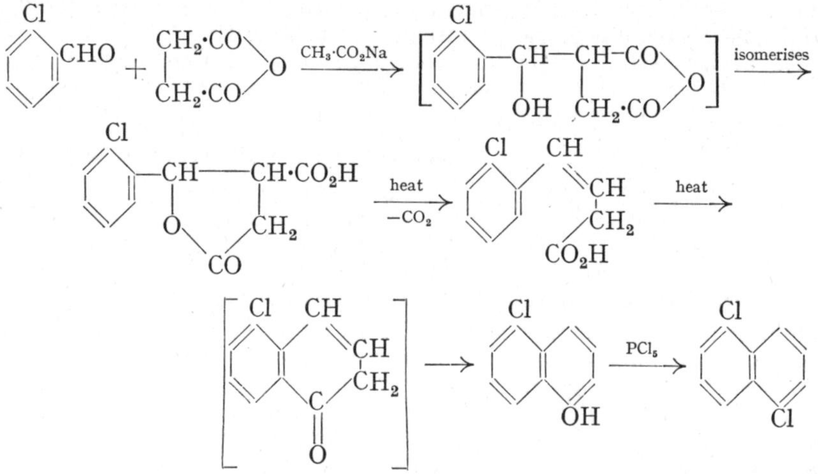

o-ClC_6H_4·CHO + $(CH_2·CO)_2O$ —($CH_3·CO_2Na$)→ [ClC_6H_4–CH(OH)–CH(CH_2·CO)–CO–O] —isomerises→ ClC_6H_4–CH–CH·CO_2H (lactone: O–CO–CH_2) —heat, $-CO_2$→ ClC_6H_4–CH=CH–CH_2–CO_2H —heat→ [cyclic ketone: Cl, CH=CH, CH_2, C=O] → 5-chloro-1-naphthol (Cl, OH) —PCl_5→ 1 : 5-dichloronaphthalene (Cl, Cl)

Similarly, *p*-chlorobenzaldehyde gives 1 : 7-dichloronaphthalene. On the other hand, *m*-chlorobenzaldehyde gives rise to an *ambiguous* synthesis, since two chloronaphthols are obtained and there is no means (from the synthesis) of ascertaining which is which:

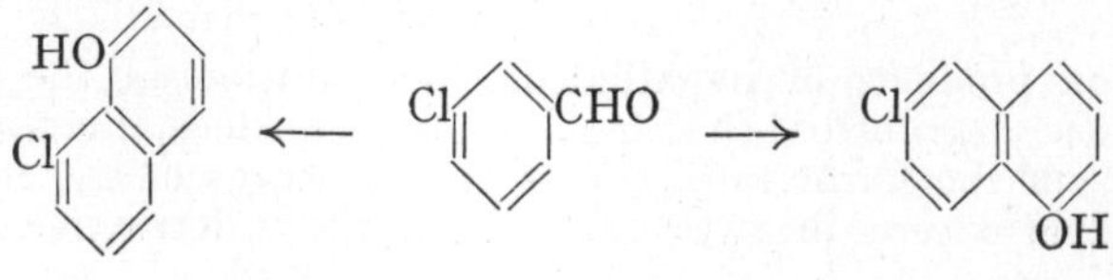

chloronaphthol (HO, Cl) ← m-ClC_6H_4·CHO → chloronaphthol (Cl, OH)

Naphthalene is an *alternant hydrocarbon* (p. 502), and the π-electron densities are unity at all positions. Hence, at first sight, it might be expected that positions 1 and 2 would be attacked equally well by the usual electrophilic

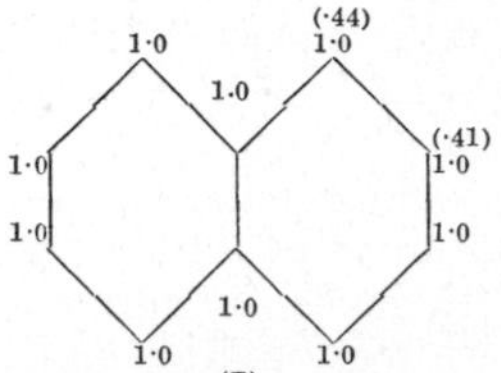

(I) 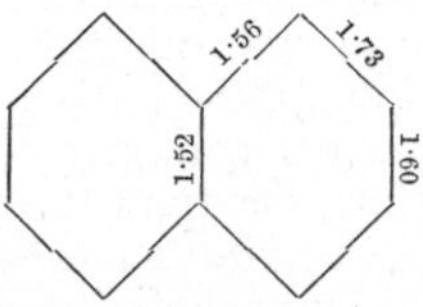 (II) 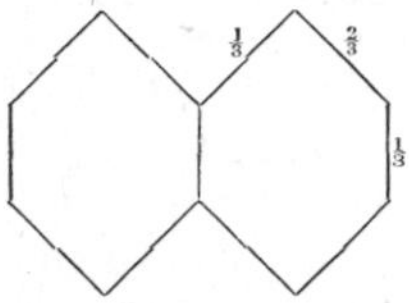 (III)

reagents. There is, however, another factor which must be considered when the charge densities are equal at various positions. This is the *self-polarisability* of the position, and the larger the magnitude of this self-polarisability, the more reactive will that point be to electrophilic (or nucleophilic) reagents. In benzene all the carbon atoms carry a charge of unity, and the self-polarisabilities are also equal (as shown by calculation). Hence no particular carbon atom in benzene is preferentially attacked. The case of naphthalene, however, is different. The self-polarisability is greater at position 1 than 2 (figures in parentheses in I), and hence the former is more readily attacked than the latter; this is the case in practice.

Bond order (or double-bond character) may also be used to study the reactivities of the various positions of the naphthalene molecule (*cf.* p. 502). (II) shows the bond orders obtained by calculation. (III) shows the double-bond character of the various bonds, and is obtained by taking the average of the three resonating structures of naphthalene given on p. 681. This average has been obtained on the *assumption* that each resonating structure contributes *equally* to the resonance hybrid. The problem that always arises in polynuclear hydrocarbons is the weighting of the various possible valency structures. The usual practice is to omit Dewar structures (*i.e.*, structures with formal bonds) and also polar structures, and to take the Kekulé structures as being of equal weights. On this basis, it can be seen that the π-electron density is greater in the 1 : 2- than in the 2 : 3-bond. It might therefore be expected that the former would be more reactive than the latter, since, although neither is a double bond, both can function as double bonds, the 1 : 2-bond being " nearer " to a double bond than the 2 : 3. Badger (1948–50) has shown that double-bond reagents add to the bond having the highest order (*cf.* the ozonide of naphthalene, p. 683). It might also be noted that these bonds with the highest orders are those which were supposed to be " fixed " double bonds, *i.e.*, in naphthalene the 1 : 2-bond was a " fixed " double bond, in accordance with the Fries rule (p. 681).

Still another way of studying organic reactions has been to calculate the energy of activation for the various positions in a molecule. When the attacking reagent forms the transition state, two of the delocalised π-electrons in the naphthalene molecule must be polarised to form a σ-bond with the attacking electrophilic reagent (p. 491). The lower the bond localisation energy, the more readily will the transition state be formed. Furthermore, the higher the bond order, *i.e.*, the greater the π-electron density in that bond, the smaller will be the bond localisation energy. This accounts for substitution of 2-naphthol in

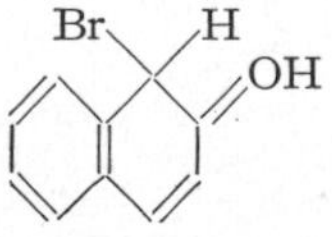

(IV) 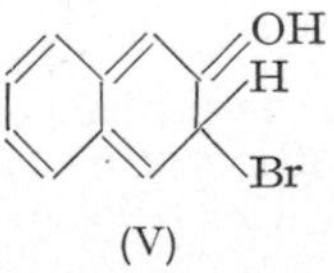 (V) 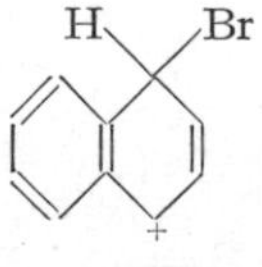 (VI) 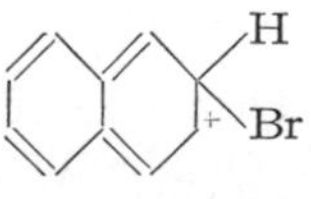 (VII)

position 1 and not in 3. In (IV), the transition state is formed by localisation of the 1 : 2-bond; in (V), by that of the 2 : 3-bond. Since the former has the higher bond order, this one will be more readily localised, *i.e.*, the energy of activation of (IV) is lower than that of (V), and so the reaction proceeds via (IV) and not via (V). In the substitution of naphthalene itself, two transition states are possible, (VI) and (VII); the former is the more stable, and so 1-substitution occurs rather than 2- (*cf.* self-polarisabilities, above).

The Friedel–Crafts reaction with naphthalene. Naphthalene is attacked by aluminium chloride when vigorous conditions are used (dinaphthyls and compounds with one of the naphthalene rings opened are formed). Hence to carry out the Friedel–Crafts reaction successfully, mild conditions (low temperatures) must be used, and even then the maximum yield is about 60 per cent. With methyl iodide, 1- and 2-methylnaphthalenes are formed; with ethyl bromide, only 2-ethylnaphthalene; and with *n*-propyl bromide, 2-*iso*propylnaphthalene. With alcohols and aluminium chloride, 2 : 6-dialkylnaphthalenes are obtained but with alcohols and boron trifluoride, 1 : 4-dialkylnaphthalenes (Price, 1943). Introduction of an acyl group in the presence of aluminium chloride gives a mixture of 1- and 2-ketones, the nature of the solvent affecting the percentage of each; *e.g.*, with acetyl chloride in carbon disulphide as solvent, 1- and 2-naphthyl methyl ketone are formed in a ratio of 3 : 1; in nitrobenzene, 1 : 9:

$$C_{10}H_8 \xrightarrow[AlCl_3]{CH_3\cdot COCl} \text{1-}C_{10}H_7\cdot CO\cdot CH_3 + \text{2-}C_{10}H_7\cdot CO\cdot CH_3$$

Chloromethylation of naphthalene using a mixture of paraformaldehyde, hydrochloric acid, glacial acetic acid and phosphoric acid gives mainly the 1-derivative and a small amount of the 1 : 5-bischloromethyl-derivative:

$$C_{10}H_8 + CH_2O + HCl \longrightarrow \text{1-}C_{10}H_7\cdot CH_2Cl \quad (56\%)$$

When naphthalene is chloromethylated with boiling aqueous formaldehyde and concentrated hydrochloric acid, a mixture of compounds is obtained from which 1 : 4- and 1 : 5-bischloromethylnaphthalenes have been isolated (Badger *et al.*, 1947).

Halogen derivatives. Naphthalene is very easily halogenated, *e.g.*, when brominated in boiling carbon tetrachloride solution, naphthalene forms 1-bromonaphthalene (yield 72–75 per cent.). Further bromination gives mainly the 1 : 4-dibromo-derivative, and some 1 : 2-. Sulphuryl chloride (1 equivalent) in the presence of aluminium chloride at 25° chlorinates naphthalene to give the 1-chloro-derivative; with 2 equivalents of sulphuryl chloride (at 100–140°), 1 : 4-dichloronaphthalene is formed.

2-Halogeno-naphthalenes are conveniently prepared from 2-naphthylamine by diazotisation, etc., *e.g.*,

$$\text{2-}C_{10}H_7NH_2 \xrightarrow[HCl]{NaNO_2} \text{2-}C_{10}H_7N_2Cl \xrightarrow[HCl]{CuCl} \text{2-}C_{10}H_7Cl$$

Chlorination of naphthalene at 250°, in the presence of iodine, gives 1- and 2-monochloronaphthalenes in the proportion of 9 : 1; above 340°, the proportion is 1 : 1 (Wibaut *et al.*, 1950). The halogen atom in naphthalene behaves similarly as in the benzene ring, but is more reactive.

Nitronaphthalenes. Nitric acid attacks naphthalene at room temperature to form 1-nitronaphthalene. This is a yellow solid, m.p. 60°, which behaves like nitrobenzene, but differs in that it forms 1-chloro-naphthalene when treated with phosphorus pentachloride (nitrobenzene does not react).

Nitration of naphthalene at high temperature gives a mixture of 1:5- and 1:8-dinitronaphthalenes. Other dinitro-derivatives are prepared by special means.

2-Nitronaphthalene (m.p. 79°) may be prepared by heating 2-naphthalenediazonium borofluoride with sodium nitrite and copper powder.

Naphthalenesulphonic acids. When naphthalene is treated with concentrated sulphuric acid at 40°, the main product is the 1-derivative (m.p. 91°); at 160°, the main product is the 2-derivative (m.p. 102°):

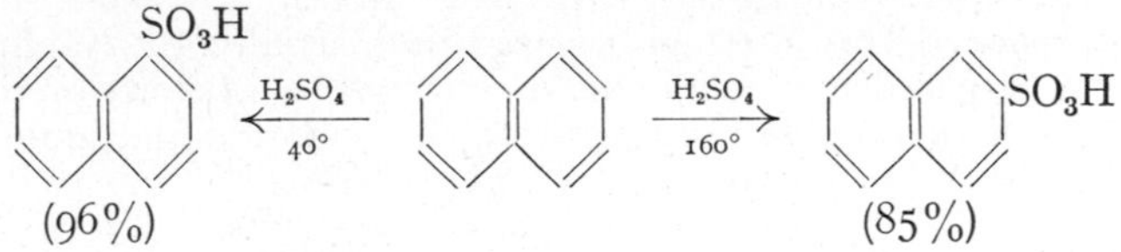

SO_3H (96%) $\xleftarrow[40°]{H_2SO_4}$ naphthalene $\xrightarrow[160°]{H_2SO_4}$ SO_3H (85%)

The two isomeric acids may be separated by means of their calcium or lead salts, those of the 1-acid being more soluble than the 2-. The 2-acid may be obtained pure by treating the mixture of 1- and 2-naphthalenesulphonic acids with superheated steam; the 1-acid is decomposed into naphthalene, the 2-acid being practically unaffected.

1- and 2-Naphthalenesulphonic acids behave similarly to benzenesulphonic acid, but the sulphonic acid group in the former is more easily replaced; *e.g.*, when fused with phosphorus pentachloride, both acids give the corresponding chloronaphthalenes. Both acids are oxidised to phthalic acid by acid permanganate. When heated with concentrated sulphuric acid, the 1-acid is converted into the 2-isomer.

β-Naphthalenesulphonic acid is the starting point of practically all β-naphthalene derivatives.

Sulphonation of the 1-sulphonic acid with concentrated sulphuric acid below 40° gives 1 : 5- (70 per cent.) and 1 : 6-disulphonic acids (25 per cent.); at 130°, the main products are 1 : 6- and 1 : 7-disulphonic acids. Sulphonation of the 2-acid at 60° gives 1 : 6- (80 per cent.) and 1 : 7-disulphonic acid (20 per cent.); above 140°, the main product is 2 : 7-disulphonic acid, and a small amount of 2 : 6-. Armstrong and Wynne's rule (1890) for the orientation of naphthalene-

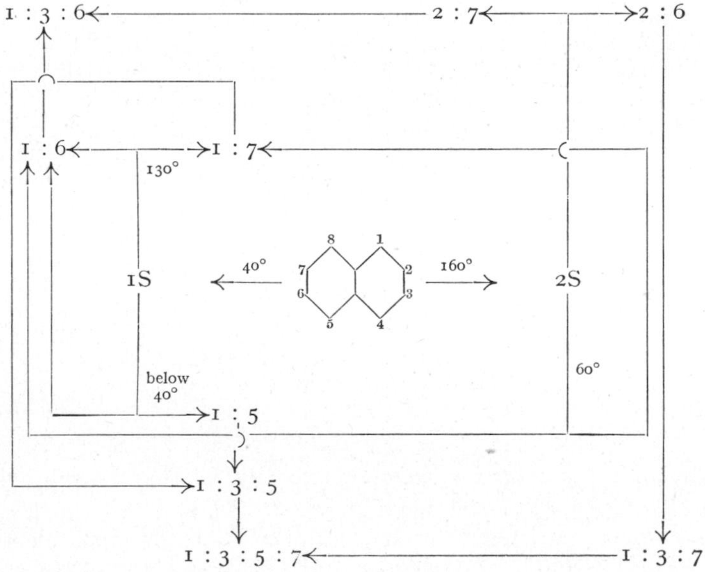

1 : 3 : 6 2 : 7 2 : 6
1 : 6 1 : 7
130°
1S 40° 8 1 7 2 6 3 5 4 160° 2S
below 40° 60°
1 : 5
1 : 3 : 5
1 : 3 : 5 : 7 1 : 3 : 7

polysulphonic acids is useful: two sulpho-groups never occupy positions *o*, *p* or *peri* to each other. This rule limits the number of isomers that can be formed by direct sulphonation of naphthalene to two mono-, six di-, three tri-, and one tetra-sulphonic acid. The table on p. 687 summarises the products obtained by the sulphonation of naphthalene with concentrated sulphuric acid (note the various migrations).

Many of these sulphonic acids are very important dye-intermediates.

Naphthylamines. 1-Naphthylamine (**α-naphthylamine**) may be prepared by reducing 1-nitronaphthalene with iron and hydrochloric acid (yield 80–85 per cent.). This method is used industrially. 1-Naphthylamine may also be prepared by the Bucherer reaction (see below) or by heating 1-naphthol with the double compound of zinc chloride and ammonia (this amination occurs more easily than with phenol):

$$C_{10}H_7OH + NH_3 \xrightarrow[250^\circ]{ZnCl_2} C_{10}H_7NH_2 + H_2O$$

1-Naphthylamine has recently been prepared by heating 1-naphthoic acid with hydroxylamine and polyphosphoric acid (Snyder *et al.*, 1953).

1-Naphthylamine is a colourless solid, m.p. 50°, almost insoluble in water but very soluble in ethanol and ether. It has an unpleasant odour, and turns red on exposure to air. It reduces ammoniacal silver nitrate, and solutions of its salts give a blue precipitate with ferric chloride. Oxidation with boiling chromic acid gives β-naphthaquinone; with permanganate, phthalic acid is obtained. 1-Naphthylamine is reduced by sodium and *iso*pentanol to *ar*-tetrahydro-1-naphthylamine; the prefix *ar*- is the abbreviation of *aromatic* and indicates that the four hydrogen atoms are *not* in the ring containing the amino-group:

$$C_{10}H_7NH_2 \xrightarrow{[H]} C_{10}H_{11}NH_2$$

The systematic name is 5 : 6 : 7 : 8-tetrahydro-1-naphthylamine.

1-Naphthylamine couples with diazonium salts in the 4-position.

2-Naphthylamine (**β-naphthylamine**) is prepared industrially from 2-naphthol by the **Bucherer reaction** (1904). This is the reversible conversion of a naphthol into a naphthylamine in the presence of an aqueous sulphite or hydrogen sulphite. The mechanism of the formation of 2-naphthylamine from 2-naphthol, sodium hydrogen sulphite and ammonia is believed to be as follows:

$$C_{10}H_7OH \rightleftharpoons \left[C_{10}H_8{=}O \right] \xrightleftharpoons{NaHSO_3} C_{10}H_8(OH)SO_3Na \xrightleftharpoons[H_2O]{NH_3} C_{10}H_8(NH_2)SO_3Na \xrightleftharpoons{NH_3} C_{10}H_7NH_2 + (NH_4)NaSO_3$$

2-Naphthylamine is prepared commercially by heating 2-naphthol with aqueous ammonium hydrogen sulphite at 150° under pressure (yield: 94–96 per cent.). 2-Naphthylamine has also been prepared from 2-naphthoic acid (*cf.* the 1-isomer above).

2-Naphthylamine is a colourless solid, m.p. 112°, insoluble in water but soluble in ethanol and ether. It is odourless, reduces ammoniacal silver nitrate, but gives *no* coloration with ferric chloride. It is oxidised by permanganate to phthalic acid and reduced by sodium and *iso*pentanol to *ac*-tetrahydro-2-naphthylamine (1 : 2 : 3 : 4-tetrahydro-2-naphthylamine); the prefix *ac*- is the abstraction of *alicyclic* and indicates that the four hydrogen atoms are in the ring containing the amino-group (*cf.* above):

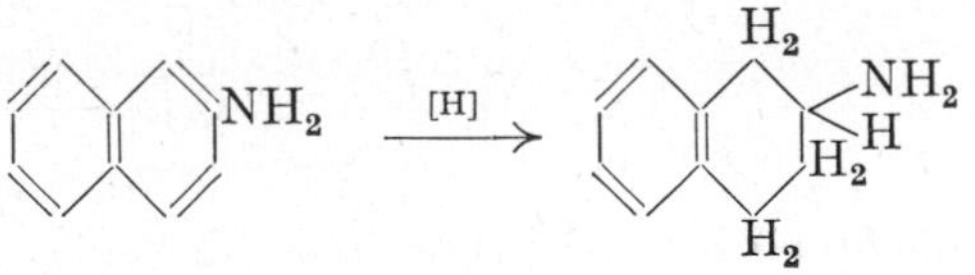

$$C_{10}H_7NH_2 \xrightarrow{[H]} C_{10}H_{11}NH_2$$

2-Naphthylamine couples with diazonium salts only in the 1-position; if this is occupied, no coupling occurs.

Naphthylaminesulphonic acids. These are very important industrially for making dyes. When heated with excess concentrated sulphuric acid at 130°, 1-naphthylamine forms 1-naphthylamine-4-sulphonic acid (*naphthionic acid*). This is used in the preparation of Congo red (p. 753), and is manufactured by the baking process of naphthylamine hydrogen sulphate (*cf.* sulphanilic acid). Prolonged action of sulphuric acid at 130° converts 1-naphthylamine into 1-naphthylamine-5-sulphonic acid (*Laurent's acid*). If the heating is prolonged still further, Laurent's acid rearranges to 1-naphthylamine-6-sulphonic acid (*Cleve's acid*).

1-Naphthylamine-8-sulphonic acid (*Schollkopf's acid*) may be prepared by reduction of the corresponding nitro-sulphonic acid. When heated with phosphoryl chloride, 1-naphthylamine-8-sulphonic acid forms *naphthsultam*:

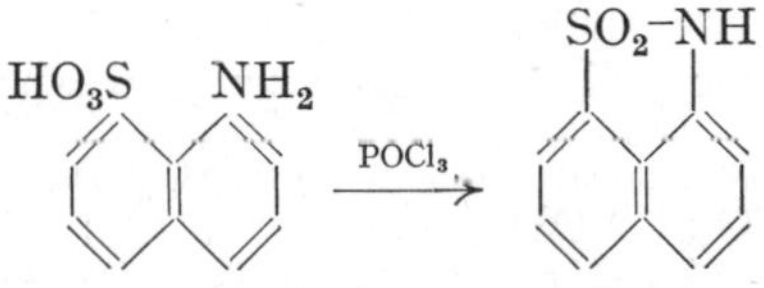

$$HO_3S \cdot C_{10}H_6 \cdot NH_2 \xrightarrow{POCl_3} C_{10}H_6(SO_2\text{–}NH)$$

Sultams may be regarded as *inner* sulphonamides.

When heated with concentrated sulphuric acid, 2-naphthylamine gives four different sulphonic acids according to the temperature: 2-naphthylamine-5-sulphonic acid (*Dahl's acid*), 2-naphthylamine-6-sulphonic acid (*Bronner's acid*), 2-naphthylamine-7-sulphonic acid (F-*acid*), and 2-naphthylamine-8-sulphonic acid (*Badische's acid*).

Naphthols. Both 1- and 2-naphthols are present in coal-tar. They are prepared industrially by fusing the corresponding naphthalenesulphonic acid with sodium hydroxide:

$$C_{10}H_7 \cdot SO_3Na + NaOH \xrightarrow{300^\circ} C_{10}H_7OH + Na_2SO_3 \quad (70\text{–}80\%)$$

Pure 1-naphthol may be prepared by heating 1-naphthylamine with dilute sulphuric acid at 290° under pressure:

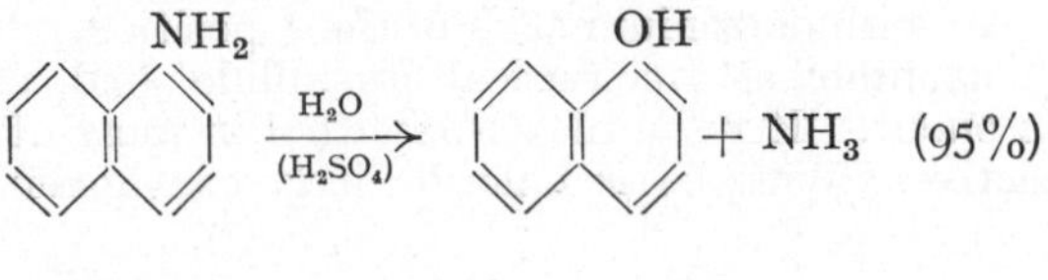

$$C_{10}H_7NH_2 \xrightarrow[(H_2SO_4)]{H_2O} C_{10}H_7OH + NH_3 \quad (95\%)$$

A most interesting preparation of 1-naphthol is by the reaction between *o*-bromofluorobenzene and lithium amalgam in the presence of furan (Wittig *et al.*, 1955). The reaction proceeds via a benzyne intermediate (p. 521):

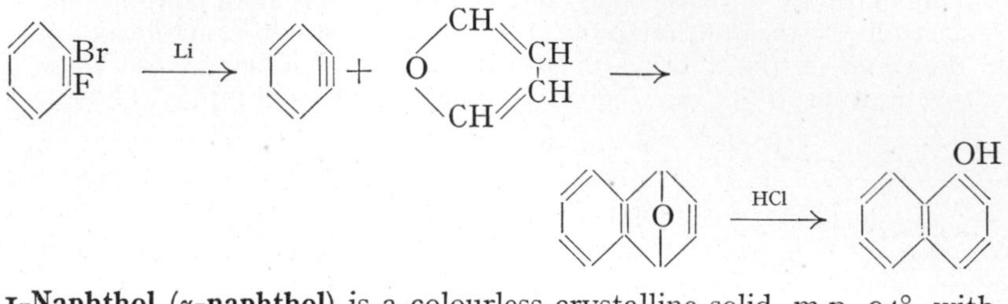

Br F —Li→ + O CH CH CH CH →

O —HCl→ OH

1-Naphthol (**α-naphthol**) is a colourless crystalline solid, m.p. 94°, with a faint phenolic odour. It is sparingly soluble in water, but is readily soluble in alkalis to form naphthoxides, *e.g.*, $C_{10}H_7ONa$. With ferric chloride it gives a violet-blue precipitate of *α-dinaphthol* (4 : 4′-bis-1-naphthol):

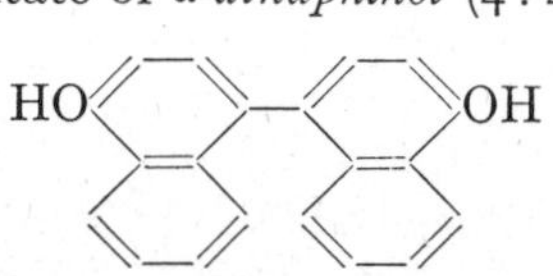

HO OH

1-Naphthol reduces ammoniacal silver nitrate, is oxidised by alkaline permanganate to phthalonic acid and by chromic acid to α-naphthaquinone. It is reduced by sodium and *iso*pentanol to *ar*-tetrahydro-1-naphthol (*ar-1-tetralol*).

Direct sulphonation of 1-naphthol under mild conditions gives a mixture of 1-naphthol-2-sulphonic acid (*Schaeffer's acid*) and 1-naphthol-4-sulphonic acid (*Nevile-Winther's acid*). More vigorous conditions result in the formation of 1-naphthol-2 : 4-disulphonic acid and finally 1-naphthol-2 : 4 : 7-trisulphonic acid.

1-Naphthol-8-sulphonic acid forms an *inner* ester when heated:

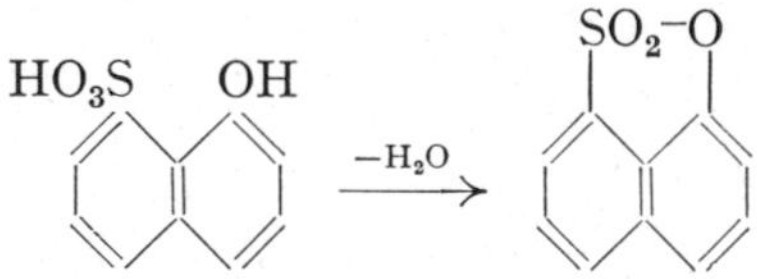

HO_3S OH $\xrightarrow{-H_2O}$ SO_2–O

This is known as *naphthsultone*, and its formation is unusual in view of the fact that sulphonic acids do not form esters directly.

Treatment of 1-naphthol with nitrous acid gives mainly the 2-oxime of β-naphthaquinone, (I), and a small amount of the 4-oxime of α-naphthaquinone, (II) (*cf.* nitrosophenol, p. 604):

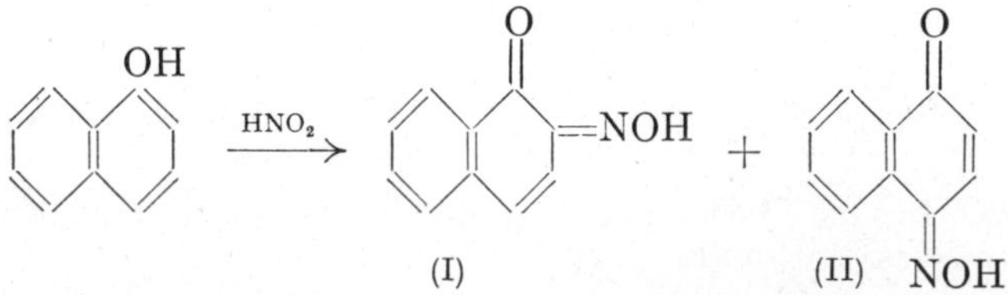

OH $\xrightarrow{HNO_2}$ O =NOH (I) + O NOH (II)

1-Naphthol couples with diazonium salts in the 4-position.

2-Naphthol (**β-naphthol**) is a colourless crystalline solid, m.p. 123°, with a faint phenolic odour. It resembles 1-naphthol in most of its properties, but is more reactive. With ferric chloride it gives a green precipitate of β-*dinaphthol* (1 : 1′-bis-2-naphthol). It reduces ammoniacal silver nitrate, and is oxidised by alkaline permanganate to phthalonic acid. It is reduced

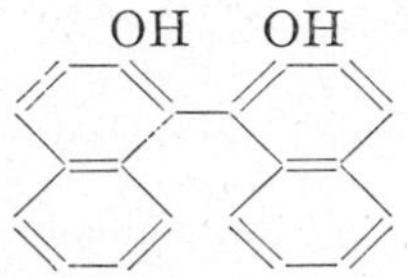

OH OH

by sodium and *iso*pentanol to mainly *ac*-tetrahydro-2-naphthol (*ac*-2-*tetralol*). With nitrous acid it forms the 1-oxime of β-naphthaquinone (nitroso-β-naphthol):

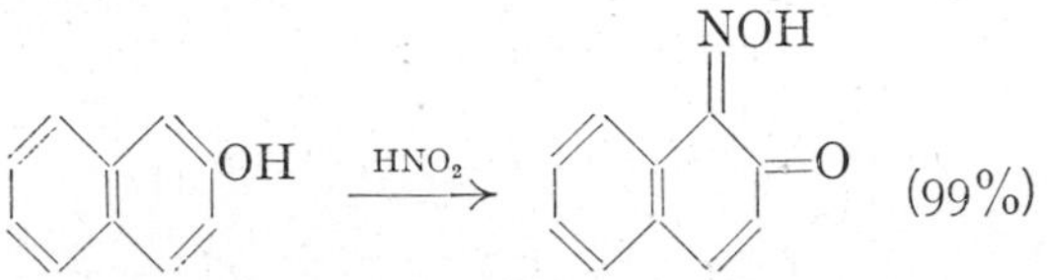

NOH

OH $\xrightarrow{HNO_2}$ =O (99%)

This is used for the detection and estimation of cobalt. 2-Naphthol couples with diazonium salts only in the adjacent 1-position; if this is occupied, no coupling takes place. Only the oxime form exists in the solid state, but in solution only the other tautomer (nitrosonaphthol) is present (Burawoy *et al.*, 1955; *cf.* *p*-nitrosophenol, p. 604).

Some 2-naphthol ethers (methyl and ethyl), known as *nerolins*, are used in perfumery. When 2-naphthol is sulphonated, the original product is 2-naphthol-1-sulphonic acid, but this is unstable and rearranges to 2-naphthol-8-sulphonic acid (*croceic acid*) at low temperature. Croceic acid, at 100°, rearranges to 2-naphthol-6-sulphonic acid (*Schaeffer's* β-*acid*). When sulphonated with larger amounts of concentrated sulphuric acid, 2-naphthol gives disulphonic acids. At low temperature the main product is 2-naphthol-6 : 8-disulphonic acid (G-*acid*); at higher temperatures, mainly 2-naphthol-3 : 6-disulphonic acid (R-*acid*). G- and R-acids are used in the manufacture of dyes.

Woodward (1940) prepared 10-methyldecal-2-one from *ar*-2-tetralol by means of the Reimer–Tiemann reaction as follows:

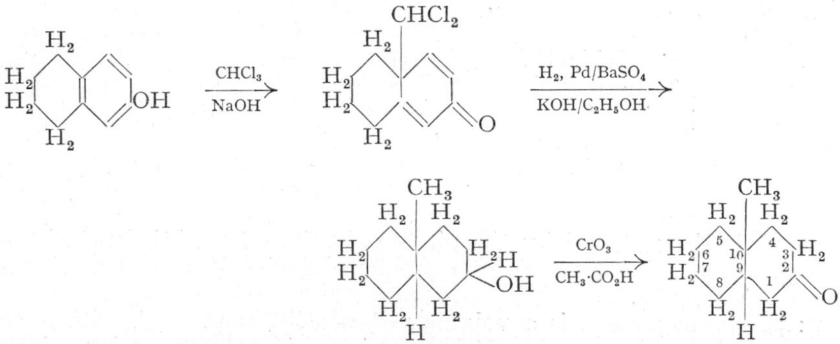

H_2 H_2 H_2 H_2 OH $\xrightarrow[NaOH]{CHCl_3}$ $CHCl_2$ H_2 H_2 H_2 H_2 O $\xrightarrow[KOH/C_2H_5OH]{H_2,\ Pd/BaSO_4}$

CH_3 H_2 H_2 H_2 H_2 H_2 H OH H_2 H_2 H $\xrightarrow[CH_3{\cdot}CO_2H]{CrO_3}$ CH_3 H_2 H_2 H_2 H_2 H_2 5 4 6 10 3 7 9 2 8 1 O H_2 H_2 H

This synthesis is based on the fact that the intermediate product in the Reimer–Tiemann reaction can be isolated when the *p*-position to the hydroxyl group is occupied by, *e.g.*, a methyl group (p. 627).

Naphthalenecarboxylic acids. **1-Naphthoic acid** (*naphthalene-1-carboxylic acid*), m.p. 161°, may be prepared by the hydrolysis of the corresponding cyanide, or by the oxidation of 1-acetylnaphthalene with sodium hypochlorite. It may also be prepared from 1-naphthylmagnesium bromide as follows:

$$1\text{-}C_{10}H_7{\cdot}MgBr + (C_2H_5O)_2CO \xrightarrow{\text{ether}} 1\text{-}C_{10}H_7{\cdot}CO_2C_2H_5 + C_2H_5OMgBr \quad (68\text{–}73\%)$$

2-Naphthoic acid, m.p. 184°, may be prepared by methods similar to those used for the 1-isomer.

1- and 2-Naphthoic acids are insoluble in cold or hot water, and both readily eliminate carbon dioxide to form naphthalene when heated with soda–lime. Both undergo most of the usual reactions of a carboxylic acid, but 1-naphthoic acid shows the proximity effect due to the carbon atom in position 8; *e.g.*, 2-chloro-1-naphthoic acid is not esterified by the Fischer–Speier method, whereas the isomeric 1-chloro-2-naphthoic acid gives the ester under the same conditions.

Naphthalic acid (*naphthalene*-1 : 8-*dicarboxylic acid*) may be prepared by oxidising acenaphthene with acid dichromate:

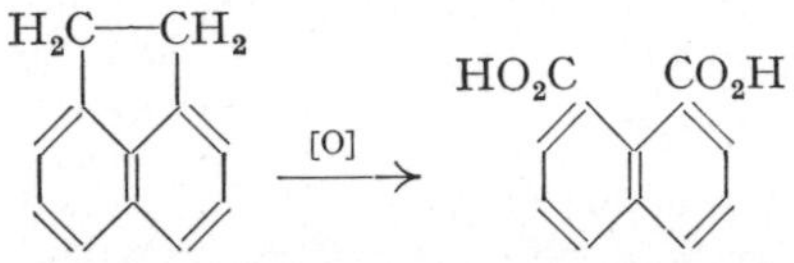

H_2C—CH_2 (acenaphthene) $\xrightarrow{[O]}$ HO_2C CO_2H (naphthalic acid)

It is a solid, and when heated at 180° forms naphthalic anhydride:

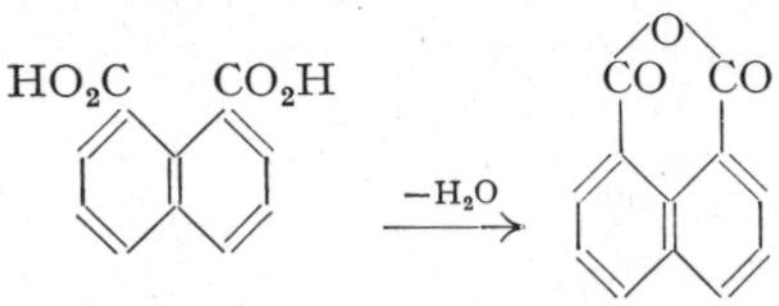

HO_2C CO_2H $\xrightarrow{-H_2O}$ CO–O–CO (naphthalic anhydride)

This is in keeping with the fact that all *peri*-(1 : 8-) substituents interact if possible (*cf.* sultams and sultones).

Naphthaquinones. Theoretically, six naphthaquinones are possible: 1 : 2-, 1 : 4-, 1 : 5-, 1 :7-, 2 : 3- and 2 : 6. Only three are known, the 1 :2-, 1 : 4- and 2 : 6-, but it appears that derivatives of 2 : 3-naphthaquinone have been prepared.

1 : 4-Naphthaquinone (**α-naphthaquinone,** 1 : 4-*dihydronaphthalene*-1 : 4-*dione*) may be prepared by the oxidation of 1 : 4-diamino-, dihydroxy- or aminohydroxynaphthalene, *e.g.*,

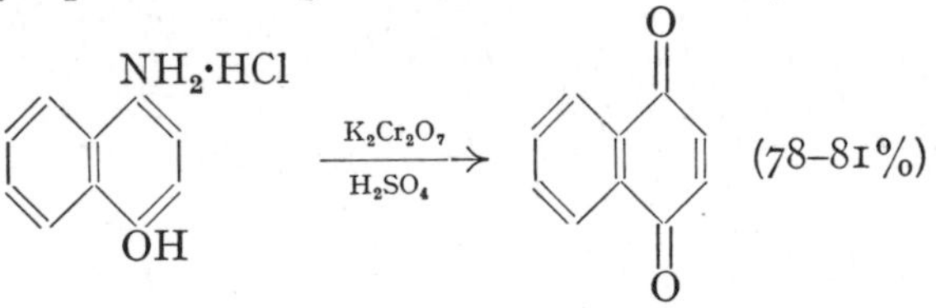

$NH_2{\cdot}HCl$ / OH (4-amino-1-naphthol hydrochloride) $\xrightarrow[H_2SO_4]{K_2Cr_2O_7}$ 1 : 4-naphthaquinone (O, O) (78–81%)

It may also be prepared by the direct oxidation of naphthalene with dichromate and sulphuric acid, or chromium trioxide in glacial acetic acid (yield 40 per cent.).

1 : 4-Naphthaquinone is a volatile yellow solid, m.p. 125°, with a pronounced odour. It resembles *p*-benzoquinone in many ways chemically, but it is not reduced by sulphurous acid. It is reduced by metal and acid to 1 : 4-*dihydroxynaphthalene* (*naphthalene*-1 : 4-*diol*) and oxidised by nitric acid to phthalic acid. It forms a monoxime; this is tautomeric, and in the solid state it exists as the oxime, and in solution this form predominates in equilibrium with the nitrosophenol form (Havinga *et al.*, 1955; Hadži,

1956). A most remarkable reaction is its conversion into *indane*-1 : 3-*dione* (1 : 3-*diketohydrindene*) on treatment with nitrous acid:

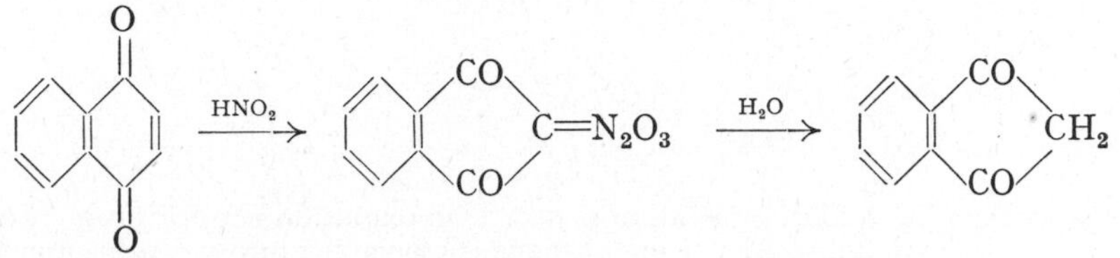

$\xrightarrow{HNO_2}$ C=N_2O_3 $\xrightarrow{H_2O}$ CH_2

Vitamin K (the antihaemorrhagic factor) is a derivative of 1 : 4-naphthaquinone.

1 : 2-Naphthaquinone (**β-naphthaquinone,** 1 : 2-*dihydronaphthalene*-1 : 2-*dione*) may be prepared by oxidising 1-amino-2-naphthol with dichromate and sulphuric acid (yield 75 per cent.). It is a non-volatile, odourless, red solid which decomposes at 115–120°. A most remarkable reaction is the fission of the quinone ring with simultaneous hydroxylation when 1 : 2-naphthaquinone is treated with chlorine-water (or with hypochlorous acid); phenylglyceric-*o*-carboxylic lactone is the final product:

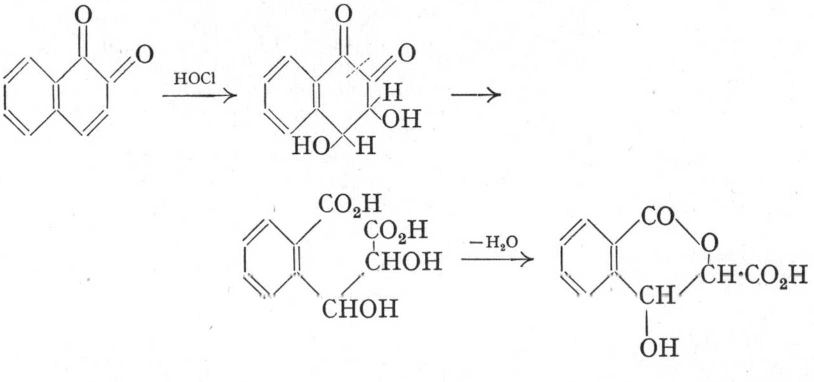

$\xrightarrow{HOCl}$ → $\xrightarrow{-H_2O}$ $CH{\cdot}CO_2H$

2 : 6-Naphthaquinone (***amphi*-naphthaquinone,** 2 : 6-*dihydronaphthalene*-2 : 6-*dione*) may be prepared by oxidising 2 : 6-dihydroxynaphthalene in benzene solution with " active " lead dioxide (this may be prepared by decomposing lead tetra-acetate with water; Kuhn *et al.*, 1950):

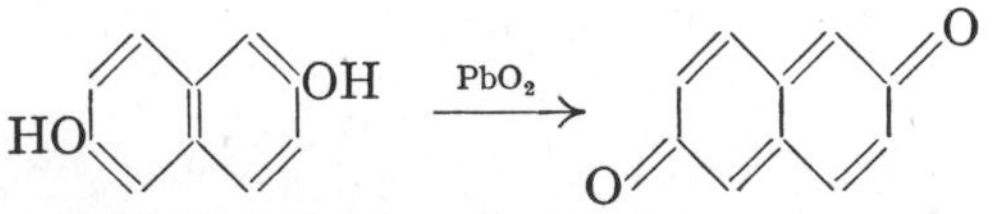

$\xrightarrow{PbO_2}$

It is an orange, non-volatile, odourless solid, m.p. 135°.

Acenaphthene, $C_{12}H_{10}$, occurs in coal-tar; it may be prepared by passing 1-ethylnaphthalene through a red-hot tube:

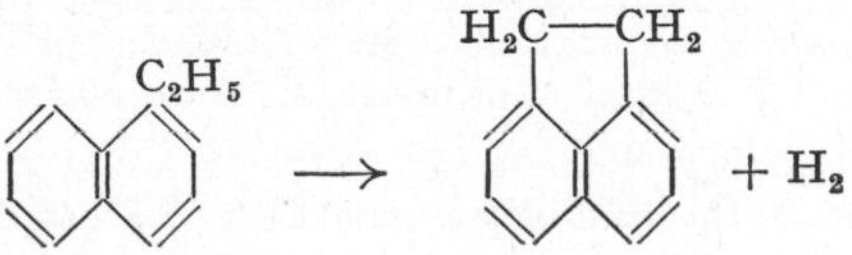

C_2H_5 → H_2C—CH_2 + H_2

It may also be prepared by a Friedel–Crafts reaction using naphthalene and oxalyl chloride and reducing the product, 7 : 8-*acenaphthaquinone*,* by the Wolff–Kishner method (p. 143):

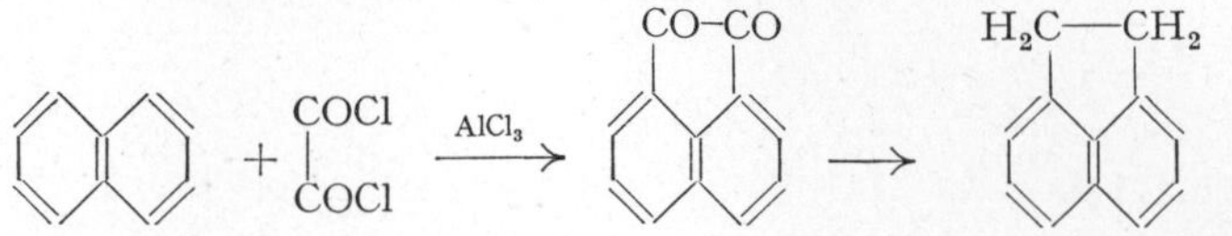

Acenaphthene is a colourless solid, m.p. 96°. On oxidation with dichromate and sulphuric acid, acenaphthene is converted into 7 : 8-acenaphthaquinone which, by further action of the oxidising agent, gives naphthalic acid. This shows that the ethylene group occupies the 1 : 8-positions of naphthalene. Substitution in acenaphthene occurs most readily in the 3- and 4-positions, *e.g.*, bromination, nitration and sulphonation give the corresponding 3-derivatives. When oxidised with lead peroxide or passed through a red-hot tube, acenaphthene forms *acenaphthylene*:

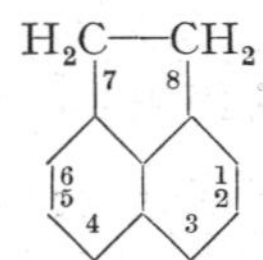

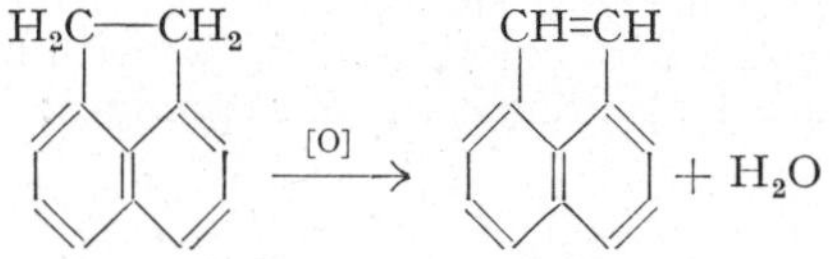

Indene (benzo*cyclo*pentadiene), C_9H_8, occurs in the coal-tar fraction boiling at 175–185°. It may be obtained from this fraction by precipitating with picric acid and purifying the picrate by recrystallisation. When the picrate is steam-distilled, it is decomposed, the indene passing over in the distillate. Alternatively, indene may be obtained from the coal-tar fraction by heating the latter with sodium, separating the sodioindene formed (solid) and steam-distilling it, whereupon indene distils over.

Indene is a colourless liquid, b.p. 182°, which readily polymerises (*cf. cyclo*pentadiene). It is reduced by sodium and ethanol to 2 : 3-*dihydroindene* (*indane* or *hydrindene*):

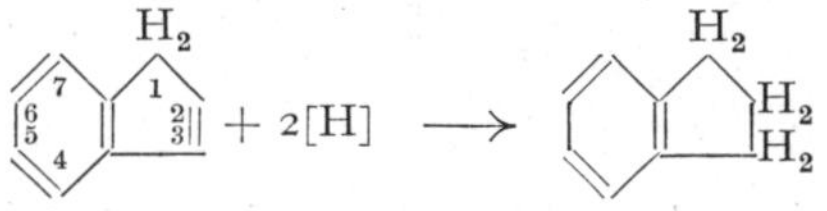

Oxidation of indene with acid dichromate gives homophthalic acid.

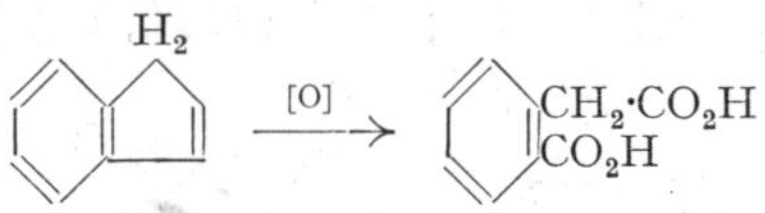

(66–77%)

Indane, b.p. 177°, occurs in coal-tar. Indene combines with halogen to form 2 : 3-dihalogeno-indane. The methylene group in indene is very reactive, *e.g.*, indene forms a sodio-derivative:

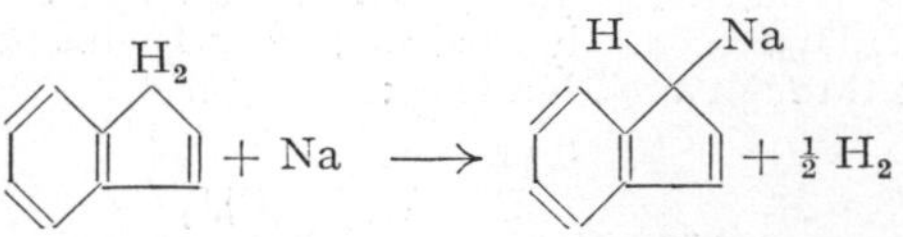

$$+ Na \longrightarrow + \tfrac{1}{2} H_2$$

* In American journals, number 1 starts at 7 (as shown above) and numbering proceeds clockwise; hence this compound would be 1 : 2-acenaphthaquinone.

It liberates paraffins from alkyl-magnesium halides, condenses with ethyl oxalate in the presence of sodium ethoxide to form indene-oxalic ester, and with aldehydes or ketones in the presence of alkali to form benzofulvenes:

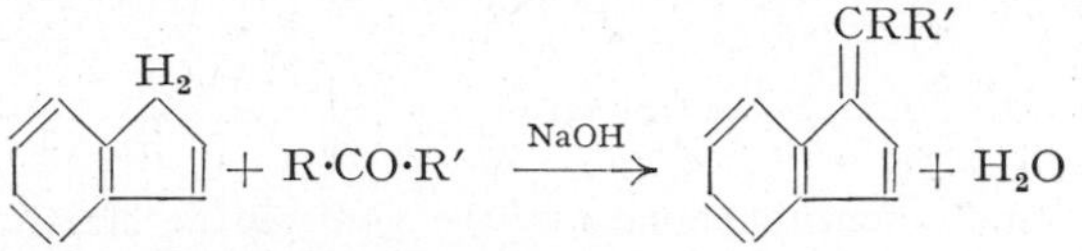

$$\text{(indene, } H_2\text{)} + R\cdot CO\cdot R' \xrightarrow{NaOH} \text{(benzofulvene, } CRR'\text{)} + H_2O$$

These benzofulvenes are highly coloured; *benzofulvene* has been prepared (R = R′ = H). All the foregoing reactions are characteristic of the methylene group in *cyclo*pentadiene.

Indan-1-one (*α-hydrindone*), m.p. 42°, may be synthesised by an internal Friedel–Crafts reactions on β-phenylpropionyl chloride:

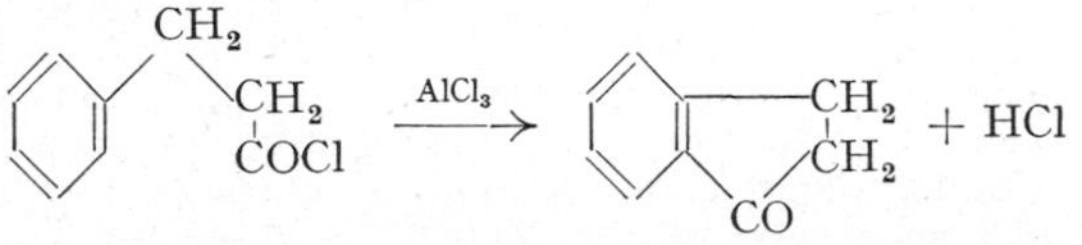

$$C_6H_5\cdot CH_2\cdot CH_2\cdot COCl \xrightarrow{AlCl_3} \text{(indan-1-one: } CH_2, CH_2, CO\text{)} + HCl$$

It may also be prepared by treating indene with hydrochloric acid and oxidising the product, 1-chloroindane, with chromium trioxide in acetic acid:

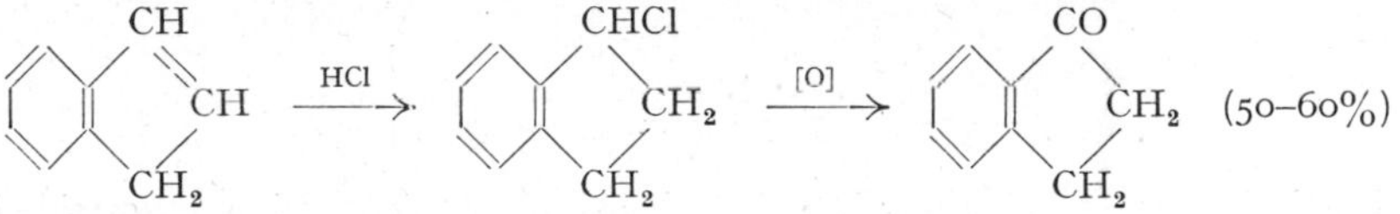

$$\text{(CH, CH, } CH_2\text{)} \xrightarrow{HCl} \text{(CHCl, } CH_2, CH_2\text{)} \xrightarrow{[O]} \text{(CO, } CH_2, CH_2\text{)} \quad (50\text{–}60\%)$$

Indan-2-one (*β-hydrindone*), m.p. 61°, may be prepared by heating xylylene-*o*-dicarboxylic acid:

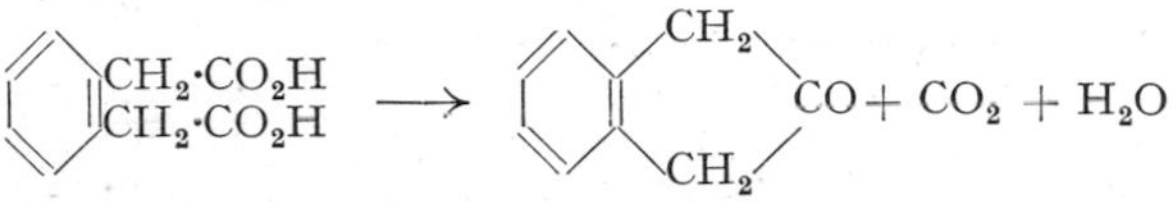

$$C_6H_4(CH_2\cdot CO_2H)_2 \longrightarrow \text{(}CH_2, CO, CH_2\text{)} + CO_2 + H_2O$$

Indane-1 : 3-dione may be prepared by the action of nitrous acid on 1 : 4 naphthaquinone (p. 692).

Fluorene (*diphenylenemethane*), $C_{13}H_{10}$, occurs in coal-tar (fraction 270–300°) and can be separated from the other compounds by means of its sodio-derivative (*cf.* indene). It may be prepared:

(i) By passing diphenylmethane through a red-hot tube:

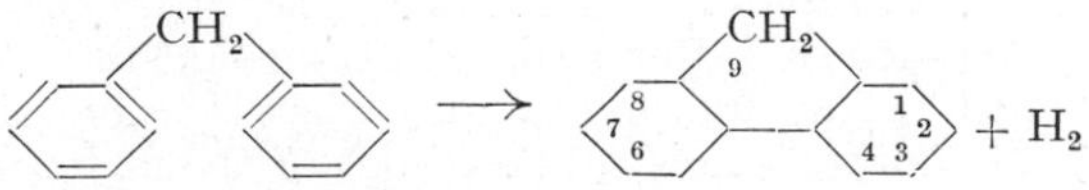

$$C_6H_5\cdot CH_2\cdot C_6H_5 \longrightarrow \text{fluorene (}CH_2\text{, positions 1–9)} + H_2$$

(ii) By passing *o*-methyldiphenyl over palladium at 450°:

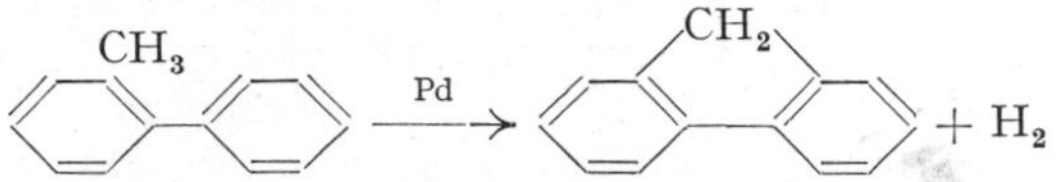

$$\text{(}CH_3\text{-diphenyl)} \xrightarrow{Pd} \text{fluorene (}CH_2\text{)} + H_2$$

(iii) By heating the calcium salt of diphenic acid, reducing the product, fluorenone, with zinc dust and ethanolic sodium hydroxide, and then reducing the fluorenol so produced by the Clemmensen method:

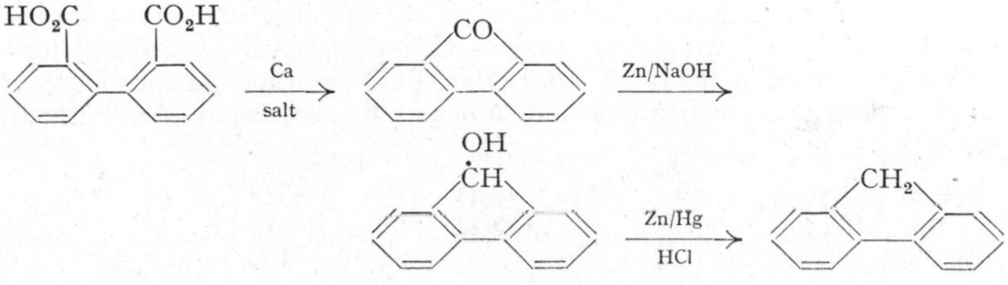

$$\text{(}HO_2C, CO_2H\text{)} \xrightarrow[\text{salt}]{Ca} \text{(CO)} \xrightarrow{Zn/NaOH} \text{(OH, CH)} \xrightarrow[HCl]{Zn/Hg} \text{(}CH_2\text{)}$$

(iv) Fluorene may be prepared by means of the Pschorr synthesis (p. 705), starting with *o*-aminodiphenylmethane.

$$\text{o-}NH_2C_6H_4\cdot CH_2\cdot C_6H_5 \xrightarrow[H_2SO_4]{NaNO_2} \text{o-}HSO_4N_2C_6H_4\cdot CH_2\cdot C_6H_5 \xrightarrow{Cu} \text{fluorene}$$

Alternatively, *o*-aminobenzophenone may be used as the starting material and the product, fluorenone, reduced to fluorene as in (iii).

Methods (iii) and (iv) are useful for preparing substituted fluorenes with the substituents in known positions.

Fluorene is a colourless solid, m.p. 116°, with a blue fluorescence. The methylene group is active (*cf. cyclo*pentadiene), *e.g.*, fluorene forms a sodio-derivative, liberates hydrocarbons from Grignard reagents, and condenses with aldehydes and ketones in the presence of alkali. These condensation products are colourless or slightly coloured (*cf.* indene). When fluorene is halogenated, nitrated or sulphonated, the first substituent enters the 2-position, and the second the 7-position. Fluorene is oxidised by chromium trioxide in glacial acetic acid to *fluorenone* (m.p. 84°). This is oxidised by permanganate to phthalic acid. When fused with potassium hydroxide, fluorenone is converted into diphenyl-2-carboxylic acid:

$$\text{fluorenone} \xrightarrow{KOH} C_6H_5\cdot C_6H_4\cdot CO_2H$$

This acid is also formed when fluorenone is heated with potassium hydroxide in diphenyl ether at 180° (Huntress and Seikel, 1939). The opening of the five-membered ring in this manner offers a means of determining the orientation of substituted fluorenones (and fluorenes).

ANTHRACENE

Anthracene, $C_{14}H_{10}$, is obtained from the anthracene oil fraction of coal-tar by cooling the latter and pressing the solid (which crystallises out) free from liquid. The crude anthracene contains phenanthrene and carbazole. The anthracene cake is powdered and washed with "solvent naphtha" which dissolves the phenanthrene, and the remaining solid is then washed with pyridine which dissolves the carbazole. The anthracene is purified by sublimation. Alternatively, after removal of phenanthrene, the remaining solid is fused with potassium hydroxide, whereby potassio-carbazole is formed; unreacted anthracene is sublimed out of the melt and recovered.

Until recently, there has been very little use for carbazole, and thus the recovery of anthracene was expensive. Since anthracene is mainly used as the starting point of anthraquinone, a cheaper method of isolating anthracene from coal-tar is to remove the phenanthrene first, and then catalytically oxidise the remaining mixture of anthracene and carbazole by air and vanadium pentoxide at 300–500°. Under these conditions, anthracene is oxidised to anthraquinone and carbazole is completely oxidised (to carbon dioxide, etc.).

Structure of anthracene. Bromination of anthracene gives bromo-anthracene, $C_{14}H_9Br$, which, on fusion with potassium hydroxide, forms hydroxyanthracene, $C_{14}H_9\cdot OH$, and this, on vigorous oxidation, gives phthalic acid and a small amount of *o*-benzoylbenzoic acid (Anschutz and Japp, 1878):

$$C_{14}H_9OH \xrightarrow{[O]} C_6H_4(CO_2H)_2 + \text{o-}HO_2C\cdot C_6H_4\cdot CO\cdot C_6H_5$$

This suggests that anthracene contains at least two benzene rings, and that its skeleton is as shown. The presence of two benzene rings is confirmed by the fact that on fusion with potassium hydroxide at 250°, anthraquinone (which may be obtained from anthracene by direct oxidation) gives *two* molecules of benzoic acid. The above skeleton contains 14 carbon atoms, and to fit in 10 hydrogen atoms and retain the quadrivalency of carbon, the middle ring must be closed, *i.e.*, a structure of anthracene which is consistent with the foregoing reactions is three benzene rings fused together in a linear manner. This structure has been amply confirmed by many syntheses.

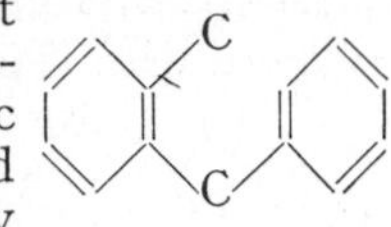

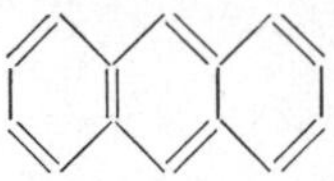

Synthesis of anthracene. (i) By a Friedel–Crafts reaction using benzyl chloride; 9 : 10-*dihydroanthracene*, which is first formed, readily eliminates two hydrogen atoms under the conditions of the experiment to form anthracene:

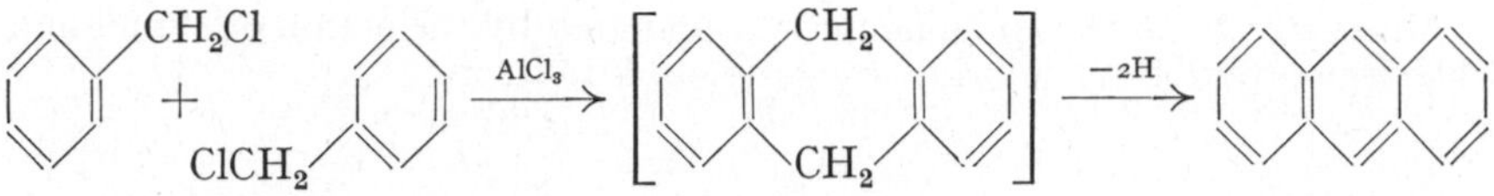

$C_6H_5CH_2Cl + ClCH_2C_6H_5 \xrightarrow{AlCl_3} [C_6H_4(CH_2)_2C_6H_4] \xrightarrow{-2H}$ anthracene

Anthracene is also formed by the Friedel–Crafts condensation between benzene and methylene bromide, or between benzene and acetylene tetrabromide:

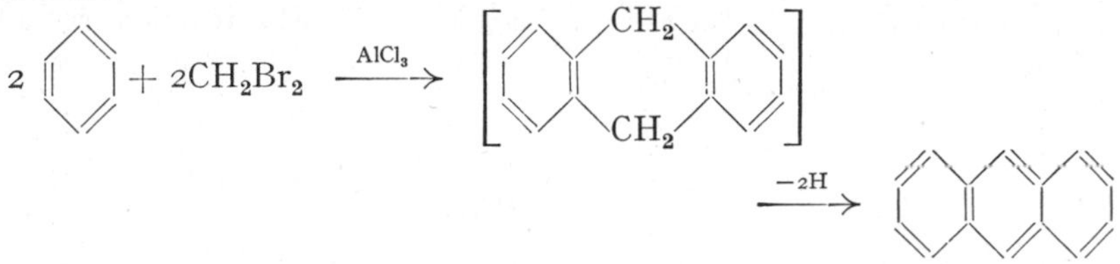

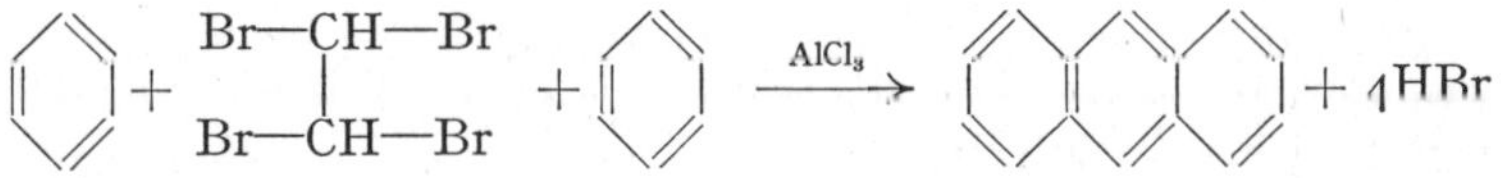

$2C_6H_6 + 2CH_2Br_2 \xrightarrow{AlCl_3} [C_6H_4(CH_2)_2C_6H_4] \xrightarrow{-2H}$ anthracene

$C_6H_6 + Br—CH(Br)—CH(Br)—Br + C_6H_6 \xrightarrow{AlCl_3}$ anthracene $+ 4HBr$

(ii) By heating *o*-bromobenzyl bromide with sodium; the product, dihydroanthracene, is converted into anthracene by mild oxidation:

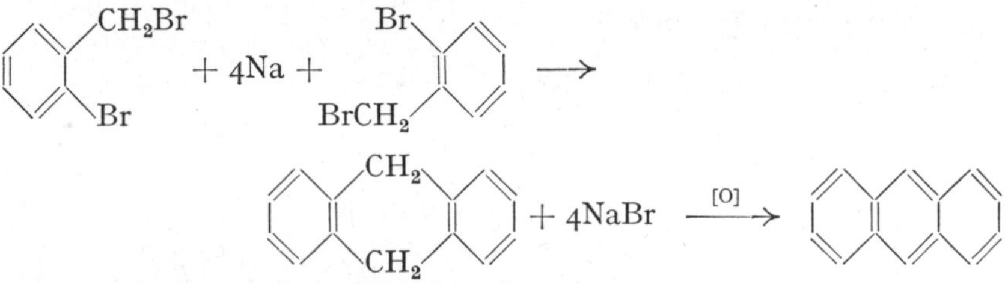

o-$BrC_6H_4CH_2Br + 4Na + o$-$BrCH_2C_6H_4Br \longrightarrow C_6H_4(CH_2)_2C_6H_4 + 4NaBr \xrightarrow{[O]}$ anthracene

Some phenanthrene is formed at the same time:

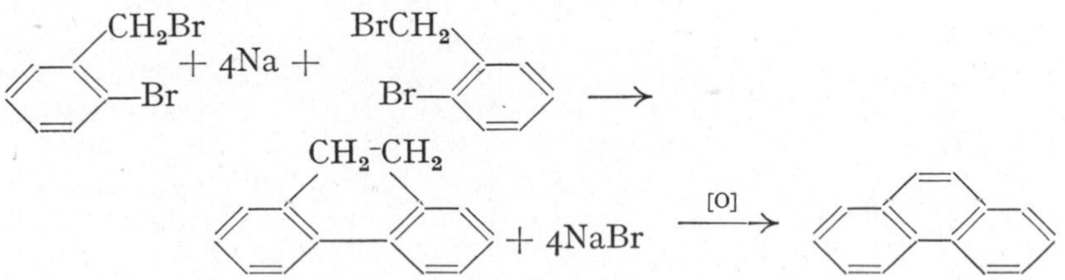

o-$BrC_6H_4CH_2Br + 4Na + o$-$BrCH_2C_6H_4Br \longrightarrow C_6H_4(CH_2\text{-}CH_2)C_6H_4 + 4NaBr \xrightarrow{[O]}$ phenanthrene

(iii) When phthalic anhydride in benzene solution is treated with aluminium chloride, *o*-benzoylbenzoic acid is formed. This, on heating with concentrated sulphuric acid at 100°, forms anthraquinone, which, on distillation with zinc dust, gives anthracene:

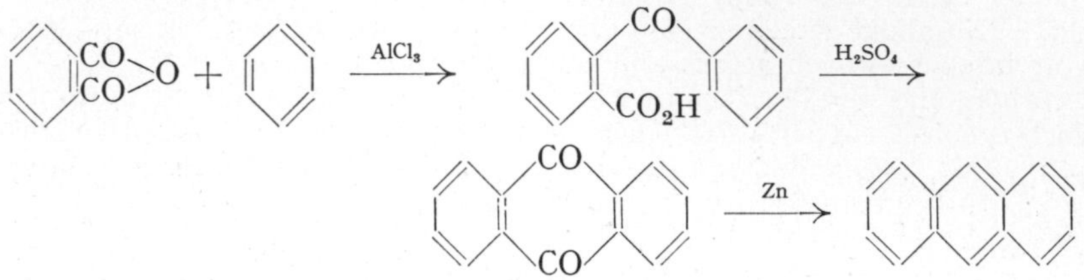

CO>O (phthalic anhydride) + benzene $\xrightarrow{AlCl_3}$ $C_6H_4(CO_2H)COC_6H_5$ $\xrightarrow{H_2SO_4}$ anthraquinone $\xrightarrow{Zn}$ anthracene

According to Koo (1953), polyphosphoric acid is the best reagent for cyclising *o*-benzoylbenzoic acid.

Alternatively, anthraquinone may be prepared by the action of aluminium chloride on phthaloyl chloride in benzene solution:

$C_6H_4(COCl)_2$ + benzene $\xrightarrow{AlCl_3}$ anthraquinone $\xrightarrow{Zn}$ anthracene

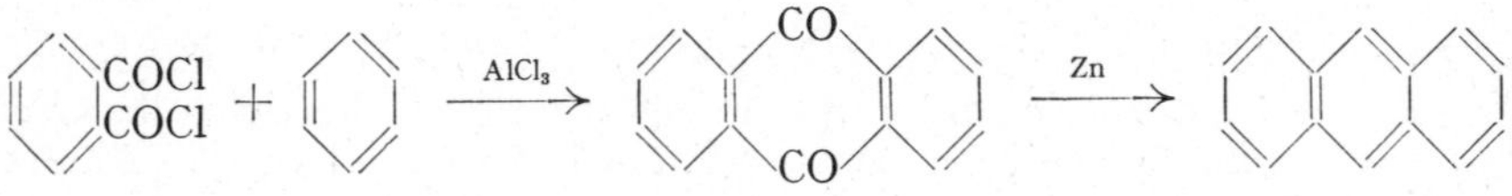

(iv) Anthracene may be prepared by means of the **Elbs reaction** (see also p. 637):

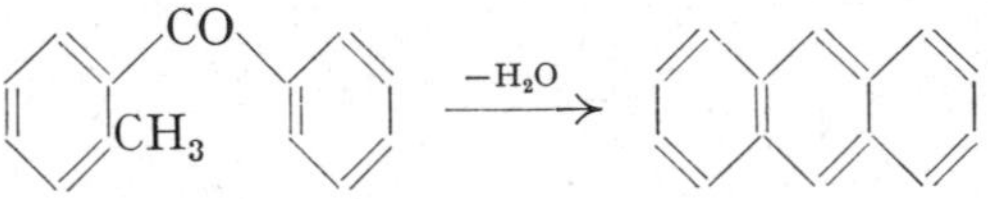

$o\text{-}CH_3C_6H_4COC_6H_5$ $\xrightarrow{-H_2O}$ anthracene

This reaction is usually carried out by heating the ketone under reflux or at 400–450° until water is no longer evolved. The yield of hydrocarbon is usually low, but often the Elbs reaction is the only means of preparing certain polynuclear hydrocarbons.

(v) Anthracene may be synthesised in the following ways starting with naphthalene (thereby showing the presence of the naphthalene nucleus in anthracene):

(*a*) 1 : 4-Naphthaquinone undergoes the Diels–Alder reaction with butadiene to form 1 : 4-dihydroanthraquinone. This, on oxidation with chromium trioxide in glacial acetic acid, gives anthraquinone:

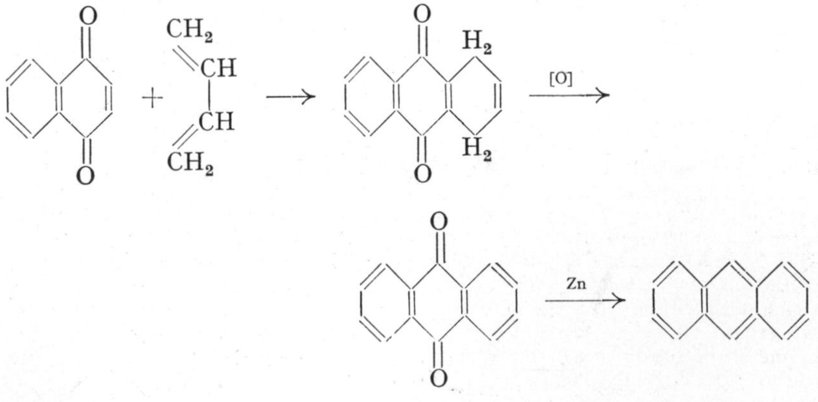

1 : 4-naphthaquinone + $CH_2{=}CH{-}CH{=}CH_2$ $\longrightarrow$ 1 : 4-dihydroanthraquinone $\xrightarrow{[O]}$ anthraquinone $\xrightarrow{Zn}$ anthracene

(*b*) In this method, naphthalene is converted into 1 : 4-dihydronaphthalene-2-carboxylic ester, and this is then made to undergo the Michael condensation (p. 262) with acetoacetic ester, etc.:

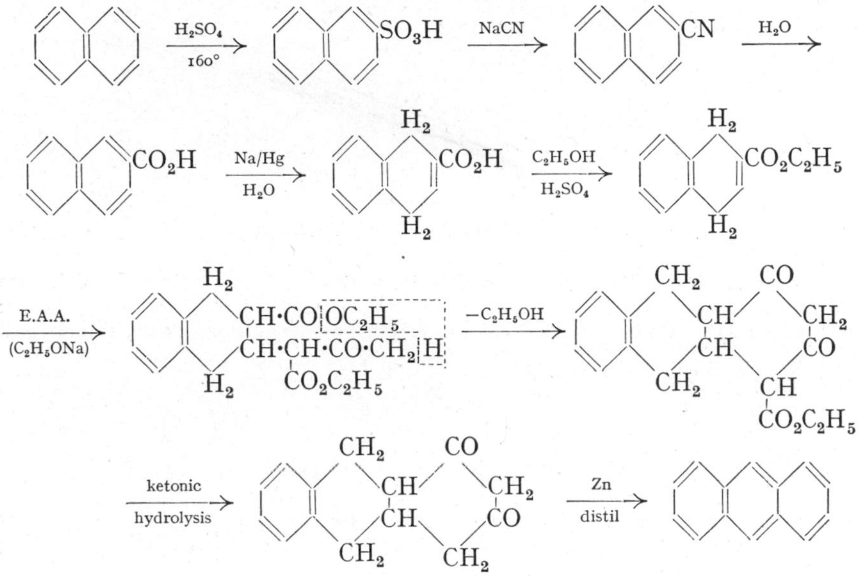

SO_3H $\xrightarrow[160°]{H_2SO_4}$ ... $\xrightarrow{NaCN}$ CN $\xrightarrow{H_2O}$

CO_2H $\xrightarrow[H_2O]{Na/Hg}$ H_2, CO_2H, H_2 $\xrightarrow[H_2SO_4]{C_2H_5OH}$ H_2, $CO_2C_2H_5$, H_2

$\xrightarrow[(C_2H_5ONa)]{E.A.A.}$ H_2, $CH \cdot CO | OC_2H_5$, $CH \cdot CH \cdot CO \cdot CH_2 | H$, $CO_2C_2H_5$, H_2 $\xrightarrow{-C_2H_5OH}$ CH_2, CO, CH, CH_2, CH, CO, CH_2, CH, $CO_2C_2H_5$

$\xrightarrow[hydrolysis]{ketonic}$ CH_2, CO, CH, CH_2, CH, CO, CH_2, CH_2 $\xrightarrow[distil]{Zn}$

Positions of the double bonds in anthracene. Many structures have been proposed for anthracene.

Structure (I) was accepted by many because of the synthesis of anthracene from benzene and acetylene tetrabromide (see method (i)). This structure,

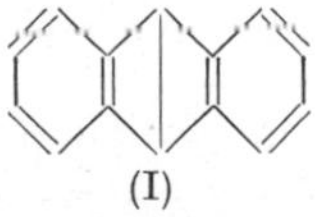

(I) 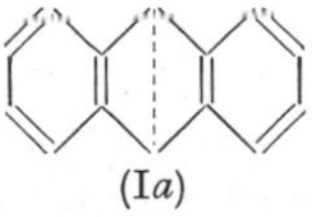 (I*a*)

however, has been considered unlikely for various reasons, *e.g.*,

(i) The synthesis of anthracene from naphthalene (and other syntheses) indicates the absence of a *para*-bond.

(ii) Anthracene adds on maleic anhydride to form *endoanthracenemaleic anhydride*, the addition occurring in the middle ring:

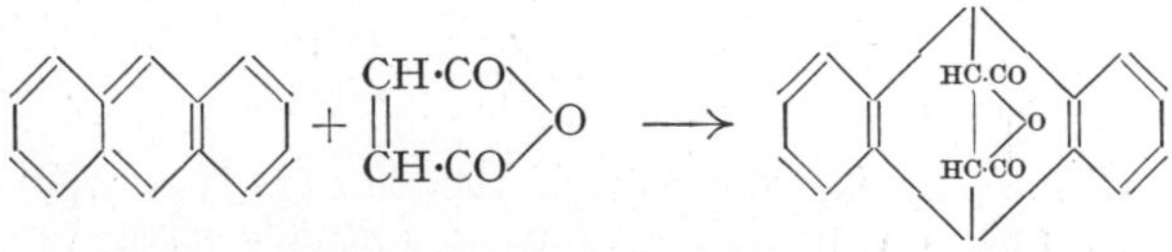

$+$ $CH \cdot CO$, O, $CH \cdot CO$ $\longrightarrow$ HC·CO, O, HC·CO

Since the middle ring behaves as a diene, this indicates it contains conjugated double bonds (*cf.* Diels–Alder reaction).

(iii) X-Ray analysis studies have shown that all the carbon atoms of anthracene lie in a plane, and that the distance between the *para*-carbon atoms in each ring is the same as in benzene. According to calculations of Oakley *et al.* (1949), however, (I) is a contributing structure to the resonance hybrid, *i.e.*, one of the resonating structures has a 9 : 10 formal bond, (I*a*) (*cf.* the Dewar structures of benzene, p. 484).

All the evidence points towards anthracene being a resonance hybrid of the four resonating structures (II–V):

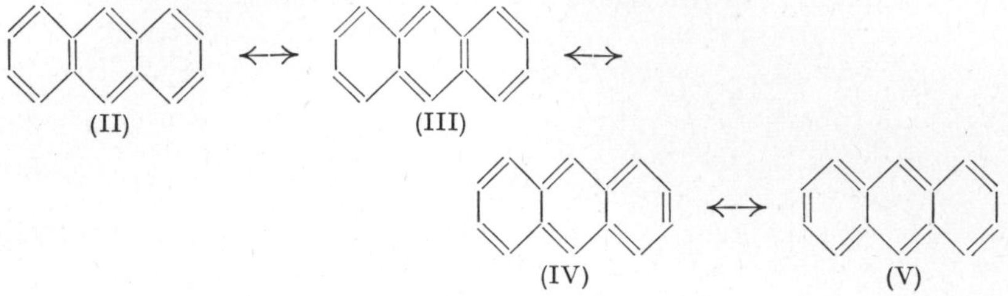

(II) ↔ (III) ↔

(IV) ↔ (V)

The resonance energy of anthracene is 105 k. cal./mole.

Anthracene is an *alternant hydrocarbon* (p. 502), and the π-electron densities are unity at all positions. The self-polarisabilities are in the following order: $9 > 1 > 2$ (I). Consequently position 9 will be the most reactive, then 1 and

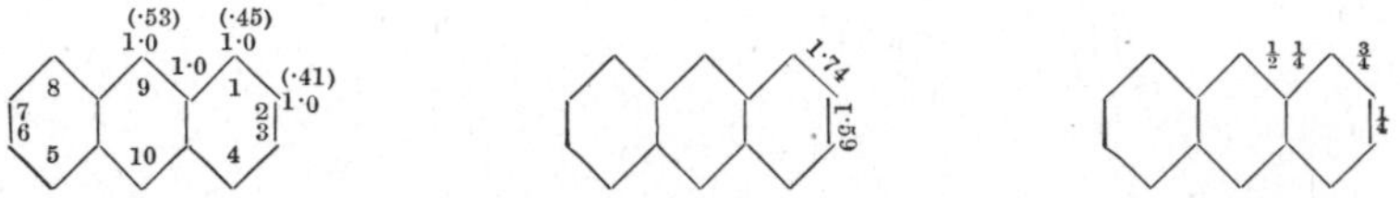

(I) (II) (III)

finally 2. (II) shows bond orders (obtained by calculation), and (III) shows double-bond characters (obtained by taking the average of the four resonating structures of anthracene; *cf.* naphthalene, p. 685).

Isomerism of anthracene derivatives. There are three possible monosubstitution products: 1- or α-, 2- or β- and 9- or γ- (or *meso*-). There are 15 possible disubstitution products if both substituents are identical; if the substituents are not identical, the number of isomers is larger.

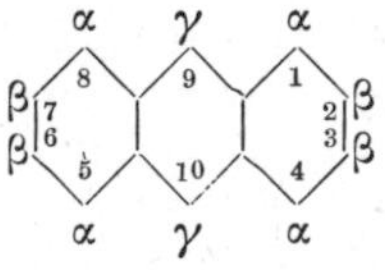

Orientation of anthracene derivatives. It is usually difficult to determine the orientation of anthracene derivatives except in the case where the substituents occupy the 9- and 10-positions. When a mono- or disubstituted anthracene is oxidised with dichromate and sulphuric acid, an *unsubstituted anthraquinone* is generally obtained if the substituents were in the 9 : 10-positions:

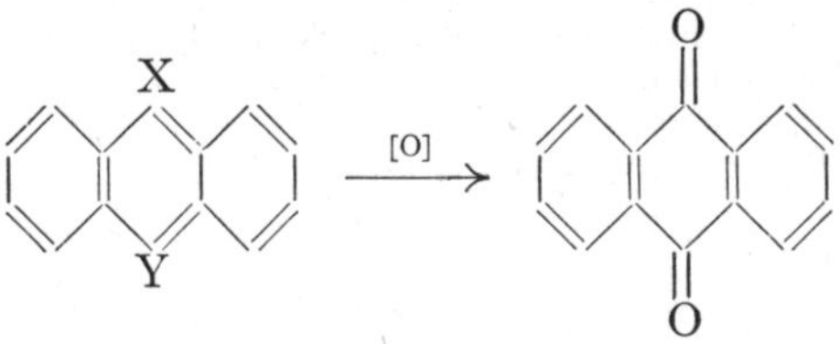

A *substituted anthraquinone* results if the substituents were not in the 9 : 10-positions, and on further oxidation phthalic acid or substituted phthalic acids are obtained, *e.g.*,

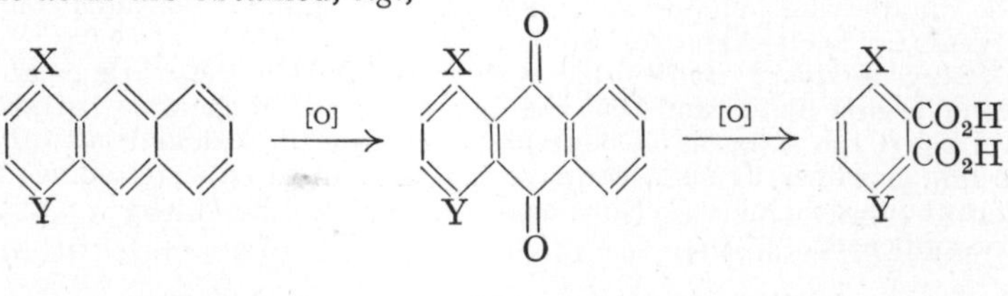

Orientation of anthracene derivatives may also be ascertained by unambiguous syntheses using method (iii).

Properties of anthracene. Anthracene is a colourless solid, m.p. 216°, with a blue fluorescence. It is insoluble in water and sparingly soluble in organic solvents. Anthracene is very reactive in the 9 : 10-positions. The reason for this is not clear, but it has been suggested that anthracene is in equilibrium with a free diradical (Clar, 1932). This may possibly account for the reactivity at these positions:

A saturated solution of anthracene in xylene, on exposure to light, forms crystals of the dimer, dianthracene (paranthracene). X-Ray analysis studies led to the suggestion that the two anthracene molecules are linked in the 9 : 9′ : 10 : 10′-positions to give the structure shown (Hengstenberg *et al.*, 1932). For this structure to be possible, each anthracene molecule must be folded about the line joining the 9 : 10-carbon atoms (since this dimer is actually a derivative of 9 : 10-dihydroanthracene; the 9 : 10-carbon atoms are *tetrahedrally* hybridised). This structure has been confirmed by ultraviolet spectrum studies of dianthracene (Weiss *et al.*, 1955). When dianthracene is melted, it reforms anthracene.

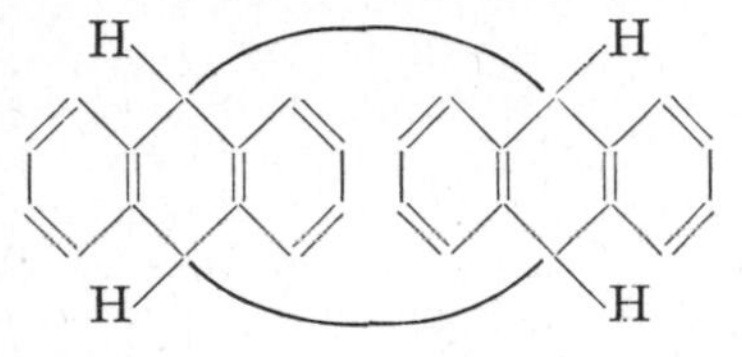

Anthracene adds on one molecule of oxygen in the presence of light to form a colourless photo-oxide (anthracene peroxide), the structure of which is also believed to be folded, since this oxide is also actually a derivative of 9 : 10-dihydroanthracene. Anthracene forms a red picrate (m.p. 138°) which dissociates into its constituents when treated with a large amount of ethanol; phenanthrene picrate is stable under these conditions.

Anthracene undergoes the Diels–Alder reaction in the 9 : 10-positions (see above); phenanthrene does not give the Diels–Alder reaction. When reduced with sodium and *iso*pentanol, anthracene forms 9 : 10-dihydroanthracene, m.p. 107°, which is not fluorescent and which, on heating or on treatment with concentrated sulphuric acid, loses the two hydrogen atoms to reform anthracene. Catalytic reduction of anthracene using nickel at 200–250° gives, according to the amount of hydrogen used, tetra-, hexa- and octahydroanthracene, and finally perhydro-anthracene, $C_{14}H_{24}$ (the prefix *per* is often used to denote complete hydrogenation of a ring system).

When chlorine is passed into a cold solution of anthracene in carbon disulphide, anthracene dichloride is formed:

$$+ Cl_2 \longrightarrow \quad CHCl \quad CHCl \quad \xrightarrow[\text{(heat)}]{-HCl} \quad Cl$$

If this is heated or treated with alkali, hydrogen chloride is eliminated with the formation of 9-chloroanthracene. This is also obtained by chlorinating anthracene at 100°, together with some 9 : 10-dichloroanthracene. Bromine reacts similarly, *e.g.*, bromination of anthracene in boiling carbon tetrachloride solution gives 9 : 10-dibromoanthracene (yield: 83–88 per cent.). Sulphuryl chloride, at room temperature, converts anthracene into 9 : 10-dichloroanthracene. Oxidation of all these halogeno-anthracenes converts them into anthraquinone (thereby indicating the positions of the halogen atoms; *cf.* above).

Anthracene can be chloromethylated in the 9- and 9 : 10-positions, and can be formylated in the 9-position:

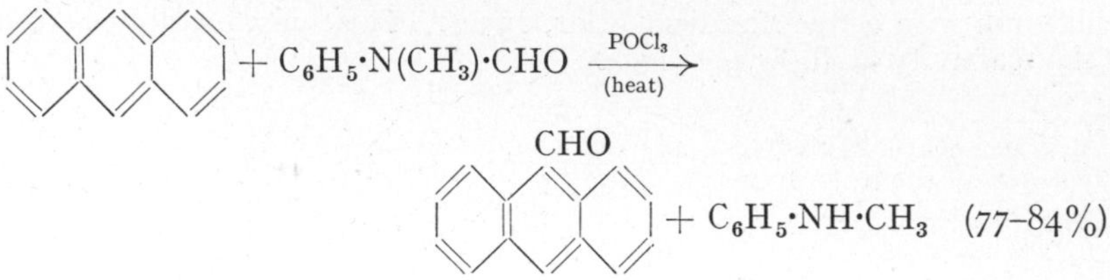

$$\text{(anthracene)} + C_6H_5\cdot N(CH_3)\cdot CHO \xrightarrow[\text{(heat)}]{POCl_3} \text{(9-CHO-anthracene)} + C_6H_5\cdot NH\cdot CH_3 \quad (77\text{–}84\%)$$

Attempts to nitrate anthracene with aqueous nitric acid lead to the formation of anthraquinone by oxidation. If, however, the nitration is carried out in acetic anhydride at 15–20°, 9-nitroanthracene (m.p. 145°) and 9 : 10-dinitroanthracene (m.p. 294°) can be isolated. Anthracene is readily sulphonated to a mixture of the 1- and 2-sulphonic acids, some disulphonic acids also always being obtained; the 2-position is favoured at high temperature. If the sulphonation of anthracene is carried out in glacial acetic acid, a mixture of about equal amounts of 1- and 2-anthracenesulphonic acid is obtained; these acids may be separated by means of their barium salts, that of the former acid being more soluble. The 1-sulphonic acid shows no tendency to rearrange to the 2-acid (*cf.* naphthalenesulphonic acids, p. 687). With excess concentrated sulphuric acid, anthracene gives disulphonic acids, the 1 : 8- at low temperatures, and the 2 : 7- at higher temperatures.

Hydroxyanthracenes. 1- and 2-*Hydroxyanthracenes* are known as **anthrols.** Each may be obtained from the corresponding anthracenesulphonic acid by alkaline fusion. 1-Anthrol is a yellow solid, m.p. 152°; 2-anthrol is a brownish solid which decomposes at 200°.

10-*Hydroxyanthracene,* also known as **anthranol,** is an unstable yellow solid, m.p. 120°, and when quickly heated, forms **anthrone** (10-*keto*-9 : 10-*dihydroanthracene*—the keto-group is numbered last and consequently its isomer is known as 10- and *not* 9-hydroxyanthracene). Anthrone is the stable form and is a colourless solid, m.p. 154°:

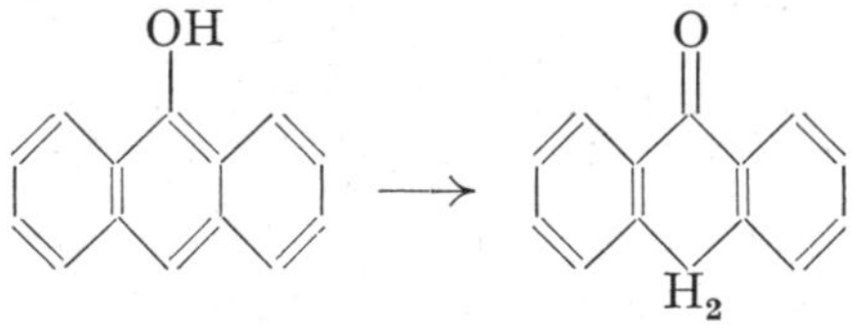

$$\text{(anthranol, OH)} \longrightarrow \text{(anthrone, O, } H_2\text{)}$$

Since the hydrogen atom migrates across the ring, this type of tautomerism is called *trans-annular tautomerism.* Infra-red spectroscopy studies by Flett (1948) indicate that solid anthrone does not exist in equilibrium with the enol form (anthranol). Anthrone may be prepared by heating *o*-benzylbenzoic acid with concentrated sulphuric acid, or by reducing anthraquinone with tin and hydrochloric acid in glacial acetic acid. Anthrone dissolves in warm dilute alkalis, and these solutions, on acidification, precipitate the enol form.

Reduction of anthraquinone with zinc dust and aqueous sodium hydroxide gives *anthracene*-9 : 10-*diol* or *anthraquinol* (*anthrahydroquinone*). This is a brown solid, m.p. 180°; its alkaline solutions (deep red) oxidise in air to give anthraquinone. When anthraquinol in alkaline solution is immediately acidified, it partly tautomerises to *oxanthranol*, m.p. 167° (*trans*-annular tautomerism):

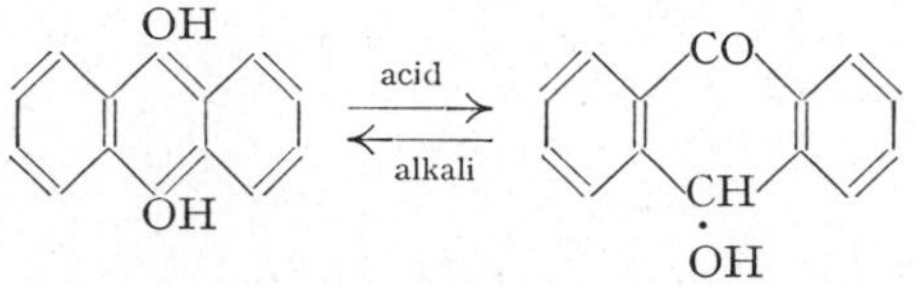

OH OH acid alkali CO CH OH

Anthracenecarboxylic acids. **1- and 2-Anthroic acids** may be prepared by the hydrolysis of the corresponding cyanides (prepared by fusion of the sodium sulphonate with sodium cyanide). **9-Anthroic acid** may be prepared by hydrolysing its acid chloride which may be prepared by heating anthracene with oxalyl chloride at 160°. 9-Anthroic acid exhibits the spatial effect.

Anthraquinone (9 : 10-*dihydroanthracene*-9 : 10-*dione*). There are nine possible isomeric quinones of anthracene, but only three are known: 1 : 2-, 1 : 4- and 9 : 10-. The most important one is the 9 : 10-compound, and this is referred to simply as anthraquinone.

Before 1914, anthraquinone was made by oxidising anthracene with sodium dichromate and sulphuric acid (yield: 90 per cent.). Later, instead of isolating anthracene free from carbazole, the mixture of these two compounds was oxidised under conditions whereby anthracene was converted into anthraquinone and the carbazole completely oxidised. This method is cheaper than the original, but the cheapest method to-day is a synthetic one:

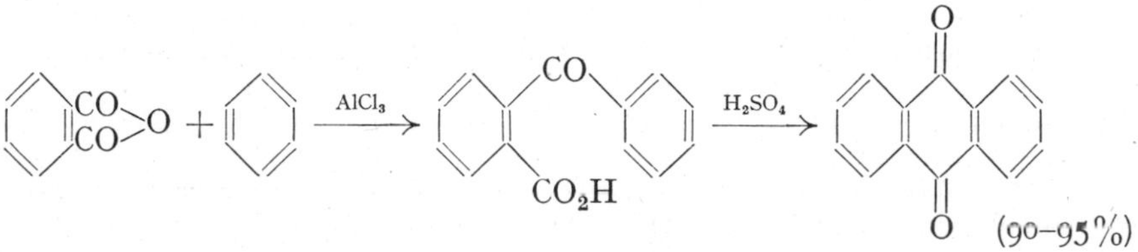

CO CO O + $\xrightarrow{AlCl_3}$ CO CO_2H $\xrightarrow{H_2SO_4}$ O O (90–95%)

By using chlorobenzene or toluene instead of benzene, chloro- or methylanthraquinone is obtained; these are used in the manufacture of dyes.

A possible future industrial method may be that of Sachanen and Caesar (1946), who showed that anthraquinone can be obtained in one step from phthalic anhydride and benzene by using a silica-alumina catalyst at 370°:

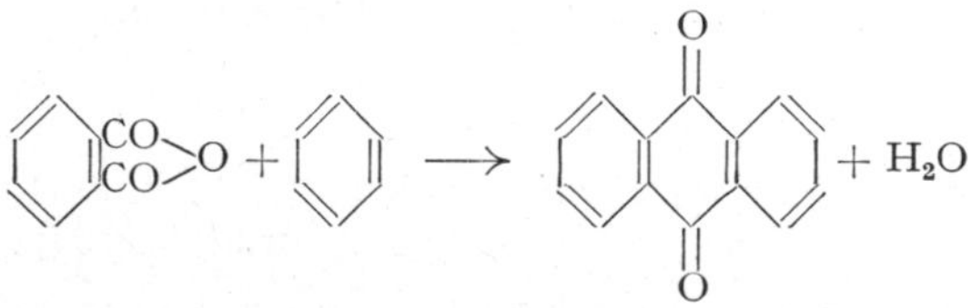

CO CO O + ⟶ O O + H_2O

Anthraquinone is a pale yellow compound which sublimes in needles that melt at 268°. When distilled with zinc dust, or heated with hydriodic acid at 150°, anthraquinone forms anthracene. Anthraquinone is very stable and shows very little resemblance to *p*-benzoquinone, *e.g.*, it has no smell, is not very volatile, and is not reduced by sulphurous acid. When anthraquinone is reduced, the nature of the reduction product depends on the reducing agent used, *e.g.*, with tin and hydrochloric acid in acetic acid, anthrone is formed; using zinc instead of tin, the main product is *dianthryl*,

(I); with zinc dust and aqueous sodium hydroxide, anthraquinol; and with zinc dust and aqueous ammonium hydroxide, 9 : 10-dihydroanthranol, (II):

OH
CH
CH_2
(I) (II)

Nitration of anthraquinone with mixed acid gives 1-nitroanthraquinone; further nitration gives mainly 1 : 5- and 1 : 8-dinitroanthraquinones, and small amounts of the 1 : 6- and 1 : 7-dinitro-compounds. The nitro-group in the 1-position is very reactive, *e.g.*, it is replaced by an amino-group when 1-nitroanthraquinone is heated with ammonia.

Anthraquinone is very difficult to sulphonate with concentrated sulphuric acid, but it is readily sulphonated with oleum at 160°. The first product is the 2-sulphonic acid and a small amount of the 1-isomer; prolonged heating gives a mixture of 2 : 6- and 2 : 7-anthraquinonedisulphonic acids in about equal amounts. If mercuric sulphate is used as a catalyst, the sulphonation takes an entirely different course. The first product now is the 1-sulphonic acid, and then a mixture of the 1 : 5- and 1 : 8-disulphonic acids. The sulphonic acid group in the 1- or 2-positions is easily displaced; *e.g.*, when 1 or 2-anthraquinonesulphonic acid is treated with chlorine, the corresponding chloroanthraquinone is obtained.

Anthraquinone does not undergo the Friedel–Crafts reaction, and is halogenated with very great difficulty; in fact, monohalogeno-anthraquinones cannot be obtained directly.

2-Aminoanthraquinone, m.p. 304°, is very important as an intermediate in the preparation of indanthrene dyes. It is prepared industrially by heating the sodium salt of anthraquinone-2-sulphonic acid with a solution of ammonia, ammonium chloride and sodium arsenate under pressure at 200°. The sodium arsenate oxidises the liberated sulphite which otherwise would attack the amine produced:

$$SO_3Na + NH_3 + [O] \longrightarrow NH_2 + NaHSO_4$$

Alizarin (1 : 2-*dihydroxyanthraquinone*) is the most important dihydroxy-derivative of anthraquinone, and is used as a mordant dye (p. 776).

PHENANTHRENE

Phenanthrene, $C_{14}H_{10}$, is isomeric with anthracene; it is an example of an *angular* polynuclear hydrocarbon. It occurs in the anthracene oil fraction of coal-tar, and is separated from anthracene by means of solution in solvent naphtha (see p. 696). Phenanthrene is structurally related to certain alkaloids, *e.g.*, morphine, and to the steroids, *e.g.*, cholesterol.

Structure of phenanthrene. When oxidised with sodium dichromate and acetic acid, phenanthrene forms phenanthraquinone which, on further oxidation with dichromate and sulphuric acid, gives diphenic acid. This, on distillation with soda-lime, gives diphenyl. The structures of the last two compounds are known. Therefore phenanthrene contains the skeleton (I).

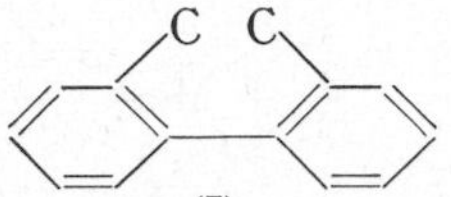

(I) 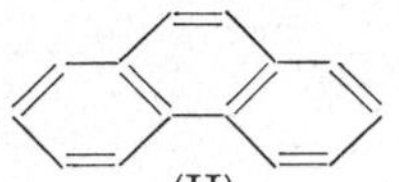 (II)

This is equivalent to $C_{14}H_8$. Thus two hydrogen atoms are missing; these may be fitted in by closing the middle ring, *i.e.*, a possible structure for phenanthrene is (II). This structure has been amply confirmed by many syntheses.

Synthesis of phenanthrene. (i) By passing 2 : 2′-dimethyldiphenyl, dibenzyl or stilbene through a red-hot tube; the yields are poor in each case:

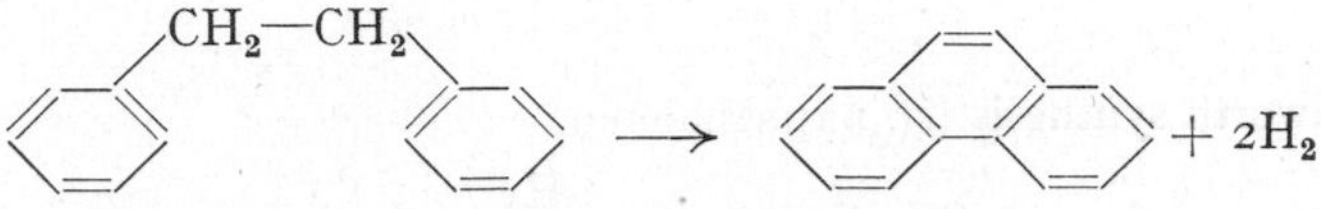

$CH_2—CH_2$ → + $2H_2$

An interesting preparation is the *cyclo*dehydrogenation of 2 : 2′-dimethyldiphenyl by means of sulphur:

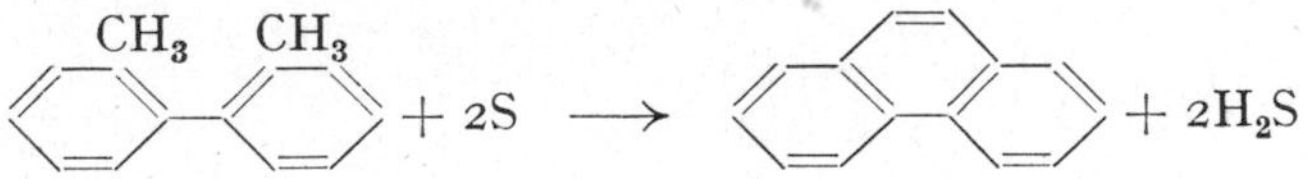

CH_3 CH_3 + 2S → + $2H_2S$

(ii) By treating benzil with aluminium chloride at 120° and then heating the product, phenanthraquinone, with zinc dust:

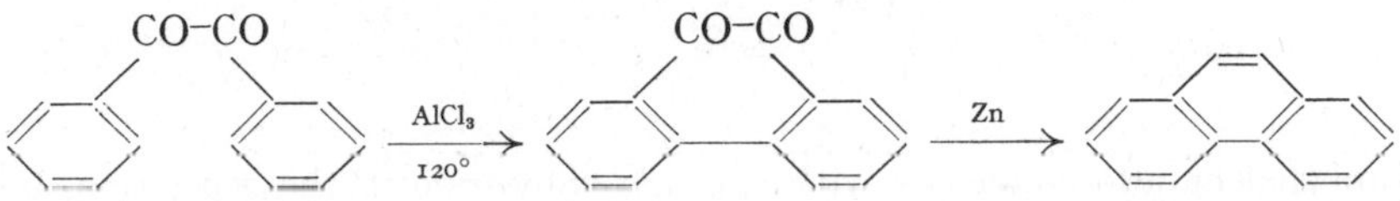

CO–CO $\xrightarrow[120°]{AlCl_3}$ CO–CO $\xrightarrow{Zn}$

(iii) By treating *o*-bromobenzyl bromide with sodium; anthracene is also formed (see method ii, p. 697).

(iv) **Pschorr synthesis** (1896). This is carried out by heating *o*-nitrobenzaldehyde with sodium β-phenylacetate in the presence of acetic anhydride (Perkin's reaction), reducing and diazotising the product, α-phenyl-*o*-nitrocinnamic acid, and treating the diazonium salt with sulphuric acid and copper powder. Phenanthrene-9-carboxylic acid is produced and this, on strong heating, forms phenanthrene:

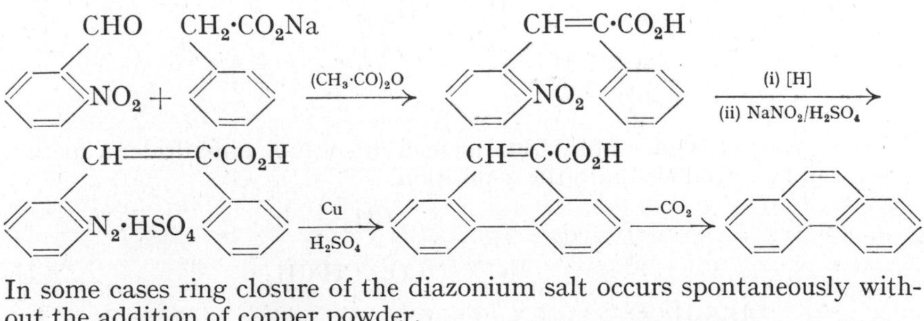

CHO NO_2 + $CH_2·CO_2Na$ $\xrightarrow{(CH_3·CO)_2O}$ CH=C·CO_2H NO_2 $\xrightarrow[(ii)\ NaNO_2/H_2SO_4]{(i)\ [H]}$

CH=C·CO_2H $N_2·HSO_4$ $\xrightarrow[H_2SO_4]{Cu}$ CH=C·CO_2H $\xrightarrow{-CO_2}$

In some cases ring closure of the diazonium salt occurs spontaneously without the addition of copper powder.

The Pschorr synthesis offers a means of preparing substituted phenanthrenes with the substituents in known positions. In those cases, however, where isomerism in the cyclised product is possible, it is usual to obtain both isomers, *e.g.*,

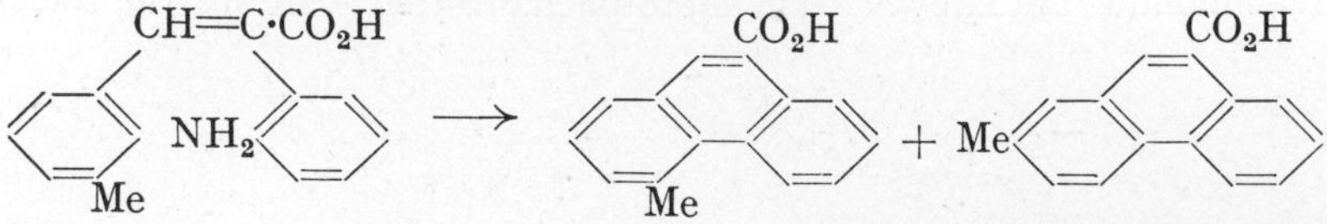

$CH{=}C{\cdot}CO_2H$ NH_2 Me → CO_2H Me + Me CO_2H

A further point to note is that since ring closure is effected between two rings, these rings must be in the *cis* position, *e.g.*, *cis*-*o*-aminostilbene gives phenanthrene, but the *trans* isomer does not.

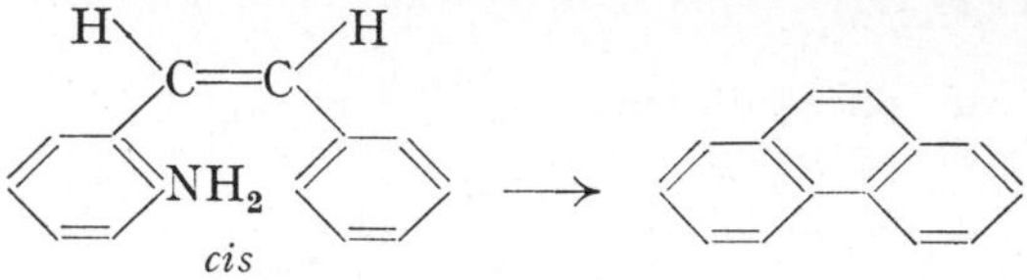

H H C=C NH_2 *cis* →

(v) **Haworth synthesis** (*cf.* naphthalene):

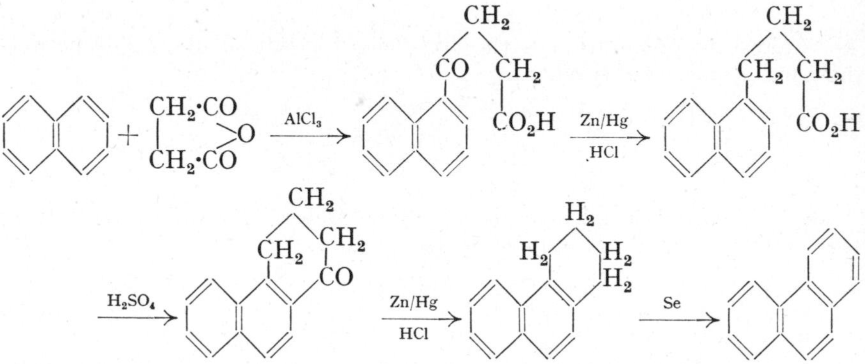

$$+ \begin{matrix} CH_2{\cdot}CO \\ | \quad >O \\ CH_2{\cdot}CO \end{matrix} \xrightarrow{AlCl_3} CO{\cdot}CH_2{\cdot}CH_2{\cdot}CO_2H \xrightarrow[HCl]{Zn/Hg} CH_2{\cdot}CH_2{\cdot}CH_2{\cdot}CO_2H$$

$$\xrightarrow{H_2SO_4} \xrightarrow[HCl]{Zn/Hg} \xrightarrow{Se}$$

Naphthalene also condenses with succinic anhydride in the 2-position, but this also gives phenanthrene when treated as above; no anthracene is formed since ring closure in only the 1-position of naphthalene, and not in 3.

The Haworth synthesis is very useful for preparing alkylphenanthrenes with the alkyl groups in known positions; *e.g.*, after ring closure, 1-methylphenanthrene may be obtained by the action of methylmagnesium iodide on the ketone, etc.:

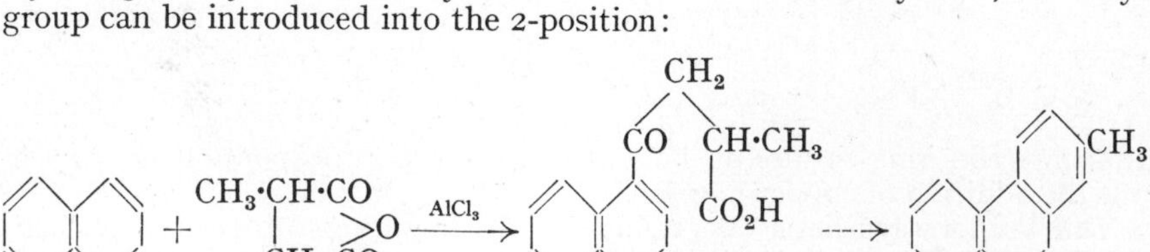

$$\xrightarrow[(ii)\ H_2O]{(i)\ CH_3{\cdot}MgI} \xrightarrow{Pd/C} CH_3$$

By using methylsuccinic anhydride instead of succinic anhydride, a methyl group can be introduced into the 2-position:

$$+ \begin{matrix} CH_3{\cdot}CH{\cdot}CO \\ | \quad >O \\ CH_2{\cdot}CO \end{matrix} \xrightarrow{AlCl_3} CO{\cdot}CH_2{\cdot}CH(CH_3){\cdot}CO_2H \dashrightarrow CH_3$$

(vi) **Stobbe condensation** (1893). This is the condensation between succinic ester and a carbonyl compound in the presence of sodium ethoxide. Johnson (1944) has improved the yield by using potassium *tert.*-butoxide in *tert.*-butanol as the condensating agent, and has used this method to introduce a propionic acid residue at the site of the carbonyl group in an aromatic ketone. The condensation product is refluxed with concentrated hydrobromic acid in glacial acetic acid and the γ-lactone formed is catalytically reduced (using copper oxide-chromic oxide) via the sodium salt:

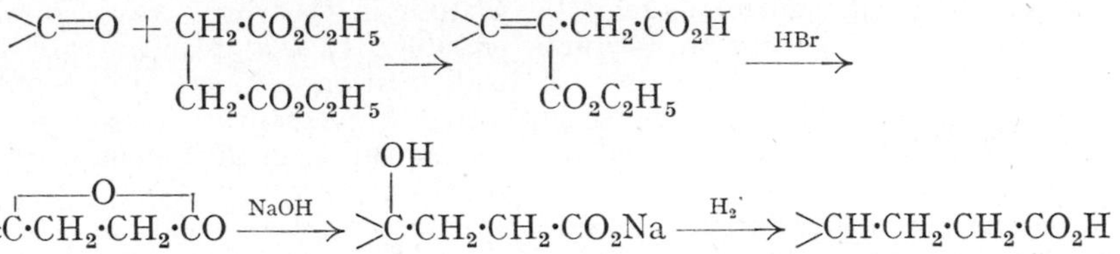

$$>C{=}O + \begin{matrix} CH_2{\cdot}CO_2C_2H_5 \\ | \\ CH_2{\cdot}CO_2C_2H_5 \end{matrix} \longrightarrow \ >C{=}\underset{\underset{CO_2C_2H_5}{|}}{C}{\cdot}CH_2{\cdot}CO_2H \xrightarrow{HBr}$$

$$>\overset{\lceil\text{------}O\text{------}\rceil}{C{\cdot}CH_2{\cdot}CH_2{\cdot}CO} \xrightarrow{NaOH} \ >\overset{\overset{OH}{|}}{C}{\cdot}CH_2{\cdot}CH_2{\cdot}CO_2Na \xrightarrow{H_2} \ >CH{\cdot}CH_2{\cdot}CH_2{\cdot}CO_2H$$

Johnson has used this procedure to prepare polynuclear compounds, *e.g.*, 1-methylphenanthrene from 2-acetylnaphthalene. After introduction of the propionic acid residue at the site of the carbonyl group, the ring is closed by means of anhydrous hydrogen fluoride, and the product dehydrogenated over heated palladium on charcoal:

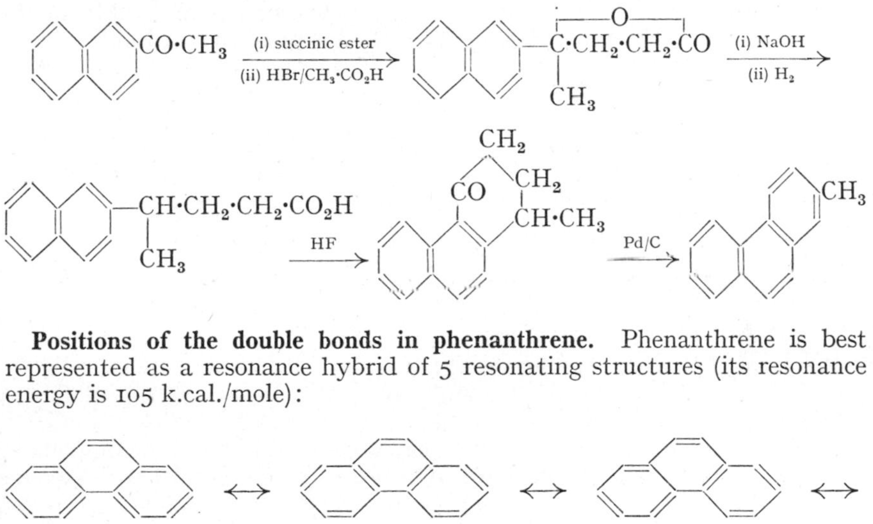

CO·CH$_3$ —(i) succinic ester; (ii) HBr/CH$_3$·CO$_2$H→ C(CH$_3$)·CH$_2$·CH$_2$·CO (lactone, —O—) —(i) NaOH; (ii) H$_2$→

—CH(CH$_3$)·CH$_2$·CH$_2$·CO$_2$H —HF→ (CO, CH$_2$, CH$_2$, CH·CH$_3$) —Pd/C→ CH$_3$

Positions of the double bonds in phenanthrene. Phenanthrene is best represented as a resonance hybrid of 5 resonating structures (its resonance energy is 105 k.cal./mole):

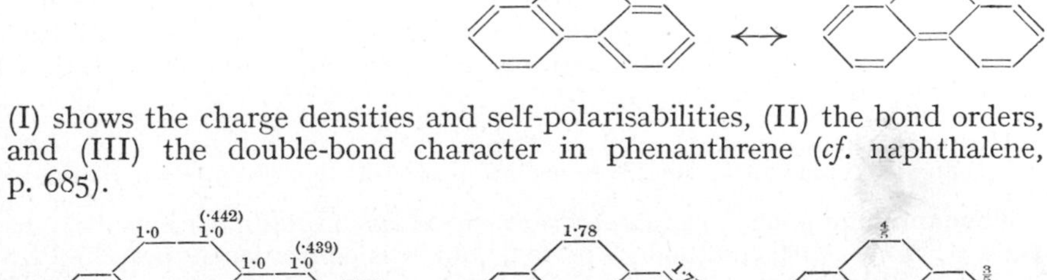

↔ ↔ ↔

↔

(I) shows the charge densities and self-polarisabilities, (II) the bond orders, and (III) the double-bond character in phenanthrene (*cf.* naphthalene, p. 685).

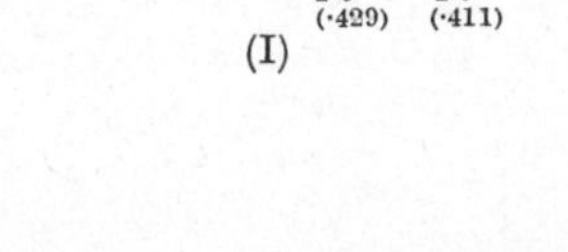

(I): 1·0, 1·0 (·442); 1·0, 1·0 (·439); 1·0 (·403); 1·0; 1·0 (·429); 1·0 (·411)

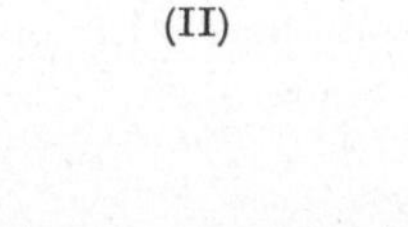

(II): 1·78; 1·71; 1·62; 1·70

(III): 4/5; 3/5; 2/5; 3/5

(I) (II) 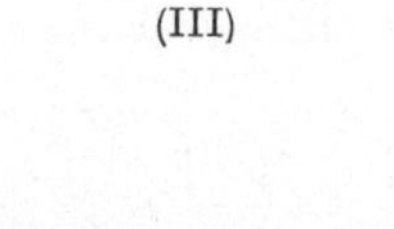 (III)

Isomerism of phenanthrene derivatives.

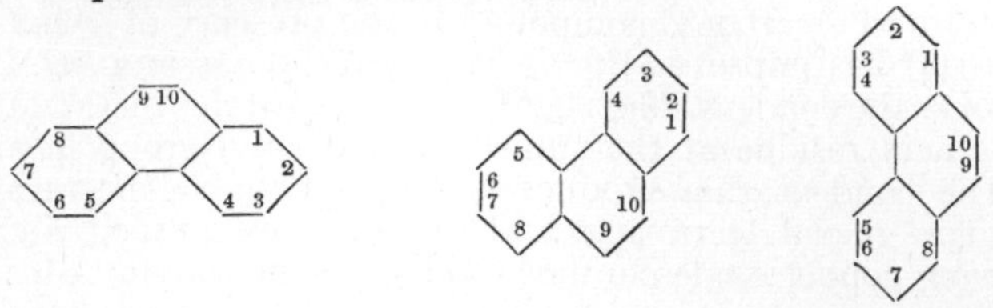

The formula of phenanthrene may be written in the three ways shown. There are 5 monosubstitution products possible: 1, 2, 3, 4 and 9. If the two substituents are identical, then 25 disubstitution products are possible. Due to the great number of isomers, derivatives of phenanthrene are usually prepared synthetically and not by direct substitution in the phenanthrene nucleus.

Properties of phenanthrene. Phenanthrene is a white solid, m.p. 99°; its solution in benzene shows a blue fluorescence. It is very reactive in the 9 : 10-positions, and this reactivity may possibly be due to the large amount ($\frac{4}{5}$) of double bond character; *e.g.*, phenanthrene is readily catalytically reduced (using copper oxide-chromic oxide) to 9 : 10-dihydrophenanthrene, and it adds on bromine to form 9 : 10-phenanthrene dibromide. These addition reactions occur almost as easily as with a pure ethylenic bond. Dichromate in glacial acetic acid oxidises phenanthrene to phenanthraquinone. Schmitt *et al.* (1955) have prepared a stable monoozonide of phenanthrene. This has been shown to be the 9 : 10-compound by conversion into diphenic acid.

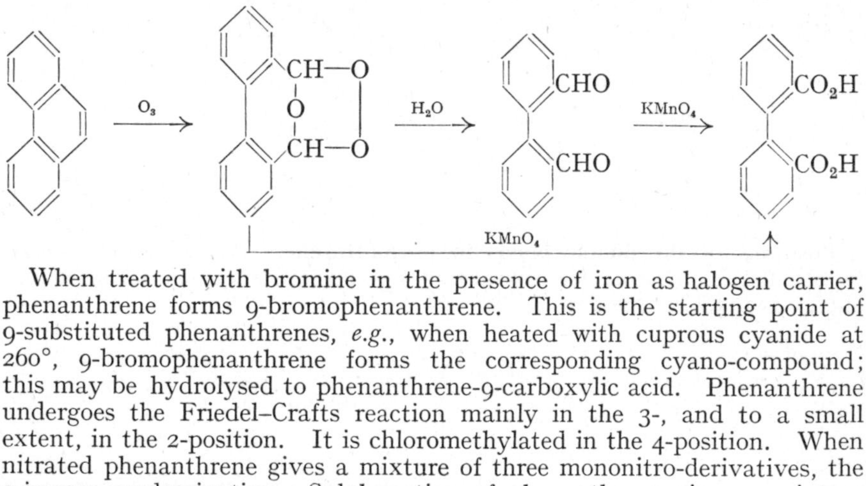

When treated with bromine in the presence of iron as halogen carrier, phenanthrene forms 9-bromophenanthrene. This is the starting point of 9-substituted phenanthrenes, *e.g.*, when heated with cuprous cyanide at 260°, 9-bromophenanthrene forms the corresponding cyano-compound; this may be hydrolysed to phenanthrene-9-carboxylic acid. Phenanthrene undergoes the Friedel–Crafts reaction mainly in the 3-, and to a small extent, in the 2-position. It is chloromethylated in the 4-position. When nitrated phenanthrene gives a mixture of three mononitro-derivatives, the 3-isomer predominating. Sulphonation of phenanthrene gives a mixture of 1-, 2-, 3- and 9-phenanthrenesulphonic acids, and the ratio of these isomers depends on the temperature.

Hydroxyphenanthrenes. Five *phenanthrols* are known: 1-, 2-, 3-, 4- and 9-. 3 : 4-Dihydroxyphenanthrene is a degradation product of morphine (an alkaloid).

Phenanthraquinone (9 : 10-*dihydrophenanthrene*-9 : 10-*dione*) may be synthesised from benzil (method ii, p. 705), but it is conveniently prepared by oxidising phenanthrene with sodium dichromate or chromium trioxide in glacial acetic acid (yield is excellent).

Phenanthraquinone is an orange solid, m.p. 208°, which is odourless and not steam-volatile. It combines with one or two molecules of hydroxylamine to form phenanthraquinone monoxime and dioxime, respectively, and it is reduced by sulphurous acid to **phenanthrene-9 : 10-diol** (*phenanthraquinol*). In all of these reactions phenanthraquinone resembles *o*-benzoquinone.

When nitrated, phenanthraquinone gives a mixture of 2- and 4-nitrophenanthraquinones; more vigorous nitration produces a mixture of the 2 : 7- and 4 : 5-dinitro-compounds. Oxidation with sodium dichromate and sulphuric acid converts phenanthraquinone into diphenic acid. When warmed with alkali, phenanthraquinone undergoes the benzilic-acid rearrangement (p. 678) to form 9-hydroxyfluorene-9-carboxylic acid:

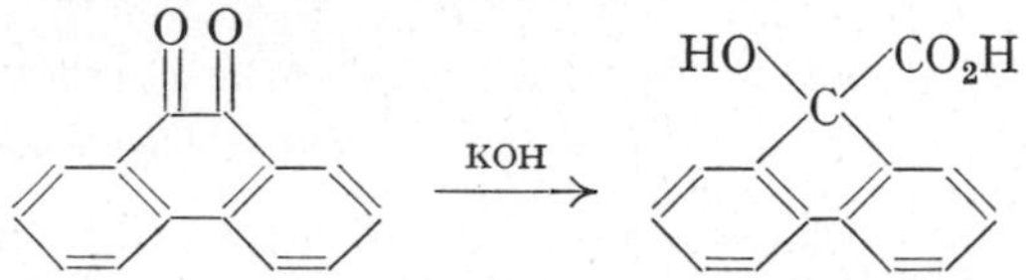

O O — KOH → HO C CO_2H

This, on heating in air, eliminates carbon dioxide and the product, fluorenol, is oxidised to fluorenone:

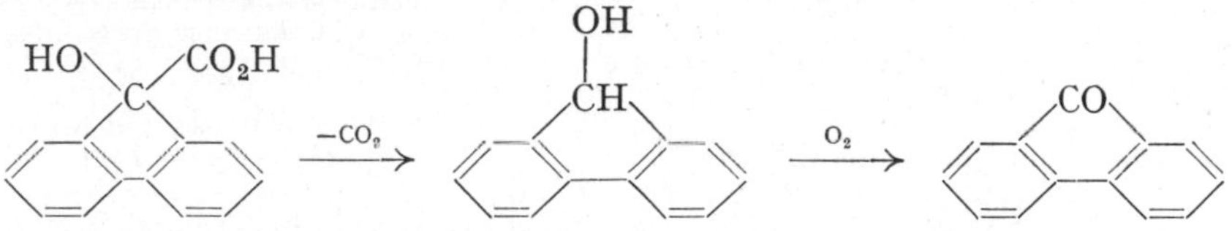

HO C CO_2H — $-CO_2$ → OH CH — O_2 → CO

Phenanthraquinone readily reacts with *o*-phenylenediamines to form phenazines which, since they are insoluble in many organic solvents, are very useful for characterising *o*-phenylenediamines (see also p. 553).

1 : 2-, 1 : 4- and 3 : 4-Phenanthraquinones have also been prepared.

QUESTIONS

1. Discuss the preparation and properties of diphenyl and diphenic acid.
2. Starting with benzene or toluene, show how you would synthesise:—(*a*) 4 : 4′-dimethyldiphenyl, (*b*) 2 : 2′-diaminodiphenyl, (*c*) benzidine, (*d*) dibenzyl, (*e*) stilbene, (*f*) benzoin, (*g*) deoxybenzoin, (*h*) hydrobenzoin, (*i*) benzil, (*j*) benzilic acid, (*k*) diphenylacetic acid, (*l*) 2 : 4 : 6-trinitrostilbene.
3. How may each of the following compounds be prepared:—(*a*) CH_2Ph_2, (*b*) $CHPh_3$, (*c*) CPh_4, (*d*) C_2Ph_6?
Name the compounds and state the conditions under which they are formed when each of the above hydrocarbons is treated with:—(*a*) HNO_3, (*b*) H_2SO_4, (*c*) Br_2, (*d*) I_2, (*e*) oxidising agents, (*f*) NO, (*g*) Na.
4. Write an essay on the preparation and properties of free radicals.
5. Formulate the course of the reaction when each of the two benzil monoximes and three benzil dioximes undergoes the Beckmann transformation.
6. Write an account of the analytical and synthetic evidence for the structure of:—(*a*) naphthalene, (*b*) anthracene, (*c*) phenanthrene.
7. Name the compounds and state the conditions under which they are formed when naphthalene, anthracene and phenanthrene are each treated with:—(*a*) reducing agents, (*b*) oxidising agents, (*c*) Br_2, (*d*) MeI, (*e*) HCHO, (*f*) HNO_3, (*g*) H_2SO_4, (*h*) Na, (*i*) AcCl, (*j*) SO_2Cl_2.
8. Describe the preparation and properties of:—(*a*) 1-, 2- and 10-hydroxyanthracenes, (*e*) anthrone, (*f*) anthraquinone, (*g*) phenanthraquinone.
9. Starting with any aromatic hydrocarbon you like, show how you would synthesise:—1 : 5-dichloronaphthalene, (*b*) 7-chloro-1-naphthylamine, (*c*) 2-naphthoic acid, (*d*) 1-naphthylacetic acid, (*e*) 2-bromonaphthalene, (*f*) 2 : 6-dihydroxynaphthalene, (*g*) indene, (*h*) acenaphthene, (*i*) 2-chlorofluorene, (*i*) 2-nitroanthracene, (*k*) 9-anthroic acid, (*l*) 2-chloroanthraquinone, (*m*) 3-chlorophenanthrene, (*n*) 1 : 2-dimethylphenanthrene, (*o*) 9-phenanthroic acid.
10. Define and give examples of:—(*a*) Fittig's reaction, (*b*) Ullmann's synthesis, (*c*) benzoin condensation, (*d*) benzilic acid rearrangement, (*e*) Haworth synthesis, (*f*) Fries rule, (*g*) Alternant hydrocarbon, (*h*) Elbs reaction, (*i*) Pschorr synthesis, (*j*) Stobbe condensation.

READING REFERENCES

Gilman, *Advanced Organic Chemistry*, Wiley (1942, 2nd Ed.). Vol. I, Ch. 3. Aromatic Character. Ch. 6. Free Radicals.
Bunnett and Zahler, Ullmann Reactions, *Chem. Reviews*, 1951, **49**, 392.
Organic Reactions, Wiley. (i) Vol. IV (1948), Ch. 5. The Synthesis of Benzoins. Vol. V (1949). The Friedel–Crafts Reaction with Aliphatic Dibasic Anhydrides.
The Benzilic Acid Rearrangement.
(i) Westheimer, *J. Amer. Chem. Soc.*, 1936, **58**, 2209.
(ii) Roberts and Urey, *ibid.*, 1938, **60**, 880.
Hodgson *et al.*, Studies on Naphthalene Substitution. *J. Soc. Dyers and Col.*, 1945, **61**, 283; 1946, **62**, 241; 1947, **63**, 46, 109, 141, 177.
Organic Reactions, Wiley. Vol. I (1942), (i) Ch. 5. The Bucherer Reaction. (ii) Ch. 6. The Elbs Reaction.
Cowdry *et al.*, The Mechanism of the Bucherer Reaction, *J.C.S.*, **1946**, 1036, 1041, 1044, 1046.
Organic Reactions, Wiley. Vol. VI (1951), Ch. 1. The Stobbe Condensation.
Waters, *The Chemistry of Free Radicals.* Oxford Press (1946).
Badger, The Aromatic Bond, *Quart. Reviews* (*Chem. Soc.*), 1951, **5**, 147.
Brown, Molecular Orbitals and Organic Reactions, *ibid.*, 1952, **6**, 63.
Jacobs, Electron Distribution in Conjugated Free Radicals, *J.C.S.*, **1952**, 292.
Finar, *Organic Chemistry*, Vol. II, Longmans, Green (1956). Ch. V. Stereochemistry of Diphenyl Compounds. Ch. X. Polycyclic Aromatic Hydrocarbons.
Badger, *The Structure and Reactions of the Aromatic Compounds*, Cambridge Press (1954).
Fanta, The Ullmann Synthesis of Biaryls, *Chem. Reviews*, 1946, **38**, 139.
Leake, The Pschorr Synthesis, *ibid.*, 1956, **56**, 27.
Organic Reactions, Wiley. Vol. IX (1957), Ch. 7. The Pschorr Synthesis and Related Diazonium Ring Closure Reactions.

CHAPTER XXX

HETEROCYCLIC COMPOUNDS

HETEROCYCLIC compounds are cyclic compounds with the ring containing carbon and other elements, the commonest being oxygen, nitrogen and sulphur. There are a number of heterocyclic rings which are easily opened and do not possess any aromatic properties, *e.g.*, ethylene oxide, γ- and δ-lactones, etc. These are not considered to be heterocyclic compounds. Heterocycles are those compounds with five- or six-membered heterocyclic rings which are stable, contain conjugated double bonds, and exhibit aromatic character.

FIVE-MEMBERED RINGS

FURAN AND ITS DERIVATIVES

Furan (*furfuran*) contains one oxygen atom in its ring, and its structure is as shown. The position of side-chains or substituents is indicated by numbers (or by Greek letters), number 1 being given to the oxygen atom:

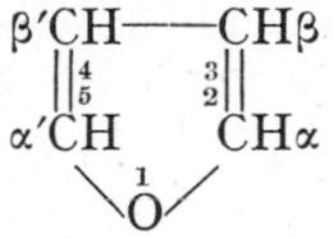

$$\begin{array}{ccc} \beta'CH & — & CH\beta \\ \|^{4}_{5} & & ^{3}_{2}\| \\ \alpha'CH & & CH\alpha \\ & \diagdown \overset{1}{O} \diagup & \end{array}$$

When a heterocyclic compound contains only one hetero-atom, this atom is always given the number 1. If the heterocyclic ring is part of a condensed system, the number given to the hetero-atom depends on the type of compound in question (see later).

There are two monosubstituted derivatives of furan, 2 (or α) and 3 (or β); there are four disubstitution products: 2 . 3 (α . β), 2 : 4 (α : β'), 2 : 5 (α : α') and 3 : 4 (β : β').

Furan is obtained when wood, especially pine-wood, is distilled. It may be prepared by the dry distillation of mucic acid, and heating the product, *furoic acid*, at its b.p.:

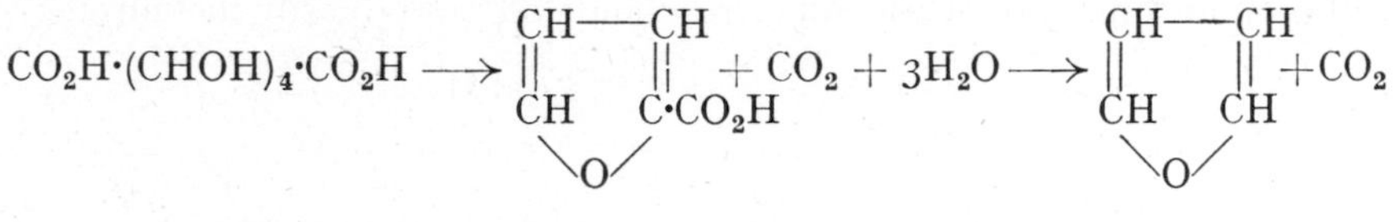

$$CO_2H\cdot(CHOH)_4\cdot CO_2H \longrightarrow \begin{array}{ccc} CH & — & CH \\ \| & & \| \\ CH & & C\cdot CO_2H \\ & \diagdown O \diagup & \end{array} + CO_2 + 3H_2O \longrightarrow \begin{array}{ccc} CH & — & CH \\ \| & & \| \\ CH & & CH \\ & \diagdown O \diagup & \end{array} + CO_2$$

A general method of preparing furan derivatives is to dehydrate 1 : 4-diketones or dialdehydes with, *e.g.*, phosphorus pentoxide:

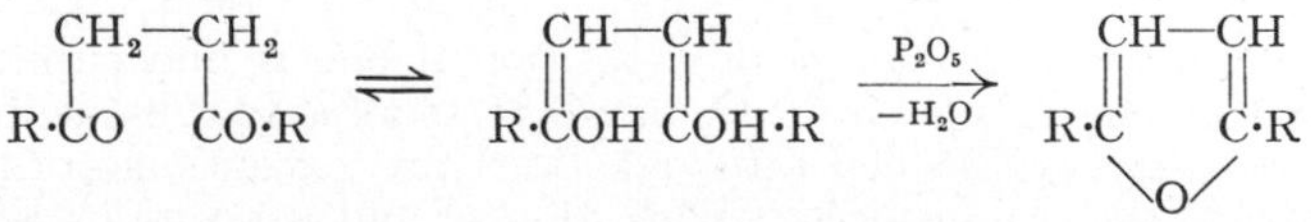

$$\begin{array}{cc} CH_2 — & CH_2 \\ | & | \\ R\cdot CO & CO\cdot R \end{array} \rightleftharpoons \begin{array}{cc} CH — & CH \\ \| & \| \\ R\cdot COH & COH\cdot R \end{array} \xrightarrow[-H_2O]{P_2O_5} \begin{array}{ccc} CH & — & CH \\ \| & & \| \\ R\cdot C & & C\cdot R \\ & \diagdown O \diagup & \end{array}$$

Alternatively, furan derivatives may be prepared from ethyl acetoacetate as follows:

$$2CH_3\cdot CO\cdot CHNa\cdot CO_2C_2H_5 + I_2 \longrightarrow 2NaI + \begin{array}{c} CH_3\cdot CO\cdot CH\cdot CO_2C_2H_5 \\ | \\ CH_3\cdot CO\cdot CH\cdot CO_2C_2H_5 \end{array}$$

When diacetosuccinic ester is heated with dilute sulphuric acid, 2 : 5-dimethylfuran-3 : 4-dicarboxylic acid is formed:

$$\begin{array}{c} C_2H_5O_2C{\cdot}CH{-}CH{\cdot}CO_2C_2H_5 \\ \quad | \qquad\quad | \\ CH_3{\cdot}CO \quad CO{\cdot}CH_3 \end{array} \rightleftharpoons \begin{array}{c} C_2H_5O_2C{\cdot}C{-}{-}{-}C{\cdot}CO_2C_2H_5 \\ \| \qquad\qquad \| \\ CH_3{\cdot}COH \quad HOC{\cdot}CH_3 \end{array} \xrightarrow{H_2SO_4} \begin{array}{c} HO_2C{\cdot}C{-}{-}C{\cdot}CO_2H \\ \| \qquad \| \\ CH_3{\cdot}C \diagdown_{O} \diagup C{\cdot}CH_3 \end{array}$$

If ammonia is used instead of sulphuric acid, 2 : 5-dimethylpyrrole-3 : 4-dicarboxylic ester is obtained.

Furan is a colourless liquid, b.p. 32°, which turns green a pine splint moistened with hydrochloric acid. It is catalytically reduced (palladium-palladium oxide) to *tetrahydrofuran*:

$$\text{furan} + 2H_2 \longrightarrow \begin{array}{c} CH_2{-}CH_2 \\ | \qquad | \\ CH_2 \quad CH_2 \\ \diagdown O \diagup \end{array}$$

Tetrahydrofuran may be manufactured synthetically from butyne-1 : 4-diol (*cf.* p. 257):

$$CH_2OH{\cdot}C{:}C{\cdot}CH_2OH \xrightarrow{H_2} CH_2OH{\cdot}CH_2{\cdot}CH_2{\cdot}CH_2OH \xrightarrow[\text{(heat)}]{-H_2O} \begin{array}{c} CH_2{-}CH_2 \\ | \qquad | \\ CH_2 \quad CH_2 \\ \diagdown O \diagup \end{array}$$

Tetrahydrofuran is a valuable solvent, and it can be made to react with carbon monoxide and water to give adipic acid. With ammonia it forms pyrrolidine, and with hydrogen chloride, tetramethylene chlorohydrin:

$$\begin{array}{c} CH_2{-}CH_2 \\ | \qquad | \\ CH_2 \quad CH_2 \\ \diagdown NH \diagup \end{array} \xleftarrow{NH_3} \begin{array}{c} CH_2{-}CH_2 \\ | \qquad | \\ CH_2 \quad CH_2 \\ \diagdown O \diagup \end{array} \xrightarrow{HCl} CH_2Cl{\cdot}CH_2{\cdot}CH_2{\cdot}CH_2OH$$

Furan undergoes the Diels–Alder reaction, and can be easily mercurated:

$$\text{furan} + \begin{array}{c} CH{\cdot}CO \diagdown \\ \| \qquad\quad O \\ CH{\cdot}CO \diagup \end{array} \longrightarrow \text{adduct (CH bridged by O, fused to } \begin{array}{c} CH{\cdot}CO \diagdown \\ | \qquad\quad O \\ CH{\cdot}CO \diagup \end{array})$$

Substituents usually enter the 2- or 5-position if one is unoccupied, even though a *m*-orienting group, *e.g.*, NO_2 or SO_3H, is already present in one of these positions (some Friedel–Crafts reactions are exceptional, the alkyl radical entering the 3-position). When the 2- and 5-positions are both occupied, the substituent enters the 3-position. Furan is very readily attacked by oxidising agents, *e.g.*, it cannot be directly nitrated with nitric acid; the furan nucleus is completely oxidised. 2-Nitrofuran may be prepared by nitrating furan with acetyl nitrate. Similarly, furan cannot be directly sulphonated (resinified products are obtained), but the 2-sulphonic acid may be prepared by the action of pyridine-sulphur trioxide on furan. If a negative group is present in the ring, then sulphonation can be carried out directly, *e.g.*, furoic acid gives furoic-5-sulphonic acid. The direct halogenation of furan is also not possible (the ring is destroyed), but if a negative group is present, halogenation can be carried out, *e.g.*, furoic acid gives 5-bromofuroic acid.

$$\text{(furan ring)}CO_2H \xrightarrow{Br_2} Br\text{(furan ring)}CO_2H \xrightarrow{\text{heat}} Br\text{(furan ring)} + CO_2$$

Furan undergoes the Gattermann reaction (p. 618) to form furfural. Since aluminium chloride attacks the ring, Friedel–Crafts reactions are best carried out with stannic chloride as catalyst. If, however, a negative group is present in the ring, then alkylation may be carried out using aluminium chloride.

Furan behaves as a resonance hybrid. It appears that (I), (II) and (III) are

(I) ⟷ (II) ⟷ (III) ⟷ (IV) ⟷ (V)

the main contributing structures, since, as pointed out above, 2- (or 5-) substitution (with electrophilic reagents) occurs most readily. At the same time, (IV) and (V) would account for 3-substitution when the 2- and 5-positions are both occupied. Calculations of the bond lengths and comparison with the measured values show that (I) contributes about 85 per cent. to the resonance hybrid.

It should be noted that one of the lone pairs of the oxygen atom enters into resonance with the ring; we now have six electrons involved as in benzene. From the M.O. point of view, one lone pair of the oxygen atom conjugates with the four p_z electrons of the ring, thereby producing a "closed circuit" of six π-electrons (these will be in three M.O.s; *cf.* benzene, p. 485). Furan and all other *five-membered* rings are *non-alternant* compounds (p. 502), and since the oxygen atom has supplied *two* electrons to form the closed circuit, the π-electron densities at each carbon atom will be *greater* than unity, and are greatest at the 2- and 5-positions (see pyrrole, p. 719). Thus electrophilic attack will occur most readily at position 2 (or 5), but if these are occupied, and provided the substituent groups leave the ring π-electron distribution very little affected, electrophilic attack can now occur at position 3 (or 4), since the charge density here is also greater than unity.

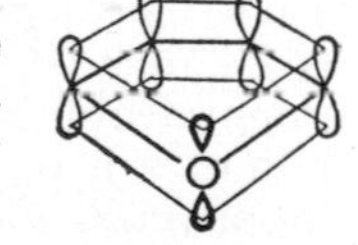

Furfural (*furfuraldehyde*) may be prepared by distilling pentoses with dilute sulphuric acid (p. 416):

$$CH_2OH{\cdot}(CHOH)_3{\cdot}CHO \longrightarrow \text{(furan ring)}CHO + 3H_2O \quad (100\%)$$

It is manufactured by treating oat husks, cotton-seed hulls or maize cobs with dilute sulphuric acid followed by steam distillation (the starting materials are rich in pentoses).

Furfural is a colourless liquid, b.p. 162°. Chemically it is very similar to benzaldehyde, *e.g.*, with aqueous sodium hydroxide furfural forms *furfuryl alcohol* and *furoic acid*:

$$2\,\text{(furan ring)}CHO + NaOH \longrightarrow \text{(furan ring)}CH_2OH + \text{(furan ring)}CO_2Na$$

With ethanolic potassium cyanide *furoin* is formed and this, on oxidation, gives *furil*:

$$2\,C_4H_3O{\cdot}CHO \xrightarrow{KCN} C_4H_3O{\cdot}CHOH{\cdot}CO{\cdot}C_4H_3O \xrightarrow{[O]} C_4H_3O{\cdot}CO{\cdot}CO{\cdot}C_4H_3O$$

When heated with aqueous potassium hydroxide, furil gives *furilic acid*:

$$C_4H_3O{\cdot}CO{\cdot}CO{\cdot}C_4H_3O \xrightarrow{KOH} (C_4H_3O)_2C(OH)CO_2K$$

Furfural reacts with ammonia to form *furfuramide*, $(C_5H_4O)_3N_2$, and can undergo the Perkin reaction and the Claisen reaction. It is easily oxidised by silver oxide to the corresponding acid; it is oxidised by sodium chlorate to maleic acid, and Salchinkin *et al.* (1955) have shown that 30 per cent. hydrogen peroxide oxidises furfural to succinic acid. Furfural condenses with dimethylaniline in the presence of zinc chloride to form *furfuraldehyde green* (analogous to malachite green, p. 756). A characteristic reaction of furfural is the red coloration it gives with aniline and hydrochloric acid; it also turns green a pine splint moistened with hydrochloric acid (*cf.* furan, above).

Furfural is used for the preparation of dyes, plastics and maleic acid. It is also used as a solvent in synthetic rubber manufacture, and as an extraction liquid in petroleum refining.

Furfuryl alcohol, b.p. 170°, may be prepared by reducing furfural, or by means of the Cannizzaro reaction on furfural (see above).

Furoic acid (furan-2-carboxylic acid, *pyromucic acid*) may be prepared by the dry distillation of mucic acid, or by the oxidation of furfural with acid dichromate.

It is a solid, m.p. 133°, and behaves more like an unsaturated aliphatic acid rather than benzoic acid (*cf.* furfural); *e.g.*, furoic acid is readily oxidised by alkaline permanganate, brominated by bromine vapour (it adds on four bromine atoms), and oxidised by bromine-water to fumaric acid. The sodium salt of furoic acid is decarboxylated by mercuric chloride to give the mercuri-chloride (this does not occur with furan-3-carboxylic acid):

$$C_4H_3O{\cdot}CO_2Na + HgCl_2 \longrightarrow C_4H_3O{\cdot}HgCl + CO_2 + NaCl$$

Furan-3-carboxylic acid occurs naturally.

Benzofuran (benzfuran, *coumarone*) occurs in coal-tar. It is a liquid, b.p. 174°, and is used in the manufacture of plastics.

Dibenzofuran (dibenzfuran, *diphenylene oxide*) may be prepared by heating phenol with lead oxide at 150°:

$$2\,C_6H_5OH \xrightarrow{PbO} (C_6H_4)_2O \quad (28\%)$$

It may also be prepared by passing diphenyl ether through a red hot tube. It is a white solid, m.p. 87°.

THIOPHEN AND ITS DERIVATIVES

Thiophen occurs in coal-tar and shale oils. Its b.p. (84°) is close to that of benzene and hence it is difficult to separate from the benzene fraction obtained from coal-tar. Thiophen can be sulphonated more readily than benzene, and this property is used to separate the two compounds by repeatedly shaking benzene (from coal-tar) with cold concentrated sulphuric acid, whereby the water-soluble thiophensulphonic acid is formed. A better means of separation is to reflux the benzene with aqueous mercuric acetate whereupon thiophen is mercurated and benzene is not. Thiophen may be recovered from its mercurated derivative by distilling the latter with hydrochloric acid. The presence of thiophen in benzene may be detected by the *indophenin reaction*. This is the development of a blue colour when benzene is treated with isatin and sulphuric acid.

β′CH——CHβ
‖4 3‖
‖5 2‖
α′CH CHα
\ 1 /
S

Thiophen may be prepared by passing a mixture of acetylene and hydrogen sulphide through a tube containing alumina at 400°:

$$2C_2H_2 + H_2S \longrightarrow C_4H_4S + H_2$$

This method is used commercially. It is also manufactured by reaction between *n*-butane and sulphur in the vapour phase. Since butadiene also forms thiophen under these conditions, and since sulphur is a dehydrogenating agent, the reaction with *n*-butane probably proceeds via butadiene as an intermediate. Thiophen may also be prepared by heating sodium succinate with phosphorus trisulphide:

$$\begin{array}{l} CH_2{\cdot}CO_2Na \\ | \\ CH_2{\cdot}CO_2Na \end{array} \xrightarrow{P_2S_3} \begin{array}{l} CH{=}CH \diagdown \\ | \qquad\qquad S \\ CH{-}CH \diagup \end{array} \quad (30\%)$$

Derivatives of thiophen may be prepared by heating 1 : 4-diketones with phosphorus trisulphide (*cf.* furan derivatives):

$$\begin{array}{cc} CH_2{-}CH_2 \\ | \qquad | \\ R{\cdot}CO \quad CO{\cdot}R \end{array} \rightleftharpoons \begin{array}{cc} CH{-}CH \\ \| \qquad \| \\ R{\cdot}C{\cdot}OH \quad COH{\cdot}R \end{array} \xrightarrow{P_2S_3} \begin{array}{c} CH{-}CH \\ \| \qquad \| \\ R{\cdot}C \qquad C{\cdot}R \\ \diagdown S \diagup \end{array}$$

Thiophen is a liquid which is easily sulphonated, nitrated or chlorinated in the α-position. It was this close chemical similarity to benzene that masked the presence of thiophen in benzene from coal-tar. V. Meyer (1882) found that a sample of benzene prepared by heating sodium benzoate with soda-lime did not give the indophenin test. Subsequently he showed that it was a sulphur-containing compound, which he called *thiophene*, that was responsible for the indophenin reaction.

Thiophen undergoes substitution mainly in the 2-position; some substitution may also occur in the 3-position, particularly when alkylated. Thiophen is fairly readily polymerised by acids, and stannic chloride is better than aluminium chloride for Friedel–Crafts reactions (*cf.* furan). It can be nitrated by fuming nitric acid in acetic anhydride to give mainly 2-nitrothiophen, and is readily sulphonated in the 2-position with *cold* concentrated sulphuric acid. 2-Halogeno-chiophens may be prepared by direct action between the halogen and thiophen under suitable conditions, *e.g.*, chlorination at 100° gives almost 100 per cent. 2-chlorothiophen. Thiophen may be catalytically hydrogenated to *thiophan* (tetrahydrothiophen), provided a very large amount of the catalyst (palladium) is used to overcome the poisoning effect of the sulphur (Mozingo *et al.*, 1945). On the other hand, reduction of thiophen with sodium in liquid ammonia gives 2 : 3- and 2 : 5-dihydrothiophen (Birch *et al.*, 1951).

Various derivatives of thiophen may be prepared from the monobromo-derivative, *e.g.*,

Thiophen does not form sulphonium salts and cannot be oxidised to a sulphoxide or sulphone; hydrogen peroxide *opens* the thiophen ring, the sulphur being oxidised to sulphuric acid. Thiophensulphone (thiophen-1 : 1-dioxide) has, however, been prepared indirectly as follows (Melles *et al.*, 1953):

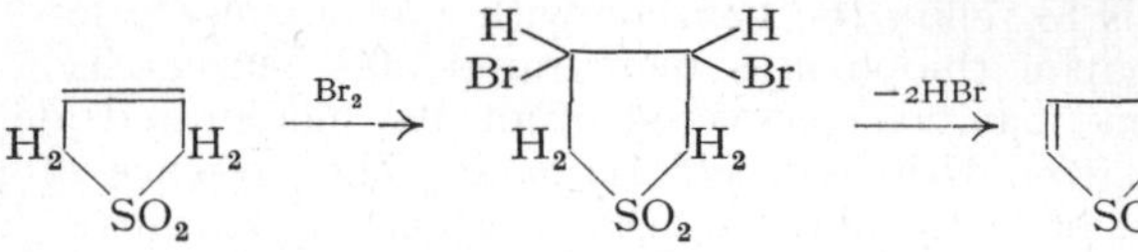

Many thiophen *derivatives* may be directly oxidised to the sulphone by perbenzoic acid.

Thiophen is a resonance hybrid (V.B. method), or forms a " closed circuit ", the sulphur atom contributing *two* electrons (see furan, p. 713; replace the oxygen atom by sulphur). The problem of thiophen, however, appears to be more complicated than this because of the fact that sulphur can use a 3*d* orbital (oxygen cannot). The valency angle of C–S–C in thiophen is about 91°, and not the expected value of about 105°. Schomaker *et al.* (1939) explained this by assuming that some of the sulphur 3*d* orbitals are used in the V.B. structures (II–IV).

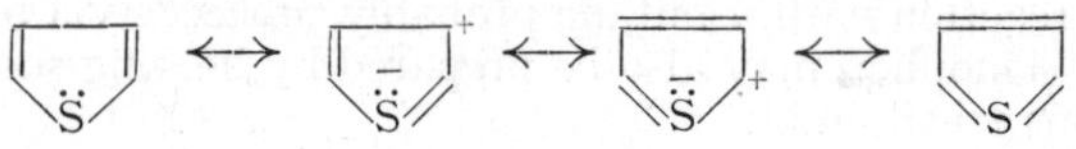

(I) (II) (III) (IV)

This has been supported and extended by calculations using the M.O. method (Longuet-Higgins, 1949).

A number of condensed thiophen systems are known, *e.g.*, *benzothiophen* (V) (also known as *thionaphthen* because it closely resembles naphthalene), *dibenzothiophen* (VI), and *thiophthen* (VII).

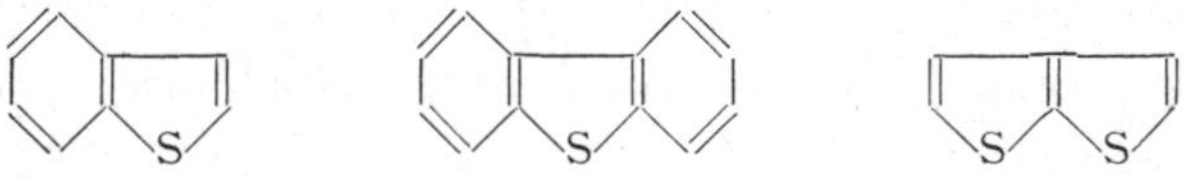

(V) (VI) (VII)

PYRROLE AND ITS DERIVATIVES

Pyrrole is a very important five-membered heterocyclic ring because its nucleus occurs in many natural compounds, *e.g.*, alkaloids, chlorophyll, hæmatin, etc. In addition to the 2- and 3-derivatives, pyrrole can form 1- or *N*-derivatives in which imino-hydrogen is replaced.

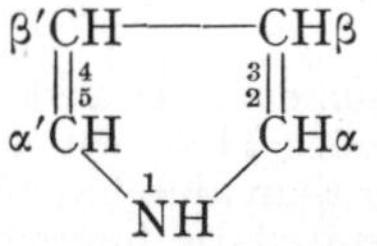

Pyrrole occurs in coal-tar and bone oil. It may be isolated from bone oil by washing the latter with dilute alkali to remove acidic substances, then with acid to remove strongly basic substances, and finally fractionating. Pyrrole distils over in the fraction boiling between 100° and 150°, and may be purified by fusing with potassium hydroxide. Solid potassiopyrrole is formed and this, on steam distillation, gives pure pyrrole.

Pyrrole may be synthesised by passing a mixture of acetylene and ammonia through a red-hot tube:

$$2C_2H_2 + NH_3 \longrightarrow C_4H_5N + H_2$$

It is conveniently prepared by distilling a mixture of ammonium mucate and glycerol at 200°:

$$CO_2NH_4\cdot(CHOH)_4\cdot CO_2NH_4 \longrightarrow C_4H_5N + 2CO_2 + NH_3 + 4H_2O \quad (37\text{–}40\%)$$

If salts of mucic acid with primary amines are decomposed as above, then *N*-substituted pyrroles are obtained, *e.g.*, aniline mucate gives *N*-phenylpyrrole.

Pyrrole is also formed when succinimide is distilled with zinc dust:

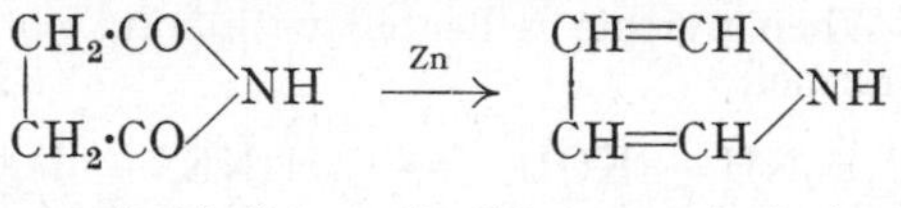

$$\begin{array}{l} CH_2\cdot CO \\ | \qquad\qquad \rangle NH \\ CH_2\cdot CO \end{array} \xrightarrow{Zn} \begin{array}{l} CH{=}CH \\ | \qquad\qquad \rangle NH \\ CH{=}CH \end{array}$$

Many methods are available for synthesising pyrrole derivatives, *e.g.*,

(i) **Paal–Knorr synthesis** (1885). This is carried out by treating a 1 : 4-diketone with ammonia, primary amines, hydrazines, etc., *e.g.*,

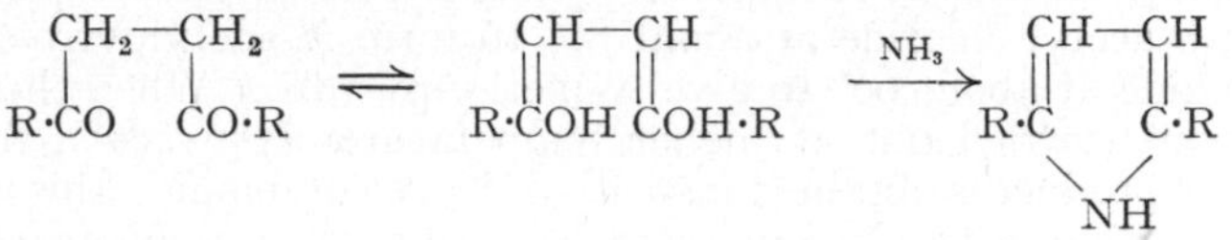

$$\begin{array}{cc} CH_2 & \!\!-\!\! CH_2 \\ | & | \\ R\cdot CO & CO\cdot R \end{array} \rightleftharpoons \begin{array}{cc} CH & \!\!-\!\! CH \\ \| & \| \\ R\cdot COH & COH\cdot R \end{array} \xrightarrow{NH_3} \begin{array}{ccc} CH & - & CH \\ \| & & \| \\ R\cdot C & & C\cdot R \\ & \diagdown\ \diagup & \\ & NH & \end{array}$$

If succinaldehyde is used as the 1 : 4-dicarbonyl compound, pyrrole itself is obtained

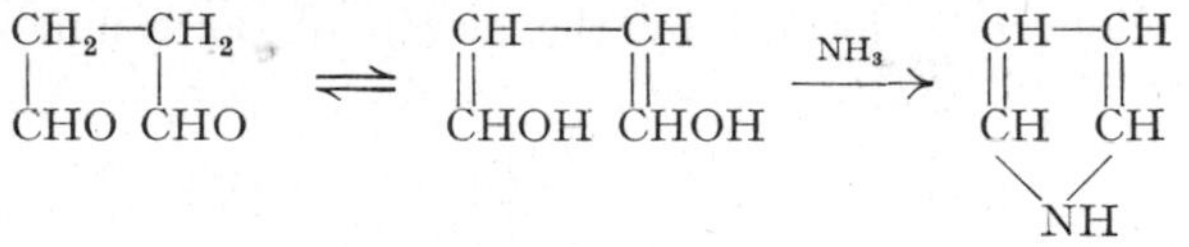

$$\begin{array}{cc} CH_2 & \!\!-\!\! CH_2 \\ | & | \\ CHO & CHO \end{array} \rightleftharpoons \begin{array}{cc} CH & \!\!-\!\! CH \\ \| & \| \\ CHOH & CHOH \end{array} \xrightarrow{NH_3} \begin{array}{ccc} CH & - & CH \\ \| & & \| \\ CH & & CH \\ & \diagdown\ \diagup & \\ & NH & \end{array}$$

(ii) **Knorr synthesis** (1884; 1886). This is the most general method, and involves the condensation between an α-aminoketone and a β-diketone or β-ketoester; *e.g.*, 3 : 5-dimethylpyrrole-2 : 4-dicarboxylic ester may be prepared from acetoacetic ester as follows:

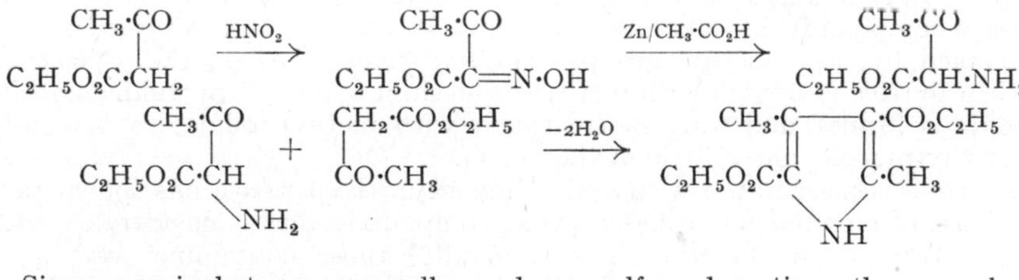

$$\begin{array}{r} CH_3\cdot CO \\ | \\ C_2H_5O_2C\cdot CH_2 \end{array} \xrightarrow{HNO_2} \begin{array}{r} CH_3\cdot CO \\ | \\ C_2H_5O_2C\cdot C{=}N\cdot OH \end{array} \xrightarrow{Zn/CH_3\cdot CO_2H} \begin{array}{r} CH_3\cdot CO \\ | \\ C_2H_5O_2C\cdot CH\cdot NH_2 \end{array}$$

$$\begin{array}{r} CH_3\cdot CO \\ | \\ C_2H_5O_2C\cdot CH \\ \diagdown NH_2 \end{array} + \begin{array}{l} CH_2\cdot CO_2C_2H_5 \\ | \\ CO\cdot CH_3 \end{array} \xrightarrow{-2H_2O} \begin{array}{ccc} CH_3\cdot C & - & C\cdot CO_2C_2H_5 \\ \| & & \| \\ C_2H_5O_2C\cdot C & & C\cdot CH_3 \\ & \diagdown\ \diagup & \\ & NH & \end{array}$$

Since α-aminoketones generally undergo self-condensation, they are best prepared *in situ* (as illustrated above).

(iii) **Hantzsch synthesis** (1890). This is the condensation between chloroacetone, a β-ketoester, and a primary amine, *e.g.*,

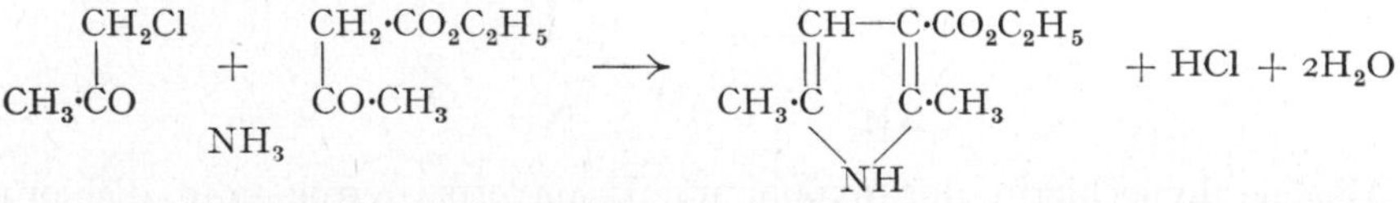

$$\begin{array}{r} CH_2Cl \\ | \\ CH_3\cdot CO \end{array} + \begin{array}{l} CH_2\cdot CO_2C_2H_5 \\ | \\ CO\cdot CH_3 \end{array} \longrightarrow \begin{array}{ccc} CH & - & C\cdot CO_2C_2H_5 \\ \| & & \| \\ CH_3\cdot C & & C\cdot CH_3 \\ & \diagdown\ \diagup & \\ & NH & \end{array} + HCl + 2H_2O$$
$$NH_3$$

Some furan derivative is also formed.

Properties of pyrrole. Pyrrole is a colourless liquid, b.p. 131°, which rapidly darkens on exposure to air. It is sparingly soluble in water but readily soluble in ethanol and ether. A characteristic reaction is the turning red of a pine splint moistened with hydrochloric acid when exposed to the vapour of pyrrole (and many of its derivatives). Pyrrole is a very weak secondary base, dissolving very slowly in cold dilute acids, and these solutions, on warming, form pyrrole-red (pyrrole polymers); concentrated acids resinify pyrrole rapidly. Pyrrole, however, gives 2-nitropyrrole (21% yield) when nitrated with nitric acid in acetic anhydride at $-10°$ (Rinkes, 1934). Sulphonation of pyrrole with pyridine-sulphur trioxide in ethylene chloride gives the 2-sulphonic acid (Terentyev, 1949).

Pyrrole shows a number of resemblances to phenols and aromatic amines. The imino-hydrogen of pyrrole is replaceable by sodium, potassium, alkyl or acyl radicals. When pyrrole is heated with solid potassium hydroxide, potassiopyrrole is formed:

$$C_4H_4NH + KOH \longrightarrow C_4H_4\bar{N}K^+ + H_2O$$

Potassiopyrrole reacts with carbon dioxide and with chloroform as do phenols in the Kolbe–Schmitt and Reimer–Tiemann reactions, to form 2- and 3-pyrrolecarboxylic acids and pyrrole-2-aldehyde, respectively. It reacts with acetyl chloride at about 80° to form *N*-acetylpyrrole, and with methyl iodide at about 60° to give *N*-methylpyrrole. When these last two reactions are carried out at higher temperatures (150–220°), the 2- or 3-substituted product is obtained instead of the *N*-compound; this may be due to rearrangement of the *N*-compound (*cf.* Hofmann–Martius rearrangement, p. 549).

Pyrrole may be readily halogenated, the most important halogeno-pyrrole being tetraiodopyrrole, formed by the action of potassium iodide-iodine solution on pyrrole:

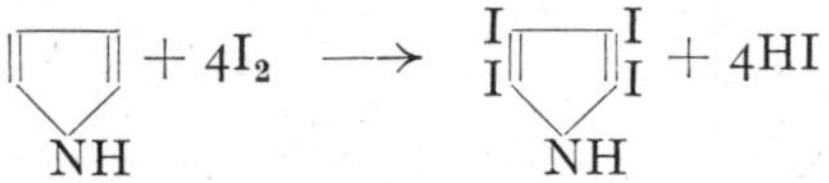

$$\text{pyrrole (NH)} + 4I_2 \longrightarrow \text{2,3,4,5-tetraiodopyrrole (NH)} + 4HI$$

This is often used as a substitute (under the name of *iodole*) for iodoform, but is much more expensive. Pyrrole couples with diazonium salts in the 2-position in weakly acid solution, and in the 2- and 5-positions (to give the bisazo-compound) in alkaline solution. If the 2- and 5-positions are occupied by, *e.g.*, methyl groups, coupling takes place in the 3-position. When pyrrole is treated with methylmagnesium iodide, *N*-pyrrylmagnesium iodide is formed and this, on treatment with methyl iodide, gives mainly 3-methylpyrrole, and a little of the 2-isomer.

Pyrrole is mercurated with great difficulty. Experience has shown that the ease of mercuration of heterocyclic compounds varies considerably with the nature of the hetero-atom. Generally, those containing oxygen or sulphur are easily mercurated (*cf.* thiophen), whereas those containing nitrogen are mercurated with great difficulty.

Pyrrole is oxidised by chromium trioxide in sulphuric acid to maleic-imide:

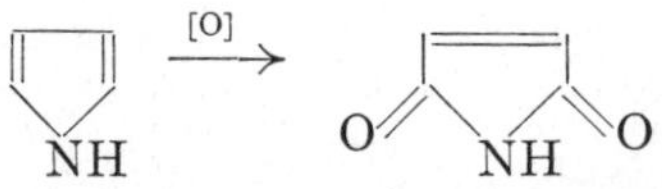

$$\text{pyrrole (NH)} \xrightarrow{[O]} \text{maleic-imide (O=C–CH=CH–C=O, NH)}$$

Alkaline hypochlorite (or hypobromite) converts pyrrole into dichloro- (or dibromo-) maleic-imide. When pyrrole is treated with hydroxylamine, *the ring is opened* and succinaldehyde dioxime is formed:

$$\begin{array}{l}CH{=}CH\diagdown \\ | \qquad\qquad NH \\ CH{=}CH\diagup\end{array} + 2NH_2{\cdot}OH \longrightarrow \begin{array}{l}CH_2{\cdot}CH{=}N{\cdot}OH \\ | \\ CH_2{\cdot}CH{=}N{\cdot}OH\end{array} + NH_3$$

When potassiopyrrole is heated with chloroform and sodium ethoxide, *ring expansion* takes place, the product being 3-chloropyridine:

$$\text{Potassiopyrrole } (C_4H_4N^- K^+) \xrightarrow[C_2H_5ONa]{CHCl_3} \text{3-chloropyridine}$$

The yields are better if lithiopyrrole is used instead of potassiopyrrole (Alexander *et al.*, 1950).

The same result may be achieved by passing a mixture of pyrrole and chloroform through a glass tube at 550° (Rice *et al.*, 1955).

Reduction products of pyrrole. Pyrrole is reduced by zinc and acetic acid to **pyrroline** (2 : 5-*dihydropyrrole*), b.p. 91°. This, on heating with hydriodic acid and red phosphorus, gives **pyrrolidine** (*tetrahydropyrrole*), b.p. 88°:

$$\text{pyrrole} \xrightarrow[CH_3\cdot CO_2H]{Zn} \text{pyrroline (CH=CH, } CH_2, CH_2, NH) \xrightarrow{HI/P} \text{pyrrolidine } (CH_2-CH_2, CH_2, CH_2, NH)$$

Pyrrolidine may also be prepared by catalytically reducing pyrrole using nickel at 200°, or by the electrolytic reduction of succinimide. A potential source of pyrrolidine is its preparation by the action of ammonia on tetrahydrofuran (p. 712).

Pyrroline and pyrrolidine are both strong bases, and do not show any tendency to polymerise.

2-Pyrrolidone, m.p. 25°, may be prepared by the electrolytic reduction of succinimide:

$$\text{succinimide } (CH_2-CH_2, CO, CO, NH) \xrightarrow{[H]} \text{2-pyrrolidone } (CH_2-CH_2, CH_2, CO, NH)$$

2-Pyrrolidone is the *lactam* (*cf.* lactones) of γ-aminobutyric acid.

3-*Pyrrolidone* is also known.

Pyrrole behaves as a resonance hybrid, the main contributing structures being (I), (II) and (III). From the M.O. point of view, the lone pair on the nitrogen

(I) $\longleftrightarrow$ (II) $\longleftrightarrow$ (III) $\longleftrightarrow$ (IV) $\longleftrightarrow$ (V)

atom (which is hybridised trigonally) conjugates with the four p_z electrons of the ring, thereby producing a " closed circuit " of six π-electrons (which are accommodated in three M.O.s). Like all odd-membered rings, pyrrole is *non-alternant* (p. 502), and the charge densities will not be unity at each position in the molecule. Since the nitrogen atom has supplied *two* electrons to form the closed circuit, the charge density at each carbon atom is *greater* than unity, being greater at the α-positions than the β- (as shown by calculation). Hence electrophilic attack occurs most readily at the α-position. Had the nitrogen atom retained

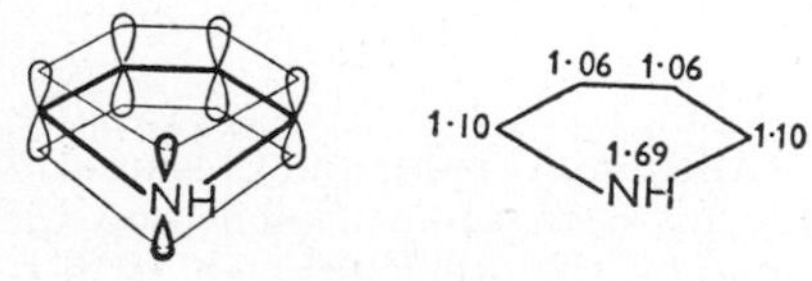

FIG. 30.1.

its lone pair, its charge density would have been 2, but owing to conjugation, it is less than this, and so acquires a small positive charge.

Indole (*benzopyrrole*) occurs in coal-tar, jasmine flowers and orange blossoms. Some indole derivatives, *e.g.*, indole-3-acetic acid, indole-3-propionic acid, etc., have great growth-promoting action on plants (and are known as *heteroauxins*). Indole is the parent substance of indigotin (p. 770). It may be synthesised in many ways, *e.g.*,

(i) **Lipp synthesis** (1884). This is carried out by heating *o*-amino-ω-chlorostyrene with sodium ethoxide.

$$C_6H_4(NH_2)CH{=}CHCl \xrightarrow{C_2H_5ONa} \text{indole}$$

(ii) When heated with potassium alkoxides, formyl-*o*-toluidide gives indole (Friedman, 1948).

$$C_6H_4(CH_3)NH{\cdot}CHO \xrightarrow{ROK} \text{indole} \quad (79\%)$$

(iii) **Fischer's indole synthesis** (1886) This is the most important method of preparing indole derivatives, and is carried out by heating the phenylhydrazone or substituted phenylhydrazone of an appropriate aldehyde, ketone, or ketonic acid with zinc chloride as catalyst. Boron trifluoride has been found to be a very good reagent for converting phenylhydrazones into indole derivatives.

The mechanism of the reaction is uncertain, but a highly favoured one is that of Robinson (1918). According to him acetone phenylhydrazone forms 2-methylindole by first tautomerising, the tautomer then undergoing the *o*-benzidine rearrangement, and the diamino-compound so produced eliminating a molecule of ammonia with ring closure:

$$C_6H_5NH{-}N{=}C(CH_3){-}CH_3 \rightleftharpoons C_6H_5NH{-}NH{-}C(CH_3){=}CH_2 \rightarrow$$

$$o\text{-}NH_2C_6H_4{-}CH{=}C(NH_2){-}CH_3 \xrightarrow{-NH_3} \text{2-methylindole}$$

Allen *et al.* (1943) and Clusius *et al.* (1952), using ^{15}N, have shown that it is the nitrogen atom attached to the aromatic ring that is retained in the product, the other nitrogen atom being eliminated as ammonia.

(iv) **Reissert synthesis** (1897). This is a very good method, and is carried out with *o*-nitrotoluene (or its substituted derivatives) and ethyl oxalate as follows:

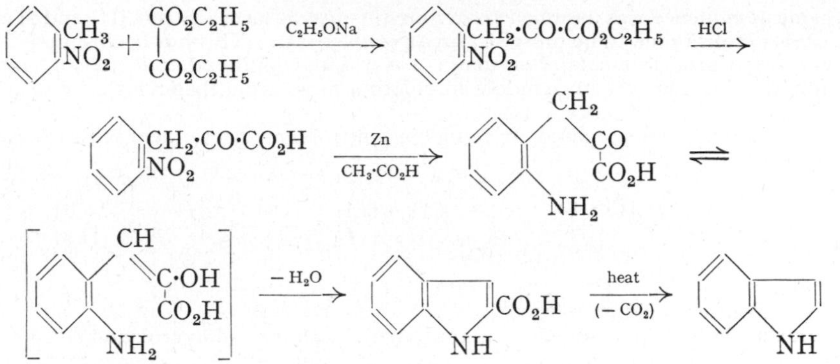

$$C_6H_4(CH_3)(NO_2) + \begin{matrix} CO_2C_2H_5 \\ | \\ CO_2C_2H_5 \end{matrix} \xrightarrow{C_2H_5ONa} C_6H_4(NO_2)\cdot CH_2\cdot CO\cdot CO_2C_2H_5 \xrightarrow{HCl}$$

$$C_6H_4(NO_2)\cdot CH_2\cdot CO\cdot CO_2H \xrightarrow[CH_3\cdot CO_2H]{Zn} C_6H_4(NH_2)\cdot CH_2\cdot CO\cdot CO_2H \rightleftharpoons$$

$$\left[C_6H_4(NH_2)\cdot CH{=}C(OH)\cdot CO_2H \right] \xrightarrow{-H_2O} \text{indole-2-carboxylic acid } (CO_2H, NH) \xrightarrow[(-CO_2)]{heat} \text{indole } (NH)$$

Indole is a crystalline solid, m.p. 52°. It resembles pyrrole in many of its properties, and is oxidised by ozone to indigotin.

Indole is most readily substituted in the 3-position, *e.g.*, treatment with iodine gives 3-iodoindole; the Reimer–Tiemann reaction produces indole-3-aldehyde; the rearrangement of, for example, *N*-acetylindole gives 3-acetylindole. The calculated charge densities for indole are as shown.

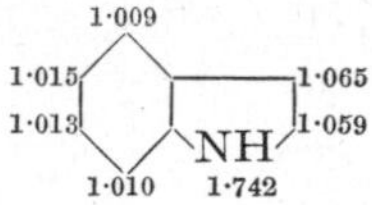

1·009; 1·015; 1·065; 1·013; 1·059; NH; 1·010; 1·742

Indole behaves in some ways as a tautomeric substance, the tautomer being known as *indolenine*. Indolenine itself has never yet been isolated, but its

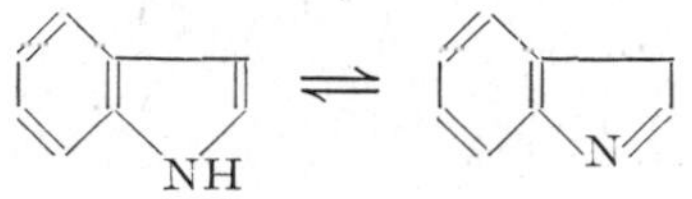

NH ⇌ N

derivatives are known, and these may be prepared, *e.g.*, by condensation between indoles and aldehydes.

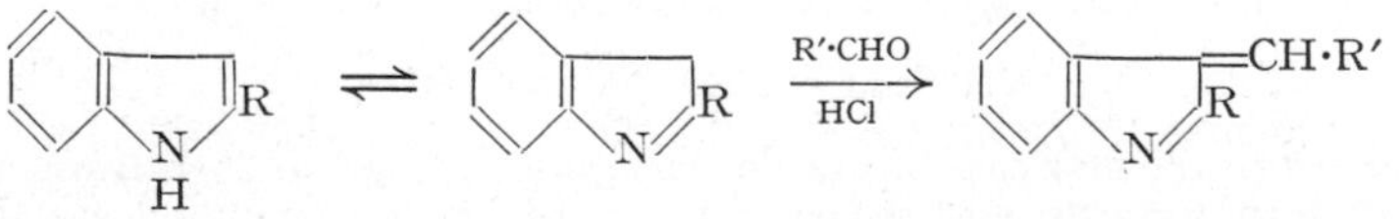

$$\text{2-R-indole (NH)} \rightleftharpoons \text{2-R-indolenine (N)} \xrightarrow[HCl]{R'\cdot CHO} \text{3-}({=}CH\cdot R')\text{-2-R-indolenine (N)}$$

Indoxyl is the term usually applied to the keto-form of **3-hydroxyindole** (the enolic form):

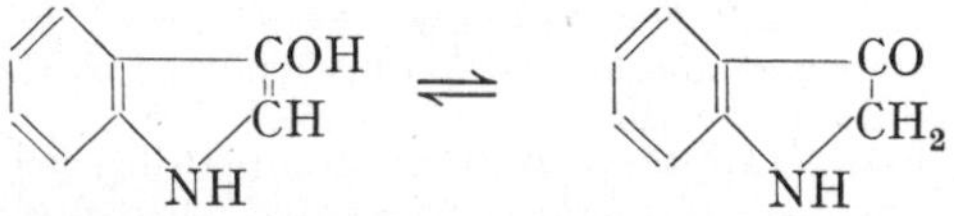

$$C_6H_4\langle{}^{COH}_{NH}\rangle CH \rightleftharpoons C_6H_4\langle{}^{CO}_{NH}\rangle CH_2$$

Derivatives of both are known (see p. 772 for its preparation). Indoxyl is a bright yellow solid, m.p. 85°, and is readily oxidised in alkaline solution by air to indigotin.

Oxindole. There are three possible formulæ for oxindole:

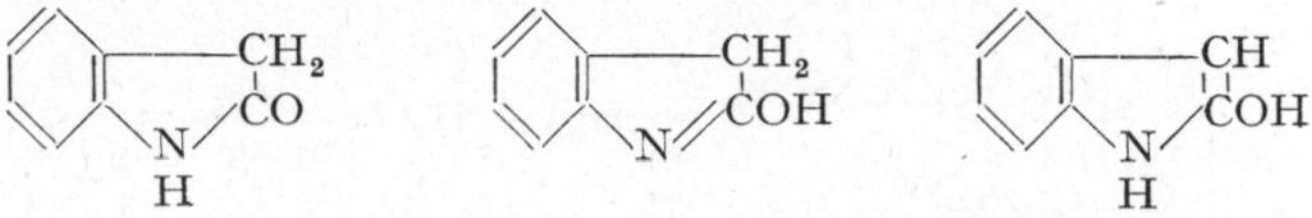

$$C_6H_4\langle{}^{CH_2}_{NH}\rangle CO \quad (I) \qquad C_6H_4\langle{}^{CH_2}_{N}\rangle\!\!=\!COH \quad (II) \qquad C_6H_4\langle{}^{CH}_{NH}\rangle\!\!=\!COH \quad (III)$$

Chemical evidence was assumed to favour the *lactam* form (I), but (II) and (III) were also considered to be present (Julian *et al.*, 1935). This has been supported by infrared measurements (Bergmann, 1955), but O'Sullivan *et al.* (1956), from infrared measurements of oxindole in chloroform solution, believe that only (I) is present.

Oxindole may be prepared by reducing *o*-nitrophenylacetic acid with tin and hydrochloric acid.

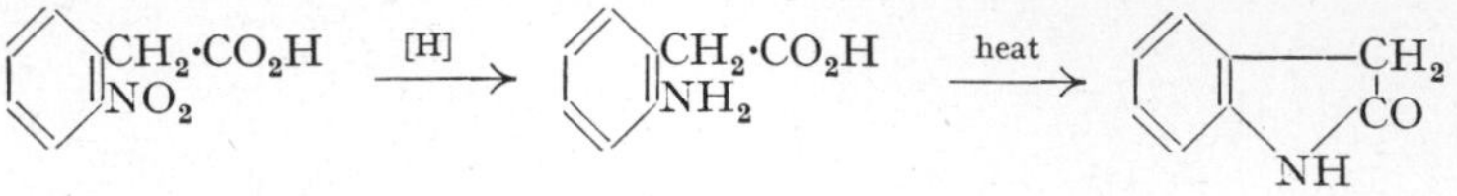

$$C_6H_4(CH_2{\cdot}CO_2H)(NO_2) \xrightarrow{[H]} C_6H_4(CH_2{\cdot}CO_2H)(NH_2) \xrightarrow{heat} C_6H_4\begin{matrix}—CH_2\\|\\CO\\NH\end{matrix}$$

It is a colourless solid, m.p. 120°.

Dioxindole (3-*hydroxyoxindole*) is tautomeric with **2 : 3-dihydroxyindole:**

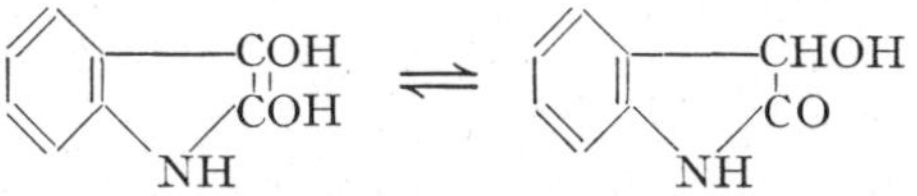

$$C_6H_4\begin{matrix}—COH\\||\\COH\\NH\end{matrix} \rightleftharpoons C_6H_4\begin{matrix}—CHOH\\|\\CO\\NH\end{matrix}$$

It may be prepared by reducing isatin with zinc and hydrochloric acid:

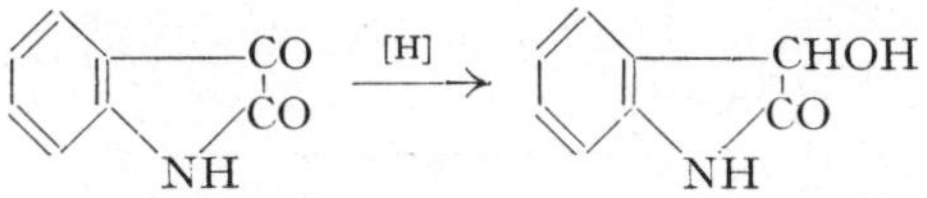

$$C_6H_4\begin{matrix}—CO\\|\\CO\\NH\end{matrix} \xrightarrow{[H]} C_6H_4\begin{matrix}—CHOH\\|\\CO\\NH\end{matrix}$$

It is colourless solid, m.p. 180°.

Isatin exists in two forms, the term ψ-isatin being applied to the *lactam* form (I), and isatin to the *lactim* form (II) (both are derivatives of 2 : 3-dihydroindole; and the name isatin is often applied to I):

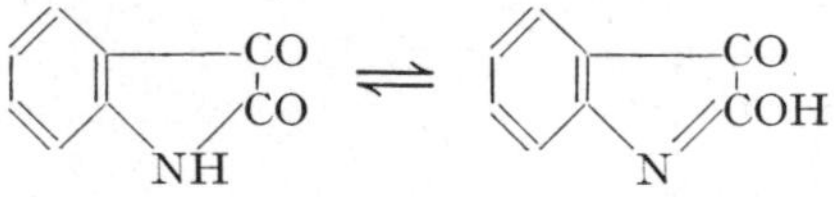

$$C_6H_4\begin{matrix}—CO\\|\\CO\\NH\end{matrix} \rightleftharpoons C_6H_4\begin{matrix}—CO\\|\\COH\\N\end{matrix}$$

(I) (II)

This is an example of the *amido–imidol* tautomeric system:

$$—NH—CO— \rightleftharpoons —N{=}C(OH)—$$

It appears to be the first case of tautomerism to be recognised. Isatin reacts as the lactam form towards most reagents, *e.g.*, the N atom is readily acetylated by heating with acetic anhydride, and when the sodium salt is heated with methyl iodide, the *N*-methyl ether is formed. On the other hand, when the silver salt is heated with methyl iodide, the *O*-ether is obtained (*cf.* amides). Infrared measurements of isatin (and a series of substituted isatins), however, provide no support for the existence of a classical lactim structure in the solid state or in dilute chloroform solution (O'Sullivan *et al.*, 1956).

Isatin was first obtained by the oxidation of indigotin with nitric acid. It is best prepared by heating a solution of concentrated hydrochloric acid containing aniline, chloral hydrate, hydroxylamine and sodium sulphate. "*iso*Nitroso-acetanilide" (oximinoacetanilide) crystallises out and this, on treatment with concentrated sulphuric acid, forms isatin:

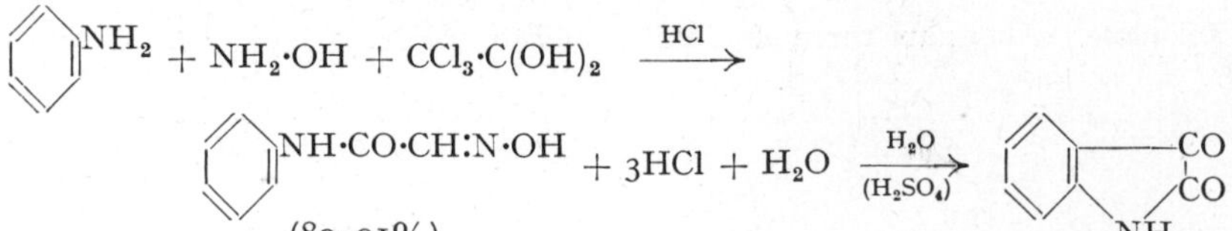

$$C_6H_5NH_2 + NH_2{\cdot}OH + CCl_3{\cdot}C(OH)_2 \xrightarrow{HCl}$$

$$C_6H_5NH{\cdot}CO{\cdot}CH{:}N{\cdot}OH + 3HCl + H_2O \xrightarrow[(H_2SO_4)]{H_2O} C_6H_4\begin{matrix}—CO\\|\\CO\\NH\end{matrix}$$

(80–91%) (71–78%)

The following synthesis from *o*-nitrobenzoyl chloride clearly shows the structure of isatin (Claisen *et al.*, 1879):

$$C_6H_4(COCl)(NO_2) \xrightarrow{NaCN} C_6H_4(CO{\cdot}CN)(NO_2) \xrightarrow{H_2O} C_6H_4(CO{\cdot}CO_2H)(NO_2) \xrightarrow[NH_3]{FeSO_4} C_6H_4(CO{\cdot}CO_2H)(NH_2) \xrightarrow[(warm)]{-H_2O} \text{isatin (CO, CO, NH)}$$

Isatin is a red solid, m.p. 200°. With phosphorus pentachloride it forms *isatin chloride*, and with warm sodium hydroxide, *isatic acid*:

$$\text{isatin chloride (CO, CCl, N)} \xleftarrow{PCl_5} \text{isatin (CO, CO, NH)} \xrightarrow{NaOH} C_6H_4(CO{\cdot}CO_2Na)(NH_2)$$

Carbazole (*dibenzopyrrole*) may be isolated from the anthracene fraction of coal-tar (see p. 696). It may be synthesised by passing diphenylamine through a red hot tube, or better, by heating 2 : 2′-diaminodiphenyl at 200° with concentrated phosphoric acid (the yield is almost quantitative; Leditschke, 1953).

$$(C_6H_5)_2NH \longrightarrow \text{carbazole (positions 1–9, NH at 9)} \xleftarrow{H_3PO_4} NH_2C_6H_4{-}C_6H_4NH_2$$

Carbazole is a colourless solid, m.p. 245°. Silver oxide converts it into N : N′-*dicarbazyl*, which is a colourless compound but gives coloured solutions due to its dissociation into free carbazyl radical (*cf.* p. 551). Carbazole is used in the preparation of polyvinylcarbazole plastics.

AZOLES

Azole is the suffix used for five-membered rings containing two or more hetero-atoms, at least one of which is nitrogen.

Nomenclature. (i) When the heterocyclic compound contains two or more hetero-atoms, the starting point is the hetero-atom of as high a group in the periodic table and as low an atomic number in that group. Thus the order of naming will be O, S, N.

(ii) With the atom of the preferred kind as number 1, the ring is numbered in such a way that the hetero-atoms are given the lowest numbers possible.

(iii) Of two or more numberings conforming to rules (i) and (ii), the one that is chosen is that which assigns low numbers most nearly in the order of precedence established by rule (i).

(iv) Of two or more numberings conforming to rules (i)–(iii), the one that is chosen is that which gives hydrogen atoms the lowest numbers possible.

Hetero-atoms are indicated by prefixes: **O** by **oxa, S** by **thia** and **N** by **aza.**

Pyrazoles. Pyrazole may be prepared by passing acetylene into a cold ethereal solution of diazomethane.

$$CH{\equiv}CH + CH_2{=}N_2 \longrightarrow \text{pyrazole: } {}^4CH{=}{}^3CH,\ {}^5CH{=}{}^2N,\ {}^1NH$$

Pyrazole is a colourless solid, m.p. 70°. It has aromatic properties, readily undergoing substitution (with the usual electrophilic reagents) in the 4-position.

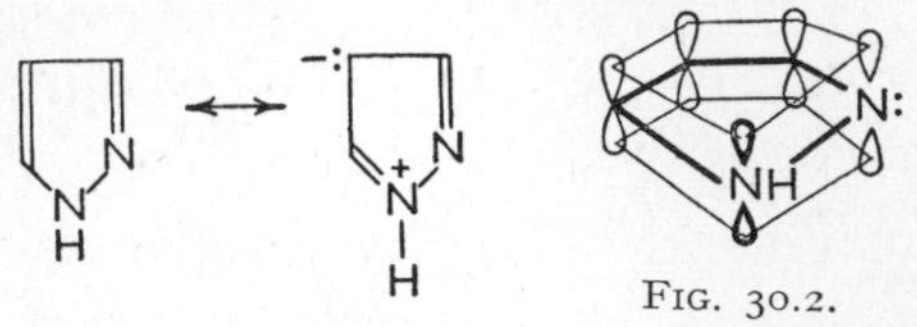

FIG. 30.2.

Pyrazole is a tautomeric substance; this cannot be demonstrated in pyrazole itself, but may be shown as follows. If pyrazole is tautomeric, then positions 3 and 5 are identical; if not tautomeric, these positions are different. When the phenyl group in 3-methyl-1-phenyl- and 5-methyl-1-phenylpyrazole is removed, *both* compounds give the *same* methylpyrazole. Hence positions 3 and 5 are equivalent, and this can only be explained by assuming that pyrazole is tautomeric.

$$\text{CH—CH, CH}^5\ {}^2\text{N, }{}^1\text{NH} \rightleftharpoons \text{CH=CH, CH}^3\ {}^1\text{NH, }{}^2\text{N}$$

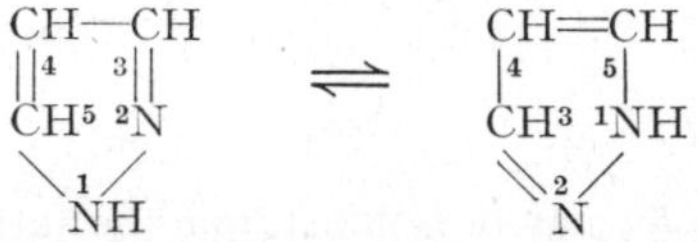

Pyrazole may be catalytically reduced to pyrazoline (I) and then to pyrazolidine (II). Both are stronger bases than pyrazole. 5-Ketopyrazoline or *pyrazol-5-one* is (III) (see below).

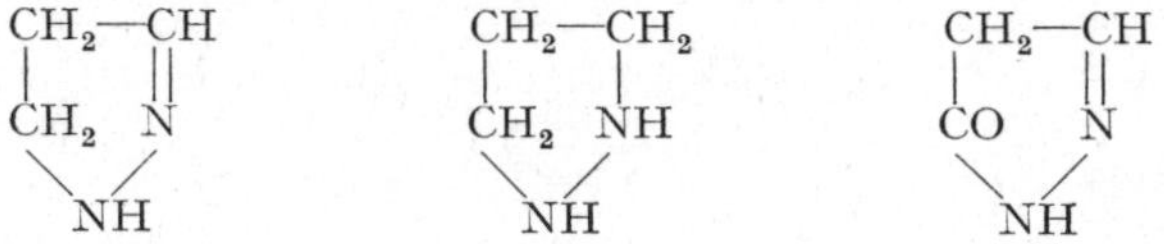

(I) CH_2—CH, CH_2 N, NH (II) CH_2—CH_2, CH_2 NH, NH (III) CH_2—CH, CO N, NH

Pyrazole derivatives. One of the chief methods for preparing these is by reaction between hydrazines and 1 : 3-dicarbonyl compounds, *e.g.*, hydrazine and acetylacetone form 3 : 5-dimethylpyrazole.

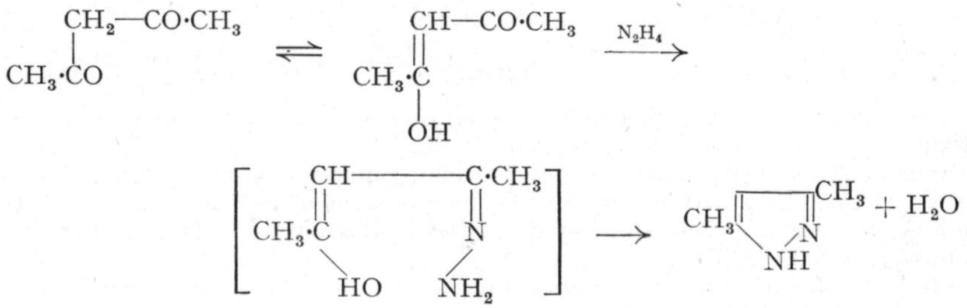

$$CH_3\cdot CO\cdot CH_2\cdot CO\cdot CH_3 \rightleftharpoons CH_3\cdot C(OH){=}CH\cdot CO\cdot CH_3 \xrightarrow{N_2H_4} [CH_3\cdot C(HO){=}CH\text{—}C(CH_3){=}N\cdot NH_2] \longrightarrow \text{3:5-dimethylpyrazole} + H_2O$$

5-Pyrazolones are formed by reaction between hydrazines and β-ketonic esters, *e.g.*, 3-methyl-1-phenylpyrazolone from phenylhydrazine and ethyl acetoacetate. This, on methylation, gives *antipyrine* (*phenazone*, 2 : 3-dimethyl-1-phenylpyrazol-5-one), which is used in medicine as a febrifuge.

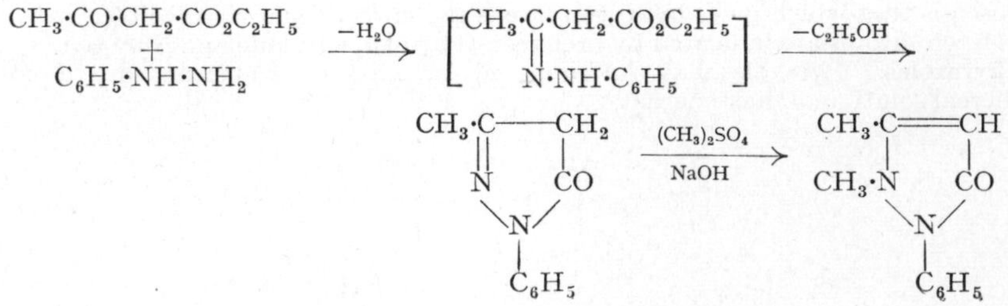

$$CH_3\cdot CO\cdot CH_2\cdot CO_2C_2H_5 + C_6H_5\cdot NH\cdot NH_2 \xrightarrow{-H_2O} [CH_3\cdot C(=N\cdot NH\cdot C_6H_5)\cdot CH_2\cdot CO_2C_2H_5] \xrightarrow{-C_2H_5OH}$$

$$CH_3\cdot C{=}N\text{—}N(C_6H_5)\text{—}CO\text{—}CH_2 \xrightarrow[NaOH]{(CH_3)_2SO_4} CH_3\cdot C{=}CH\text{—}CO\text{—}N(C_6H_5)\text{—}N\cdot CH_3$$

Glyoxalines (iminazoles, imidazoles). Glyoxaline is isomeric with pyrazole, and occurs in the purine nucleus (p. 369) and in histidine (p. 307).

A general method for preparing glyoxalines is by reaction between α-dicarbonyl compounds, ammonia and an aldehyde.

$$\begin{matrix} R{-}C{=}O \\ | \\ R'{-}C{=}O \end{matrix} + 2NH_3 + R''{\cdot}CHO \longrightarrow \begin{matrix} R{\cdot}C \text{———} N \\ \|^4 \quad {}^3\| \\ R'{\cdot}C^5 \quad {}^2C{\cdot}R'' \\ \diagdown {}^1 \diagup \\ NH \end{matrix} + 3H_2O$$

Glyoxal, ammonia and formaldehyde produce glyoxaline itself. This, however, is best prepared as follows: tartaric acid is treated with a mixture of concentrated nitric and sulphuric acids, the product, tartaric acid dinitrate (" dinitrotartaric acid "), then treated with formalin and ammonia solution, and the glyoxaline-4 : 5-dicarboxylic acid formed is then decarboxylated by heating with copper oxide.

$$\begin{matrix} CO_2H \\ | \\ CHOH \\ | \\ CHOH \\ | \\ CO_2H \end{matrix} \xrightarrow[H_2SO_4]{HNO_3} \begin{matrix} CO_2H \\ | \\ CHONO_2 \\ | \\ CHONO_2 \\ | \\ CO_2H \end{matrix} \longrightarrow \left[\begin{matrix} CO_2H \\ | \\ CO \\ | \\ CO \\ | \\ CO_2H \end{matrix}\right] \xrightarrow[2NH_3]{CH_2O}$$

$$\begin{matrix} HO_2C{\cdot}C \text{———} N \\ \| \qquad \| \\ HO_2C{\cdot}C \qquad CH \\ \diagdown \diagup \\ NH \\ (43\text{–}48\%) \end{matrix} \xrightarrow{CuO} \begin{matrix} CH{-}N \\ \| \qquad \| \\ CH \quad CH \\ \diagdown \diagup \\ NH \\ (68\text{–}76\%) \end{matrix}$$

Glyoxaline is a solid, m.p. 90°. It appears to be tautomeric (positions 4 and 5 are identical).

Oxazoles are formed by reaction between acid amides and α-halogeno-ketones, *e.g.*, acetamide and bromoacetone form 2 : 4-dimethyloxazole (the enol forms have been written to simplify the equation).

$$\begin{matrix} CH_3{\cdot}C{\cdot}OH \\ \| \\ CHBr \end{matrix} + \begin{matrix} HN \\ \| \\ HO{\cdot}C{\cdot}CH_3 \end{matrix} \xrightarrow{130^\circ} \begin{matrix} CH_3{\cdot}C \text{——} N \\ \|^4 \quad {}^3\| \\ CH^5 \quad {}^2C{\cdot}CH_3 \\ \diagdown {}^1 \diagup \\ O \end{matrix} + H_2O + HBr$$

Only derivatives of oxazole are known.

***iso*-Oxazoles.** These are formed by warming the mono-oximes of 1 : 3-diketones, *e.g.*, 3 : 5-dimethyl*iso*oxazole from acetylacetonemonoxime.

$$\begin{matrix} CH_3{\cdot}C \text{———} CH_2 \\ \| \qquad\quad | \\ NOH \quad CO{\cdot}CH_3 \end{matrix} \rightleftharpoons \begin{matrix} CH_3{\cdot}C \text{———} CH \\ \| \qquad\quad \| \\ NOH \quad HOC{\cdot}CH_3 \end{matrix} \xrightarrow{-H_2O} \begin{matrix} CH_3{\cdot}C \text{——} CH \\ \|^3 \quad {}^4\| \\ N^2 \quad {}^5C{\cdot}CH_3 \\ \diagdown {}^1 \diagup \\ O \end{matrix}$$

Thiazoles may be prepared by reaction between an α-chloro-carbonyl compound and a thioacid amide (enol forms have been written in the equation).

$$\begin{matrix} R{\cdot}COH \\ \| \\ R'{\cdot}CCl \end{matrix} + \begin{matrix} HN \\ \| \\ C{\cdot}R'' \\ \diagup \\ HS \end{matrix} \longrightarrow \begin{matrix} R{\cdot}C \text{——} N \\ \|^4 \quad {}^3\| \\ R'{\cdot}C^5 \quad {}^2C{\cdot}R'' \\ \diagdown {}^1 \diagup \\ S \end{matrix} + H_2O + HCl$$

Thiazole itself may be prepared from chloroacetaldehyde and thioformamide. Thiazole is a liquid, b.p. 117°. Vitamin B_1 contains the thiazole nucleus.

Triazoles and **tetrazoles** are also known.

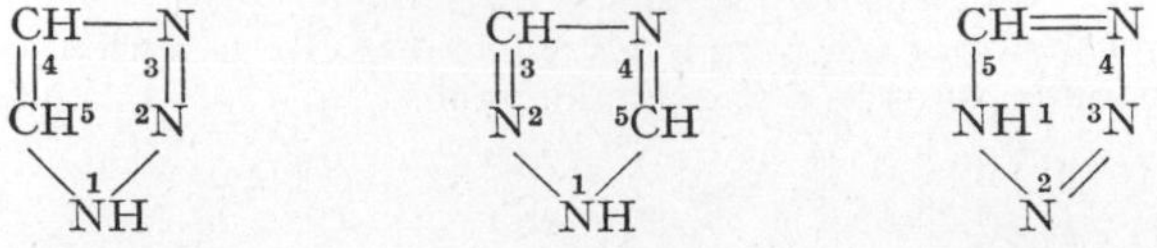

```
CH——N            CH——N            CH══N
||4   3||        ||3   4||        |5    4|
CH5  2N          N2   5CH         NH1  3N
  \ 1 /            \ 1 /            \ 2 //
   NH               NH                N
osotriazole       triazole        tetrazole
```

All are tautomeric substances. Osotriazoles may be prepared by oxidising osazones (p. 423).

A very remarkable five-membered ring is that in **sydnones**. These were prepared by Earl and Mackney (1935), and the peculiar feature of these compounds is that it is not possible to give them a structure which represents covalent bonds by the usual paired electrons, *e.g.*, sydnone (I, II, III). Dipole and infra-red studies indicate this compound is a resonance hybrid; it has been named a *meso-ionic structure* and may be written as (IV) (Baker *et al.*, 1955).

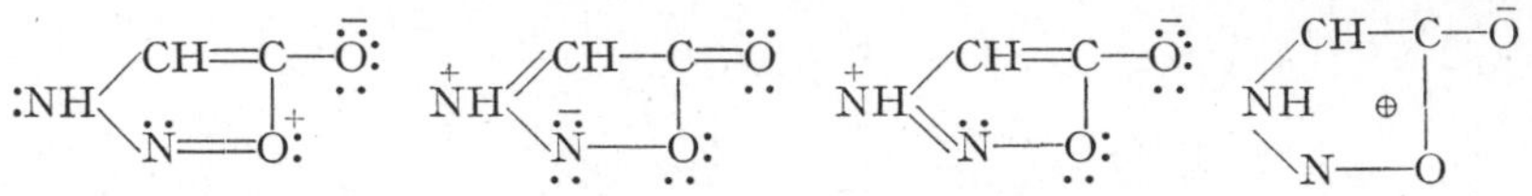

```
      /CH=C—Ö:        +  /CH—C=Ö       +  /CH=C—Ö:        /CH—C—Ō
:NH<       |+   ··    NH<  -   |  ··   NH<      |  ··    NH   ⊕  |
    \N==O:               \N——O:           \\N——O:          \N——O
                          ··  ··              ··
     (I)                  (II)             III)            (IV)
```

SIX-MEMBERED RINGS

PYRIDINE AND ITS DERIVATIVES

Pyridine occurs in the light oil fraction of coal-tar and in bone oil, and is a decomposition product of several alkaloids. Pyridine is obtained from light oil by treating the latter with dilute sulphuric acid. This dissolves pyridine and other basic substances. The acid layer is neutralised with sodium hydroxide and the liquid repeatedly fractionated.

Pyridine is a colourless liquid, b.p. 115°, with a disagreeable odour. It is completely miscible with water and is hygroscopic. It is basic, and is only very slowly attacked by boiling concentrated nitric acid or chromic acid. It resembles benzene in many of its properties and this partly led Körner (1864) to adopt the ring structure for pyridine, a structure which is confirmed by synthesis.

Synthesis of pyridine. There are many methods available for the synthesis of pyridine, *e.g.*,

(i) By passing a mixture of acetylene and hydrogen cyanide through a red-hot tube:

$$2C_2H_2 + HCN \longrightarrow C_5H_5N \text{ (pyridine)}$$

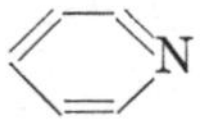

(ii) By passing a mixture of formaldehyde (1 part by volume), acetaldehyde (2 parts) and ammonia (1 part) over heated alumina (other compounds are also formed).

(iii) By heating the hydrochloride of pentamethylenediamine and oxidising the product, *piperidine*, with concentrated sulphuric acid at 300°:

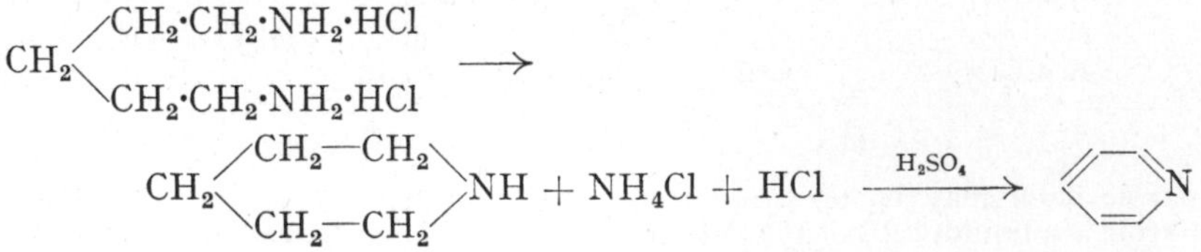

$$CH_2\begin{cases}CH_2{\cdot}CH_2{\cdot}NH_2{\cdot}HCl\\CH_2{\cdot}CH_2{\cdot}NH_2{\cdot}HCl\end{cases} \longrightarrow$$

$$CH_2\begin{cases}CH_2{-}CH_2\\CH_2{-}CH_2\end{cases}NH + NH_4Cl + HCl \xrightarrow{H_2SO_4} C_5H_5N \text{ (pyridine)}$$

(iv) By heating pyrrole with methylene iodide and sodium methoxide at 200°:

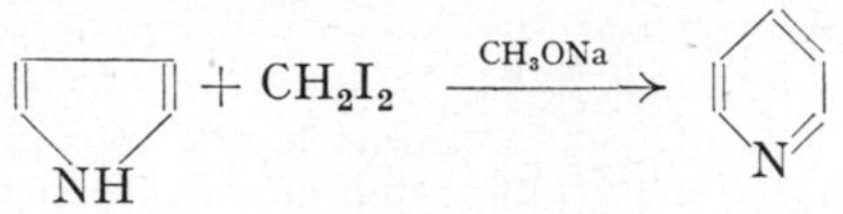

$$\text{pyrrole (NH)} + CH_2I_2 \xrightarrow{CH_3ONa} \text{pyridine (N)}$$

Pyridine derivatives may be prepared by various methods. One important method is the *Hantzsch pyridine synthesis* (1882). A β-dicarbonyl compound (2 mol.) is condensed with an aldehyde (1 mol.) and ammonia (1 mol.). The dihydropyridine derivative is obtained, and this gives the pyridine derivative on oxidation with nitric acid, *e.g.*,

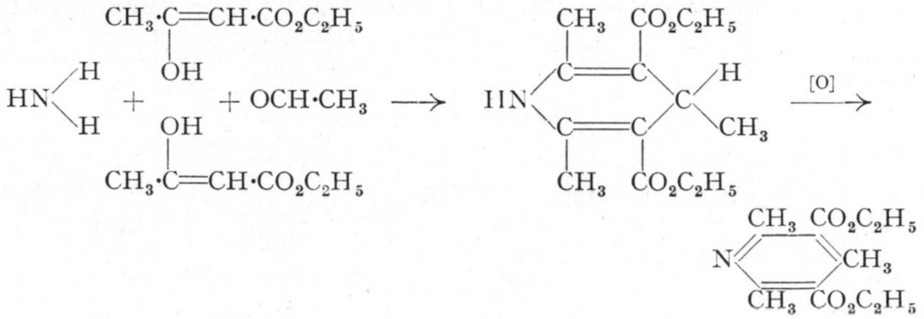

$$HN\begin{matrix}H\\H\end{matrix} + \begin{matrix}CH_3\cdot C{=}CH\cdot CO_2C_2H_5\\ |\\ OH\\ OH\\ |\\ CH_3\cdot C{=}CH\cdot CO_2C_2H_5\end{matrix} + OCH\cdot CH_3 \longrightarrow HN\begin{matrix}\overset{CH_3}{C}{=}\overset{CO_2C_2H_5}{C}\\ \underset{CH_3}{C}{=}\underset{CO_2C_2H_5}{C}\end{matrix}C\begin{matrix}H\\CH_3\end{matrix} \xrightarrow{[O]}$$

$$N\begin{matrix}\overset{CH_3}{=}\ \overset{CO_2C_2H_5}{}\\ \underset{CH_3}{=}\ \underset{CO_2C_2H_5}{}\end{matrix}CH_3$$

This ester can be hydrolysed and then decarboxylated to 2 : 4 : 6-trimethyl-pyridine.

If one molecule of ethyl acetoacetate and two molecules of acetaldehyde are used, the *dimethyl* derivative is obtained.

$$HN\begin{matrix}H\\H\end{matrix} + \begin{matrix}CH_3\cdot C{=}CH\cdot CO_2C_2H_5\\ |\\ OH\\ OH\\ |\\ CH{=}CH_2\end{matrix} + OCH\cdot CH_3 \longrightarrow HN\begin{matrix}\overset{CH_3}{C}{=}\overset{CO_2C_2H_5}{C}\\ CH{=}CH\end{matrix}C\begin{matrix}H\\CH_3\end{matrix} \xrightarrow[\text{(ii) } -CO_2]{\text{(i) [O]}}$$

$$N\begin{matrix}\overset{CH_3}{}\\ {=}\end{matrix}CH_3$$

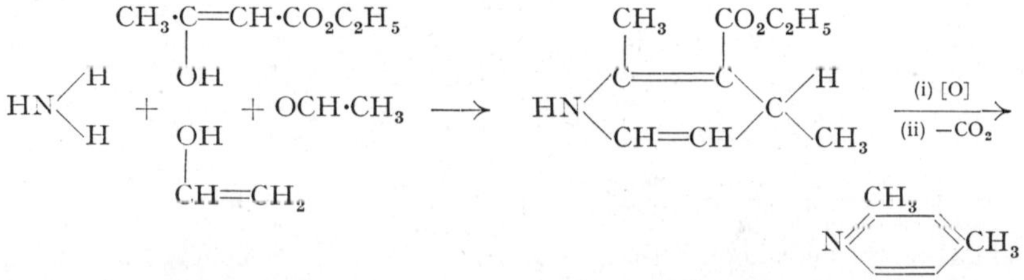

Reactions of pyridine. Pyridine can undergo substitution just as does benzene, but less easily than the latter. There are three possible mono-substitution products, and six disubstitution products if the two substituent groups are identical.

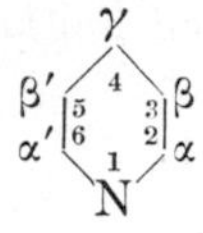

(pyridine ring numbered: N 1, α 2, β 3, γ 4, β′ 5, α′ 6)

(i) At ordinary temperatures, pyridine adds on halogen to form dihalides, *e.g.*, $C_5H_5\overset{+}{N}Br\}Br^-$. If, however, pyridine and bromine (or chlorine) are passed over a catalyst of pumice or charcoal at 300°, a mixture of 3-bromopyridine and 3 : 5-dibromopyridine is obtained; at 500° a mixture of the 2- and 2 : 6-bromo-derivatives is obtained. At 300° the reaction is probably electrophilic in character, whereas at 500° the mechanism is probably via free radicals. 3-Chloropyridine may be obtained by heating potassiopyrrole with chloroform and sodium ethoxide (see p. 719). 2- and 4-Chloropyridines may be obtained by diazotising the corresponding amino-compounds in concentrated hydrochloric acid and treating with cuprous chloride.

Halogen in the 2- or 4-position is reactive, being fairly readily replaced by OH, CN, NH_2, etc. In this respect these halogeno-pyridines resemble *o*- and *p*-chloronitrobenzenes (see later).

(ii) Pyridine reacts with nitric acid fairly readily only if a hydroxyl or an amino-group is present in the ring. Pyridine itself is nitrated to 3-nitro-pyridine by heating with concentrated sulphuric acid and potassium nitrate at 300°. 2- and 4-Nitropyridines may be obtained by oxidising the corresponding amino-compounds with hydrogen peroxide in sulphuric acid.

(iii) Sulphonation of pyridine is difficult, but when heated with concentrated sulphuric acid at 350° for some hours, pyridine gives pyridine-3-sulphonic acid. 2- and 4-Pyridinesulphonic acids may be prepared by oxidation of the corresponding thiols (prepared by the action of potassium hydrogen sulphide on the chloropyridine).

The sulphonic acid group can be replaced by hydroxyl or by the cyano-group. Fusion of pyridinesulphonic acid with potassium hydroxide is one method of preparing the monohydroxypyridines (*pyridols*). The structures of 2- and 4-hydroxypyridine have been the subject of much work. Originally, the hydroxy-structure, (I), was proposed, but it soon became apparent that this was unsatisfactory and so the ketonic formula (2-pyridone), (II), was proposed. X-Ray studies (Penfold, 1953) and infrared work (Gibson *et al.*, 1955) have indicated that the structure is (II) rather than (I).

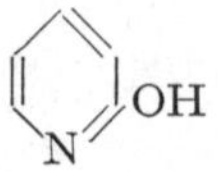

OH N (I) N O H (II)

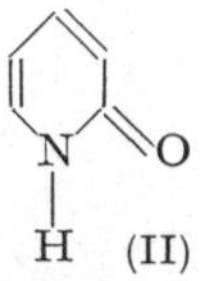

3-Hydroxypyridine exhibits true phenolic properties.

(iv) Pyridine may be fairly easily mercurated in the 3-position with aqueous mercuric acetate.

(v) When heated with sodamide in toluene solution, pyridine forms 2-aminopyridine; excess of sodamide produces 2 : 6-diaminopyridine (**Tschitschibabin (Chichibabin) reaction,** 1914). Actually, the sodium salts are formed, but on treatment with water, are hydrolysed to the amine.

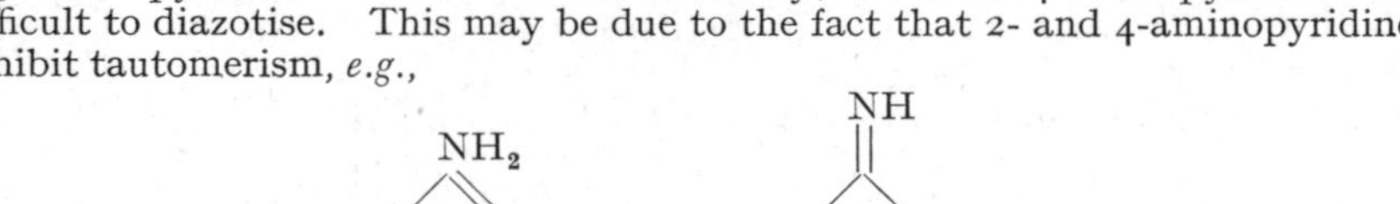

$$\text{C}_5\text{H}_5\text{N} + \text{NaNH}_2 \longrightarrow \text{(2-)NH}_2\text{-pyridine} + \text{NaH} \longrightarrow \text{(2-)NHNa-pyridine} + \text{H}_2$$

The three monoaminopyridines can be obtained by means of the Hofmann reaction on the amides of the pyridine monocarboxylic acids.

3-Aminopyridine can be diazotised easily; 2- and 4-aminopyridines are difficult to diazotise. This may be due to the fact that 2- and 4-aminopyridines exhibit tautomerism, *e.g.*,

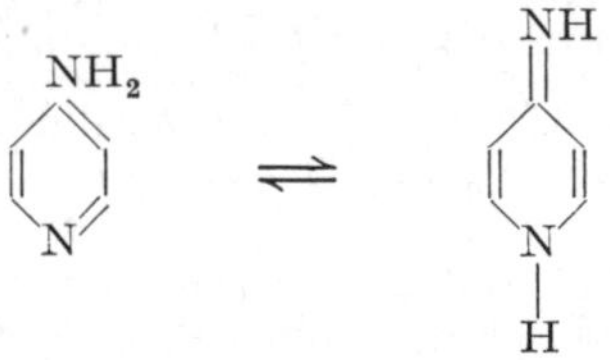

$$\text{NH}_2\text{ (4-aminopyridine)} \rightleftharpoons \text{NH (4-imino-1H-pyridine, N–H)}$$

Angyal *et al.* (1952), from an examination of the infrared absorption spectra, have concluded that 2- and 4-aminopyridine (and aminoquinolines) are mainly in the amino form.

(vi) Pyridine is a strong tertiary base, forming salts with inorganic acids, *e.g.*, *pyridine hydrochloride* or *pyridinium chloride*, $\{C_5H_5\overset{+}{N}H\}Cl^-$. Pyridine forms quaternary salts when heated with alkyl halides, *e.g.*, *pyridine methiodide* or N-*methylpyridinium iodide*, $\{C_5H_5\overset{+}{N}{\cdot}CH_3\}I^-$. This, when heated at 300°, gives 2- and 4-methylpyridines (*cf.* alkylanilines, p. 549).

(vii) Sodium and ethanol, electrolytic reduction, or catalytic reduction using nickel, convert pyridine into piperidine (see later). On the other hand, when pyridine is heated with hydriodic acid at 300°, the ring is opened with the formation of *n*-pentane and ammonia.

(viii) Pyridine is oxidised by perbenzoic acid to pyridine-1-oxide. Dipole moment studies have shown it to be a resonance hybrid of the following resonating structures (Linton, 1940; Ochiai, 1953):

$$\overset{+}{N}-O^- \longleftrightarrow \overset{+}{N}=O \longleftrightarrow \overset{+}{N}=O \longleftrightarrow N-O^- \longleftrightarrow N-O^-$$

In general, *N*-oxides may be prepared by direct oxidation with peracetic acid, but in a number of cases perbenzoic or monoperphthalic acid may be used.

(ix) When pyridine is treated with sodium, and the disodio-derivative so produced is exposed to the air, 4 : 4′-dipyridyl is formed:

$$2Na + 2\,C_5H_5N \longrightarrow NaN{<}C_5H_4{>}CH\text{—}CH{<}C_5H_4{>}NNa \xrightarrow{O_2} N{<}C_5H_4{>}\text{—}{<}C_5H_4{>}N$$

(x) When heated with *n*-butyl-lithium, pyridine forms 2-*n*-butylpyridine (Ziegler *et al.*, 1930).

$$C_5H_5N + C_4H_9Li \longrightarrow \text{(N-Li, 2-H, 2-}C_4H_9\text{ dihydropyridine)} \longrightarrow 2\text{-}C_4H_9C_5H_4N + LiH$$

Pyridine is a resonance hybrid of two Kekulé structures (the resonance energy is 31 k. cal./mole), and this leaves the lone pair of the nitrogen atom free to unite with a proton:

$$\ddot{N} \longleftrightarrow \ddot{N} \qquad \ddot{N}H \longleftrightarrow \overset{+}{N}H \longleftrightarrow \overset{+}{N}H$$

In pyrrole the lone pair takes part in the resonance, and consequently is not so free to unite with a proton. Hence pyrrole is a much weaker base than pyridine.

Two types of electromeric effects are possible in pyridine, (I) and (II):

In (I) the 2, 4 and 6 positions are points of electron-deficiency, and hence attack at these positions is easy for nucleophilic reagents and difficult for electrophilic, and vice-versa at positions 3 and 5; *e.g.*, nitration and sulphonation (electrophilic reagents) give 3-substitution, whereas sodamide (the $:\ddot{N}H_2^-$ ion is the attacking reagent, and is nucleophilic) gives 2-substitution. In (II), the 3- and 5-positions are points of high electron-density, and consequently will be attacked by electrophilic reagents as in (I). Positions 2, 4 and 6 are unaffected and hence attack at these points is difficult. In any case, substitution in pyridine is not so easy as in benzene, thereby resembling nitrobenzene rather than benzene. This may be due to the fact that since electrophilic reagents are used in acid solution, pyridine is converted into the pyridinium ion, thereby preventing the lone pair of the nitrogen atom from participating in the electromeric effect.

In pyridine each carbon atom supplies one p_z electron, and the nitrogen atom (in the trigonal state) also one p_z electron to form the "closed circuit". Pyridine is an even-membered ring, and so is an *alternant* compound (p. 502). The nitrogen atom, however, is strongly electron-attracting, and so the electron cloud

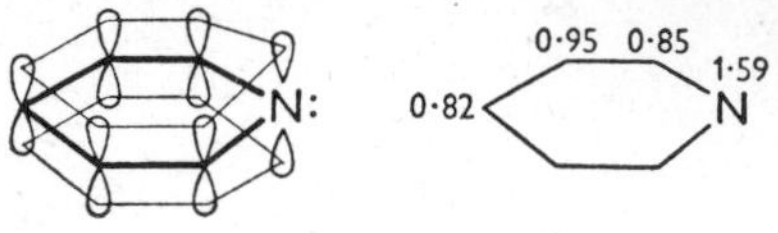

N: 0·95 0·85 1·59 0·82 N

FIG. 30.3.

is concentrated round the nitrogen atom, thereby decreasing *below unity* all charge densities on the carbon atoms. Position 3 has the highest π-electron density, and so *electrophilic* substitution will occur here most easily. *Nucleophilic* substitution will occur most readily at position 4 and almost as easily at position 2; actually substitution in the latter position usually takes place in practice. Some other factors, *e.g.*, bond order, polarisability, must therefore operate. It should be noted that pyridine is less easily attacked by electrophilic agents than is benzene, *i.e.*, the nitrogen atom deactivates the ring, a condition similar to that in nitrobenzene.

Pyridine finds great use in organic chemistry due mainly to its strong basic property and solvent properties. Because of its basic property, pyridine is used in many reactions where halogen acid is produced, or where it is desired to remove a molecule of halogen acid to form an unsaturated compound; *e.g.*, acetylation (with acetyl chloride), benzoylation (with benzoyl chloride), removal of hydrogen bromide from bromosuccinic ester to form the unsaturated ester (ethanolic potassium hydroxide would saponify the ester at the same time). Pyridine is used as a halogen carrier in Dam's solution (pyridine, bromine and sulphuric acid dissolved in glacial acetic acid) which is used for the determination of the iodine number (p. 247) of unsaturated compounds. Pyridine is used as a catalyst in the formation of Grignard reagents, and also as a solvent in the estimation of active hydrogen (see p. 333); it may be used in epimerisation (p. 425). Pyridine dissolves copper oxide (to give a modified Fehling's solution) and potassium permanganate, and these solutions may be used for oxidation purposes where aqueous solutions fail or are undesirable. Pyridine acts as a catalyst in the Perkin and Knoevenagel reactions, and forms complexes with many metallic salts and so may be used for their identification.

Pyridine homologues occur in coal-tar and bone oil. There are three methylpyridines and these are known as **picolines**. The methyl group in 2- and 4-picolines is reactive (*cf.* nitrotoluenes, p. 534); *e.g.*, 2-picoline condenses with acetaldehyde in the presence of warm aqueous sodium hydroxide to form 2-propenylpyridine:

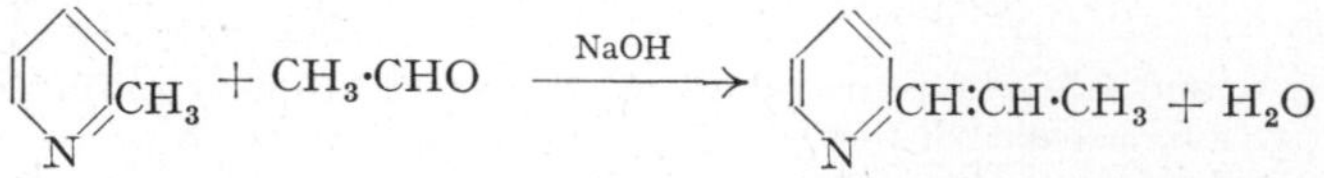

$$C_5H_4N{\cdot}CH_3 + CH_3{\cdot}CHO \xrightarrow{NaOH} C_5H_4N{\cdot}CH{:}CH{\cdot}CH_3 + H_2O$$

Oxidation of gaseous picolines with air at 380° over mixed vanadium–molybdenum oxides gives mainly the pyridine–aldehydes (Mathes *et al.*, 1955). There are six *dimethylpyridines* (**lutidines**) and six *trimethylpyridines* (**collidines**).

Pyridinecarboxylic acids. There are three monocarboxylic acids, and each may be obtained by oxidising the corresponding picoline:

picolinic acid — nicotinic acid — *iso*nicotinic acid

All three acids may be reduced to the corresponding piperidinecarboxylic acids by means of sodium and ethanol, or better, catalytically.

There are six pyridinedicarboxylic acids, but only two are important: **quinolinic acid** (*pyridine*-2 : 3-*dicarboxylic acid*), which is an oxidation product of quinoline, and **cinchomeronic acid** (*pyridine*-3 : 4-*dicarboxylic acid*), an oxidation product of *iso*quinoline.

Piperidine occurs in the alkaloid piperine. It may be prepared by reducing pyridine (see reaction vii), or by heating the hydrochloride of pentamethylenediamine:

$$CH_2\begin{cases}CH_2{\cdot}CH_2{\cdot}NH_2{\cdot}HCl\\CH_2{\cdot}CH_2{\cdot}NH_2{\cdot}HCl\end{cases} \longrightarrow \text{piperidine } (C_5H_{10}NH) \xleftarrow{Na/C_2H_5OH} \text{pyridine}$$

It is a colourless liquid, b.p. 106°, and gives the reactions of a secondary aliphatic amine. It is oxidised by concentrated sulphuric acid at 300° to pyridine.

Methods of ring fission. Many heterocyclic compounds (containing nitrogen) occur naturally, and an extremely important step in the determination of their structure is to ascertain the disposition of the carbon atoms. A common procedure is to first reduce the heterocyclic compounds, and then open the ring of the product by the following methods (in which piperidine is used as the example):

(i) *Secondary* cyclic amines may be opened by treatment with 3 per cent. hydrogen peroxide, *e.g.*, piperidine gives δ-aminovaleraldehyde:

$$CH_2\begin{cases}CH_2{-}CH_2\\CH_2{-}CH_2\end{cases}NH \xrightarrow{H_2O_2} NH_2{\cdot}CH_2{\cdot}CH_2{\cdot}CH_2{\cdot}CH_2{\cdot}CHO$$

(ii) *Von Braun's method* (1910) may be used to open *secondary* cyclic amines by treating them with benzoyl chloride in the presence of aqueous sodium hydroxide, adding phosphorus tribromide and cooled bromine to the product, and then distilling under reduced pressure, *e.g.*,

$$CH_2\begin{cases}CH_2{-}CH_2\\CH_2{-}CH_2\end{cases}NH \xrightarrow{C_6H_5{\cdot}COCl} CH_2\begin{cases}CH_2{-}CH_2\\CH_2{-}CH_2\end{cases}N{\cdot}CO{\cdot}C_6H_5 \xrightarrow{PBr_3/Br_2}$$

benzoylpiperidine

$$\left[CH_2\begin{cases}CH_2{-}CH_2\\CH_2{-}CH_2\end{cases}NCBr_2{\cdot}C_6H_5\right] \longrightarrow Br{\cdot}(CH_2)_5{\cdot}Br + C_6H_5{\cdot}CN$$

It might be noted that this provides a good method of preparing 1 : 5-dibromopentane.

(iii) *von Braun cyanogen bromide reaction* (1900). This is the reaction of a tertiary amine with cyanogen bromide to form an alkyl bromide and a disubstituted cyanamide (p. 301):

$$R_3N + BrCN \longrightarrow RBr + R_2N{\cdot}CN$$

This reaction has been used in alkaloid chemistry for opening tertiary *cyclic* amines. The tertiary amine is treated with cyanogen bromide, and the product is then heated with constant boiling hydrobromic acid, *e.g.*, an *N*-alkylpiperidine:

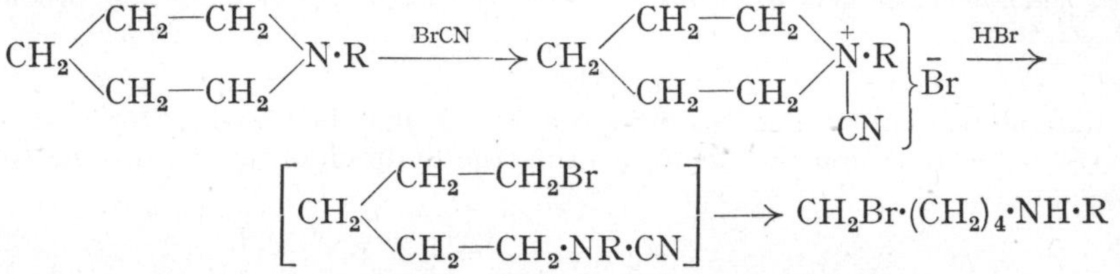

$$CH_2\begin{matrix}\diagup CH_2-CH_2 \diagdown \\ \diagdown CH_2-CH_2 \diagup\end{matrix}N{\cdot}R \xrightarrow{BrCN} CH_2\begin{matrix}\diagup CH_2-CH_2 \diagdown \\ \diagdown CH_2-CH_2 \diagup\end{matrix}\left.\overset{+}{N}{\cdot}R \atop \underset{CN}{|}\right\}\overset{-}{Br} \xrightarrow{HBr}$$

$$\left[CH_2\begin{matrix}\diagup CH_2-CH_2Br \\ \diagdown CH_2-CH_2{\cdot}NR{\cdot}CN\end{matrix}\right] \longrightarrow CH_2Br{\cdot}(CH_2)_4{\cdot}NH{\cdot}R$$

(iv) Piperidine may be converted into *n*-pentane by heating with hydriodic acid at 300°:

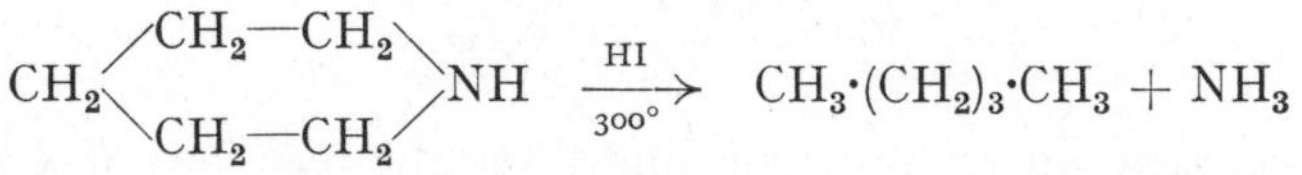

$$CH_2\begin{matrix}\diagup CH_2-CH_2 \diagdown \\ \diagdown CH_2-CH_2 \diagup\end{matrix}NH \xrightarrow[300^\circ]{HI} CH_3{\cdot}(CH_2)_3{\cdot}CH_3 + NH_3$$

(v) **Hofmann's exhaustive methylation method** (1881) is the most important method of opening heterocyclic rings, but it fails with unhydrogenated pyridine, quinoline and *iso*quinoline derivatives, and with hydrogenated quinolines. Consider piperidine as our example. This is heated with methyl iodide and the quaternary salt produced, dimethylpiperidinium iodide, is converted into the corresponding hydroxide by moist silver oxide. When this is heated, water is eliminated, a hydrogen atom in the β-*position* with respect to the nitrogen atom being eliminated, and the ring opened at the nitrogen atom on the *same* side as the β-hydrogen atom eliminated. The product is dimethyl-4-pentenylamine and this, when the above treatment is repeated, eliminates water (the β-hydrogen atom being removed) and trimethylamine, forming penta-1 : 4-diene. This, however, isomerises to *piperylene* (penta-1 : 3-diene). This isomerisation is general, an isolated double bond system always rearranging, if possible, to form a conjugated system (the double bond moving to the middle of the chain; see also p. 302 for mechanism):

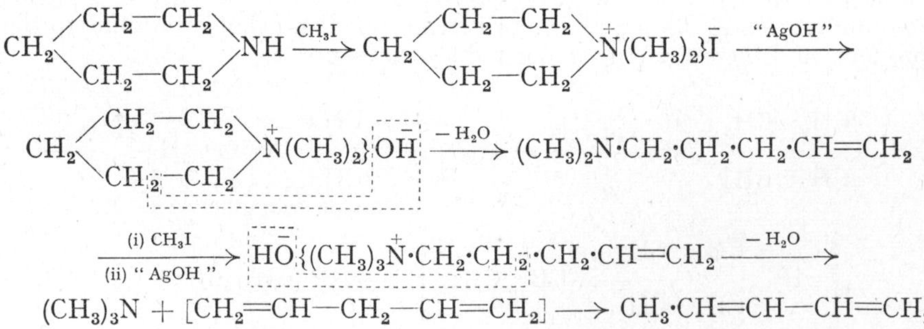

$$CH_2\begin{matrix}\diagup CH_2-CH_2 \diagdown \\ \diagdown CH_2-CH_2 \diagup\end{matrix}NH \xrightarrow{CH_3I} CH_2\begin{matrix}\diagup CH_2-CH_2 \diagdown \\ \diagdown CH_2-CH_2 \diagup\end{matrix}\overset{+}{N}(CH_3)_2\}\overset{-}{I} \xrightarrow{\text{"AgOH"}}$$

$$CH_2\begin{matrix}\diagup CH_2-CH_2 \diagdown \\ \diagdown CH_2-CH_2 \diagup\end{matrix}\overset{+}{N}(CH_3)_2\}\overset{-}{OH} \xrightarrow{-H_2O} (CH_3)_2N{\cdot}CH_2{\cdot}CH_2{\cdot}CH_2{\cdot}CH{=}CH_2$$

$$\xrightarrow[\text{(ii) "AgOH"}]{\text{(i) } CH_3I} H\overset{-}{O}\{(CH_3)_3\overset{+}{N}{\cdot}CH_2{\cdot}CH_2{\cdot}CH_2{\cdot}CH{=}CH_2 \xrightarrow{-H_2O}$$

$$(CH_3)_3N + [CH_2{=}CH-CH_2-CH{=}CH_2] \longrightarrow CH_3{\cdot}CH{=}CH-CH{=}CH_2$$

Quinoline is present in coal-tar and bone oil, and was first obtained from the alkaloid *quinine* by alkaline decomposition. It is obtained commercially from coal-tar, or prepared synthetically.

(i) **Skraup synthesis** (1880) is a very important method, and may be carried out by heating a mixture of aniline, nitrobenzene, glycerol, concentrated sulphuric acid and ferrous sulphate. Nitrobenzene acts as an oxidising agent, and ferrous sulphate makes the reaction less violent. Arsenic acid may be used instead of nitrobenzene and the former is better since the reaction is less violent. The mechanism of the Skraup synthesis is not certain. It is generally believed that the glycerol is converted into acraldehyde, and that the aniline adds on to this in the 3 : 4-positions (*cf.* p. 261):

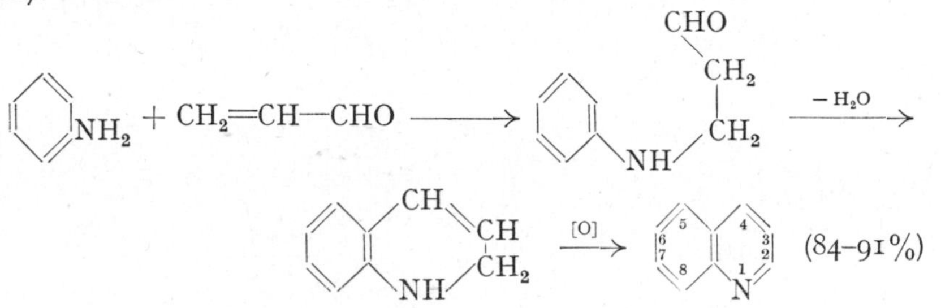

$C_6H_5NH_2 + CH_2{=}CH{-}CHO \longrightarrow C_6H_5NH{-}CH_2{-}CH_2{-}CHO \xrightarrow{-H_2O}$ (dihydroquinoline: CH, CH, CH_2, NH) $\xrightarrow{[O]}$ quinoline (84–91%)

In general, the Skraup synthesis may be carried out with any primary aromatic amine in which at least one position *ortho* to the amino-group is vacant. If both *o*-positions are vacant, then both quinolines are usually formed, *e.g.*,

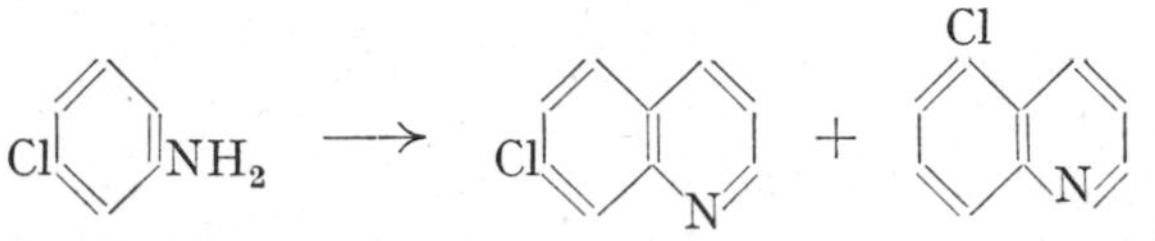

Cl-C$_6$H$_4$-NH$_2$ (*m*-chloroaniline) $\longrightarrow$ 7-chloroquinoline + 5-chloroquinoline

(ii) **Friedländer's synthesis** (1882) is another important method for synthesising quinoline and many of its derivatives; *e.g.*, quinoline is formed when *o*-aminobenzaldehyde is condensed with acetaldehyde in aqueous sodium hydroxide:

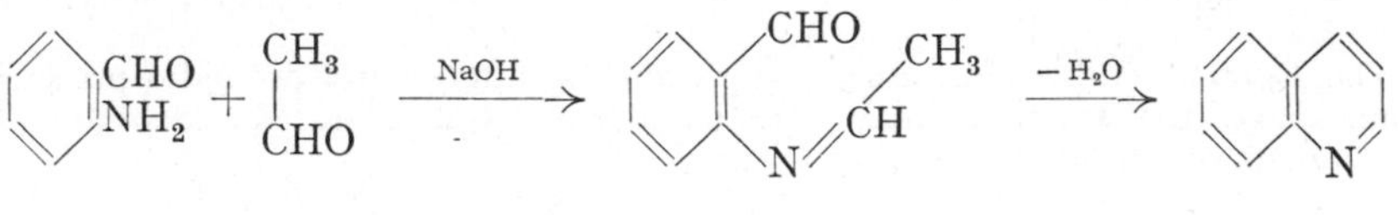

o-$C_6H_4(CHO)NH_2 + CH_3CHO \xrightarrow{NaOH} o$-$C_6H_4(CHO){-}N{=}CH{-}CH_3 \xrightarrow{-H_2O}$ quinoline

Derivatives of quinoline may be prepared by condensing *o*-aminoaldehydes or ketones with any aliphatic aldehyde or ketone containing the grouping $-CH_2{\cdot}CO-$:

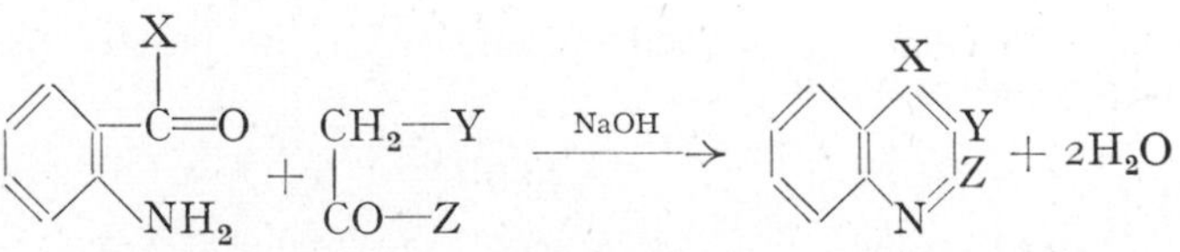

o-$C_6H_4(CX{=}O)NH_2 + CH_2Y{-}CO{-}Z \xrightarrow{NaOH}$ quinoline (4-X, 3-Y, 2-Z) $+ 2H_2O$

e.g., if X is CH_3, Y $CO_2C_2H_5$, and Z CH_3 (*i.e.*, the compound $YCH_2{\cdot}COZ$ is ethyl acetoacetate), the product is 2 : 4-dimethylquinoline-3-carboxylic ester.

(iii) Condensation between β-ketonic esters and primary aromatic amines produces quinolines, the nature of the product depending on the conditions, *e.g.*, aniline and E.A.A.

(*a*)

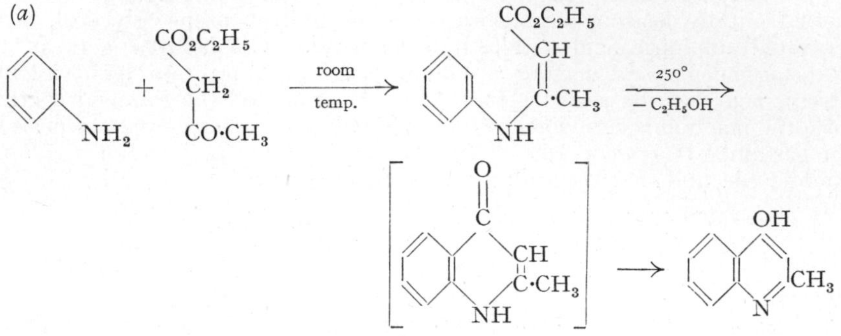

$$C_6H_5NH_2 + CH_2(CO_2C_2H_5)(CO \cdot CH_3) \xrightarrow[\text{temp.}]{\text{room}} C_6H_5NH\cdot C(CH_3){=}CH\cdot CO_2C_2H_5 \xrightarrow[-C_2H_5OH]{250^\circ} \left[\text{4-keto-2-methyl-1,4-dihydroquinoline}\right] \rightarrow \text{4-hydroxy-2-methylquinoline}$$

(*b*)

$$C_6H_5NH_2 + CH_2(CO\cdot CH_3)(CO_2C_2H_5) \xrightarrow{110^\circ} C_6H_5NH\cdot CO\cdot CH_2\cdot CO\cdot CH_3 \xrightarrow[-H_2O]{H_2SO_4} \left[\text{4-methyl-2-quinolone}\right] \rightarrow \text{2-hydroxy-4-methylquinoline}$$

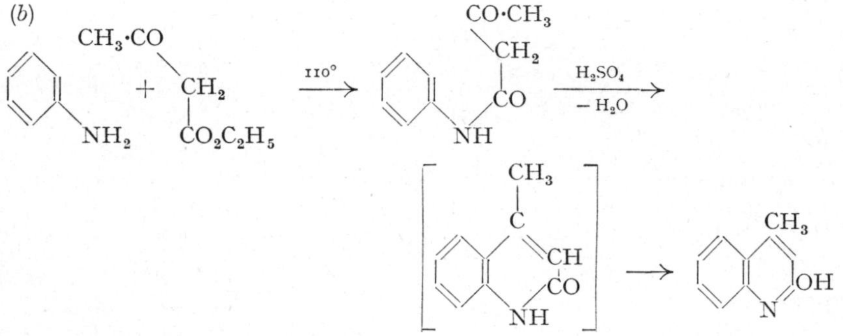

(iv) Homologues of quinoline may be prepared by the **Doebner–Miller synthesis** (1881); *e.g.*, aniline and paraldehyde heated with sulphuric acid form *quinaldine* (2-methylquinoline).

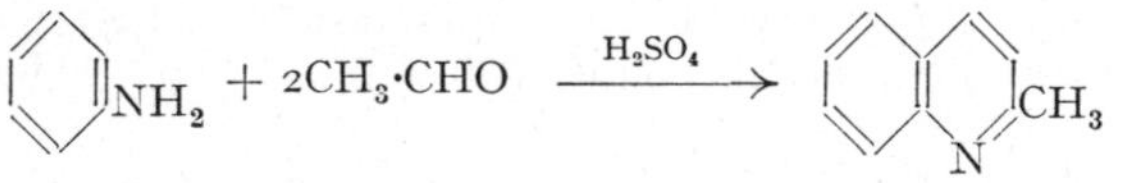

$$C_6H_5NH_2 + 2CH_3\cdot CHO \xrightarrow{H_2SO_4} \text{2-methylquinoline}$$

The Doebner–Miller synthesis is applicable to almost any aromatic primary amine, and the aldehyde may also be any α : β-unsaturated aldehyde (*cf.* mechanism of Skraup reaction):

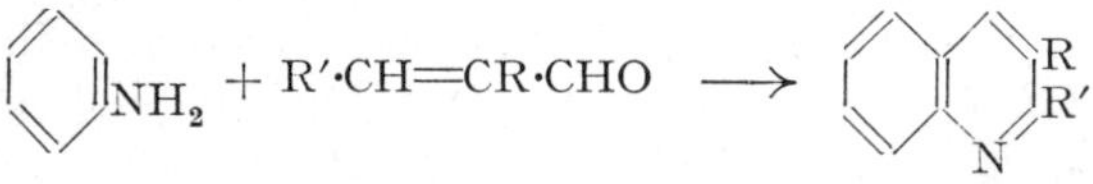

$$C_6H_5NH_2 + R'\cdot CH{=}CR\cdot CHO \longrightarrow \text{3-R-2-R'-quinoline}$$

(v) **Pfitzinger reaction** (1886). This is carried out by heating isatin with alkali in the presence of a ketone, *e.g.*,

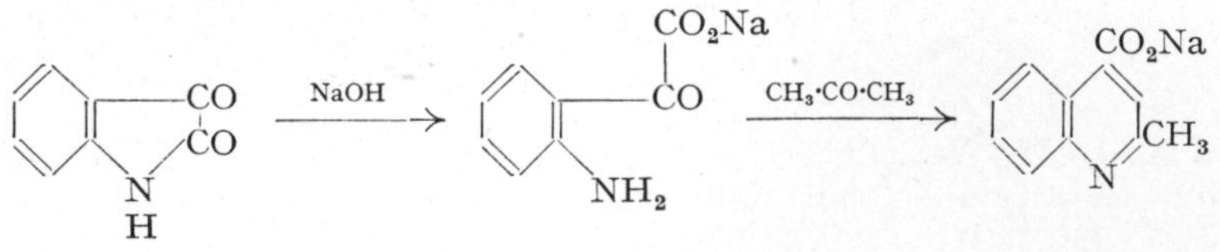

$$\text{isatin} \xrightarrow{NaOH} o\text{-}NH_2C_6H_4\cdot CO\cdot CO_2Na \xrightarrow{CH_3\cdot CO\cdot CH_3} \text{2-methylquinoline-4-}CO_2Na$$

Quinoline is a colourless oil, b.p. 238°, sparingly soluble in water but completely miscible with ethanol and ether. It is a tertiary base and forms salts with inorganic acids; with alkyl halides it forms *quinolinium salts* (quaternary salts), *e.g.*, with methyl iodide it forms *quinoline methiodide* or N-*methylquinolinium iodide*, (I); with methyl sulphate in forms *quinoline methylmethosulphate* or N-*methylquinolinium methyl sulphate*, (II):

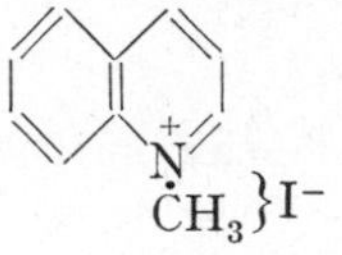

$\overset{+}{N}$ $CH_3\}I^-$
(I)

$\overset{+}{N}$ $CH_3\}\bar{S}O_4CH_3$
(II)

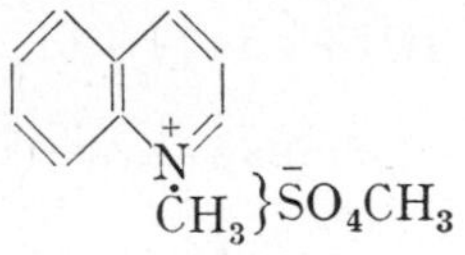

Quinoline is oxidised by permanganate to quinolinic acid (p. 731). The methyl group in the 2-position (quinaldine) and in the 4-position (lepidine) is very active and undergoes many condensation reactions (see cyanine dyes, p. 766).

The nitrogen atom deactivates the pyridine ring, and so substituents enter the benzene ring. Calculation of charge densities shows that position 8 will be attacked preferentially by electrophilic reagents, and position 2 by nucleophilic reagents. In practice, nitration gives a mixture of 5- and 8-nitroquinolines; therefore some other factors must operate (*cf.* pyridine).

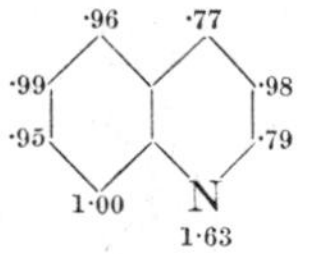

·96 ·77 ·99 ·98 ·95 ·79 1·00 N 1·63

***iso*Quinoline** is always present with quinoline, and it may be separated from the latter by converting both compounds into their sulphates; these are separated by fractional crystallisation from ethanol in which *iso*quinoline sulphate is only sparingly soluble. *iso*Quinoline is a decomposition product of many alkaloids. It may be synthesised in many ways, *e.g.*, (i) By passing benzylidene-ethylamine vapour through a red-hot tube:

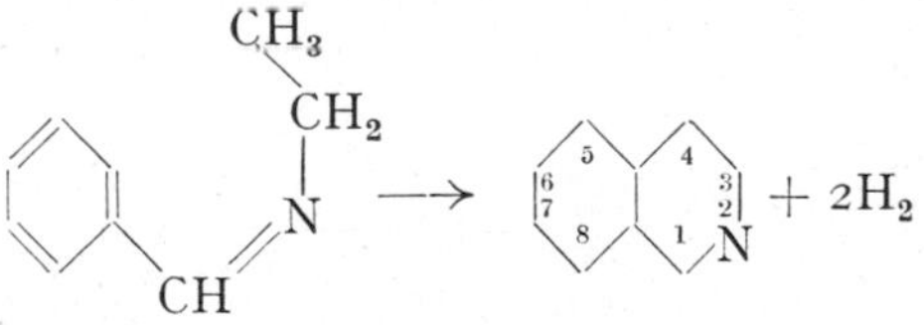

CH_3 CH_2 N CH $\longrightarrow$ 5 4 6 7 8 1 3 2 N $+ 2H_2$

(ii) By heating ammonium homophthalate, treating the product, homophthalimide, with phosphoryl chloride, and reducing the dichloro-compound so produced with hydriodic acid and red phosphorus:

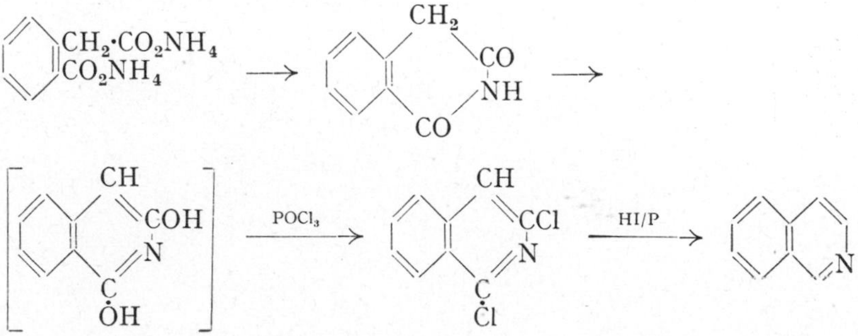

$CH_2 \cdot CO_2NH_4$ CO_2NH_4 $\longrightarrow$ CH_2 CO NH CO $\longrightarrow$

[CH COH N C OH] $\xrightarrow{POCl_3}$ CH CCl N C Cl $\xrightarrow{HI/P}$ N

(iii) By heating the oxime of cinnamaldehyde with phosphorus pentoxide:

CH CH CH N·OH → [CH CH N CHOH] $\xrightarrow{-H_2O}$ N

The formation of *iso*quinoline, and not quinoline, can only be explained by assuming that the oxime first undergoes the Beckmann transformation (p. 638), which is then followed by ring closure.

In addition to the above methods for *iso*quinoline itself, there are also three important methods which have a wide application. In the first two, partially reduced *iso*quinolines are obtained, but these may be readily dehydrogenated to the corresponding *iso*quinolines.

Bischler–Napieralski reaction (1893). In this method a β-phenylethylamide is made to undergo cyclodehydration to a 3 : 4-dihydro*iso*quinoline by heating with phosphorus pentoxide or anhydrous zinc chloride at high temperature; or better still, with phosphoryl chloride, phosphorus pentachloride, etc., at lower temperatures (about 140°).

CH_2 CH_2 NH R·CO $\xrightarrow{-H_2O}$ N R $\xrightarrow[(-H_2)]{Pd}$ N R

Dehydrogenation to the *iso*quinoline may be effected by heating the dihydro-compound with sulphur or selenium, or catalytically with, *e.g.*, palladium black.

*iso*Quinolines can be obtained directly by using β-hydroxyethylamides, *e.g.*,

OH CH CH_2 NH HCO $\xrightarrow{P_2O_5}$ N

Pictet–Spengler reaction (1911). Condensation between a β-arylethylamine and an aldehyde in the presence of a large excess of hydrochloric acid at 100° produces a 1 : 2 : 3 : 4-tetrahydro*iso*quinoline. This reaction, however, is successful only if the aromatic nucleus contains a hydroxyl or an alkoxyl group *para* to the position of ring closure. The tetrahydro-compound may be

RO CH_2 CH_2 NH_2 + R′·CHO → RO CH_2 CH_2 N R′·CH $\xrightarrow[100°]{20\% \ HCl}$

RO CH_2 CH_2 NH CH R′

converted into the *iso*quinoline by catalytic dehydrogenation, or by heating with an ethanolic solution of iodine containing sodium acetate, or by heating with mercuric acetate.

Pomeranz–Fritsch reaction (1893). This is carried out by condensing an aromatic aldehyde with an aminoacetal and then cyclising the product with sulphuric acid, *e.g.*,

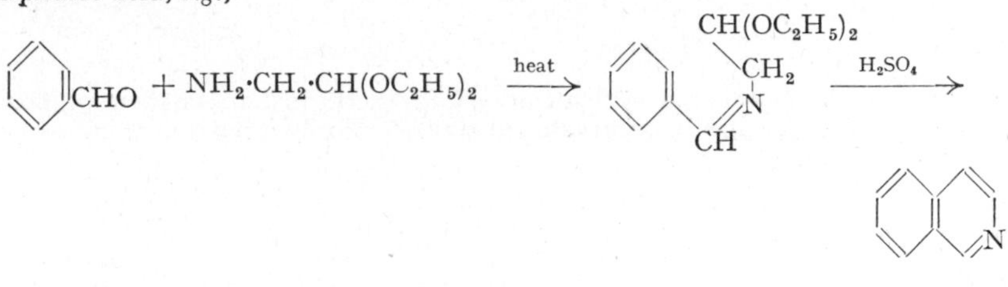

If an aromatic ketone is used instead of the aldehyde, then the product is a 1-substituted *iso*quinoline, *e.g.*,

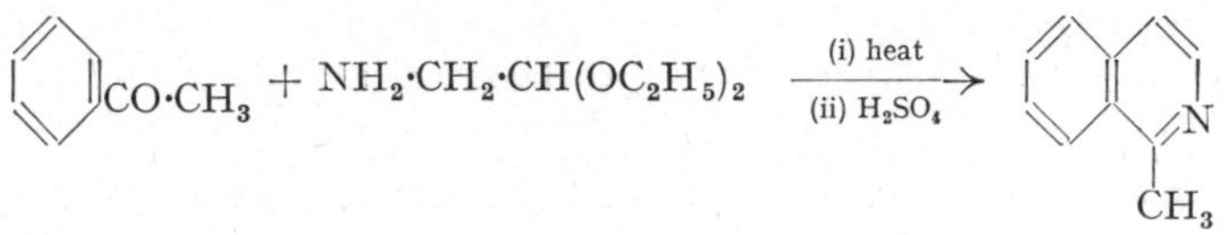

*iso*Quinoline is a colourless solid (or liquid), m.p. 23°, and resembles quinoline in many of its properties. It is oxidised by permanganate to a mixture of phthalic and cinchomeronic acids (p. 731).

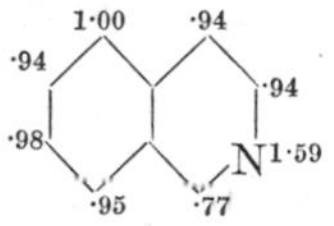

Nitration occurs at positions 5 and 8 in *iso*quinoline; the former agrees with expectations from charge densities, but position 7 would have been expected to be the next position to be attacked (*cf.* quinoline).

Acridine occurs in the anthracene fraction of coal-tar. It may be synthesised by passing the vapour of benzylaniline or *o*-aminodiphenylmethane through a red hot tube (note the two methods of numbering):

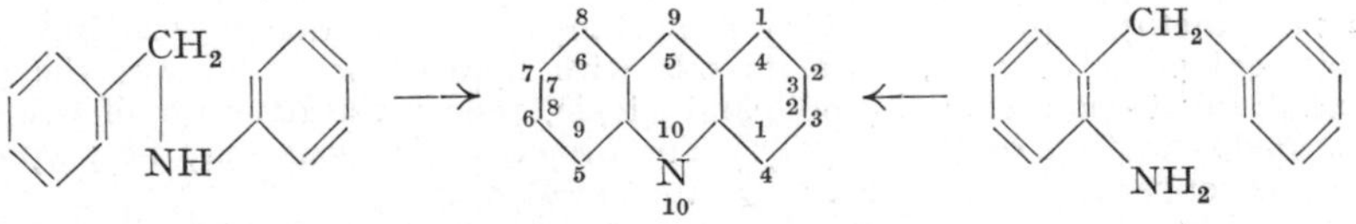

Acridine is a colourless solid, m.p. 110°; it is a tertiary base, but weaker than quinoline. It is the parent substance of a number of dyes and antiseptics (p. 765).

SIX-MEMBERED RINGS WITH ONE OXYGEN ATOM

The simplest six-membered rings with one oxygen atom are **1 : 2-** (or α-) **pyran,** (I), and **1 : 4-** (or γ) **pyran,** (II). These, however, are unknown, but *dihydro-*

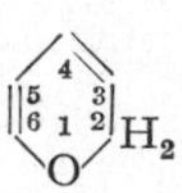

(I)

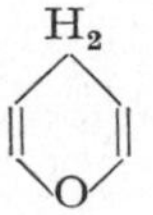

(II)

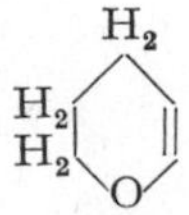

(III)

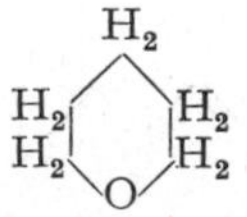

(IV)

(III) and *tetrahydropyran* (IV) have been prepared. The pyranose sugars (p. 431) are derivatives of tetrahydropyran.

The corresponding keto-derivatives of the pyrans are known as **pyrones**:

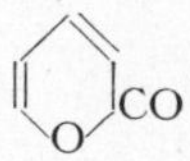

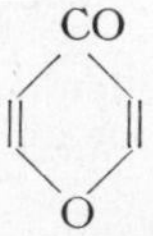

α-pyrone γ-pyrone

γ-Pyrone may be prepared by heating *chelidonic acid* just above its m.p. (262°). Chelidonic acid (a naturally occurring substance) may be prepared from acetone and ethyl oxalate.

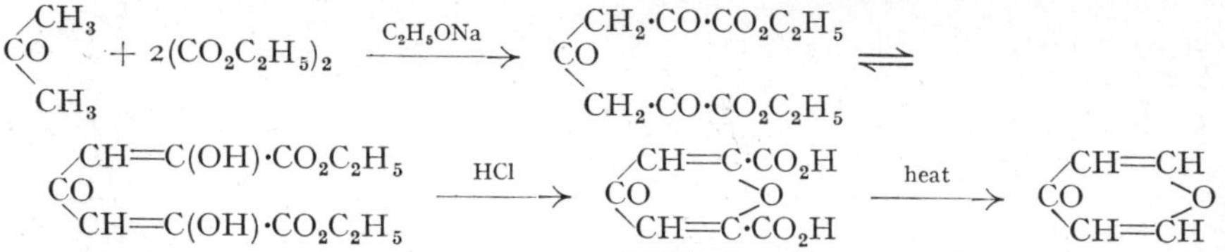

$$CO(CH_3)_2 + 2(CO_2C_2H_5)_2 \xrightarrow{C_2H_5ONa} CO(CH_2\cdot CO\cdot CO_2C_2H_5)_2 \rightleftharpoons$$

$$CO(CH{=}C(OH)\cdot CO_2C_2H_5)_2 \xrightarrow{HCl} \text{chelidonic acid} \xrightarrow{heat} \gamma\text{-pyrone}$$

chelidonic acid

γ-Pyrone, m.p. 32·5°, is basic and shows some aromatic properties, and so it is possibly a resonance hybrid with contributing structures such as (III). γ-Pyrone

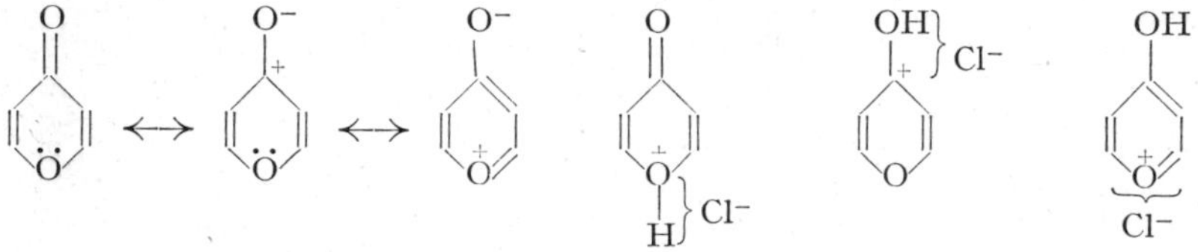

(I) (II) (III) (IV) (V) (VI)

does *not* form an oxime or phenylhydrazone. Similarly, the structure of γ-pyrone salts may be (VI) rather than (IV). According to Brown (1951), however, calculation of general charge distribution suggests (V) as the structure of the oxonium salts (this corresponds to (II) for γ-pyrone itself).

2 : 6-Dimethyl-γ-pyrone is a very important derivative of γ-pyrone from the theoretical point of view, since its salt with hydrochloric acid was the first *oxonium* salt to be prepared (Collie and Tickle, 1899); the structure of this salt corresponds to that of (V) or (VI). The dimethyl-γ-pyrone may be prepared from the copper salt of ethyl acetoacetate as follows:

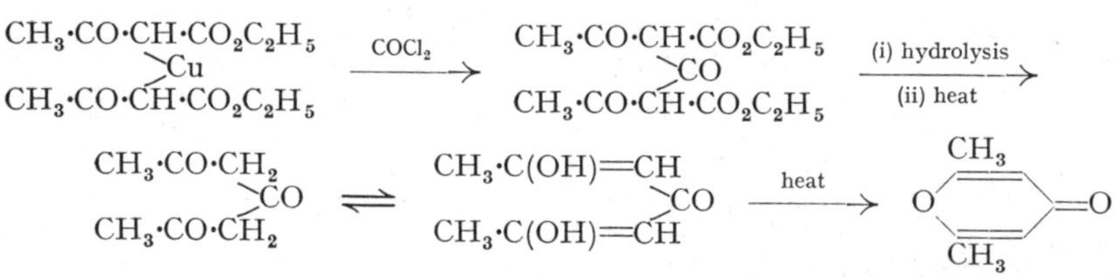

$$(CH_3\cdot CO\cdot CH\cdot CO_2C_2H_5)_2Cu \xrightarrow{COCl_2} (CH_3\cdot CO\cdot CH\cdot CO_2C_2H_5)_2CO \xrightarrow[\text{(ii) heat}]{\text{(i) hydrolysis}}$$

$$(CH_3\cdot CO\cdot CH_2)_2CO \rightleftharpoons (CH_3\cdot C(OH){=}CH)_2CO \xrightarrow{heat} \text{2:6-dimethyl-}\gamma\text{-pyrone}$$

Condensed pyrone systems are important since many occur naturally:

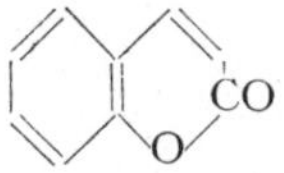

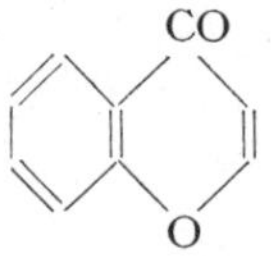

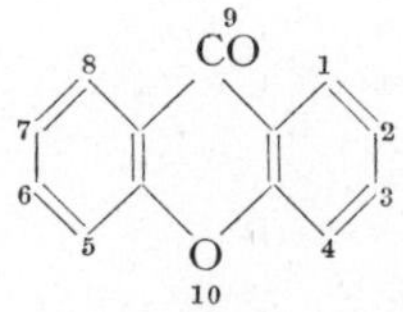

α-benzopyrone *or* coumarin (α-chromone)

γ-benzopyrone (γ-chromone)

xanthone

α-**Flavone** is 2-phenyl-γ-chromone, and many of its derivatives are the colouring matter of flowers:

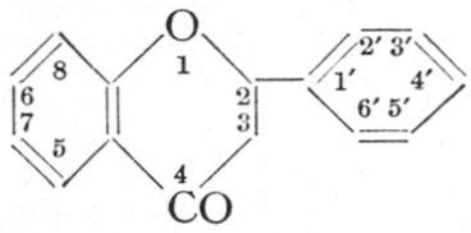

O 1 2 3 4 CO 5 6 7 8 2′ 3′ 1′ 4′ 6′ 5′

SIX-MEMBERED RINGS WITH TWO NITROGEN ATOMS

These are known collectively as the *diazines*, and the *o*-, *m*- and *p*-isomers are called *pyridazines* (*oiazines*), *pyrimidines* (*miazines*) and *pyrazines* (*piazines*), respectively:

pyridazine b.p. 208° | pyrimidine m.p. 22° | pyrazine m.p. 53°

The corresponding *benzodiazines* are:

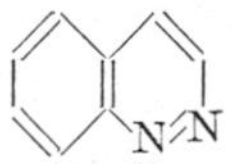

cinnoline 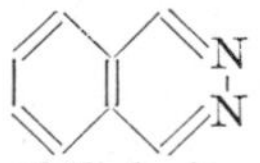 | phthalazine  | quinazoline 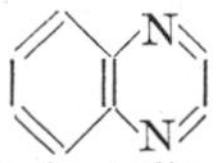 | quinoxaline

The pyrimidines are a particularly important group of compounds, since the pyrimidine nucleus occurs in purines, nucleic acids and synthetic barbiturates (p. 369). Barbituric acid may be regarded as 2 : 4 : 6-trihydroxypyrimidine, and pyrimidine may be prepared from barbituric acid as follows:

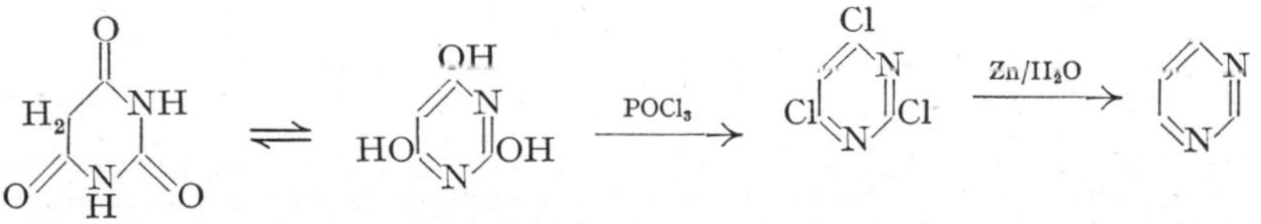

$\rightleftharpoons$ (HO, OH, OH pyrimidine) $\xrightarrow{POCl_3}$ (Cl, Cl, Cl pyrimidine) $\xrightarrow{Zn/H_2O}$ pyrimidine

A very important general method for preparing pyrimidines is the condensation between a β-dicarbonyl compound and a compound which has the amidine structure, *e.g.*, 6-hydroxy-2 : 4-dimethylpyrimidine from ethyl acetoacetate and acetamidine.

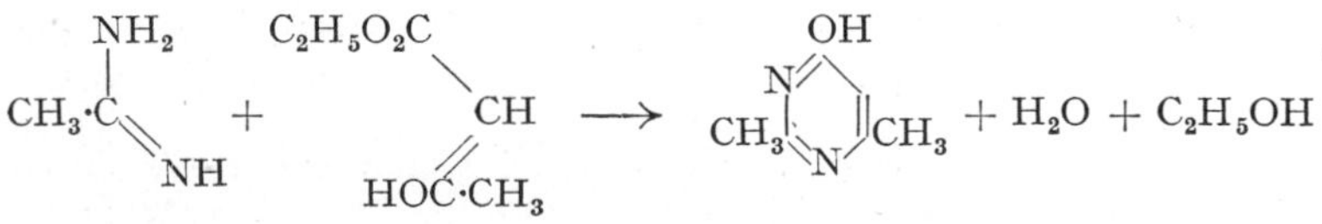

$$CH_3{\cdot}C(NH_2){=}NH + C_2H_5O_2C{\cdot}CH{=}C(OH){\cdot}CH_3 \longrightarrow \text{(OH, }CH_3\text{, }CH_3\text{ pyrimidine)} + H_2O + C_2H_5OH$$

Some pyrimidines found in nucleic acids are:

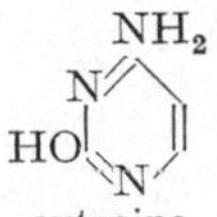

cytosine 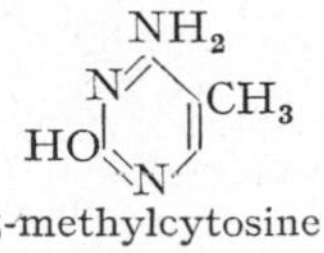 | 5-methylcytosine 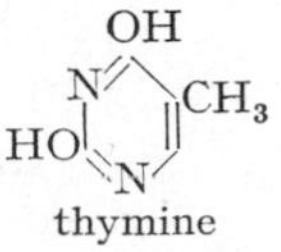 | thymine 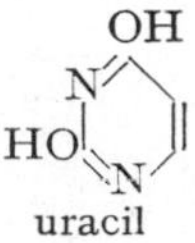 | uracil

QUESTIONS

1. Discuss the preparation and properties of furan, furfural and furoic acid.
2. Describe the preparation of thiophen, and compare and contrast the behaviour of the sulphur atom in thiophen with that in the alkyl sulphides.
3. Describe the preparation of pyrrole and compare and contrast its reactions with phenol and aniline.
4. Name the compounds and state the conditions under which they are formed when pyridine is treated with:—(*a*) reducing agents, (*b*) oxidising agents, (*c*) Br_2, (*d*) HNO_3, (*e*) H_2SO_4, (*f*) $(AcO)_2Hg$, (*g*) $NaNH_2$, (*h*) MeI, (*i*) Na.
5. Write an essay on the methods of opening heterocyclic rings containing one nitrogen atom.
6. Suggest a synthesis for each of the following compounds:—(*a*) furan-3 : 4-dicarboxylic acid, (*b*) 6-nitroquinoline, (*c*) 7-methylquinoline, (*d*) 2 : 3 : 4-trimethylquinoline, (*e*) 7-nitro-2 : 3-dimethylquinoline, (*f*) 1-methyl*iso*quinoline.
7. Write an account of the analytical and synthetic evidence for the structure of:—(*a*) quinoline, (*b*) *iso*quinoline.
8. Discuss the use of E.A.A. in the synthesis of heterocyclic compounds.
9. Define and give examples of:—(*a*) Paal–Knorr synthesis, (*b*) Knorr synthesis, (*c*) Hantzsch synthesis, (*d*) Fischer's indole synthesis, (*e*) Hofmann's exhaustive methylation method, (*f*) Skraup's synthesis, (*g*) Friedländer's quinoline synthesis, (*h*) Hantzsch pyridine synthesis, (*i*) Doebner–Miller synthesis, (*j*) Lipp synthesis, (*k*) Reissert synthesis, (*l*) Chichibabin reaction, (*m*) Pfitzinger reaction, (*n*) Bischler–Napieralski reaction, (*o*) Pictet–Spengler reaction, (*p*) Pomeranz–Fritsch reaction.
10. Discuss the procedure and results of the exhaustive methylation of:—(*a*) 3-methylpyrrole, (*b*) indole, (*c*) quinoline, (*d*) *iso*quinoline.
11. Describe the preparation and properties of:—(*a*) pyrazole, (*b*) glyoxaline, (*c*) oxazoles, (*d*) *iso*-oxazoles, (*e*) thiazole, (*f*) sydnones, (*g*) pyrones, (*h*) pyrimidine, (*i*) antipyrine.

READING REFERENCES

The Ring Index, Reinhold Publishing Co.
Mitchell, *British Chemical Nomenclature*, Arnold (1948).
Sidgwick, *The Organic Chemistry of Nitrogen*. Oxford Press (New Ed. by Taylor and Baker, 1937). Ch. XVII. Five-Membered Rings. Ch. XVIII. Six-Membered Rings.
Morton, *The Chemistry of Heterocyclic Compounds*. McGraw-Hill (1946).
Schofield, The Nitration of Heterocyclic Nitrogen Compounds. *Quart. Reviews (Chem. Soc.)*, 1950, **4**, 382.
Elderfield (Editor), *Heterocyclic Compounds*, Wiley (1950—).
Gilman, *Advanced Organic Chemistry*, Wiley (1953). Vol. IV, Ch. 8. Heterocyclic Chemistry.
Finar, *Organic Chemistry*, Vol. II. Longmans, Green (1956). Ch. XII. Heterocyclic Compounds Containing Two or more Hetero-atoms.
Organic Reactions, Wiley. Vol. VI (1951), Chh. 2, 3, 4. The Synthesis of *iso*Quinolines. Vol. VII (1953). Ch. 2. The Skraup Synthesis of Quinolines. Ch. 4. The von Braun Cyanogen Bromide Reaction.
Katritzky, The Chemistry of the Aromatic Heterocyclic *N*-Oxides, *Quart. Reviews (Chem. Soc.)*, 1956, **10**, 395.
Baker and Ollis, Meso-ionic Compounds, *ibid.*, 1957, **11**, 15.

CHAPTER XXXI

DYES

For a substance to act as a dye, certain conditions must be fulfilled, *viz.*,

(i) It must have a suitable colour.
(ii) It must be able to " fix " itself or be capable of being " fixed " to the fabric.
(iii) When fixed, it must not be fugitive, *i.e.*, it must be fast to light; and it must be resistant to the action of water and, to a certain extent (the more the better), to dilute acids and alkalis (particularly the latter on account of the alkaline nature of " washing soda ").

Many natural dyes have been known for a long time. These were obtained from animal and vegetable sources. Today, however, practically all dyes are synthetic and are prepared from aromatic compounds, the only source of which, until recently, was coal-tar; hence the name *coal-tar dyes*.

Colour. When white light (7,500–4,000 A) falls on a substance, the light may be totally reflected or totally absorbed. In the former case, the substance appears white; in the latter, black. If a certain proportion of the light is absorbed and the rest reflected, the substance has the colour of the *reflected* light. If only a *single* band is absorbed, the substance has the *complementary* colour (of the absorbed band).

TABLE X

(A)	Colour absorbed	Visible (complementary) colour
4000–4350	violet	yellow-green
4350–4800	blue	yellow
4800–4900	green-blue	orange
4900–5000	blue-green	red
5000–5600	green	purple
5600–5800	yellow-green	violet
5800–5950	yellow	blue
5950–6050	orange	green-blue
6050–7500	red	blue-green

If a substance absorbs all visible light except one band, which it reflects, the substance will have the colour of that reflected band. Thus a substance can appear blue because it absorbs the yellow portion of the spectrum only; or because it absorbs *all the visible spectrum except blue*. The shades, however, will be different. Apparently no dye gives a pure shade, *i.e.*, does not reflect only one band of wave-lengths; *e.g.*, malachite green reflects green light, but also, to a small extent, red, blue and violet.

Many substances which appear to be colourless nevertheless have absorption spectra, but in these cases, absorption takes place in the infrared or ultraviolet, and not in the region of the visible spectrum.

RELATION BETWEEN COLOUR AND CONSTITUTION

Graebe and Liebermann (1868) observed that organic colouring matter could be reduced to colourless compounds, and that when the hydrogen atoms (added by the reduction) were removed by oxidation, the original colour was regenerated. It was Witt (1876), however, who was the first to point out that colour usually appeared in an organic compound when that compound contained certain "unsaturated groups". Consider, for example, diazomethane and glyoxal. These are the simplest coloured organic compounds. Both contain "unsaturated groups", and on reduction diazomethane gives methylhydrazine, and glyoxal, glycol; both reduction products are colourless. It is important to note that the carbonyl group is referred to as an *unsaturated group* (by Witt). Its presence in a compound, however, does not give rise to unsaturation (see definition of unsaturation, p. 8). As will be seen subsequently, a more appropriate term than unsaturated group would have been a *group with multiple bonds*.

Witt called these groups with multiple bonds **chromophores**; some of the more important chromophoric groups are:

Nitro —$N\begin{smallmatrix}\nearrow\!\!\!\!/ O \\ \searrow O\end{smallmatrix}$ nitroso —N=O; azo —N=N—

azoxy —N=N→O (with a bond up from the second N) azoamino —N=N—NH—

carbonyl C=O thiocarbonyl C=S

Witt named the compound containing the chromophoric group, a **chromogen.** Experience has shown that if the chromogen contains only one chromophore, it is usually coloured (yellow), and that the depth of colour (see later) generally increases with the number of chromophores. A single C=C group is not sufficient to produce colour, but if a number of them are present in conjugation, colour may develop, *e.g.*, $CH_2{=}CH_2$ is colourless; $CH_3\cdot(CH{=}CH)_6\cdot CH_3$ is yellow.

Witt also pointed out that the presence of certain groups in the chromogen deepen colour, although these groups are not chromophores. These he called **auxochromes.** Auxochromes are acidic (phenolic) or basic, the most important being: OH, NH_2, NH·R and NR_2.

Radicals which bring about deepening of colour are known as **bathochromic groups,** and those which bring about the opposite effect, **hypsochromic groups.** Deepening of colour (in colour chemistry) means the change in colour as follows: yellow→orange→red→purple→violet→blue→green→black. Since visible colour is the complementary colour of the absorbed band, bathochromic groups shift the absorption maxima from the violet towards the red (*i.e.*, they *lower* the frequency of the light absorbed). Conversely, hypsochromic groups shift the absorption maxima from the red to the violet (*i.e.*, they *raise* the frequency of the light absorbed). Experience has shown that auxochromes are usually bathochromic, and that replacement of hydrogen in the NH_2 group by R or Ar generally has a bathochromic effect. On the other hand, acetylation of OH or NH_2 (*i.e.*, replacement of hydrogen by an acetyl group) generally has a hypsochromic effect.

Nietzki (1879) stated that increase in molecular weight deepened colour; *e.g.*, substitution of a naphthalene nucleus for benzene in azo-dyes, deepens the colour from yellow to red. Schütze (1892) showed that there were many exceptions to Nietzki's rule (it was Schütze who introduced the terms bathochrome and hypsochrome). Piccard (1913) also found that Nietski's rule was not always true, and showed that in these cases the introduction of the heavier group introduced a second absorption band at the blue end of the spectrum.

It has already been pointed out that in order to act as a dye, a substance must be capable of fixing itself or being fixed to the fabric. No chromogens act as a dye; the presence of a salt-forming group is necessary. Auxochromes are such groups and so, apart from their auxochromic properties (of deepening colour), they are also necessary to make the chromogen a dye. Thus auxochromes perform two functions. The sulphonic acid and carboxyl groups possess very little auxochromic properties; their presence, however, makes a chromogen a dye, the sulphonic acid group making the dye soluble in water, and the carboxyl group usually enabling the dye to form lakes (see later).

Armstrong (1885) pointed out that quinones (*o*- and *p*-) are coloured, and suggested that all colouring matters of known structure could generally be represented by a quinonoid structure. This meant that if the quinonoid structure was present, the substance would be coloured; if absent, colourless. This view was accepted quickly, but before long it was shown that the quinonoid formula could not be given to some coloured compounds, *e.g.*, fulvenes. It is important to note, however, that these compounds all contain conjugated double bonds (see later).

Armstrong's quinonoid theory was very useful since it stimulated further work on this problem of the relation between colour and constitution. Armstrong believed that the quinonoid structure accounted for the colour of nitrophenols, but no proof of this belief was forthcoming until Hantzsch (1906) prepared the two kinds of ethers (p. 600). Hantzsch was thus led to believe that change in colour involved a change in structure, and he also thought that the quinonoid structure was essential for the production of colour in compounds containing benzene rings. As time went on, however, Hantzsch changed his views about the significance of conjugation with respect to colour, and by 1919, he believed that some other factor played a part, *viz.*, the state of the molecule as a whole, and that it cannot be represented by a static formula (inset).

OH ⇌ O
NO_2 NO_2H

The relation between colour and constitution discussed above is empirical, and it is only recently that some headway has been made on the theoretical side of the problem. When light (this term will be used for electromagnetic waves of any wavelength) is absorbed by a molecule, the molecule undergoes transition from a state of lower to a state of higher energy. If E_1 is the original energy content of the molecule and E_2 the higher energy content, then $h\nu = E_2 - E_1 = \Delta E$, where h is Planck's constant and ν the frequency of the absorbed light. If the molecule is monatomic, the energy absorbed can only be used to raise the energy levels of the electrons, thereby changing the atom from its *ground* state to some *excited* state. If, however, the molecule consists of more than one atom, the light absorbed may bring about changes in electronic, rotational or vibrational energy. Since electronic transitions are associated with large amounts of energy relative to rotational and vibrational transitions, ΔE is large for the former, *i.e.*, ν is large (and consequently the wavelength is short); for the latter, ΔE is small, *i.e.*, ν is small (and consequently the wavelength is long). Thus changes in electronic states give absorption (or emission) in the visible and ultraviolet parts of the spectrum, whereas changes in rotational and vibrational energies give absorption (or emission) respectively in the far and near infra-red. Since we are concerned with colour, we shall deal mainly with the visible part of the spectrum.

As we have seen (p. 21) an electron must occupy some *particular* orbital. Thus ΔE must have *definite* values (for physically stable molecules, *i.e.*, molecules not undergoing any type of dissociation), and hence the frequency of the light absorbed (or emitted) will have definite values, *i.e.*, each value will be associated with a particular line in the spectrum. In complex molecules there will be a very large number of possible excited states, and since, when we examine the absorption spectrum of a compound, we are dealing with very large numbers of molecules, all these excited states will be produced (under the right conditions), *i.e.*, the spectrum will consist of a very large number of lines, and where these lines are very close together (owing to the values of ΔE being very close), bands will appear in the spectrum (see also later). Thus the absorption spectra of complex molecules will appear as bands, these bands appearing in *definite* regions. It is the existence of these bands in definite parts of the spectrum that gives rise to colour. In practice the *first* absorption band of a compound is the most important, *i.e*, the band which occurs at the *lowest* frequency (ΔE smallest), and is due to transition from the ground state to the lowest (first) excited state.

Not only must the *frequency* of the light be considered, but also whether transitions between different energy levels in the molecule can occur, *i.e.*, whether they are " permitted " or " forbidden " transitions. The *probability of transition* is related to the *dipole moment of transition* or *transition dipole* of the molecule. Light absorption by a molecule can occur only when the dipole moment changes in that molecule. The more symmetrical the molecule, the smaller is the possibility of a transition dipole, and therefore the less likely is the molecule to absorb light. Calculation has also shown that the greater is the transition dipole, the greater is the *intensity* of the absorption. If the *electric* dipole is zero, absorption may still occur if the transition *magnetic* dipole is not zero, but absorption of light in this case is usually weak. The introduction of any group into a molecule which decreases symmetry will thus increase the transition dipole and consequently increase the intensity of absorption. At the same time, however, new " resonance paths " may be introduced, and hence not only is there a change in intensity of absorption (due to an increase in the transition dipole), but there is also a shift of the band to longer wavelengths (see below).

As pointed out on p. 28, an important difference between V.B. and M.O. theories is that in the former electrons are dealt with in *pairs*, whereas in the latter they can be dealt with *singly*. This has produced some differences in the theory of light absorption, but nevertheless there is a large amount of ground common to both theories (V.B. and M.O.).

According to the V.B. theory, oscillating (vibrating) electrons in a molecule permit absorption of light by the substance. When light is absorbed by a molecule, there is an *induced* oscillation of the electron pairs (in bonds) throughout the length of the molecule. Lewis and Calvin, and Mulliken have assumed that the electrons are oscillating in the ground state of the molecule, the character of these oscillations being the same as that of the induced oscillation in the excited state. When the molecule is raised to its first excited state, the absorption spectrum corresponding to this will have the lowest frequency. If the molecule is raised to its second excited state, *i.e.*, the amplitude of vibration of the oscillating electrons is increased, then the second absorption band will appear. For a *long* molecule which has an absorption band of low frequency, the electron displacements must be small compared to the dimensions of the molecule, and so the first two excited states occur close together. If the frequency of the absorption band is relatively high for a *short* molecule, the electronic displacements are effectively those in the resonating structures (see later), and so the two excited states are widely separated.

Absorption of light raises the molecule from its ground state to an (electronically) excited state, and the difference in energy between the two states will determine the frequency of the light absorbed. Whether the molecule is symmetrical or not, oscillation of electron pairs produces a changing dipole moment, since they become associated with one or other of the bonded pair of atoms. Thus a changing dipole moment is present in both ground and excited states. It has been shown experimentally that the ease of excitation of the following groups is:

$$N{=}O > C{=}S > N{=}N > C{=}O > C{=}N > C{=}C$$

Thus colour (due to the presence of one of these groups) will *deepen from right to left*.

The smaller the difference in energy between ground and excited states, the lower is the frequency, or longer the wavelength, of the light absorbed. Anything that decreases ΔE will therefore displace the bands to the longer wavelengths. It has been shown that resonance among *charged* structures lowers the energies of both ground and excited states, and since charged structures contribute more to the excited than to the ground state, the energy of the former will be lowered more than that of the latter. Thus, in general, *colour is deeper the greater is the resonance among the various charged forms.* It was Bury (1935) who first pointed out that many dyes could be represented as resonance hybrids.

All the above unsaturated groups (N=O, etc.) are easily polarised, *i.e.*, readily produce charged structures in the excited state; hence their presence in a molecule tends to produce colour. Let us now consider benzene. Its charged structures contribute relatively little to the ground or excited states, and so benzene absorbs only in the ultraviolet, and the absorption is weak due to the symmetry of the molecule. In nitrobenzene the contribution of charged structures is larger than in benzene, and consequently the absorption band is shifted to the longer wavelengths (blue), thereby producing a pale yellow colour (which is the complementary colour of the blue band); the intensity of absorption is also increased because of the loss of symmetry. In *p*-nitroaniline there is a still larger contribution of charged structures, and hence the colour is deeper (orange-red) and still more intense.

The colour of quinones may be explained by resonance among charged structures:

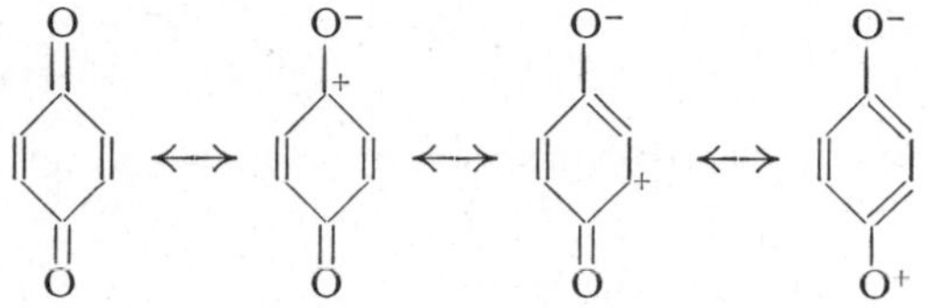

There are similar resonating structures for *o*-benzoquinone:

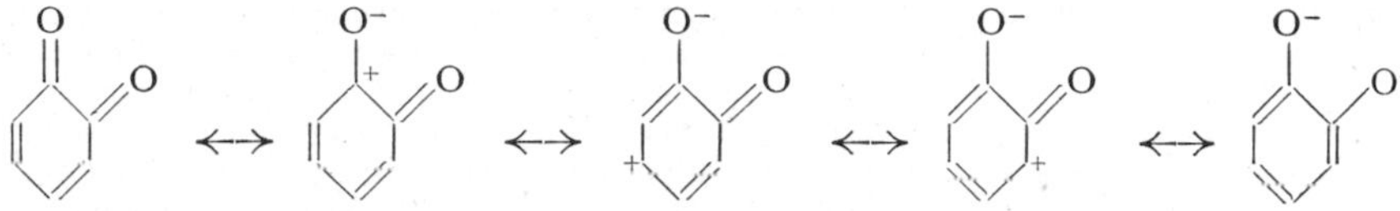

Thus all compounds which can be represented as a quinonoid structure (*ortho* or *para*) will probably be coloured. Moreover, since the number of resonating structures is greater for the *o*-compound than for the *p*-, the former will be deeper in colour (*o*-quinone is red and *p*-quinone is yellow).

Let us now consider aminoazobenzene. This is a resonance hybrid of a number of resonating structures of which only the following two will be considered:

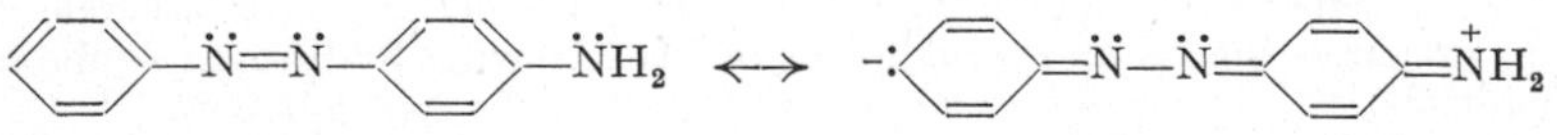

Aminoazobenzene is yellow, only one charged structure contributing to the resonance. In acid solution, aminoazobenzene exists as the following resonance hybrid:

This is violet, and the deepening of colour is due to the fact that only *charged* structures contribute to the resonance hybrid. Here is an example where the addition of acid produces a greater bathochromic effect than is caused by adding an auxochrome.

From the foregoing it can be seen that chromophores give rise to the potentiality of colour by introducing the possibility of resonance involving *charged* structures. Auxochromes (the " key atoms " of which have a lone pair of electrons) change the colour of the chromogen by enhancing resonance, or by producing new forms involving separation of charge.

The longer the conjugation in a molecule, the deeper will be the colour. Conjugation of chromophores also deepens colour. Lewis and Calvin showed that the effect of conjugation is due to the increase in the number of electrons involved in the oscillation. When the conjugated system also contains atoms such as N, S, O, etc., then the absorption frequency is much lower than that of the corresponding conjugated carbon compound, *e.g.*, the absorption frequency of (II) is lower than that of (I) because (II) has a charge and is less symmetrical than (I). Furthermore, the more the charge can be made to reside on the *terminal* atoms, the longer will be the wavelength of the absorbed light.

C=C—C=C—C (I) O=C—C=C—$\bar{O}$ (II)

From the foregoing account it might have been expected that resonance among an increasingly larger number of resonating structures would deepen colour. Consider crystal violet (III), and malachite green (IV).

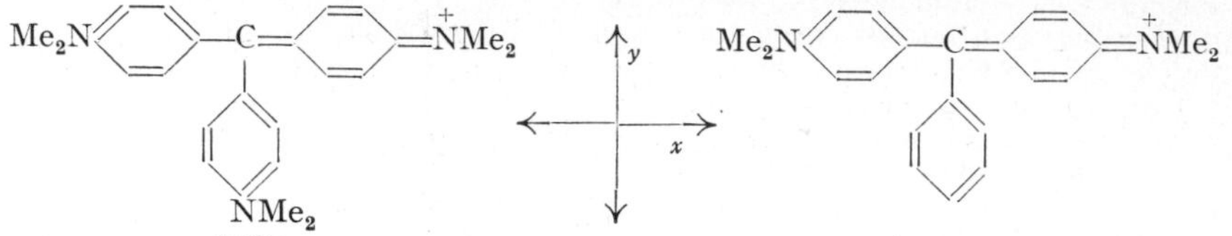

(III) (IV)

(III) has a larger number of resonating structures than (IV), yet the colour of the latter is deeper than that of the former. In (III) the charge on each N atom is approximately two-thirds that on each N in (IV). Therefore the charge that migrates in (III) is smaller than that in (IV), and so the absorption frequency of (III) is higher (or the wavelength is shorter) than that of (IV).

There is, however, another factor introduced. When a molecule has a conjugated system extending in two directions, there may be two optical axes, *i.e.*, absorption will give rise to excited states of different energies and therefore to absorption bands of *different* frequencies. Lewis and Calvin associated the band of *lowest* frequency with the *longest* axis in the molecule. This is called the *x*-band, and the band corresponding to the axis at right angles to this *major axis* is the *y*-band. Generally the *x*-axis of a molecule can readily be determined from the structural formula. (IV) has *x*- and *y*-bands, but (III) has only *one* band (the *x*- and *y*-axes in (III) are identical). Furthermore, if each axis acts independently, the *x*-bands of both (III) and (IV) should be about the same wavelength. This has been found to be so in practice. (IV), however, also has a *y*-absorption band, and it is the presence of this that makes the colour of (IV) different from that of (III).

Another factor that plays a part in colour is the steric factor. Brode *et al.* (1952) prepared the *cis* and *trans* forms of the following hydroxyazo compound (azophenol):

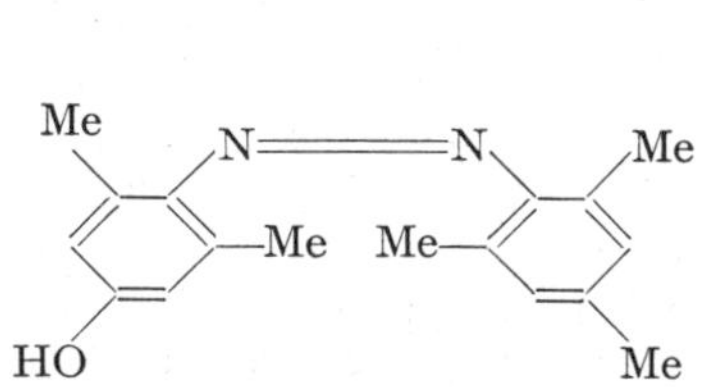

cis

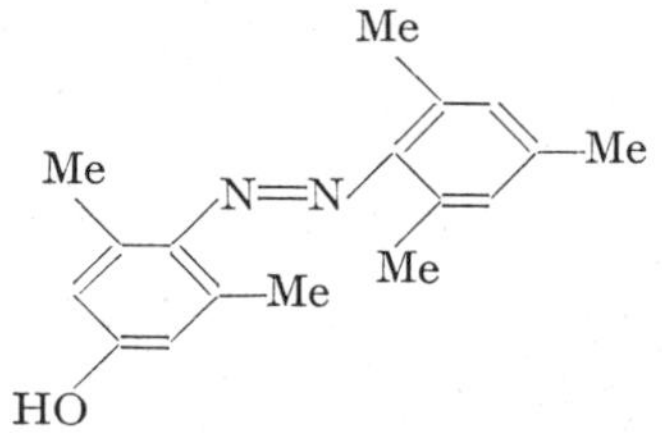

trans

The *trans* form is coloured, whereas the *cis* is colourless; the former can undergo resonance, but in the latter a planar configuration is prevented by the spatial effect of the *o*-methyl groups, and consequently resonance is inhibited and there is therefore no colour (this is an example of steric inhibition of resonance, p. 659). The colourless *cis* form, on standing, changes to the coloured *trans* form. It is of interest to note, in this connection, that fading, with azo-dyes, may be due, at least partly, to the conversion of the *trans* form into the *cis*.

In general, when two conjugated fragments R and S are joined by a single bond, the electronic spectrum depends largely on the coplanarity between the two fragments. If R and S lie in mutually perpendicular planes, the spectrum of the molecule is very similar to the superimposed spectra of RH and SH. Furthermore, in such a molecule the intensity of the absorption band usually decreases with increasing steric distortion from the coplanar configuration. There are, however, many cases where the frequency of a band remains unchanged or is shifted in either direction as the molecule is distorted.

Now let us consider the problem of light absorption from the M.O. point of view. In M.O. theory, an atom or a molecule is excited when *one* electron is transferred from an orbital of lower to one of higher energy. Such transitions can occur only between " permitted " orbitals. In *atoms*, allowable transitions are $s \longleftrightarrow p$, $p \longleftrightarrow d$, etc.; $s \longrightarrow s$ is forbidden (p. 22). In *molecules*, a g state must go to a u state, or *vice-versa*; transitions $u \longrightarrow u$, and $g \longrightarrow g$ are forbidden (p. 28).

An unsymmetrical molecule in the ground state has a dipole moment, and the dipole moment will generally change if the internuclear distances change. Absorption of light increases the amplitude of vibration. On the other hand, a symmetrical molecule will not have a dipole moment, but one may be produced in an excited state. In a diatomic molecule, transition of an electron from a bonding to the corresponding anti-bonding orbital is always an allowed transition.

Let us first consider the hydrogen molecule. The electron pair in the σ-bond can be excited, and excitation can be effected by absorption of light, *e.g.*, the hydrogen molecule in the ground state (Fig. 1*a*) can be raised to its first excited state (Fig. 1*b*). In the ground state we have a σ_g orbital (*bonding* orbital), and

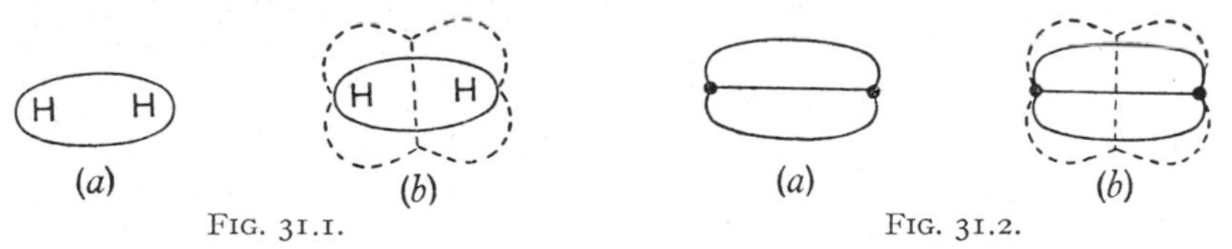

(*a*) (*b*) FIG. 31.1. (*a*) (*b*) FIG. 31.2.

in the first excited state we have *one* electron in the σ_g orbital and the *other* electron in a σ_u orbital (*antibonding* orbital; see p. 27). Absorption of light of the *requisite* amount of energy can transfer one electron from a σ_g to a σ_u orbital (this is an allowable transition). Now the amount of energy required to raise one electron from a σ_g to a σ_u orbital is large, *i.e.*, the frequency of the incident light must be high, and so the wavelength is very short. Thus the hydrogen molecule absorbs in the ultraviolet (we are not considering rotational and vibrational spectra).

The ethylene molecule in its ground state has, in addition to a σ-bond, a π_u (bonding) orbital (Fig. 2*a*), and in the first excited state a π_g (antibonding) orbital (Fig. 2*b*) in which *one* electron has been excited (this is an allowable transition; see p. 28). Since it requires less energy to excite a π-electron than a σ-electron, the wavelength of the absorbed light necessary to raise one electron from a π_u to a π_g orbital will therefore be longer, *i.e.*, the absorption spectrum of ethylene will be in the longer wavelength region (than that of hydrogen).

In a compound containing two *isolated* double bonds (p. 76), the absorption band has about the same frequency as that of one double bond, but the intensity is greater. In a compound containing two bonds in conjugation we now have delocalised bonds. Let us consider the simple case of butadiene (p. 81, Fig. 4.1). (*d*) represents the molecule in the ground state; (*e*) and (*f*) represent excited states, that of (*f*) being a higher state. Excitation of butadiene can therefore cause the transfer of *one* electron from (*b*) to (*e*) or (*f*), or *one* from (*c*) to (*e*) or (*f*). If all these occurred, *four* absorption bands would be produced. Calculation has shown that the energy difference between (*c*) and (*e*) is lower than that of any other transition; (it should be noted that this transition is from the highest level of the ground state to the lowest level of the excited state; see also below). Thus when butadiene absorbs light (of requisite wavelength), the absorption band of *longest* wavelength corresponds to excitation of one electron from (*c*) to (*e*), and other bands of *shorter* wavelength correspond to the other transitions.

As we have seen (p. 82), in a conjugated system containing $2n$ π-electrons, there are n bonding and n antibonding orbitals. Calculation and experimental work have shown that as conjugation increases, the energy difference between the highest occupied and the lowest unoccupied π-orbitals decreases. Thus, as conjugation extends, the wavelength of the absorption band increases. When it reaches the *visible* part of the spectrum, colour will appear in the compound, *e.g.*, in the polyenes, $CH_3\cdot(CH{=}CH)_n\cdot CH_3$, when $n = 6$, the absorption band occurs in the blue region, and so the compound is yellow (complementary colour). Thus increased conjugation deepens colour, and this effect offers an explanation for Nietzki's rule (p. 742); *e.g.*, when benzene rings are replaced by naphthalene, conjugation is extended.

Although it always requires less energy to transfer π-electrons than σ-electrons from one orbital to another, nevertheless all π-electrons are not transferred with equal ease. The energy required depends on the nature of the atoms embraced in the M.O.

Now let us consider benzene. This is a symmetrical molecule, all the carbon atoms carrying equal charges of unity. Thus benzene has no transition dipole, and so would not be expected to absorb light. In practice, however, it shows *weak* absorption in the ultraviolet (one electron passes from (II) or (III) to (IV) or (V), p. 485; also see p. 745). When a nitro-group is introduced into the benzene ring, the molecule is no longer symmetrical; the nitro-group is conjugated with the rest of the molecule, and the carbon atoms are no longer equally charged (p. 502). Nitrobenzene therefore has a dipole moment and consequently a large transition dipole, and so strong absorption bands can be expected. Furthermore, because of the extended conjugation, the energy difference between the highest occupied and the lowest unoccupied orbitals is decreased, and so the absorption band will have a longer wavelength than that of benzene. It actually occurs in the blue region, and so nitrobenzene is yellow.

In aniline, the lone pair on the nitrogen atom becomes conjugated with the ring (p. 501), and the molecule now has a dipole moment and therefore a transition dipole. At the same time the absorption band of aniline has a longer wavelength than that of benzene. The absorption spectrum of aniline in *acid* solution, however, is almost the same as that of benzene. This is because the lone pair (on the " key atom ", p. 492) has been removed from conjugation by co-ordination with a proton.

In *p*-nitroaniline, the conjugation is more extended than in either nitrobenzene or aniline, the separation of charge is greater, and so the wavelength of the absorbed light is longer. In general, any group which conjugates with the benzene ring will shift the frequency of the absorbed light to longer wavelengths (auxochromes behave like chromophores in this respect). Thus, for a compound to act as a dye (as far as *colour* is concerned), it is necessary for the molecule to have as large a changing dipole moment as possible, and this may be achieved by the presence of two or more polar groups as far apart as possible but connected by a conjugated system.

Free radicals are usually coloured, and this is because ΔE is small.

The V.B. resonance approach to colour is satisfactory from a qualitative point of view, but the M.O. method appears to be more promising from a quantitative point of view. It has now been possible to calculate the light absorption of many molecules, and good agreement has been obtained between calculated and observed values. A simplified version of the M.O. method has now been developed (Coulson *et al.*, 1947; Dewar, 1952).

NOMENCLATURE OF DYES. There is no systematic nomenclature of dyes. Many have names that have been given to them by the manufacturers, and so it is not unusual to find a given dye having several names. Generally, each dye has a trade name (or names), and the shade is indicated by a letter, *e.g.*, Y or G = yellow (*gelb*); O = orange; R = red; B = blue. Sometimes the letter is repeated, the number of letters indicating roughly the intensity of the colour, *e.g.*, methyl violet 6B is a very deep purple (close to blue). Sometimes the letters have other meanings, *e.g.*, alizarin blue D; here the D means that this dye is a *direct* cotton colour; fuchsine S, the S indicating that the dye is an *acid* (*sauer*) colour. The letter F is often used to indicate that the dye is fast to light.

To avoid difficulties, the Society of Dyers and Colourists have compiled a Colour Index in which each dye is assigned its individual colour number (**C.I. no.**).

Classification of Dyes. Dyes are classified according to their chemical constitution or by their application to the fibre. The former is of theoretical value to the chemist but of little importance to the dyer who is mainly concerned with the reaction of dyes towards the fibre being dyed.

Chemical classification. The chemical constitutions of dyes are so varied that it is difficult to classify them into distinct groups. The following classification is used in this book; in some cases a particular dye could be placed in one or other group.

(1) Nitro-dyes; (2) Nitroso-dyes; (3) Azo-dyes; (4) Diphenylmethane dyes; (5) Triphenylmethane dyes; (6) Xanthen dyes; (7) Diphenylamine dyes: (i) *indamines*, (ii) *indophenols*; (8) Heterocyclic dyes: (i) *acridine group*, (ii) *quinoline group*, (iii) *azine group*, (iv) *thiazine group*, (v) *oxazine group*; (9) Vat dyes: (i) *indigoid group*, (ii) *anthraquinone group*; (10) Anthraquinoid dyes (not vat dyes); (11) Sulphur dyes; (12) Phthalocyanine dyes.

Classification according to application

1. **Acid dyes** are the sodium salts of sulphonic acids and nitrophenols. They dye animal fibres directly, but not vegetable; they are mostly applied to wool and silk.

2. **Basic dyes** are mostly the salts of colour bases (p. 756) with hydrochloric acid or zinc chloride. They dye animal fibres directly, and vegetable fibres which have been mordanted with tannin. Basic dyes are mostly applied to cotton and silk.

3. **Direct dyes** (*substantive dyes*) dye animal and vegetable fibres directly.

4. **Mordant dyes** (*adjective dyes*) dye neither animal nor vegetable fibres directly, but require a mordant. If the dye is acidic, the mordant must be basic; if the dye is basic, then the mordant must be acidic. For acidic dyes the mordants are metallic hydroxides; for basic dyes the mordant generally used is tannin (tannic acid). For metal mordanting, the fabric is dipped into a solution of the metallic salt and the "padded" fibre is then dipped into the solution of the dye; this produces an insoluble coloured lake which is fast to washing. For tannin mordanting, the fabric is dipped into a tannin bath, but since the lakes are dull and tend to be fugitive, potassium antimonyl tartrate (tartar emetic) is added to the tannin bath; this produces brighter and more insoluble lakes.

The colour of the lake depends on the metal used; the commonest metals are chromium, aluminium, iron and tin. Lakes are believed to be chelate compounds formed between the metal and the dye. The majority of mordant dyes owe their special properties to the presence of hydroxyl groups, and it appears that dyes containing one hydroxyl group will be mordanted if this hydroxyl group is *ortho* to a carboxyl, nitroso-, azo- or imino-group, *e.g.*,

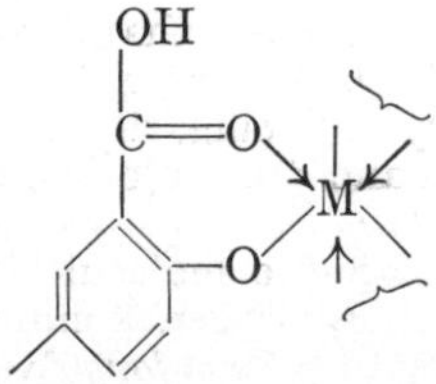

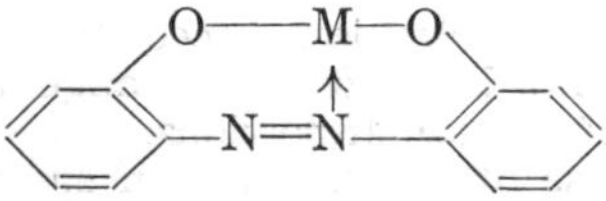

Chromium, aluminium and iron usually form chelate compounds containing *three* dye molecules. It is important to note that the sulphonic acid group cannot form lakes.

5. **Vat dyes** are insoluble in water, but are reduced by alkaline sodium hyposulphite (dithionite) to alkali-soluble compounds which are readily reoxidised to the dye. These reduced compounds are often white or colour-

less, and so are called **leuco-compounds**. Dyes in the leuco-condition dye both animal and vegetable fibres directly. Vat dyes are used mostly on cotton.

6. **Ingrain** or **developed dyes** are dyes which are produced in the fibre. They are divided into three broad groups:

(i) *Ice-colours.* These are produced generally on cotton by soaking the fibre (" padding ") in the secondary component (phenol or amine) of the azo-dye, and developing the colour by immersion in the diazonium salt solution. The name *ice-colours* was given because diazotisation and coupling are carried out at *low* temperatures.

(ii) A direct cotton-dye containing a free amino-group is applied to the fibre and diazotised by dipping into a nitrous acid solution, followed by dipping into a solution of the secondary component (phenol or amine), whereupon the azo-dye is produced.

(iii) *Aniline-black.* This is produced by the oxidation of aniline hydrochloride either by oxidising the fibre impregnated with the amine salt, or by heating the fibre with a solution of aniline hydrochloride containing the oxidising agent (potassium chlorate, and vanadium salts as catalyst).

7. **Sulphur dyes** are dyes containing sulphur, and are soluble in aqueous sodium sulphide. Sulphur dyes are used exclusively for vegetable fibres, the dye being regenerated in the fabric by oxidation in the atmosphere, or by oxidation with dilute aqueous potassium dichromate.

8. **Rayon dyes.** Viscose rayon and *cupra silk* (p. 443) can be dyed in the usual way; acetate rayon, however, requires special dyes and techniques.

9. **Organic pigments.** These are not dyes in the sense that they dye fibres, but are solids which are generally insoluble in water, and are used for colouring paints, varnishes, etc. Some pigments have been made water soluble and then are used as dyes, *e.g.*, phthalocyanine dyes.

Theory of Dyeing. It appears that the mechanism of dyeing depends on the nature of both the dye and the fibre. Textile fibres fall into two main groups, vegetable and animal. *Vegetable fibres* are cellulose fibres, *e.g.*, cotton, linen, flax, hemp and jute. *Animal fibres* are protein fibres, *e.g.*, wool, silk and leather.

There is also a third type of fibres, the *artificial* and *synthetic fibres, e.g.*, rayons (cellulose-type) and nylons (protein-type).

X-Ray photographs show that textile fibres are built up from long-chain molecules which are present as amorphous material containing crystalline regions which are known as *crystallites* or *micelles*. In these micelles the long-chain molecules are arranged parallel to one another, and are held together by the usual crystal forces, and in the case of wool, by cross-linkages between the chains. The edges of the micelles are not clearly defined but merge into amorphous material of the same chemical structure as the micelles, though not arranged in a definite oriented pattern. Thus a fibre consists of a number of micelles linked by amorphous parts.

When a fibre is placed in water, it swells owing to the osmotic pressure developed internally. It has been shown (by X-ray studies) that swelling takes place in the amorphous parts, producing open pores large enough to permit the passage of dye molecules. According to one theory of dyeing, the dye molecules enter the fibre by diffusing through these pores and then along the parallel channels in the micellar portions.

In cellulose fibres, it has been suggested that the dye molecule is oriented parallel to the micellar chains, and is attached by hydrogen bonding. Since hydrogen bonding is not very strong, it is necessary to have a *long* dye molecule in order to get a number of points of attachment by hydrogen bonding. As the dye molecule becomes longer (bigger), however, it becomes less soluble and so less easily dissolved out, *i.e.*, it becomes faster to washing. On the other hand, if the dye molecule becomes too large, it becomes too insoluble to be applied. In such cases it can be made soluble by reduction and then regenerated by oxidation, thereby giving a very fast dye since it is so highly insoluble. Furthermore, as far as cellulose is concerned, the shape of the dye must be linear and planar.

Thus, with azo-dyes the *cis* form, which is neither linear nor planar, cannot align itself parallel to the micellar chains (see p. 746).

Protein fibres contain free amino- and carboxyl groups. In acid solution the carboxyl group is undissociated, and the charged $—\overset{+}{N}H_3$ ion is produced. These ions are capable of attracting dye anions to form salts. In alkaline solution it is the carboxylate ion, $—CO_2^-$, which is present, and this is capable of attracting a dye cation to form a salt.

Nitro-dyes. These contain the nitro-group as the chromophore, and hydroxyl group usually as the auxochrome. The simplest nitro-dye is picric acid and was first prepared by Woulfe (1771), who noted its capacity to dye silk bright yellow; the colour, however, is fugitive. Picric acid is really the first synthetic dye, but it was Perkin (1856) who founded the synthetic coal-tar dye industry (see p. 768).

Martius Yellow (*Manchester Yellow*) is 2 : 4-dinitro-1-naphthol (I; Martius, 1864), and is prepared by nitrating 1-naphthol-2 : 4-disulphonic acid (*cf.* picric acid, p. 584). It has been used as the sodium, calcium or ammonium salt, but it

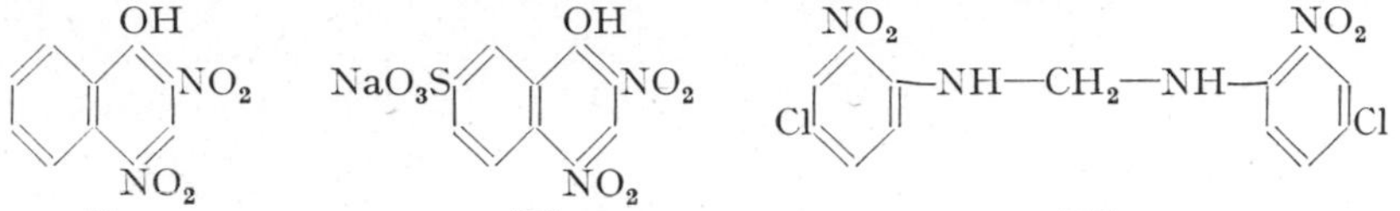

(I) (II) (III)

is fugitive and readily sublimes off the fibre. It has therefore been replaced by **Naphthol Yellow S** (Caro, 1879), 2 : 4-dinitro-1-naphthol-7-sulphonic acid (sodium or potassium salt; II). This is the most important nitro-dyestuff, and is now made by nitrating 1-naphthol-2 : 4 : 7-trisulphonic acid or 4-nitroso-1-naphthol-2 : 7-disulphonic acid. This dye has been very much used as an acid dye for wool and silk.

Lithol Fast Yellow GG (III) is a pigment, and is used as a non-poisonous substitute for *Chrome Yellow* (lead chromate). It is prepared by condensing *p*-chloro-*o*-nitroaniline with formaldehyde.

Nitroso-dyes. In these the chromophore is the nitroso-group, and the auxochrome the hydroxyl group. Nitroso-dyes are prepared by the action of nitrous acid on phenols and naphthols. Only the *o*-nitroso-compounds are useful, and these are used mainly in the form of their green iron lakes in dyeing and printing; *e.g.*, **Fast Green O** (Fitz, 1875) is prepared by the action of nitrous acid on resorcinol, and it is the oxime form which produces the lakes (the oxime form is stabilised by intramolecular hydrogen bonding):

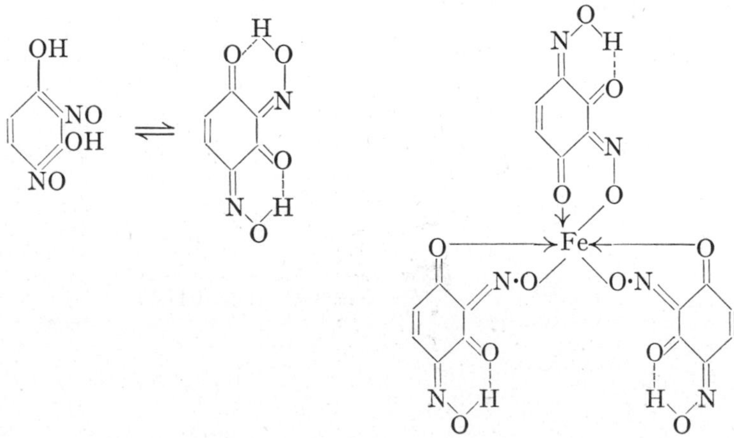

Two other nitroso-dyes are **Gambine R** (2-nitroso-1-naphthol, I) and **Gambine Y** (1-nitroso-2-naphthol, II).

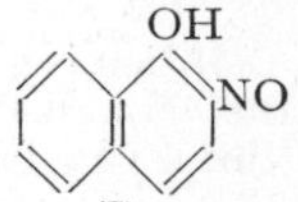

(I) 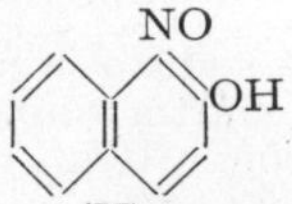 (II)

AZO-DYES

In azo-dyes the chromophore is the azo-group, and the common auxochromes are NH_2, NR_2 and OH. Azo-dyes, as far as application is concerned, are classified as *basic, acid, direct, ingrain* and *mordant dyes*.

The structure of an azo-dye is readily found by reduction with stannous chloride and hydrochloric acid, or with sodium hyposulphite (dithionite), whereupon the azo-group is ruptured with the formation of primary amines which are then identified:

$$Ar{\cdot}N{=}N{\cdot}Ar' \xrightarrow{[H]} Ar{\cdot}NH_2 + Ar'{\cdot}NH_2$$

Basic Azo-dyes contain NH_2 or NR_2 as the auxochrome. **Aniline Yellow** (*aminoazobenzene*, p. 571) and **Butter Yellow** (p-*dimethylaminoazobenzene*, p. 572) are the simplest basic azo-dyes, but are of very little value as dyes since they are sensitive to acids. **Phenylene Brown** or **Bismarck Brown G** (Martius, 1863) was the first commercially important azo-dye, and was manufactured by the action of nitrous acid on excess of *m*-phenylenediamine. It consists of a mixture of the hydrochlorides of mono- and bisazo-derivatives (see p. 554). **Chrysoidine G** (Caro, 1875; Witt, 1876) is prepared by coupling diazotised aniline with *m*-phenylenediamine:

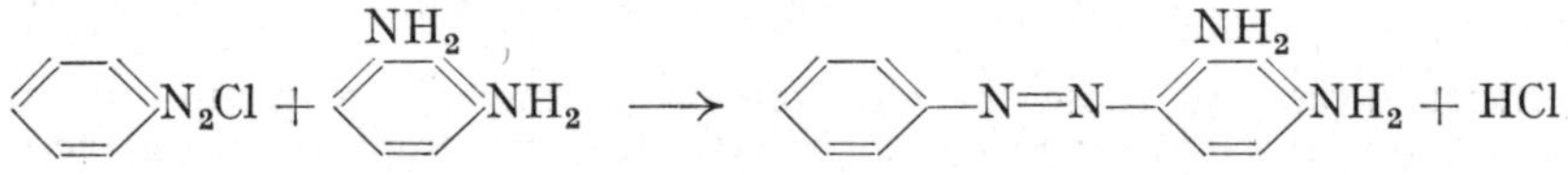

$$C_6H_5N_2Cl + C_6H_4(NH_2)_2 \longrightarrow C_6H_5{-}N{=}N{-}C_6H_3(NH_2)_2 + HCl$$

It is an orange dye, and is still used for dyeing cotton on a tannin mordant.

Acid Azo-dyes contain a sulphonic acid group. **Methyl Orange** (*helianthin*) is prepared by coupling diazotised sulphanilic acid with dimethylaniline:

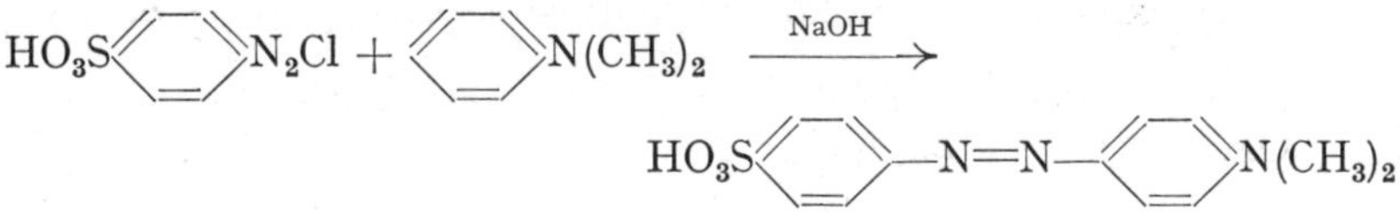

$$HO_3S{-}C_6H_4{-}N_2Cl + C_6H_5N(CH_3)_2 \xrightarrow{NaOH} HO_3S{-}C_6H_4{-}N{=}N{-}C_6H_4{-}N(CH_3)_2$$

It dyes only in fugitive shades; it is used as an indicator, being orange in alkaline solution and red in acid solution (*cf.* Congo red, below):

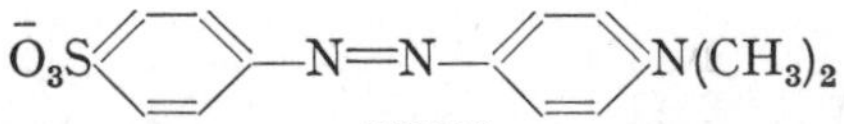

$$\bar{O}_3S{-}C_6H_4{-}N{=}N{-}C_6H_4{-}N(CH_3)_2$$

orange

$$\bar{O}_3S{-}C_6H_4{-}NH{-}N{=}C_6H_4{=}\overset{+}{N}(CH_3)_2$$

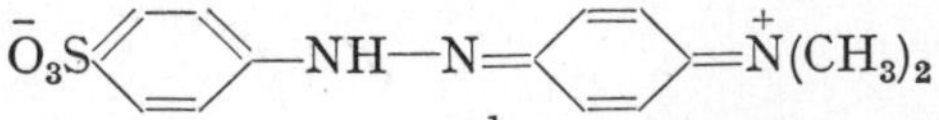

red

Coupling diazotised sulphanilic acid with 1-naphthol gives **Orange I** (Griess, 1876), and with 2-naphthol it gives **Orange II** (Roussin, 1876). These Orange dyes were the first acidic azo-dyes to be put on the market.

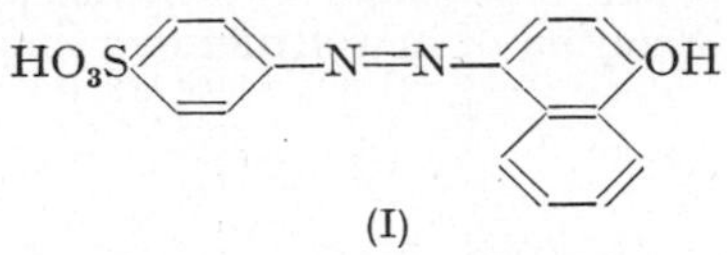

HO_3S—N=N—OH (I)

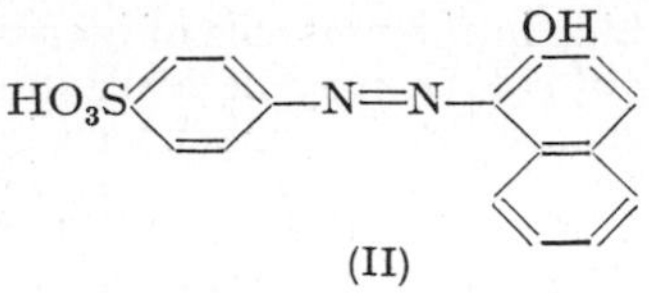

HO_3S—N=N— (OH) (II)

Fast Red AV, (III), (Caro, 1877) is made by coupling diazotised naphthionic acid (p. 689) with 2-naphthol. **Ponceau 2R,** (IV), is prepared by coupling diazotised *m*-xylidine with the sodium salt of R-acid (p. 691).

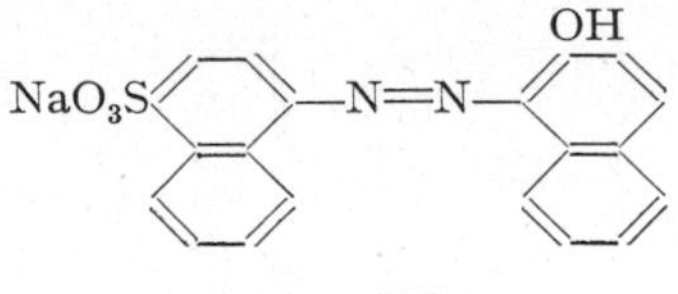

NaO_3S—N=N— (OH) (III)

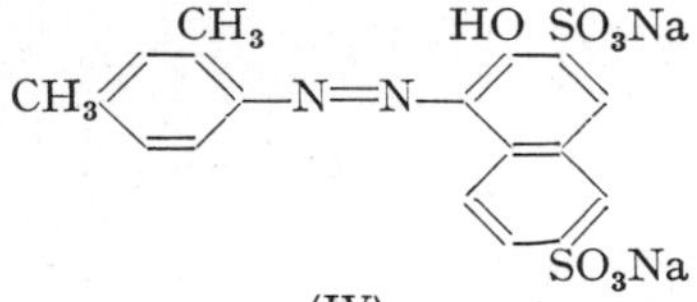

CH_3, CH_3—N=N— (HO, SO_3Na, SO_3Na) (IV)

Crystal Ponceau 6R is prepared by coupling diazotised 1-naphthylamine with the sodium salt of G-acid (p. 691).

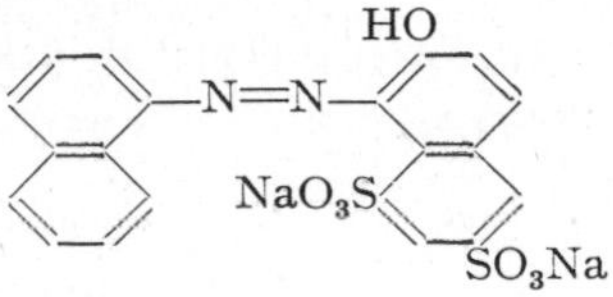

—N=N— (HO, NaO_3S, SO_3Na)

Naphthol Blue Black B (Hofmann, 1891) is one of the most largely used black acid dyes. It is made by coupling H-acid with one molecule of diazotised *p*-nitroaniline in *acid* solution (coupling occurs in the 2-position), and then coupling the product, in alkaline solution, with one molecule of diazotised aniline (coupling occurs in the 7-position):

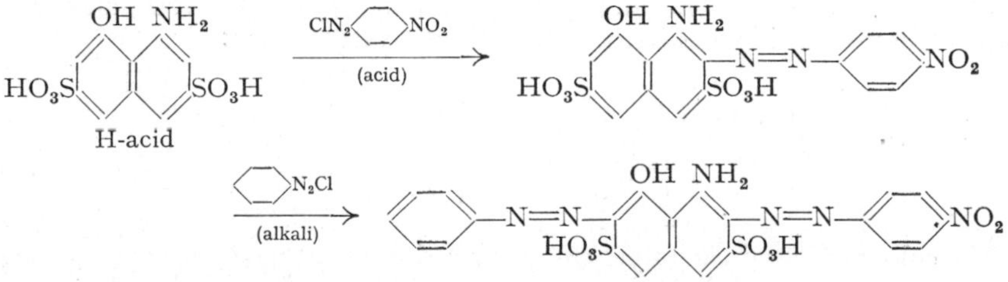

OH NH_2, HO_3S, SO_3H (H-acid) —[ClN_2—NO_2 (acid)]→ OH NH_2, HO_3S, SO_3H, —N=N—NO_2

—[N_2Cl (alkali)]→ —N=N— OH NH_2, HO_3S, SO_3H, —N=N—NO_2

Direct Azo-dyes. Congo Red (Bottiger, 1885) is a bisazo-dye which is prepared by coupling tetrazotised benzidine with two molecules of 1-naphthylamine-4-sulphonic acid:

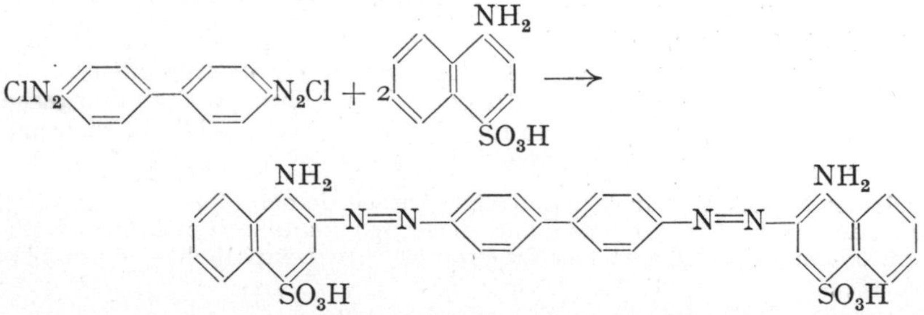

ClN_2——N_2Cl + 2 (NH_2, SO_3H) →

(NH_2, SO_3H)—N=N———N=N—(NH_2, SO_3H)

This is red in alkaline solution, and its sodium salt dyes cotton a full red. Congo red was the first synthetic dye produced that was capable of dyeing cotton directly. It is very sensitive to acids, the colour changing from red to blue in the presence of inorganic acids. This blue colour, *i.e.*, the deepening of colour, may be attributed to the formation of new structures similar to those of aminoazobenzene (see p. 745):

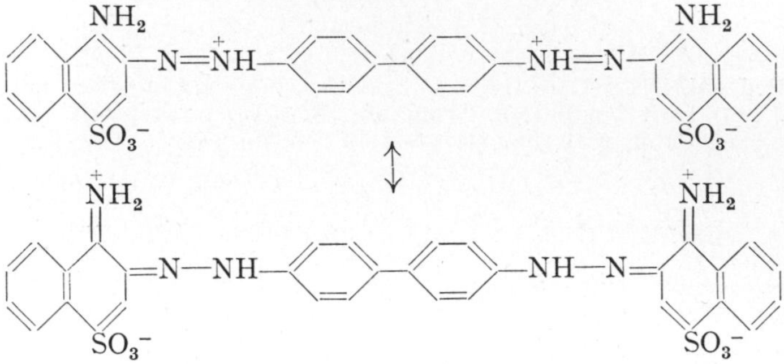

Stilbene dyes. These are examples of direct azo-dyes without the use of diazotisation and coupling, *e.g.*, **Sun Yellow** (Walter, 1883) is made by heating 4-aminotoluene-2-sulphonic acid with sodium hydroxide solution. The structures of these stilbene dyes were elucidated by Green, Wahl *et al.* (1897–1908).

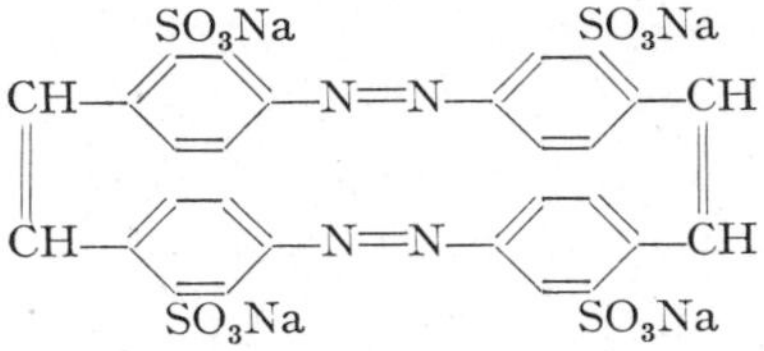

Ingrain Azo-dyes. These insoluble azo-dyes are known as **azoic dyes.** Dyeing with **Para Red** is carried out by "padding" the fibre with an alkaline solution of 2-naphthol containing Turkey-red oil, drying the cloth, and then immersing it in an ice-cold bath of diazotised *p*-nitroaniline:

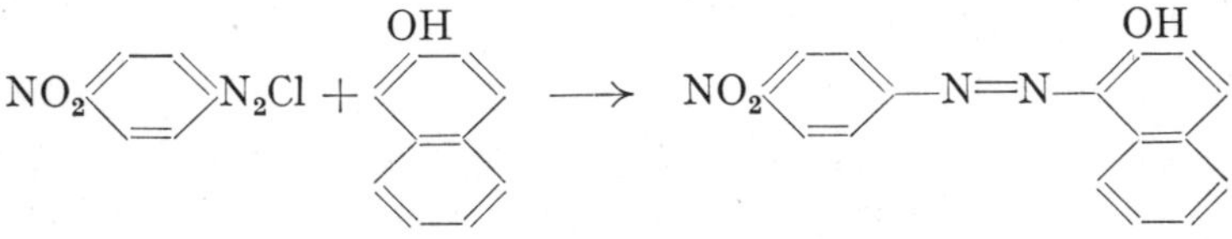

The colour of ingrain azo-dyes can be varied from orange to blue by varying the amine component (diazotised), *e.g.*,

2-naphthol + *m*-nitroaniline = *Nitroaniline Orange*
" + 2 : 4-dinitroaniline = *Permanent Red 2G*
" + dianisidine = *Dianisine Blue*

Mordant Azo-dyes. Chromium is the most important metal used in mordanting azo-dyes, producing the so-called *azo-chrome mordant dyes.* The fibre is mordanted by boiling with potassium dichromate solution, usually with a reducing agent such as formic, lactic, or oxalic acid (the dichromate is converted into chromic hydroxide).

Diamond Black F (Lauch and Krekeler, 1889) is one of the earliest chrome dyes, and is produced by coupling diazotised 5-aminosalicylic acid with 1-naphthylamine, and diazotising the product with 1-naphthol-4- or 5-sulphonic acid, *e.g.*,

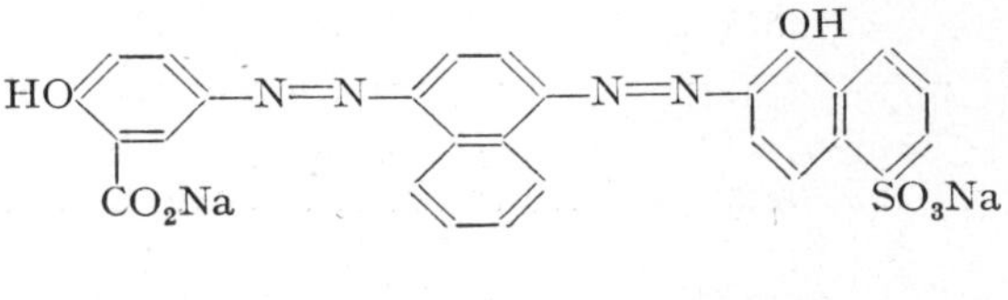

Instead of mordanting the fibre first, the azo-dye may be applied to the fibre first, and then the dye " chromed " by boiling with sodium dichromate and a reducing agent. By this procedure the colour may be changed completely. Most of the azo-dyes that are " after-chromed " on the fibre are derived from *chromotropic acid* (1 : 8-dihydroxynaphthalene-3 : 6-disulphonic acid); *e.g.*, **Chromotrope 2B** (Kuzel, 1890) is prepared by coupling *p*-nitroaniline with chromotropic acid:

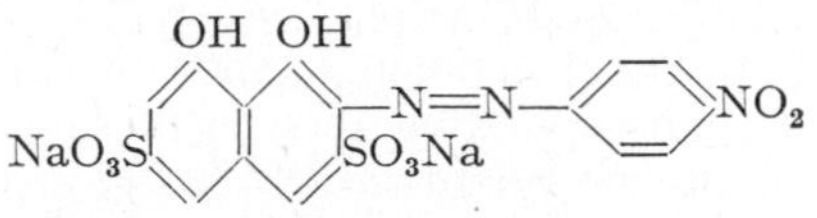

This dyes wool a bluish-red; the colour is changed into blue to black by " after-chroming ".

Cellulose acetate rayon dyes. It was found to be very difficult to dye rayon by the usual dyestuffs, since the dyeings were not fast. The first dyes specially designed for dyeing rayon were the *Ionamine dyes* (Green and Saunders, 1922). These are methyl-ω-sulphonates of insoluble aminoazo-compounds which are slowly hydrolysed in the hot dye bath (65–75°), giving formaldehyde bisulphite and the aminoazo-compound in a form readily absorbed by the fibre, *e.g.*, **Ionamine Red KA.**

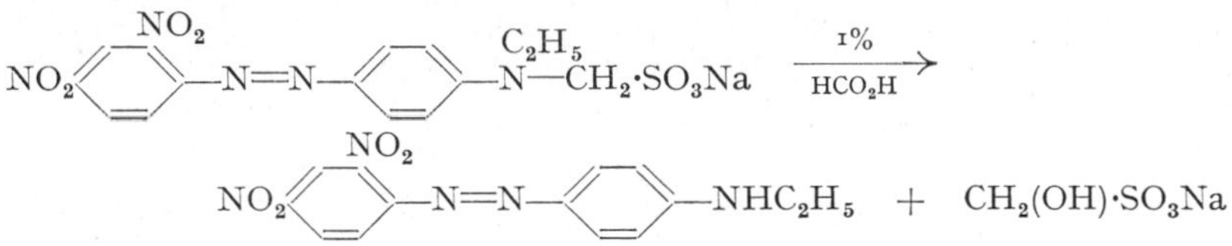

$$\text{NO}_2\text{C}_6\text{H}_3(\text{NO}_2)\text{—N=N—C}_6\text{H}_4\text{—N(C}_2\text{H}_5)\text{—CH}_2\cdot\text{SO}_3\text{Na} \xrightarrow[\text{HCO}_2\text{H}]{1\%} \text{NO}_2\text{C}_6\text{H}_3(\text{NO}_2)\text{—N=N—C}_6\text{H}_4\text{—NHC}_2\text{H}_5 + \text{CH}_2(\text{OH})\cdot\text{SO}_3\text{Na}$$

A more general method is one discovered independently by Shepherdson and Ellis (1923). The insoluble dye, by means of dispersing agents—originally sulphoricinoleic acid, but now replaced by more effective reagents—is prepared in a state of uniform fine dispersions in the dye bath. These dispersions are not satisfactory for all purposes.

DIPHENYLMETHANE DYES

Auramine O was discovered independently by Kern and Caro (1883). They prepared it by fusing Michler's ketone (p. 637) with ammonium and zinc chlorides at 150–160°. It is now prepared by heating *p* : *p'*-tetramethyldiaminodiphenylmethane with sulphur, ammonium chloride and a large excess of sodium chloride in a current of ammonia at about 200° (Sandmeyer, 1889); this produces *Auramine Base*. This, with hydrochloric acid forms the hydrochloride, *Auramine O*, a yellow basic dye. It has a low fastness, being readily hydrolysed

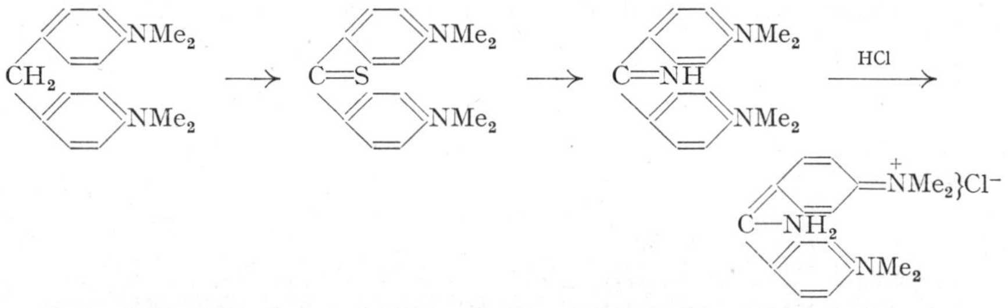

$$\text{CH}_2(\text{C}_6\text{H}_4\text{NMe}_2)_2 \longrightarrow \text{C=S}(\text{C}_6\text{H}_4\text{NMe}_2)_2 \longrightarrow \text{C=NH}(\text{C}_6\text{H}_4\text{NMe}_2)_2 \xrightarrow{\text{HCl}} \left\{\text{Me}_2\text{N}\text{C}_6\text{H}_4\text{—C(NH}_2)\text{=C}_6\text{H}_4\text{=}\overset{+}{\text{N}}\text{Me}_2\right\}\text{Cl}^-$$

to the corresponding ketone. Nevertheless, it is largely used for dyeing cotton, paper, leather, wool, silk and jute; it is also used for lake-making.

Auramine G (Grehn and Schmid, 1892) is made in a similar way from the condensation product of monomethyl-*o*-toluidine and formaldehyde, which is

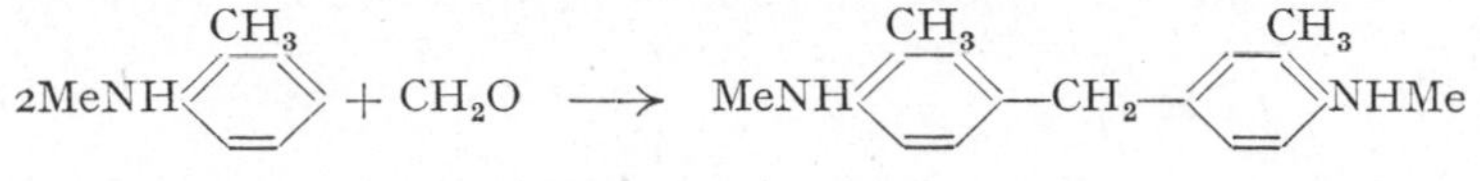

$$2\text{MeNH}\text{C}_6\text{H}_4(\text{CH}_3) + \text{CH}_2\text{O} \longrightarrow \text{MeNH}\text{C}_6\text{H}_3(\text{CH}_3)\text{—CH}_2\text{—C}_6\text{H}_3(\text{CH}_3)\text{NHMe}$$

heated with sulphur in a current of ammonia. Auramine G is a greenish-yellow basic dye.

TRIPHENYLMETHANE DYES

Triphenylmethane dyes are obtained by the introduction of NH_2, NR_2 or OH groups into the rings of triphenylmethane. The compounds so obtained are colourless—the **leuco-compounds**—and these, on oxidation, are converted into the corresponding tertiary alcohols, the **colour bases,** which readily change from the colourless benzenoid forms to the quinonoid dyes in the presence of acid, due to salt formation. The salts are easily reconverted into the leuco-base:

$$\underset{\text{(colourless)}}{\text{leuco-base}} \underset{\text{reduction}}{\overset{\text{oxidation}}{\rightleftharpoons}} \underset{\text{(colourless)}}{\text{colour base}} \underset{\text{alkali}}{\overset{\text{acid}}{\rightleftharpoons}} \underset{\text{(coloured)}}{\text{dye}}$$

Malachite Green (O. Fischer, 1877) is prepared by condensing dimethylaniline (2 molecules) with benzaldehyde (1 molecule) at 100° in the presence of concentrated sulphuric acid. The leuco-base produced is oxidised with lead dioxide in a solution of acetic acid containing hydrochloric acid; the resulting colour base gives malachite green with excess hydrochloric acid:

$$C_6H_5CHO + 2\,C_6H_5N(CH_3)_2 \xrightarrow{H_2SO_4} C_6H_5{-}CH[C_6H_4N(CH_3)_2]_2 \xrightarrow{[O]}$$

$$C_6H_5{-}C(OH)[C_6H_4N(CH_3)_2]_2 \xrightarrow{HCl} \{C_6H_5{-}C(C_6H_4N(CH_3)_2){=}C_6H_4{=}\overset{+}{N}(CH_3)_2\}Cl^-$$

Malachite green dyes wool and silk directly, and cotton mordanted with tannin. **Fast Green** or **Brilliant Green** (Bindschedler and Busch, 1879) is the sulphate of the corresponding ethyl derivative; it gives a more yellow shade than malachite green, and is also a powerful antiseptic.

Pararosaniline is prepared by oxidising a mixture of *p*-toluidine (1 molecule) and aniline (2 molecules) with arsenic acid or nitrobenzene:

$$2\,NH_2C_6H_4{-}H + 2[O] + H_2{-}CH{-}C_6H_4NH_2 \longrightarrow$$

$$(NH_2C_6H_4)_2CH{-}C_6H_4NH_2 + 2H_2O \xrightarrow{[O]}$$

$$(NH_2C_6H_4)_2C(OH){-}C_6H_4NH_2 \xrightarrow{HCl} \{(NH_2C_6H_4)_2C{=}C_6H_4{=}\overset{+}{N}H_2\}Cl^-$$

In the newer process, pararosaniline hydrochloride is prepared by starting with aniline (2 molecules) and formaldehyde (1 molecule), and treating the product, 4:4'-diaminodiphenylmethane, with aniline hydrochloride in the presence of an oxidising agent:

$$2C_6H_5\cdot NH_2 + CH_2O \longrightarrow NH_2\cdot C_6H_4-CH_2-C_6H_4\cdot NH_2 \xrightarrow[\text{[O]}]{C_6H_5\cdot NH_2\cdot HCl} (NH_2\cdot C_6H_4-)_2C=C_6H_4=\overset{+}{N}H_2\}Cl^-$$

Rosaniline, Magenta, Fuchsine (Verguin, 1859) is the *o*-methyl derivative of pararosaniline. It is produced by oxidising an equimolecular mixture of aniline, *o*- and *p*-toluidines, and their hydrochlorides, with nitrobenzene in the presence of iron filings. The product is a mixture of rosaniline and pararosaniline, in which the former predominates:

$$NH_2\cdot C_6H_4-CH-H_2 + 2[O] + H\cdot C_6H_3(CH_3)\cdot NH_2 + H\cdot C_6H_4\cdot NH_2 \longrightarrow$$

$$NH_2\cdot C_6H_4-CH(C_6H_3(CH_3)\cdot NH_2)(C_6H_4\cdot NH_2) + 2H_2O \xrightarrow{[O]} NH_2\cdot C_6H_4-C(OH)(C_6H_3(CH_3)\cdot NH_2)(C_6H_4\cdot NH_2)$$

$$\xrightarrow{HCl} \overset{-}{Cl}\{\overset{+}{N}H_2=C_6H_4=C(C_6H_3(CH_3)\cdot NH_2)(C_6H_4\cdot NH_2)$$

Crystals of rosaniline show a green metallic lustre, and dissolve in water to form a deep-red solution. This solution is decolorised by sulphur dioxide and is then known as Schiff's reagent, which is used as a test for aldehydes (see p. 148). The chemical changes involved in the preparation of Schiff's reagent are still uncertain.

Rosaniline (and pararosaniline) dyes wool and silk directly, producing a violet-red colour; cotton must first be mordanted with tannin.

Structure of rosaniline dyes. Determination of the structures of the rosaniline dyes was carried out by E. and O. Fischer (1878, 1880) as follows. Pararosaniline, on reduction, gives *leucaniline* (the leuco-base). This was shown to be a primary triamine which, on treatment with nitrous acid and subsequent boiling with ethanol, gave triphenylmethane ($C_{19}H_{16}$). Triphenylmethane, on treatment with fuming nitric acid, gave a trinitro-derivative which, on reduction, gave leucaniline, and this, on oxidation, gave pararosaniline base (the colour base):

$$HC(C_6H_5)_3 \xrightarrow{HNO_3} HC(C_6H_4\cdot NO_2)_3 \xrightarrow{[H]} HC(C_6H_4\cdot NH_2)_3 \underset{[H]}{\overset{[O]}{\rightleftharpoons}} HO\cdot C(C_6H_4\cdot NH_2)_3$$

$$HC(C_6H_4\cdot NH_2)_3 \xrightarrow{HNO_2/C_2H_5OH} HC(C_6H_5)_3$$

Thus pararosaniline base is a triaminotriphenylcarbinol. Each benzene ring probably contains one amino-group since the colour base is synthesised from 2 molecules of aniline and one of *p*-toluidine. Also, nitration of triphenylmethane is likely to introduce one nitro-group into each ring, and furthermore, it is probable that each nitro-group is in the *p*-position (*cf.* diphenyl and diphenylmethane). The positions of the three amino-groups, however, were found as follows. Condensation of benzaldehyde with aniline in the presence of zinc chloride gives diaminotriphenylmethane. This, on treatment with nitrous acid and followed by boiling with water, gives dihydroxytriphenylmethane which, on fusion with potassium hydroxide, gives *p* : *p*′-dihydroxybenzophenone. These reactions may be formulated as follows:

$$C_6H_5CHO + 2\,H\text{-}C_6H_4\text{-}NH_2 \longrightarrow C_6H_5\text{-}CH(C_6H_4NH_2)_2 \xrightarrow[\text{(ii) } H_2O]{\text{(i) } HNO_2} C_6H_5\text{-}CH(C_6H_4OH)_2 \xrightarrow{KOH} CO(C_6H_4OH)_2$$

The two amino-groups in diaminotriphenylmethane are therefore in the *p*-positions. Since *p*-nitrobenzaldehyde condenses with aniline to give a product which, on reduction, gives leucaniline, it follows that all three amino-groups are in the *p*-positions to the methane carbon atom.

The structure of rosaniline was found in a similar manner. The hydrocarbon obtained was $C_{20}H_{18}$, and one structure that agrees with this is diphenyltolylmethane. The position of the methyl group in the tolyl ring is indicated by the fact that, in order to obtain rosaniline, *o*-toluidine must be used as one of the starting materials (see above). This position (*ortho* to the *p*-amino-group) is confirmed by condensing 4-nitro-3-methylbenzaldehyde with aniline, and reducing the product; leucorosaniline is obtained.

Aniline Blue (Girard and de Laire, 1861) is the diphenyl derivative of rosaniline, and is prepared by heating the latter with aniline and benzoic acid (the function of the acid in this reaction is obscure). The *o*-methyl group prevents phenylation of the amino-group in this ring (spatial effect). If pararosaniline is used, the *triphenyl* derivative is obtained.

$$NH_2(CH_3)C_6H_3\text{-}C(OH)(C_6H_4NH_2)_2 + 2C_6H_5{\cdot}NH_2 \longrightarrow$$

$$NH_2(CH_3)C_6H_3\text{-}C(OH)(C_6H_4NH{\cdot}C_6H_5)_2 \xrightarrow{HCl} NH_2(CH_3)C_6H_3\text{-}C(C_6H_4NH{\cdot}C_6H_5)(=C_6H_4=NH{\cdot}C_6H_5\}Cl^-)$$

Aniline Blue is readily sulphonated, the sulphonic acid group entering the *substituted phenyl radicals.* Nicholson (1862) thus prepared **Alkali Blue** (the monosulphonic acid) and **Soluble Blue** (the trisulphonic acid). These compounds dye wool and silk directly.

Crystal Violet (Kern, 1883) may be prepared by heating *Michler's ketone* with dimethylaniline in the presence of phosphoryl chloride or carbonyl chloride. If the latter compound is used, then crystal violet may be prepared directly by heating carbonyl chloride and dimethylaniline:

$$COCl_2 + 2\,C_6H_5N(CH_3)_2 \longrightarrow CO[C_6H_4N(CH_3)_2]_2$$

$$CO\left(C_6H_4N(CH_3)_2\right)_2 + C_6H_5N(CH_3)_2 + COCl_2 \longrightarrow$$

$$\left\{(CH_3)_2N\text{—}C_6H_4\text{—}C\left(C_6H_4N(CH_3)_2\right)\text{=}C_6H_4\text{=}\overset{+}{N}(CH_3)_2\right\}Cl^- + HCl + CO_2$$

A weakly acid solution of crystal violet is purple. In *strongly* acid solution the colour is green, and in still more strongly acid solution, the colour is yellow. The explanation of these colour changes may be as follows (*cf.* p. 745). In weakly acid solution crystal violet exists as the singly charged ion (I). In this state two-thirds of the charge can oscillate in the horizontal direction. In strongly acid solution, if crystal violet exists as the *doubly* charged ion (II), the whole unit of charge can oscillate in the horizontal

$$(CH_3)_2N\text{—}C_6H_4\text{—}C\left(C_6H_4N(CH_3)_2\right)\text{=}C_6H_4\text{=}\overset{+}{N}(CH_3)_2 \qquad \text{(I)}$$

$$(CH_3)_2N\text{—}C_6H_4\text{—}C\left(C_6H_4\overset{+}{N}H(CH_3)_2\right)\text{=}C_6H_4\text{=}\overset{+}{N}(CH_3)_2 \qquad \text{(II)}$$

$$(CH_3)_2\overset{+}{N}H\text{—}C_6H_4\text{—}C\left(C_6H_4\overset{+}{N}H(CH_3)_2\right)\text{=}C_6H_4\text{=}\overset{+}{N}(CH_3)_2 \qquad \text{(III)}$$

direction, and consequently the colour *deepens* (the vertical direction of oscillation is inhibited due to the fixation of the lone pair by proton addition). In very strongly acid solution another proton is added to form the ion (III) with three charges. In this ion relatively little resonance (with oscillation of charge) is possible, and consequently the colour lightens.

Rosolic acid, Aurin is prepared by diazotising rosaniline and boiling the

$$HO\text{—}C_6H_4\text{—}C\left(C_6H_3(CH_3)OH\right)\text{=}C_6H_4\text{=}O$$

diazonium compound with water. It crystallises in red prisms which are soluble in alkalis to form intense red solutions. It is used as an indicator, and has been used in the form of lakes for the printing of wall-papers. **Para-aurin** is the corresponding hydroxy-compound of pararosaniline.

XANTHEN DYES

The parent substance of this group of dyes is **xanthen** (*dibenzo*-1 : 4-*pyran*). This, on oxidation, yields **xanthone** (9-*ketoxanthen*) which, on reduction, yields **xanth-hydrol** (9-*hydroxyanthen*). This forms *oxonium salts* with inorganic acids (*cf*. p. 738):

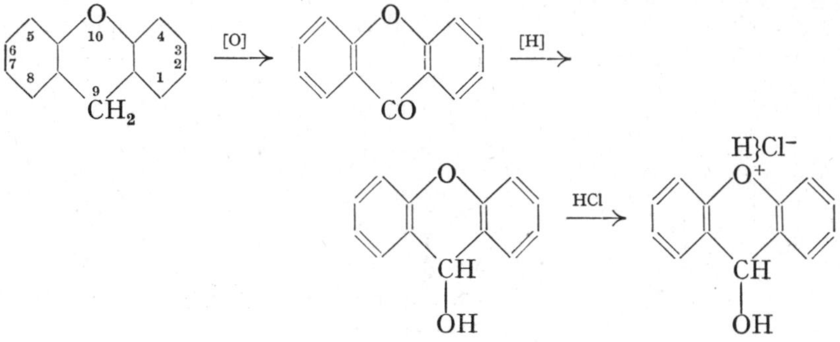

Dyes are obtained from xanthen by the introduction of auxochromes into positions 3 and 6 (*i.e.*, the *p*-positions with respect to the carbon atom linking the two benzene nuclei).

Pyronines. *Pyronine G* (Bender, 1889) is prepared by condensing formaldehyde (1 mol.) with *m*-dimethylaminophenol (2 mols.) in the presence of concentrated sulphuric acid, and then oxidising the leuco-compound with ferric chloride.

Pyronine G dyes silk and cotton mordanted with tannin a crimson red.

Since two electronic structures are possible in which the conjugation is totally different, more information is necessary to say which form predominates, or even whether both forms are present.

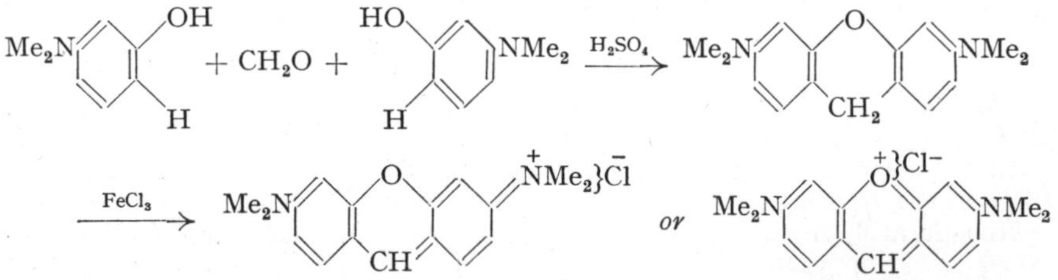

Phthaleins. A sub-group of the xanthen dyes is the **phthaleins.** These are obtained by condensing phenols with phthalic anhydride in the presence of certain dehydrating agents, *viz*., concentrated sulphuric acid, zinc chloride or anhydrous oxalic acid.

Phenolphthalein (Baeyer, 1871) is not a xanthen derivative but a triphenylmethane derivative. Since, however, it is prepared from phenol and phthalic anhydride, it is more closely allied to the phthaleins in (preparation and properties), and hence is here considered in the phthalein group. Phenolphthalein is prepared by heating phthalic anhydride (1 molecule) with phenol (2 molecules) in the presence of concentrated sulphuric acid:

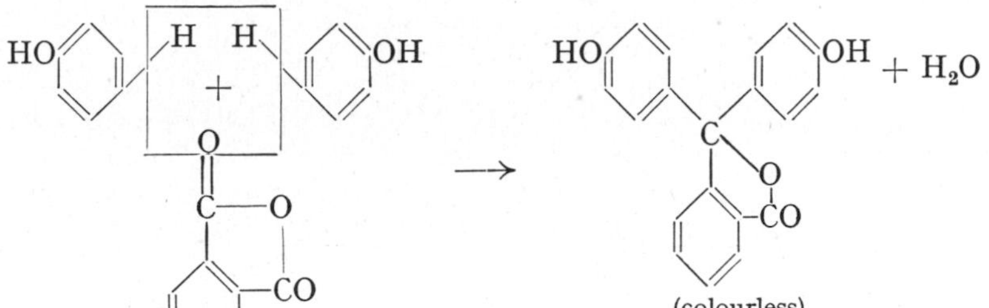

HO–C₆H₄–H + H–C₆H₄–OH + phthalic anhydride → (HO–C₆H₄)₂C(lactone) + H_2O

(colourless)

It is a white crystalline solid, insoluble in water, but soluble in alkalis to form deep red solutions:

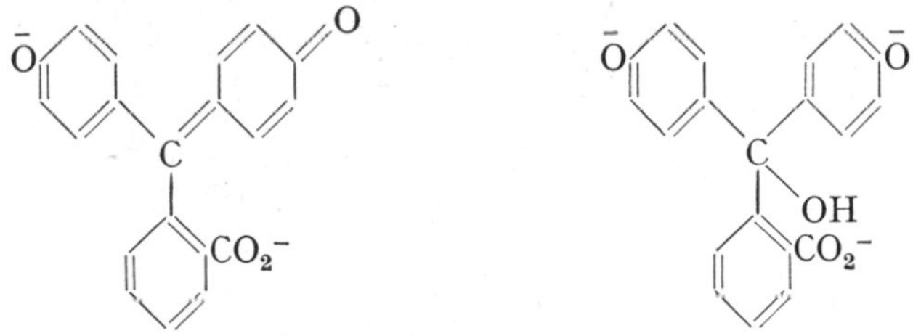

deep red

colourless

In the presence of *excess* strong alkali, the solution of phenolphthalein becomes colourless again due to the loss of the quinonoid structure and resonance (but see fluorescein, below).

Structure of phenolphthalein. Phthaloyl chloride condenses with benzene in the presence of aluminium chloride to form 3 : 3-diphenylphthalide (phthalophenone), (I). This, on heating with ethanolic potassium hydroxide, gives triphenylcarbinol-*o*-carboxylic acid, (II), which, on treatment with zinc dust and ethanolic sodium hydroxide, gives triphenylmethane-*o*-carboxylic acid, (III). This on dry distillation gives triphenylmethane, (IV). When 3 : 3-diphenylphthalide is nitrated, a mixture of two dinitro-derivatives is obtained. Reduction of these two dinitro-compounds results in the formation of two diamino-compounds, one of which, being much less soluble than the other, crystallises out first. This less soluble diamino-compound gives phenolphthalein when treated with nitrous acid. These reactions show that phenolphthalein contains the triphenylmethane nucleus, and that it is a dihydroxy-derivative of 3 : 3-diphenylphthalide. The problem now is to ascertain the positions of the two hydroxyl groups. That they are in different rings is indicated by the fact that phenolphthalein is formed when phthalic anhydride (1 molecule) is heated with phenol (2 molecules). Thus, when 3 : 3-diphenylphthalide is nitrated, we may assume that the dinitro-compound produced contains one nitro-group in each benzene ring, the phthalic acid ring remaining unsubstituted (this ring may be regarded as already substituted, and hence the nitro-groups will enter the *unsubstituted* rings, and probably in the *p*-positions; *cf.* diphenyl). When phenolphthalein is fused with potassium hydroxide, it gives benzoic acid and *p* : *p*′-dihydroxybenzophenone. Thus each hydroxyl group occupies a *p*-

position with respect to the methane carbon atom. The foregoing reactions may therefore be formulated:

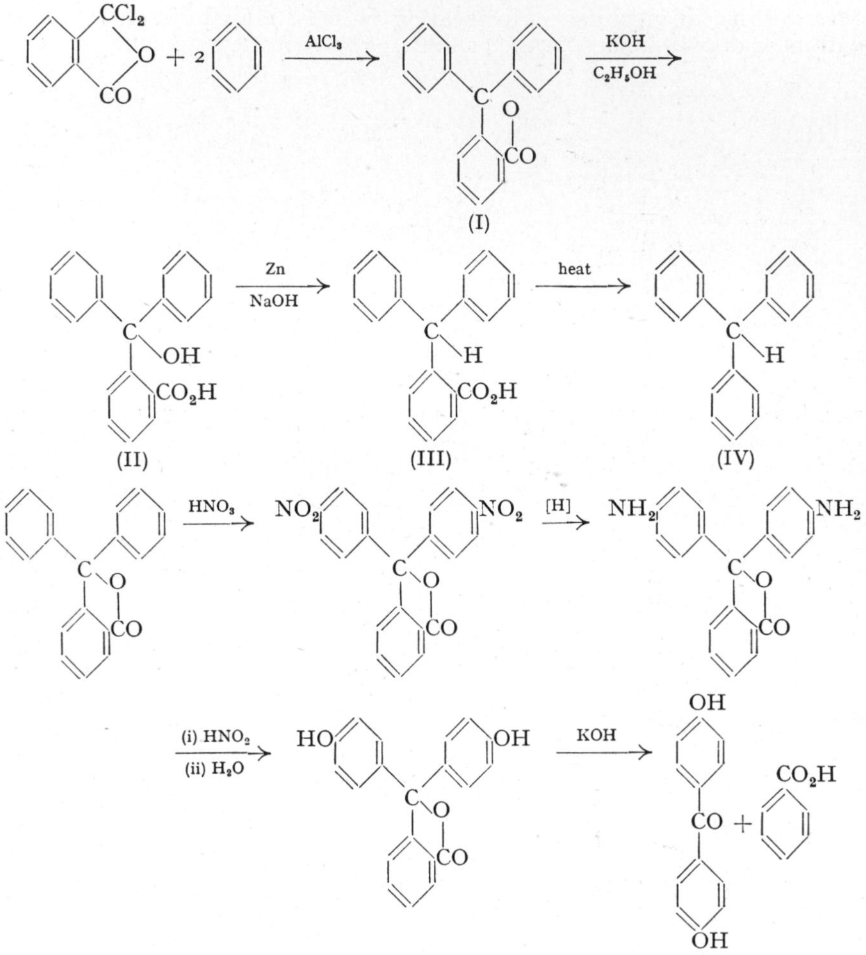

CCl_2 ... O + 2 (benzene) $\xrightarrow{AlCl_3}$ (I) $\xrightarrow[C_2H_5OH]{KOH}$

(II) $\xrightarrow[NaOH]{Zn}$ (III) $\xrightarrow{heat}$ (IV)

$\xrightarrow{HNO_3}$ NO_2 ... NO_2 $\xrightarrow{[H]}$ NH_2 ... NH_2

$\xrightarrow[(ii)\ H_2O]{(i)\ HNO_2}$ HO ... OH $\xrightarrow{KOH}$ OH, CO, OH + CO_2H (benzoic acid)

Fluorescein is a xanthen derivative, and is prepared by heating phthalic anhydride (1 molecule) with resorcinol (2 molecules) at 200°, or at 110–120° with anhydrous oxalic acid:

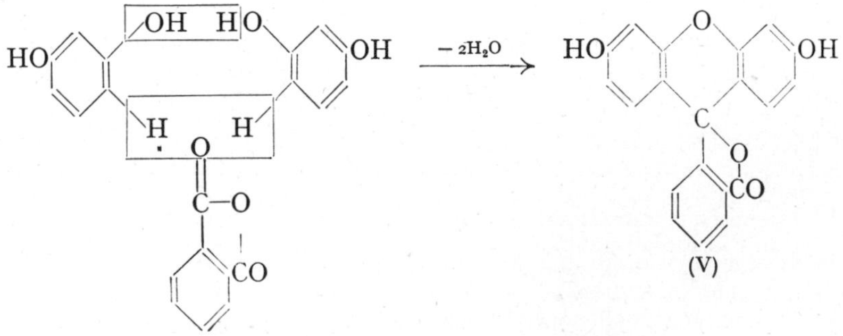

HO ... OH H O ... OH; H H; O; C—O; CO $\xrightarrow{-2H_2O}$ HO ... O ... OH; C; O; CO

(V)

Fluorescein in a red powder insoluble in water. Since it is coloured, the non-quinonoid uncharged structure V has been considered unsatisfactory. Two quinonoid structures are possible in which the conjugation is totally different, one having the *p*-quinonoid structure, VI, and the other the *o*-quinonoid, VII (which contains tercovalent oxygen):

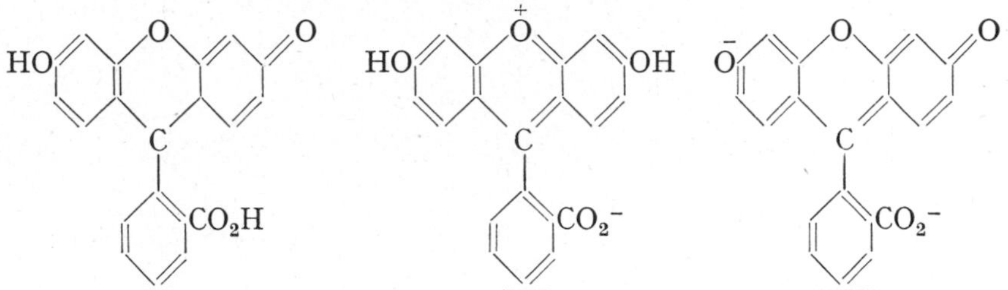

(VI) (VII) (VIII)

Davies *et al.* (1954) have examined the infrared absorptions of phenol, phenolphthalein, fluorescein, and some of their alkali derivatives, and have concluded that the classical representation of fluorescein (V) is to be preferred. (VI) is eliminated because of the absence of the characteristic absorption of the carboxyl group, and similarly, the frequencies of the carboxylate ion (in VII) are also absent.

Fluorescein dissolves in alkalis to give a reddish-brown solution which, on dilution, gives a strong yellowish-green fluorescence. The structure of the fluorescein anion is (VIII) (oxygen becomes tercovalent unielectrovalent only in acid solution). The sodium salt of fluorescein is known as **Uranine,** and dyes wool and silk yellow from an acid bath; the colours are fugitive.

Eosin (Caro, 1871) is tetrabromofluorescein, and is prepared by the action of bromine on fluorescein in glacial acetic acid solution:

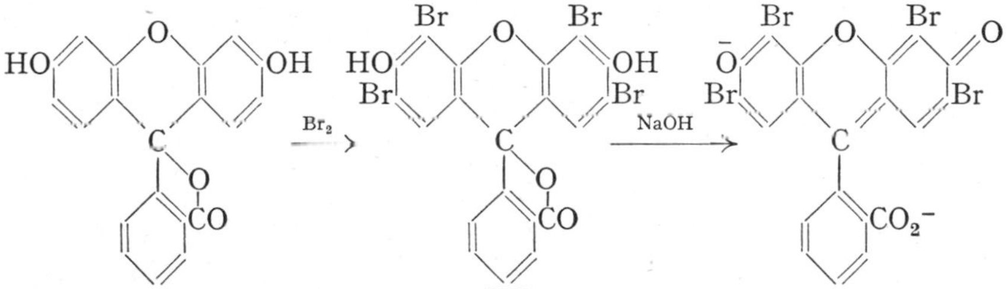

$\xrightarrow{Br_2}$ (IX) $\xrightarrow{NaOH}$

Eosin itself is a red powder and so its structure may not be (IX), but may be (X) or (XI) (*cf.* fluorescein):

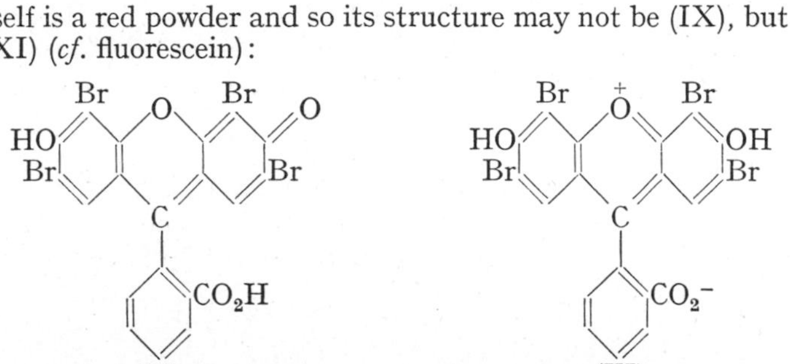

(X) (XI)

Eosin dyes wool and silk a pure red, with a yellow fluorescence in the case of silk. Eosin is also used as the lead lake *Vermilionette* for poster printing. Most red inks are dilute solutions of eosin.

Mercurochrome 220 is a derivative of fluorescein, and is used as an antiseptic.

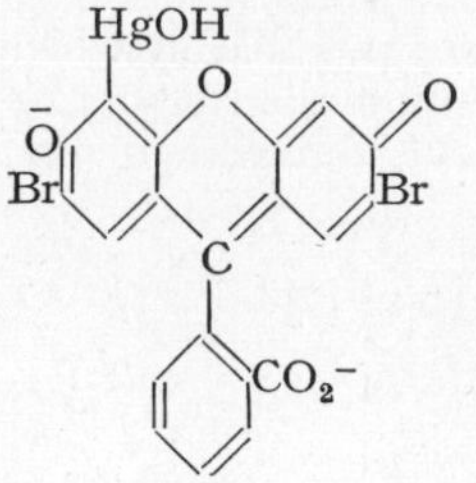

Rhodamines are prepared by condensing phthalic anhydride (1 molecule) with *m*-aminophenol (2 molecules) or its derivatives, *e.g.*, **Rhodamine B**:

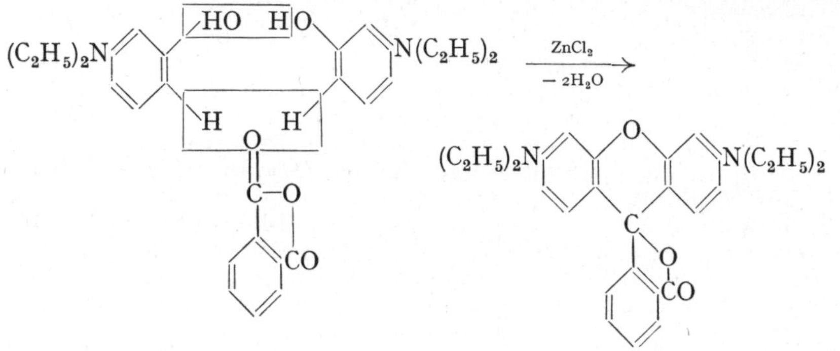

The hydrochloride of Rhodamine B may be (XII) or (XIII) (*cf.* above):

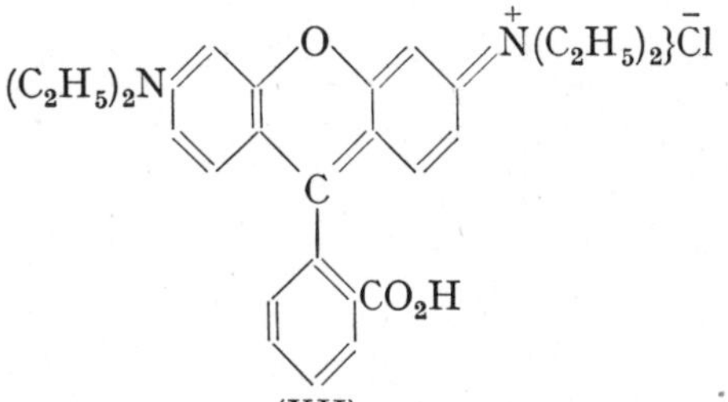

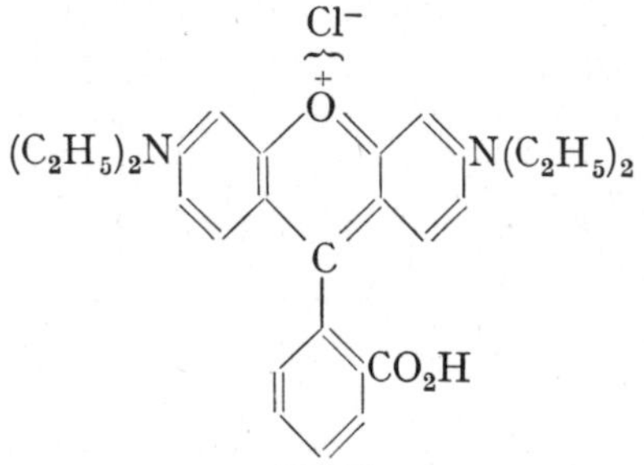

Rhodamine 6G is the ethyl ester of diethylrhodamine.

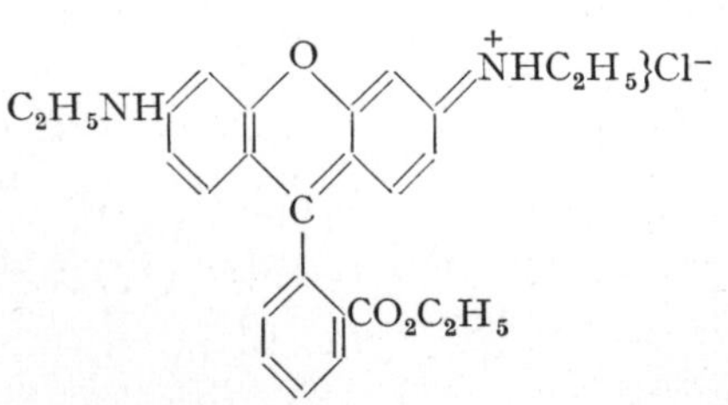

or the *o*-form

The rhodamines are red basic dyes, the *N*-alkylated derivatives being more highly coloured than the unsubstituted compounds. They dye wool and silk directly, and cotton mordanted with tannin.

DIPHENYLAMINE (QUINONE-IMINE) DYES

One group of these dyes are the **Indamines** (Nietzki, 1877). The simplest indamine is **Phenylene Blue,** and is prepared by oxidising a solution of a mixture of *p*-phenylenediamine and aniline with potassium dichromate in acetic acid–concentrated hydrochloric acid.

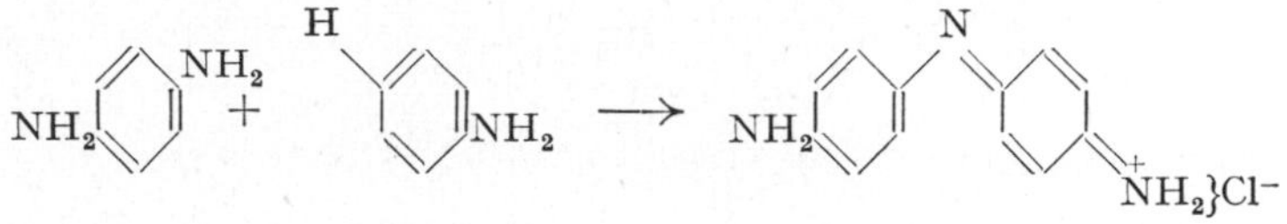

The indamines (which form blue or green salts) are very sensitive to the action of acids, which hydrolyse them to quinones. Hence they are not used as dyes but mainly as starting materials for the manufacture of azines, thiazines and oxazines.

The **Indophenols** are another group of diphenylamine dyes. The simplest is **Indophenol** (Blue), and is prepared by oxidising a mixture of *p*-phenylenediamine and phenol with alkaline hypochlorite solution:

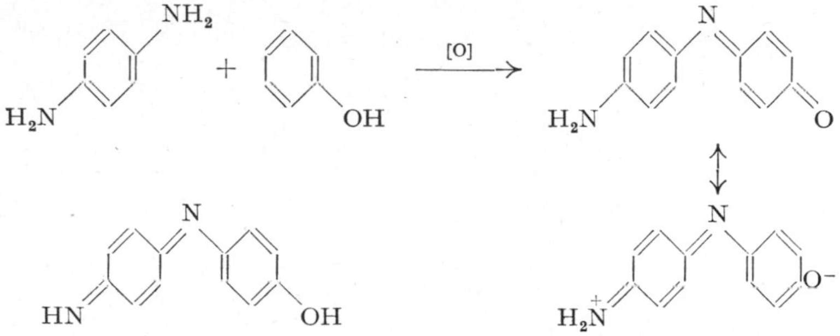

Indophenol is usually given the amino-structure and not the imino-structure because it is insoluble in alkalis but soluble in acids which hydrolyse them to quinones.

The indophenols are blue in colour, and owing to their sensitivity to acids, are not used now as dyestuffs, but only as the starting materials for various sulphur dyes.

HETEROCYCLIC DYES

Acridine Group. Acridine dyes are all yellow to orange and brown, basic dyes; they are used in calico printing, dyeing cotton, silk and particularly leather. Some acridine dyes have medicinal and antiseptic properties.

2 : 8-Diaminoacridine is made by heating a mixture of *m*-phenylenediamine, glycerol, oxalic acid and zinc chloride, and oxidising the leuco-compound:

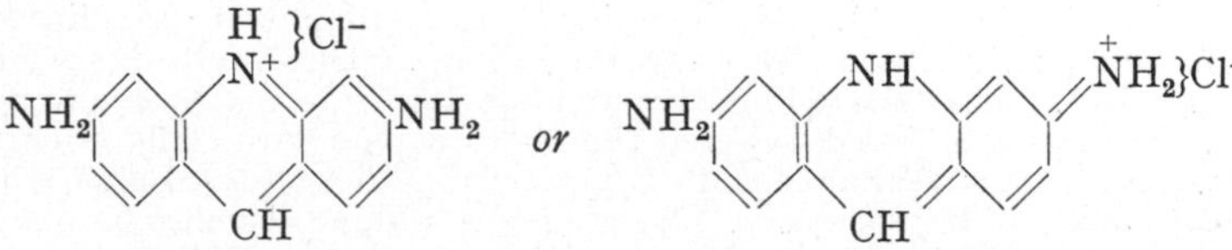

The corresponding sulphate is the antiseptic **proflavine.** On acetylating 2 : 8-diaminoacridine, methylating the 10-N atom by means of methyl *p*-toluenesulphonate, and then hydrolysing the product with dilute hydrochloric acid, 2 : 8-diamino-10-methylacridinium chloride is produced. This is known as **acriflavine,** and possesses trypanocidal action (*i.e.*, the power to kill trypanosomes which are micro-organisms causing sleeping sickness and other diseases). It has now been replaced by more potent trypanocides, but it is still used as an antiseptic:

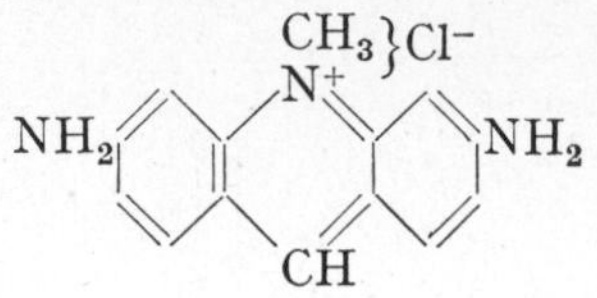

Acridine Yellow is one of the more important acridine dyes, and is prepared from 2 : 4-diaminotoluene and formaldehyde:

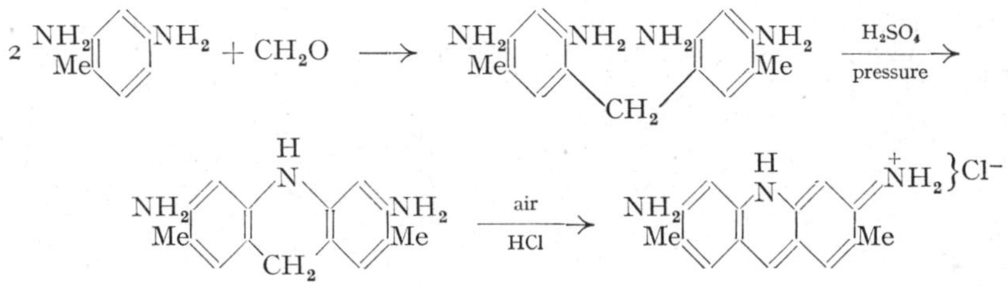

Quinoline group. Most of these dyes are more important as photographic sensitisers than as dyes for fabrics.

Quinoline Yellow (Jacobsen, 1882) is the most important quinoline compound used as a dyestuff for textiles. It is prepared by condensing phthalic anhydride with quinaldine in the presence of zinc chloride.

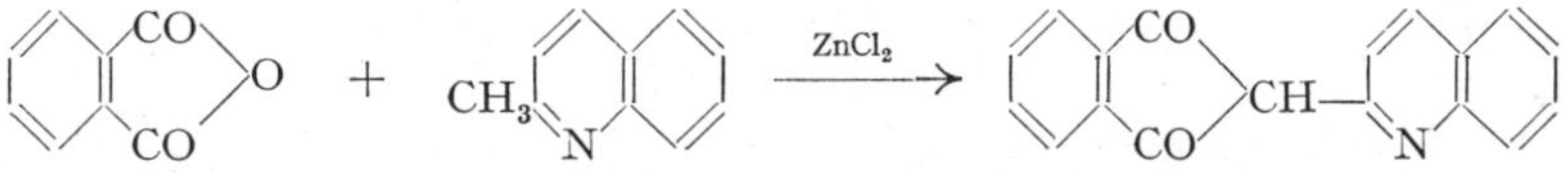

This structure is probably incorrect, since the dye is coloured and so requires a charged structure; it also forms an *N*-methyl derivative which has almost the same absorption spectrum as Quinoline Yellow, thereby indicating a similarity in structure. Hence Quinoline Yellow is considered to be the following resonance hybrid (the *extended* conjugation in the dipolar ion should be noted).

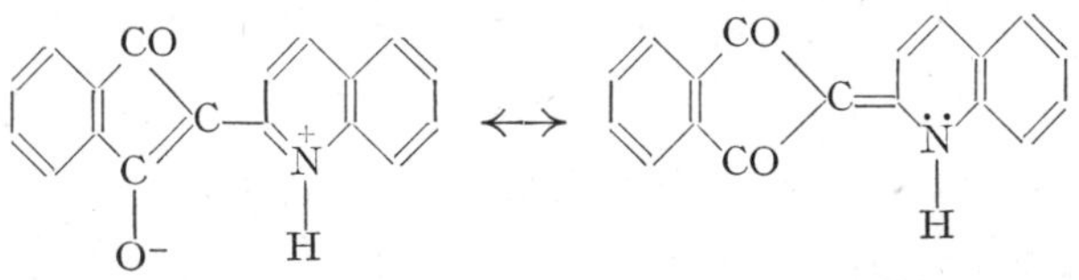

Cyanine (*Quinoline Blue*). The cyanine dyes contain two quinoline nuclei linked in the 4 : 4′-positions by a =CH— group. They were discovered by Williams (1856). They are too fugitive and apparently too expensive to be used as dyes. Vogel (1873) first discovered the photographic sensitising properties of cyanine. Ordinary silver halide photographic plates are sensitive only to the blue and violet regions of the spectrum. By adding a suitable cyanine compound the plates are made sensitive to other regions of the spectrum: yellow, orange, red or green. Plates can also be made sensitive to *all* parts of the spectrum; they are then said to be *panchromatic*.

Cyanine is formed by the air oxidation of a mixture of amylquinolinium and amyllepidinium iodides in the presence of aqueous alkali.

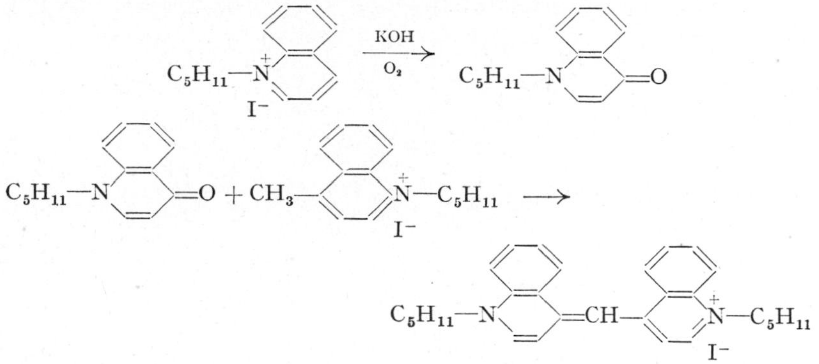

C_5H_{11}—$\overset{+}{N}$ I^- $\xrightarrow[O_2]{KOH}$ C_5H_{11}—N =O

C_5H_{11}—N =O + CH_3— $\overset{+}{N}$—C_5H_{11} I^- $\longrightarrow$

C_5H_{11}—N =CH— $\overset{+}{N}$—C_5H_{11} I^-

***iso*Cyanine dyes** contain two quinoline nuclei linked in the 2 : 4′-positions by a =CH— group. The first *iso*cyanine was **Ethyl Red** (Hoogewerff and van Dorp, 1883), and is prepared from quinoline and quinaldine ethiodides by air oxidation in the presence of alkali.

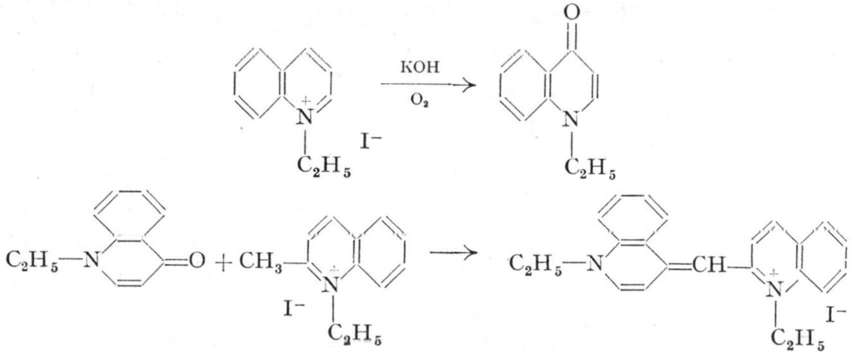

$\overset{+}{N}$ I^- C_2H_5 $\xrightarrow[O_2]{KOH}$ O N C_2H_5

C_2H_5—N =O + CH_3— $\overset{+}{N}$ I^- C_2H_5 $\longrightarrow$ C_2H_5—N =CH— $\overset{+}{N}$ I^- C_2H_5

Ethyl Red sensitises plates evenly from orange to the ultraviolet.

Pseudocyanine dyes contain two quinoline nuclei linked in the 2 : 2′-positions by a =CH— group. They are prepared by the action of ethanolic potassium hydroxide on a mixture of a 2-iodoquinoline alkiodide and a quinaldine alkiodide, *e.g.*

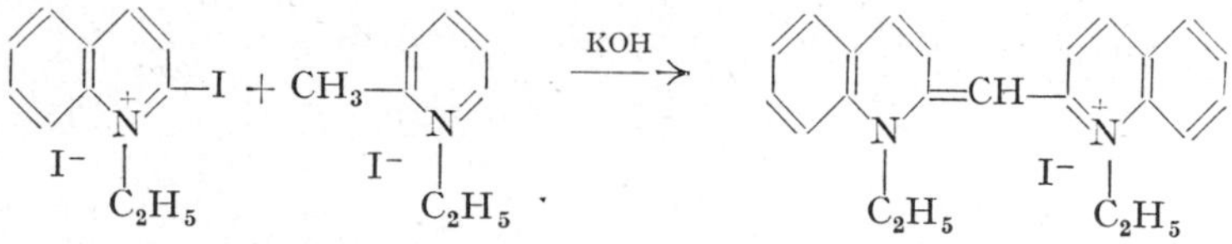

$\overset{+}{N}$—I I^- C_2H_5 + CH_3— $\overset{+}{N}$ I^- C_2H_5 $\xrightarrow{KOH}$ N C_2H_5 =CH— $\overset{+}{N}$ I^- C_2H_5

The pseudocyanines are sensitisers for the blue to the green part of the spectrum.

Acidification destroys the colour of cyanine dyes. This is due to the fact that *both* nitrogen atoms become charged, a proton is taken into the chain, and so resonance is prevented between the two nitrogen atoms (see p. 745).

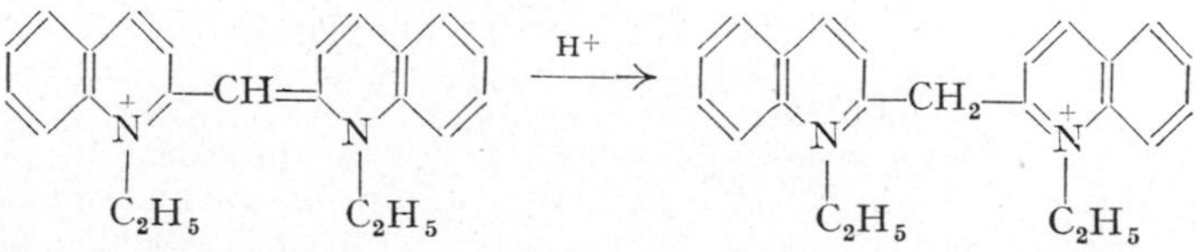

$\overset{+}{N}$ C_2H_5 —CH= N C_2H_5 $\xrightarrow{H^+}$ $\overset{+}{N}$ C_2H_5 —CH_2— $\overset{+}{N}$ C_2H_5

Sensitol Red or **Pinacyanole** (König, 1905) is a *carbocyanine*, and sensitises in the red-to-orange region. Carbocyanines are compounds containing two quinoline nuclei linked in the 2 : 2′-positions by =CH—CH=CH—. *Sensitol Red* is prepared by the action of excess ethyl orthoformate on quinaldine ethiodide in boiling pyridine solution.

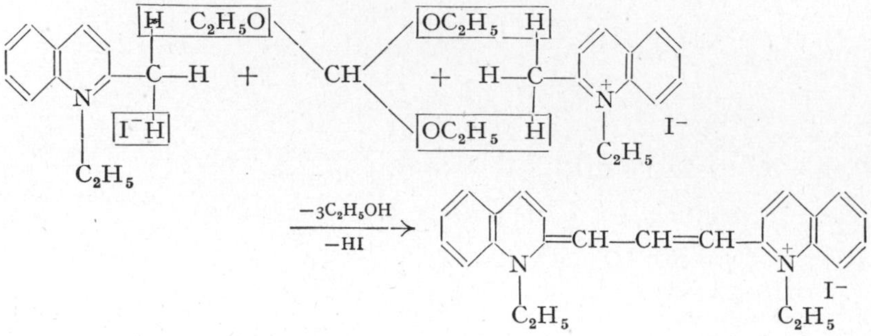

$$\text{Quinaldine ethiodide}\;(\text{CH}_3\text{ group: } \boxed{H}\ \ \boxed{I^-H}) + \text{CH}(\boxed{C_2H_5O})(\boxed{OC_2H_5})_2 + \text{quinaldine ethiodide} \xrightarrow[-HI]{-3C_2H_5OH} \text{quinoline}(N\text{-}C_2H_5)\text{=CH—CH=CH—quinolinium}(\overset{+}{N}\text{-}C_2H_5)\ I^-$$

The isomeric 4 : 4′-carbocyanines are known as *kryptocyanines*, and are sensitisers for the red and infrared regions. 2 : 4′-Carbocyanines are known as *dicyanines*.

Azine Dyes. Perkin (1856), in a search for the synthesis of the alkaloid quinine, oxidised crude aniline sulphate with potassium dichromate, and obtained a black precipitate from which he extracted a mauve colouring matter with methylated spirit. Perkin found that this material had the properties of a dye. This was the first synthetic dye to be used, and was used for dyeing silk under the name of *Aniline Purple* or *Tyrian Purple*. Aniline Purple was the first basic dye to be used, but no method was known (when it was discovered) for applying it to cotton. Perkin and Pullar, independently in 1857, discovered the general method of applying basic dyes to cotton mordanted with insoluble inorganic compounds of tannin. Aniline Purple was used in France under the name of *Mauve*, and the dye afterwards became known by this name; it is also known as *mauveine*.

Perkin found that his material contained two products, one from pure aniline—*pseudo-mauveine*, and the other from aniline and *o*-toluidine (the latter was an impurity in crude aniline)—*mauveine*. The structure of pseudomauveine was established by Nietzki who prepared it by oxidising a mixture of *p*-phenylenediamine and diphenyl-*m*-phenylenediamine:

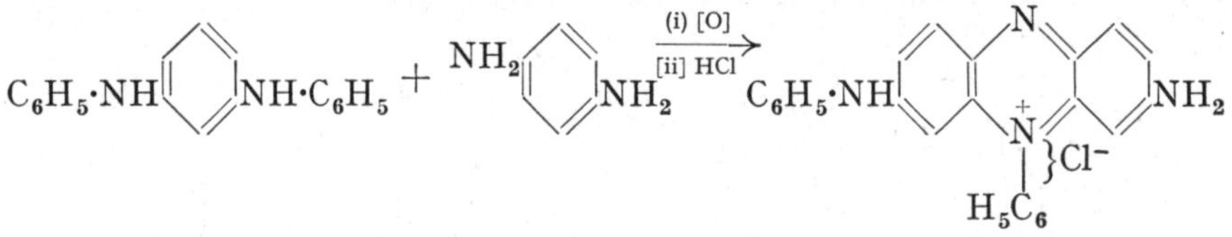

$$C_6H_5\cdot NH\text{—}C_6H_4\text{—}NH\cdot C_6H_5 + NH_2\text{—}C_6H_4\text{—}NH_2 \xrightarrow[\text{(ii) HCl}]{\text{(i) [O]}} C_6H_5\cdot NH\text{—(phenazinium, }\overset{+}{N}\text{—}C_6H_5\text{)—}NH_2\ \}Cl^-$$

The structure may be the *p*-quinonoid instead of the *o*- shown above (*cf.* fluorescein, etc.).

Mauveine is a mixture of compounds of the type

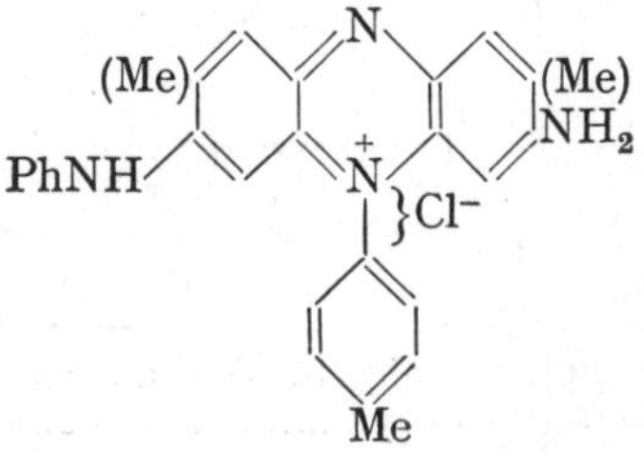

$$\text{PhNH—(Me)phenazinium(Me)—}NH_2,\ \overset{+}{N}\text{—}C_6H_4\text{—Me}\ \}Cl^-$$

More useful dyes than Mauveine are the **Safranines**—these are more strongly basic than the mauveines. **Safranine T** (Williams, 1859) is prepared by oxidising a mixture of 2 : 5-diaminotoluene, *o*-toluidine and aniline with sodium dichromate and hydrochloric acid (an indamine is formed as an intermediate).

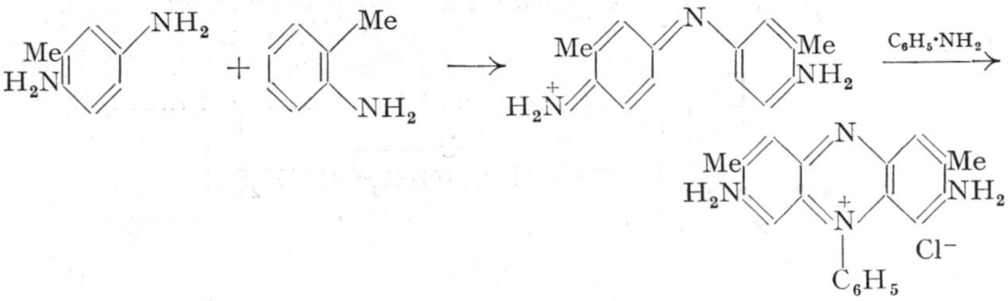

Me, H_2N, NH_2 + Me, NH_2 → Me, $H_2\overset{+}{N}$, N, Me, NH_2 $\xrightarrow{C_6H_5\cdot NH_2}$

Me, H_2N, N, $\overset{+}{N}$, Me, NH_2, Cl^-, C_6H_5

It is a red basic dye, dyeing wool, silk and " tanned " cotton red shades.

Indulines (Caro, 1863) are phenylamino-derivatives of the mauveines, and are prepared by heating a mixture of aminoazobenzene, aniline and its hydrochloride under pressure. They are very much used for colouring leather polishes, for printing cotton and for newspapers.

Induline Blue 6B is insoluble in water (as are other indulines), but is made water soluble by sulphonation; the alkaline solutions are used as dyes and for making lakes and inks.

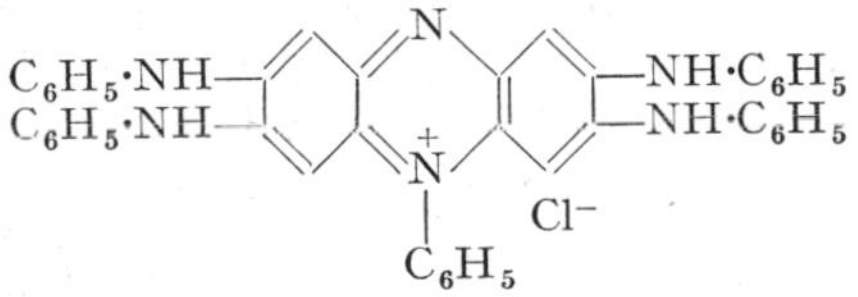

$C_6H_5\cdot NH$—, $C_6H_5\cdot NH$—, N, $\overset{+}{N}$, —$NH\cdot C_6H_5$, —$NH\cdot C_6H_5$, Cl^-, C_6H_5

Thiazine dyes. *Lauth's Violet* (1876) was the first thiazine dye to be prepared; it is made by oxidising with ferric chloride in hydrochloric acid a hydrochloric acid solution of *p*-phenylenediamine saturated with hydrogen sulphide.

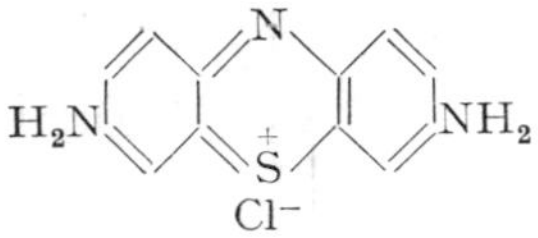

H_2N, N, $\overset{+}{S}$, NH_2, Cl^-

Methylene Blue (Caro, 1876) may be prepared in a similar way to Lauth's violet, but *p*-aminodimethylaniline is used instead of *p*-phenylenediamine. A better preparation is to oxidise a mixture of *p*-aminodimethylaniline and

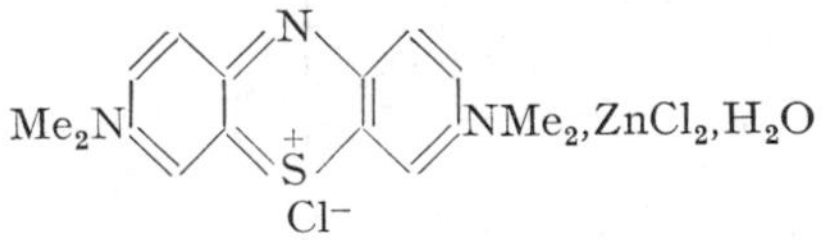

Me_2N, N, $\overset{+}{S}$, $NMe_2,ZnCl_2,H_2O$, Cl^-

dimethylaniline with potassium dichromate in the presence of sodium thiosulphate and aluminium sulphate (Bernthsen). The zinc double chloride is used in dyeing, and is largely used for dyeing cotton mordanted with tannin. Methylene Blue, free from the zinc, is used in calico printing, as an indicator and in medicine.

Oxazine dyes. **Meldola's Blue** or **Naphthol Blue** (1879) is prepared by the action of excess *p*-nitrosodimethylaniline hydrochloride on 2-naphthol in hot methanol solution.

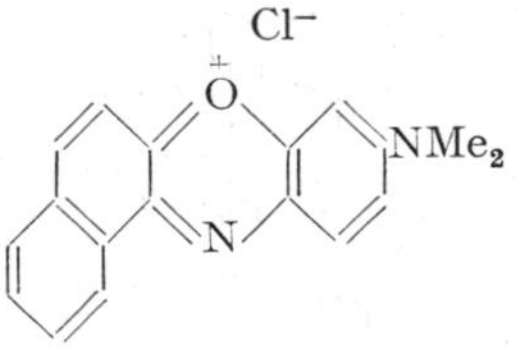

Cl^-, $\overset{+}{O}$, NMe_2, N

It is used commercially as the zinc double chloride for dyeing cotton mordanted with tannin; it dyes the fabric an indigo blue. It is also used as a leather dye.

VAT DYES

Indigoid Group. India appears to be the birth-place of **indigo—indigotin** is its official name. It is the oldest known dye—mummy cloths, 5000 years old, have been found that were dyed with indigotin. *Woad*, which is an impure form of indigotin (and is obtained from the plant *Isatis tinctoria*), contains a small amount of *indican* which is the glucoside of indoxyl:

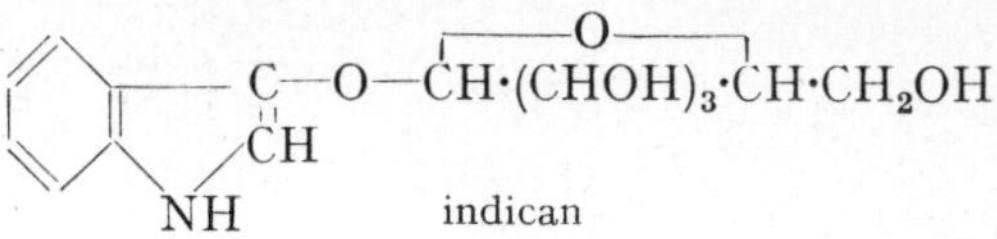

$$C—O—CH·(CHOH)_3·CH·CH_2OH \quad \text{(ring O between the CH groups; indole: } C=CH—NH)$$

indican

Indigotin used to be obtained from plants of the *indigofera* group, but is now prepared synthetically. These plants do not contain indigotin but indican which, on hydrolysis with hydrochloric acid or by enzymes which occur in the crushed plant, is converted into indoxyl and this, on oxidation by atmospheric oxygen, gives indigotin:

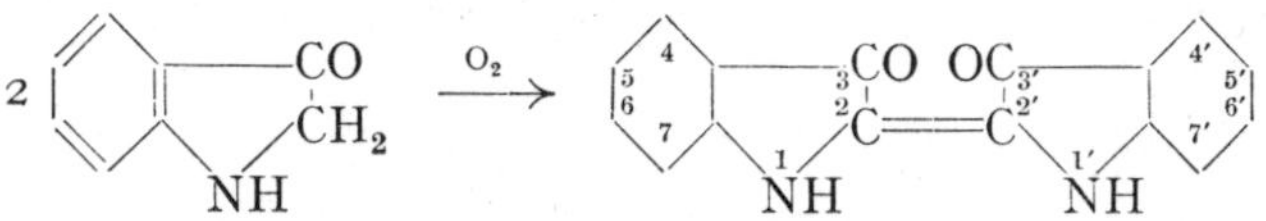

$$2\ C_6H_4(CO)(CH_2)NH \xrightarrow{O_2} C_6H_4(CO)(NH)C{=}C(NH)(CO)C_6H_4$$

Structure of indigotin. Vapour density determination shows that the molecular formula of indigotin is $C_{16}H_{10}O_2N_2$. Oxidation of indigotin with nitric acid gives two molecules of isatin only, two oxygen atoms being added on in the process. This implies that the indigotin molecule contains two identical units joined together, and that each unit, when indigotin is oxidised, gives a molecule of isatin. There are three possible structures of indigotin which meet these requirements:

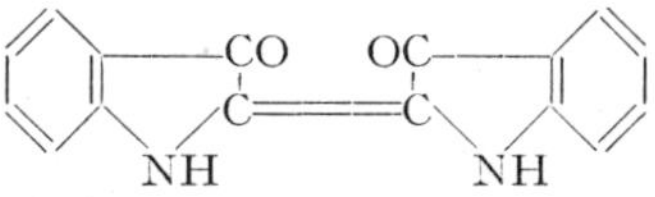

(I) 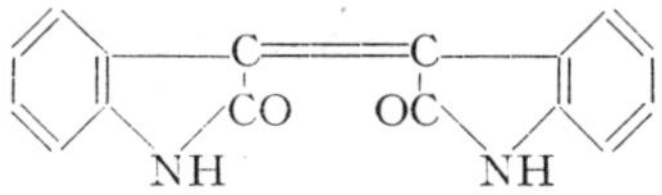 (II) 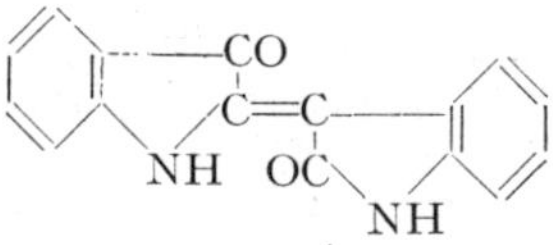 (III)

The carbon skeletons of these are different, *viz.*,

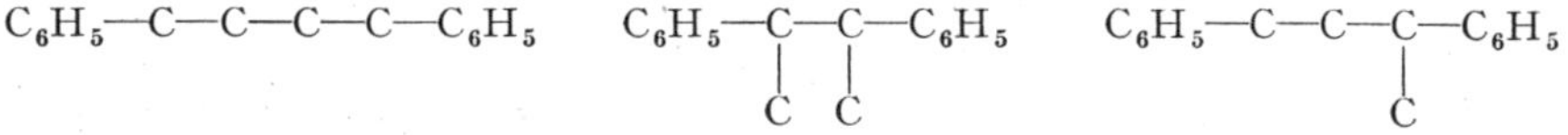

$$C_6H_5—C—C—C—C—C_6H_5 \quad \text{(I)}$$

$$C_6H_5—C(—C)—C(—C)—C_6H_5 \quad \text{(II)}$$

$$C_6H_5—C—C—C(—C)—C_6H_5 \quad \text{(III)}$$

Synthesis (iv) below, in particular, indicates (I), and this structure is supported by the fact that on hydrolysis with dilute alkali, indigotin gives anthranilic acid and indoxyl-2-aldehyde. Only structure (I) can give rise to these two products. Actually, all three compounds (I), (II) and (III), are known: (I) is

$$C_6H_4(CO_2H)(NH_2) \qquad HO—C=C(—CHO)—NH \text{ (indoxyl-2-aldehyde)}$$

indigotin, (II) *iso*indigotin, and (III) indirubin. Furthermore, indigotin is the *trans*-isomer of (I) (see below).

Synthesis of indigotin. Many syntheses of indigotin are known, and they may be divided into two groups:

A. *Syntheses of historical and theoretical interest (these show the structure of indigotin.)* All are due to Baeyer.

(i) When isatin is treated with phosphorus pentachloride and the product, isatin chloride, reduced with zinc dust in glacial acetic acid, indoxyl is formed and this, on atmospheric oxidation, gives indigotin (Baeyer, 1878):

$\xrightarrow{PCl_5}$ $\xrightarrow[CH_3 \cdot CO_2H]{Zn}$ $\xrightarrow[O_2]{\text{2 molecules}}$

(ii) When *o*-nitrobenzaldehyde is warmed with acetone in the presence of a little sodium hydroxide, indigotin is formed (Baeyer, 1882):

$$2\,C_6H_4(CHO)(NO_2) + 2CH_3 \cdot CO \cdot CH_3 \xrightarrow{NaOH} \text{indigotin} + 2CH_3 \cdot CO_2H + 2H_2O$$

(iii) Bromination of *o*-nitrocinnamic acid, followed by treatment with ethanolic potassium hydroxide, produces *o*-nitrophenylpropiolic acid. This, on heating with glucose and aqueous sodium hydroxide, gives indigotin, possibly via *isatogenic acid* (Baeyer, 1880):

$$C_6H_4(NO_2)CH{=}CH \cdot CO_2H \xrightarrow[\text{(ii) } KOH/C_2H_5OH]{\text{(i) } Br_2} C_6H_4(NO_2)C{\equiv}C \cdot CO_2H \xrightarrow[NaOH]{C_6H_{12}O_6} [\text{isatogenic acid}] \longrightarrow \text{indigotin}$$

(iv) *o*-Nitrophenylacetylene, produced by heating *o*-nitrophenylpropiolic acid, forms the copper salt when treated with ammoniacal cuprous chloride. On treatment with potassium ferricyanide, this salt is converted into a diyne derivative which, by means of concentrated sulphuric acid, is converted into *di-isatogen* and this, on reduction with aqueous ammonium polysulphide, gives indigotin (Baeyer, 1882):

$$o\text{-}NO_2C_6H_4C{:}C\cdot CO_2H \xrightarrow{\text{heat}} o\text{-}NO_2C_6H_4C{:}CH \xrightarrow[NH_4OH]{CuCl} o\text{-}NO_2C_6H_4C{:}CCu \xrightarrow{K_3Fe(CN)_6}$$

$$o\text{-}NO_2C_6H_4\text{—}C{:}C\cdot C{:}C\text{—}C_6H_4NO_2\text{-}o \xrightarrow{H_2SO_4} \text{di-isatogen} \xrightarrow{(NH_4)_2S_x} \text{indigotin}$$

This synthesis shows clearly that the carbon skeleton of indigotin is C_6H_5—C—C—C—C—C_6H_5 (*cf.* above).

B. *Commercial syntheses of indigotin.* Natural indigotin is now produced only on a very small scale. It is interesting to note that Noelting (1886) expressed the opinion that although Baeyer had synthesised indigotin (in 1878), he (Noelting) did not think it was possible to manufacture synthetic indigotin on a scale large enough to compete with natural indigotin:

(i) Anthranilic acid (prepared from naphthalene as the starting material) is heated with chloroacetic acid and the product, phenylglycine-*o*-carboxylic acid, is heated with a mixture of potassium hydroxide and sodamide. Indoxylic acid is thereby produced, and this decarboxylates into indoxyl which, on exposure to air, is oxidised to indigotin:

$$o\text{-}C_6H_4(CO_2H)NH_2 + CH_2Cl\cdot CO_2H \longrightarrow o\text{-}C_6H_4(CO_2H)NH\cdot CH_2\cdot CO_2H \xrightarrow[NaNH_2]{KOH}$$

$$\left[C_6H_4\begin{matrix}COH\\ \| \\ C\cdot CO_2H\end{matrix}\ (NH)\right] \xrightarrow{-CO_2} C_6H_4\begin{matrix}CO\\ | \\ CH_2\end{matrix}\ (NH) \xrightarrow{O_2} \text{indigotin}$$

This method is due to Heumann (1896).

(ii) Aniline is heated with chloroacetic acid, the product, phenylglycine, converted into a mixture of its sodium and potassium salts, and these fused with sodamide and a mixture of sodium and potassium hydroxides at 220–240°. Indoxyl which is thereby obtained is converted into indigotin by atmospheric oxygen (the "mixed salt" requires a lower temperature of fusion, and consequently the yield of indoxyl is better):

$$C_6H_5NH_2 + CH_2Cl\cdot CO_2H \longrightarrow C_6H_5NH\cdot CH_2\cdot CO_2H \xrightarrow[KOH]{NaOH}$$

$$C_6H_5NH\cdot CH_2\cdot CO_2\begin{cases}Na\\K\end{cases} \xrightarrow[NaOH/KOH]{NaNH_2} C_6H_4\begin{matrix}CO\\ | \\ CH_2\end{matrix}\ (NH) \xrightarrow{O_2} \text{indigotin}$$

This method was first used in 1890, the fusion, however, being carried out with potassium hydroxide alone (Heumann). In 1896 this method was abandoned, and method (i) was used due to the cheap cost of phthalic anhydride from naphthalene. This oxidation was successful due to the accidental breaking of a thermometer, an accident which led to the discovery in 1893 that mercury catalyses the oxidation of naphthalene with sulphuric acid. Furthermore, method (i) gave better yields than (ii). About 1898, however, it was found that the addition of sodamide in the fusion in method (ii) increased the yield, and so (ii) was used again. Still later the preparation of phenylglycine was modified as follows. Formaldehyde is converted into its bisulphite compound on treatment with an aqueous saturated solution of sodium hydrogen sulphite at 50–80°. This compound is then warmed with aniline at 50–70°, then treated with aqueous sodium cyanide, and the product hydrolysed with water at 70°:

$$CH_2O + NaHSO_3 \longrightarrow CH_2(OH){\cdot}SO_3Na \xrightarrow{C_6H_5{\cdot}NH_2} C_6H_5{\cdot}NH{\cdot}CH_2{\cdot}SO_3Na$$

$$\xrightarrow{NaCN} C_6H_5{\cdot}NH{\cdot}CH_2{\cdot}CN \xrightarrow{H_2O} C_6H_5{\cdot}NH{\cdot}CH_2{\cdot}CO_2H$$

(iii) Aniline, on treatment with ethylene oxide, forms *N*-phenyl-2-hydroxyethylamine and this, on fusion with a mixture of sodium and potassium hydroxides at 200°, gives the sodium (and potassium) alkoxide. When this sodium salt is heated with sodamide and a mixture of sodium and potassium hydroxides at 200°, the *N*-sodio-derivative is produced. This is dehydrogenated on heating rapidly to 300°, and on rapid cooling to 235°, ring closure takes place with the formation of the sodium salt of indoxyl. This, when treated with water and allowed to stand exposed to the air, gives indigotin:

$$C_6H_5{\cdot}NH_2 + CH_2{-}CH_2\ (\text{with bridging O}) \longrightarrow C_6H_5{\cdot}NH{\cdot}CH_2{\cdot}CH_2OH \xrightarrow[200^\circ]{NaOH/KOH}$$

$$C_6H_5{\cdot}NH{\cdot}CH_2{\cdot}CH_2ONa \xrightarrow[NaNH_2]{NaOH/KOH} C_6H_5{\cdot}N(Na){\cdot}CH_2{\cdot}CH_2ONa \xrightarrow[(ii)\ 235^\circ]{(i)\ 300^\circ}$$

$$\text{(indoxyl sodium salt: benzene ring fused, C(ONa)=CH, NH)} \xrightarrow{air/H_2O} \text{indigotin}$$

CONa, CH, NH

Properties of indigotin. Indigotin is a dark blue powder with a coppered lustre. It is insoluble in water, but when its paste is agitated with alkaline sodium hyposulphite in large vats, the insoluble indigotin is reduced to the soluble leuco-compound, *indigotin-white*:

$$\text{indigotin (CO, NH, C=C, NH, CO)} \underset{[O]}{\overset{[H]}{\rightleftharpoons}} \text{indigotin-white (C(ONa), NH, C—C, NH, C(ONa))}$$

The material to be dyed is soaked in this alkaline solution and then exposed to the air, whereupon the original blue dye is regenerated in the cloth.

In vat-colour printing (of calico), "local dyeing" is achieved by making the dye pigment into a thick paste (by means of a "thickener", *e.g.*, starch), and applying this locally in the presence of alkali and a reducing agent, *e.g.*, sodium formaldehyde-sulphoxylate (*Rongalite*, *formosul*), $CH_2(OH){\cdot}SO_2Na$, which is prepared by reducing formaldehyde bisulphite with zinc and acetic acid. The colour is finally developed by means of an oxidising agent, *e.g.*, sodium nitrite.

In textile printing, *e.g.*, shirtings, dress materials, etc., indigotin-white is not sufficiently stable to be used. Hence textile printing (and ordinary dyeing) may be effected by first converting indigotin into **indigosol O** by treating indigotin-white with chlorosulphonic acid in the presence of pyridine. This produces the disulphuric ester which, by means of sodium hydroxide, is converted into its sodium salt, indigosol O. This is readily applied to animal or vegetable fibres

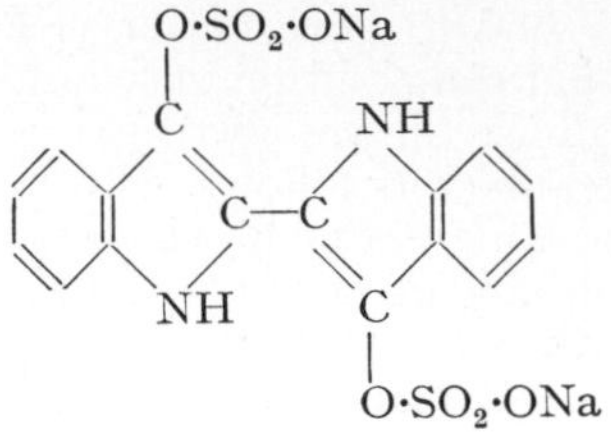

$O{\cdot}SO_2{\cdot}ONa$
C NH
C—C
NH C
$O{\cdot}SO_2{\cdot}ONa$

by soaking the fabric in the solution, and then oxidising the indigosol O in *acid* solution (with sodium nitrite) to the original insoluble vat dye. Here we have an example of a vat dye being applied without the vatting process. Indigosol O is stable in neutral or alkaline solution, but is hydrolysed to indigotin-white in acid solution.

When heated with concentrated alkali, indigotin gives a brownish-red solid which, on distillation, gives aniline. Aniline was actually first obtained this way (Fritzsche, 1840). When refluxed first with dilute alkali and then with sulphuric acid, indigotin gives anthranilic acid. If the acid stage is omitted, indoxyl-2-aldehyde can be isolated, but this tends to condense with the anthranilic acid; the acid decomposes this complex and also any free aldehyde.

With metals indigotin forms complexes, the structure of which is not certain, but is probably chelate.

Two geometrical isomers are possible for indigotin:

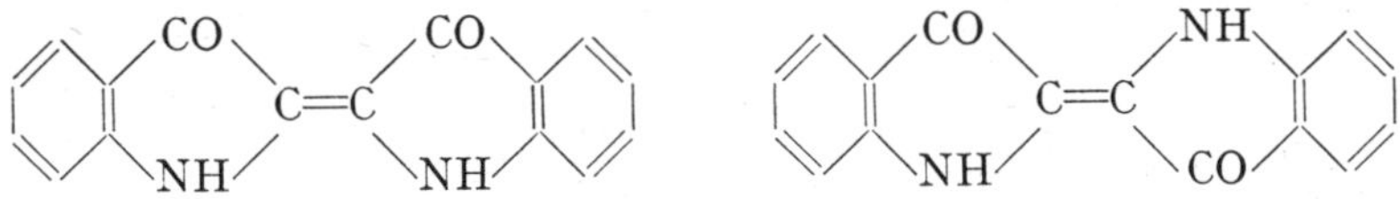

CO CO
C=C
NH NH
cis-form

CO NH
C=C
NH CO
trans-form

Derivatives of both are known, but the stable form is the *trans*-; X-ray analysis shows that the indigotin molecule contains a centre of symmetry. There is, however, some evidence to show that it is the *cis*-form which is produced in the cloth, and that it slowly changes into the stable *trans*-form.

The colour of indigotin requires explanation by charged structures, *e.g.*, the *o*-quinonoid charged structure (IV) is a possibility; at the same time, this structure would be stabilised by hydrogen bonding:

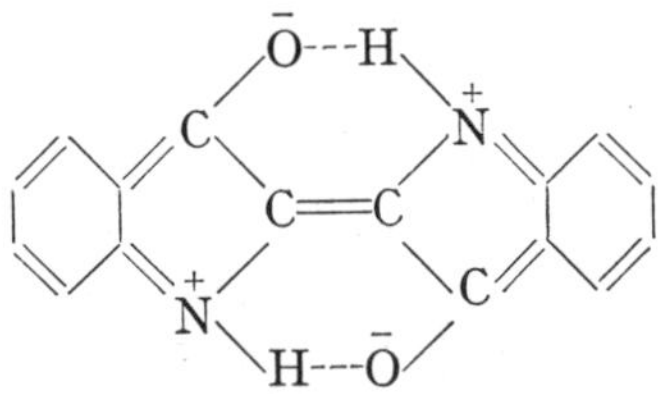

$\bar{O}$---H
C $\overset{+}{N}$
C=C
$\overset{+}{N}$ C
H---$\bar{O}$
(IV)

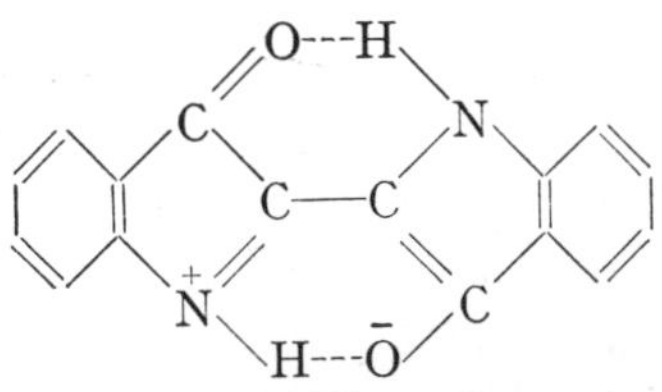

O---H
C N
C—C
$\overset{+}{N}$ C
H---$\bar{O}$
(V)

An alternative charged structure for indigotin is V; this does not involve any quinonoid structures, but it is again stabilised by hydrogen bonding. Furthermore, the presence of this resonating structure may be used to explain the conversion of the labile *cis*-form into the stable *trans*-form since it contains a *single* bond linking the two units together. If we imagine that the *cis* form is formed first, and that (VI) is the main contributing resonating structure, then due to the repulsion between the strongly electron-attracting oxygen atoms, and the attraction between the negatively charged oxygen atom and the positively charged nitrogen atom, rotation will take place about the

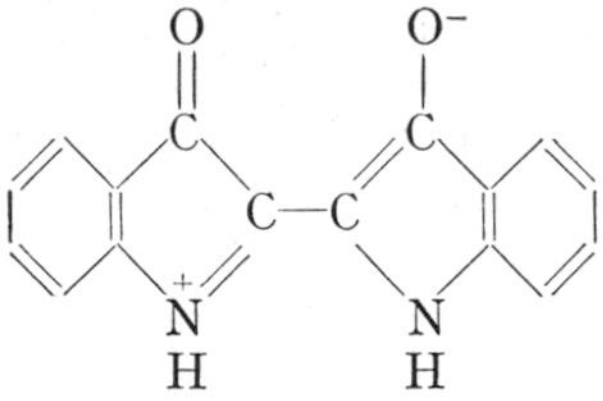

(VI)

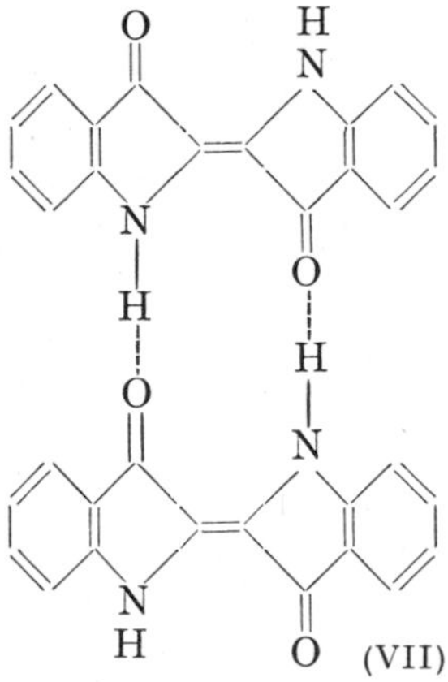

(VII)

C—C *single* bond to give the stable *trans*-form V. This form is so stabilised by intramolecular hydrogen bonding that it cannot be isomerised to the *cis* form by the action of light (Brode *et al.*, 1954). The problem, however, cannot be regarded as settled. According to Holt *et al.* (1956), the hydrogen bonding in indigotin is intermolecular and *not* intramolecular; thus (VII) represents the molecule. Furthermore, indigotin has been shown to be dimeric in *p*-toluidine solution.

Derivatives of indigotin. Indigotin can be chlorinated or brominated directly in the 5, 5′, 7 and 7′ positions. The tetrachloro-derivative, **Brilliant Indigo B,** and the tetrabromo-derivative, **Brilliant Indigo 2B,** are both used commercially; both are brighter than indigotin. **Tyrian Purple** (" *Purple of the Ancients* ") is 6 : 6′-dibromoindigotin, and was originally obtained from a species of molluscs in the Mediterranean. It is not commercially important since much cheaper dyes of similar colour are available. **Indigo Carmine** is the sodium salt of indigotin 5 : 5′-disulphonic acid. **Thioindigo Red** (Friedländer, 1905) is an important vat dye. An interesting point about this compound is that, as in the case of indigotin, two geometrical isomers are possible, but since hydrogen bonding is not possible in the sulphur compound, neither form is stabilised, and in solution both forms appear to exist in equilibrium (Wyman *et al.*, 1951).

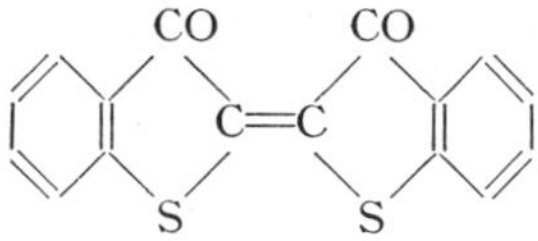

Anthraquinone type of vat dyes. The *algol colours* are acylaminoanthraquinones, *e.g.*, **Algol Yellow W.G.** This dyes cotton in yellow shades, and is

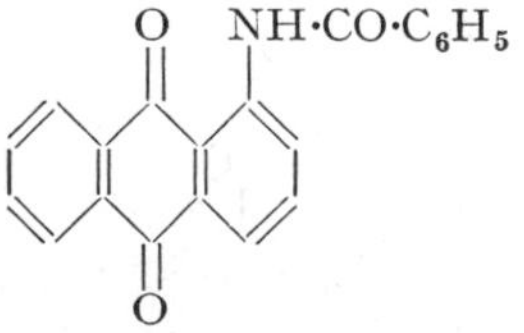

$NH{\cdot}CO{\cdot}C_6H_5$

readily prepared by heating the corresponding amino-compound with benzoic acid.

Indanthrone (*Indanthrene Blue R*; Bohn, 1901) is prepared by fusing 2-

aminoanthraquinone with potassium hydroxide in the presence of potassium chlorate or nitrate at 250°.

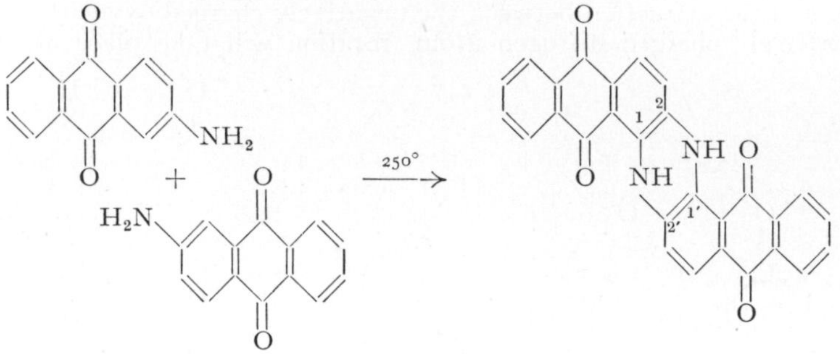

It is reduced by alkaline sodium hyposulphite to the alkali-soluble form (leuco-compound; brown) which is oxidised to the dye by exposure to air.

Substituted indanthrones are also very important vat dyes, *e.g.*, 4 : 4′-di-chloro- and dibromo-derivatives give greener blues than the parent compound.

Flavanthrone (*Flavanthrene, Indanthrene Yellow G.*; Bohn, 1901) is formed by fusing 2-aminoanthraquinone with potassium hydroxide at 350° (*cf.* above).

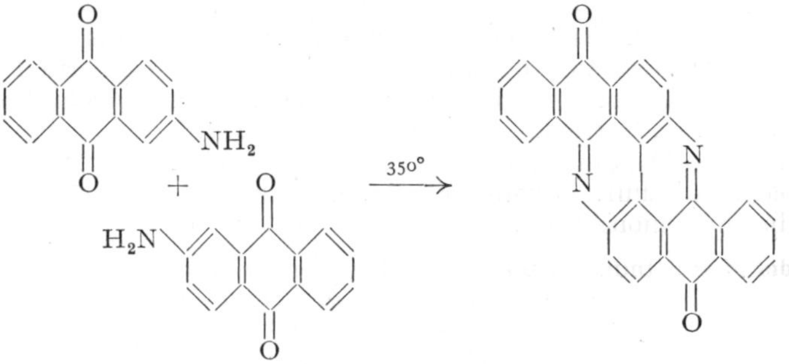

It is now made by the action of antimony pentachloride on 2-aminoanthra-quinone in boiling nitrobenzene solution.

ANTHRAQUINOID DYES

Alizarin is one of the most important anthraquinoid dyes; it is the chief constituent of the madder root. Alizarin is 1 : 2-dihydroxyanthraquinone, and is now manufactured synthetically by sulphonating anthraquinone with fuming sulphuric acid at high temperatures, and fusing the sodium salt of the product, anthraquinone-2-sulphonic, acid, with sodium hydroxide and the calculated quantity of potassium chlorate at 180–200° under pressure:

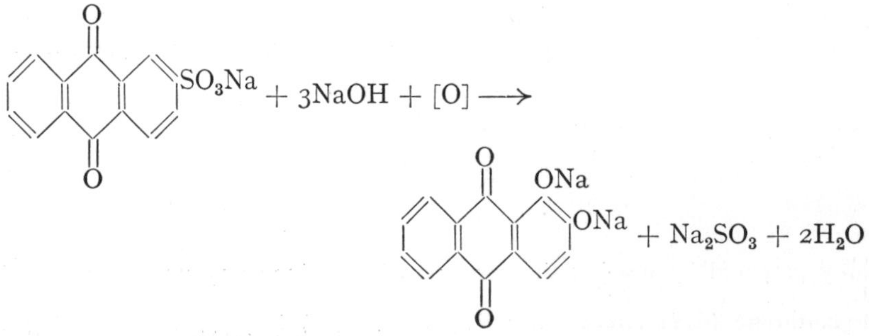

$$C_{14}H_7O_2SO_3Na + 3NaOH + [O] \longrightarrow C_{14}H_6O_2(ONa)_2 + Na_2SO_3 + 2H_2O$$

The function of the potassium chlorate is to provide oxygen for the oxidation of the 1-carbon atom to COH.

Structure of alizarin. Analysis and molecular weight determinations show that the molecular formula of alizarin is $C_{14}H_8O_4$. When distilled with zinc dust, alizarin gives anthracene; this shows that it is an anthracene derivative. When heated with the calculated quantity of bromine, anthraquinone forms dibromoanthraquinone and this, on fusion with potassium hydroxide, gives alizarin; this indicates that alizarin is dihydroxyanthraquinone. Actually this was the method used by Graebe and Liebermann, who were the first to synthesise alizarin. A most interesting feature of this synthesis is that these authors thought they had obtained 1 : 2-dibromoanthraquinone. Much later work has shown that they were actually working with 2 : 3-dibromoanthraquinone, and that rearrangement had therefore taken place during the fusion with alkali.

Vigorous oxidation of alizarin gives phthalic acid, thereby indicating that the two hydroxyl groups are in the same ring; otherwise an hydroxyphthalic acid would have been obtained, or the whole molecule broken down completely. Thus alizarin must be the 1 : 2-, 1 : 3-, 1 : 4- or 2 : 3-dihydroxy-derivative of anthraquinone. Since alizarin may be obtained by heating a mixture of phthalic anhydride and catechol with a little sulphuric acid at 130°, the two hydroxyl groups must be in the *o*-positions in alizarin:

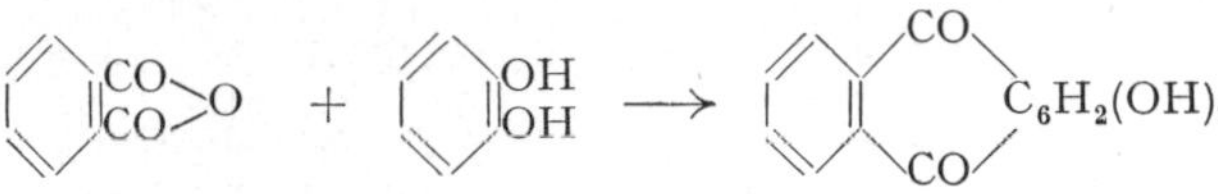

There are two possibilities, *viz.*, 1 : 2- (I) and 2 : 3- (II):

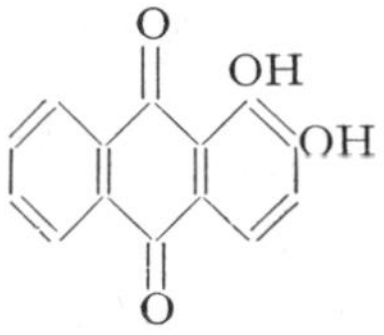

(I) 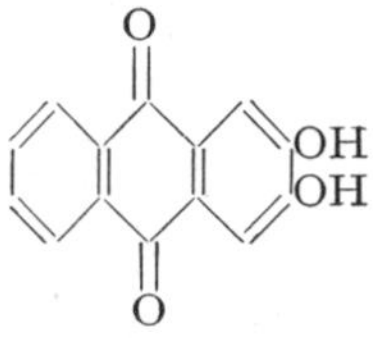 (II)

When oxidised with manganese dioxide and sulphuric acid, alizarin forms *purpurin*, a trihydroxy-derivative of anthraquinone in which the three hydroxyl groups are in the *same* ring (as shown by oxidation to phthalic acid). (I) can give rise to two trihydroxy-derivatives, 1 : 2 : 3- and 1 : 2 : 4-; (II), only one, 1 : 2 : 3-. Purpurin has been shown to be 1 : 2 : 4-trihydroxyanthraquinone by condensing phthalic anhydride with quinol, and oxidising the product, *quinizarin*:

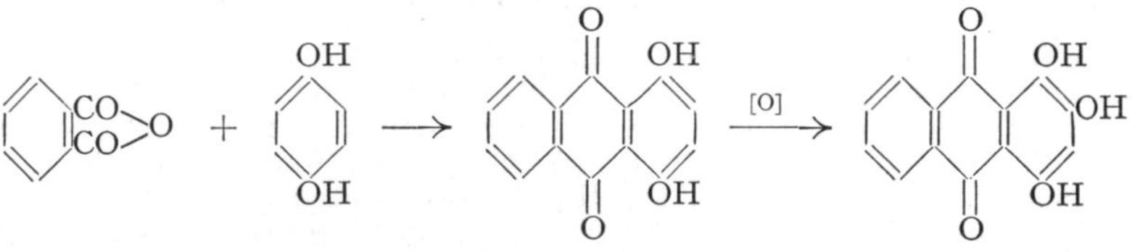

Thus structure (I) is alizarin, and this is supported by the facts (i) that nitration of alizarin under different conditions gives *two* isomeric mononitro-derivatives in both of which the nitro-group is in the same ring as the hydroxyl groups (oxidation gives no nitrophthalic acid), and (ii) that alizarin forms *two* monoacyl derivative (1- and 2-).

Properties of alizarin. Alizarin forms ruby red crystals, m.p. 290°, almost insoluble in water but fairly soluble in ethanol. It dissolves in alkalis to give purple solutions. It is a mordant dye, and the colour of the lake depends on the metal used. Aluminium gives a red lake (*Turkey Red*), iron (ferric) a violet-black and chromium a brown-violet. Aluminium and iron lakes are usually employed for cotton dyeing and for printing, and aluminium and chromium lakes for wood dyeing.

In addition to the aluminium compound, the lake contains calcium salts, Turkey-red oil and sodium phosphate. These additional compounds affect the brightness of the lake and increase its stability towards acids and alkalis. It appears that aluminium hydroxide alone does not yield a lake with alizarin, but only after the addition of a calcium salt.

Alizarin Orange (Rosenstiehl, 1876) is prepared by nitrating alizarin in sulphuric acid solution in the presence of boric acid. It forms orange lakes with aluminium. **Alizarin Blue** (Prud'homme, 1877) may be prepared by first reducing Alizarin Orange to the corresponding amino-compound and then heating this with glycerol, sulphuric acid and nitrobenzene (Skraup's synthesis). It dyes

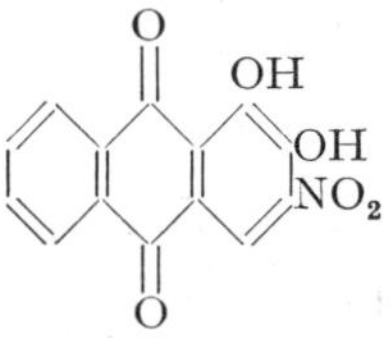

Alizarin Orange

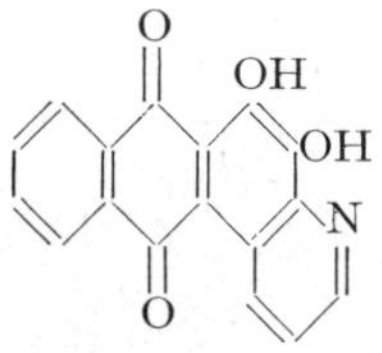

Alizarin Blue

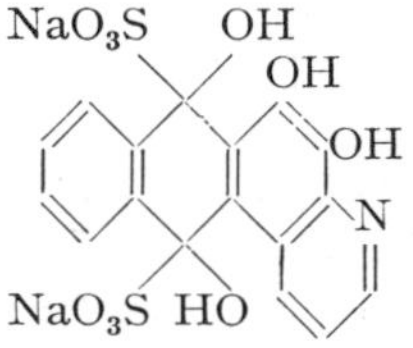

Alizarin Blue S

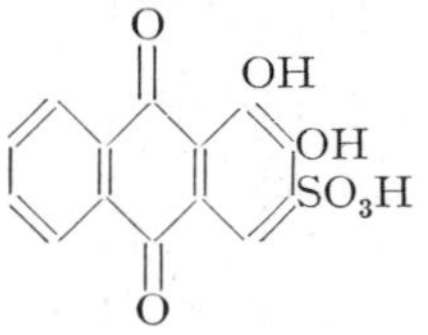

Alizarin Red S

wool mordanted with chromium a blue colour. **Alizarin Blue S** (Brunck, 1881) is the soluble bisulphite compound of Alizarin Blue. It gives a reddish-blue lake with chromium. **Alizarin Red S** (Graebe and Liebermann, 1871) is prepared by sulphonating alizarin with fuming sulphuric acid. It dyes wool mordanted with aluminium a scarlet red, and a bordeaux when mordanted with chromium.

SULPHUR DYES

Sulphur dyes are prepared by heating various organic compounds such as amines, aminophenols and nitrophenols, with sodium polysulphide. Sulphur dyes are coloured solids, insoluble in water and acids, but soluble in cold alkaline solutions of sodium sulphide, in which the dyes are reduced to the leuco-compound. Cotton is dipped and then exposed to the air, whereupon the leuco-compound is oxidised to the dye. Oxidation may also be effected by immersion in a warm bath of dilute potassium dichromate.

Sulphur dyes have complex structures, many of which are uncertain or unknown.

A largely used sulphur dye is that for dyeing cloth khaki. This dye is made by heating *p*-phenylenediamine, *p*-aminoacetanilide and sulphur, with or without benzidine, and then heating the product with sodium sulphide.

PHTHALOCYANINE PIGMENTS AND DYES

The **phthalocyanines** are a very important new class of organic dyes and pigments; they are coloured blue to green. They are very fast to light, heat, acids and alkalis, and are very useful for paints, printing inks, synthetic plastics and fibres, rubber, etc.

The phthalocyanine dyes were discovered by accident at the works of Scottish Dyes Ltd. in 1928. It was there observed that some lots of phthalimide, manufactured by the action of ammonia on molten phthalic anhydride in an iron vessel, were contaminated with a blue pigment. The structure and method of formation of this iron compound were established by Linstead and his co-workers (1934).

The first commercial phthalocyanine dye was **Monastral Fast Blue BS.** This is copper phthalocyanine, the copper atom taking place of the hydrogen atoms in the two NH groups of phthalocyanine itself, and being co-ordinated with the other two nitrogen atoms. The colour depends on the metal (copper, magnesium, lead, etc.), and greener shades are obtained by direct chlorination or bromination.

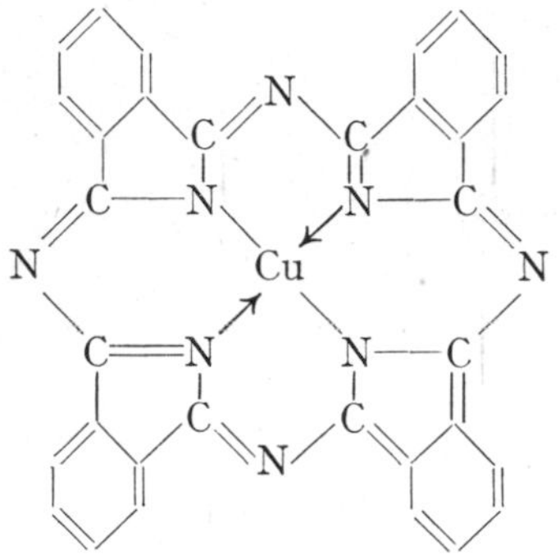

Metal phthalocyanines may be prepared:

(i) By passing ammonia into molten phthalic anhydride or phthalimide in the presence of a metal salt.

(ii) By heating *o*-cyanoarylamides or phthalonitriles with metals or metallic salts.

(iii) By heating phthalic anhydride or phthalimide with urea and a metallic salt, preferably in the presence of a catalyst such as boric acid.

Phthalocyanine may be prepared by heating phthalonitrile with a little triethanolamine.

Phthalocyanines are made water soluble by sulphonation, and these soluble salts are used as direct dyes.

QUESTIONS

1. Write an essay on the relation between colour and constitution.
2. Discuss the classification of dyes according to their application.
3. Write an essay on the azo-dyes.
4. Discuss the analytical and synthetic evidence for the structure of:—(*a*) triphenylmethane dyes, (*b*) indigotin, (*c*) alizarin.
5. Describe the preparation of:—Bismarck Brown G, (*b*) Methyl Orange, (*c*) Congo Red, (*d*) Chromotrope 2B, (*e*) Malachite Green, (*f*) Pararosaniline, (*g*) Rosaniline, (*h*) Crystal Violet, (*i*) Phenolphthalein, (*j*) Fluorescein, (*k*) Rhodamine B, (*l*) Indigotin, (*m*) Alizarin, (*n*) Copper phthalocyanine, (*o*) Naphthol Yellow S, (*p*) Aniline Blue, (*q*) Pyronine G, (*r*) Quinoline Yellow, (*s*) Methylene Blue, (*t*) Meldola's Blue.
6. Write an essay on the Cyanine dyes.
7. Write an account of the Vat Dyes.

READING REFERENCES

Lewis and Calvin, The Colour of Organic Substances, *Chem. Reviews*, 1939, **25**, 273.
Symposium on Colour and the Electronic Structure of Complex Molecules, *ibid.*, 1947, **41**, 201.
Maccoll, Colour and Constitution, *Quart. Reviews* (*Chem. Soc.*), 1947, **1**, 16.
Absorption Spectra, *Ann. Reports*, 1939, **36**, 47; 1941, **38**, 7; 1943, **40**, 12; 1945, **42**, 105.
Cain and Thorpe, *Synthetic Dye-Stuffs*, Griffin and Co. (1933).
Rowe, Perkin Centenary Lecture, *J. Soc. Dyers and Col.*, 1938, **54**, 551.
Rowe, The Development of the Chemistry of Commercial Synthetic Dyes (1856–1938), Institute of Chemistry of Great Britain and Ireland (1938).
Phthalocyanines. (i) Linstead *et al.*, *J.C.S.*, **1934**, 1016–1039.
(ii) Dahlen, *Ind. Eng. Chem.*, 1939, **31**, 839.
Bowen, Light Absorption and Photochemistry, *Quart. Reviews* (*Chem. Soc.*), 1950, **4**, 236.
Bowen, *The Chemical Aspects of Light*, Oxford Press (2nd ed., 1946).
Dewar, *The Electron Theory of Organic Chemistry*, Oxford Press (1949). Ch. XV. Light Absorption and Colour.
Dewar, Colour and Constitution, *J.C.S.*, **1950**, 2329; **1952**, 3532, 3544.
Ferguson, Relationship between Absorption Spectra and Chemical Constitution of Organic Molecules, *Chem. Reviews*, 1948, **43**, 385.
Fierz-David and Blangey, *Fundamental Processes of Dye Chemistry*, Interscience Publishers (1949; translated by Vittum).
Gilman, *Advanced Organic Chemistry*, Wiley (1953). Vol. III, Ch. 4. Organic Dyes.
Wheland, *Resonance in Organic Chemistry*, Wiley (1955), Ch. 6. Resonance and Molecular Spectra.
Lubs (Ed.), *The Chemistry of Synthetic Dyes and Pigments*, Reinhold (1955).
Recent Advances in the Chemistry of Colouring Matters. Special Publication No. 4. Chemical Society (1956).

EXAMINATION QUESTIONS

1. By means of equations and short notes indicate some typical examples of the use of (*a*) malonic ester in the synthesis of homocyclic compounds, and (*b*) acetoacetic ester in the synthesis of heterocyclic compounds (B.Sc. Special, U.L., 1948).

2. A hydrocarbon of molecular formula $C_{12}H_{10}$ is nitrated to a substance $C_{12}H_9NO_2$ which is converted by the action of chromic acid mixture into a dicarboxylic acid $C_{12}H_7NO_6$. Further oxidation of this acid yields 4-nitrobenzene-1 : 2 : 3-tricarboxylic acid, whereas reduction of the nitro-group followed by drastic oxidation produces benzene-1 : 2 : 3-tricarboxylic acid.

Explain these facts and give the structural formula of the original hydrocarbon (A.R.I.C., 1948).

3. Write an essay on *one* of the following topics:—

(*a*) The concept of resonance (mesomerism) in relation to the structure of molecules.

(*b*) The influence of substituents on the strengths of organic acids and bases.

(*c*) Keto-enol tautomerism—including methods for the estimation of the proportions of tautomerides in such equilibrium mixtures (B.Sc. Special, U.L., 1948).

4. Outline the methods of preparation and the characteristic reactions of *five* of the following compounds:—(*a*) urea, (*b*) ethyl chloroformate, (*c*) keten, (*d*) chloroform, (*e*) diacetyl, (*f*) acetonylacetone, (*g*) phenyl *iso*cyanate (phenylcarbimide) (B.Sc. Special, U.L., 1945).

5. Indicate briefly by means of formulæ and equations how each of the following substances may be prepared from nitrobenzene:—nitrosobenzene, diphenyl, phenacetin, quinoline, phenylhydrazine, azoxybenzene, Bismarck Brown, *p*-aminoacetophenone (A.R.I.C., 1946).

6. Classify the different types of isomerism which are known and give formulæ illustrating one example of each type (A.R.I.C., 1948).

7. A substance is believed to possess the following structure:

CH_3O (top), CH_3O— (left) on the first benzene ring —CH=N— second benzene ring with NO_2 (top) and —Br (right)

Suggest reactions you would carry out in order to confirm it. Indicate a method of synthesising this compound (B.Sc. Special, U.L., 1945).

8. Describe methods for the preparation of aromatic sulphonic acids, and indicate the most important reactions of these compounds (B.Sc. General, U.L., 1939).

9. Write an account of the preparation of aromatic aldehydes, and give three condensation reactions of benzaldehyde (B.Sc. General, U.L., 1946).

10. Give an account of methods which have been used to convert aldohexoses into aldopentoses and aldoheptoses. Outline the essential proof of the structure of glucose (B.Sc General, U.L., 1944).

11. Discuss the work which has been carried out in investigating the kinetics of any *one* organic reaction or class of reactions (F.R.I.C., *Branch C*, 1948).

12. Describe and explain the reactions which have been observed in aromatic compounds where substitution or displacement is effected by an anionoid (nucleophilic) reagent (F.R.I.C., *Branch C*. 1948).

13. State briefly how any *five* of the following substances could be conveniently prepared in the laboratory, ethyl alcohol and acetic acid being available as starting materials:—

Methyldiethylcarbinol, diethylacetic acid, dichloroacetic acid, methyl ethyl ketone, sulphonal, methylamine (A.R.I.C., 1947).

14. Give the approximate conditions under which phenol (or a simple derivative of phenol) may be caused to react with (*a*) carbon dioxide, (*b*) chloroform, (*c*) a diazo solution, (*d*) hydrogen and (*e*) methylating agent. Indicate the products in each case and give any necessary explanation of the process involved (B.Sc. General, U.L., 1943).

15. Mention *six* general reactions used in organic chemistry by which a new carbon–carbon bond is formed. Give one example of each, indicate any essential experimental conditions and explain the range of applicability of the reaction (A.R.I.C., 1945).

16. Give an account of the ways in which acetylene has been used for synthetic purposes (F.R.I.C., *Branch C*, 1947).

17. Classify the more important reactions of the diazo-compounds, differentiating between reactions in which nitrogen is eliminated and reactions in which it is not (B.Sc. General, U.L., 1943).

18. Suggest methods by which *five* of the following compounds can be obtained from easily accessible materials. Write notes on any points of interest in connection with the substances you select:

(*a*) [benzene ring with OH, OCH_3, CHO]   (*b*) $NH_2{\cdot}(CH_2)_6{\cdot}NH_2$ (*c*) [ring: CO, NH, NH, CO, CO, $C(CH_2{\cdot}CH{:}CH_2)_2$]

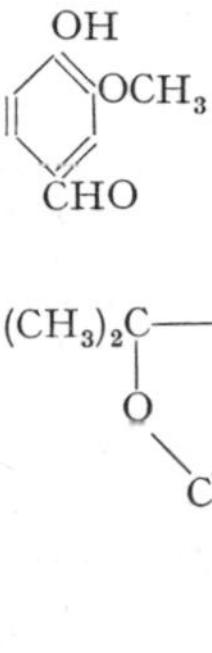

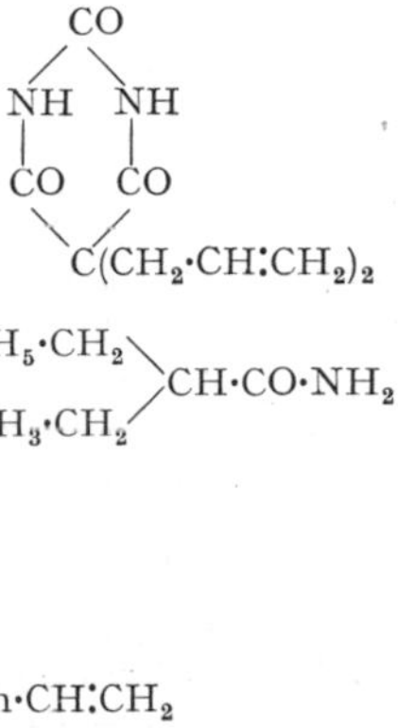

(*d*) $(CH_3)_2C$——$CH{\cdot}CO_2H$ [ring with O, CH_2, CO]   (*e*) [phenanthroline structure with N, N]   (*f*) $C_6H_5{\cdot}CH_2$ / $CH_3{\cdot}CH_2$ > $CH{\cdot}CO{\cdot}NH_2$

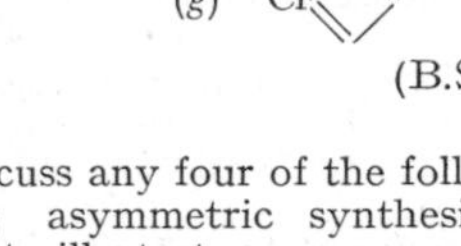

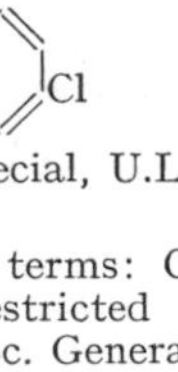

(*g*) Cl–C_6H_4–$CH(CCl_3)$–C_6H_4–Cl   (*h*) $Ph{\cdot}CH{:}CH_2$

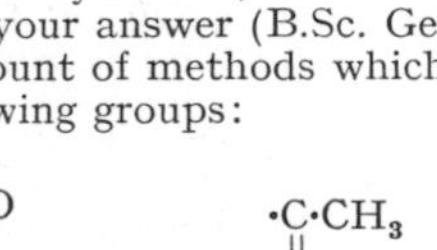

(B.Sc. Special, U.L., 1945).

19. Discuss any four of the following terms: Centre of symmetry; optical (Walden) inversion; asymmetric synthesis; restricted rotation; racemisation. Give clear examples to illustrate your answer (B.Sc. General, U.L., 1943).

20. Give a brief account of methods which have been used to prove the presence in a molecule of the following groups:

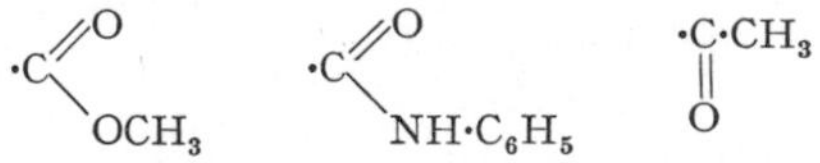

$\cdot C(=O)OCH_3$ $\cdot C(=O)NH{\cdot}C_6H_5$ $\cdot C(=O){\cdot}CH_3$ $\cdot C{\equiv}CH$ $\cdot CH(OH)\cdot$ $\cdot NH{\cdot}CH_3$

(B.Sc. General, U.L., 1939).

21. Explain, giving examples, the use of any *six* of the following substances in organic chemistry: selenium, maleic anhydride, diazoacetic ester, periodic acid, sodamide, thoria, copper powder, phenyl *iso*cyanate (F.R.I.C., *Branch C*, 1946).

22. Indicate briefly by means of formulæ and equations how the following substances may be conveniently prepared from phenol:—(*a*) chloropicrin, (*b*) *p*-hydroxy-

acetophenone, (*c*) pimelic acid, (*d*) *p*-dinitrobenzene, (*e*) adipic acid, (*f*) aurin, (*g*) *p*-hydroxybenzene-azo-naphthalene (A.R.I.C., 1946).

23. Give the more important methods available for the synthesis of pyrrole and its derivatives. Describe the characteristic properties and behaviour of these compounds. In which respects do they show resemblance to aromatic substances?

How can pyrrole be converted into (*a*) an open-chain compound, (*b*) a pyridine derivative, (*c*) a strong cyclic base? (A.R.I.C., 1946).

24. Indicate the methods available for the preparation of the aliphatic amines. In what ways do primary, secondary and tertiary amines differ in their chemical behaviour? (B.Sc. General, 1937).

25. Write a general account of the use of organo-metallic compounds for synthetic purposes, giving examples.

In which circumstances is zinc used in preference to magnesium? (A.R.I.C., 1945).

26. What are the main classes of dye-stuffs? Give an example of each class, referring to its mode of manufacture and its use in dyeing (B.Sc. Special, U.L., 1947).

27. Write a concise essay on *one* of the following subjects:—(*a*) Free radicals, (*b*) alcoholic fermentation, (*c*) " aromatic character " (B.Sc. Special, U.L., 1943).

28. Write a full account of the formation and properties of formaldehyde and its polymeric modifications (B.Sc. Special, U.L., 1948).

29. What methods are available for the preparation of ketones of the aliphatic and aromatic series, including aromatic hydroxy-ketones?

What is Michler's ketone? How is it prepared, and how may it be used in the preparation of dyes? (A.R.I.C., 1945).

30. Review the methods by which cyclic polymethylene compounds have been obtained, with special reference to the methods of Ruzicka and of Ziegler (B.Sc. Special, U.L., 1945).

31. Indicate *three* methods of synthesising aliphatic monocarboxylic acids, and *three* methods of introducing the carboxyl group into an aromatic nucleus. In each case give examples, and mention the reagents employed and the essential conditions for reaction (B.Sc. Special, U.L., 1944).

32. Discuss the influence of neighbouring groups or atoms on the reactivity of hydrogen which is in combination with carbon (B.Sc. Special, U.L., 1943).

33. Write notes on *three* of the following:—Hofmann's conversion of amides into primary amines, (*b*) Perkin's reaction, (*c*) the benzidine change, (*d*) Sandmeyer's reaction, (*e*) catalytic hydrogenation (B.Sc. Special, U.L., 1943).

34. Outline the important advances which have been made in recent years in the utilisation of petroleum as an initial material for the preparation of organic compounds (B.Sc. Special, U.L., 1943).

35. Write notes on *two* of the following:—(*a*) Friedel–Crafts' reaction, (*b*) the reduction of nitrobenzene, (*c*) hydroxy-azo-dyestuffs, (*d*) quinones (B.Sc. Special, U.L., 1944).

36. Write a general account of the industrially important esters of glycerol (B.Sc. Special, U.L., 1946).

37. Discuss *one* of the following physical properties in relation to molecular structure:—(*a*) dipole moment, (*b*) molecular refraction, (*c*) diamagnetic susceptibility, (*d*) colour (*i.e.*, the electronic absorption spectrum) (B.Sc. Special, U.L., 1946).

38. Discuss the significance of the terms " electrophilic reagent " and " nucleophilic reagent " with reference to:—(*a*) addition to the carbonyl double bond, (*b*) addition to the ethylenic double bond, (*c*) substitution in the benzene nucleus (B.Sc. Special, U.L., 1946).

39. Discuss the structure of any three of the following substances: urea, glycine, glucose, anthraquinone, phenolphthalein, sulphanilic acid (B.Sc. General, U.L., 1939).

40. Compare and contrast the reactions of (*a*) acetaldehyde and acetone, (*b*) ethyl nitrite and nitroethane (B.Sc. General, U.L., 1936).

41. Describe briefly the experiments you would carry out in order to confirm the constitution of substances which are stated to have the following formulæ:

(*a*) $CN{\cdot}CH(NH_2){\cdot}CO_2H$; (*b*) $CH_3{\cdot}CH_2{\cdot}CH{:}CH{\cdot}CH_2{\cdot}O{\cdot}CH_3$; (*c*) CH_3, Cl, NO_2 (benzene ring)

(B.Sc. Special, U.L. 1943).

42. Review both direct and indirect methods which are available for the introduction of halogen atoms into an aromatic nucleus. Include a brief statement indicating the causes of the known results of the direct chlorination and dichlorination of benzene (B.Sc. General, U.L., 1944).

43. Review the methods which are available for methylating hydroxylic compounds (B.Sc. Special, U.L., 1939).

44. Suggest practicable syntheses, from readily accessible materials, of any five of the following:

(a) CH_3 — CH — CH_2 — CO (ring fused to benzene)

(b) CH_3 ⟨benzene⟩ $CO\cdot CH{:}CH$ ⟨benzene⟩ OCH_3

(c) $(CH_3)_3C\cdot CBr(CH_3)_2$

(d) O — CO — $C\cdot CH_3$ — CH (ring fused to benzene)

(e) $CH_3\cdot CH$ — O — $CH_3\cdot CH$ (ring)

(f) ⟨benzene, CH_3⟩ —NH— ⟨benzene⟩ NO_2, NO_2

(g) $CH_3\cdot CH_2$ ⟨benzene⟩ CH_3

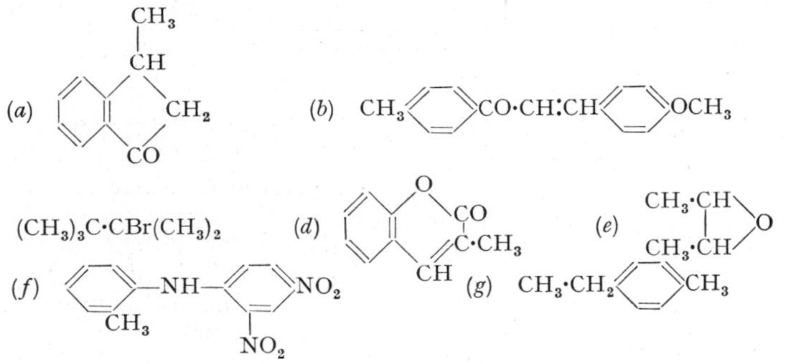

(B.Sc. Special, U.L., 1942).

45. Describe (*a*) a method of manufacture, and (*b*) an alternative small scale method of preparation of each of the following: acetaldehyde; phenol; benzoic acid (B.Sc. Special, U.L., 1939).

46. Describe the main uses of any five of the following in the organic chemical laboratory:—Aluminium tri-*iso*propoxide; selenium dioxide; perbenzoic acid; pyridine; maleic anhydride; picric acid; metallic palladium (B. Sc. Special, U.L., 1940).

47. To what uses have metals been put as catalysts in organic chemistry? (B.Sc. Special, U.L., 1938).

48. Compare and contrast the reactions of (*a*) acetaldehyde and benzaldehyde, (*b*) ethyl alcohol and phenol, (*c*) ethyl iodide and iodobenzene (B.Sc. General, U.L., 1935).

49. By means of suitable examples show how the electronic theory of valency has proved helpful in explaining the reactivity of organic compounds (A.R.I.C., 1940).

50. Give an account of the structure and synthesis of *either* alizarin *or* indigotin (A.R.I.C., 1945).

APPENDIX

NOMENCLATURE

In dealing with the systematic methods of nomenclature, no attempt has been made to indicate whether a particular system is described in the Geneva system, or whether it is described in the I.U.C. rules. Irrespective of its origin, the method of nomenclature has been referred to in the text as the I.U.C. system. In any case, the reader should appreciate that organic nomenclature is in a state of flux. This is unfortunate, but inevitable. What is more unfortunate is that there is no complete agreement among the various publishing societies. Thus the reader, at times, may be confused, and in some cases misled, when changing from British to American journals, particularly in the case of numbering of various ring systems, *e.g.*, acenaphthene (p. 694).

Many of the I.U.C. rules have been given in the text. The reader should find the following remarks of some assistance in nomenclature.

Order of radicals. In British usage, the following order was adopted for naming radicals prior to April, 1950: Cl, Br, I, F, NO_2, NO, NH_2, $NH{\cdot}CO{\cdot}CH_3$, NH, OH, CHO, CO, CN, CNS, CO_2H, $R{\cdot}CO_2$, RO, R·CO, R, H. R is an alkyl or aryl radical, and these radicals were named in the following order:

(i) Cyclic precede acyclic radicals.
(ii) More saturated precede less saturated radicals.
(iii) Less complex precede more complex radicals.
(iv) Univalent precede bivalent radicals.

Since April, 1950, the *Chemical Society* has adopted an order for prefixes denoting substituents, which, in general, follows American usage, except for differences in nomenclature, spelling, italicising or punctuation.

(i) The names of substituents cited as prefixes are arranged alphabetically, regardless of the number of each (see list above, and also p. 41); *e.g.*,

3-**a**mino-4-chloro-2-naphthol
ethyl **m**ethyl ketone
5-**n**itro-1 : 4-di**p**henylnaphthalene
1-**a**cetyl-2-**a**mino-4-**h**ydroxy-3 : 5 : 6-tri**m**ethylanthracene
methyl **p**ropyl succinate
N.B. **m**ethyl **h**ydrogen phthalate

(ii) Compound radical names are treated as *units*, and when several prefixes begin with the same letter, short names precede longer ones, *e.g.*,

1-(2 : 4-**d**initrophenyl)-3-**m**ethylnaphthalene
1-**methyl**-4-**methylamino**anthracene
1-**d**imethylamino-2-**e**thylnaphthalene

(iii) Italicised prefixes are neglected when assembling substituents; but isomeric substituents are arranged in alphabetical order of the italicised prefixes, except that *iso* follows directly after *n*, and *o* precedes *m*. The following are some of the more important italicised prefixes: *aci*, *allo*, *amphi*, *anti*, *as*, *cis*, *cyclo*, *endo*, *gem*, *iso*, *meso*, *neo*, *peri*, *sec*, *spiro*, *syn*, *tert*, *trans*, *vic*.

1-**f**luoro-4-*cyclo***p**entylbenzene
n-**p**ropyl *iso***p**ropyl ether
o-**n**itrophenyl-*m*-**n**itrophenylacetic acid

(iv) When a compound contains one principal function, then this is expressed in the ending of the name, *e.g.*,

3-ethyl-2-methyl*cyclo*hexane-1-carboxylic acid

This rule also applies to aromatic compounds (p. 478).

(v) When a compound contains more than one functional group, the compound is named by using the suffix of the principal function and the prefixes of all the other functions (p. 221). This rule also applies to aromatic compounds (p. 479).

(vi) In some cases the order may be changed to avoid ambiguity, *e.g.*, phenyldichloroarsine is used for $C_6H_5{\cdot}AsCl_2$, as dichlorophenylarsine might be taken as $C_6H_3Cl_2{\cdot}AsH_2$.

Use of Greek letters. The Greek alphabet is:

α	alpha
β	beta
γ	gamma
δ (Δ)	delta
ε	epsilon
ζ	zeta
η	eta
θ	theta
ι	iota
κ	kappa
λ	lambda
μ	mu
ν	nu
ξ	xi
ο	omicron
π	pi
ρ	rho
σ	sigma
τ	tau
υ	upsilon
φ	phi
χ	chi
ψ	psi
ω	omega

The use of Greek letters to indicate the positions of substituents in a chain is to be avoided; numerals should be used. Greek letters, however, may be used (and are preferable) to indicate positions of substituents in compounds described by trivial names, *e.g.*, α-hydroxypropionic acid (lactic acid). Greek letters are also used to indicate the *class* of compound, *e.g.*, α, β, γ-, . . . diketones; γ- and δ-lactones, etc.

***iso*- as a prefix.** Although the prefixes *iso*- and *neo*- are not used in the I.U.C. system, there is now a tendency to incorporate *iso*- in the names of olefins, alcohols, etc. *e.g.*, *iso*butene, *iso*propanol. This practice has been adopted in this book.

Position of numerals used in enumeration of substituents, etc. There is no definite rule for this purpose, and three methods are still in use, *e.g.*, $CH_3{\cdot}CH_2{\cdot}CH(OH){\cdot}CH_3$ is described as 2-butanol, butan-2-ol and butanol-2. In this book the numbers have (usually) been placed immediately before the suffix of each functional group.

Writing of names. The general practice is to " run on " the names of radicals replacing hydrogen atoms in a compound, *e.g.*, chlorobenzene, 1-nitropropane, ethylmethylcarbinol, etc. If the compound is named by any general term, then each part of the name is written separately, *e.g.*, ethyl alcohol, ethyl methyl ether, acetic acid, methyl propyl ketone, butyraldehyde oxime (but butyraldoxime), acetaldehyde phenylhydrazone, etc.

ORGANIC CHEMISTRY PUBLICATIONS

Before using any book, consult the preface for information about the contents. The preface usually gives all the information necessary. Also note the date of the publication.

Chemical Dictionaries

Thorpe's Dictionary of Applied Chemistry. This contains short articles on a very wide field of subjects, and also contains a large bibliography of original literature.

Heilbron's Dictionary of Organic Compounds. This gives a concise account of the physical and chemical properties of organic compounds, and references to good methods of preparation.

Physical Constants

Heilbron's Dictionary of Organic Compounds.
International Critical Tables.
Kaye and Laby, *Tables of Physical and Chemical Constants.*
Landolt and Bornstein, *Physikalisch-Chemische Tabellen.*
Chemist's Year Book (British: yearly).
Handbook of Chemistry and Physics (American: yearly).
Lange's *Handbook of Chemistry.*

Reference Books

There are many excellent single volume texts available on Organic Chemistry. The following, however, are of a more specialised character:

Sidgwick, *The Organic Chemistry of Nitrogen.*
Morton, *The Chemistry of Heterocyclic Compounds.*
Cohen, *Organic Chemistry for Advanced Students* (3 vols.).
Gilman, *Advanced Organic Chemistry* (4 vols.).
Richter's Organic Chemistry (4 vols.).
Hückel, *Theoretische Grundlagen der Organischen Chemie* (2 vols.).
Stewart, *Recent Advances in Organic Chemistry* (3 vols.).
Elderfield (Ed.), *Heterocyclic Compounds* (1950—).
Chemistry of the Carbon Compounds (Edited by Rodd), Elsevier (1951—).
Radt (Ed.), *Elsevier's Encyclopædia of Organic Chemistry* (1940—).
Wheeler and Gowan, *Name Index of Organic Reactions* (J.S.C.I., 1950).
Beilstein's Handbuch der Organischen Chemie.

In addition to the above reference books which are mainly theoretical in character, there are also a number of reference books on practical organic chemistry, *e.g.*,

Houben-Weyl, *Die Methoden der Organischen Chemie.*
Organic Syntheses. These are published annually (1921—). There are now also three collected volumes.
Organic Reactions (1942—). These contain detailed discussions of a large number of organic reactions, and also include an account of the practical methods.
Weissberger, *Physical Methods of Organic Chemistry.*
Theilheimer, *Synthetic Methods of Organic Chemistry* (1947—).
Migrdichian, *Organic Synthesis*, Reinhold (Vol. I and II, 1957).

LITERATURE

The more important periodicals are:

American: **Journal of the American Chemical Society** (*J. Amer. Chem. Soc.*). It was first issued in 1879, and was incorporated with the American Chemical Journal since 1913. It is now issued twice a month.
Belgian: **Bulletin de la Société chimique de Belgique** (*Bull. Soc. chim. Belg.*). It was first issued in 1887. Monthly.
British: **Journal of the Chemical Society** (*J.C.S.*). Issued since 1848. Monthly.
Dutch: **Recueil des travaux chimiques des Pays-Bas** (*Rec. trav. chim.*). Issued since 1882. Monthly.
French: **Bulletin de la Société chimique de France** (*Bull. Soc. chim.*). Issued since 1858. Monthly.
German: **Berichte der deutschen chemischen Gesellschaft** (*Ber.*). Issued since 1868. Monthly.
Italian: **Gazzetta chimica italiana** (*Gazzetta*). Issued since 1871. Monthly.
Russian: **Journal of General Chemistry** (U.S.S.R.) (*J. Gen. Chem.* (*U.S.S.R.*). This is a U.S. translation of *Zhurnal obschei Khimii*.
Swiss: **Helvetica Chimica Acta** (*Helv. Chim. Acta*). Issued since 1918. Intermittent.

The above journals are general in that they publish research on all branches of chemistry. Besides these, however, are a large number of specialised journals which deal with only Organic, Physical, Analytical, Biological, Industrial chemistry, etc.

Other useful sources of Organic Chemistry are:

Justus Liebig's Annalen der Chemie (*Annalen*).
Journal of Organic Chemistry (*J. Org. Chem.*).
Journal für praktische Chemie (*J. pr. Chem.*).
Monatshefte für Chemie und verwandte Teile anderer Wissenschaften (*Monatsh.*).
Transactions of the Faraday Society (*Trans. Faraday Soc.*).

Owing to the large number of journals, it is impossible to read everything published. Hence abstracting journals have appeared for the benefit of the chemist. The most important abstracting journals are:

Chemical Abstracts. These are American, were begun in 1907, and are issued twice a month. Four decennial indexes have appeared: 1917, 1927, 1937 and 1947.

British Chemical Abstracts. These began in 1871 and were issued monthly until January, 1954, when the publication of the abstracts in " Pure Chemistry " was discontinued.

Current Chemical Papers. This is a new publication of the Chemical Society, and began January 1954. It is issued monthly, and its aim is to inform chemists of new work as quickly as possible. Since only the titles of papers are given, this periodical does not replace abstracts.

Chemisches Zentrallblatt. This began in 1830 (under the name of Pharmaceutisches Zentrallblatt, and subsequently modified several times). It is issued weekly.

All good abstracts have the following three indexes: author, subject and formula.

Author index. This is arranged alphabetically. To search the author index it is necessary to know the name of the author and also how to spell it; care must be exercised with some surnames, *e.g.*, Tschitschibabin or Chichibabin.

Subject index. This is arranged alphabetically. When searching the literature about a particular subject, the word (name) and related words (names) should be looked up, *e.g.*, suppose we wish to ascertain the work that has been done on *fats*. The procedure would be to look up:

(i) Fats.
(ii) Oils.
(iii) Esters.
(iv) Individuals, *e.g.*, olein, palmitin, etc.
(v) Saponification.
(vi) Soaps.
(vii) Hydrolysis.
(viii) Edible fats and oils.
(ix) The author index of the various papers, since it is quite likely that the author has published more than one paper on the subject.

When using the subject index, it is advisable to work backwards chronologically, since recent papers will give references to older ones.

When searching for a particular compound, the reader should bear in mind alternative names for that particular compound, and also the possibility of alternative methods of numbering.

Formula Index should offer no difficulties. It is probably best to search this.

In addition to journals containing original papers, there are reviews published by various societies. These are critical surveys of literature published during a certain period, and are extremely valuable sources of information, *e.g.*,

Annual Reports of the Chemical Society (published annually). There is now a cumulative (subject) index for volumes **1–46** (1904–1949).

Quarterly Reviews (**Chem. Soc.**). These began in 1947.

Chemical Reviews (six a year).

Journal of Chemical Education (monthly).

Many journals also give critical surveys, or publish lectures that have been given by specialists, *e.g.*, **Journal of the Chemical Society, Journal of Industrial and Engineering Chemistry, Journal of the Society of Chemical Industry.** The periodicals **Nature** and **Chemistry and Industry** are used as a means of correspondence as well as for publications. The Chemical Society also now issues monthly the (new) **Proceedings of the Chemical Society** (1957—) in which communications and lectures are printed.

SEARCHING THE LITERATURE

Some indication of searching the literature has already been given in the foregoing.

Finding a paper given the reference. Original papers are given as author, name of periodical, year of publication, volume number (in heavy print, or underlined in written work), and page, *e.g.*,

E. F. Armstrong, *J.C.S.*, 1903, **83**, 1305. This is British practice. American practice is slightly different, *viz.*

E. F. Armstrong, *J.C.S.*, **83**, 1305 (1903).

Sometimes mistakes are made in giving a reference.

Wrong author. No difficulty will be encountered here, provided the nature of the article is known.

Wrong Journal. In this case it is best to consult the author or subject indexes of the abstracting journals.

Wrong year. If the volume number is correct, there should be no difficulty.

Wrong volume. If the year is correct, there should be no difficulty.

Wrong page. In this case one should look up the annual index of the authors or subjects, or both.

When consulting a reference in an abstracting journal, the reader should look up the same year and at least two years afterwards. The more efficient the abstracting journal, the sooner will an abstract of a publication appear.

Finding information about a compound of known formula (and structure). This is usually done by looking up Beilstein, and then the Chemical Abstracts.

Beilstein's Handbuch. There is now a fourth edition, and this is intended to give a complete survey of organic chemistry up to Jan. 1st, 1910. The plan of the arrangement is described in volume I, pp. 1–46 and pp. 939–944. The subject matter is divided into four main divisions:

(i) *Acyclic compounds.*	Volumes I–IV.
(ii) *Isocyclic compounds.*	Volumes V–XVI.
(iii) *Heterocyclic compounds.*	Volumes XVII–XXVII.
(iv) *Natural products.*	Volumes XXX and XXXI.

Volume XXVIII is the general names index: part 1, A-G; part 2, H–Z. Volume XXIX is the general formulæ index: part 1, C_1–C_{13}; part 2, C_{14}–C_{195}.

The names index is arranged alphabetically. To look up the formulæ index, the molecular formula of the compound is written down with the elements in the following order:

C H O N Cl Br I F S P

After P the elements appear in alphabetical order. Each page is marked at the top by (*a*) an arabic number which gives the number of carbon atoms in the compound listed on that page, and (*b*) a Roman number which gives the number of other elements present in the compounds listed *e.g.*, *m*-chloronitrobenzene:

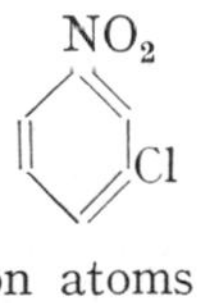

NO_2, Cl (benzene ring) $\equiv C_6H_4O_2NCl$

This contains six carbon atoms and four other elements. Therefore the page marked 6IV is found, and looking down the pages marked in this way, the desired compound will soon be found.

There is a first supplement to Beilstein's fourth edition, in most cases one to each volume; otherwise, the supplements may be combined, *e.g.*, the supplements for volumes III and IV are combined into one volume. The literature survey of the first supplement is from Jan. 1st, 1910 to Jan. 1st, 1920. There is also a second supplement giving the literature survey from Jan. 1st, 1920 to Jan. 1st, 1930. A third supplement has now been begun.

How to use Beilstein. Each volume and supplement has a table of contents and an index consisting partly of names and partly of formulæ. The simplest way to find a compound is to look up the collected indexes of names and formulæ. Having found the compound in the main volumes, the searcher will then find later information (if any) in the corresponding supplements. System numbers are used for cross-reference purposes.

In Beilstein will be found an account of methods of preparation, properties, derivatives, etc.

Each main division of Beilstein is subdivided into functional group compounds in the following order:

Acyclic and Isocyclic. Hydrocarbons, hydroxy-compounds, carbonyl compounds, hydroxy-carbonyl compounds, carboxylic acids, hydroxy-acids, carbonyl acids, hydroxy-carbonyl acids, sulphinic acids, sulphonic acids, hydroxy-sulphonic acids, carbonyl-sulphonic acids, carboxy-sulphonic acids, amines, hydroxyamines, carbonyl-amines, hydroxy-carbonyl-amines, aminoacids, hydroxylamines, hydrazines, azo-compounds, diazo-compounds, azoxy-compounds, metallic compounds.

Heterocyclic. 1 cyclic oxygen (S, Se, Te); 2 cyclic oxygen; 3 cyclic oxygen; 4 cyclic oxygen; 5 cyclic oxygen.

1 cyclic nitrogen; 2 cyclic nitrogen; . . . . 8 cyclic nitrogen.

Natural products. Hydrocarbons (petroleum), ethereal oils, sterols, fats, waxes, carbohydrates, alkaloids, proteins.

The division of a particular compound is determined by its *stem-nucleus.* This is obtained by replacing in the formula all the atoms or groups attached to carbon by the equivalent number of hydrogen atoms, except where replacement involves the breaking of a cyclic chain. When the stem-nucleus has been obtained, the following general rule is applied: when the compound is derived from two or more compounds, or contains two or more functional groups, that compound is discussed under the parent compound to be found *last* in the classification.

Example 1.

Cl

—CH_2—

NH

The stem nuclei are:

CH_4

NH

Since pyrrole is described last in the classification of these three compounds, the compound under consideration will be found under pyrrole.

Example 2.

$$ClCH_2{\cdot}CH_2OH$$

This is a derivative of ethanol, and will therefore be found under the substitution products of ethanol (described immediately after ethanol).

It is important to note that X, NO, NO_2 and N_3 are *not* functional groups, and that their order (of discussion) is F, Cl, Br, I, NO, NO_2, N_3 (immediately after the parent compound).

Difficulty may be encountered when more than one functional group, or one functional group and one or more *apparent* functional groups are attached to the *same* carbon atom. The following examples show how to find the compound:

(i)

$$R{\cdot}C\begin{cases}=O\\ -NH_2\end{cases} \quad \text{(I)} \qquad\qquad R{\cdot}C\begin{cases}-OH\\ -OH\\ -OH\end{cases} \quad \text{(II)}$$

Replace the functional groups in (I) by hydroxyl groups. This gives (II), which is an acid (ortho-acid). (I) will therefore be found under the derivatives of the acid $R{\cdot}CO_2H$:

(ii)

$$R{\cdot}CH\begin{cases}OH\\ NH_2\end{cases} \equiv R{\cdot}CH\begin{cases}OH\\ OH\end{cases} \equiv R{\cdot}CHO$$

(iii)

$$NH_2{\cdot}C(:NH){\cdot}NH_2 \equiv HO{\cdot}C(OH)_2{\cdot}OH \equiv H_2CO_3$$

(iv) $R\cdot CCl_3$. Since there is no functional group present, this compound will be found under $R\cdot CH_3$:

(v)
$$CH_3 \,|\, O{-}C_2H_5 \equiv CH_3OH + C_2H_5OH$$
$$HO \,|\, H$$

This compound will be found under the derivatives of ethanol (ethanol occurs later than methanol):

(vi)
$$R\cdot CO \,|\, \cdot OR' \equiv R\cdot CO_2H + R'OH$$
$$HO \,|\, H$$

This will be found under $R\cdot CO_2H$, since this is discussed later than R′OH.

Note however:
$$RO\cdot \,|\, NO_2 \equiv ROH + HNO_3$$
$$H \,|\, OH$$

This compound will be described under ROH, since HNO_3 is inorganic. Inorganic acid derivatives are discussed in the following order: hydrogen peroxide, halogen-oxyacids, sulphur-oxyacids, nitrogen-oxyacids, phosphorus-oxyacids, arsenic-oxyacids, silicon-oxyacids, halogen acids, . . .

(vii)
$$NH_2\cdot CH_2\cdot CO \,|\, \cdot NH\cdot CH(CH_3)\cdot CO_2H \qquad NH_2\cdot CH_2\cdot CO\cdot NH \,|\, \cdot CH(CH_3)\cdot CO_2H$$
$$HO \,|\, H \qquad\qquad\qquad H \,|\, OH$$

(III) (IV)

This is an example where a compound may be broken up in two (or more) ways. In such cases, the decomposition is carried out in the way which gives the stem-nucleus described later than any obtained in any other way. (III) gives glycine and alanine; (IV) gives glycine (amide derivative) and lactic acid. Since alanine is described later than any other decomposition product, the compound will be found under alanine:

(viii)
$$\begin{matrix} CH_2\cdot CO \\ | \\ CH_2\cdot CO \end{matrix} \!\!>\! O \equiv \begin{matrix} CH_2\cdot CH_2 \\ | \\ CH_2\cdot CH_2 \end{matrix} \!\!>\! O$$

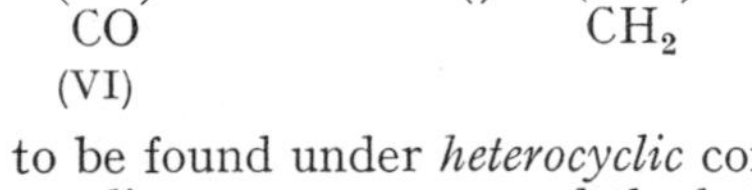

(V)

$$C_6H_4 \begin{matrix} CO \\ CO \end{matrix} \!\!>\! NH \equiv C_6H_4 \begin{matrix} CH_2 \\ CH_2 \end{matrix} \!\!>\! NH$$

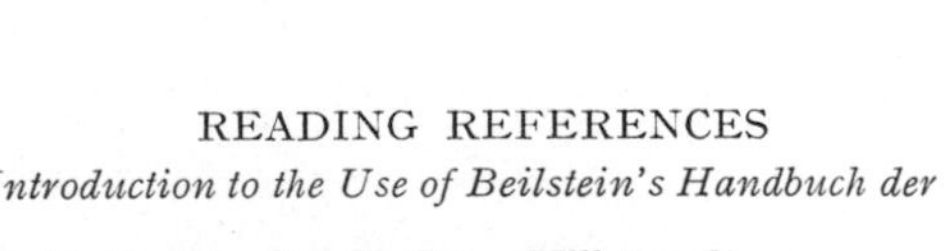

(VI)

(V) and (VI) are both to be found under *heterocyclic* compounds, the former under the division of 1 cyclic oxygen atom, and the latter, 1 cyclic nitrogen atom.

READING REFERENCES

Huntress, *A Brief Introduction to the Use of Beilstein's Handbuch der Organischen Chemie*, Wiley (1930).
Soule, *Library Guide for the Chemist*, McGraw-Hill (1938).
Dyson, *A Short Guide to Chemical Literature*, Longmans, Green (1951).
Patterson *et al.*, Nomenclature of Organic Compounds, *C.A.*, 1945, **39**, 5875.
Editorial Report on Nomenclature, 1952; *J.C.S.*, **1952**, 5057.
Crane, Patterson and Marr, *A Guide to the Literature of Chemistry*, Wiley (2nd ed., 1957).

INDEX

Pages printed in bold type are the more important references. Letters marking the pages have the following meanings: **d** indicates definitions (of reactions, etc.); **n**, nomenclature; **p**, preparations; **r**, reactions. These letters are not used for single page references. Physical constants of a compound will be found described immediately after the methods of preparation. Derivatives of a parent substance will be found under the initial letter of the name, *e.g.*, nitrobenzene will be found under N. Names with prefixes will be found under the initial letter, *e.g.*, *iso*butanes will be found under I; *cyclo*propane under C. The alphabetical order has been used to name prefixes (see p. 784 for the old order). Also the suffix *methanol* has been used as well as *carbinol* (p. 113). Salts are not listed separately, but are included with the references of the corresponding acids or bases. Names of authors are indexed only when they are associated with a particular reaction, condensation, etc. Dyestuffs are listed under Dyes; individual dyes are listed separately.

A

B

C

D

E

F

G

H

I

J

K

L

N

O

Q

R

T

U

V

W

X

Z